Stanley Gib
Stamp Catal

PART 18

Japan & Korea

5th edition 2008

Stanley Gibbons Ltd

London and Ringwood

By Appointment to Her Majesty The Queen
Stanley Gibbons Ltd, London
Philatelists

Published by Stanley Gibbons Ltd
Editorial, Publications Sales Offices
and Distribution Centre:
Parkside, Christchurch Road, Ringwood,
Hants BH24 3SH

1st Edition in this form – February 1980
2nd Edition – November 1984
3rd Edition – January 1992
4th Edition – January 1997
5th Edition – April 2008

© Stanley Gibbons Ltd 2008

Stanley Gibbons Holdings Plc.
HEAD OFFICE, 399 STRAND, LONDON WC2R 0LX
Telephone 020 7836 8444 and
Fax 020 7836 7342
Website: *www.stanleygibbons.com* for all departments.

Stanley Gibbons Ltd, Stanley Gibbons Auctions.
Auction Room and Specialist Stamp Departments:
Open Monday-Friday,
9.30 a.m. to 5 p.m.
Shop: Open Monday-Friday 9 a.m. to 5.30 p.m. and
Saturday 9.30 a.m. to 5.30 p.m.
E-mail: *enquiries@stanleygibbons.co.uk*

Fraser's. Autographs, photographs, letters, documents.
Open Monday-Friday 9 a.m. to 5.30 p.m.
and Saturday 10 a.m. to 4 p.m.
Website: *www.frasersautographs.com*
E-mail: *info@frasersautographs.co.uk*

RINGWOOD OFFICE,
PARKSIDE, CHRISTCHURCH ROAD, RINGWOOD,
HANTS BH24 3SH
Telephone 01425 472363
(24 hour answer phone service),
Fax 01425 470247.
Website: *www.stanleygibbons.com*
E-mail: *info@stanleygibbons.co.uk*

Stanley Gibbons Publications.
Publications Mail Order: FREEPHONE 0800 611 622
Monday-Friday 8.30 a.m. to 5 p.m.
Stanley Gibbons Publications has overseas licensees and distributors for Australia, Belgium, Canada, Denmark, Finland, France, Hong Kong, Israel, Italy, Japan, Luxembourg, Netherlands, New Zealand, Norway, Singapore, Sweden and Switzerland. Please contact the Ringwood address for details.

ISBN 13: 978-0-85259-667-8
ISBN 10: 0-85259-667-7

Item No. 2836 (08)

Printed in the United Kingdom
by Cambridge University Press

Contents

Stanley Gibbons
Foreign Catalogues Parts 2 –22

Edward Stanley Gibbons published his first catalogue of postage stamps from Plymouth in November 1865. Its unillustrated twenty pages listed stamps and postal stationery from Antigua to Wurttemburg with price columns provided for unused or used, either as singles or by the dozen.

Since 1865 the catalogue range has grown to over forty current titles, all profusely illustrated and reflecting current research and price information.

The foreign listings, of which this volume forms a part, were published as Part 2 of the Stanley Gibbons catalogue from 1897 to 1945. Circumstances were difficult in the austerity period following the Second World War so the foreign listings were split into seven smaller catalogues. From 1951 to 1970 these were consolidated into Part 2 Europe and Colonies and Part 3 America, Asia and Africa.

Collecting patterns do change, however, so in 1970–71 an experimental series of Sectional catalogues appeared which were, in turn, replaced by a series of three alphabetical volumes covering Europe and four covering Overseas.

The present system of twenty-one catalogues, covering individual countries or collecting groups, was initiated in 1979. Full details of each volume and its contents are provided on page xviii. The scheme has the advantage of allowing flexibility in response to changing collecting habits with the listings being continually improved, currently by notes covering certain postal history aspects and by the addition of stamp booklet listings and stamp design indexes.

About this edition

This new edition, the first to be published since 1997, has been completely reset and for the first time is in colour.

We have included a new design index for Japan as well as a complete and comprehensive listing of all the Japanese Prefecture stamps, with illustrations.

Following requests from collectors, the stamps issued for the Japanese Occupations of China, the Philippines and the British and Dutch colonies in the Far East, previously listed only in Parts 1, 17, 21 and 22 of this catalogue, now appear in this volume for the first time.

Pricing has been carefully revised throughout with notable price increases in both early Japan and early used South Korea.

Addresses of specialist societies for this area follow.

Hugh Jefferies
Clare de la Feuillade
Barbara Hawkins
Sue Price
Geoff Wilson

New issues

The first supplement to this catalogue appeared in *Gibbons Stamp Monthly* for January 2008.

Specialist Societies:

International Society for Japanese Philately

Washington Chapter: Lee R. Wilson
4216 Jenifer Street
NW Washington
DC 20015-1954
USA
Email: *lerwilson@aol.com*

UK Chapter: Alan Cowie
Highview
102 Gidley Way
Horspath
Oxford
OX33 1TD
UK
Email: *alancowie@talk21.com*

Scandinavian Chapter: Dr. Borge Tilt
Kratvej 45
DK-2760 Malov
Denmark
Email: *botilt@tiscali.dk*
Website: *www.ssjp.dk*

Ryukyu Philatelic Specialist Society Ltd
Secretary: Laura Edmonds
PO BOX 240177
Charlotte NC 28224-0177
USA
Email: *secretary@ryukyustamps.org*
Website: *www.ryukyustamps.org*

Korean Stamp Society
Secretary: John Talmage, Jr.
129 Hendrix Avenue
Oak Ridge
TN 37830
USA
Email: *jtaslmage@usit.net*
Website: *www.pennfamily.org/KSS-USA/*

General Philatelic Information and Guidelines to the Scope of Stanley Gibbons Foreign Catalogues

The notes which follow seek to reflect current practice in compiling the Foreign Catalogue.

It scarcely needs emphasising that the Stanley Gibbons Stamp *Catalogue* has a very long history and that the vast quantity of information it contains has been carefully built up by successive generations through the work of countless individuals. Philately itself is never static and the Catalogue has evolved and developed during this long time-span. Thus, while these notes are important for today's criteria, they may be less precise the farther back in the listings one travels. They are not intended to inaugurate some unwanted series of piecemeal alterations in a widely respected work, but it does seem to us useful that Catalogue users know as exactly as possible the policies currently in operation.

THE CATALOGUE IN GENERAL

Contents. The Catalogue is confined to adhesive postage stamps, including miniature sheets. For particular categories the rules are

(a) Revenue (fiscal) stamps or telegraph stamps are listed only where they have been expressly authorised for postal duty.

(b) Stamps issued only precancelled are included, but normally issued stamps available additionally with precancel have no separate precancel listing unless the face value is changed.

(c) Stamps prepared for use but not issued, hitherto accorded full listing, are nowadays footnoted with a price (where possible).

(d) Bisects (trisects, etc.) are only listed where such usage was officially authorised.

(e) Stamps issued only on first day covers and not available separately are not listed but priced (on the cover) in a footnote.

(f) New printings, as such, are not listed, though stamps from them may qualify under another category, e.g. when a prominent new shade results.

(g) Official and unofficial reprints are dealt with by footnote.

(h) Stamps from imperforate printings of modern issues which also occur perforated are covered by footnotes or general notes, but are listed where widely available for postal use.

Exclusions. The following are excluded:

(a) non-postal revenue or fiscal stamps;
(b) postage stamps used fiscally;
(c) local carriage labels and private local issues;
(d) telegraph stamps;
(e) bogus or phantom stamps;
(f) railway or airline letter fee stamps, bus or road transport company labels;
(g) cut-outs;
(h) all types of non-postal labels;
(i) documentary labels for the postal service, e.g. registration, recorded delivery, airmail etiquettes, etc.;
(j) privately applied embellishments to official issues and privately commissioned items generally;
(k) stamps for training postal officers;
(l) specimen stamps.

Full listing. "Full listing" confers our recognition and implies allotting a catalogue number and (wherever possible) a price quotation.

In judging status for inclusion in the catalogue broad considerations are applied to stamps. They must be issued by a legitimate postal authority, recognised by the government concerned, and must be adhesives valid for proper postal use in the class of service for which they are inscribed. Stamps, with the exception of such categories as postage dues and officials, must be available to the general public, at face value, in reasonable quantities without any artificial restrictions being imposed on their distribution.

We record as abbreviated Appendix entries, without catalogue numbers or prices, stamps from countries which either persist in having far more issues than can be justified by postal need or have failed to maintain control over their distribution so that they have not been available to the public in reasonable quantities at face value. Miniature sheets and imperforate stamps are not mentioned in these entries.

The publishers of this catalogue have observed, with concern, the proliferation of "artificial" stamp-issuing territories. On several occasions this has resulted in separately inscribed issues for various component parts of otherwise united states or territories.

Stanley Gibbons Publications have decided that where such circumstances occur, they will not, in the future, list these items in the SG catalogue without first satisfying themselves that the stamps represent a genuine political, historical or postal division within the country concerned. Any such issues which do not fulfil this stipulation will be recorded in the Catalogue Appendix only.

For errors and varieties the criterion is legitimate (albeit inadvertent) sale over a post office counter in the normal course of business. Details of provenance are always important; printers' waste and fraudulently manufactured material is excluded.

Certificates. In assessing unlisted items due weight is given to Certificates from recognised Expert Committees and, where appropriate, we will usually ask to see them.

New issues. New issues are listed regularly in the Catalogue Supplement in *Gibbons Stamp Monthly*, whence they are consolidated into the next available edition of the Catalogue.

Date of issue. Where local issue dates differ from dates of release by agencies, "date of issue" is the local date. Fortuitous stray usage before the officially intended date is disregarded in listing.

Catalogue numbers. Stamps of each country are catalogued chronologically by date of issue. Subsidiary classes (e.g. postage due stamps) are integrated into one list with postage and commemorative stamps and distinguished by a letter prefix to the catalogue number.

The catalogue number appears in the extreme left column. The boldface type numbers in the next column are merely cross-references to illustrations. Catalogue numbers in the *Gibbons Stamp Monthly* Supplement are provisional only and may need to be altered when the lists are consolidated. Miniature sheets only purchasable intact at a post office have a single MS number; sheetlets – individual stamps available – number each stamp separately. The catalogue no longer gives full listing to designs originally issued in normal sheets, which subsequently appear in sheetlets showing changes of colour, perforation, printing process or face value. Such stamps will be covered by footnotes.

Once published in the Catalogue, numbers are changed as little as possible; really serious renumbering is reserved for the occasions when a complete country or an entire issue is being rewritten. The edition first affected includes cross-reference tables of old and new numbers.

Our catalogue numbers are universally recognised in specifying stamps and as a hallmark of status.

Illustrations. Stamps are illustrated at three-quarters linear size. Stamps not illustrated are the same size and format as the value shown unless otherwise indicated. Stamps issued only as miniature sheets have the stamp alone illustrated but sheet size is also quoted. Overprints, surcharges, watermarks and postmarks are normally actual size. Illustrations of varieties are often enlarged to show the detail.

CONTACTING THE CATALOGUE EDITOR

The editor is always interested in hearing from people who have new information which will improve or correct the Catalogue. As a general rule he must see and examine the actual stamps before they can be considered for listing; photographs or photocopies are insufficient evidence. Neither he nor his staff give opinions as to the genuineness of stamps.

Submissions should be made in writing to the Catalogue Editor, Stanley Gibbons Publications, 7 Parkside, Christchurch Road, Ringwood, Hants BH24 3SH. The cost of return postage for items submitted is appreciated, and this should include the registration fee if required.

Where information is solicited purely for the benefit of the enquirer, the editor cannot undertake to reply if the answer is already contained in these published notes or if return postage is omitted. Written communications are greatly preferred to enquiries by telephone or e-mail and the editor regrets that he or his staff cannot see personal callers without a prior appointment being made.

The editor welcomes close contact with study circles and is interested, too, in finding local correspondents who will verify and supplement official information in overseas countries where this is deficient.

We regret we do not give opinions as to the genuineness of stamps, nor do we identify stamps or number them by our Catalogue.

TECHNICAL MATTERS

The meanings of the technical terms used in the Catalogue will be found in *Philatelic Terms Illustrated*, published by Gibbons (Price £14.95 plus postage).

1. Printing

Printing errors. Errors in printing are of major interest to the Catalogue. Authenticated items meriting consideration would include background, centre or frame inverted or omitted; centre or subject transposed; error of colour; error or omission of value; double prints and impressions; printed both sides; and so on. Designs *tête-bêche*, whether intentionally or by accident, are listable. *Se-tenant* arrangements of stamps are recognised in the listings and footnotes. Gutter pairs (a pair of stamps separated by blank margin) are excluded unless they have some philatelic importance. Colours only partially omitted are not listed, neither are stamps printed on the gummed side.

Printing varieties. Listing is accorded to major changes in the printing base which lead to completely new types. In recess-printing this could be a design re-engraved, in photogravure or photolithography a screen altered in whole or in part. It can also encompass flat-bed and rotary printing if the results are readily distinguishable.

To be considered at all, varieties must be constant.

Early stamps, produced by primitive methods, were prone to numerous imperfections; the lists reflect this, recognising re-entries, retouches, broken frames, misshapen letters, and so on. Printing technology has, however, radically improved over the years, during which time photogravure and lithography have become predominant. Varieties nowadays are more in the nature of flaws and these, being too specialised for a general catalogue, are almost always outside the scope. We therefore do not list such items as dry prints, kiss prints, doctor-blade flaws, blanket set-offs, doubling through blanket stretch, plate cracks and scratches, registration flaws (leading to colour shifts), lithographic ring flaws, and so on. Neither do we recognise fortuitous happenings like paper creases or confetti flaws.

Overprints (and surcharges). Overprints of different types qualify for separate listing. These include overprints in different colours; overprints from different printing processes such as litho and typo; overprints in totally different typefaces, etc.

Overprint errors and varieties. Major errors in machine-printed overprints are important and listable. They include overprint inverted or omitted; overprint double (treble, etc.); overprint diagonal; overprint double, one inverted; pairs with one overprint omitted, e.g. from a radical shift to an adjoining stamp; error of colour; error of type fount; letters inverted or omitted, etc. If the overprint is handstamped, few of these would qualify and a distinction is drawn.

Varieties occurring in overprints will often take the form of broken letters, slight differences in spacing, rising spacers, etc. Only the most important would be considered for footnote mention.

Sheet positions. If space permits we quote sheet positions of listed varieties and authenticated data is solicited for this purpose.

2. Paper
All stamps listed are deemed to be on "ordinary" paper of the wove type and white in colour; only departures from these are mentioned.

Types. Where classification so requires we distinguish such other types of paper as, for example, vertically and horizontally laid; wove and laid bâtonné; card(board); carton; cartridge; enamelled; glazed; GC (Grande Consommation); granite; native; pelure; porous; quadrillé; ribbed; rice; and silk thread.

Our chalky (chalk-surfaced) paper is specifically one which shows a black mark when touched with a silver wire. This and other coatings are easily lost or damaged through immersion in water.

The various makeshifts for normal paper are listed as appropriate. They include printing on: unfinished banknotes, war maps, ruled paper, Post Office forms, and the unprinted side of glossy magazines. The varieties of double paper and joined paper are recognised.

Descriptive terms. The fact that a paper is hand-made (and thus probably of uneven thickness) is mentioned where necessary. Usual descriptive terms as "hard" and "soft"; "smooth" and "rough"; "thick", "medium" and "thin" are applied where there is philatelic merit in classifying papers.

Coloured, very white and toned papers. A coloured paper is one that is coloured right through (front and back of the stamp). In the Catalogue the colour of the paper is given in italics, thus

black/*rose* = black design on rose paper.

Papers have been made specially white in recent years by, for example, a very heavy coating of chalk. We do not classify shades of whiteness of paper as distinct varieties. There does exist, however, a type of paper from early days called toned. This is off-white, often brownish or buffish, but it cannot be assigned a definite colour. A toning effect brought on by climate, incorrect storage or gum staining is disregarded here, as this was not the state of the paper when issued.

Safety devices. The Catalogue takes account of such safety devices as varnish lines, grills, burelage or imprinted patterns on the front or moiré on the back of stamps.

Modern developments. Two modern developments also affect the listings, printing on self-adhesive paper and the tendency, philatelic in origin, for conventional paper to be reinforced or replaced by different materials. Some examples are the use of foils in gold, silver, aluminium, palladium and steel; application of an imitation wood veneer; printing on plastic moulded in relief; and use of a plastic laminate to give a three-dimensional effect. Examples also occur of stamps impregnated with scent; printed on silk; and incorporating miniature gramophone records.

3. Perforation and Rouletting
Perforation gauge. The gauge of a perforation is the number of holes in a length of 2 cm. For correct classification the size of the holes (large or small) may need to be distinguished; in a few cases the actual number of holes on each edge of the stamp needs to be quoted.

Measurement. The Gibbons Instanta gauge is the standard for measuring perforations. The stamp is viewed against a dark background with the transparent gauge put on top of it. Though the gauge measures to decimal accuracy, perforations read from it are generally quoted in the Catalogue to the nearest half. For example:

Just over perf.
12¾ to just under perf. 13¼   = perf. 13
Perf. 13¼ exactly, rounded up = perf. 13½
Just over perf.
13¼ to just under perf. 13¾   = perf. 13½
Perf. 13¾ exactly, rounded up = perf. 14

However, where classification depends on it, actual quarter-perforations are quoted.

Notation. Where no perforation is quoted for an issue it is imperforate. Perforations are usually abbreviated (and spoken) as follows, though sometimes they may be spelled out for clarity. This notation for rectangular stamps (the majority) applies to diamond shapes if "top" is read as the edge to the top right.

P 14: perforated alike on all sides (read: "perf. 14").

P 14×15: the first figure refers to top and bottom, the second to left and right sides (read: "perf. 14 by 15"). This is a compound perforation. For an upright triangular stamp the first figure refers to the two sloping sides and the second to the base. In inverted triangulars the base is first and the second figure refers to the sloping sides.

P 14-15: perforation measuring anything between 14 and 15: the holes are irregularly spaced, thus the gauge may vary along a single line or even along a single edge of the stamp (read: "perf. 14 to 15").

P 14 irregular. perforated 14 from a worn perforator, giving badly aligned holes irregular spaced (read "irregular perf. 14").

P *comp(ound)* 14×15: two gauges in use but not necessarily on opposite sides of the stamp. It could be one side in one gauge and three in the other, or two adjacent sides with the same gauge (Read: "perf. compound of 14 and 15"). For three gauges or more, abbreviated as "P 14, 14½, 15 or compound" for example.

P 14, 14½: perforated approximately 14¼ (read: "perf. 14 or 14½"). It does not mean two stamps, one perf. 14 and the other perf. 14½. This obsolescent notation is gradually being replaced in the Catalogue.

Imperf: imperforate (not perforated).

Imperf × P 14: imperforate at top and bottom and perf 14 at sides.

P 14 × *imperf* = perf 14 at top and bottom and imperforate at sides.

Such headings as "P 13 × 14 (vert) and P 14 × 13 (horiz)" indicate which perforations apply to which stamp format – vertical or horizontal.

Some stamps are additionally perforated so that a label or tab is detachable; others have been perforated suitably for use as two halves. Listings are normally for whole stamps, unless stated otherwise.

Other terms. Perforation almost always gives circular holes; where other shapes have been used they are specified, e.g. square holes; lozenge perf. Interrupted perfs are brought about by the omission of pins at regular intervals. Perforations have occasionally been simulated by being printed as part of the design. With few exceptions, privately applied perforations are not listed.

Perforation errors and varieties. Authenticated errors, where a stamp normally perforated is accidentally issued imperforate, are listed provided no traces of perforation (blind holes or indentations) remain. They must be provided as pairs, both stamps wholly imperforate, and are only priced in that form.

Stamps merely imperforate between stamp and margin (fantails) are not listed.

Imperforate-between varieties are recognised, where one row of perfs has been missed. They are listed and priced in pairs:

Imperf between (horiz pair): a horizontal pair of stamps with perfs all around the edges but none between the stamps.

Imperf between (vert pair): a vertical pair of stamps with perfs all around the edges but none between the stamps.

Where several of the rows have escaped perforation the resulting varieties are listable. Thus:

Imperf vert (horiz pair): a horizontal pair of stamps perforated top and bottom; all three vertical directions are imperf – the two outer edges and between the stamps.

Imperf horiz (vert pair): a vertical pair perforated at left and right edges; all three horizontal directions are imperf – the top, bottom and between the stamps.

Straight edges. Large sheets cut up before issue to post offices can cause stamps with straight edges, i.e. imperf on one side or on two sides at right angles. They are not usually listable in this condition and are worth less than corresponding stamps properly perforated all round. This does not, however, apply to certain stamps, mainly from coils and booklets, where straight edges on various sides are the manufacturing norm affecting every stamp. The listings and notes make clear which sides are correctly imperf.

Malfunction. Varieties of double, misplaced or partial perforation caused by error or machine malfunction are not listable, neither are freaks, such as perforations placed diagonally from paper folds. Likewise disregarded are missing holes caused by broken pins, and perforations "fading out" down a sheet, the machinery progressively disengaging to leave blind perfs and indentations to the paper.

Centering. Well-centred stamps have designs surrounded by equal opposite margins. Where this condition affects the price the fact is stated.

Type of perforating. Where necessary for classification, perforation types are distinguished. These include:

Line perforation from one line of pins punching single rows of holes at a time.

Comb perforation from pins disposed across the sheet in comb formation, punching out holes at three sides of the stamp a row at a time.

Harrow perforation applied to a whole pane or sheet at one stroke.

Rotary perforation from the toothed wheels operating across a sheet, then crosswise.

Sewing-machine perforation. The resultant condition, clean-cut or rough, is distinguished where required.

Pin-perforation is the commonly applied term for pin-roulette in which, instead of being punched out, round holes are pricked by sharp-pointed pins and no paper is removed.

Punctured stamps. Perforation holes can be punched into the face of the stamp. Patterns of small holes, often in the shape of initial letters, are privately applied devices against pilferage. These "perfins" are outside the scope. Identification devices, when officially inspired, are listed or noted; they can be shapes, or letters or words formed from holes, sometimes converting one class of stamp into another.

Rouletting. In rouletting the paper is cut, for ease of separation, but none is removed. The gauge is measured, when needed, as for perforations. Traditional French terms descriptive of the type of cut are often used and types include:

Arc roulette (percé en arc). Cuts are minute, spaced arcs, each roughly a semicircle.

Cross roulette (percé en croix). Cuts are tiny diagonal crosses.

Line roulette (parcé en ligne or en ligne droite). Short straight cuts parallel to the frame of the stamp. The commonest basic roulette. Where not further described, "roulette" means this type.

Rouletted in colour or coloured roulette (percé en lignes colorees or en lignes de coleur). Cuts with coloured edges, arising from notched rule inked simultaneously with the printing plate.

Saw-tooth roulette (percé en scie). Cuts applied zigzag fashion to resemble the teeth of a saw.

Serpentine roulette (percé en serpentin). Cuts as sharply wavy lines.

Zigzag roulettes (percé en zigzags). Short straight cuts at angles in alternate directions, producing sharp points on separation. U.S. usage favours "serrate(d) roulette" for this type.

Pin-roulette (originally percé en points and now perforés trous d'epingle) is commonly called pin-perforation in English.

4. Gum

All stamps listed are assumed to have gum of some kind; if they were issued without gum this is stated. Original gum (o.g.) means that which was present on the stamp as issued to the public. Deleterious climates and the presence of certain chemicals can cause gum to crack and, with early stamps, even make the paper deteriorate. Unscrupulous fakers are adept in removing it and regumming the stamp to meet the unreasoning demand often made for "full o.g." in cases where such a thing is virtually impossible.

Until recent times the gum used for stamps has been gum arabic, but various synthetic adhesives – tinted or invisible-looking – have been in use since the 1960s. Stamps existing with more than one type of gum are not normally listed separately, though the fact is noted where it is of philatelic significance, e.g. in distinguishing reprints or new printings.

The distinct variety of grilled gum is, however, recognised. In this the paper is passed through a gum breaker prior to printing to prevent subsequent curling. As the patterned rollers were sufficient to impress a grill into the paper beneath the gum we can quote prices for both unused and used examples.

Self-adhesive stamps are issued on backing paper from which they are peeled before affixing to mail. Unused examples are priced as for backing paper intact. Used examples are best kept on cover or on piece.

5. Watermarks
Stamps are on unwatermarked paper except where the heading to the set says otherwise.
Detection. Watermarks are detected for Catalogue description by one of four methods:
(1) holding stamps to the light;
(2) laying stamps face down on a dark background;
(3) adding a few drops of petroleum ether 40/60 to the stamp laid face down in a watermark tray; or
(4) by use of the Stanley Gibbons Detectamark, or other equipment, which works by revealing the thinning of the paper at the watermark. (Note that petroleum ether is highly inflammable in use and can damage photogravure stamps.)
Listable types. Stamps occurring on both watermarked and unwatermarked papers are different types and both receive full listing.
Single watermarks (devices occurring once on every stamp) can be modified in size and shape as between different issues; the types are noted but not usually separately listed. Fortuitous absence of watermark from a single stamp or its gross displacement would not be listable.
To overcome registration difficulties the device may be repeated at close intervals (a multiple watermark); single stamps thus showing parts of several devices. Similarly a large sheet watermark (or all-over watermark) covering numerous stamps can be used. We give informative notes and illustrations for them. The designs may be such that numbers of stamps in the sheet automatically lack watermark; this is not a listable variety. Multiple and all-over watermarks sometimes undergo modifications, but if the various types are difficult to distinguish from single stamps notes are given but not separate listings.
Papermakers' watermarks are noted where known but not listed separately, since most stamps in the sheet will lack them. Sheet watermarks which are nothing more than officially adopted papermakers' watermarks are, however, given normal listing.
Marginal watermarks, falling outside the pane of stamps, are ignored except where misplacement causes the adjoining row to be affected, in which case they are footnoted.
Watermark errors and varieties. Watermark errors are recognised as of major importance. They comprise stamps intended to be on unwatermarked paper but issued watermarked by mistake, or stamps printed on paper with the wrong watermark. Watermark varieties, on the other hand, such as broken or deformed bits on the dandy roll, are not listable.
Watermark positions. Paper has a side intended for printing and watermarks are usually impressed so that they read normally when looked through from that printed side.

Illustrations in the Catalogue are of watermarks in normal positions (from the front of the stamps) and are actual size where possible.
Differences in watermark position are collectable as distinct varieties. In this Catalogue, however, only normal sideways watermarks are listed (and "sideways inverted" is treated as "sideways"). Inverted and reversed watermarks have always been outside its scope: in the early days of flat-bed printing, sheets of watermarked paper were fed indiscriminately through the press and the resulting watermark positions had no particular philatelic significance. Similarly, the special make-up of sheets for booklets can in some cases give equal quantities of normal and inverted watermarks.

6. Colours
Stamps in two or three colours have these named in order of appearance, from the centre moving outwards. Four colours or more are usually listed as multicoloured.
In compound colour names the second is the predominant one, thus:
orange-red = a red tending towards orange;
red-orange = an orange containing more red than usual.
Standard colours used. The 200 colours most used for stamp identification are given in the Stanley Gibbons Colour Key. The Catalogue has used the Key as a standard for describing new issues for some years. The names are also introduced as lists are rewritten, though exceptions are made for those early issues where traditional names have become universally established.
Determining colours. When comparing actual stamps with colour samples in the Key, view in a good north daylight (or its best substitute: fluorescent "colour-matching" light). Sunshine is not recommended. Choose a solid portion of the stamp design; if available, marginal markings such as solid bars of colour or colour check dots are helpful. Shading lines in the design can be misleading as they appear lighter than solid colour. Postmarked portions of a stamp appear darker than normal. If more than one colour is present, mask off the extraneous ones as the eye tends to mix them.
Errors of colour. Major colour errors in stamps or overprints which qualify for listing are: wrong colours; one colour inverted in relation to the rest; albinos (colourless impressions), where these have Expert Committee certificates; colours completely omitted, but only on unused stamps (if found on used stamps the information is footnoted).
Colours only partially omitted are not recognised. Colour shifts, however spectacular, are not listed.
Shades. Shades in philately refer to variations in the intensity of a colour or the presence of differing amounts of other colours. They are particularly significant when they can be linked to specific printings. In general, shades need to be quite marked to fall within the scope of this Catalogue; it does not favour nowadays listing the often numerous shades of a stamp, but chooses a single applicable colour name which will indicate particular groups of outstanding shades. Furthermore, the listings refer to colours as issued: they may deteriorate into something different through the passage of time.
Modern colour printing by lithography is prone to

marked differences of shade, even within a single run, and variations can occur within the same sheet. Such shades are not listed.

Aniline colours. An aniline colour meant originally one derived from coal-tar; it now refers more widely to colour of a particular brightness suffused on the surface of a stamp and showing through clearly on the back.

Colours of overprints and surcharges. All overprints and surcharges are in black unless otherwise in the heading or after the description of the stamp.

7. Luminescence

Machines which sort mail electronically have been introduced in recent years. In consequence some countries have issued stamps on fluorescent or phosphorescent papers, while others have marked their stamps with phosphor bands.

The various papers can only be distinguished by ultraviolet lamps emitting particular wavelengths. They are separately listed only when the stamps have some other means of distinguishing them, visible without the use of these lamps. Where this is not so, the papers are recorded in footnotes or headings. (Collectors using the lamps should exercise great care in their use as exposure to their light is extremely dangerous to the eyes.)

Phosphor bands are listable, since they are visible to the naked eye (by holding stamps at an angle to the light and looking along them, the bands appear dark). Stamps existing with and without phosphor bands or with differing numbers of bands are given separate listings. Varieties such as double bands, misplaced or omitted bands, bands printed on the wrong side, are not listed.

8. Coil Stamps

Stamps issued only in coil form are given full listing. If stamps are issued in both sheets and coils the coil stamps are listed separately only where there is some feature (e.g. perforation) by which singles can be distinguished. Coil strips containing different stamps *se-tenant* are also listed.

Coil join pairs are too random and too easily faked to permit of listing; similarly ignored are coil stamps which have accidentally suffered an extra row of perforations from the claw mechanism in a malfunctioning vending machine.

9. Booklet Stamps

Single stamps from booklets are listed if they are distinguishable in some way (such as watermark or perforation) from similar sheet stamps. Booklet panes, provided they are distinguishable from blocks of sheet stamps, are listed for most countries; booklet panes containing more than one value *se-tenant* are listed under the lowest of the values concerned.

Lists of stamp booklets are given for certain countries and it is intended to extend this generally.

10. Forgeries and Fakes

Forgeries. Where space permits, notes are considered if they can give a concise description that will permit unequivocal detection of a forgery. Generalised warnings, lacking detail, are not nowadays inserted since their value to the collector is problematic.

Fakes. Unwitting fakes are numerous, particularly "new shades" which are colour changelings brought about by exposure to sunlight, soaking in water contaminated with dyes from adherent paper, contact with oil and dirt from a pocketbook, and so on. Fraudulent operators, in addition, can offer to arrange: removal of hinge marks; repairs of thins on white or coloured papers; replacement of missing margins or perforations; reperforating in true or false gauges; removal of fiscal cancellations; rejoining of severed pairs, strips and blocks; and (a major hazard) regumming. Collectors can only be urged to purchase from reputable sources and to insist upon Expert Committee certification where there is any doubt.

The Catalogue can consider footnotes about fakes where these are specific enough to assist in detection.

PRICES

Prices quoted in this Catalogue are the selling prices of Stanley Gibbons Ltd at the time when the book went to press. They are for stamps in fine condition for the issue concerned; in issues where condition varies they may ask more for the superb and less for the sub-standard.

All prices are subject to change without prior notice and Stanley Gibbons Ltd may from time to time offer stamps at other than catalogue prices in consequence of special purchases or particular promotions.

No guarantee is given to supply all stamps priced, since it is not possible to keep every catalogued item in stock. Commemorative issues may, at times, only be available in complete sets and not as individual values.

Quotations of prices. The prices in the left-hand column are for unused stamps and those in the right-hand column are for used.

Prices are expressed in pounds and pence sterling. One pound comprises 100 pence (£1 = 100p).

The method of notation is as follows: pence in numerals (e.g. 10 denotes ten pence); pounds and pence up to £100, in numerals (e.g. 4·25 denotes four pounds and twenty-five pence); prices above £100 expressed in whole pounds with the "£" sign shown.

Unused stamps. Prices for stamps issued up to the end of the Second World War (1945) are for lightly hinged examples and more may be asked if they are in unmounted mint condition. Prices for all later unused stamps are for unmounted mint. Where not available in this condition, lightly hinged stamps are often available at a lower price.

Used stamps. The used prices are normally for stamps postally used but may be for stamps cancelled-to-order where this practice exists.

A pen-cancellation on early issues can sometimes correctly denote postal use. Instances are individually noted in the Catalogue in explanation of the used price given.

Prices quoted for bisects on cover or on large piece are for those dated during the period officially authorised.

Stamps not sold unused to the public but affixed by postal officials before use (e.g. some parcel post stamps) are priced used only.

Minimum price. The minimum catalogue price quoted is 10p. For individual stamps prices between 10p and 95p are provided as a guide for catalogue users. The lowest price charged for individual stamps purchased from Stanley Gibbons Ltd. is £1.

Set prices. Set prices are generally for one of each value, excluding shades and varieties, but including major coulour changes. Where there are alternative shades, etc, the cheapest is usually included. The number of stamps in the set is always stated for clarity.

Where prices are given for *se-tenant* blocks or strips, any mint set price quoted for such an issue is for the complete *se-tenant* strip plus any other stamps included in the set. Used set prices are always for a set of single stamps.

Repricing. Collectors will be aware that the market factors of supply and demand directly influence the prices quoted in this Catalogue. Whatever the scarcity of a particular stamp, if there is no one in the market who wishes to buy it it cannot be expected to achieve a high price. Conversely, the same item actively sought by numerous potential buyers may cause the price to rise.

All the prices in this Catalogue are examined during the preparation of each new edition by expert staff of Stanley Gibbons and repriced as necessary. They take many factors into account, including supply and demand, and are in close touch with the international stamp market and the auction world.

GUARANTEE

All stamps are guaranteed genuine originals in the following terms:

If not as described, and returned by the purchaser, we undertake to refund the price paid to us in the original transaction. If any stamp is certified as genuine by the Expert Committee of the Royal Philatelic Society, London, or by B.P.A. Expertising Ltd, the purchaser shall not be entitled to make claim against us for any error, omission or mistake in such certificate. Consumers' statutory rights are not affected by this guarantee.

The establishment Expert Committees in this country are those of the Royal Philatelic Society, 41 Devonshire Place, London W1N 1PE, and B.P.A. Expertising Ltd, P.O. Box 137, Leatherhead, Surrey KT22 0RG. They do not undertake valuations under any circumstances and fees are payable for their services.

Abbreviations

Printers

A.B.N. Co.	American Bank Note Co, New York.
A. & M.	Alden & Mowbray Ltd., Oxford.
Aspioti-Elka (Aspiotis)	Aspioti-Elka, Corfu, Greece
B.A.B.N.	British American Bank Note Co. Ottawa
B.D.T.	B.D.T. International Security Printing Ltd, Dublin, Ireland.
B.W.	Bradbury Wilkinson & Co, Ltd.
C.B.N.	Canadian Bank Note Co, Ottawa.
Chalot -Deheneffe	Chalot-Deheneffe S.A. Brussels, Belgium.
Continental B.N. Co.	Continental Bank Note Co.
Courvoisier	Imprimerie Courvoisier S.A., La-Chaux-de-Fonds, Switzerland.
D.L.R.	De La Rue & Co, Ltd, London.
Edila	Editions de l'Aubetin S.A.
Enschedé	Joh. Enschedé en Zonen, Haarlem, Netherlands.
Harrison	Harrison & Sons, Ltd. London
Heraclio Fournier	Heraclio Fournier S.A. Vitoria, Spain.
J.W.	John Waddington of Kirkstall Ltd
P.B.	Perkins Bacon Ltd, London.
Questa	Questa Colour Security Printers Ltd
Walsall	Walsall Security Printers Ltd
Waterlow	Waterlow & Sons, Ltd, London.

General Abbreviations

Alph	Alphabet
Anniv	Anniversary
Comp	Compound (perforation)
Des	Designer; designed
Diag	Diagonal; diagonally
Eng	Engraver; engraved
F.C.	Fiscal Cancellation
H/S	Handstamped
Horiz	Horizontal; horizontally
Imp, Imperf	Imperforate
Inscr	Inscribed
L	Left
Litho	Lithographed
mm	Millimetres
MS	Miniature sheet
N.Y.	New York
Opt(d)	Overprint(ed)
P or P-c	Pen-cancelled
P, Pf or Perf	Perforated
Photo	Photogravure
Pl	Plate
Pr	Pair

Ptd	Printed
Ptg	Printing
R	Right
R.	Row
Recess	Recess-printed
Roto	Rotogravure
Roul	Rouletted
S	Specimen (overprint)
Surch	Surcharge(d)
T.C.	Telegraph Cancellation
T	Type
Typo	Typographed
Un	Unused
Us	Used
Vert	Vertical; vertically
W or wmk	Watermark
Wmk s	Watermark sideways

(†) = Does not exist
(−) (or blank price column) = Exists, or may exist, but no market price is known.
/ between colours means "on" and the colour following is that of the paper on which the stamp is printed.

Colours of Stamps

Bl (blue); blk (black); brn (brown); car, carm (carmine); choc (chocolate); clar (claret); emer (emerald); grn (green); ind (indigo); mag (magenta); mar (maroon); mult (multicoloured); mve (mauve); ol (olive); orge (orange); pk (pink); pur (purple); scar (scarlet); sep (sepia); turq (turquoise); ultram (ultramarine); verm (vermilion); vio (violet); yell (yellow).

Colour of Overprints and Surcharges

(B.) = blue, (Blk.) = black, (Br.) = brown, (C.) = carmine, (G.) = green, (Mag.) = magenta, (Mve.) = mauve, (Ol.) = olive, (O.) = orange, (P.) = purple, (Pk.) = pink, (R.) = red, (Sil.) = silver, (V.) = violet, (Vm.) or (Verm.) = vermilion, (W.) = white, (Y.) = yellow.

Arabic Numerals

As in the case of European figures, the details of the Arabic numerals vary in different stamp designs, but they should be readily recognised with the aid of this illustration.

٠	١	٢	٣	٤	٥	٦	٧	٨	٩
0	1	2	3	4	5	6	7	8	9

International Philatelic Glossary

English	French	German	Spanish	Italian
Agate	Agate	Achat	Agata	Agata
Air stamp	Timbre de la poste aérienne	Flugpostmarke	Sello de correo aéreo	Francobollo per posta aerea
Apple Green	Vert-pomme	Apfelgrün	Verde manzana	Verde mela
Barred	Annulé par barres	Balkenentwertung	Anulado con barras	Sbarrato
Bisected	Timbre coupé	Halbiert	Partido en dos	Frazionato
Bistre	Bistre	Bister	Bistre	Bistro
Bistre-brown	Brun-bistre	Bisterbraun	Castaño bistre	Bruno-bistro
Black	Noir	Schwarz	Negro	Nero
Blackish Brown	Brun-noir	Schwärzlichbraun	Castaño negruzco	Bruno nerastro
Blackish Green	Vert foncé	Schwärzlichgrün	Verde negruzco	Verde nerastro
Blackish Olive	Olive foncé	Schwärzlicholiv	Oliva negruzco	Oliva nerastro
Block of four	Bloc de quatre	Viererblock	Bloque de cuatro	Bloco di quattro
Blue	Bleu	Blau	Azul	Azzurro
Blue-green	Vert-bleu	Blaugrün	Verde azul	Verde azzuro
Bluish Violet	Violet bleuâtre	Bläulichviolett	Violeta azulado	Violtto azzurrastro
Booklet	Carnet	Heft	Cuadernillo	Libretto
Bright Blue	Bleu vif	Lebhaftblau	Azul vivo	Azzurro vivo
Bright Green	Vert vif	Lebhaftgrün	Verde vivo	Verde vivo
Bright Purple	Mauve vif	Lebhaftpurpur	Púrpura vivo	Porpora vivo
Bronze Green	Vert-bronze	Bronzegrün	Verde bronce	Verde bronzo
Brown	Brun	Braun	Castaño	Bruno
Brown-lake	Carmin-brun	Braunlack	Laca castaño	Lacca bruno
Brown-purple	Pourpre-brun	Braunpurpur	Púrpura castaño	Porpora bruno
Brown-red	Rouge-brun	Braunrot	Rojo castaño	Rosso bruno
Buff	Chamois	Sämisch	Anteado	Camoscio
Cancellation	Oblitération	Entwertung	Cancelación	Annullamento
Cancelled	Annulé	Gestempelt	Cancelado	Annullato
Carmine	Carmin	Karmin	Carmín	Carminio
Carmine-red	Rouge-carmin	Karminrot	Rojo carmín	Rosso carminio
Centred	Centré	Zentriert	Centrado	Centrato
Cerise	Rouge-cerise	Kirschrot	Color de ceresa	Color Ciliegia
Chalk-surfaced paper	Papier couché	Kreidepapier	Papel estucado	Carta gessata
Chalky Blue	Bleu terne	Kreideblau	Azul turbio	Azzurro smorto
Charity stamp	Timbre de bienfaisance	Wohltätigkeitsmarke	Sello de beneficenza	Francobollo di beneficenza
Chestnut	Marron	Kastanienbraun	Castaño rojo	Marrone
Chocolate	Chocolat	Schokolade	Chocolate	Cioccolato
Cinnamon	Cannelle	Zimtbraun	Canela	Cannella
Claret	Grenat	Weinrot	Rojo vinoso	Vinaccia
Cobalt	Cobalt	Kobalt	Cobalto	Cobalto
Colour	Couleur	Farbe	Color	Colore
Comb-perforation	Dentelure en peigne	Kammzähnung, Reihenzähnung	Dentado de peine	Dentellatura e pettine

English	French	German	Spanish	Italian
Commemorative stamp	Timbre commémoratif	Gedenkmarke	Sello conmemorativo	Francobollo commemorativo
Crimson	Cramoisi	Karmesin	Carmesí	Cremisi
Deep Blue	Blue foncé	Dunkelblau	Azul oscuro	Azzurro scuro
Deep bluish Green	Vert-bleu foncé	Dunkelbläulichgrün	Verde azulado oscuro	Verde azzurro scuro
Design	Dessin	Markenbild	Diseño	Disegno
Die	Matrice	Urstempel. Type Platte,	Cuño	Conio, Matrice
Double	Double	Doppelt	Doble	Doppio
Drab	Olive terne	Trüboliv	Oliva turbio	Oliva smorto
Dull Green	Vert terne	Trübgrün	Verde turbio	Verde smorto
Dull purple	Mauve terne	Trübpurpur	Púrpura turbio	Porpora smorto
Embossing	Impression en relief	Prägedruck	Impresión en relieve	Impressione a relievo
Emerald	Vert-eméraude	Smaragdgrün	Esmeralda	Smeraldo
Engraved	Gravé	Graviert	Grabado	Inciso
Error	Erreur	Fehler, Fehldruck	Error	Errore
Essay	Essai	Probedruck	Ensayo	Saggio
Express letter stamp	Timbre pour lettres par exprès	Eilmarke	Sello de urgencia	Francobollo per espresso
Fiscal stamp	Timbre fiscal	Stempelmarke	Sello fiscal	Francobollo fiscale
Flesh	Chair	Fleischfarben	Carne	Carnicino
Forgery	Faux, Falsification	Fälschung	Falsificación	Falso, Falsificazione
Frame	Cadre	Rahmen	Marco	Cornice
Granite paper	Papier avec fragments de fils de soie	Faserpapier	Papel con filamentos	Carto con fili di seta
Green	Vert	Grün	Verde	Verde
Greenish Blue	Bleu verdâtre	Grünlichblau	Azul verdoso	Azzurro verdastro
Greenish Yellow	Jaune-vert	Grünlichgelb	Amarillo verdoso	Giallo verdastro
Grey	Gris	Grau	Gris	Grigio
Grey-blue	Bleu-gris	Graublau	Azul gris	Azzurro grigio
Grey-green	Vert gris	Graugrün	Verde gris	Verde grigio
Gum	Gomme	Gummi	Goma	Gomma
Gutter	Interpanneau	Zwischensteg	Espacio blanco entre dos grupos	Ponte
Imperforate	Non-dentelé	Geschnitten	Sin dentar	Non dentellato
Indigo	Indigo	Indigo	Azul indigo	Indaco
Inscription	Inscription	Inschrift	Inscripción	Dicitura
Inverted	Renversé	Kopfstehend	Invertido	Capovolto
Issue	Émission	Ausgabe	Emisión	Emissione
Laid	Vergé	Gestreift	Listado	Vergato
Lake	Lie de vin	Lackfarbe	Laca	Lacca
Lake-brown	Brun-carmin	Lackbraun	Castaño laca	Bruno lacca
Lavender	Bleu-lavande	Lavendel	Color de alhucema	Lavanda
Lemon	Jaune-citron	Zitrongelb	Limón	Limone
Light Blue	Bleu clair	Hellblau	Azul claro	Azzurro chiaro

English	French	German	Spanish	Italian
Lilac	Lilas	Lila	Lila	Lilla
Line perforation	Dentelure en lignes	Linienzähnung	Dentado en linea	Dentellatura lineare
Lithography	Lithographie	Steindruck	Litografía	Litografia
Local	Timbre de poste locale	Lokalpostmarke	Emisión local	Emissione locale
Lozenge roulette	Percé en losanges	Rautenförmiger Durchstich	Picadura en rombos	Perforazione a losanghe
Magenta	Magenta	Magentarot	Magenta	Magenta
Margin	Marge	Rand	Borde	Margine
Maroon	Marron pourpré	Dunkelrotpurpur	Púrpura rojo oscuro	Marrone rossastro
Mauve	Mauve	Malvenfarbe	Malva	Malva
Multicoloured	Polychrome	Mehrfarbig	Multicolores	Policromo
Myrtle Green	Vert myrte	Myrtengrün	Verde mirto	Verde mirto
New Blue	Bleu ciel vif	Neublau	Azul nuevo	Azzurro nuovo
Newspaper stamp	Timbre pour journaux	Zeitungsmarke	Sello para periódicos	Francobollo per giornali
Obliteration	Oblitération	Abstempelung	Matasello	Annullamento
Obsolete	Hors (de) cours	Ausser Kurs	Fuera de curso	Fuori corso
Ochre	Ocre	Ocker	Ocre	Ocra
Official stamp	Timbre de service	Dienstmarke	Sello de servicio	Francobollo di
Olive-brown	Brun-olive	Olivbraun	Castaño oliva	Bruno oliva
Olive-green	Vert-olive	Olivgrün	Verde oliva	Verde oliva
Olive-grey	Gris-olive	Olivgrau	Gris oliva	Grigio oliva
Olive-yellow	Jaune-olive	Olivgelb	Amarillo oliva	Giallo oliva
Orange	Orange	Orange	Naranja	Arancio
Orange-brown	Brun-orange	Orangebraun	Castaño naranja	Bruno arancio
Orange-red	Rouge-orange	Orangerot	Rojo naranja	Rosso arancio
Orange-yellow	Jaune-orange	Orangegelb	Amarillo naranja	Giallo arancio
Overprint	Surcharge	Aufdruck	Sobrecarga	Soprastampa
Pair	Paire	Paar	Pareja	Coppia
Pale	Pâle	Blass	Pálido	Pallido
Pane	Panneau	Gruppe	Grupo	Gruppo
Paper	Papier	Papier	Papel	Carta
Parcel post stamp	Timbre pour colis postaux	Paketmarke	Sello para paquete postal	Francobollo per pacchi postali
Pen-cancelled	Oblitéré à plume	Federzugentwertung	Cancelado a pluma	Annullato a penna
Percé en arc	Percé en arc	Bogenförmiger Durchstich	Picadura en forma de arco	Perforazione ad arco
Percé en scie	Percé en scie	Bogenförmiger Durchstich	Picado en sierra	Foratura a sega
Perforated	Dentelé	Gezähnt	Dentado	Dentellato
Perforation	Dentelure	Zähnung	Dentar	Dentellatura
Photogravure	Photogravure, Heliogravure	Rastertiefdruck	Fotograbado	Rotocalco
Pin perforation	Percé en points	In Punkten durchstochen	Horadado con alfileres	Perforato a punti
Plate	Planche	Platte	Plancha	Lastra, Tavola
Plum	Prune	Pflaumenfarbe	Color de ciruela	Prugna
Postage Due stamp	Timbre-taxe	Portomarke	Sello de tasa	Segnatasse

English	French	German	Spanish	Italian
Postage stamp	Timbre-poste	Briefmarke, Freimarke, Postmarke	Sello de correos	Francobollo postale
Postal fiscal stamp	Timbre fiscal-postal	Stempelmarke als Postmarke verwendet	Sello fiscal-postal	Fiscale postale
Postmark	Oblitération postale	Poststempel	Matasello	Bollo
Printing	Impression, Tirage	Druck	Impresión	Stampa, Tiratura
Proof	Épreuve	Druckprobe	Prueba de impresión	Prova
Provisionals	Timbres provisoires	Provisorische Marken. Provisorien	Provisionales	Provvisori
Prussian Blue	Bleu de Prusse	Preussischblau	Azul de Prusia	Azzurro di Prussia
Purple	Pourpre	Purpur	Púrpura	Porpora
Purple-brown	Brun-pourpre	Purpurbraun	Castaño púrpura	Bruno porpora
Recess-printing	Impression en taille douce	Tiefdruck	Grabado	Incisione
Red	Rouge	Rot	Rojo	Rosso
Red-brown	Brun-rouge	Rotbraun	Castaño rojizo	Bruno rosso
Reddish Lilac	Lilas rougeâtre	Rötlichlila	Lila rojizo	Lilla rossastro
Reddish Purple	Poupre-rouge	Rötlichpurpur	Púrpura rojizo	Porpora rossastro
Reddish Violet	Violet rougeâtre	Rötlichviolett	Violeta rojizo	Violetto rossastro
Red-orange	Orange rougeâtre	Rotorange	Naranja rojizo	Arancio rosso
Registration stamp	Timbre pour lettre chargée (recommandée)	Einschreibemarke	Sello de certificado lettere	Francobollo per raccomandate
Reprint	Réimpression	Neudruck	Reimpresión	Ristampa
Reversed	Retourné	Umgekehrt	Invertido	Rovesciato
Rose	Rose	Rosa	Rosa	Rosa
Rose-red	Rouge rosé	Rosarot	Rojo rosado	Rosso rosa
Rosine	Rose vif	Lebhaftrosa	Rosa vivo	Rosa vivo
Roulette	Percage	Durchstich	Picadura	Foratura
Rouletted	Percé	Durchstochen	Picado	Forato
Royal Blue	Bleu-roi	Königblau	Azul real	Azzurro reale
Sage green	Vert-sauge	Salbeigrün	Verde salvia	Verde salvia
Salmon	Saumon	Lachs	Salmón	Salmone
Scarlet	Écarlate	Scharlach	Escarlata	Scarlatto
Sepia	Sépia	Sepia	Sepia	Seppia
Serpentine roulette	Percé en serpentin	Schlangenliniger Durchstich	Picado a serpentina	Perforazione a serpentina
Shade	Nuance	Tönung	Tono	Gradazione de colore
Sheet	Feuille	Bogen	Hoja	Foglio
Slate	Ardoise	Schiefer	Pizarra	Ardesia
Slate-blue	Bleu-ardoise	Schieferblau	Azul pizarra	Azzurro ardesia
Slate-green	Vert-ardoise	Schiefergrün	Verde pizarra	Verde ardesia
Slate-lilac	Lilas-gris	Schierferlila	Lila pizarra	Lilla ardesia
Slate-purple	Mauve-gris	Schieferpurpur	Púrpura pizarra	Porpora ardesia
Slate-violet	Violet-gris	Schieferviolett	Violeta pizarra	Violetto ardesia
Special delivery stamp	Timbre pour exprès	Eilmarke	Sello de urgencia	Francobollo per espressi
Specimen	Spécimen	Muster	Muestra	Saggio

English	French	German	Spanish	Italian
Steel Blue	Bleu acier	Stahlblau	Azul acero	Azzurro acciaio
Strip	Bande	Streifen	Tira	Striscia
Surcharge	Surcharge	Aufdruck	Sobrecarga	Soprastampa
Tête-bêche	Tête-bêche	Kehrdruck	Tête-bêche	Tête-bêche
Tinted paper	Papier teinté	Getöntes Papier	Papel coloreado	Carta tinta
Too-late stamp	Timbre pour lettres en retard	Verspätungsmarke	Sello para cartas retardadas	Francobollo per le lettere in ritardo
Turquoise-blue	Bleu-turquoise	Türkisblau	Azul turquesa	Azzurro turchese
Turquoise-green	Vert-turquoise	Türkisgrün	Verde turquesa	Verde turchese
Typography	Typographie	Buchdruck	Tipografía	Tipografia
Ultramarine	Outremer	Ultramarin	Ultramar	Oltremare
Unused	Neuf	Ungebraucht	Nuevo	Nuovo
Used	Oblitéré, Usé	Gebraucht	Usado	Usato
Venetian Red	Rouge-brun terne	Venezianischrot	Rojo veneciano	Rosso veneziano
Vermilion	Vermillon	Zinnober	Cinabrio	Vermiglione
Violet	Violet	Violett	Violeta	Violetto
Violet-blue	Bleu-violet	Violettblau	Azul violeta	Azzurro violetto
Watermark	Filigrane	Wasserzeichen	Filigrana	Filigrana
Watermark sideways	Filigrane couché liegend	Wasserzeichen	Filigrana acostado	Filigrana coricata
Wove paper	Papier ordinaire, Papier uni	Einfaches Papier	Papel avitelado	Carta unita
Yellow	Jaune	Gelb	Amarillo	Giallo
Yellow-brown	Brun-jaune	Gelbbraun	Castaño amarillo	Bruno giallo
Yellow-green	Vert-jaune	Gelbgrün	Verde amarillo	Verde giallo
Yellow-olive	Olive-jaunâtre	Gelboliv	Oliva amarillo	Oliva giallastro
Yellow-orange	Orange jaunâtre	Gelborange	Naranja amarillo	Arancio giallastro
Zig-zag roulette	Percé en zigzag	Sägezahnartiger Durchstich	Picado en zigzag	Perforazione a zigzag

Complete List of Parts

1   Commonwealth & British Empire Stamps 1840–1970
(Annual)

Foreign Countries

2   Austria & Hungary (6th edition, 2002)
• Austria • U.N. (Vienna) • Hungary

3   Balkans (4th edition, 1998)
• Albania • Bosnia & Herzegovina • Bulgaria
• Croatia • Greece & Islands • Macedonia
• Romania • Slovenia • Yugoslavia

4   Benelux (5th edition, 2003)
• Belgium & Colonies • Luxembourg
• Netherlands & Colonies

5   Czechoslovakia & Poland (6th edition, 2002)
• Czechoslovakia • Czech Republic • Slovakia
• Poland

6   France (6th edition, 2006)
• France • Colonies • Post Offices • Andorra
• Monaco

7   Germany (8th edition, 2008)
• Germany • States • Colonies • Post Offices

8   Italy & Switzerland (6th edition, 2003)
• Italy & Colonies • Liechtenstein • San Marino
• Switzerland • U.N. (Geneva) • Vatican City

9   Portugal & Spain (5th edition, 2004)
• Andorra • Portugal & Colonies
• Spain & Colonies

10 Russia (5th edition, 1999)
• Russia • Armenia • Azerbaijan • Belarus
• Estonia • Georgia • Kazakhstan • Kyrgyzstan
• Latvia • Lithuania • Moldova • Tajikistan
• Turkmenistan • Ukraine • Uzbekistan
• Mongolia

11 Scandinavia (5th edition, 2001)
• Aland Islands • Denmark • Faroe Islands
• Finland • Greenland • Iceland • Norway
• Sweden

12 Africa since Independence A-E
(2nd edition, 1983)
• Algeria • Angola • Benin • Burundi • Cameroun
• Cape Verde • Central African Republic
• Chad • Comoro Islands • Congo • Djibouti
• Equatorial Guinea • Ethiopia

13 Africa since Independence F-M
(1st edition, 1981)
• Gabon • Guinea • Guinea-Bissau • Ivory Coast
• Liberia • Libya • Malagasy Republic • Mali
• Mauritania • Morocco • Mozambique

14 Africa since Independence N-Z
(1st edition, 1981)
• Niger Republic • Rwanda • St. Thomas & Prince
• Senegal • Somalia • Sudan • Togo • Tunisia
• Upper Volta • Zaire

15 Central America (3rd edition, 2007)
• Costa Rica • Cuba • Dominican Republic
• El Salvador • Guatemala • Haiti • Honduras
• Mexico • Nicaragua • Panama

16 Central Asia (4th edition, 2006)
• Afghanistan • Iran • Turkey

17 China (6th edition, 1998)
• China • Taiwan • Tibet • Foreign P.O.s
• Hong Kong • Macao

18 Japan & Korea (5th edition, 2008)
• Japan • Korean Empire • South Korea
• North Korea

19 Middle East (6th edition, 2005)
• Aden • Bahrain • Egypt • Iraq • Israel • Jordan
• Kuwait • Lebanon • Oman • Qatar
• Saudi Arabia • Syria • U.A.E. • Yemen

20 South America (3rd edition, 1989)
• Argentina • Bolivia • Brazil • Chile • Colombia
• Ecuador • Paraguay • Peru • Surinam
• Uruguay • Venezuela

21 South-East Asia (4th edition, 2004)
• Bhutan • Cambodia • Indo-China • Indonesia
• Laos • Myanmar • Nepal • Philippines
• Thailand • Timor • Vietnam

22 United States (6th edition, 2005)
• U.S. & Possessions • Canal Zone
• Marshall Islands • Micronesia • Palau
• U.N. (New York, Geneva, Vienna)

Thematic Catalogues

Stanley Gibbons Catalogues for use
with **Stamps of the World.**

Collect Aircraft on Stamps	(out of print)
Collect Birds on Stamps	(5th edition, 2003)
Collect Chess on Stamps	(2nd edition, 1999)
Collect Fish on Stamps	(1st edition, 1999)
Collect Fungi on Stamps	(2nd edition, 1997)
Collect Motor Vehicles on Stamps	
	(1st edition, 2004)
Collect Railways on Stamps	(3rd edition, 1999)
Collect Shells on Stamps	(1st edition, 1995)
Collect Ships on Stamps	(3rd edition, 2001)

Japan

EMPEROR MUTSUHITO
30 January 1867–30 July 1912

The Emperor succeeded to the Imperial throne in 1867 and Imperial rule replaced that of the last Shogun on 3 January 1868.

"Sumiten"   "Mihon"

(*Actual size*)

"SPECIMEN" OVERPRINTS. Most Japanese stamps exist with overprints signifying "Specimen" and these are illustrated above so that they are not confused with ordinary stamps. The "sumiten" dot overprint always occurs in black but the "mihon" overprints are known in black or red. There is a second type of the latter comprising two different characters.

The "DRAGON" Series

1 (48 mon)   **2** (100 mon)

3 (200 mon)   **4** (500 mon)

(Pair of Dragons facing Value Characters)

48 MON

 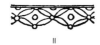

I   II

I. Dots in inner frame
II. Circles in inner frame

100 MON

I   II

Note differences in Dragon claws; right foreleg of western dragon; right hind leg of eastern dragon.

200 MON

I   II

Plate I has dot as shown in top north-west corner ornament.

500 MON

I   II

Note difference in bottom south-east corner ornament.

(Eng A. Matsuda. Recess Matsuda, Kyoto)

1871 (20 Apr). Value inscription in black. Imperf. Ungummed. Two plates for each value.

A. Native LAID paper

			Un	Used
1	1	48m. brown (I)	£250	£375
2		48m. brown (II)	£275	£375
3	2	100m. blue (I)	£225	£300
4		100m. deep blue (II)	£500	£450
		a. Missing foreleg, East dragon (No. 18)	£25000	£20000
		b. Retouched head (No. 26)	£13000	£9000
5	3	200m. vermilion (I)	£375	£325
		a. Reddish orange (I)	£375	£325
		b. Missing foreleg. West dragon (No. 31)	£14000	£9000
6		200m. orange-vermilion (II)	£1700	£1500
7	4	500m. pale yellow-green (I)	£1900	£1200
		aa. Value characters inverted	—£164000	
		a. Green (I)	£1400	£1100
		b. Blue-green (I)	£550	£475
		c. Deep greenish blue (I)	£500	£500
		d. Missing stroke, top character (No. 2)	—	£50000
		e. Missing dot and stroke, top character (No. 3)	—	£50000
8		500m. deep greenish blue (II)	£550	£3250
		a. Blue-green (II)	£550	£3250

The laid paper exists vertically laid, horizontally laid and quadrillé laid in all values.

B. Native WOVE paper

9	1	48m. brown (I)	£300	£375
10		48m. brown (II)	£300	£375
11	2	100m. blue (I)	£475	£400
12		100m. deep blue (II)	£800	£800
		a. Missing foreleg, East dragon (No.18)	£12000	£9000
		b. Retouched head (No. 26)	£3750	£3500
13	3	200m. vermilion (I)	£450	£425
		a. Missing foreleg. West dragon (No. 31)	£6500	£5500
		b. *Reddish orange* (I)	£450	£425
14		200m. orange-vermilion (I)	—	£3500
15	4	500m. pale yellow-green (I)	£1000	£800
		a. *Green* (I)	£1000	£800
		b. *Blue-green* (I)	£550	£550
		c. Missing stroke, top character (No. 2)	—	£50000
		d. Missing dot and stroke, top character (No. 3)		£50000
16		500m. deep greenish blue (II)	£2000	£4500
		a. *Blue-green* (II)	£2000	£4500

The plates were hand-engraved with forty varieties to each plate.

1 (½ sen)   2 (1 sen)   3 (2 sen)   4 (5 sen)

The "SEN" issue. The frame plates of the "Mon" issue, with new centre plates as illustrated, were used for this issue. In addition *new* frame plates were made later for the ½ sen and 1 sen. We list the third plate of the 1 sen separately, but not the ½ sen third plate, which is very difficult to distinguish.

1 SEN

I and II   III

Plate III has the Dragon faces much spottier and there is a much wider space between the outer frameline) than in Plates I and II.

1872 (Feb–May). Currency changed. Value in black. Rough irregular perfs from 9 to 12½ approx. With and without gum.

A. Thin Native LAID paper

17		½s. brown (II, III)	90·00	£130
		a. Grey	£140	£225
18		1s. deep blue (I)	£1100	£2500
19		1s. blue (II)	£325	£325
		a. Missing foreleg, East dragon (No. 18)	£600	£600
		b. Retouched head (No. 26)	—	£1000
20		1s. blue (III)	£8000	£1900
21		2s. orange-vermilion (II)	£475	£500
22		5s. green to blue-green (II)	£650	£650

B. Medium to thick Native WOVE paper

23		½s. brown (II, III)	£1700	£900
24		1s. deep blue (I, II, III)	£4500	£1000
25		2s. vermilion (II)	—	£700
26		5s. green (II)	—	£2500

C. Thin Native PELURE Wove Paper

27		½s. brown (II)	£150	£160
29		1s. pale blue (II)	£800	£1500
		a. Missing foreleg. East dragon (No.18)	£2000	£2500
31		2s. vermilion (II)	£475	£500
32		5s. green (II)	£650	£550

Official imitations were made in 1894 of the 1s. and 2s. on thin ordinary white laid paper, imperf.

Genuine stamps of the first two issues bearing forged cancellations are not infrequently met with, often upon what purports to be the original cover.

The "CHERRY BLOSSOM" Series

5   6   7

8   9   10

(Eng A. Matsuda. Recess Matsuda, Tokyo)

1872 (23 Aug–3 Oct). Various hard native wove papers. Short perf 9½ to 12½ and compounds.

34	5	½s. red-brown (3 Oct)	20·00	25·00
		a. Brown	23·00	28·00
35	6	1s. intense blue	80·00	46·00
36	7	2s. vermilion	£170	60·00
37	8	10s. blue-green	£300	£190
		a. Green	£300	£190
38	9	20s. violet (3 Oct)	£400	£275
		a. Lilac	£425	£325
39	10	30s. black (3 Oct)	£550	£450

Medium paper except for scarce thin paper (0.06–0.07 mm).

(Eng A. Matsuda and S. Umemura. Recess Govt Ptg Works, Tokyo)

1872 (6 Oct). Various soft native laid papers. Long perf 10 to 13 and compounds.

40	5	½s. grey-brown	70·00	
		a. Wove paper	75·00	
41	6	1s. blue	70·00	45·00
		a. Wove paper	75·00	45·00
42	7	2s. red	£160	60·00
		a. Wove paper	£160	65·00
43	8	10s. pale yellow-green	£400	£275
		a. Wove paper	£450	£375
44	9	20s. red-violet	—£146000	

Paper varies between thick (over 0.12 mm), medium, and thin (less than 0.07 mm). The ½s. was not issued but a few are known used. Hand-engraved with forty varieties to each plate. Four plates are known for the ½s., twenty-six for the 1s. (of which only the first four were used for No. 35), and two for the 2s. Only one plate for the 10s., 20s. and 30s.

In the above issues there are many varieties such as incomplete characters which are of interest to specialists but they are beyond the scope of this catalogue.

11   12

(Eng A. Matsuda and S. Umemura. Recess Govt Ptg Works, Tokyo)

1873. As last but colour changed and new value.

45	7	2s. yellow (5 June)	£140	43·00
		a. Wove paper	£550	£180
46	11	4s. dull rose (1 April)	£140	33·00
		a. Wove paper	£300	41·00

Fourteen plates are known for the 4s.

KATAKANA (Syllabic Alphabet)
As used for the notation of plate numbers

イ	1 (i)	ワ	13 (wa)
ロ	2 (ro)	カ	14 (ka)
ハ	3 (ha)	ヨ	15 (yo)
ニ	4 (ni)	タ	16 (ta)
ホ	5 (ho)	レ	17 (re)
ヘ	6 (he)	ソ	18 (so)
ト	7 (to)	ツ	19 (tsu)
チ	8 (chi)	ネ	20 (ne)
リ	9 (ri)	ナ	21 (na)
ヌ	10 (nu)	ラ	22 (ra)
ル	11 (ru)	ム	23 (mu)
ヲ	12 (o)		

Position of syllabics

½, 1, 2, 4, 30s.	At foot of central design.
10s., 20s.	Immediately below central design (slightly to left in 20s.).
6s. violet-brown	Immediately below buckle.
6s. orange	Just below the ribbon or as 6s. violet-brown.
12, 15, 45s. birds	Between value and "SEN".

1874 (1 Jan–Feb). First Transitional Group. (a) Ordinary wove paper. Without syllabics. P 11 to 12 and compounds.

47	**11**	4s. red	£650	£250
48	**10**	30s. grey-black	£28000	£7000

The plates for the 4s. and 30s. were those used for the 1873 and 1872 issues respectively.

(b) Wove and laid soft native papers. With syllabics. P 9 to 12½ and compounds

49	**7**	2s. yellow	£425	£400
		Syll 1	£24000	£400
		Syll 16		£425
50	**12**	6s. violet brown (1 Jan)	£1600	£475
		Syll 1	£1600	£475
		Syll 2	£1900	£500
		Syll 3	£23000	£1200
		Syll 4	£23000	£650
		Syll 5	£23000	£650
		Syll 6	£23000	£800
		Syll 7	£28000	£600
		Syll 8	£28000	£550
		Syll 9	£23000	£750
		Syll 10	—	£3500
		Syll 11	—	£17000
		Syll 12	£23000	£1900
51	**9**	20s. red-violet	£11000	
		Syll 1	—	
		Syll 2	£11000	
		Syll 3	£11000	
52	**10**	30s. black (syll 1)	£3000	£3250

The 2s. syll 16 and the 20s. syll 1, 2 and 3 were never issued. The 20s. with syll 1 only exists with the specimen dot.

In February 1874 the Government changed from native to ordinary wove paper.

1874 (Feb). Ordinary wove paper, also porous (2s., 6s.) and laid (2s.). With syllabics. P 11 to 13 and compounds.

53	**5**	½s. brown	27·00	28·00
		Syll 1	27·00	28·00
		Syll 2	44·00	55·00
54	**6**	1s. blue	£160	38·00
		Syll 1	£160	38·00
		Syll 2	£250	42·00
		Syll 3	£225	42·00
		Syll 4	£180	42·00
		Syll 5	£750	£160
		Syll 6	£160	42·00
		Syll 7	£375	49·00
		Syll 8	£160	42·00
		Syll 9	£160	42·00
		Syll 10	£250	75·00
		Syll 11	£225	70·00
		Syll 12	£275	75·00
55	**7**	2s. yellow	£225	33·00
		Syll 1	£425	38·00
		Syll 2	£225	33·00
		Syll 3	£225	33·00
		Syll 4	£225	33·00
		Syll 5	£450	33·00
		Syll 6	£2250	55·00
		Syll 7	£2250	33·00
		Syll 8	£225	60·00
		Syll 9	£225	38·00
		Syll 10	£3250	55·00
		Syll 11	£225	33·00
		Syll 12	£3000	33·00
		Syll 13	£2750	33·00
		Syll 14	£3000	49·00
		Syll 15	£225	33·00
		Syll 16	£2750	33·00
		Syll 17	£225	33·00
		Syll 18	£225	33·00
		Syll 19 on porous paper	£225	33·00
		Syll 20	£225	33·00
		Syll 20 on porous paper	£225	33·00
		Syll 21	£275	33·00
		Syll 21 on laid paper	—	£140
		Syll 22	£3250	33·00
		Syll 22 on laid paper	—	£140
		Syll 23	£300	35·00
		Syll 23 on laid paper	—	£100
56	**11**	4s. red (syll 1)	£2750	£500
57	**12**	6s. violet-brown	£180	75·00
		Syll 10	£550	£550
		Syll 11 on porous paper	£550	
		Syll 13	£14000	£5000
		Syll 14	£325	£300
		Syll 16	£23000	£2500
		Syll 16	£180	75·00
		Syll 17	£225	90·00
		Syll 18	£325	£130
58	**8**	10s. green	£160	65·00
		Syll 1	£325	£100
		Syll 2	£160	65·00
		Syll 3	£700	£700
59	**9**	20s. violet	£325	£100
		Syll 4	£325	£100
		Syll 5	£325	£100
60	**10**	30s. grey-black (syll 1)	£375	£100

The 6s. syll 11 was never issued.

13 Bean Goose

14 Pied Wagtail (Arrow refers to Nos. 62a/b)

15 Northern Goshawk

(Des R. Yanagida (45s.), G. Nakamura (others). Eng and recess Govt Ptg Wks, Tokyo)

1875 (1 Jan). Bird issues. Ordinary wove paper. With syllabics. P 9 to 12½ and compound.

61	**13**	12s. rose	£375	£160
		Syll 1	£375	£160
		Syll 2	£425	£190
		Syll 3	£3750	£550

62	14	15s. violet	£375	£160
		a. Right character + omitted (syll 2, Pl. II, No. 5)	—	£15000
		b. Character inserted by hand	£13000	£10000
		Syll 1	£375	£160
		Syll 2	£425	£180
		Syll 3	£375	£190
63	15	45s. carmine	£475	£190
		Syll 1	£475	£190
		Syll 2	£1300	£500
		Syll 3	£1100	£450

69	12	6s. orange	£110	27·00
		Syll 10	£190	55·00
		Syll 11	£160	42·00
		Syll 13	£160	33·00
		Syll 14	£250	44·00
		Syll 15		
		Syll 16	£110	27·00
		Syll 17	£110	27·00
		Syll 19	£110	26·00
		Syll 20	£110	26·00
		Syll 21	£200	60·00
		Syll 21 on porous paper	£110	20·00
		Syll 22 on porous paper	£4500	£1900
70	16	10s. ultramarine	£190	30·00
		Syll 4	£190	30·00
		Syll 5 on porous paper	£4500	£375
71	17	20s. red (syll 8	£150	21·00
72	18	30s. violet	£190	70·00
		Syll 2	£200	£110
		Syll 3	£190	70·00
		Syll 4	£190	70·00

The plates for the ½s. grey syll 2, the 1s. brown syll 5, 7, 8, 12, the 4s. green syll 1 and the 6s. orange syll 10, 11, 13 to 17 were those used for the issue of 1874.

16	17	18

(Recess Govt Ptg Wks)

1875 (4 Feb). Colours changed and all designs in unified size. P 10½ to 12½ and compounds.

(a) Without syllabics. Wove paper

64	6	1s. brown	£7500	£700
65	11	4s. green	£275	£100

The plates for the 1s. and 4s. were those used for the issues of 1872 and 1873 respectively.

(b) With syllabics. Wove, laid or porous paper

66	5	½s. grey	24·00	22·00
		Syll 2	24·00	22·00
		Syll 3	24·00	22·00
		Syll 4 on porous paper	38·00	£1100
67	6	1s. brown	38·00	24·00
		Syll 5	£400	55·00
		Syll 7	£25000	£300
		Syll 8	£37000	£300
		Syll 12	£900	£250
		Syll 13	55·00	24·00
		Syll 14	55·00	24·00
		Syll 14 on porous paper	35·00	
		Syll 15	38·00	24·00
		Syll 16	44·00	24·00
		Syll 17	85·00	38·00
		Syll 17 on porous paper	£200	25·00
		Syll 17 on laid paper	—	£225
68	11	4s. green	£140	30·00
		Syll 1	£140	30·00
		Syll 1 on porous paper	£500	£200
		Syll 2	£160	30·00
		Syll 2 on porous paper	£450	75·00
		Syll 3	£400	£120
		Syll 3 on porous paper	£170	49·00

19

(Recess Govt Ptg Wks)

1875 (Aug)–**76**. Second Transitional Group. As T **6/7** but with branches tied with ribbon, and new value, T **19**. No syllabics. Porous paper. P 9 to 13 and compound.

73	6	1s. brown	85·00	16·00
74	7	2s. yellow	£120	16·00
75	19	5s. green (19.3.76)	£200	£110

Plates of all issues 1872–76 were hand-engraved like the Dragon issues, with forty varieties to the sheet.

Innumerable forgeries, of native origin, exist of the 1871–76 issues, some of which are very deceptive. Many are found with native characters signifying *facsimile*, in various positions on the different stamps, and on some they are more prominent than on others. The imitations usually have heavy Japanese obliterations, often over the characters, in order to make it appear that they have done postal duty.

PRINTERS. Unless otherwise stated, all the following stamps were printed by the Government Printing Works, Tokyo.

The "KOBAN" Series

20	21	22	23	24

(Des E. Chiossone. Dies eng G. Furuya. K. Ishii and T. Saito. Typo)

First Issue

1876–86. As T **20/22** (details of ornaments and backgrounds of each value differ).

I. Medium to thick paper, sometimes tinted. P 9–10 (large holes)

76	**20**	5r. slate (17.5.76)	30·00	20·00
		b. P 9, 11 or compound		
		(small holes)	22·00	15·00
		c. P 11–12	30·00	20·00
		d. P 12½	£200	£100
		e. Compounds	—	—
77		1s. black (17.5.76)	45·00	5·00
		b. P 9, 11 or compound		
		(small holes)	45·00	5·00
		c. P 11–12	45·00	5·00
		d. P 12½	45·00	5·00
		e. Compounds	45·00	5·00
78		1s. brown (11.10.79)	15·00	2·00
		c. P 11–12	15·00	2·00
		d. P 12½	20·00	4·00
		e. Compounds	£170	12·50
79		2s. drab (17.5.76)	90·00	12·50
		b. P 9, 11 or compound		
		(small holes)	£110	4·50
		c. P 11–12	£120	15·00
		d. P 12½	£120	15·00
		e. Compounds	£120	16·00
80		2s. violet (11.10.79)	50·00	2·50
		c. P 11–12	85·00	5·00
		d. P 12½	75·00	3·00
		e. Compounds	£250	15·00
81		3s. dull orange (30.6.79)	80·00	32·00
		e. Compounds	—	—
82		4s. green (23.6.76)	75·00	7·50
		b. P 9, 11 or compound		
		(small holes)	75·00	7·50
		c. P 11–12	75·00	7·50
		d. P 12½	50·00	4·00
		e. Compounds	60·00	12·50
82a		4s. blue	50·00	6·25
		b. P 9, 11 or compound		
		(small holes)	55·00	6·50
		e. Compounds	—	—
83	**21**	5s. brown (23.6.76)	65·00	25·00
		b. P 9, 11 or compound		
		(small holes)	55·00	20·00
		c. P 11–12	60·00	25·00
		d. P 12½	£225	£110
		e. Compounds	£120	95·00
84		6s. orange-buff (29.6.76)	£200	£120
85		8s. purple-brown (20.11.77)	65·00	7·50
		d. P 12½	95·00	47·00
		e. Compounds	£200	35·00
86		10s. pale blue (29.6.77)	50·00	4·00
		b. P 9, 11 or compound		
		(small holes)	50·00	4·00
		c. P 11–12	50·00	4·00
		d. P 12½	50·00	2·50
		e. Compounds	55·00	7·50
87		12s. pink (29.6.77)	£225	£170
88	**22**	15s. dull green (29.6.77)	£150	12·50
		e. Compounds	£150	12·50
89		20s. dull blue (18.8.77)	£160	15·00
		d. P 12½	—	—
90		30s. dull mauve (18.8.77)	£250	£110
		b. P 9, 11 or compound		
		(small holes.	—	—
91		45s. rose (18.8.77)	£500	£650
		b. P 9, 11 or compound		
		(small holes.	—	—
92		50s. deep carmine (30.6.79)	£225	17·00
		b. P 9, 11 or compound		
		(small holes)	£225	£225

Shades of the above issue vary considerably. The 5r. perf 11–12 and 2s. and 6s. in various perfs on thick white porous paper are from the earliest printing.

II. Thin pale white paper (1878). P 9–10 (large holes)

93	**20**	1s. black	25·00	5·00
		b. P 9, 11 or compound (small holes)	75·00	15·00
		c. P 11–12	75·00	15·00
		d. P 12½	25·00	1·50
		e. Compounds	£250	60·00

94		2s. drab	40·00	5·00
		b. P 9, 11 or compound		
		(small holes)	£100	15·00
		c. P 11–12	60·00	4·00
		d. P 12½	35·00	1·00
		e. Compounds	£250	60·00
95		3s. salmon	75·00	30·00
		c. P 11–12	—	—
96		4s. green	55·00	4·00
		b. P 9, 11 or compound		
		(small holes)	—	—
		c. P 11–12	£120	12·50
		d. P 12½	£120	12·50
		e. Compounds	—	—
97	**21**	5s. brown	30·00	12·50
		b. P 9, 11 or compound		
		(small holes)	£120	30·00
		d. P 12½	£200	50·00
		e. Compounds	—	—
98		10s. blue	£100	10·00
		d. P 12½	£120	20·00
99	**22**	50s. rose	£225	17·00
		c. P 11–12	£250	25·00
		e. Compounds	—	—
		a. Carmine	£250	25·00

III. Medium to thick paper. Brighter (aniline) colours. P 8½–10 (large holes) (1882)

100	**20**	5r. grey	10·00	90
		e. Compounds	—	—
		f. P 11 (large holes) (1882)	22·00	15·00
		g. P 13½–14 (1886)	12·50	2·00
101		1s. brown	—	—
		e. Compounds	—	—
		f. P 11 (large holes) (1882)	—	20·00
102		2s. violet	—	—
		e. Compounds	—	—
		f. P 11 (large holes) (1882)	70·00	2·50
103		4s. green	50·00	5·00
		e. Compounds	—	—
		f. P 11 (large holes) (1882)	80·00	2·50
		g. P 13½–14 (1886)	50·00	1·00
103a	**21**	5s. brown		
		g. P 13½–14 (1886)	—	50·00
104		6s. orange	£190	90·00
		e. Compounds	—	—
		f. P 11 (large holes) (1882)	£200	£120
		g. P 13½–14 (1886)	£225	£110
105		8s. brown-purple	37·00	3·00
		e. Compounds	—	—
		f. P 11 (large holes) (1882)	50·00	5·00
		g. P 13½–14 (1886)	37·00	3·00
106		10s. bright blue	40·00	1·50
		e. Compounds	—	—
		f. P 11 (large holes) (1882)	40·00	1·50
		g. P 13½–14 (1886)	30·00	1·00
107		12s. rose	£225	£170
		e. Compounds	£250	£170
108	**22**	15s. bright green	£150	1·50
		e. Compounds	—	—
		f. P 11 (large holes) (1882)	£170	5·00
		g. P 13½–14 (1886)	£160	10·00
109		20s. deep blue	£160	10·00
		e. Compounds	—	—
		f. P 11 (large holes) (1882)	£160	15·00
		g. P 13½–14 (1886)	£160	15·00
110		30s. bright mauve	£250	£110
		f. P 11 (large holes) (1882)	—	—
111		45s. carmine	£500	£650
		f. P 11 (large holes) (1882)	—	—
112		50s. rose-red	£225	17·00
		f. P 11 (large holes) (1882)	£250	25·00
		a. Pink	—	—
		e. Compounds	—	—
		g. P 13½–14 (1886)	£300	17·00

Second Issue

1883 (1 Jan)–**92**. As T **20/21**. Dull shades in early printings and brighter (aniline) colours for later printings. Medium to thick paper. P 8½–10 (large holes).

113	**20**	1s. green	25·00	4·00
		c. P 11–12	15·00	1·20
		d. P 12½	75·00	20·00
		f. P 11 (large holes)	15·00	1·20
		g. P 13–14	25·00	1·50
		h. P 11½–12 (1892)	15·00	1·20

114		2s. rose	25·00	2·50
		c. P 11–12	25·00	25
		d. P 12½	75·00	20·00
		f. P 11 (large holes)	22·00	1·00
		g. P 13–14	35·00	1·00
		h. P 11½–12 (1892)	20·00	25
115	**21**	5s. blue	40·00	1·00
		c. P 11–12	40·00	2·50
		f. P 11 (large holes)	35·00	1·00
		g. P 13–14	30·00	2·00
		h. P 11½–12 (1892)	25·00	1·00

Third Issue

1888 (10 Mar)–**92**. As T **20/24**. T **24** has large chrysanthemum embossed in colourless relief in centre. Medium to thick paper. P 13–14

116	**20**	5r. slate (19.8.89)	10·00	90
		e. Compounds	—	—
		h. P 11½–12 (1892)	7·50	75
117		3s. pale claret (6.5.92)	25·00	1·00
		e. Compounds	—	—
		h. P 11½–12 (1892)	20·00	75
118		4s. bistre	20·00	90
		e. Compounds	—	90·00
		h. P 11½–12 (1892)	17·00	75
119	**21**	8s. bright orange	37·00	3·00
		e. Compounds	—	—
		h. P 11½–12 (1892)	37·00	3·00
120		10s. orange-brown	30·00	1·00
		e. Compounds	—	40·00
		h. P 11½–12 (1892)	25·00	75
121	**22**	15s. bright violet	70·00	1·50
		e. Compounds	—	£100
		h. P 11½–12 (1892)	60·00	1·00
122		20s. orange	80·00	4·00
		e. Compounds	—	£150
		h. P 11½–12 (1892)	75·00	3·00
123	**23**	25s. green (28.4.88)	£130	4·00
		e. Compounds	—	£150
		h. P 11½–12 (1892)	£110	3·00
124	**22**	50s. brown	£140	6·50
		e. Compounds	—	40·00
		h. P 11½–12 (1892)	£120	6·00
125	**24**	1y. scarlet (28.4.88)	£170	6·50
		e. Compounds	—	—
		h. P 11½–12 (1892)	£150	6·00

Shades of the above exist.

Cancellations consisting of two concentric circles with Japanese characters between the circles only are telegraph cancellations which are often found in this issue, particularly on the 15, 20 and 50s. values. These are worth much less than our prices which are for postally used specimens.

Some of the rarer perforations of both the "Koban" and "Chrysanthemum" issues have been faked.

25 Imperial Crest and Cranes

26 Prince
Kitashirakawa

27 Prince
Arisugawa

(Des T. Honda. Dies eng T. Saito. Typo)

1884 (9 Mar). Emperor's Silver Wedding. P 11½–12.

126	**25**	2s. carmine)	37·00	3·50
		b. P 12½–13½	40·00	6·00
		c. Compounds	—	£100

127		5s. ultramarine	50·00	15·00
		b. P 12½–13½	55·00	16·00

(T **26** des T. Honda; die eng T. Hosogai. T **27** des T. Saito; die eng S. Katsuyama. Typo)

1896 (1 Aug). War with China. P 11½–12.

128	**26**	2s. carmine	32·00	4·00
		b. P 12½–13½	42·00	12·50
		c. Compounds	42·00	12·50
129	–	2s. carmine	32·00	4·00
		b. P 12½–13½	45·00	12·50
		c. Compounds	47·00	12·50
130	**27**	5s. violet-blue	75·00	4·00
		b. P 12½–13½	80·00	9·00
		c. Compounds	90·00	10·00
131	–	5s. violet-blue	75·00	4·00
		b. P 12½–13½	80·00	9·00
		c. Compounds	90·00	10·00

No. 129 has portrait T **27** with frame as T **26**; No. 131 has portrait T **26** with frame as T **27**.

The "CHRYSANTHEMUM" Series

28    **29**    **30**

31    **32** Princess Jingu

(T **28/31** des and die eng T. Saito. T **32** des T. Isobe. Eng S. Oyama. Recess)

1899 (1 Jan)–**1908**. P 11½–12 (line).

132	**28**	5r. slate (1.4.99)	14·00	1·50
		b. P 12½ (line)	17·00	75
		c. Compounds (line)	—	—
133		½s. slate (27.3.01)	7·50	25
		b. P 12½ (line)	17·00	75
		c. Compounds (line)	—	—
		d. P 12×12½ (comb)	75·00	1·00
		e. P 13×13½ (comb)	9·00	25
134		1s. pale brown (1.4.99)	10·00	25
		b. P 12½ (line)	25·00	50
		c. Compounds (line)	—	£100
		d. P 12×12½ (comb)	75·00	1·00
		e. P 13×13½ (comb)	10·00	25
135		1½s. pale ultramarine (1.10.00)	30·00	1·70
		b. P 12½ (line)	30·00	1·20
		c. Compounds (line)	—	50·00
		e. P 13×13½ (comb)	35·00	1·70
136		1½s. violet (15.5.06)	22·00	60
		b. P 12½ (line)	40·00	5·00
		c. Compounds (line)	—	—
		d. P 12×12½ (comb)	£150	2·00
		e. P 13×13½ (comb)	20·00	50
137		2s. yellow-green	20·00	25
		b. P 12½ (line)	40·00	2·50
		c. Compounds (line)	—	75·00
		d. P 12×12½ (comb)	£200	1·50
		e. P 13×13½ (comb)	20·00	25
138		3s. dull maroon (1.4.99)	20·00	30
		b. P 12½ (line)	27·00	40
		c. Compounds (line)	—	40·00
		e. P 13×13½ (comb)	27·00	35
139		3s. rosine (15.5.06)	15·00	25
		b. P 12½ (line)	15·00	25
		c. Compounds (line)	—	75·00
		d. P 12×12½ (comb)	75·00	1·70
		e. P 13×13½ (comb)	12·50	25

140		4s. rosine	20·00	2·50
		b. P 12½ (line)	27·00	3·00
		c. Compounds (line)	—	75·00
		d. P 12×12½ (comb)	£275	25·00
		e. P 13×13½ (comb)	35·00	3·50
141		5s. orange-yellow (1.10.99.	30·00	30
		b. P 12½ (line)	35·00	50
		c. Compounds (line)	—	—
		d. P 12×12½ (comb)	£275	3·50
		e. P 13×13½ (comb)	30·00	30
142	29	6s. maroon (20.8.07)	50·00	5·00
		b. P 12½ (line)	£100	20·00
		c. Compounds (line)	—	—
		d. P 12×12½ (comb)	—	—
		e. P 13×13½ (comb)	65·00	6·00
143		8s. olive (1.10.99	60·00	7·50
		b. P 12½ (line)	80·00	10·00
		c. Compounds (line)	—	90·00
		d. P 12×12½ (comb)	£200	40·00
		e. P 13×13½ (comb)	85·00	10·00
144		10s. deep blue	25·00	25
		b. P 12½ (line)	30·00	30
		c. Compounds (line)	—	—
		d. P 12×12½ (comb)	£250	1·50
		e. P 13×13½ (comb)	25·00	35
145		15s. purple (1.10.99	£100	2·50
		b. P 12½ (line)	£225	5·00
		c. Compounds (line)	—	—
		d. P 12×12½ (comb)	—	—
		e. P 13×13½ (comb)	£275	3·00
146		20s. orange (1.10.99)	50·00	30
		b. P 12½ (line)	65·00	35
		c. Compounds (line)	—	65·00
		d. P 12×12½ (comb)	£750	1·50
		e. P 13×13½ (comb)	50·00	25
147	30	25s. pale blue-green (1.10.99)	£110	1·50
		b. P 12½ (line)	£120	2·20
		c. Compounds (line)	—	—
		e. P 13×13½ (comb)	£225	2·50
148		50s. brown (1.10.99)	£110	2·00
		b. P 12½ (line)	£120	3·00
		c. Compounds (line)	—	65·00
		d. P 12×12½ (comb)	£6000	£350
		e. P 13×13½ (comb)	£170	3·75
149	31	1y. carmine (1.10.99)	£150	2·50
		b. P 12½ (line)	£190	3·50
150	32	5y. green (20.2.08)	£1000	11·00
151		10y. violet (20.2.08)	£1500	15·00

There are numerous marked shades in this issue. For 5y. and 10y. watermarked, see Nos. 183/4.

33 Rice Cakes, etc

34 Symbols of Korea and Japan

35 Gun an. Japanese Flag

(M **36**)

(Des T. Saito. Die eng T. Honda. Typo)

1900 (10 May). Wedding of Prince Imperial. P 11½–12.
152	33	3s. carmine	36·00	1·10
		b. P 12½	41·00	2·30
		c. Compounds	65·00	18·00

No. 152 was on sale from 28 April but was not valid for postage until 10 May.

(Des T. Isobe. Die eng T. Hosogai. Typo)

1905 (1 July). Amalgamation of Japanese and Korean Postal Services. P 11½–12.
153	34	3s. rose-re	£130	23·00
		b. P 12½	£160	26·00
		c. Compounds	£325	£110

No. 153 was valid for inland mail and mail to Japanese offices in China and Korea only.

(Des T. Isobe. Die eng T. Hosogai. Typo)

1906 (29 Apr). Triumphal Military Review of Russo–Japanese War. P 11½–12.
154	35	1½s. blue	55·00	7·00
		b. P 12½	55·00	8·50
155		3s. rose-red	£110	29·00
		b. P 12½	£110	40·00

1910 (1 Dec). MILITARY FRANK. No. 139 optd with Type M **36**.
M156	28	3s. rosine (P 11½–12)	£300	75·00
		a. P 12×12½	—	—
		b. P 13×13½	£275	65·00

This and subsequent issues overprinted with Type M **36** were for the use of military and naval forces in China and Korea.

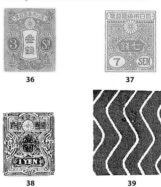
36   **37**
38   **39**

(Des M. Tazawa. Die eng S. Morimoto. Typo)

1913 (31 Aug–31 Oct). White paper. No wmk. P 11½–12 (line).
156	36	½s. brown (31.10)	60·00	5·00
		b. P 12×12½ (comb)	12·50	1·50
		c. P 13×13½ (comb)	12·50	1·50
157		1s. orange (31.10)	£200	5·00
		b. P 12×12½ (comb)	20·00	1·50
		c. P 13×13½ (comb)	20·00	1·50
158		1½s. pale blue	60·00	7·50
		b. P 12×12½ (comb)	27·00	2·50
		c. P 13×13½ (comb)	27·00	2·50
159		2s. green (31.10)	£300	7·50
		b. P 12×12½ (comb)	30·00	1·50
		c. P 13×13½ (comb)	30·00	1·50
160		3s. carmine	50·00	4·00
		b. P 12×12½ (comb)	50·00	1·50
		c. P 13×13½ (comb)	37·00	1·50
161	37	4s. scarlet (31.10)	80·00	25·00
		b. P 12×12½ (comb)	50·00	17·00
		c. P 13×13½ (comb)	50·00	17·00
162		5s. violet (31.10)	90·00	7·50
		b. P 12×12½ (comb)	60·00	3·00
		c. P 13×13½ (comb)	60·00	3·00
163		10s. deep blue (31.10)	£250	12·50
		b. P 12×12½ (comb)	£170	2·00
		c. P 13×13½ (comb)	£170	2·00
164		20s. claret (31.10)	£350	10·00
		b. P 12×12½ (comb)	£200	3·50
		c. P 13×13½ (comb)	£250	5·00
165		25s. olive (31.10)	—	£400
		b. P 12×12½ (comb)	£225	7·50
		c. P 13×13½ (comb)	£200	6·00
166	38	1y. pale green and chocolate (31.10.	£950	40·00

1913 (31 Aug). MILITARY FRANK. No. 160 optd with Type M **36**. P 11½–12 (line).
M167	36	3s. carmin	—	£800
		b. P 12×12½ (comb)	£325	£130
		c. P 13×13½ (comb)	£325	£130

1914 (20 May)–**25**. Granite paper. W 39. Large Die, size 19×22½ mm. P 11 (line).

167	**36**	½s. brown			
		b. P 11½–12 (line)		£160	20·00
		d. P 12×12½ (comb)		12·50	1·00
		e. P 13×13½ (comb)		5·00	25
168		1s. orange			
		b. P 11½–12 (line)		75·00	15·00
		d. P 12×12½ (comb)		12·50	1·00
		e. P 13×13½ (comb)		6·50	25
169		1½s. pale blue.		—	—
		b. P 11½–12 (line)		£150	15·00
		d. P 12×12½ (comb)		12·50	1·00
		e. P 13×13½ (comb)		6·50	25
		a. Booklet pane of 6*		50·00	—
		ab. Booklet pane of 6*		40·00	—
		ac. Booklet pane of 6*		£1100	—
		ad. Booklet pane of 6*		—	—
		ae. Booklet pane of 6*		£100	—
170		2s. green			
		b. P 11½–12 (line)		£140	15·00
		d. P 12×12½ (comb)		17·00	1·00
		e. P 13×13½ (comb)		9·00	25
171		3s. carmine		—	£500
		b. P 11½–12 (line)		£100	10·00
		d. P 12×12½ (comb)		12·50	1·00
		e. P 13×13½ (comb)		6·00	25
		a. Booklet pane of 6*		50·00	—
		ab. Booklet pane of 6*		40·00	—
		ac. Booklet pane of 6*		£900	—
		ad. Booklet pane of 6*		—	—
		ae. Booklet pane of 6*		£100	—
172	**37**	4s. scarlet			
		b. P 11½–12 (line)		55·00	15·00
		d. P 12×12½ (comb)		55·00	5·00
		e. P 13×13½ (comb)		25·00	2·20
173		5s. violet			
		b. P 11½–12 (line)		£225	17·00
		d. P 12×12½ (comb)		45·00	2·50
		e. P 13×13½ (comb)		25·00	9·50
174		6s. brown			
		b. P 11½–12 (line).		—	—
		d. P 12×12½ (comb)		£250	£120
		e. P 13×13½ (comb)		40·00	7·50
175		8s. grey			
		b. P 11½–12 (line)		£300	£300
		d. P 12×12½ (comb)		—	£600
		e. P 13×13½ (comb)		32·00	22·00
176		10s. deep blue		—	£500
		b. P 11½–12 (line)		£250	17·00
		c. P 12½ (line)		—	—
		d. P 12×12½ (comb)		40·00	1·50
		e. P 13×13½ (comb)		22·00	25
177		13s. brown			
		e. P 13×13½ (comb)		40·00	7·50
178		20s. claret			
		b. P 11½–12 (line)		£375	50·00
		d. P 12×12½ (comb)		£190	4·00
		e. P 13×13½ (comb)		£130	2·00
179		25s. olive			
		b. P 11½–12 (line).		£650	70·00
		d. P 12×12½ (comb)		£100	6·00
		e. P 13×13½ (comb)		22·00	2·50
180	**38**	30s. chestnut (16.8.19)		—	£500
		b. P 11½–12 (line)		£750	£600
		d. P 12×12½ (comb)		£750	£600
		e. P 13×13½ (comb)		35·00	1·50
181		50s. chocolate		—	£250
		d. P 12×12½ (comb)		£350	£100
		e. P 13×13½ (comb)		50·00	2·20
182		1y. pale green and chocolat.		£200	2·20
		b. P 11½–12 (line)		£190	2·20
		c. P 12½ (line)		£325	£120
		e. P 13×13½ (comb)		£225	25·00
183	**32**	5y. green			
		b. P 11½–12 (line)		£600	6·00
183		10y. violet			
		b. P 11½–12 (line)		£900	10·00

No. 182e also exists line)perf.
*Booklet panes 169a/ae and 171a/ae are perforated as follows:
        a. 11 and 11×12
        ab. 12 and 12×11
        ac. 13×12
        ad. 12×12½
        ae. 13×13½

Booklet panes 169a/ac and 171a/ac were issued in August 1923 and have the three outer edges imperf. Booklet panes 168ae and 171ae exist both fully perforated (20.5.14) and with outer edges imperf (4.25). The 3s. perf 12×12½ only comes fully perforated (20.5.14).
See also Nos. 230/40, 269/70 and 296/312.

BOOKLET PANES. Booklets issued up to and including 1914 contained fully perforated panes of six stamps; as these cannot be distinguished from sheet blocks they are not listed. All later booklets of whatever size have two or more margins imperforate; all stamps from these booklets therefore have one, two adjacent, or three straight edges.
   A checklist of all booklets is given at the end of the country.

1914 (20 May). MILITARY FRANK. No. 171 optd with Type M **36**. P 11½–12 (line).

M185	**36**	3s. carmine			
		b. P 11½–12 (line)		—	£1200
		d. P 12×12½ (comb)		50·00	35·00
		e. P 13×13½ (comb)		40·00	25·00

40 Ceremonial Cap    **41** Imperial Throne

42 Hall of Ceremony

(Des T. Isobe. Eng S. Morimoto and K. Mizutani (**40**). Y. Kamoshita and K. Watanabe (**41**). S. Oyama (**42**). Typo (**40/1**); recess (**42**))

1915 (10 Nov). Coronation of Emperor Yoshihito. P 12½ (1½s., 3s.) or 12×12½ (others).

185	**40**	1½s. olive-grey and scarlet	4·00	85
186	**41**	3s. violet and yellow-brown	5·25	1·20
187	**42**	4s. carmine	23·00	15·00
188		10s. blue	55·00	25·00
185/188	*Set of 4*		80·00	38·00

43 Mandarin Duck    **44**"Kammuri"
                               (ceremonial headband)

(Des E. Fujishima. T **43**, die eng K. Watanabe. Typo. T **44**, eng S. Morimoto and K. Kawamura. Recess and litho)

1916 (3 Nov). Investiture of Prince Hirohito as Heir Apparent. P 12½.

189	**43**	1½s. green, red and yellow	4·25	1·60
190		3s. red and yellow	8·00	1·90
191	**44**	10s. blue.	£950	£400

45 Dove of Peace   **46** Dove of Peace   **(47)**

(Des S. Yuki. Eng S. Kurobe (**45**); Des S. Okada. Eng S. Morimoto (**46**). Recess)

1919 (1 July). Restoration of Peace. P 12½ (1½s., 4s.) or 13½×13 (others).

192	**45**	1½s. bistre-brown	3·50	1·40
		a. Perf 12	8·25	10·00
193	**46**	3s. dull green	4·75	2·20
		a. Perf 12	16·00	13·00
194	**45**	4s. rose-carmine	11·50	7·00
195	**46**	10s. indigo	34·00	20·00
192/195		Set of 4	48·00	30·00

1919 (3 Oct). AIR. First Tokyo–Osaka Airmail Service. Nos. 169E and 171E optd with T **47**.

196	**36**	1½s. pale blue (R.)	£375	£150
197		3s. carmine (B.)	£650	£450

48 7th-century Censor   **49** Meiji Shrine

(Des S. Hibata. Die eng S. Morimoto. Typo)

1920 (25 Sept). First Census (1.10.20). P 12½.

198	**48**	1½s. purple	8·25	6·00
199		3s. vermilion	9·50	6·00

The above were valid for inland mail and mail to China only.

(Des S. Hibata. Eng S. Morimoto. Recess)

1920 (1 Nov). Dedication of Meiji (Emperor Mutsuhito) Shrine. P 12½.

200	**49**	1½s. violet	4·00	2·00
201		3s. carmine	4·00	2·00

The above were valid for inland mail and mail to China only.

1921 (Apr). MILITARY FRANK. No. 37 of Japanese Post Offices in China optd with Type M **36**. P 13×13½.

M202	**36**	3s. carmine	£9500	£4500

50 Postal and National Flag.   **51** Dept of Communications, Tokyo

(T **50** des Y. Yoshida. Die eng S. Kurobe. Typo. T **51** des F. Honda. Eng S. Morimoto. Recess)

1921 (20 Apr). 50th Anniv of Japanese Post. P 12½ (1½s., 4s.) or 13 13½ (others).

202	**50**	1½s. orange-red and deep olive	3·25	1·90
203	**51**	3s. chocolate	4·50	2·50

204	**50**	4s. orange-red and rose-red	55·00	44·00
205	**51**	10s. deep blue	£300	£200
202/205		Set of 4	£325	£225

52 Warships *Katori* and *Kashima*   **53** Mt. Fuji and Sika Deer   **54** Mount Niitaka

(Des Y. Yoshida. Die eng S. Monmoto. Litho)

1921 (3 Sept). Return of Crown Prince from European Tour. P 12½.

206	**52**	1½s. violet	4·00	2·20
207		3s. bronze green	3·50	2·20
208		4s rose-red	48·00	33·00
209		10s. blue	70·00	40·00
206/209		Set of 4	£110	70·00

(Des S. Hibata and Y. Yoshida. Die eng S. Morimoto. Typo)

1922 (1 Jan). Large Die, size 19×22½ mm. Granite paper. W **39**. P 13×13½

210	**53**	4s. green	24·00	5·25
211		8s. carmine	34·00	9·75
212		20s. deep blue	45·00	2·30
210/212		Set of 3	95·00	16·00

See also Nos. 252/4, 266/8, 293, 295, 299, 303 and 305.

(Des S. Hibata. Eng S. Morimoto. Recess)

1923 (16 Apr). Visit of Crown Prince to Taiwan. P 12½.

213	**54**	1½s. orange-yellow	20·00	23·00
214		3s. violet	25·00	12·50

The above were valid for inland mail only.

55   **56**   **57**

(Des S. Morimoto (**55**), M. Yoshizaki (**56**). Dies eng S. Katsuyama. Litho Nihon Seihan Ptg Wks, Osaka and Shueisha Ptg Wks, Tokyo)

1923 (25 Oct). Granite paper. W **57**. No. gum. Imperf.

215	**55**	½s. grey	4·75	5·00
216		1½s. light blue	7·25	2·20
217		2s. red-brown	8·25	2·20
218		3s. carmine	3·75	1·40
219		4s. green	38·00	34·00
220		5s. dull violet	19·00	2·20
221		8s. red-orange	55·00	44·00
222	**56**	10s. brown	50·00	2·20
223		20s. deep blue	80·00	2·75
215/223		Set of 9	£225	85·00

These stamps may be found roughly pin-perf, perf 12 and rouletted, but these were not official.

This issue was an emergency one following the earthquake of 1 September which destroyed the printing plates of the regular series. The master dies survived from which new plates were made later in different sizes.

1924 (June). MILITARY FRANK. No. 171 optd as Type M **36**, but only 2 mm between Japanese characters. Granite paper. P 13×13½.

M224	**36**	3s. carmine	£120	£130

58 Empress Jingu   **59** Cranes   **60** Phoenix

(Des Y. Yoshida. Eng S. Morimoto. Recess)

1924 (1 Dec)–**35.** Granite paper. W **39**. P 12.

224	**58**	5y. green	£300	4·50
		a. Perf 13×13½ (4.35)	£400	11·50
225		10y. violet	£475	3·25
		a. Perf 13×13½ (4.35)	£550	10·00

See also Nos. 310/11.

(Des Y. Yoshida. Dies eng K. Kato (**59**), K. Kawamura (**60**). Litho)

1925 (10 May). Imperial Silver Wedding. P 12½.

226	**59**	1½s. dull purple	2·20	1·70
227	**60**	3s. orange-brown and silver	25·00	20·00
		a. Perf 11	4·00	3·50
		b. Perf 11×12	32·00	30·00
		c. Perf 12	4·75	4·00
		d. Perf 12×11	32·00	30·00
		e. Perf 12×12½	15·00	12·50
		f. Perf 12½×12	32·00	30·00
		g. Perf 13½×13	4·25	4·00
228	**59**	8s. red	32·00	23·00
229	**60**	20s. green and silver	£225	£100
		a. Perf 11	£100	90·00
		b. Perf 13½×13	70·00	60·00
226/229		Set of 4 (cheapest)	95·00	80·00

1926–31. Smaller Dies size 181×22½ mm (rotary) or 18½×22 mm (flat plate). Granite paper. W **39**. P 13×13½.

230	**36**	½s. brown (8.29)	5·00	2·50
231		1s. orange (3.30)	6·00	2·50
232		1½s. blue (12.28)	6·50	25
		a. Booklet pane of 6 (13.5.28)	50·00	
233		3s. carmine (2.26)	2·75	25
		a. Booklet pane of 6 (13.5.28)	50·00	
234	**37**	5s. violet (3.30)	40·00	25
235		7s. red-orange (21.1.31)	22·00	35
236		13s. brown (1930)	14·00	35
237		25s. olive (1930)	£110	1·20
238	**38**	30s. orange and green (1.9.29)	40·00	60
239		50s. chestnut and blue (1930)	17·00	90
240		1y. pale green and chocolate (3.30)	£150	1·00
230/240		Set of 11	£375	9·00

1926 (June). MILITARY FRANK. No. 233 optd as Type M **36**, but only 2 mm between Japanese characters.

M241	**36**	3s. carmine	£170	£170

61 Mt. Fuji   **61a** Yomei Gate, Tosho Shrine, Nikko   **61b** Nagoya Castle

(Des Y. Yoshida. Die eng S. Morimoto (**61**), K. Noma (**61a**), K. Kato (**61b**). Typo)

1926 (5 July). Small Dies size 22½×18½ mm (rotary) or 22×18½ mm (flat plate). Granite paper. W **39** (horiz).P 13½×13.

241	**61**	2s. green	3·00	15
242	**61a**	6s. carmine	14·00	50
243	**61b**	10s. deep blue	14·00	15
241/243		Set of 3	28·00	70

See also Nos. 294, 301 and 304.

EMPEROR HIROHITO
25 December 1926–7 January 1989

62 Baron Maeshima   **63** Globe

(Des Y. Yoshida. Dies eng K. Kato (**62**), K. Noma (**63**). Litho)

1927 (20 June). 50th Anniv of Membership of Universal Postal Union. P 12½ (T **62**) or 13×13½ (T **63**).

244	**62**	1½s. dull claret	3·75	2·20
245		3s. yellow-green	5·00	2·20
246	**63**	6s. carmine-red	90·00	65·00
247		10s. blue	£130	65·00
244/247		Set of 4	£200	£120

64 Phoenix   **65** Ceremonial Shrines   **66** Shrine of Ise

(Des Y. Yoshida. Eng K. Noma (**64**), S. Morimoto (**65**). Recess)

1928 (10 Nov). Emperor's Enthronement. P 12½.

248	**64**	1½s. green/yellow	1·00	90
249	**65**	3s. purple/yellow	1·00	85
250	**64**	6s. scarlet/yellow	5·50	3·25
251	**65**	10s. blue/yellow	5·75	4·00
248/251		Set of 4	12·00	8·00

1929 (1 Sept). Colours changed. Large Die, size 19×22½ mm. Granite paper. W **39**. P 13×13½.

252	**53**	4s. orange	£160	17·00
253		8s. olive-green	£400	£110
254		20s. purple	£160	3·25
252/254		Set of 3	£650	£120

(Des Y. Yoshida. Eng M. Aoki. Recess)

1929 (2 Oct). 58th Vicennial Removal of Shrine of Ise. P 12½.

255	**66**	1½s. violet	2·20	1·60
256		3s. carmine	2·75	2·20

67 Nakajima-built Fokker F.VIIb/3m over Lake Ashi, Hakone   **68** Map of Japan   **69** Meiji Shrine

(Des T. Kasori and Y. Yoshida. Eng K. Noma. Recess)

1929 (6 Oct)–**34.** AIR. Granite paper. W **39** (horiz). P 13½×13.

257	**67**	8½s. red-brown	65·00	50·00
258		9½s. scarlet (1.3.34)	17·00	11·00
259		16½s. emerald-green	20·00	20·00
260		18s. bright ultramarine	19·00	8·25
261		33s. grey-black	55·00	11·00
257/261		Set of 5	£160	90·00

See also No. **MS**271.

(Des Y. Yoshida. Eng M. Aoki. Recess)

1930 (25 Sept). Third Census (1 Oct). P 12½.
262   **68**   1½s. purple.. 3·75   1·90
263   3s. scarlet....................................... 4·25   2·40
Type **68** is incorrectly inscribed "Second Census".

(Des Y. Yoshida. Die eng K. Kato. Litho)

1930 (1 Nov). 10th Anniv of Dedication of Meiji Shrine. P 12½.
264   **69**   1½s. green....................................... 2·75   2·20
265   3s. orange...................................... 4·00   2·75

1930. Small Die, size 18½×22 mm. Granite paper. W **39**. P 13×13½.
266   **53**   4s. orange....................................... 15·00   55
267   8s. olive-green............................ 22·00   35
268   20s. purple...................................... 95·00   55
266/268   *Set of 3* .... £120   1·30

1933 (1 Nov). Coil stamps. Small Die, size 18½×22½ mm. Granite paper. W **39**. P 13×imperf.
269   **36**   1½s. pale blue .... 26·00   26·00
270   3s. carmine................................. 36·00   36·00

1934 (20 Apr). AIR. Establishment of Communications Commemoration Day. Sheet containing Nos. 258/61.
MS271   **67**   110×100 mm £1300   £1800

70 Insignia of Red   **71** Red Cross Society
Cross Society   Buildings, Tokyo

(Des Y. Yoshida. Eng K. Noma (**70**), K. Kato (**71**). Recess (cross typo))

1934 (1 Oct). 15th International Red Cross Conference, Tokyo. Cross in red. P 12½.
272   **70**   1½s. deep grey-green .... 2·30   1·80
273   **71**   3s. slate-violet......................... 2·75   3·00
274   **70**   6. deep carmine .... 13·50   13·00
275   **71**   10. deep blue .... 16·00   12·50
272/275   *Set of 4* .... 31·00   27·00

72 Cruiser *Hiyei* and   **73** Akasaka Palace,
Pagoda. Liaoyang   Tokyo

(Des T. Kasori. Eng M. Aoki (**72**), K. Noma (**73**). Recess)

1935 (2 Apr). Visit of Emperor of Manchukuo. P 12½.
276   **72**   1½s. olive-green....................... 1·80   1·60
277   **73**   3s. red-brown.......................... 3·00   1·80
278   **72**   6s. scarlet.................................. 10·50   8·75
279   **73**   10s. deep blue........................... 14·00   11·00
276/279   *Set of 4* .... 26·00   21·00

74 Mt. Fuji (after
Kazan Watanabe)

(Des T. Kasori. Die eng K. Kato. Typo)

1935 (1 Dec). New Year's Greetings. Granite paper. P 13×13½.
280   **74**   1½s. carmine............................ 15·00   35

No. 280 was issued both in sheets of 100 and in sheets of 20. (*Price for sheet of 20*: £600.)

In Japanese mandated territories this stamp was issued on 15 November 1935.

75 Mt. Fuji   **75a** Mt. Fuji from Lake Ashi

75b Mt. Fuji from Lake   **75c** Mt. Fuji from Mishima
Kawaguchi

(Photo Dai-Nippon Ptg Co, Tokyo)

1936 (10 July). Fuji-Hakone National Park. Granite paper. W **39**. P 13×13½.
281   **75**   1½s. reddish brown...................... 4·00   6·75
282   **75a**   3s. deep green........................... 7·25   11·50
283   **75b**   6s. carmine.............................. 16·00   22·00
284   **75c**   10s. royal blue......................... 18·00   25·00
281/284   *Set of 4* .... 41·00   60·00

76 Dove of Peace   **77** Shinto Shrine,
                           Port Arthur

(Des M. Hiromatsu. Dies eng K. Fujiki (1½s.) M. Aoki (3s.), K. Kato (10s.). Litho)

1936 (1 Sept). Thirty Years of Occupation of Kwantung. T **76/7** and similar design. Granite paper. W **39**. P 12½.
285   **76**   1½s. dull violet......................... 18·00   22·00
286   **77**   3s. red-brown.......................... 22·00   27·00
287   –   10s. grey-green........................ £200   £250
285/287   *Set of 3* £225   £275
Design: *Horiz*—10s. Govt House, Kwantung.
The above were sold only in Kwantung Leased Territory and the South Manchurian Railway Zone.

78 Imperial Diet

79 Grand Staircase

(Des T. Kasori; eng K. Noma (**78**). Des M. Kimura; eng M. Aoki (**79**). Recess)

1936 (7 Nov). Inauguration of New Houses of the Imperial Diet, Tokyo. W **39**. P 13×13½.

288	**78**	1½s. green	2·00	2·00
289	**79**	3s. maroon	2·30	2·30
290		6s. scarlet	7·75	8·75
291	**78**	10s. blue	15·00	11·00
288/291	*Set of 4*		25·00	22·00

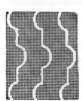

80 Wedded Rocks, Futami Bay

81

WATERMARKS. There are two types of W **81**. The illustrated type is the one usually found; the second, narrow, type has four parallel wavy line) on each stamp. This occurs on some stamps in the 1945–8 and 1946–7 definitive series (Nos. 414/34).

(Photo Dai-Nippon Ptg Co, Tokyo)

1936 (10 Dec). New Year's Greetings. W **39**. P 13×13½.

292	**80**	1½s. carmine	8·00	35

1937 (1 Apr). Colours changed. Small Die, size 22×18½ mm (10s.), 18½×22 mm (others). Granite paper. W **39** (horiz on 10s.). P 13½×13 (10s.) or 13×13½ (others).

293	**53**	4s. light green	4·50	1·10
294	**61b**	10s. maroon	12·50	22·00
295	**53**	20s. deep blue	38·00	38·00
293/295	*Set of 3*		50·00	55·00

1937 (May)–**38**. W **81** (horiz on 6s. and 10s.). White paper.

(a) P 13½×13 (6s., 10s.) or 13×13½ (others)

296	**36**	½s. olive-sepia (5.37)	3·75	3·25
297		1s. yellow-orange (8.37)	7·25	5·00
298		3s. rose-red (6 37)	3·00	45
299	**53**	4s. bright green (5.37)	8·50	35
300	**37**	5s. slate-lilac (6.37)	11·00	30
301	**61a**	6s. rose-red (5.37)	15·00	2·75
302	**37**	7s. red-orange (5.37)	14·00	30
303	**53**	8s. bistre (6.37)	19·00	2·20
304	**61b**	10s. rose-red (5.37)	12·50	30
305	**53**	20s. blue (5.37)	22·00	70
306	**37**	25s. olive-green (11.37)	85·00	3·75
307	**38**	30s. yellow-orange & yell-gn (6.37)	55·00	1·00
308		50s. chestnut and deep blue (9.37)	£275	2·75
309		1y. yellow-green & pur-brn (10.37)	£150	1·10
310	**58**	5y. green (11.37)	£450	12·50
311		10y. violet (11.37)	£600	11·00

(b) Coil stamp. P 13×imperf.

312	**36**	3s. rose-red (8.38)	7·50	7·50
296/312	*Set of 17*		£1500	50·00

82 Goshuin-sen (16th-century trading ship)

83 Gen. Nogi

84 Lake Taisho, Kamikochi

85 Mitsubishi B5N1 and Map

86 Kamatari Fujiwara

87 Plum Tree

(Des T. Kasori (1, 3, 5, 7, 14, 20s.), M. Kimura (others). Die eng K. Noma (½s.), M. Aoki (1s.), K. Kato (2s., 4s.), F. Watabe (3s., 8s., 14s., 25s., 50s., 1y.), all typo. Eng K. Kato (5s., 30s., 5y.), K. Noma (6s., 20s.), M. Aoki (7s., 10s.), F. Watabe (12s.), S. Kurihara (10y.), all recess)

1937 (10 May)–**40**. T **82/7** and similar vert designs. W **81**.

(a) P 13×13½

313		½s. violet (1.11.37)	1·30	80
314		1s. chestnut (11.12.37)	3·50	70
315		2s. bright scarlet (10.5.37)	1·00	10
		a. Booklet pane of 20 (16.10.37)	60·00	
316		3s. green (11.12.39)	1·00	10
317		4s. emerald (1.8.37)	1·30	10
		a. Booklet pane of 20 (16.10.37)	25·00	
318		5s. dull ultramarine (21.12.39)	2·30	10
319		6s. yellow-orange (1.6.39)	4·75	2·10
320		7s. green (16.10.39)	1·20	45
321		8s. violet (11.8.39)	1·50	60
322		10s. deep carmine (1.11.38)	7·00	20
323		12s. slate-blue (1.12.39)	1·00	1·00
324		14s. lake and purple-brown (1.2.38)	1·30	45
325		20s. ultramarine (1.2.40)	1·60	10
326		25s. light brown & dp brown (11.10.38)	1·20	30
327		30s. turquoise (3.4.39)	3·50	20
		a. Imperf (pair)	£1000	
328		50s. olive and bistre (11.6.39)	1·00	20
		a. Olive (forest) omitted	£800	£650
329		1y. lt brown & reddish brown (1.7.39).	6·25	80
330		5y. bronze green (21.7.39)	38·00	3·00
331		10y. maroon (21.9.39)	32·00	1·60
313/331	*Set of 19*		£100	14·00

(b) Coil stamps. P 13×imperf.

332		½s. violet (4.39)	6·75	6·75
333		2s. bright scarlet (25.1.38)	7·25	7·25
334		4s. emerald (25.1.38)	7·50	7·50
335		14s. magenta and brown-lake (12.38).	£170	£170
332/335	*Set of 4*		£170	£170

Designs: As T **82**—1s. Rice harvesting. As T **83**—4s. Admiral Togo. As T **85**—3s. Hydro-electric power station; 6s. Garambi Lighthouse, Taiwan (as T **140**); 7s. Diamond Mountains, Korea; 8s. Meiji Shrine 10s. Yomei Gate, Tosho Shrine, Nikko; 14s. Inner Gate, Kasuga Shrine; 20s. Mt. Fuji and cherry blossoms; 25s. Horyu Temple; 30s. Torii, Itsukushima Shrine at Miyajima; 50s. Temple of Golden Pavilion, Kyoto; 1y. Great Buddha, Kamakura.

For stamps in T **83**, see also Nos. 392, 394 and 414 and for stamps showing Admiral Togo, see Nos. 396 and 398. For stamps in T **86/7**. see Nos. 424/5.

88 Nakajima-built Douglas DC-2 Airline)

89 New Year's Emblem

(Des O. Masuyama and M. Kimura. Photo)

1937 (1 June). Aerodrome Fund. W **81** (horiz). P 13×13½.

336	**88**	2s. +2s. carmine-red	2·75	1·80
337		3s. +2s. violet	2·75	2·10
338		4s. +2s. green	3·50	1·90
336/338	*Set of 3*		8·00	5·25

(Des H. Otsuka. Photo)

1937 (15 Dec). New Year's Greetings. W **81**. P 13×13½.

339	**89**	2s. scarlet	13·00	20

90 Nantai Volcano

91 Kegon Falls

92 Shinkyo Bridge

93 Hiuchi Volcano

1938 (25 Dec). Nikko National Park. Photo. P 13½×13 (vert) or 13×13½ (horiz).

340	**90**	2s. yellow-orange	80	95
341	**91**	4s. yellow-green	80	95
342	**92**	10s. scarlet	9·50	8·25
343	**93**	20s. blue	9·75	8·50
340/343	*Set of 4*		19·00	17·00
MS344	128×182 mm. Nos. 340/3 (sold at 50s.)		70·00	80·00

94 Daisen Volcano and Meadow

95 Yashima Plateau and Estuary

96 Abuto Kwannon Shrine

97 Tomo Bay

1939 (20 Apr). Daisen and Setonaikai National Parks. Photo. P 13×13½.

345	**94**	2s. light brown	60	80
346	**95**	4s. yellow-green	5·00	2·75
347	**96**	10s. scarlet	10·00	10·50
348	**97**	20s. blue	10·00	10·50
345/348	*Set of 4*		23·00	31·00
MS349	127×180 mm. Nos. 345/8 (sold at 60s.)		44·00	50·00

98 Mt. Kuju and Village

99 Naka Volcano

100 Naka Crater

101 Volcanic Cones of Mt. Aso

1939 (15 Aug). Aso National Park. Photo. P 13×13½.

350	**98**	2s. olive-sepia	60	1·10
351	**99**	4s. yellow-green	3·50	6·50
352	**100**	10s. scarlet	23·00	27·00
353	**101**	20s. blue	33·00	22·00
350/353	*Set of 4*		55·00	50·00
MS354	127×181 mm. Nos. 350/3 (sold at 50s.)		£140	£160

102 Globe

103 Count Tsunetami Sano

(Des T. Kasori. Photo)

1939 (15 Nov) 75th Anniv of Membership of International Red Cross Union. Cross in red. P 12½.

355	**102**	2s. brown	1·90	2·00
356	**103**	4s. yellowish green	2·20	2·50
357	**102**	10s. scarlet	12·50	15·00
358	**103**	20s. dull ultramarine	12·50	15·00
355/358	*Set of 4*		26·00	31·00

104 Golden Bird

105 Mt. Takachiho

106 Saké Jar and Trout

107 Kashiwara Shrine

(Des T. Kasori (2s.), F. Nishizawa (4s.), M. Kimura (10s., 20s.). Eng T. Matsuura. Recess)

1940 2600th Anniv of Japanese Empire. P 12.

359	**104**	2s. orange (11.2.40)	1·10	1·60
360	**105**	4s. deep green (10.11.40)	55	85
361	**106**	10s. deep rose-red (11.2.40)	5·25	7·75
362	**107**	20s. dull ultramarine (10.11.40)	1·60	2·50
359/362	*Set of 4*		7·75	11·50

108 Mt. Hokuchin

109 Mt. Asahi

110 Sounkyo Gorge, Kobako   **111** Tokachi Range

1940 (20 Apr). Daisetsu-zan National Park. Photo. P 13½×13 (10s.) or 13×13½ (others).

363	**108**	2s. light brown	60	1·10
364	**109**	4s. yellow-green	3·25	5·50
365	**110**	10s. scarlet	10·50	11·50
366	**111**	20s. blue	13·00	11·50
363/366	*Set of 4*		25·00	27·00
MS367	127×181 mm. Nos. 363/6 (sold at 50s.)		£300	£325

112 Mt. Shimmoe   **113** Takachiho Peak

114 Kirishima Shrine   **115** Lake Roku-Kwannon

1940 (21 Aug). Kirishima National Park, Kyushu. Photo. P 13×13½.

368	**112**	2s. light brown	60	1·10
369	**113**	4s. yellowish green	1·30	2·20
370	**114**	10s. scarlet	9·75	11·50
371	**115**	20s. dull ultramarine	12·50	11·50
368/371	*Set of 4*		22·00	24·00
MS372	127×181 mm. Nos. 368/71 (sold at 50s.)		£300	£375

116 Ceremonial Shrine (after Y. Araka)   **117** "Loyalty and Filial Piety"

(Des T. Kasori. Eng T. Matsuura. Recess)

1940 (25 Oct). 50th Anniv of Promulgation of Imperial Re-script on Education. P 12½.

373	**116**	2s. violet	1·10	1·90
374	**117**	4s. green	1·50	2·40

118 Mt. Daiton   **119** Central Peak, Mt. Niitaka

120 Buddhist Temple, Mt. Kwannon   **121** View of Mt. Niitaka

1941 (10 Mar). Daiton and Niitaka-Arisan National Parks. Photo. P 13×13½.

375	**118**	2s. light brown	1·30	1·30
376	**119**	4s. emerald	2·75	2·75
377	**120**	10s. scarlet	8·25	10·00
378	**121**	20s. blue	11·50	11·50
375/378	*Set of 4*		21·00	23·00
MS379	128×182 mm. Nos. 375/8 (sold at 90s. together with No. **MS**384)		£130	£150

122 Seisui Precipice, East Taiwan Coast   **123** Mt. Tsugitaka

124 Taroko Gorge, Taiwan   **125** Mt. Taroko, source of R. Takkiri

1941 (10 Mar). Tsugitaka and Taroko National Parks. Photo. P 13½×13 (vert) or 13×13½ (horiz).

380	**122**	2s. light brown	1·30	1·30
381	**123**	4s. emerald	2·75	2·75
382	**124**	10s. scarlet	8·25	9·75
383	**125**	20s. blue	11·50	13·50
380/383	*Set of 4*		21·00	25·00
MS304	128×182 mm. Nos. 380/3 (sold at 90s. together with No. **MS**379)		£100	95·00

(126)

127 Kenkoku Shrine

128 Japanese and Manchukuan Boys

129 Orchids and Crest of Manchukuo

1942 (16 Feb). Surrender of Singapore. Nos. 315 and 317 surch as T **126**.

385	2s. +1s. scarlet (B.)	1·10	2·00
386	4s. +2s. emerald (R.)	1·10	2·00

(Des T. Kasori. Eng T. Matsuura. Recess)

1942 (1 Mar–15 Sept). 10th Anniv of Establishment of Manchukuo. P 12.

387	**127**	2s. light brown	55	85
388	**128**	5s. yellow-olive (15 Sept)	85	1·30
389	**127**	10s. scarlet	1·90	3·75
390	**129**	20s. royal blue (15 Sept)	4·00	5·75
387/390	*Set of* 4		6·50	10·50

130 Girl War-worker

131 Shipbuilding

132 Hyuga Monument and Mt. Fuji

132a Admiral Togo

133 War Worker

134 Palms and Map of Greater East Asia

135 "The Enemy will Surrender"

136 Airman

137 Yasukuni Shrine

138 Mt. Fuji

139 Torii, Itsukushima Shrine, Miyajima

140 Garambi Lighthouse. Taiwan

141 Garambi Lighthouse, Taiwan

(Des T. Yamanouchi (1s.), M. Kimura (2s. (392), 3s., 5s., 7s., 40s. (406)), H. Otsuka (2s. (393), 6s.), S.Suzuki (4s.), T. Nakano (10s. (399)), K. Fuya (10s. (400)), H. Ando (15s.), K. Mori (17s., 27s.), T. Kasori (20s., 30s., 40s. (407)). Die eng M. Matsuura (1s.), K. Kato (2s. (392), 3s., 5s., 7s., 10s. (400), 30s.), S. Kurihara (2s. (393), 17s., 27s.), K. Fujiki (4s.), F. Watabe (6s., 10s. (399), 40s. (407)), K. Noma (20s.). Eng K. Kato (15s.), K. Noma (40s. (406)). Recess (15s., 40s. (406)). Typo (others))

1942–45. W **81**. P 13×13½.

391	**130**	1s. brown (1.1.43)	15	15
392	**83**	2s. vermilion (10.44)	3·50	3·50
		a. Perf 12 (1.45)	8·00	8·00
		b. *Red* (10.44)	65	60
		ba. Perf 12. *Red* (12 44)	3·00	55
393	**131**	2s. green (2.2.45)	80	80
		a. Wmk sideways	80·00	80·00
394	**83**	3s. brown (15.7.44)	1·10	15
395	**132**	4s. yellow-green (1 10.42)	30	30
396	**132a**	5s. claret (1.4.42)	40	20
397	**133**	5s. ultramarine (22.9.44)	65	65
398	**132a**	7s. vermilion (15.6.44)	1·20	50
399	**134**	10s. carmine and pink (1.12.42)	95	10
		a. Pink (map) omitted	£400	
400	**135**	10s. grey (1 4.45)	5·25	5·25
401	**136**	15s. blue (1.10.42)	4·00	2·30
402	**137**	17s. dull slate-violet (21.2.43)	1·20	25
403	**138**	20s. blue (8.1.44)	1·60	15
404	**137**	27s. deep carmine (2 2.45)	1·20	1·10
405	**139**	30s. green (8.1.44)	4·00	2·00
406	**140**	40s. deep reddish purple (1.10.42)	1·60	15
407	**141**	40s. purple (8.1.44)	2·40	2·10
		a. Wmk sideways	£1200	
391/407	*Set of* 17		27·00	18·00

Nos. 392, 394, 396 and 399 were issued with and without gum and No. 400 only without gum.

See also Nos. 417/21.

142 Steam Locomotive

143 Tanks in action at Bataan

(Des T. Kasori. Photo)

1942 (14 Oct). 70th Anniv of First National Railway. P 12.

408	**142**	5s. blue-green	3·75	6·00

1942 (8 Dec). First Anniv of Declaration of War. T **143** and similar horiz design. Photo. P 12.

409	2s. +1s. red-brown	1·60	2·75
410	5s. +2s. blue (Attack on Pearl Harbor).	2·40	3·75

144 Yasukuni Shrine

145 Kwantung Shrine and Map of Kwantung Peninsula

(Des T. Kasori. Photo)

1944 (29 June). 75th Anniv of Yasukuni Shrine. P 13×13½.
411　**144**　7s. blue-green...................................　80　1·30

(Des M. Hiromatsu. Photo Kyodo Ptg Co, Tokyo)

1944 (1 Oct). Dedication of Kwantung Shrine. P 13½×13.
412　**145**　3s. red-brown................................　3·75　11·50
413　　　　7s. grey...　4·00　11·50

PRINTERS. Owing to post-war conditions printing of the two following issues was shared by a number of printers. Their names are indicated by letters, thus: (*a*) Govt Ptg Works, Tokyo; (*b*) Kyodo Ptg Co, Tokyo; (*c*) Teikoku Ptg Co, Tokyo; (*d*) Tokodo, Tokyo; (*e*) Tokyo-Shoken, Sapporo; (*f*) Tokyo-Shoken, Tokyo; (*g*) Toppan Ptg Co, Osaka; (*h*) Toppan Ptg Co, Tokyo.

146 Sun and Cherry Blossom

147 Sunrise and Kawasaki Ki-61 Hien Fighter

148 Coal Miners

149 Torii of Yasukuni Shrine

(Des N. Furuya (3s.), S. Suzuki (5s.), H. Otsuka (50s.), M. Hioki (1y.). Typo (2s., 10s. (417)); litho (others). Printers: 2s. (*a*), 3s. (*egh*), 5s. *deh*, 10s. (417/18) (*h*), 10s. (419) (*bdegh*), 20s., 50s. (422) (*g*), 30s. (f), 50s. (422a), 5y., 10y. (*a*), 1y. (*gh*))

1945–48. W **81**. Imperf.
414　**83**　2s. red (4.45)......................................　85　85
415　**146**　3s. carmine (1.8.45)...........................　50　40
416　**147**　5s. green (1.8.45)...............................　40　30
　　　　　a. Greenish blue..............................　20·00　17·00
417　**135**　10s. olive-grey (5.45)........................　20·00　13·50
418　　　　10s. dull blue (9 45)...........................　45·00
419　**138**　10s. orange (8.10.45).........................　60　35
420　　　　20s. dull ultramarine (3.46)..............　80　30
421　**139**　30s. dull blue (3.46).........................　2·20　70
422　**148**　50s. brown (15.4 46).........................　85　30
　　　　　a. Perf 13×13½ (16.3.48).................　5·00　1·40
423　**149**　1y. olive-green (15.4.46)...................　1·90　95
424　**86**　5y. bronze green (8.45).....................　6·25　80
425　**87**　10y. maroon (8.45)...........................　44·00　1·50
414/425 *Set of 12* ....　£110　†
414/417, 419/425 *Set of 11* ....　†　18·00

There are numerous variations of colour and paper in this issue. The following numbers exist with both versions of W **81**: 416, 419, 420 and 422.

Nos. 414/25 were all, except No. 422a, issued without gum. No. 414 also exists with gum and is rare thus.

For No. 422 in miniature sheet, see No. **MS466**.

149a Baron H. Maeshima

150 Pagoda of Horyu Temple, Nara

151 Mt. Fuji, after Hokusai

152 Snow and White-fronted Geese (after Hokusai)

152a Kintai Bridge, Iwakuni

153 Kiyomizu Temple, Kyoto

153a Goldfish

154 Noh Mask

155 Plum Tree

(Des Y. Yoshida (15s., 1y.50, 5y.), T. Yamanouchi (30s.), M. Hioki (1y.), M. Kimura (1y.30), T. Kasori (2y., 100y.), T. Kono (50y.). Eng M. Matsuura, recess (50y., 100y.), litho (others). Printers: 15s. (*b*): 30s. (without gum), 2y., 5y., 10y., 50y., 100y. (*a*); 30s. (with gum) (*h*)); 1y. (*acd*); 1y.30, 1y.50 (*ac*))

1946–47. T **150/55** and similar vert designs. W **81**. Imperf.
426　**149a**　15s. deep green (20.11.46)...............　60　55
　　　　　a. Wmk sideways (8.47)..................　27·00　27·00
427　**150**　30s. dull violet (10.8.46)..................　1·00　30
　　　　　a. Perf 12×12½ (2.47).....................　7·50　7·50
　　　　　b. Perf 12 (10.46)..........................　15·00　15·00
　　　　　c. Perf 13×13½ (10.46)...................　4·75　4·75
　　　　　d. Perf 13×12
428　**151**　1y. ultramarine (*shades*) (1.8.46).....　2·00　30
428*a*　　　1y. pale dull blue (10.46).................　1·70　30
429　**152**　1y.30 olive-bistre (15.9.46)..............　4·50　1·40
430　　　　1y.50 deep grey (20.11.46)...............　4·00　80
431　**153**　2y. vermilion (1.12.46)...................　3·25　30
432　**153a**　5y. magenta (15.11.46)..................　10·50　1·10
433　**154**　50y. yellow-brown (1.11.46)............　£100　2·20
　　　　　a. Wmk sideways............................　£100　2·20
　　　　　b. Perf 13×13½ (7.47).....................　£100　1·50
434　**155**　100y. claret (26.12.46)....................　£100　2·00
　　　　　a. Perf 13×13½ (7.47).....................　£100　1·30
426/434 *Set of 10* ....　£200　6·75

There are numerous variations of colour and paper in this issue. The following numbers exist with both versions of W **81**: 426, 427/c, 428, 429 and 430.

Nos. 427a (narrow wmk), 433b and 434a were only issued with gum; Nos. 427 (narrow wmk), 427c (wide wmk) and 432 exist both with and without gum; the rest come only without gum.

For stamps in the above designs but redrawn with characters reading from left to right, see Nos. 441, 445/6 and 449/50.

For Nos. 428*a* 431 and 432 in miniature sheets, see Nos. **MS464**, **MS457** and **MS472/3** respectively.

(Typo Hirayama-Shuzando, Tokyo)

1946 (26 Sept). As No. 427, but rouletted in coloured line). No wmk.
435   **150**   30s. dull violet..   2·10   1·90

156 Mediaeval
Postman's Bell

157 Baron
Maeshima

158 First Japanese
Postage Stamp

159 Symbols of
Communications

(15s. des M. Hioki, eng Y. Kawahara; 30s. des Y. Yoshida, eng
F. Watabe; 50s. des T. Kasori, eng H. Hasegawa; 1y. des M. Hisano,
eng M. Matsuura. Recess)

1946 (12 Dec). 75th Anniv of Govt Postal Service. P 13½×13 (30s.)
or 12½ (others).
436   **156**   15s. orange..   6·00   6·00
437   **157**   30s. myrtle green..   8·00   8·00
438   **158**   50s. deep rose-red..   4·00   4·00
439   **159**   1y. blue..   4·00   4·00
436/439 *Set of 4*   ....   20·00   20·00
MS440 183×125 mm. Nos. 436/9. Imperf. No gum
(sold at 3y.)..   £170   £190

160

160a

161 Baron
Maeshima

162 Whaling

163 National Art

(Des T. Yamanouchi (30s., 1y.20), Y. Yoshida (35s., 5y.), S. Watanabe
(45s.), M. Hioki (1y.), T. Kasori (4y., 10y. (448)). Die eng K. Kato (30s.,
1y., 1y.20, 5y.). Eng S. Kurihara (10y. (448)). Litho (45s., 10y. (449)).
Recess (10y. (448)). Typo (others))

1947–52. T **160/3** and types of 1946–47 issue but redrawn with
Japanese characters reading from left to right. (*a*) W **81**.
P 13½×13 (10y.) or 13×13½ (others). With gum.
441   **150**   30s. dull violet (12.2.47)..............................   6·00   6·00
442   **160**   35s. green (15.4.47)......................................   95   65

443   **160a**   45s. bright magenta (1.5.47)......................   1·40   1·20
                    a. Perf 11×13½...   13·50   11·50
                    b. Imperf (pair)..   £1800
444   **161**   1y. brown (10.8.47)......................................   5·00   75
445   **150**   1y.20 yellow-green (15.5.47).......................   2·50   70
446   **152**   4y. pale blue (1.9.47)...................................   6·75   30
447   **162**   5y. bright blue (10.6.47)..............................   10·00   20
                    a. Perf 11×13½...   32·00   4·50
                    b. Imperf (pair)..   £600
448   **163**   10y. dull violet (15.5.47).............................   11·00   15

(b) W **81**. Imperf. Without gum
449   **155**   10y. purple (7.3.47).....................................   46·00   2·10

(c) No wmk. P 13×13½. With gum
450   **152**   4y. pale blue (2.52)......................................   34·00   2·30
441/450 *Set of 10*   ....   £140   17·00
For No. 445 in miniature sheet, see No. **MS454**.

164 Mother and
Child

165 Roses and
Wisteria

166 National Products

(Des I. Kamaya (50s.), M Morimoto (1y.). Photo)

1947 (3 May). Inauguration of New Constitution. P 12½.
451   **164**   50s. deep carmine   65   70
452   **165**   1y. ultramarine   95   90
MS453 128×180 mm. Nos. 451/2. Imperf. No gum
(sold at 3y.) ....   10·50   12·00

1947 (15 May). Know Your Stamps Exhibition, Tokyo, May 1947. Sheet
containing No. 445 in block of fifteen. Sold at 18y.
MS454 237×76 mm £200   £180

(Des S. Watanabe. Photo)

1947 (15 Aug) Re-opening of Private Foreign Trade. P 12½.
455   **166**   1y.20 brown ....   4·00   2·10
456   4y. pale ultramarine...................................   8·00   2·75
The frame design differs in the 4y.

1947 (19 Aug). Know Your Stamps Exhibition, Kyoto, August 1947.
Sheet containing No. 431 in block of five. Imperf. No gum. Sold
at 10y.
MS457 115×69 mm...   33·00   38·00

167 Lily of the
Valley

168 Locomotive *Benkei*, 1880

(Des M. Hioki. Photo)

1947 (13 Sept). Relief of Ex-convicts Day. P 12½.
458   **167**   2y. deep blue.green....................................   6·50   3·25

(DesY. Yoshida. Eng K. Kato. Recess)

1947 (14 Oct). 75th Anniv of Japanese Railway Service. Imperf. No
gum. Sold at 5y.
MS459 116×72 mm. **168** 4y. blue ....   23·00   23·00

169 Hurdling **170**

(Des S. Watanabe, T. Kasori, Y. Yoshida and M. Hisano respectively. Photo)

1947 (25 Oct). Second National Athletic Meeting, Kanazawa. T **169** and similar vert designs. Each deep mauve. P 12½.

460	1y.20 Type **169**	13·00	12·00
	a. Block of 4. Nos. 460/3	55·00	
461	1y.20 Diving	13·00	12·00
462	1y.20 Throwing the discus	13·00	12·00
463	1y.20 Volleyball	13·00	12·00
460/463	Set of 4	47·00	42·00

Nos. 460/3 were issued together in *se-tenant* blocks of four within the sheet.

1947 (1 Nov). Philatelic Week. Sheet containing No. 428*a* in strip of five. Imperf. No gum.

MS464 114×71 mm 5·50 6·75

For No. MS464 overprinted at top and bottom with Japanese characters in purple, see No. MS476.

(Des T Kasori. Photo)

1947 (25 Nov). Community Chest. W **81** (horiz). P 12½.
465 **170** 1y.20 + 80s. rose-carmine 2·00 1·80

1947 (27 Nov). Philatelic Exhibition, Sapporo, November 1947. Sheet containing No. 422 in block of five. Imperf. No gum. Sold at 2y.50.

MS466 114×71 mm 18·00 20·00

171 **172** Kiyomizu Temple, Kyoto **173** National Art

(1y.50 des S. Watanabe, litho; 2y. des T. Kasori, die eng K. Hiranu, typo; 3y.80 des M. Hisano, litho; 10y. des T. Kasori, die eng Y. Nozawa, typo)

1948–51. Designs without chrysanthemum. P 13×13½.

(a) W **81**

467	**171**	1y.50 pale blue (10.9.48)	4·50	65
468	**172**	2y. vermilion (10.1.48)	12·00	30
469	–	3y.80 light brown (10.9.48)	12·00	7·75
470	**173**	10y. bright violet (15.4.48)	23·00	25

(b) No wmk

471	**173**	10y. bright violet (10.51)	90·00	7·50
467/471	Set of 5		£130	15·00

Design:—3y.80 Numeral type as T **171**.

For Nos. 467 and 469 imperf in miniature sheet, see No. MS484.

1948 (8 Mar). Philatelic Exhibition, Osaka. Sheet containing No. 432 twice with two Japanese characters in centre below stamps. Imperf. No gum.

MS472 114×71 mm 18·00 22·00

1948 (11 Mar). Philatelic Exhibition, Nagoya. Sheet as last but three Japanese characters in centre below stamps.

MS473 114×71 mm 21·00 23·00

For No. MS473 overprinted at top, bottom and sides with Japanese characters and flowers in green, see No. MS475 and for No. MS472 similarly overprinted in error, see No. MS475b.

174 Stylized Tree **175** Sampans, Seto Inland Sea

(Des M. Hioki. Photo)

1948 (1 Apr). Encouragement of Afforestation. P 12½.
474 **174** 1y.20 deep green 1·60 1·60

1948 (3 Apr). Philatelic Exhibition, Mishima, April, 1948. Sheet No. MS473 optd at top, bottom and sides with Japanese characters and flowers in green, at Mishima Ptg Wks, Mishima.

MS475	114×71 mm	£110	46·00
	a. Opt inverted	£250	£170
	b. Error. Optd on No. MS472	£225	£140

1948 (18 Apr). Death Centenary of Hokusai Katsushika (painter). Sheet No. MS464 optd at top and bottom with Japanese characters in purple.

MS476 114×71 mm 37·00 28·00

(Des Y. Yoshida. Eng M. Matsuura. Recess)

1948. Sheets Commemorating Various Exhibitions. Each sheet contains two stamps as T **175** (2y. red), with coloured borders and inscriptions. Imperf. No gum.

(a) Communications Exhibition, Tokyo, April 27 to May 4 1948 (27 April)

MS477 113×71 mm. Green border 21·00 11·50

(b) Newspaper and Postage Stamp Exhibition, Aomori City (20 May)

MS478 113×71 mm. Blue border 28·00 20·00

(c) Communications Exhibition, Fukushima (23 May)

MS479 113×71 mm. Turquoise-blue border 28·00 20·00

176 Boy and Girl reading **177** Horse Race

(Des M. Hoiki. Photo)

1948 (3 May). Re-organisation of Educational System. P 12½.
480 **176** 1y.20 deep carmine 1·60 1·40

(Des S. Wada. Photo)

1948 (6 June). 25th Anniv of Japanese Horse Racing Laws. P 12½.
481 **177** 5y. brown 3·50 2·00

Issued in sheets of 30 stamps and two labels showing a stylized horse.

178 Swimmer **179** Distillery Towers

(Des M. Hioki. Photo)

1948 (9 Sept). Third National Athletic Meeting, Yawata. P 12½.
482 **178** 5y. blue 4·75 2·40

Issued in sheets of 30 stamps and two labels, one showing a torch, the other Inscribed with dates of the meeting

(Des M. Hisano. Photo)

1948 (14 Sept). 10th Anniv of Government Alcohol Monopoly. P 12½.
483   **179**   5y. bistre-brown..   4·50   2·75

1948 (20 Sept). Philatelic Exhibition, Kumamoto. Sheet containing two copies each of Nos. 467 and 469. Imperf. No gum.
MS484   114×71 mm...   46·00   38·00

180 Nurse

181 Varied Tit Feeding Young

(Des S. Watanabe (**180**), T. Kasori (**181**). Photo)

1948 (1 Oct). Red Cross and Community Chest. P 12½.
485   **180**   5y. +2y.50 scarlet....................................   12·50   12·50
486   **181**   5y. +2y.50 bright green..........................   12·50   12·50
MS487   128×90 mm. T **180/1** (both 5y. + 5y.). W **81**.
    Imperf. No gum ....   95·00   80·00

182 Farm Girl

183 Harpooning

184 Miner

185 Girl plucking Tea

186 Girl Printer

187 Mill Girl

188 Mt. Hodaka

189 Tree Planting

190 Postman

191 Blast Furnace

192 Locomotive Construction

(Des M. Hioki (2y., 3y., 5y. (**184**), 8y.), Y. Yoshida (5y. (**185**), 16y.), T. Yamanouchi (6y.), S. Watanabe (15y., 100y., 500y.), T. Kasori (20y.), M. Hisano. (30y.). Die eng F. Watabe (2y., 30y.). S. Kurhara (3y.), K. Kato (5y. (**184**), 8y.), Y. Kawahara (5y. (**185**)), K. Oshikiri (6y.), M. Matsuura (15y.), H. Hasegawa (20y.), all typo. Eng M. Matsuura (16y.), S. Kurihara (100y.), F Watabe (500y.), recess)

1948–52. P 13×13½.

(a) W **81**.

488	**182**	2y. green and light green (20.11.48)....	3·25	10
		a. Optd with 4 characters in frame (R.) (27.12.48)*	1·40	1·90
		b. Opt inverted	£120	
489	**183**	3y. turquoise (20.5.49).....................	7·75	20
490	**184**	5y. olive-bistre (1.11.48)..................	18·00	1·50
		a. Booklet pane of 20 (15.2.49)	£225	
491	**185**	5y. blue-green (15.11.49).................	60·00	8·00
492	**186**	6y. red-orange (25.11.49).................	12·00	15
493	**184**	8y. chestnut (1.6.49)........................	13·00	10
		a. Booklet pane of 20 (3.11.49)	£300	
494	**187**	15y. greenish blue (16.10.48)............	4·75	20
495	**188**	16y. ultramarine (15.1.49)	12·50	6·50
496	**189**	20y. green (10.5.49)	50·00	20
497	**190**	30y. violet-blue (10.5.49)	60·00	20
498	**191**	100y. carmine (15.10.49)	£750	2·20
499	**192**	500y. blue (26.9.49)...........................	£650	3·75
488/499	*Set of* 12		£1500	21·00

(b) No wmk

500	**182**	2y. green and light green (10.51).........	3·25	25
501	**183**	3y. turquoise (11.51).........................	75·00	1·40
502	**186**	6y. red-orange (6.51)	12·50	65
503	**184**	8y. chestnut (7.51)............................	55·00	80
504	**189**	20y. green (8.51)................................	95·00	1·40
505	**190**	30y. violet-blue (7.51)........................	£300	1·60
506	**191**	100y. carmine (2.52)	£650	1·40
507	**192**	500y. blue (3.52)...............................	£550	1·60
500/507	*Set of* 8		£1500	8·25

*No. 488a was made available for candidates' mail during an election, each candidate receiving 1000 copies.

For No. 495 in bright blue, see No. 524a and for No. 490 and 494 imperf in miniature sheets see Nos. **MS**513 and **MS**508.

1948 (16 Oct). Philatelic Exhibition, Nagano. Sheet containing No. 494. Imperf. No gum.
MS508   114×71 mm..   60·00   44·00

193 Baseball

194 "Beauty Looking Back" (Moronobu Hishikawa)

(Des M. Hisano, M. Hioki. S. Watanabe and Y. Yoshida respectively. Photo)

1948 (29 Oct). Third National Athletic Meeting, Fukuoka. T **193** and similar sports designs. P 12½.
509   5y. green (Type **193**)................................   13·50   6·75
    a. Block of 4. Nos. 509/12......................   60·00

510		5y. green (Bicycle race)	13·50	6·75
511		5y. green (Sprinter)	13·50	6·75
512		5y. green (High jumper)	13·50	6·75
509/512	*Set of 4*		50·00	24·00

Nos. 509/12 were issued together in *se-tenant* blocks of four within the sheet.

1948 (2 Nov). Commemorating the Shikoku Travelling Philatelic Exhibition, November 1948. Sheet containing two copies of No. 490. Imperf. No gum.

MS513	115×72 mm	70·00	55·00

1948 (29 Nov). Philatelic Week. Photo. P 13½×13.

514	**194**	5y. brown	95·00	49·00

No. 514 was issued in small sheets consisting of a horizontal strip of five stamps.

1948 (3 Dec). Postal Service Exhibition, Kanazawa and Takaoka. Sheet containing No. 514. Imperf. No gum.

MS515	71×115 mm	65·00	39·00

195 Girl playing with Shuttlecock   **196** Skater   **197** Ski Jumping

(Des M. Hioki. Photo)

1948 (13 Dec). New Year's Greetings. P 13½.

516	**195**	2y. vermilion	6·50	6·00

(Des M. Hioki. Photo)

1949 (27 Jan). Fourth National Athletic Meeting, Suwa City. P 12.

517	**196**	5y. violet	3·75	2·30

(Des S. Watanabe. Photo)

1949 (3 Mar). Fourth National Athletic Meeting, Sapporo, Hokkaido. P 12.

518	**197**	5y. ultramarine	4·50	2·30

198 *Koan Maru* (ferry) in Beppu Harbour   **199** Exhibition Grounds

(Des K. Nakamura and T. Kasori. Eng K. Kato. Recess)

1949 (10 Mar). P 13½.

519	**198**	2y. blue and scarlet	1·60	1·20
520		5y. blue and green	6·75	1·70

(Des M. Kimura. Photo)

1949 (15 Mar). Foreign Trade Fair, Yokohama. P 13½.

521	**199**	5y. rose-carmine	4·25	2·75

No. 521 was also issued imperforate in sheets of 20, sold only at the exhibition. (Price for imperforate single, £3.25 unused, £2.10 used).

200 Seto Inland Sea   **201** Stylized Trees

(Des Y. Yoshida. Eng M. Matsuura. Recess)

1949 (20 Mar). Matsuyama, Okayama and Takamatsu Exhibitions. W **81**. P 13×13½.

522	**200**	10y. scarlet (Matsuyama)	37·00	23·00
523		10y. carmine (Okayama)	30·00	21·00
524		10y. claret (Takamatsu)	55·00	26·00
522/524	*Set of 4*		£110	65·00

1949 (1 Apr). Nagano Peace Exhibition. As No. 495 but colour changed.

524*a*	**188**	16y. bright blue	11·00	6·50

No. 524*a* was issued in sheets of 20.

(Des M. Hioki. Photo)

1949 (1 Apr). Encouragement of Afforestation. P 12.

525	**201**	5y. bright green	12·50	2·40

202 Shishi-Iwa (Lion Rock)   **203** Mt. Omine

204 Doro Hatcho River Pool   **205** Hashikui-Iwa

1949 (10 Apr). Yoshino Kumano National Park. Photo. P 13×13½.

526	**202**	2y. light brown	1·70	1·00
527	**203**	5y. yellow-green	5·50	1·60
528	**204**	10y. bright scarlet	21·00	12·00
529	**20S**	16y. blue	10·00	5·50
526/529	*Set of 4*		34·00	18·00
MS530	126×182 mm. Nos. 526/9. No gum (sold at 40y.)		50·00	37·00

206 Boy   **207** Radio Mast

(Des M. Hioki, Photo)

1949 (5 May). Children's Day. P 12.
531   **206** 5y. purple and buff.. 7·50   2·40
             a. Buff omitted.................................. £300

1949 (5 May). Children's Exhibition, Inuyama. Sheet containing No. 531 in block of ten. Imperf.
MS532 143×90 mm £400   £375

(Des S. Watanabe. Photo)

1949 (11 May). Electrical Communications Week. Sheet containing T **207**. P 13½×13.
MS533 71×108 mm. 20y. blue £140   £120

208 Observatory Tower

209 Radio Mast, Pigeon and Globe

(Des T. Kasori. Eng M. Matsuura. Recess)

1949 (1 June). 75th Anniv of Central Meteorological Observatory, Tokyo. P 12.
534   **208** 8y. green .... 4·50   2·20

(Des M. Kimura. Eng S. Kurihara. Recess)

1949 (1 June). Establishment of Joint Ministries of Postal Administration and Electrical Communications. P 12.
535   **209** 8y. blue... 4·50   2·20

210 Park in Autumn

211 Park in Spring

212 Park in Summer

213 Park in Winter

1949 (15 July–20 Nov). Fuji–Hakone National Park. Various views of Mt. Fuji. Photo. P 13×13½.
536   **210** 2y. light brown.................................. 4·50   1·10
537   **211** 8y. yellow-green.............................. 4·75   1·60
538   **212** 14y. deep rose-red........................... 2·20   65
539   **213** 24y. blue... 7·50   80
536/539 *Set of 4* .... 28·00   3·75
MS540 127×180 mm. Nos. 536/9 (sold at 56y.)
   (20 Nov)... 47·00   47·00

214 Woman holding Rose   **215** Doves

(Des S. Watanabe. Photo)

1949 (6 Aug). Establishment of Memorial City at Hiroshima. P 13×13½.
541   **214** 8y. olive-brown.............................. 10·50   2·75

(Des M. Hisano. Photo)

1949 (9 Aug). Establishment of International Cultural City at Nagasaki. P 13½×13.
542   **215** 8y. yellow-green.............................. 6·25   2·75

216 Swimmer   **217** Boy Scout   **218** Symbolical of Writing and Printing

(Des S. Watanabe. Photo)

1949 (15 Sept). Fourth National Athletic Meeting, Yokohama. P 13½.
543   **216** 8y. blue... 5·25   2·10
   Issued in sheets of 30 stamps and two labels, one showing a torch, the other dated "1949".

(Des M. Kimura. Photo)

1949 (22 Sept). First National Scout Jamboree, Tokyo. P 13½.
544   **217** 8y. yellow-brown .... 8·75   2·75

(Des M. Hisano. Photo)

1949 (1 Oct). Press Week. P 13½×13.
545   **218** 8y. deep blue.................................. 6·75   2·75

219 Map or Japan and Letters   **220** Globe and Forms of Transport

(Des T. Kasori; eng M. Matsuura (**219**). Des S. Watanabe; eng S. Kurihara (**220**). Recess)

1949 (10 Oct–1 Nov). 75th Anniv of Universal Postal Union. P 12 (2y., 14y.) or 13½×13½ (others).
546   **219** 2y. deep dull green .... 3·50   2·10
547   **220** 8y. carmine-lake............................ 4·50   2·10

548	**219**	14y. deep rose-red	12·50	9·00
549	**220**	24y. deep turquoise-blue	17·00	10·00
546/549	Set of 4		34·00	21·00

MS550 115×70 mm. Nos. 546/7. Imperf.

No gum (1 Nov)   5·75   6·75

Nos. 547 and 549 were each issued in sheets of 30 stamps and two labels inscribed "U.P.U".

221 Throwing the Javelin

(Des T. Yamanouchi, Y. Higashitsunoi, R. Tsunashima and T. Shimada, respectively. Photo)

1949 (30 Oct). Fourth National Athletic Meeting, Tokyo. T **221** and similar horiz designs, each deep olive-brown. A. P 12. B. P 12½.

			A		B	
551	8y. Type **221**		8·50	3·50	12·50	4·75
	a. Block of 4. Nos. 551/4		40·00		55·00	
552	8y. Yachting		8·50	3·50	12·50	4·75
553	8y. Relay racing		8·50	3·50	12·50	4·75
554	8y. Tennis		8·50	3·50	12·50	4·75
551/554	Set of 4		30·00	12·50	46·00	17·00

Nos. 551/4 were issued together in se-tenant blocks of four within the sheet.

222 Telescope

223 "Moon and Brent Geese" (after Hiroshige)

(Des S. Watanabe. Photo)

1949 (30 Oct). 50th Anniv of Establishment of Latitude Observatory, Mizusawa. P 12.

555	**222**	8y. blue-green	4·75	2·10

1949 (1 Nov). Postal Week. Photo. P 13½×13.

556	**223**	8y. violet	£140	50·00

The above was issued in small sheets consisting of a horizontal strip of five stamps.

A   B   C   D

E   F   G   H   I

J   K   L   M   N

O   P   Q   R

(Des M. Kimura (557/60, 562/4, 566, 570/1, 573), Y. Yoshida (others). Eng K. Kato (557), K. Oshikiri (561, 574), S. Kurihara (562/3, 571), T. Kasano (568), F. Watabe (others). Recess)

1949–52. T **224** and similar portraits. P 12½.

557	A	8y. deep emerald (23·3 mm wide) (3.11.49)	11·50	1·40
		a. Redrawn (23·7 mm wide)	£120	8·00
558	B	8y. grey-olive (3.2.50)	4·75	1·40
		a. Imperf (pair)	£650	
559	C	8y. deep green (10.4.50)	4·75	1·40
560	D	8y. deep blue-green (23.5.50)	4·50	1·40
561	E	8y. deep reddish violet (13.9.50)	12·50	4·50
562	F	8y. brown-purple (22.11.50)	4·50	1·40
563	G	8y. grey-green (27.2.51)	11·50	2·75
564	H	8y. reddish violet (23.3.51)	11·50	2·75
565	I	8y. carmine (10.4.51)	18·00	2·75
566	J	8y. brown-lake (9.7.51)	30·00	3·00
567	K	8y. brown (19.9.51)	18·00	3·00
568	L	8y. blue (21.9.51)	14·00	3·00
569	M	10y. dull green (31.1.52)	60·00	5·50
570	N	10y. maroon (25.8.52)	12·50	1·80
571	O	10y. carmine (26.9.52)	4·50	1·60
572	P	10y. slate (16.10.52)	6·00	1·60
573	Q	10y. brown (3.11.52)	5·50	1·60
574	R	10y. deep grey-blue (3.11.52)	6·00	1·60
557/574		Set of 18	£225	38·00

Portraits:—A, Hideyo Noguchi (bacteriologist). B, Y. Fukuzawa (educationist). C, Soseki Natsume (novelist). D, Shoyo Tsubouchi (dramatist). E, Danjuro Ichikawa (actor). F, Jo Niijima (religious leader). G, Hogai Kano (painter). H, Kanzo Uchimura (religious leader). I, Mme. Higuchi (author). J, Ogai Mori (doctor). K, S. Masaoka (poet). L, S. Hishida (painter). M, A. Nishi (scholar). N, K. Ume (lawyer). O, H. Kimura (astrophysicist). P, I. Ninobe (statesman). Q, T. Torada (physicist). R, Tenshin Okakura (writer).

225 Japanese Pheasant and Pampas Grass

226 Tiger (after Maruyama Okyo)

224 Dr. H. Noguchi

(Des T. Kasori. Eng S. Kurihara. Recess)

1950 (10 Jan)–**51**. AIR. Greyish paper. P 13×13½.

575	**225**	16y. grey	41·00	27·00
576		34y. purple	70·00	24·00
577		59y. rose-carmine	95·00	17·00
		a. White paper (10.51)	£110	18·00
578		103y. yellow-orange	65·00	21·00
579		144y. olive	70·00	30·00
575/579	*Set of* 5		£300	£110

(Des T. Kasori. Photo)

1950 (1 Feb). New Year's Greetings. P 12.

580	**226**	2y. carmine	9·75	2·75

NEW YEAR MINIATURE SHEETS. Miniature sheets which contain New Year's greetings stamps were not sold at post offices but were given as prizes in the annual New Year Lottery. These sheets are listed separately at the end of the country.

227 Microphones of 1925 and 1950

228 Dove

(Des S. Watanabe. Photo)

1950 (22 Mar). 25th Anniv of Japanese Broadcasting System. P 13½.

582	**227**	8y. ultramarine	4·50	2·10

(Des T. Kasori. Photo)

1950 (20 Apr). First Anniv of Establishment of Joint Ministries of Postal Administration and Electrical Communications. P 12.

583	**228**	8y. olive-green	4·25	1·60

229 Lake Akan and Mt. O-Akani

230 Lake Kutcharo

231 Mt. Akan-Fuji

232 Lake Mashu

1950 (15 July). Akan National Park. Photo. P 13×13½.

584	**229**	2y. light brown	1·60	1·20
585	**230**	8y. green	3·25	1·80
586	**231**	14y. carmine-red	15·00	6·75
587	**232**	24y. blue	16·00	7·75
584/587	*Set of* 4		32·00	16·00
MS588		127×181 mm. Nos. 584/7 (sold at 55y.)	50·00	49·00

233 Gymnast on Rings

(Des T. Shimada, Y. Higashitsunoi, T. Yamanouchi and R. Tsunashima, respectively. Photo)

1950 (28 Oct). Fifth National Athletic Meeting. T **233** and similar sports designs. P 13½.

589		8y. brown-red (Type **233**)	32·00	17·00
		a. Block of 4. Nos. 589/92	£200	
590		8y. brown-red (Pole vaulting)	32·00	17·00
591		8y. brown-red (Soccer)	32·00	17·00
592		8y. brown-red (Horse jumping)	32·00	17·00
589/592	*Set of* 4		£120	60·00

Nos. 589/92 were issued together in *se-tenant* blocks of four within the sheet.

234 Tahoto Pagoda, Ishiyama Temple

235 Baron Maeshima

236 Long-tailed Cock

237 Kannon Bosatsu (detail of wall painting, Horyu Temple)

238 Himeji Castle

239 Phoenix Temple, Uji

240 Buddhisattva Statue, Chugu Temple

(Des Y. Yoshida (80s., 50y.), T. Kasori (1y., 5y., 24y.), T. Yamanouchi (10y.), Y. Higashitsunoi (14y.). Die eng Y. Kawahara (80s.), M. Matsuura (5y., 10y.). Eng K. Oshikiri (14y.), S. Kurihara (24y.). Photo (1y., 50y.), recess (14y., 24y.), typo (others))

1950–51. With noughts for sen after numerals of value. P 13½×13 (14y.) or 13×13½ (others).

593	**234**	80s. carmine (21.5.51)	2·30	2·10
594	**235**	1y. brown (14.4.51)	3·00	45
595	**236**	5y. green & orange-brn (25.12.51)	6·75	20
596	**237**	10y. lake and mauve (10.12.51)	13·50	15
597	**238**	14y. lake-brown (27.3.51)	55·00	44·00
598	**239**	24y. blue (1.11.50)	44·00	23·00
599	**240**	50y. reddish brown (1.5.51)	£160	1·00
593/599	*Set of* 7		£250	65·00

For stamps without noughts for sen after value, see Nos. 653 etc. and for stamps additionally inscribed "NIPPON", see Nos. 1041 and 1058/9.

For miniature sheet containing No. 594, see No. **MS**610.

1950–51. Miniature sheets, each 76×50 mm, and each containing one of stamps from the above issue.
MS600 **234** 80s. carmine (21.5.51) .... 10·50   14·00
MS601 **238** 14y. lake-brown (27.3.51) .... 75·00   80·00
MS602 **239** 24y. blue (1.11.50) .... 47·00   60·00
MS603 **240** 50y. reddish brown (1.5.51) £300   £350

241 Girl and Rabbit

(Des S. Watanabe. Photo)

1951 (1 Jan). New Year's Greetings. P 12.
604   **241**   2y. rose .... 8·00   1·10

242 Skiing, Mt. Zao   **242a** Skiing, Mt. Zao

(Des R. Tsunashima (8y), K. Maeno (24y). Photo)

1951 (15 Feb). Tourist issue. Mt. Zao. P 13½.
606   **242**   8y. olive-green............................... 18·00   3·75
607   **242a** 24y. light blue................................. 20·00   8·75
See also Nos. 608/9, 612/17, 623/4, 639/44 and 702/3.

243 Nihon-Daira   **244** Mt. Fuji from Nihon-Daira

(Des A. Tango (8y.), T. Yamada (24y.). Photo)

1951 (2 Apr). Tourist Issue. Nihon-Daira. P 13½.
608   **243**   8y. olive-green............................... 18·00   3·75
609   **244**   24y. blue.. £130   35·00

1951 (14 Apr). 80th Anniv of Japanese Postal Service. Sheet containing No. 594 in block of four.
MS610   86×64 mm.. 25·00   22·00

245 Child's Head

(Des S. Watanabe. Photo)

1951 (5 May). Children's Charter. P 13½.
611   **245**   8y. orange-brown......................... 30·00   4·50

246 Hot Springs, Owaki Valley   **247** Lake Ashi

(Des R. Tsunashima (8y.), T. Shimada (24y.). Photo)

1951 (25 May). Tourist Issue. Hakone Spa. P 13½.
612   **246**   8y. red-brown............................... 11·00   3·00
613   **247**   24y. ultramarine .... 9·25   4·50

248 Senju Waterfall   **249** Ninai Waterfall

(Des T. Yamanouchi (8y.), K. Maeno (24y.). Photo)

1951 (1 June). Tourist Issue. Akame Waterfalls. P 13½.
614   **248**   8y. green.. 13·00   3·00
615   **249**   24y. light blue............................... 12·00   4·50

250 Waka-no-Ura   **251** Tomo-ga-Shima

(Des R. Tsunashima (8y.), T. Yamanouchi (24y.). Photo)

1951 (25 June). Tourist Issue. Waka-no-Ura and Tomo-ga-Shima Coastal Resorts. P 13½.
616   **250**   8y. yellow-brown.......................... 9·25   3·00
617   **251**   24y. light blue............................... 8·75   4·50

252 Oirase River   **253** Lake Towada

254 View from Kankodai   **255** Hakkoda Mountains

1951 (20 July). Towada National Park. Photo. P 13×13½.

618	**252**	2y. deep brown	3·00	1·10
619	**253**	8y. yellowish green	11·00	1·60
620	**254**	14y. brown-red	12·50	6·75
621	**255**	24y. blue	14·00	7·75
618/621 *Set of* 4			36·00	15·00
MS622 128×182 mm. Nos. 618/21 (sold at 55y.)			47·00	47·00

256 Uji River   **257** Uji Bridge

(Des Y. Yoshida. Eng M. Matsuura (8y.), S. Kurihara (24y.). Recess)

1951 (1 Aug). Tourist Issue. Uji River. P 13½.

623	**256**	8y. reddish brown	9·75	3·00
624	**257**	24y. blue	9·00	4·50

258 Douglas DC-4 Airliner over Horyuji Pagoda   **259** Airplane over Mt. Tate

(Des S. Watanabe. Photo)

1951 (1 Sept)–**52**. AIR. With noughts for sen after numerals of value. P 13×13½.

625	**258**	15y. violet	5·75	4·50
626		20y. light blue	38·00	2·75
627		25y. green (20.12.51)	37·00	50
628		30y. brown-red (20.12.51)	29·00	45
629		40y. grey-black	9·75	50
630	**259**	55y. bright blue (11.2.52)	£250	46·00
631		75y. brownish red (11.2.52)	£180	25·00
632		80y. magenta (11.2.52)	37·00	5·75
633		85y. black (11.2.52)	60·00	21·00
634		125y. yellow-brown (11.2.52)	20·00	5·75
635		160y. deep bluish green (11.2.52)	46·00	6·25
625/635 *Set of* 11			£650	£110

For similar designs, but without noughts after numerals of value, see Nos. 671/81.

260 Chrysanthemum   **261** Japanese Flag

(Des T. Kasori (260), S. Watanabe (261). Photo)

1951 (9 Sept). Peace Treaty. P 13½.

636	**260**	2y. yellow-brown	2·75	1·40
637	**261**	8y. red and slate-blue	8·00	3·75
638	**260**	24y. blue-green	25·00	8·75
636/638 *Set of* 3			32·00	12·50

262 Oura Catholic Church, Nagasaki   **263** Gateway, Sofuku Temple

(Des M. Kimura (8y.), T. Kasori (24y.). Photo)

1951 (15 Sept). Tourist Issue. Nagasaki. P 13½.

639	**262**	8y. carmine	13·00	3·00
640	**263**	24y. deep blue	9·75	4·50

264 Lake Marunuma   **265** Lake Sugenuma

(Des K. Hirano (8y.), T. Shimada (24y.). Photo)

1951 (1 Oct). Tourist Issue. Marunuma and Sugenuma. P 13½.

641	**264**	8y. purple	17·00	2·75
642	**265**	24y. blue-green	8·25	4·50

266 Shosenkyo Valley   **267** Nagatoro Bridge

(Des A. Tango (8y.), T. Yamada (24y.). Photo)

1951 (15 Oct). Tourist issue. Shosenkyo. P 13½.

643	**266**	8y. red	12·50	3·00
644	**267**	24y. greenish blue	13·50	4·50

268 Putting the Shot   **268a** Hockey   **269** Noh Mask

(Des S. Watanabe (T **268**), M. Hisano (T **268a**). Photo)

1951 (27 Oct). Sixth National Athletic Meeting. P 13½.
645	**268**	2y. orange-brown	4·50	2·50
		a. Pair. Nos. 645/6	13·50	13·50
646	**268a**	2y. grey-blue	4·50	2·50

Sheets contain alternate copies of each design.

(Des Y. Yoshida. Photo)

1952 (16 Jan). New Year's Greetings. P 13½.
647	**269**	5y. carmine	14·00	1·10

270 Ship's Davit and Southern Cross

270a Earth and Ursa Major

(Des S. Watanabe (5y.), M. Hisano (10y.). Photo)

1952 (19 Feb). 75th Anniv of Japan's Membership of Universal Postal Union. P 13½.
649	**270**	5y. violet	7·75	1·80
650	**270a**	10y. deep blue-green	20·00	4·50

271 Red Cross and Lily

271a Red Cross Nurse

(Des M. Hisano (5y.), S. Miyamoto (10y.). Photo)

1952 (1 May). 75th Anniv of Japanese Red Cross. P 13½.
651	**271**	5y. scarlet	6·00	2·00
652	**271a**	10y. deep green and red	14·00	4·00

272 Akita Dog

273 Little Cuckoo

274 Tahoto Pagoda, Ishiyama Temple

275 Mandarins

276 Japanese Serow

277 Chuson Temple

278 Goldfish

279 Yomei Gate, Tosho Shrine, Nikko

280 "Marimo" (water plant) and Fish

281 Great Purple

282 Fishing with Japanese Cormorants

283 "Bridge and Irises" (from lacquered box)

(Des M. Kimura (2y., 5y., 500y.), S. Watanabe (3y., 55y.), Y. Yoshida (4y., 20y., 35y., 100y.), S. Wada (8y.), T. Kasori (45y.), M. Hisano (75y.). Die eng K. Oshikiri (4y.). Eng M. Matsuura (100 y.), T. Kasano (500y.). Typo (4y., 10y.); recess (14y., 24y., 30y., 100y., 500y.); photo (others))

1952–68. T **272**/**83** and designs as 1950–51 issue, but without noughts after numerals of value. P 13½ (500y.), 13½×13 (14y.) or 13×13½ (others).
653	**235**	1y. brown (11.8.52)	55	10
654	**272**	2y. grey-black (23.8.52)	10	10
655	**273**	3y. deep bluish green (10.5.54)	15	10
		a. Imperf (pair)	£450	
656	**274**	4y. brown-purple & scar (10.7.52)	2·50	10
657	**275**	5y. reddish brn & pale bl (10.9.55)	15	10
		a. Booklet pane. Nos. 657×4 and 659×8 (20.4.59)	35·00	
		b. Booklet pane. Nos. 657×4 and 860×8 (1.4.63)	35·00	
		c. Coil. P 13ximperf (2.10.61)	3·00	2·10
		d. Booklet pane. No. 657×4 (1.8.64)	7·00	
		e. Booklet pane. Nos. 657×2 and 1049×6 (1.6.67)	12·00	
		f. Booklet pane. Nos. 657×2 and 1050×6 (1.3.68)	15·00	
		g. Booklet pane. Nos. 657×2, 1127×3 and 1128×3 (1.7.68)	34·00	
658	**276**	8y. brown and pale brown (1.8.52)	10	10
659	**237**	10y. lake and mauve (10.7.53)	5·50	10
		a. Booklet pane. No. 659×10 plus two labels (20.11.54)	£200	
		b. Coil. P 13ximperf (20.1.59)	27·00	27·00
660	**238**	14y. deep olive (20.9.56)	7·50	2·40
661	**277**	20y. sage-green (20.1.54)	1·50	10
662	**239**	24y. violet (19.3.57)	18·00	4·50
663		30y. reddish purple (1.4.59)	43·00	80
		a. Imperf (pair)	£2000	
664	**278**	35y. red-orange (10.5.52)	12·00	10
665	**279**	45y. blue (15.10.52)	5·25	10
666	**240**	50y. reddish brown (20.6.52)	6·50	10
667	**280**	55y. dull green, blk & lt bl (15.5.56)	18·00	80
668	**281**	75y. vio, yell, blk & verm (20.6.56)	9·75	80
669	**282**	100y. deep rose-red (15.9.53)	35·00	10
		a. Imperf (pair)	£900	
670	**283**	500y. reddish purple (15.3.55)	85·00	15
653/670 Set of 18			£200	8·75

Nos. 657e/f are each arranged in two blocks of four (2×5y. and 2×15y. on the left; 4×15y. on the right) separated by a gutter. The pane is folded along the gutter and attached to the booklet cover on one side of the folded edge so that the halves face each other. All four outer edges are imperforate. No. 657g is similarly arranged with the 5y. stamps and one copy each of Nos. 1127/8 on the left and the remaining stamps on the right.

No. 657d has the outer three edges imperf, the perforated edge being along the top. Blocks of four imperf top and bottom are from Nos. 657a/b.

For 1y., 2y., 3y., 50y., 55y. and 75y. in different colours and additionally inscribed "NIPPON", see Nos. 1041, 1582a, 1226, 1058/60, 1232 and 1064.

For a different version of No. 659a, see No. 734.

1952 (1 July)–**62**. AIR. As Nos. **625/35** but without noughts after numerals of value.

671	258	15y. violet (2.4.62)	2·10	95
672		20y. light blue (11.8.52)	60·00	1·30
673		25y. green (10.7.53)	1·20	10
674		30y. brown-red (1.9.52)	4·50	10
		a. Coil. P 13ximperf (2.10.61)	46·00	35·00
675		40y. grey-black (29.10.53)	5·50	25
676	259	55y. bright blue	90·00	6·75
677		75y. brownish red	£160	16·00
678		80y. magenta	£120	4·50
679		85y. black	5·00	2·75
680		125y. yellow-brown	10·00	3·75
681		160y. deep bluish green	43·00	4·50
671/681	*Set of* 11		£450	37·00

284 Mt. Yari   **285** Kurobe Valley   **288** Central Hall

286 Mt. Shirouma   **287** Mt. Norikura

1952 (5 July–26 Sept). Chubu-Sangaku National Park. Photo. P 13½×13 (vert) or 13×13½ (horiz).

682	284	5y. reddish brown	7·00	1·20
683	285	10y. deep bluish green	33·00	4·00
684	286	14y. dull vermilion	8·50	7·75
685	287	24y. new blue	14·00	7·75
682/685	*Set of* 4		55·00	19·00
MS686	129×182 mm. Nos. 682/5 but imperf.			
	No gum (sold at 60y.) (26 Sept)		£130	£120

(Des T. Kasori. Eng M. Matsuura. Recess)

1952 (1 Oct). 75th Anniv of Tokyo University. P 13½.

687	288	10y. grey-green	21·00	3·50

288a Mountaineer   **289** Wrestlers

(Des M. Hisano (T **288a**), S. Watanabe (T **289**). Photo)

1952 (18 Oct). Seventh National Athletic Meeting. P 13½.

688	288a	5y. bright blue	8·00	2·40
		a. Pair. Nos. 688/9	21·00	12·00
689	289	5y. brown	8·00	2·40

Nos. 688/9 were issued together In *se-tenant* pairs within the sheet.

290 Mt. Azuma-Kofuji   **291** Mt. Asahi

292 Mt. Bandai   **293** Mt. Gessan

1952 (18 Oct–10 Dec). Bandai-Asahi National Park. Photo. P 13×13½.

690	290	5y. deep orange-brown	5·50	1·00
691	291	10y. olive-green	17·00	2·75
692	292	14y. scarlet	6·75	4·50
693	293	24y. turquoise-blue	14·00	7·50
690/693	*Set of* 4		39·00	14·00
MS694	128×181 mm. Nos. 690/3 but imperf.			
	No gum (sold at 60y.) (10 Dec)		£150	95·00

294 "Kirin" and Chrysanthemums   **295** Flag of Crown Prince

(T **294** des M. Kimura, eng H. Hasegawa, recess, background photo; T **295** des T. Kasori, eng T. Kasano, recess)

1952 (10 Nov–23 Dec). Investiture of Crown Prince Akihito. P 13½.

695	294	5y. orange and brown	3·00	1·20
696		10y. orange and green	3·00	2·50
697	295	24y. blue	18·00	8·75
695/697	*Set of* 3		22·00	11·00
MS698	130×130 mm. Nos. 695/7 but imperf.			
	No gum (sold at 50y.) (23 Dec)		£120	£350

296 Dancing Doll   **297** First Japanese Electric Lamp

(Des T. Kasori. Photo)

1953 (1 Jan). New Years Greetings. P 13½.

699	296	5y. rose-carmine	9·50	1·10

(Des M. Hisano. Photo)

1953 (25 Mar). 75th Anniv of Electric Lamp in Japan. P 13½.

701	297	10y. brown	9·00	3·00

298 "Kintai Bridge" (after Hiroshige)   **299** Kintai Bridge

(Des Y. Yoshida (24y.). Photo)

1953 (3 May). Tourist Issue. Kintai Bridge. P 13½.
702	**298**	10y. brown	9·25	3·00
703	**299**	24y. blue	8·50	4·50

300 Lake Shikotsu   **301** Mt. Yotei

(Des Y. Yoshida (5y.), M. Kimura (10y.). Photo)

1953 (25 July). Shikotsu Toya National Park. P 13×13½.
704	**300**	5y. ultramarine	2·75	80
705	**301**	10y. green	8·75	1·60
MS706	148×105 mm. Nos. 704/5 but imperf.			
	No gum (sold at 20y.)	50·00	47·00

302 Great Buddha, Kamakura

(Des S. Watanabe. Photo)

1953 (15 Aug). AIR. P 13½.
707	**302**	70y. lake-brown	4·00	15
708		80y. blue	5·75	15
709		115y. olive-green	2·75	20
710		145y. deep blue-green	18·00	2·10
707/710	Set of 4		27·00	2·30

303 Wedded Rocks, Futami Bay   **304** Nakiri Coast

(Des K. Maeno (5y.), Tsunashima (10y.). Photo)

1953 (2 Oct) Ise Shima National Park. P 13×13½.
711	**303**	5y. red	2·50	80
712	**304**	10y. bright blue	5·50	1·60
MS713	148×105 mm. Nos. 711/2 but imperf.			
	No gum (sold at 20y.)	39·00	21·00

305 "Ho-o" (Happy Phoenix)   **305a** Manchurian Crane in Flight

(Des R. Nakao and M. Hisano, eng Y. Kawahara, recess (5y.); Des J. Maekawa and S. Watanabe, photo (10y.))

1953 (12 Oct). Return of Crown Prince from Overseas Tour. P 12½.
714	**305**	5y. brown-lake	4·25	1·60
715	**305a**	10y. grey-blue	7·50	2·75

306 Judo   **307** Tokyo Observatory

(Des M. Hisano (716), S. Watanabe (717). Photo)

1953 (22 Oct). Eighth National Athletic Meeting, Matsuyama. T **306** and similar horiz design. P 13½.
716	**306**	5y. emerald	7·25	2·10
		a. Pair. Nos. 716/17	21·00	12·00
717	–	5y. black (Rugby footballers)	7·25	2·10
	Sheets contain alternate copies of each design.			

(Des S. Watanabe. Photo)

1953 (29 Oct). 75th Anniv of Tokyo Observatory. P 13½.
718	**307**	10y. grey-blue	13·00	3·00

308 Mt. Unzen   **309** Mt. Unzen

(Des M. Kimura. Photo)

1953 (20 Nov). Unzen National Park. P 13×13½.
719	**308**	5y. rose-red	2·75	80
720	**309**	10y. blue	6·00	1·60
MS721	148×105 mm. Nos. 719/20 but imperf.			
	No gum (sold at 20y.)	39·00	21·00

310 Wooden Horse   **311** Ice Skaters

(Des M. Kimura. Photo)

1953 (25 Dec). New Year's Greetings. P 13½.
722	**310**	5y. rose-red	7·25	80

(Des S. Watanabe. Photo)

1954 (16 Jan). World Speed Skating Championships, Sapporo.
724 **311** 10y. blue .... 6·50 2·75

312

313 Wrestlers

(Des M. Hisano. Photo)

1954 (10 Apr). International Trade Fair, Osaka. P 13½.
725 **312** 10y. carmine-red .... 5·50 2·10

(Des M. Hisano. Eng F. Watabe. Recess)

1954 (22 May). International Free-style Wrestling Championship.
P 13½.
726 **313** 10y. green .... 4·50 2·00

314 Mt. Asama

315 Mt. Tanigawa

1954 (25 June). Jo-Shin-Etsu Kogen National Park. Photo. P 13×13½.
727 **314** 5y. black-brown .... 3·00 80
728 **315** 10y. deep turquoise-green .... 5·50 1·60
MS729 148×108 mm. Nos. 727/8 but imperf.
No gum (sold at 20y.) .... 39·00 21·00

316 Archery **317** Telegraph **318** Tumbler
Table

(Des M. Hisano, eng F. Watabe (730). Des S. Watanabe,
eng K. Oshikiri (731). Recess)

1954 (22 Aug). Ninth National Athletic Meeting, Sapporo. T **316** and
similar design. P 12.
730 **316** 5y. bronze green .... 6·25 2·00
a. Pair. Nos. 730/1 .... 15·00 8·50
731 – 5y. deep brown (Table tennis) ...... 6·25 2·00
Sheets contain alternate copies of each design.

(Des Y. Yoshida, eng T. Kasano (5y.). Des M. Kimura,
eng F. Watabe (10y.). Recess)

1954 (13 Oct). 75th Anniv of Japan's Membership of International
Telecommunications Union. T **317** and another design inscr
"1879 1954". P 13½.
732 5y. plum .... 2·75 1·30
733 10y. grey-blue (I.T.U. Monument)
(horiz) .... 7·50 2·30

1954 (20 Nov). Philatelic Week. Sheet 150×50 mm containing ten of
No. 659 (arranged as one row of 6 and one row of 4 with printed
label at each end). P 13×13½ with straight edge at top and
bottom.
MS734 237 10y. lake and mauve (x10) £200 £190
Although described as a special stamp booklet, **MS**734 was issued
unfolded and unattached to the cover. It differs from No. 659a by the

labels; in No. **MS**734 they each contain two vertical inscriptions in
light characters and in No. 659a they have three vertical inscriptions
in mixed light and heavy type.

(Des S. Watanabe. Photo)

1954 (20 Dec) New Year's Greetings. P 13½.
735 **318** 5y. orange-red and grey-black .... 7·25 80

319 Tama Gorge **320** Chichibu Mountains

(Des Y. Yoshida. Eng F. Watabe (5y.), S. Kurihara 10y.). Recess)

1956 (1 Mar). Chichibu-Tama National Park. P 13½×13 (5y.) or
13×13½ (10y.).
737 **319** 5y. blue .... 2·00 80
738 **320** 10y. brown-lake .... 2·50 1·10
MS739 148×105 mm. Nos. 737/8 but imperf.
No gum (sold at 20y.) .... 39·00 21·00

321 Paper Carp

(Des M. Kimura. Photo)

1955 (16 May). 15th International Chamber of Commerce Congress,
Tokyo. P 13×13½.
740 **321** 10y. vermilion, yellow, black & brt bl ..... 7·25 2·40

322 Bentenzaki **323** Jodoga Beach
Peninsula

1955 (30 Sept–17 Oct). Rikuchu-Kaigan National Park. Photo.
P 13½×13 (5y.) or 13×13½ (10y.).
741 **322** 5y. deep green .... 1·70 65
742 **323** 10y. claret .... 2·50 1·10
MS743 147×104 mm. Nos. 741/2 but imperf.
No gum (sold at 20y.) (17 Oct) .... 37·00 21·00

324 Gymnastics   **325** "Girl Playing Glass
                             Flute" (Utamaro)

(Des S. Watanabe. Eng K. Oshikiri (744), Y. Kawahara (745). Recess)

1955 (30 Oct). Tenth National Athletic Meeting, Kanagawa. T **324** and
similar vert design. P 13½.
744   **324**   5y. brown-lake ....   4·00   1·60
               a. Pair. Nos. 744/5 ....   9·25   7·25
745   –   5y. deep violet-blue (Running)..............   4·00   1·60
       Sheets contain alternate copies of each design.

(Des M. Kimura. Photo)

1955 (1 Nov). Philatelic Week. P 13½.
746   **325**   10y. multicoloured ....   16·00   12·00

326 "Kokeshi" Dolls   **327** Table Tennis

(Des M. Hisano. Photo)

1955 (20 Dec). New Year's Greetings. P 13½.
747   **326**   5y. olive-green and vermilion ....   2·75   40

(Des M. Hisano and R. Tsunashima. Photo)

1956 (2 Apr). World Table Tennis Championships. P 13½.
749   **327**   10y. red-brown...   2·00   1·10

328 Judo   **329** Children and Paper Carps

(Des M. Kimura. Eng T. Kasano. Recess)

1956 (3 May). World Judo Championships, Tokyo. P 13½.
750   **328**   10y. reddish purple and green ....   2·20   1·10

(Des H. Hasebe. Photo)

1956 (5 May). International Children's Day. P 13×13½.
751   **329**   5y. black and light blue ....   1·70   80

330 Osezaki Lighthouse   **331** Kujuku Island

(5y. photo; 10y. des M. Kimura, eng T. Shimada. Foreground recess,
background photo)

1956 (1 Oct). 25th Anniv of National Park Law. Saikai National Park.
P 13×13½.
752   **330**   5y. red-brown...........................   1·30   65
753   **331**   10y. deep blue and blue...................   1·70   1·10
MS754   147×104 mm. Nos. 752/3 but imperf.
       No gum (sold at 20y.) ....   31·00   20·00

332 Imperial Palace and Modern   **333** Sakuma Dam
Buildings

(Des M. Kimura. Eng S. Kurihara. Recess)

1956 (1 Oct). Fifth Centenary of Tokyo. P 13×13½.
755   **332**   10y. dull purple.............................   2·75   1·20

(Des Y. Yoshida. Eng Y. Kawahara, Recess)

1956 (15 Oct). Completion of Sakuma Dam. P 13½.
756   **333**   10y. deep blue.......................................   2·75   1·20

334 Basketball   **335** Ebizo Ichikawa (actor),
                             (after Sharaku)

(Des H. Hasebe, eng K. Oshikiri (757). Des S. Watanabe, eng
Y. Kawahara (758). Recess)

1956 (28 Oct). 11th National Athletic Meeting, Kobe. T **334** and
similar vert design. P 13½.
757   **334**   5y. deep bluish green..............................   1·60   80
               a. Pair. Nos. 757/8 ....   9·25   7·25
758   –   5y. deep dull purple (Long jumping) ..   1·60   80
       Sheets contain alternate copies of each design.

(Des M. Hisano. Photo)

1956 (1 Nov). Philatelic Week. P 13½.
759   **335**   10y. black, brown-orange & sil-grey.......   13·50   9·75

336 Mount Manaslu and Mountaineer

(Des M. Hisano. Photo)

1956 (3 Nov) Conquest of Mount Manaslu. P 13×13½.
760   **336**   10y. sepia, yell-brn, ultram & flesh .... 4·50   2·40

337 View of Yui (after Hiroshige) and Electric Train

338 Cogwheel. Valve and *Nissyo Maru* (freighter)

(Des S. Watanabe. Photo)

1956 (19 Nov). Electrification of Tokaido Railway Line. P 13×13½.
761   **337**   10y. black, green and deep ochre .... 7·25   2·40

(Des M. Hisano. Eng S. Kurihara. Recess)

1956 (18 Dec). Floating Machinery Fair. P 13½.
762   **338**   10y. blue .... 1·10   1·00

339 Whale (float)   **340** UNO Emblem

(Des H. Haebe. Photo)

1956 (20 Dec). New Year's Greetings. P 13½.
763   **339**   5y. black, ultramarine, red and buff ..... 1·70   30

(Des M. Kimura. Eng F. Watabe. Centre recess, frame photo)

1957 (8 Mar). First Anniv of Japan's Admission to United Nations. P 13½.
765   **340**   10y. carmine and blue .... 1·00   80

341 IGY Emblem, Emperor Penguin and Antarctic Research Vessel *Soya*

342 Atomic Reactor   **343** Gymnast

(Des S. Watanabe. Photo)

1957 (1 July). International Geophysical Year. P 13½.
766   **341**   10y. blue, yellow and black .... 1·00   65

(Des M. Kimura. Eng T. Kasano. Recess)

1957 (18 Sept). Completion of Atomic Reactor, Tokai-Mura. P 13½.
767   **342**   10y. deep reddish violet 60   30

(Des S. Watanabe. Eng K. Oshikiri (768), T. Kasano. (769). Recess)

1957 (26 Oct). 12th National Athletic Meeting, Shizuoka. T **343** and similar vert design. P 13½.
768   **343**   5y. blue 55   35
         a. Pair. Nos. 768/9 .... 1·70   2·00
769   –   5y. brown-red (Boxing) 55   35
    Sheets contain alternate copies of each design.

344 "Girl Bouncing a Ball"   **345** Ogochi Dam
(after Harunobu)

(Des M. Kimura. Photo)

1957 (1 Nov). Philatelic Week. P 13½.
770   **344**   10y. multicoloured .... 2·10   2·40

(Des M. Kimura. Eng S. Kurihara. Recess)

1957 (26 Nov). Completion of Ogochi Dam. P 13½.
771   **345**   10y. blue 50   40

346 Japan's First Blast Furnace and Modern Plant

347 "Inu-hariko" (toy dog)

(Des Y. Yoshida. Photo)

1957 (1 Dec). Centenary of Japanese Iron Industry. P 13½.
772   **346**   10y. purple and orange 35   30

(Des M. Kimura. Photo)

1957 (20 Dec). New Year's Greetings. P 13½.
773   **347**   5y. multicoloured 35   30

348 Kan-Mon Tunnel

(Des M. Hisano. Photo)

1958 (9 Mar). Opening of Kan-Mon Undersea Tunnel. P 13×13½.
775   **348**   10y. black, pink, blue and drab 50   25

349 "Lady returning from Bath-house" (after Kiyonaga)

350 Statue of Ii Naosuke, *Powhattan* (1858 paddle-steamer) and Modern Liner

(Des M. Hisano. Photo)

1958 (20 Apr). Philatelic Week. P 13½.
776   **349**   10y. multicoloured 80   25

(Des M. Kimura. Eng K. Oshikiri. Recess)

1958 (10 May). Centenary of Opening of Ports to Traders. P 13.
777   **350**   10y. carmine & deep turquoise-blue 40   25

351 National Stadium, Tokyo

352 Emigrant Ship *Kasato Maru* and South American Map

(Des S. Watanabe (5y.), M. Kimura (10y.), H. Hasebe (14y.), M. Hisano (24y.). Photo)

1958 (24 May). Third Asian Games, Tokyo. T **351** and similar designs. P 13½.
778   5y. drab, black, rose and deep
           blue-green............................... 25   20
779   10y. brown, red, blue and yellow 50   40
780   14y. ochre, blue, black and
           carmine-red............................ 40   30
781   24y. pink, yellow, black and blue........... 50   40
778/781 *Set of 4* .... 1·40   1·30
     Designs:—10y. Flame and Games emblem; 14y. Runner breasting tape; 24y. High-diver.

(Des S. Watanabe. Photo)

1958 (18 June). 50th Anniv of Japanese Emigration to Brazil. P 13×13½.
782   **352**   10y. multicoloured 40   20

353 Sado-Okesa Dancer on Sado Island

354 Mt. Yahiko and Echigo Plain

(Des H. Hasebe. Photo)

1958 (20 Aug). Sado-Yahiko Quasi-National Park. P 13½.
783   **353**   10y. multicoloured .... 1·10   40
784   **354**   10y. multicoloured .... 1·30   60

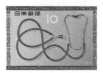

355 Stethoscope

356 "Old Kyoto Bridge" (after Hiroshige)

(Des S. Watanabe. Photo)

1958 (7 Sept). International Congresses of Chest Diseases and Bronchoesophagology, Tokyo. P 13½.
785   **355**   10y. deep turquoise-green....................... 40   25

(Des M. Hisano. Photo)

1958 (5 Oct). International Correspondence Week. P 13.
786   **356**   24y. multicoloured .... 3·50   90
     The design is taken from the series of 53 woodcuts showing stages of the Tokaido Road. Others from this series are shown on Nos. 810, 836, 878 and 908.

357 Badminton Player

358 Yukichi Fukuzawa (founder) and Keio University

(Des M. Hisano, eng K. Oshikiri (787). Des S. Watanabe, eng F. Watabe (788). Recess)

1958 (19 Oct). 13th National Athletic Meeting, Toyama. T **357** and similar vert design. P 13½.
787   **357**   5y. reddish purple 45   25
              a. Pair. Nos. 787/8 .... 1·20   80
788   —   5y. slate-blue (Weightlifting)................. 45   25
     Sheets contain alternate copies of each design.

(Des H. Otsuka. Eng T. Kasano. Recess)

1958 (8 Nov). Centenary of Keio University. P 13.
789   **358**   10y. claret............ 50   25

359 Children skipping across Globe
360 "Flame of Freedom"

(Des S. Watanabe. Photo)

1958 (23 Nov). International Child and Social Welfare Conferences, Tokyo. P 13.
790   **359**   10y. deep green   50   25

(Des M. Hisano. Photo)

1958 (10 Dec). Tenth Anniv of Declaration of Human Rights. P 12½×13.
791   **360**   10y. orange, blue, yell & bluish vio   45   25

361 Ebisu with Bream (toy)
362 Map of KojIma Bay and Tractor

(Des M. Kimura. Photo)

1958 (20 Dec). New Year's Greetings. P 13½.
792   **361**   5y. multicoloured   65   20

(Des M. Hisano. Photo)

1959 (1 Feb). Completion of Kojima Bay Reclamation Project. P 12½.
794   **362**   10y. reddish purple & brown-ochre   40   25

363 Karst Plateau
364 Akiyoshi Cavern

(Des H. Otsuka. Photo)

1959 (16 Mar). Akiyoshidai Quasi-National Park. P 13½.
795   **363**   10y. multicoloured ....   2·00   25
796   **364**   10y. multicoloured ....   3·50   25

365 Map of Asia
366 Crown Prince Akihito and Princess Michiko

(Des M. Kimura. Photo)

1959 (27 Mar). Asian Congress Commemorating 2500th Anniv of Death of Buddha. P 13½.
797   **365**   10y. carmine-red   50   25

(Des M. Kimura. Eng K. Shikiri. Recess, frame photo (10y., 30y.). Des H. Otsuka. Photo (others))

1959 (10–20 Apr). Imperial Wedding. T **366** and similar horiz design. P 13½.
798   –   5y. bluish violet and reddish purple   35   15
799   **366**   10y. maroon and brown   90   25
800   –   20y. sepia and orange-brown ....   1·20   25
801   **366**   30y. deep green and yellow-green ....   3·75   35
798/801 *Set of* 4   ....   5·25   1·00
MS802 127×88 mm. Nos. 798/9 but imperf.
  No gum (sold at 20y.) (20 Apr) ....   7·00   5·25
  Design:—5y., 20y. Ceremonial fan.

367 "Ladies reading poems" (from *Ukiyo* Genji, after Eishi)
368 Graduated Glass and Scales

(Des H. Hasebe. Photo)

1959 (20 May). Philatelic Week. P 13½.
803   **367**   10y. multicoloured ....   4·75   2·00

(Des S. Watanabe. Photo)

1959 (5 June). Ratification of Adoption of Metric System in Japan. P 13½.
804   **368**   10y. sepia and cobalt-blue   40   15

369 Stretcher-party with Casualty
370 Mt. Fuji from Lake Motosu

(Des H. Otsuka. Photo)

1959 (24 June). Red Cross. P 13½.
805   **369**   10y. red and bronze-green   50   15

(Des T. Shimada. Eng S. Kurihara. Recess)

1959 (21 July). National Parks Day. P 13½.
806   **370** 10y. deep green, maroon and blue   80   15

371 Ao Caves, Yabakei

372 Japanese Cormorant with Hita and Mt. Hito in background

(Des M. Kimura. Photo)

1959 (25 Sept). Yaba-Hita-Hikosan Quasi-National Park. P 13½.
807   **371** 10y. multicoloured ....   1·40   40
808   **372** 10y. multicoloured ....   1·40   40

373 Nagoya and Golden Dolphin

374 "Kuwana" (after Hiroshige)

(Des M. Hisano. Photo)

1959 (1 Oct). 350th Anniv of Nagoya. P 13½.
809   **373** 10y. gold, black and blue ....   1·10   15

(Des S. Watanabe. Photo)

1959 (4 Oct). International Correspondence Week. P 13.
810   **374** 30y. multicoloured ....   12·00   1·60

375 Manchurian Crane and IATA Emblem

376 Throwing the Hammer

(Des M. Hioki. Eng S. Kurihara. Recess)

1959 (12 Oct). 15th International Air Transport Association Meeting, Tokyo. P 13½.
811   **375** 10y. greenish blue...........................   80   40

(Des T. Yamanouchi, eng K. Oshikiri (812); des M. Hisano, eng T. Kasano (813). Recess)

1959 (25 Oct). 14th National Athletic Meeting, Tokyo. T **376** and similar horiz design. P 13½.
812   **376** 5y. slate-blue...............................   1·00   30
           a. Pair. Nos. 812/13.....................   2·00   95
813   –   5y. olive-brown (Fencer) ....   1·00   30
Sheets contain alternate copies of each design.

377 Open Book showing Portrait of Shoin Yoshida

378 Halves of Globe

(Des M. Hisano. Photo)

1959 (27 Oct). Death Centenary of Shoin Yoshida (educator) and National Parents and Teachers Association Convention. P 13½.
814   **377** 10y. bistre-brown...........................   70   30

(Des S. Watanabe. Photo)

1959 (2 Nov). 15th Session of the Contracting Parties to the General Agreement on Tariffs and Trade ("GATT"), Tokyo. P 13½.
815   **378** 10y. red-brown................................   70   30

379 Rice-eating Rat of Kanazawa (toy)

380 Yukio Ozaki and Clock Tower, Memorial Hall

381 Deer

(Des M. Kimura. Photo)

1959 (19 Dec). New Year's Greetings. P 13½.
816   **379** 5y. multicoloured ....   1·80   25

(Des H. Hasebe. Photo)

1960 (25 Feb). Completion of Ozaki Memorial Hall, Tokyo. P 13½.
818   **380** 10y. dull purple and cinnamon...............   70   30

(Des M. Kimura. Photo)

1960 (10 Mar). 1250th Anniv of Transfer of Capital to Nara. P 13½.
819   **381** 10y. brown-olive...........................   90   30

382 Godaido Temple, Matsushima

383 Bridge of Heaven (Sandbank), Miyazu Bay

384 Miyajima from the Sea   **385** Takeshima-Gamagon Causeway

(Des Y. Yoshida (821), M. Kimura (others). Eng S. Kurihara, K. Oshikiri and F. Watabe, respectively. Recess)

1960. "Scenic Trio". P 13½×13.

820	**382**	10y. turquoise-grn & red-brn (15.3).....	2·20	60
821	**383**	10y. deep green and blue (15.7).............	3·00	60
822	**384**	10y. blue-green & black-vio (15.11)........	3·00	60
820/822	*Set of 3*	....	7·50	1·60

(Des H. Otsuka. Photo)

1960 (20 Mar). Mikawa Bay Quasi-National Park. P 13½.

823	**385**	10y. multicoloured	1·70	40

386 "Ise" (from Satake picture scroll "Thirty-six Immortal Poets")

(Des S. Watanabe. Photo)

1960 (20 Apr). Philatelic Week. P 13½.

824	**386**	10y. black, crimson and buff..................	4·50	2·75

387 *Kanrin Maru* (barque) crossing the Pacific   **388** Japanese Crested Ibis

(Des T. Yamanouchi. Eng T. Kasano (10y.), K. Oshikiri (30y.). Recess)

1960 (17 May). Centenary of Japanese-American Treaty. T **387** and similar horiz design inscr "1960". P 13½.

825	10y. deep brown and bluish green........	80	30
826	30y. blue-black and rose-red	2·20	45

Design: —30y. Pres. Buchanan receiving Japanese mission.
For Nos. 825/6 in miniature sheet, see No. **MS**835.

(Des S. Watanabe. Photo)

1960 (24 May). 12th International Bird Preservation Congress, Tokyo. P 13½.

827	**388**	10y. vermilion, pink and deep grey........	90	45

389 Radio Waves around Globe   **390** Abashiri Flower Gardens

(Des M. Hisano. Eng S. Nakada. Recess)

1960 (1 June). 25th Anniv of Japanese Overseas Broadcasting Service, "Radio Japan". P 13½.

828	**389**	10y. carmine.....................................	70	30

(Des H. Hasebe. Photo)

1960 (15 June). Abashiri Quasi-National Park. P 13½.

829	**390**	10y. multicoloured	1·70	45

391 Cape Ashizuri   **392** Rainbow linking Hawaii and Japan

(Des M. Hisano. Photo)

1960 (1 Aug). Ashizuri Quasi-National Park. P 13½ .

830	**391**	10y. multicoloured	1·70	45

(Des H. Otsuka. Photo)

1960 (20 Aug). 75th Anniv of Japanese Emigration to Hawaii. P 13½.

831	**392**	10y. multicoloured	1·10	30

393 Douglas DC-8 Jetliner and Farman H.F.III Biplane   **394** Seat Plan of the Diet

(Des M. Hisano. Photo)

1960 (20 Sept). 50th Anniv of Japanese Aviation. P 13½.

832	**393**	10y. brown and blue-grey	80	30

(Des S. Watanabe (5y), T. Kono (10y.). Photo)

1960 (27 Sept). 49th Inter-Parliamentary Union Conference. T **394** and another horiz design. P 13½.

833	5y. orange and indigo..............................	70	25
834	10y. red-brown and slate-blue.................	1·00	30

Design:—10y. "Clear Day with Southern Breeze" (from "36 Views of Mt. Fuji" by Hokusai Katsushika) and Diet Building.

1960 (27 Sept). Visit of Crown Prince Akihito and Princess Michiko to the United States. Sheet containing Nos. 825/6.

MS835 120×76 mm..	39·00	31·00

395 "Kambara" (after Hiroshige) **396** Okayama Observatory

(Des S. Watanabe. Photo)

1960 (9 Oct). International Correspondence Week. P 13.
836 **395** 30y. black, blue, yellow & red-brown..... 25·00 5·50

(Des M. Kimura. Eng T. Kasano. Recess)

1960 (19 Oct). Opening of Okayama Astrophysical Observatory. P 13½.
837 **396** 10y. violet... 1·10 25

397 *Kendo* (Japanese fencing) **398** Lieut. Shirase and Map of Antarctica

(Des H. Otsuka, eng S. Nakada (838); des S. Watanabe, eng K. Oshikiri (839). Recess)

1960 (23 Oct). 15th National Athletic Meeting, Kumamoto. T **397** and similar vert design. P 13½.
838 **397** 5y. greenish blue............................... 80 30
   a. Pair. Nos. 838/9 .... 2·00 1·00
839   – 5y. maroon (Vaulting) 80 30
Sheets contain alternate copies of each design.

(Des M. Hisano. Photo)

1960 (29 Nov). 50th Anniv of First Japanese Antarctic Expedition. P 13½.
840 **398** 10y. black and light red-brown.............. 1·10 25

399 Red Beko and Golden Bekokko (Japanese toys) **400** Diet Building and Stars

(Des M. Kimura. Photo)

1960 (20 Dec). New Year's Greetings. P 13½.
841 **399** 5y. multicoloured .... 1·10 25

(Des M. Kimura; Photo (5y.). Des H. Otsuka; eng T. Kawahara. Recess (10y.))

1960 (24 Dec). 70th Anniv of Diet. T **400** and similar horiz design inscr "1890 1960". P 13½.
843   5y. deep violet-blue and black 70 25
844   10y. deep carmine .... 1·00 25
Design: –10y. Opening ceremony of first session of Diet.

401 Narcissus **402** Pearl-divers at Shirahama

(Des K. Maeno (845, 853), Y. Higashitsunoi (846), A. Tango (847), T. Shimada (848, 854), H. Otsuka (849, 855/6), T. Nozawa (850), H. Hasebe (851), K. Nakajima (852). Photo)

1961 Flowers. T **401** and similar vert designs. P 13½.
845   10y. yellow, grey, green and purple (30.1)...... 6·00 1·10
846   10y. yellow, black, green & brown (28.2)....... 2·50 1·10
847   10y. yellow, carmine, green & bis (20.3) .... 1·80 1·10
848   10y. pink, olive, brown and grey (28.4)........... 1·80 1·10
849   10y. rose, yellow, green and sepia (25.5)......... 1·40 1·00
850   10y. yellow, violet, grn & ol-grey (15.6).......... 75 85
851   10y. yellow, chest, grn & turq-grn (15.7)........ 60 50
852   10y. purple, yellow, green & pale bl (1.8) 60 50
853   10y. bluish vio, bl, grn & sage-grn (1.9)........... 60 50
854   10y. violet-blue, grn, yell & orge (2.10) 60 50
855   10y. yellow, green, brown & brt bl (1.11) 60 50
856   10y. yellow, pink, green and slate (1.12)......... 60 50
845/856 Set of 12 .... 16·00 8·00
Designs:—Nos. 845, T **401**; 846, Plum blossom; 847, Camellia (*japonica*); 848, Cherry blossom; 849, Peony; 850, Iris; 851, Lily; 852, Morning Glory; 853, Bellflower; 854, Gentian; 855, Chrysanthemum; 856, Camellia (*sasanqua*).

(Des H. Otsuka. Photo)

1961 (15 Mar). Minami-Boso Quasi-National Park. P 13½.
857 **402** 10y. multicoloured .... 1·00 30

403 Hirase's Slit Shell **404** Nanten **405** Cherry Blossoms

406 Engaku Temple **407** Yomei Gate, Tosho Shrine, Nikko **408** Noh Mask

409 Copper Pheasant **410** "The Wind God" **411** Manchurian Cranes

412 "Kalavinka"
(legendary bird)

413 Baron
Maeshima

(Des W. Emori (4y., 80y.), H. Hasebe (6y., 10y., 100y.), M. Kimura (30y., 40y.), I. Norimatsu (70y.), M. Hisano (90y., 120y.). Photo)

1961 (1 April)–**65**. P 13×13½.

858	**403**	4y. vermilion and brown (15.5.63)........	15	10
859	**404**	6y. red and green (20.2.62)....................	15	10
860	**405**	10y. magenta and purple	35	10
		a. Imperf (pair)...	£500	
		b. Magenta (background) omitted.....	£300	
		c. Purple (stems) omitted.....................	£300	
		d. Coil. P 13ximperf (25.4.61)...............	8·00	2·50
		e. Booklet pane of 4 (1.8.64)...............	6·00	
861	**406**	30y. slate-violet (15.6.62)......................	6·25	10
		a. Coil. P 13ximperf (1.3.63)	6·25	2·75
862	**407**	40y. carmine-red (10.5.62).....................	7·50	10
863	**408**	70y. black and ochre (20.8.65)..............	3·00	10
864	**409**	80y. bistre-brn & rosine (1.12.65)...........	1·50	10
865	**410**	90y. deep blue-green (2.7.62).................	42·00	30
866	**411**	100y. grey, black and pink (25.7.63)........	15·00	10
867	**412**	120y. reddish violet (1.11.62)	14·50	75
858/867		*Set of 10*	80·00	1·70

No. 860e has the outer three edges imperf, the perforated edge being along the top. Blocks of four imperf top and bottom, with the right side perf or with a selvedge attached, are from No. 657b.

For 70y., 80y., 90y., 100y. and 120y. in different colours and additionally inscribed "NIPPON", see Nos. 1065, 1066, 1068, 1234/6 and 1238.

(Des S. Watanabe. Photo)

1961 (20 Apr). 90th Anniv of Japanese Postal Service. P 13×13½.

868	**413**	10y. olive-green and black	2·00	25

414 "Dancing Girl" (from
17th-century screen)

415 Lake Biwa

(Des S. Watanabe. Photo)

1961 (20 Apr). Philatelic Week. P 13½.

869	**414**	10y. Venetian red, black, blue & bistre ..	2·00	1·60

(Des H. Hasebe. Photo)

1961 (25 Apr). Lake Biwa Quasi-National Park. P 13½.

870	**415**	10y. multicoloured	1·10	30

416 Rotary Emblem and
"Peoples of the World"

417 "Benefits of
Irrigation"

(Des S. Watanabe. Eng F. Watabe. Recess)

1961 (29 May). 52nd Rotary International Convention. P 13½.

871	**416**	10y. orange and black	50	25

(Des M. Kimura. Photo)

1961 (7 July). Inauguration of Aichi Irrigation System. P 13½.

872	**417**	10y. blue and deep purple	50	30

418 Globe showing
Longitude 135°E. and
Sun

419 Parasol Dancer, Tottori
Beach

(Des S. Watanabe. Photo)

1961 (12 July). 75th Anniv of Japanese Standard Time. P 13½.

873	**418**	10y. vermilion, black and ochre..............	70	25

(Des M. Kimura. Photo)

1961 (15 Aug). San'in Kaigan Quasi-National Park. P 13½.

874	**419**	10y. multicoloured	1·40	30

420 Komagatake Volcano

421 Gymnast

(Des M. Kimura. Photo)

1961 (15 Sept). Onuma Quasi-National Park. P 13½.

875	**420**	10y. multicoloured	1·40	30

(Des H. Hasebe, eng S. Okamura (876); des M. Hisano, eng K. Oshikiri (877). Recess)

1961 (8 Oct). 16th National Athletic Meeting, Akita. T **421** and similar design. P 13½.

876	**421**	5y. blue-green..	80	30
		a. Pair. Nos. 876/7	1·80	1·00
877	–	5y. ultramarine (Rowing)	80	30

Sheets contain alternate copies of each design.

422 "Hakone" (after Hiroshige)　**423** Throwing the Javelin

(Des S. Watanabe. Photo)

1961 (8 Oct). International Correspondence Week. P 13.
878　**422**　30y. multicoloured ....　9·75　6·25

(Des M. Kimura, eng T. Kasano (879); des H. Hasebe, eng S. Kurihara (880); des H. Otsuka, eng K. Oshikiri (881). Recess)

1961 (11 Oct). Olympic Games, Tokyo, 1964 (1st issue). T **423** and similar designs. P 13½.
879　5y.+5y. yellow-brown (T **423**).....................　1·30　1·60
880　5y.+5y. deep green (Wrestling)....................　1·30　1·60
881　5y.+5y. carmine (Woman diver)...................　1·30　1·60
879/881　Set of 3 ....　3·50　4·25
　See also Nos. 899/901, 909/11, 935/7, 949/52, 969/72, **MS**974/9 and 981/**MS**986.

424 Library and Book　**425** Tiger (Izumo toy)

(Des M. Hisano. Photo)

1961 (1 Nov). Opening of National Diet Library. P 13½.
882　**424**　10y. ultramarine and gold ....　50　30

(Des W. Emori. Photo)

1961 (15 Dec). New Year's Greetings. P 13½.
883　**425**　5y. multicoloured ....　90　10

426 Mt. Fuji from Lake Ashi　**427** Minokake-Iwa, Irozaki

428 Mt. Fuji from Mitsutoge　**429** Mt. Fuji from Osezaki

1962 (16 Jan). Fuji-Hakone-Izu National Park. Photo. P 13½.
885　**426**　5y. green ....　1·00　30
886　**427**　5y. deep blue...........................　90　30
887　**428**　10y. reddish brown...........................　1·40　45
888　**429**　10y. black . ...　1·80　55
885/888　Set of 4 ....　4·50　1·40

430 Omishima Island　**431** Doll Festival

(Des H. Otsuka. Photo)

1962 (15 Feb). Kitanagato-Kaigan Quasi-National Park. P 13½.
889　**430**　10y. multicoloured ....　80　30

(Des H. Otsuka. Photo)

1962 (3 Mar)–**63**. National Festivals. T **431** and similar vert designs. Multicoloured. P 13½.
890　10y. Type **431** ....　1·70　60
891　10y. Children and decorated tree (Star Festival) (7.7.62)...........................　60　30
892　10y. Three children ("Seven-Five-Three" Festival) (15.11.62)...........................　60　30
893　10y. Child throwing beans (Spring Festival) (3.2 63)...........................　50　30
890/893　Set of 4 ....　3·00　1·30

432 "Dancer" (after N. Kano)　**433** Sakurajima Volcano

(Des S. Watanabe. Photo)

1962 (20 Apr). Philatelic Week. P 13½.
894　**432**　10y. red, brown, yellow and black...........　2·00　1·60

(Des M. Hisano. Photo)

1962 (30 Apr). Kinkowan Quasi-National Park. P 13½.
895　**433**　10y. multicoloured ....　60　30

434 Mount Kongo　**435** Suigo View

(Des S. Watanabe. Photo)

1962 (15 May). Kongo-Ikoma Quasi-National Park. P 13½.
896　**434**　10y. multicoloured ....　60　30

(Des M. Kimura. Photo)

1962 (1 June). Suigo Quasi-National Park. P 13½.
897   **435** 10y. multicoloured 80   30

436 Diesel Train   **437** Scout's Hat on
emerging from Tunnel   Map

(Des H. Hasebe. Photo)

1962 (10 June). Opening of Hokuriku Railway Tunnel. P 13½.
898   **436** 10y. olive-brown.. 3·00   40

(Des S. Watanabe, eng K. Oshikiri (899), des H. Hasebe, eng F. Watabe (900), des M. Kimura, eng T. Kasano (901). Recess)

1962 (23 June). Olympic Games, Tokyo, 1964 (2nd issue). Designs as
T **423**. P 13½.
899   5y. + 5y. brown-red (Judo) 80   1·10
900   5y. + 5y. bluish green (Water-polo) 80   1·10
901   5y. + 5y. purple (Gymnastics (female)) 80   1·10
899/901 *Set of* 3 .... 2·20   3·00

(Des M. Hisano. Photo)

1962 (3 Aug). Asian Scout Jamboree, Mt. Fuji. P 13½.
902   **437** 10y. black, bistre and orange-red 40   30

438 Mt. Shibutsu and   **439** Smoking Summit of
Ozegahara Swamp   Mt. Chausu, Nasu

440 Lake Chuzenji and   **441** Senryu-kyo Narrows,
Mt. Nantai   Shiobara

1962 (1 Sept). Nikko National Park. Photo. P 13½.
903   **438** 5y. turquoise-blue............................... 40   25
904   **439** 5y. brown-lake.. 40   25
905   **440** 10y. deep purple................................... 60   25
906   **441** 10y. brown-olive.................................... 60   25
903/906 *Set of* 4 .... 1·80   90

442 Wakato   **443** "Nihonbashi" (after
Suspension Bridge   Hiroshige)

(Des M. Hisano. Eng S. Mizutani. Recess)

1962 (26 Sept). Opening of Wakato Suspension Bridge. P 13½×13.
907   **442** 10y. carmine-red .... 1·10   45

(Des S. Watanabe. Photo)

1962 (7 Oct). International Correspondence Week. P 13.
908   **443** 40y. multicoloured .... 8·25   5·50

(Des M. Kimura, eng T. Kasano (909); des H. Otsuka, eng K. Oshikiri (910), des H. Hasebe, eng F. Watabe (911). Recess)

1962 (10 Oct). Olympic Games, Tokyo, 1964 (3rd issue). Designs as
T **423**. P 13½.
909   5y. + 5y. slate-green (Basketball).................... 70   55
910   5y. + 5y. deep lilac (Rowing) 70   55
911   5y. + 5y. red (Fencing) 70   55
909/911 *Set of* 4 .... 1·90   1·50

444 Rifle-shooting   **444a** Softball

(Des M. Kimura, eng S. Mizutani (912). Des H. Hasebe, eng S. Nakada (913). Recess)

1962 (21 Oct). 17th National Athletic Meeting, Okayama. P 13½.
912   **444** 5y. maroon 40   30
          a. Pair. Nos. 912/13 .... 1·00   1·00
913   **444a** 5y. indigo 40   30
  Sheets contain alternate copies of each design.

445 Hare-bell   **446** Mt. Ishizuchi and
(Nogomi toy)   Kamega Forest

(Des W. Emori. Photo)

1962 (15 Dec). New Year's Greetings. P 13½.
914   **445** 5y. multicoloured 60   10

(Des H. Hasebe. Photo)

1963 (11 Jan). Ishizuchi Quasi-National Park. P 13½.
916   **446** 10y. multicoloured 50   30

447 "Five Towns"

(Des M. Kimura. Photo)

1963 (10 Feb). Amalgamation of Five Towns as Kita-Kyushu. P 13½.
917　**447**　10y. brown..　40　　25

448 Frosted Foliage, Fugen Peak
449 Amakusa Islands and Mt. Unzen

1963 (15 Feb). Unzen-Amakusa National Park. Photo. P 13½.
918　**448**　5y. grey-blue..　40　　25
919　**449**　10y. carmine..　40　　25

450 Midorigaike (Green Pond)
451 Hakusan Mountains

1963 (1 Mar). Hakusan National Park. Photo. P 13½.
920　**450**　5y. chocolate..　30　　25
921　**451**　10y. deep grey-green............................　30　　25

452 Great Rocks, Keya
453 Globe and Emblem

(Des M. Kimura. Photo)

1963 (15 Mar). Genkai Quasi-National Park. P 13½.
922　**452**　10y. multicoloured............................　50　　10

(Des M. Kimura. Photo)

1963 (21 Mar). Freedom from Hunger. P 13½.
923　**453**　10y. deep grey-green............................　40　　25

454 "Portrait of Heihachiro Honda" (anon — Yedo period)
455 Centenary Emblem and World Map

(Des S. Watanabe. Photo)

1963 (20 Apr). Philatelic Week. P 13½.
924　**454**　10y. multicoloured............................　1·20　　70

(Des S. Watanabe. Photo)

1963 (8 May). Centenary of Red Cross. P 13½.
925　**455**　10y. multicoloured............................　40　　25

456 Globe and Leaf
459 Purple Jay

457 Mt. Ito, Asahi Range
458 Mt. Bandai across Lake Hibara

(Des M. Hisano. Photo)

1963 (15 May). Fifth International Irrigation and Drainage Commission Congress, Tokyo. P 13½.
926　**456**　10y. blue..　40　　25

1963 (25 May). Bandai-Asahi National Park. Photo. P 13½.
927　**457**　5y. green..　40　　30
928　**458**　10y. red-brown............................　50　　30

(Des H. Otsuka (929), H. Hasebe (930, 932), W. Emori (931), M. Kimura (933), S. Watanabe (934). Photo)

1963 (10 June)–**64**. Japanese Birds. T **459** and similar bird designs. Design multicoloured; background colour given. P 13½.
929　10y. pale green............................　1·20　　70
930　10y. pale blue (10.8.63)............................　60　　30
931　10y. pale yellow (20.11.63)............................　60　　30
932　10y. turquoise-blue (10.1.64)............　60　　30
933　10y. green (10.2.64)............................　60　　30
934　10y. Venetian red (1.5.64)............　60　　30
929/934 *Set of 6*............................　3·75　2·00
Birds:—Nos. 929, T **459**; 930, Rock ptarmigan; 931, Eastern turtle dove; 932, White stork; 933, Japanese bush warbler; 934, Siberian meadow bunting.

(Des M. Hisano, eng S. Nakada (935); des H. Otsuka, eng K. Oshikiri (936); des S. Watanabe, eng T. Kasano (937). Recess)

1963 (23 June). Olympic Games, Tokyo,1964 (4th issue). Designs as T **423**. P 13½.

935		5y.+5y. blue (Yachting)	60	30
936		5y.+5y. chocolate (Boxing)	60	30
937		5y.+5y. bistre-brown (Volleyball)	60	30
935/937	Set of 3		1·60	80

460 Road Junction, Ritto, Shiga

461 Girl Scout and Flag

(Des S. Watanabe. Photo)

1963 (15 July). Opening of Nagoya-Kobe Expressway. P 13½.
938   **460**   10y. bluish green, black & yell-orge 40   10

(Des H. Otsuka. Photo)

1963 (1 Aug). Asian Girl Scout Camp, Nagano. P 13½.
939   **461**   10y. yellow, blue, maroon & lt salmon... 40   25

462 Mt. Washiu

463 Whirlpool at Naruto

1963 (20 Aug). Seto Inland Sea National Park. Photo. P 13½.
940   **462**   5y. bistre-brown 40   25
941   **463**   10y. bronze-green 50   25

464 Lake Shikaribetsu

465 Mt. Kurodake

1963 (1 Sept). Daisetsuzan National Park. Photo. P 13½.
942   **464**   5y. greenish blue........................... 40   25
943   **465**   10y. purple........................... 50   25

466 Antenna

467 "Great Wave off Kanagawa" (from "36 Views of Mt. Fuji" by Hokusai Katsushika)

(Des M. Hioki. Photo)

1963 (9 Sept). 14th International Scientific Radio Union Conference, Tokyo. P 13½.
944   **466**   10y. multicoloured 40   25

(Des S. Watanabe. Photo)

1963 (6 Oct). International Correspondence Week. P 13.
945   **467**   40y. multicoloured .... 6·75   2·30
The design is taken from the series of 36 woodcuts showing Mt. Fuji. Others from this series are shown as Nos. 989, 1010, 1075, 1100, 1140 and 1185.

468 Athletes

469 Wrestling

(Des M. Kimura. Photo)

1963 (11 Oct). "Pre-Olympic" Athletic Meeting, Tokyo. P 13½.
946   **468**   10y. multicoloured 40   25

(Des M. Kimura, eng S. Nakada (947), des H. Otsuka, eng S. Okamura (948). Recess)

1963 (27 Oct). 18th National Athletic Meeting, Yamaguchi. T **469** and similar horiz design. P 13½.
947   **469**   5y. reddish brown........................... 40   25
           a. Pair. Nos 947/8 .... 1·00   70
948   5y. deep olive-green........................... 40   25
Design:—No. 948, Free-style gymnastics.
Sheets contain alternate copies of each design.

(Des H. Hasebe, eng S. Mizutani (949); des M. Hisano, eng S. Kurihara (950); des H. Otsuka, eng T. Kasano (951); des M. Kimura, eng H. Hasegawa (952). Recess)

1963 (11 Nov). Olympic Games, Tokyo, 1964 (5th issue). Designs as T **423**. P 13½.

949		5y.+5y. deep blue (Cycling)	50	25
950		5y.+5y. yellow-olive (Show jumping)	50	25
951		5y.+5y. black (Hockey)	50	25
952		5y.+5y. reddish purple (Pistol-shooting)	50	25
949/952	*Set of 4*		1·80	90

470 Hachijo Island

471 Kai and Iwai Dragon Toys

(Des M. Kimura. Photo)

1963 (10 Dec). Izu Islands Quasi-National Park. P 13½.
953   **470**   10y. multicoloured 50   25

(Des M. Kimura. Photo)

1963 (16 Dec). New Year's Greetings. P 13½.
954   **471**   5y. multicoloured 60   25

472 Wakasa Bay

473 View from Horikiri Pass and Agave plant

(Des H. Hasebe. Photo)

1964 (25 Jan). Wakasa Bay Quasi-National Park. P 13½.
956   **472** 10y. multicoloured 50   25

(Des M. Hisano. Photo)

1964 (20 Feb). Nichinan-Kaigan Quasi-National Park. P 13½.
957   **473** 10y. multicoloured 50   25

474 Uji Bridge   **475** View of Toba

1964 (15 Mar). Ise-Shima National Park. Photo. P 13½.
958   **474** 5y. bistre-brown........................ 40   25
959   **475** 10y. bright purple 50   45

476 Festival Float   **477** "Yamaboko"
and Mt. Norikura   Shrine (Gion
(Tokayama Festival)   Festival)

478 Warriors on Horseback
(Soma Horse Festival)

479 Festival Scene (Chichibu
Festival)

(Des M. Kimura. Photo)

1964 (15 Apr)–**65**. Regional festivals. P 13½×13 (vert) or 13×13½
(horiz).
960   **476** 10y. multicoloured 40   25
961   **477** 10y. multicoloured (15.7.64) 40   25
962   **478** 10y. multicoloured (16.7.65) 40   15
963   **479** 10y. multicoloured (3.12.65) 50   15
960/963 *Set of 4* .... 1·50   70

480 Prince Niou playing for Lady
Nakanokimi (detail of Takayoshi
"Yadorigi" scroll illustrating *Tale of Genji*
by Lady Murasaki)

(Des S. Watanabe. Photo)

1964 (20 Apr). Philatelic Week. P 13½.
964   **480** 10y. multicoloured 60   30

481 Himeji Castle   **482** Handball

(Des H. Otsuka. Photo)

1964 (1 June). Rebuilding of Himeji Castle. P 13½.
965   **481** 10y. chocolate 50   30

(Des. Y. Higashitsunoi, eng S. Nakada (966); des H. Otsuka, eng
H. Hasegawa (967). Recess)

1964 (6 June). 19th National Athletic Meeting, Niigata. T **482** and
similar vert design. P 13½.
966   **482** 5y. deep bluish green........................ 40   25
         a. Pair. Nos. 966/7 .... 1·20   95
967   –   5y. carmine-red (Gymnastics) 40   25
Sheets contain alternate copies of each design.

483 Cross-section of Cable   **484** Nihonbashi
                                  Bridge

(Des M. Kimura. Photo)

1964 (19 June). Opening of Japan–US Submarine Telephone Cable.
P 13½.
968   **483** 10y. multicoloured 40   25

(Des M. Hisano, eng S. Mizutani (969); des H. Hasebe,
eng Y. Kawahara (970); des M. Kimura, eng T. Kasano (971);
des S. Watanabe, eng S. Kurihara (972). Recess)

1964 (23 June). Olympic Games, Tokyo (6th issue). Designs as T **423**.
P 13½.
969   5y.+5y. violet (Modern pentathlon) 50   25
970   5y.+5y. turquoise-blue (Canoeing).............. 50   25
971   5y.+5y. lake (Football)........................ 50   25
972   5y.+5y. olive-brown (Weightlifting) 50   25
969/972 *Set of 4* .... 1·80   90

(Des M. Kimura. Photo)

1964 (1 Aug). Opening of Tokyo Expressway. P 13½.
973   **484** 10y. green, silver and black 40   25

1964 (20 Aug). Olympic Games, Tokyo (7th issue). Set of six miniature sheets each 135×60 mm containing stamps as indicated below.

MS974	Nos. 879/81	9·25	9·75
MS975	Nos. 899/901	6·00	6·75
MS976	Nos. 909/11	4·50	5·00
MS977	Nos. 935/7	11·00	12·00
MS978	Nos. 949/52	11·00	12·00
MS979	Nos. 969/72	11·00	12·00
	Price for six sheets	48·00	50·00

485 "Coins"

486 Olympic Flame

(Des M. Hisano. Photo)

1964 (7 Sept). International Monetary Fund Convention, Tokyo. P 13½.
980   **485**   10y. gold and red 40   25

(Des S. Watanabe. Photo)

1964 (9 Sept–10 Oct). Olympic Games, Tokyo (8th issue). T **486** and similar designs. P 13½.

981	5y. red, black, gold and deep blue	30	25
982	10y. gold, red, black & dp sepia (10.10).	40	25
983	30y. gold, red, black & brt blue (10.10)..	80	30
984	40y. black, red, blue and gold (10.10)....	1·00	30
985	50y. black, blue, gold & vermilion (10.10)	1·10	30
981/985	*Set of 5*	3·25	1·30
MS986	93×144 mm. Nos. 981/5 (10.10)	6·00	6·25

Designs: Horiz.—10y. Main stadium; 30y. Fencing hall; 40y. Indoor stadium; 50y. Komazawa hall.

487 "Agriculture"

488 Electric Express Train

(Des H. Hasebe. Photo)

1964 (15 Sept). Reclamation of Hachirogata Lagoon. P 13½.
987   **487**   10y. gold and brown-purple 60   25

(Des H. Otsuka. Photo)

1964 (1 Oct). Inauguration of Tokyo–Osaka Railway. P 13½.
988   **488**   10y. light blue and black 90   15

489 "Tokaido Highway" (from "36 Views of Mt. Fuji" by Hokusai Katsushika)

490 Straw Snake

(Des S. Watanabe. Photo)

1964 (4 Oct). International Correspondence Week. P 13.
989   **489**   40y. multicoloured .... 2·00   60

(Des M. Hioki. Photo)

1964 (15 Dec). New Year's Greetings. P 13½.
990   **490**   5y. multicoloured 50   25

491 Mt. Daisen and Akamatsu Pond

492 Jodo-ga-Ura (Paradise Islands) of Oki

1965 (20 Jan). Daisen-Oki National Park. Photo. P 13½.
992   **491**   5y. chalky blue 30   25
993   **492**   10y. chestnut 40   25

493 Niseko-Annupuri Mountains

494 Radar Station

(Des Hasebe. Photo)

1965 (15 Feb). Niseko Shakotan Otaru Quasi-National Park. P 13½.
994   **493**   10y. multicoloured 40   25

(Des H. Otsuka. Photo)

1965 (10 Mar). Completion of Meteorological Radar Station, Mt. Fuji. P 13½.
995   **494**   10y. multicoloured 40   25

495 Kiyotsu Gorge

496 Mt. Myoko across Lake Nojiri

1965 (15 Mar). Jo-Shin-Etsu Kogen National Park. Photo. P 13½.
996   **495**   5y. bistre-brown 30   25
997   **496**   10y. bright purple 40   25

497 Postal Museum

(Des M. Hisano. Photo)

1965 (25 Mar). Inauguration of Postal Museum, Ote-machi, Tokyo and Stamp Exhibition. P 13½.

998	**497**	10y. green	40	15

504 ICY Emblem and Doves

(Des M. Hisano. Photo)

1965 (26 June). International Co-operation Year. P 13.

1005	**504**	40y. multicoloured	90	10

498 "The Prelude" (after Shoen Uyemura)

499 Children at Play

505 *Meiji Maru* (cadet ship) and Japanese Gulls

506 "Blood Donation"

(Des H. Hasebe. Photo)

1965 (20 Apr). Philatelic Week. P 13½.

999	**498**	10y. multicoloured	50	25

(Des M. Kimura. Photo)

1965 (5 May). Inauguration of National Children's Garden. P 13½.

1000	**499**	10y. multicoloured	50	10

(Des H. Hasebe. Photo)

1965 (20 July). 25th Maritime Day. P 13½.

1006	**505**	10y. multicoloured	60	25

(Des M. Hisano. Photo)

1965 (1 Sept). Campaign for Blood Donors. P 13½.

1007	**506**	10y. multicoloured	40	25

500 Tree within "Leaf"

501 Globe and Symbols

507 Atomic Power Station, Tokyo

508 "Population"

(Des H. Hasebe. Photo)

1965 (9 May). Reafforestation. P 13½.

1001	**500**	10y. multicoloured	40	25

(Des M. Kimura. Photo)

1965 (21 Sept). Ninth International Atomic Energy Authority Conference, Tokyo. P 13½.

1008	**507**	10y. multicoloured	40	25

(Des Y. Higashitsunoi. Photo)

1965 (17 May). Centenary of International Telecommunications Union. P 13½.

1002	**501**	10y. multicoloured	40	25

(Des S. Watanabe. Photo)

1965 (25 Sept). 10th National Census. P 13½.

1009	**508**	10y. multicoloured	40	25

502 Mt. Naka Crater

503 Aso Peaks

509 "Water at Misaka" (from "36 Views of Mt. Fuji" by Hokusai Katsushika)

510 Emblems and Plan of Diet

(Des S. Watanabe. Photo)

1965 (6 Oct). International Correspondence Week. P 13.

1010	**509**	40y. multicoloured	1·30	70

1965 (15 June). Aso National Park. Photo. P 13½.

1003	**502**	5y. cerise	30	25
1004	**503**	10y. deep green.....................................	40	25

(Des H. Otsuka. Photo)

1965 (15 Oct). 75th Anniv of National Suffrage. P 13½.

1011	**510**	10y. multicoloured	40	25

511 Walking

512 Outline of Face, and Baby

(Des T. Yamanouchi, eng S. Okamura (1012); des H. Otsuka, eng S. Nakada (1013). Recess)

1965 (24 Oct). 20th National Athletic Meeting, Gifu. T **511** and similar vert design. P 13½.
1012	**511**	5y. yellow-green	40	30
		a. Pair. Nos 1012/13	85	80
1013	–	5y. red-brown (Gymnastics)	40	30

Sheets contain alternate copies of each design.

(Des S. Watanabe. Photo)

1965 (30 Oct). International Conferences on Otology, Rhinology and Laryngology (ICORL) and Pediatrics (ICP), Tokyo. P 13.
1014	**512**	30y. multicoloured	70	25

513 Mt. Iwo

514 Mt. Rausu

1965 (15 Nov). Shiretoko National Park. Photo. P 13½.
1015	**513**	5y. turquoise	30	25
1016	**514**	10y. blue	40	25

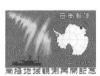
515 Antarctic Map, Research Vessel *Fuji* and Aurora Australis

516 "Straw Horse"

(Des I. Norimatsu. Photo)

1965 (20 Nov). Antarctic Expedition of 1965. P 13½.
1017	**515**	10y. multicoloured	50	10

(Des W. Emori. Photo)

1965 (10 Dec). New Year's Greetings. P 13½.
1018	**516**	5y. Multicoloured	60	30

517 Telephone Switchboard (1890) and Modern Dial

518 Spiny Lobster

(Des M. Hoiki. Photo)

1965 (16 Dec). 75th Anniv of Japanese Telephone Service. P 13½.
1020	**517**	10y. multicoloured	40	25

NIPPON. From this point onwards all stamps are additionally inscribed "NIPPON".

(Des E. Kato (1021), N. Katayama (1022), S. Mayeda (1023), M. Hashimoto (1024), Y. Sugiyama (1025), K. Yoshioka (1026), S. Uemura (1027), S. Morita (1028), D. Okumura (1029), S. Yamada (1030), T. Takayama (1031), H. Yamaguchi (1032). Photo)

1966 (31 Jan)–**67**. Fishery Products. T **518** and similar multicoloured designs. P 13.
1021		10y. Type **518**	40	15
1022		10y. Carp (28.2.66)	40	15
1023		10y. Bream (25.3.66)	40	15
1024		10y. Bonito (16.5.66)	40	15
1025		10y. Ayu (trout) (1.6.66)	40	15
1026		15y. Eel (1.8.66)	50	15
1027		15y. Mackerel (1.9.66)	50	15
1028		15y. almon (1.12.66)	50	15
1029		15y. Buri (10.2.67)	80	15
1030		15y. Globefish (10.3.67)	80	25
1031		15y. Japanese common squid (30.6.67)	1·00	30
1032		15y. Horned turban (shellfish) (25.7.67)	1·40	30
1021/1032	*Set of* 12		6·75	2·00

519 Pleasure Garden, Mito

519a Pleasure Garden and Manchurian Cranes, Okayama

519b Kenrokuen Garden, Kanazawa

520 Crater of Mt. Zao

(Des M. Hisano. Photo)

1966 (25 Feb)–**67**. Famous Japanese Gardens. P 13½.
1033	**519**	10y. deep green, black and gold	40	10
1034	**519a**	15y. blk, carm & lt bl (3.11.66)	50	10
1035	**519b**	15y. choc, grn & silver (25.1.67)	50	10
1033/1035	*Set of* 3		1·30	25

(Des H. Otsuka. Photo)

1966 (15 Mar). Zao Quasi-National Park. P 13½.
1036	**520**	10y. multicoloured	40	25

521 Muroto Cape

522 Senba Cliffs, Anan

(Des S. Watanabe. Photo)

1966 (22 Mar). Muroto-Anan Kaigan Quasi-National Park. P 13½.
1037 **521** 10y. multicoloured 40 25
1038 **522** 10y. multicoloured 40 25

523 AIPPI Emblem

(Des S. Watanabe. Photo)

1966 (11 Apr). General Assembly of International Association for Protection of Industrial Property (AIPPI). P 13.
1039 **523** 40y. multicoloured .... 1·20 25

524 "Butterflies" (after T. Fujishima)

(Des H. Hasebe. Photo)

1966 (20 Apr). Philatelic Week. P 13½.
1040 **524** 10y. multicoloured 90 30

525 Goldfish

526 Chrysanthemums

527 Fuji (wisteria)

528 Hydrangea

529 Golden Hall, Chuson Temple

530 Watasenia scintillans (squid)

531 Yomei Gate, Tosho Shrine, Nikko

532 Mizubasho

533 Konponchudo Hall, Enryaku Temple

534 Ancient Clay Horse

535 Garden of Katsura Palace

536 Onjo Bosatsu (relief from bronze lantern, Todai Temple)

537 Kongo-Rikishi Statue, Todai Temple, Nara

Two types of 20y.

I

II

(Des T. Yamanouchi (7y., 65y., 200y.), Y. Higashitsunoi (15y., 25y.), H. Otsuka (20y., 30y.), H. Hasebe (35y., 60y.), M. Kimura (40y., 110y.), S. Watanabe (45y.), W. Emori (500y.). Eng S. Kurihara (60y.), S. Mizutani (110y., 500y.), S. Okamura (120y.), T. Kasano (200y.); recess. Others photo)

1966–79. T **525/37** and designs of 1952–61 and 1961–65 but inscr "NIPPON". P 13½×13 (60y.), 13½ (200y., 500y.) or 13×13½ (others).
1041 **235** 1y. deep bistre (as 653) (10.1.68)...... 15 10
1046 **525** 7y. red-orange & ol-grn (1.7.66)...... 2·00 20
p. Phosphor frame (18.7.66)................ 17·00 13·00
1047 7y. orange-red and bright yellow-green (1.8.67)............ 25 20
1049 **526** 15y. yellow and blue (1.7.66) .... 1·80 20
a. Imperf (pair)............ £500
b. Booklet pane. No. 1049×6 plus label (1.6.67) .... 9·50
c. Booklet pane. No. 1049×4 (1.6.67). 4·50
p. Phosphor frame (18.7.66)................ 12·50 3·25
1050 15y. yellow and blue* (1.7.67) 35 20
a. Coil. P 13×imperf (9.1.68).......... 80 30
b. Booklet pane. No. 1050×6 (1.3.68). 30·00
d. Pack pane. No. 1050×10 (16.12.68)............ 3·00
1051 **527** 20y. bright yellow-green and bluish violet (I) (1.4.67)............ 3·75 2·75
1052 20y. bright yellow-green and bluish violet (II) (1.4.69)............ 2·10 20
1053 **528** 25y. blue & dp olive-grn (1.7.66) 80 10
1054 **529** 30y. gold and ultramarine (1.5 68)...... 1·30 15
1055 **530** 35y. black, brown & blue (1.7.66) .... 2·50 20
1056 **531** 40y. turquoise-grn & sep (20.5.68)...... 80 10
1057 **532** 45y. multicoloured (15.5.67)............ 80 20
1058 **240** 50y. lake (as 666) (26.12.66)............ 12·50 20
1059 50y. cerise (as 666) (1.7.67)............ 1·10 20
1060 **280** 55y. green, black & lt blue (1.9.69) .... 1·20 10
1061 **533** 60y. bronze-green (20.6.66) .... 1·30 20

1062	**534**	65y. orange-brown (1.7.66)	20·00	20
1063		65y. orange (20.7.67)	1·40	20
1064	**281**	75y. violet, yell, blk & pk (1.9.66)	1·40	20
1065	**410**	90y. sepia and gold (20.12.66)	2·75	20
1066	**411**	100y. grey, black & verm (1.8.68)	2·00	10
		a. Coil. P 13×imperf (2.4.79)	2·40	25
1067	**535**	110y. red-brown (5.12.66)	2·00	20
1068	**412**	120y. scarlet (20.12.66)	3·50	20
1069	**536**	200y. deep bluish green (20.6.66)	7·25	20
1070	**537**	500y. deep plum (1.2.69)	8·00	25
1041/1070		*Set of 25*	£110	6·50

The phosphor bands on the 7y. and 15y. run horizontally and vertically between the stamps, producing a frame effect. These stamps were produced to test automatic sorting machines and were on sale at the normal windows in Ohmiya, although they could also be obtained from philatelic counters elsewhere. Examples of the 15y. left unsold after the experiment were placed on sale at Hachinohe.

*No. 1050 has clear (white) figures of value.

No. 1049b is arranged with a block of four on the right separated by a gutter from a horizontal pair and a double-sized label on the left. The pane is folded along the gutter and attached to the booklet cover on one side of the folded edge so that the halves face each other. No. 1050b is similarly arranged except that the label is imperforate and forms an extension to the gutter. Nos. 1049b and 1050b/d have all four outer edges imperforate. No. 1049c has the three outer edges imperforate, being attached to the cover by a selvedge along the left side.

Although Nos. 1047, 1050, 1052, 1059, 1063, 1066 and 1070 are not phosphorescent, they were issued in connection with optical letter facing and cancelling machines.

For No. 1049 in booklet pane in combination with 5y., see No. 657e and for No. 1050 in similar combination, see No. 657f.

For redrawn versions of 25y. and 200y., together with other definitives inscr "NIPPON", see Nos. 1226/49.

538 UN and UNESCO Emblems

539 Pacific Ocean

(Des H. Otsuka. Photo)

1966 (2 July). 20th Anniv of United Nations Educational, Scientific and Cultural Organization. P 13½.
1071   **538**   15y. multicoloured 40   25

(Des S. Watanabe. Photo)

1966 (22 Aug). 11th Pacific Science Congress, Tokyo. P 13½.
1072   **539**   15y. multicoloured 40   25

540 Amakusa Bridges

541 Family and Emblem

(Des S. Watanabe. Photo)

1966 (24 Sept). Completion of Amakusa Bridges. P 13½.
1073   **540**   15y. multicoloured 40   25

(Des T. Yamanouchi. Photo)

1966 (1 Oct). 50th Anniv of Post Office Life Insurance Service. P 13½.
1074   **541**   15y. multicoloured 40   25

542 "Sekiya on the Sumida" (from "36 Views of Mt. Fuji" by Hokusai Katsushika)

543 Rotary Cobalt Radiator

(Des S. Watanabe. Photo)

1966 (6 Oct). International Correspondence Week. P 13.
1075   **542**   50y. multicoloured .... 2·20   85

(Des T. Takahashi (7y.), K. Kamishima (15y.). Photo)

1966 (21 Oct). Ninth International Cancer Congress, Tokyo. T **543** and similar design. P 13½.
1076   7y.+3y. black and orange-yellow 30   25
1077   15y.+5y. multicoloured 40   25
Design: Vert—15y. Detection by X-rays.

544 Triple Jump

544a Clay-pigeon Shooting

(Des H. Otsuka, eng S. Nakada (T **544**). Des M. Kimura, eng T. Kasano (T **544a**). Recess)

1966 (23 Oct). 21st National Athletic Meeting, Oita. P 13½.
1078   **544**   7y. carmine-red 40   25
           a. Pair. Nos. 1078/9 .... 1·20   1·10
1079   **544a**   7y. blue 40   25
Sheets contain alternate copies of each design.

545 National Theatre Building

545b "Bunraku" Puppet Act

545a "Kabuki" Performance

546 Rice Year Emblem

(Des H. Otsuka (50y.), H. Hasebe (others). Photo;

1966 (1 Nov). Inauguration of Japanese National Theatre. P 13×13½ (15y.) or 13½ (others).

1080	**545**	15y. multicoloured	40	25
1081	**545a**	25y. multicoloured	1·10	40
1082	**545b**	50y. multicoloured	1·30	60
1080/1082	*Set of 3*		2·50	1·20

(Des M. Hisano. Photo)

1966 (21 Nov). International Rice Year. P 13½.

1083	**546**	15y. black, ochre and red	40	25

547 Ittobori Sheep (sculpture)

548 Satellite "Intelsat 2", Earth and Moon

(Des M. Kimura. Photo)

1966 (10 Dec). New Year's Greetings. P 13½.

1084	**547**	7y. gold, black, pink and new blue	60	30

(Des S. Watanabe. Photo)

1967 (27 Jan). Inauguration of International Commercial Satellite Communications in Japan. P 13½.

1086	**548**	15y. blackish brown & greenish blue	40	10

549 Douglas DC-8 Jetliner and Flight Route

550 Literature Museum

(Des H. Otsuka. Photo)

1967 (6 Mar). Inauguration of Round-the-World Air Service. P 13½.

1087	**549**	15y. multicoloured	40	10

(Des H. Otsuka. Photo)

1967 (11 Apr). Opening of Japanese Modern Literature Museum, Meguro-ku, Tokyo. P 13½.

1088	**550**	15y. multicoloured	40	25

551 "Lakeside" (after S. Kuroda)

(Des H. Hasebe. Photo)

1967 (20 Apr). Philatelic Week. P 13½.

1089	**551**	15y. multicoloured	50	30

552 Port of Kobe

(Des S. Watanabe. Photo)

1967 (8 May). Fifth International Association of Ports and Harbours Congress, Tokyo. P 13×13½.

1090	**552**	50y. multicoloured	1·30	40

553 Emblem of Welfare Service

554 Pedestrian Road Crossing

(Des M. Kimura. Photo)

1967 (12 May). 50th Anniv of Welfare Commissioner Service. P 13½.

1091	**553**	15y. gold and agate	50	10

(Des H. Hasebe. Photo)

1967 (22 May). 20th Anniv of Road Safety Campaign. P 13½.

1092	**554**	15y. multicoloured	40	25

555 Mts. Kita and Koma

556 Mts. Akashi, Hijiri and Higashi

(Des S. Watanabe. Photo)

1967 (10 July). Southern Alps National Park. P 13½.

1093	**555**	7y. Prussian blue	30	10
1094	**556**	15y. purple	40	10

557 Protein Molecules

558 Gymnast

(Des H. Otsuka. Photo)

1967 (19 Aug). Seventh International Biochemistry Congress, Tokyo.
P 13½.
1095   **557**   15y. multicoloured   40   25

(Des T. Yamanouchi (15y.), M. Hioki (50y.). Photo)

1967 (26 Aug). "Universiade 1967" (Sports Meeting), Tokyo. T **558** and
similar multicoloured design. P 13½ (15y.) or 13 (50y.).
1096   15y. Type **558**   40   25
1097   50y. Universiade "U" emblem
               (25×35½ mm) ....   1·30   40

559 Paper Lantern   **560** Mt. Fuji (after T. Yokoyama)

(Des M. Hisano (15y.), H. Hasebe (50y.). Photo)

1967 (2 Oct). International Tourist Year. P 13½.
1098   **559**   15y. multicoloured   60   30
1099   **560**   50y. multicoloured ....   2·40   1·70

561 "Kajikazawa in Kai   **562** Athlete
Province" (from "36 Views of
Mt. Fuji" by Hokusai
Katsushika)

(Des S. Watanabe. Photo)

1967 (6 Oct). International Correspondence Week. P 13.
1100   **561**   50y. multicoloured ....   3·00   80

(Des T. Yamanouchi. Photo)

1967 (22 Oct). 22nd National Athletic Meeting, Saitama. P 13.
1101   **562**   15y. multicoloured ....   1·00   30

563 Buddha, Koryu   **564** Kudara Kannon
Temple, Kyoto   (Buddha), Horyu
                          Temple, Nara

565 Horyu Temple, Nara

(Des H. Hasebe; photo (1102). Des S. Watanabe, eng T. Kasano; recess
(1103). Des M. Hisano, eng S. Mizutani; recess and photo (1104))

1967 (1 Nov). National Treasures. Asuka Period. P 13½.
1102   **563**   15y. multicoloured   60   40
1103   **564**   15y. multicoloured   60   40
1104   **565**   50y. multicoloured ....   2·50   1·00
1002/1004   Set of 3 ....   3·25   1·70
      See also Nos. 1113/5, 1120/2, 1134/6, 1152/4, 1170/2 and
1177/80.

566 Motor Expressway   **569** "Noborizaru"
                                 (Miyazaki toy)

567 Mt. Kumotori   **568** Lake Chichibu

(Des S. Watanabe. Photo)

1967 (5 Nov). 13th World Road Congress, Tokyo. P 13.
1105   **566**   50y. multicoloured ....   1·30   30

(Des H. Otsuka. Photo)

1967 (27 Nov). Chichibu-Tama National Park. P 13½.
1106   **567**   7y. yellow-olive   30   10
1107   **568**   15y. bright reddish violet   40   10

(Des H. Hasebe. Photo)

1967 (11 Dec). New Year's Greetings. P 13½.
1108   **569**   7y. multicoloured   60   30

570 Mt. Sobo   **571** Takachiho Gorge

(Des M. Hisano. Photo)

1967 (20 Dec). Sobo-Katamuki Quasi-National Park. P 13½.
1110   **570**   15y. multicoloured   40   10
1111   **571**   15y. multicoloured   40   10

572 Boy and Girl, and Cruise Liner *Sakura Maru*

573 Asura Statue, Kofuku Temple, Nara

574 Gakko Bosatsu, Todai Temple, Nara

575 Srimaha devi (painting), Yakushi Temple, Nara

(Des T. Yamanouchi. Photo)

1968 (19 Jan). Youth Goodwill Cruise to mark Meiji Centenary. P 13½.
1112 **572** 15y. blackish vio, orge-yell & brt bl......... 30 10

(Des M. Hisano, eng S. Okamura; recess (1113). Des S. Watanabe, eng K. Oshikiri; recess and photo (1114). Des H. Hasebe; photo (1115))

1968 (1 Feb). National Treasures. Nara Period (710–784). P 13½.
1113 **573** 15y. multicoloured 50 30
1114 **574** 15y. multicoloured 60 30
1115 **575** 50y. multicoloured .... 2·20 1·40
1113/1115 *Set of 3* .... 3·00 1·90

576 Mt. Yatsugatake and Cattle

577 Mt. Tateshina and Lake

(Des H. Otsuka. Photo)

1968 (21 Mar). Yatsugatake-Chushin Kogen Quasi-National Park. P 13½.
1116 **576** 15y. multicoloured 50 30
1117 **577** 15y. multicoloured 50 30

578 "Dancer in a Garden" (after Bakusen Tsuchida)

579 View of Rishiri Island from Rebun Island

(Des H. Hasebe. Photo)

1968 (20 Apr). Philatelic Week. P 13½.
1118 **578** 15y. multicoloured 80 30

(Des S. Watanabe. Photo)

1968 (10 May). Rishin-Rebun Quasi-National Park. P 13½.
1119 **579** 15y. multicoloured 40 25

580 Lacquer Casket

581 "The Origin of Shigisan" (painting in Chogo-sonshi Temple)

582 "Fugen Bosatsu" (painting of Bodishattva Samantabhadra)

583 Centenary Tower and Star

(Des S. Watanabe, eng S. Nakada; recess and photo (1120). Des H. Hasebe (1121), M. Hisano (1122); photo)

1968 (1 June). National Treasures. Heian Period (794–1185). P 13½.
1120 **580** 15y. multicoloured 50 40
1121 **581** 15y. multicoloured 60 40
1122 **582** 50y. multicoloured .... 4·75 2·00
1120/1122 *Set of 3* .... 5·25 2·50

(Des H. Otsuka. Photo)

1968 (14 June). Hokkaido Centenary. P 13½.
1123 **583** 15y. multicoloured 40 25

584 Biro Trees and Pacific Sunrise

585 "Map of Japan" in Figures

(Des M. Hisano. Photo)

1968 (26 June). Return of Ogasawara Islands to Japan. P 13½.
1124 **584** 15y. multicoloured 40 25

A. Inscr 11 mm reading "Don't omit postal code on the address".
B. Inscr 12 mm reading "Postal code also on your address"

(Des M. Hisano. Photo)

1968 (1 July). Postal Codes Campaign. T **585** and similar design.
P 13×13½.

1125	**585**	7y. red, brown & brt yellow-grn (A)	1·50	30
		a. Pair. Nos. 1125/6	3·50	65
1126		7y. red, brown & brt yellow-grn (B)	1·50	30
1127		15y. magenta, violet & new blue (A)	1·50	30
		a. Pair. Nos 1127/8	3·50	
		b. Coil. Perf 13×imperf	1·80	1·40
		ba. Coil pair. Nos. 1127b and 1128a	3·75	
1128		15y. magenta, violet & new blue (B)	1·50	30
		a. Coil. Perf 13×imperf	1·80	1·40

Sheets of each denomination and coils of 15y. contain alternate copies of each inscription.

For Nos 1127/8 in booklet pane in combination with 5y. see No. 657g.

591 "Minamoto Yoritomo" (Jingo Temple Collection)

593 Red braided Armour (Kasuga Grand Shrine Collection)

586 River Kiso

587 Inuyama Castle and View

(Des S. Watanabe. Photo)

1968 (20 July). Hida-Kisogawa Quasi-National Park. P 13½.

1129	**586**	15y. multicoloured	40	10
1130	**587**	15y. multicoloured	40	10

592 Emperor Nijo escaping from Black Palace (from "Tale of Heiji" picture scroll)

(Des S. Watanabe; photo (1134/5). Des H. Hasebe, eng Y. Kawahara; recess (1136))

1968 (2 Sept). National Treasures. Kamakura Period (1185–1334). P 13½.

1134	**591**	15y. multicoloured	60	40
1135	**592**	15y. multicoloured	60	40
1136	**593**	50y. multicoloured	3·00	1·60
1134/1136		Set of 3	3·75	2·20

588 Federation Emblem and "Sun"

(Des I. Norimatsu. Photo)

1968 (6 Aug). International Youth Hostel Conference, Tokyo. P 13½.

1131	**588**	15y. multicoloured	40	25

594 Mount Iwate

595 Lake Towada

(Des H. Otsuka. Photo)

1968 (16 Sept). Towada-Hachimantai National Park. P 13½.

1137	**594**	7y. chestnut	30	10
1138	**595**	15y. emerald	40	10

589 Humans forming Emblem

590 Baseball "Pitcher"

(Des H. Hasebe. Photo)

1968 (9 Aug). 50th All-Japan High School Baseball Championships, Koshi-en, Tokyo. P 13½.

1132	**589**	15y. multicoloured	1·20	40
		a. Pair. Nos. 1132/3	2·50	85
1133	**590**	15y. multicoloured	1·20	40

Sheets contain alternate copies of each design.

596 Gymnastics

597 "Fujimihara in Owari Province" (from "36 Views of Mt. Fuji" by Hokusai Katsushika)

(Des T. Yamanouchi. Photo)

1968 (1 Oct). 23rd National Athletic Meeting. P.13.
1139   **596**   15y. multicoloured   50   30

(Des S. Watanabe. Photo)

1968 (7 Oct). International Correspondence Week. P 13.
1140   **597**   50y. multicoloured ....   1·90   95

598 Centenary Emblem and Sail Warship *Shohei Maru*, 1868

599 "Arrival of the Imperial Carriage in Tokyo" (after Tomone Kobori)

(Des M. Kimura (1141), H. Otsuka (1142). Photo)

1968 (23 Oct). Centenary of Meiji Era. P 13.
1141   **598**   15y. multicoloured   40   25
1142   **599**   15y. multicoloured   40   25

600 Old and New Kannonzaki Lighthouses

601 Ryo's Dancer and State Hall

(Des S. Watanabe. Photo)

1968 (1 Nov). Centenary of Japanese Lighthouses. P 13½.
1143   **600**   15y. multicoloured   50   10

(Des H. Hasebe. Photo)

1968 (14 Nov). Completion of Imperial Palace. P 13½.
1144   **601**   15y. multicoloured   60   30

602 Mount Takachiho

603 Mount Motobu, Yaku Island

(Des S. Watanabe (7y.), H. Hasebe (15y.). Photo)

1968 (20 Nov). Kirishima-Yaku National Park. P 13½.
1145   **602**   7y. bright reddish violet   60   30
1146   **603**   15y. bright orange   60   30

604 "Niwatori" (Yamagata toy)

605 Human Rights Emblem and Dancers

(Des M. Masumi. Photo)

1968 (5 Dec). New Year's Greetings. P 13½.
1147   **604**   7y. multicoloured   60   30

(Des M. Masumi. Photo)

1968 (10 Dec). Human Rights Year. P 13½.
1149   **605**   50y. multicoloured ....   1·10   30

606 Siberian Chipmunk with Nuts

607 Coastal Scenery

(Des H. Hasebe. Photo)

1968 (14 Dec). Savings Promotion. P 13×13½.
1150   **606**   15y. sepia and bright green   70   25

(Des S. Watanabe. Photo)

1969 (27 Jan). Echizen-Kaga-Kaigan Quasi-National Park. P 13½.
1151   **607**   15y. multicoloured   60   30

608 Silver Pavilion, Jisho Temple, Kyoto

609 Pagoda, Anraku Temple, Nagano

610 "Winter Landscape" (Sesshu)

611 Mt. Chokai, from Tobishima

(Des H. Otsuka (1152), S. Watanabe (1153), M. Hisano (1154). Recess and photo (1153) or photo (others)).

1969 (10 Feb). National Treasures. Muromachi Period. P 13 (No. 1153) or 13½ (others).
1152   **608**   15y. multicoloured   50   30
1153   **609**   15y. multicoloured   50   30
1154   **610**   50y. multicoloured ....   2·20   1·40
1152/1154 *Set of* 3..   2·75   1·90

(Des M. Hisano. Photo)

1969 (25 Feb). Chokai Quasi-National Park. P 13½.
1155   **611**   15y. multicoloured   50   10

612 "Expo" Emblem and Globe

613 "Cherry Blossom" (from mural, Chichakuin Temple, Kyoto)

(Des M. Kimura (15y.), M. Hisano (50y.). Photo)

1969 (15 Mar). "EXPO 70" World Fair, Osaka (1st issue). P 13½.
1156   **612**   15y. multicoloured   60   45
1157   **613**   50y. +10y. multicoloured..........................   1·60   1·20
See also Nos. 1193/**MS**1196 and 1200/**MS**1203.

614 Mt. Koya, from Jinnogamine

615 Mt. Gomadan and Rhododendrons

(Des H. Otsuka. Photo)

1969 (25 Mar). Koya-Ryujin Quasi-National Park. P 13½.
1158   **614**   15y. multicoloured   40   25
1159   **615**   15y. multicoloured   40   25

616 "Hair" (Kokei Kobayashi)

617 Woman and Child crossing "Roads"

(Des H. Hasebe. Photo)

1969 (20 Apr). Philatelic Week. P 13½.
1160   **616**   15y. multicoloured   60   40

(Des M. Hioki. Photo)

1969 (10 May). Road Safety Campaign. P 13×13½.
1161   **617**   15y. emerald, new blue & carm-verm....   40   25

618 Sakawagawa Bridge

619 Museum Building

(Des S. Watanabe. Photo)

1969 (26 May). Completion of Tokyo–Nagoya Expressway. P 13½.
1162   **618**   15y. multicoloured   50   30

(Des H. Otsuka. Photo)

1969 (11 June). Opening of National Museum of Modern Art, Tokyo. P 13½.
1163   **619**   15y. multicoloured   40   25

620 Nuclear-powered Freighter *Mutsu* and Atomic Symbol

621 Cable Ship *KDD Maru* and Map

(Des H. Otsuka. Photo)

1969 (12 June). Launching of Japan's First Nuclear-powered Ship. P 13½.
1164   **620**   16y. multicoloured   50   10

(Des H. Hasebe. Photo)

1969 (25 June). Opening of Japanese Ocean Cable. P 13½.
1165   **621**   15y. multicoloured   50   10

622 Symbol and Cards

623 Symbol, Postbox and Code Numbers

624 Lions Emblem and Rose

(Des I. Norimatsu (7y.), M. Hioki (15y.). Photo)

1969 (1 July). Postal Codes Campaign. P 13×13½.
1166   **622**   7y. red and bright yellow-green...........   30   25
1167   **623**   15y. red and light blue   80   25

(Des Y. Higashitsunoi. Photo)

1969 (2 July). 52nd Lions International Convention, Tokyo. P 13½.
1168   **624**   15y. multicoloured   60   30

625 Hotoke-ga-ura (coast)

626 Himeji Castle, Hyogo Prefecture

627 "Pinewoods"
(T. Hasegawa)

628 "The Japanese Cypress" (artist unknown)

(Des H. Hasebe. Photo)

1969 (15 July). Shimokita-Hanto Quasi-National Park. P 13½.
1169	**625**	15y. multicoloured	60	30

(Des H. Otsuka. Recess and photo (No. 1170). Des H. Hasebe (No. 1171), M. Hisano (No 1172). Photo)

1969 (21 July). National Treasures. Momoyama Period. P 13×13½ (No. 1171) or 13½ (others).
1170	**626**	15y. multicoloured	60	30
1171	**627**	15y. black and light drab	60	30
1172	**628**	50y. multicoloured	1·10	55
1170/1172		Set of 3	2·10	1·00

629 Harano-fudo Waterfalls

630 Mount Nagisan

(Des H. Hasebe. Photo)

1969 (20 Aug). Hyonosen-Ushiroyama-Nagisan Quasi-National Park. P 13½.
1173	**629**	15y. multicoloured	40	25
1174	**630**	15y. multicoloured	40	25

631 Mount O-akan

632 Mount Iwo

(Des M. Hisano. Photo)

1969 (25 Aug). Akan National Park. P 13½.
1175	**631**	7y. bright blue	30	25
1176	**632**	15y. sepia	40	25

633 "Choben" (T. Ikeno)

634 "The Red-plum Tree" (K. Ogata)

635 "The White-plum Tree" (K. Ogata)

636 "Japanese Pheasant" incense-burner (after Ninsei)

(Des H. Hasebe (No. 1177), H. Otsuka (Nos. 1178/9), M. Hisano (No. 1180). Photo)

1969 (25 Sept). National Treasures. Edo Period. P 13½.
1177	**633**	15y. multicoloured	60	45
1178	**634**	15y. multicoloured	60	45
		a. Horiz pair. Nos. 1178/9	2·50	1·90
1179	**635**	15y. multicoloured	60	45
1180	**636**	50y. multicoloured	2·40	1·40
1177/1180		Set of 4	3·75	2·75

Nos. 1178/9 were issued together in horizontal se-tenant pairs within sheets of 20 (4x5).

637 Globe and Doves

638 "Woman reading a Letter" (Utamaro Kitagawa)

639 "Reading a Letter" (Harunobu Suzuki)

640 "Miyako Dennai" (Sharaku Toshusai)

(Des H. Otsuka (Nos. 1181/2), M. Hisano (No. 1183), H. Hasebe (No. 1184). Photo)

1969 (1 Oct). 16th Universal Postal Union Congress, Tokyo. P 13½.

1181	**637**	15y. multicoloured	40	25
1182	**638**	30y. multicoloured	1·00	80
1183	**639**	50y. multicoloured	1·60	95
1184	**640**	60y. multicoloured	1·60	95
1181/1184	*Set of 4*		4·25	2·50

647 Peasants, Tsushima Island

(Des H. Otsuka. Photo)

1970 (25 Feb). Iki-Tsushima Quasi-National Park. P 13½.

1192	**647**	15y. multicoloured	50	10

641 "Mishima Pass" (from "36 Views of Mt. Fuji" by Hokusai Katsushika)

642 Rugby Player

(Des M. Masumi. Photo)

1969 (7 Oct). International Correspondence Week. P 13.

1185	**641**	50y. multicoloured	1·30	80

(Des T. Yamanouchi. Photo)

1969 (26 Oct). 24th National Athletic Meeting. P 13.

1186	**642**	15y. multicoloured	60	30

648 View of Fair and Firework Display

649 Globe and Cherry Blossom Garland

650 "Irises" (Korin Ogata)

(Des M. Hioki (7y.), Y. Higashitsunoi (15y.), M. Hisano (50y.). Photo)

1970 (14–15 Mar). "EXPO 70" World Fair, Osaka (2nd issue). P 13½.

1193	**648**	7y. multicoloured	30	25
		a. Booklet pane. Nos. 1193×5, 1194 and 1195 (15.3)	2·50	
1194	**649**	15y. multicoloured	30	25
1195	**650**	50y. multicoloured	50	25
1193/1195	*Set of 3*		1·00	70
MS1196	144×93 mm. Nos. 1193/5		3·50	3·75

No. 1193a is arranged with a block of 4×7y. at the top separated by a gutter from the remaining stamps. The pane, which has all four edges imperforate, is folded along the gutter and attached to the booklet cover on one side of the folded edge.

643 Cape Kitayama   **644** Goishi Coast

(Des M. Hisano. Photo)

1969 (20 Nov). Rikuchu-Kaigan National Park. P 13½.

1187	**643**	7y. deep blue	30	25
1188	**644**	15y. brown-red and salmon	40	25

645 Worker in Safety Helmet

646 Guardian Dog, Hokkeji Temple

(Des S. Watanabe. Photo)

1969 (26 Nov). 50th Anniv of International Labour Organization. P 13½.

1189	**645**	15y. multicoloured	40	30

(Des W. Emori. Photo)

1969 (10 Dec). New Year's Greetings. P 13½.

1190	**646**	7y. multicoloured	60	30

651 "Woman with Drum" (Saburosuke Okada)

(Des H. Hasebe. Photo)

1970 (20 Apr). Philatelic Week. P 13½.
1197 **651** 15y. multicoloured 40 25

658 Utaemon Nakamura VI as Hanako in *Musume Dojoji*

659 Danjuro Ichikawa XI as Sukeroku in *Sukeroku*

660 *Kanjincho*

661 Girl Scout saluting

652 Cherry Blossom, Mt. Yoshino

653 Waterfall, Nachi

(Des S. Watanabe. Photo)

1970 (30 Apr). Yoshino-Kumano National Park. P 13½.
1198 **652** 7y. black and pale pink 30 25
1199 **653** 15y. dp bluish gm, lt grn & pale bl 40 25

(Des H. Otsuka (No. 1206), S. Watanabe (No. 1207), H. Hasebe (No. 1208). Recess and litho (No. 1207); photo (others))

1970 (10 July). Japanese Theatre. "Kabuki". P 13½. (50y.) or 13 (others).
1206 **658** 15y. multicoloured 30 25
1207 **659** 15y. multicoloured 30 25
1208 **660** 50y. multicoloured .... 1·00 40
1206/1208 Set of 3 .... 1·40 80
For other "Theatre" stamps, see Nos. 1250/2, 1284/6 and 1300/2.

654 Kanto (lantern) Festival

655 Japanese Pavilions

(Des T. Yamanouchi. Photo)

1970 (26 July). 50th Anniv of Japanese Girl Scouts. P 13½.
1209 **661** 15y. multicoloured 50 10

662 Festival Drummer and Kinoura Coastline

663 Mt. Tate from Himi Shore

(Des M. Hisano. Photo)

1970 (1 Aug). Noto-Hanto Quasi-National Park. P 13½.
1210 **662** 15y. multicoloured 40 25
1211 **663** 15y. multicoloured 40 25

656 "Flowers of Autumn" (detail, Hoitsu Sakai)

657 Houses and Code Symbol

1970 (15–29 June). "EXPO 70" World Fair, Osaka (3rd issue). P 13½.
1200 **654** 7y. multicoloured 30 25
    a. Booklet pane. Nos. 1200×5, 1201 and 1202 (22.6) .... 2·75
1201 **655** 15y. multicoloured 30 25
1202 **656** 50y. multicoloured 80 45
1200/1202 Set of 3 .... 1·30 90
MS1203 144×93 mm. Nos. 1200/2 (29.6) .... 2·50 2·50
No. 1200a is arranged in the same way as No. 1193a.

664 "Sunflower" and UN Emblem

(Des H. Otsuka. Photo)

1970 (1 July). Postal Codes Campaign. P 13×13½.
1204 **657** 7y. violet and bright green 40 10
1205   15y. maroon and new blue 60 10

(Des S. Watanabe. Photo)

1970 (17 Aug). 4th United Nations Congress on Crime Prevention and Treatment of Offenders, Kyoto. P 13½.
1212 **664** 15y. multicoloured 40 25

665 Mt. Myogi

666 Mt. Arafune

(Des S. Watanabe. Photo)

1970 (11 Sept). Myogi-Arafune-Sakukogen Quasi-National Park. P 13½.

1213	**665**	15y. multicoloured	40	25
1214	**666**	15y. multicoloured	40	25

667 "Tokyo Post Office" (woodcut, Hiroshige III)

668 Show Jumping, Mt. Iwate and Paulownia Flowers

(Des M. Masumi. Photo)

1970 (6 Oct). International Correspondence Week. P 13.

1215	**667**	50y. multicoloured	1·10	40

(Des T. Yamanouchi. Photo)

1970 (10 Oct). 25th National Athletic Meeting, Iwate. P 13.

1216	**668**	15y. multicoloured	60	30

669 "Hodogaya Stage" (print, Hiroshige III)

(Des M. Hioki. Photo)

1970 (20 Oct). Centenary of Telegraph Service. P 13½.

1217	**669**	15y. multicoloured	60	30

670 UN Emblem within "Tree"

671 UN Emblem, New York Headquarters and Flags

(Des T. Yamanouchi (15y.), K. Aratake (50y.). Photo)

1970 (24 Oct). 25th Anniv of United Nations. P 13½ (15y.) or 13 (50y.).

1218	**670**	15y. multicoloured	40	25
1219	**671**	50y. multicoloured	1·00	30

672 Competition Emblem

673 Diet Building and Doves

(Des M. Masumi. Photo)

1970 (10 Nov). 19th International Vocational Training Competition, Chiba City. P 13½.

1220	**672**	15y. multicoloured	40	25

(Des K. Takeara. Photo)

1970 (29 Nov). 80th Anniv of Japanese Diet. P 13½.

1221	**673**	15y. multicoloured	60	30

674 "Wild Boar" (folk-handicraft)

(Des M. Kimura. Photo)

1970 (10 Dec). New Year's Greetings. P 13½.

1222	**674**	7y. multicoloured	60	30

675 Ski Jumping

676 Ice Hockey

(Des S. Watanabe (No. 1224), H. Otsuka (No. 1225). Photo)

1971 (6 Feb). Winter Olympic Games, Sapporo (1972) (1st issue). P 13.

1224	**675**	15y. +5y. multicoloured	50	40
1225	**676**	15y. +5y. multicoloured	50	20

See also Nos. 1280/**MS**1283.

677 Mute Swan

678 Sika Deer

679 *Allomyrina dichotomus*

680 "Pine Tree" (T. Kano)

680a Hydrangea

681 Narcissi

682 Golden Eagle

683 Noh Mask of Aged Man

684 Ho-o (Phoenix), Byodoin Temple, Uji

685 Onjo Bosatsu (relief), Todai Temple

686 Warrior (statuette)

687 Komainu (Guardian Dog), Katori Shrine

688 Buddha, Kofuku Temple

689 Goddess of Mercy, Yakushi Temple, Nara

690 Tentoki (Demon)

691 Buddhist Deity

692 Statue of Kissho, Joruri Temple

(Des T. Shimizu (T **677**), M. Kimura (**678, 684**), T. Yamanouchi (**679, 681, 685**), H. Otsuka (**680**), M. Hisano (**682, 686, 688, 690/1**), M. Saito (**683, 687**), Y. Irie (**689**), S. Watanabe (**692**). Recess (No. 1238), recess and photo (1249) or photo (others).)

1971 (29 Mar)–**79**. As previous issues, and some new designs, all inscr NIPPON" as T **677/92**. P 13×13½.

1226	**273**	3y. bright green (15.7.71)	30	10
		a. Booklet pane. No. 1226×20 (31.1.72)	8·00	
1227	**677**	5y. new blue (10.11.71)	20	10

1228	**678**	10y. bistre-brown and bright yellow-green (1.2.72)	20	10
		a. Booklet pane. Nos. 1228×2 and 1230×4 (1.2.72)	2·50	
		b. Coil. P 13×imperf (2.4.79)	30	15
1229	**679**	12y. brown (15.7.71)	35	10
1230	**680**	20y. blackish brown and emerald (21.1.72)	35	15
		b. Pack pane. No. 1230×10 (1.2.72)	4·00	
		c. Coil. P 13×imperf (1.2.72)	45	30
1231	**680a**	25y. violet-bl & brt grn (21.1.72)	40	15
1232	**240**	50y. bright emerald (25.1.76)	90	10
		a. Booklet pane of 6 (10.3.76)	7·00	
		b. Coil. P 13×imperf (10.3.76)	1·00	25
1233	**681**	60y. emer & orge-yell (25.5.76)	1·10	15
1234	**408**	70y. black & yell-orge (10.8.71)	1·40	15
1235	**409**	80y. bistre-brn & rosine (1.12.71)	1·40	15
1236	**410**	90y. choc & red-orange (1.12.71)	1·80	15
1237	**682**	90y. black & orge-red (19.11.73)	1·80	10
1238	**412**	120y. chocolate & lt grn (10.4.72)	1·70	10
1239	**683**	140y. bright pur & mag (25.6.76)	2·40	15
1240	**684**	150y. turquoise-grn & lt bluish green	3·00	10
1240a		150y. red-brown & vermilion (25.1.76)	2·75	15
1241	**685**	200y. lake (6.12.72)	3·75	10
1242	**686**	200y. red-brown (11.11.74)	3·25	10
1243		200y. bright vermilion (25.1.76)	1·80	10
1244	**687**	250y. greenish blue (1.7.76)	3·25	15
1245	**688**	300y. blue (27.9.74)	5·00	15
1246	**689**	350y. dull purple-brown (7.6.76)	5·00	15
1247	**690**	400y. carmine (27.9.74)	5·50	15
1248	**691**	500y. myrtle-green (11.11.74)	4·25	10
1249	**692**	1000y. multicoloured (22.4.75)	11·00	60
1226/1249		*Set of 25*	60·00	4·00
MS1249a		51×102 mm. No. 1249 (22.4.75)	15·00	13·00

No. 1228a is arranged with the 20y. stamps in a block of four on the right separated by a wide gutter from the 10y. in a vertical pair on the left. The pane is folded along the gutter and attached to the booklet cover on one side of the folded edge so that the halves face each other. No. 1232a is similarly arranged. Nos. 1228a, 1230b and 1232a have all four outer edges imperforate. No. 1226a is imperf top and bottom.

No. **MS**1249a numbered and overprinted below stamp for "JAPEX '86" stamp exhibition or with circular device inscribed "1946–86" were private productions of the Japanese Philatelic Society.

For a different version of T **680a** and a larger version of T **685** see Types **528** and **536**. For 210 and 360y. similar to Types **686** and **689** see Nos 1600 and 1604.

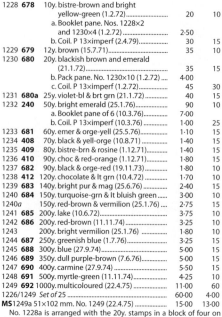

693 "Gen-jo-raku"

694 "Ko-cho"

695 "Tai-hei-raku"

Japan

1971

(Des S. Watanabe (No. 1250), M. Hisano (others). Photo)

1971 (1 Apr). Japanese Theatre. "Gagaku". P 13½. (50y.) or 13 (others).

1250	**693**	15y. multicoloured	30	25
1251	**694**	15y. multicoloured	30	25
1252	**695**	50y. multicoloured	1·00	40
1250/1252		Set of 3	1·40	80

696 Voter and Diet Building

697 Pine Tree and Maple Leaves

698 "Tsukiji-akashicho" (K. Kaburagi)

(Des T. Yamanouchi. Photo)

1971 (10 Apr). 25th Anniv of Women's Suffrage. P 13½.

1253	**696**	15y. multicoloured	40	30

(Des H. Otsuka. Photo)

1971 (18 Apr). National Afforestation Campaign. P 13×13½.

1254	**697**	7y. black, violet and bright green	30	10

(Des M. Hisano. Photo)

1971 (19 Apr). Philatelic Week. P 13½.

1255	**698**	15y. multicoloured	40	25

699 "Posting a Letter" (K. Dogishi)

700 "Postman" (K. Kasai)

701 "Railway Post Office" (S. Onozaki)

(Des from children's drawings T. Shimizu (No. 1256), M. Hisano (1257), H. Otsuka (1258). Photo)

1971 (20 Apr). Centenary of Japanese Postal Services. P 13½.

1256	**699**	15y. multicoloured	40	10
1257	**700**	7y. black and lake-brown	40	10
1258	**701**	15y. multicoloured	40	10
1256/1258		Set of 3	1·10	25

702 Great Tit

703 Adelie Penguins

(Des S. Watanabe. Photo)

1971 (10 May). 25th Bird Week. P 13½.

1259	**702**	15y. multicoloured	50	10

(Des T. Shimizu. Photo)

1971 (23 June). 10th Anniv of Antarctic Treaty. P 13½.

1260	**703**	15y. multicoloured	1·00	30

704 Goto-Wakamatsu-Seto

705 Kuzyuku-shima

(Des S. Watanabe. Photo)

1971 (26 June). Saikai National Park. P 13½.

1261	**704**	7y. deep bluish green	40	30
1262	**705**	15y. brown	40	30

706 Postal Code Numerals

707 Scout Bugler

(Des M. Hioki. Photo)

1971 (1 July). Postal Codes Campaign. P 13×13½.

1263	**706**	7y. red and bright green	30	10
1264		15y. red and light blue	50	25

(Des S. Watanabe. Photo)

1971 (2 Aug). 13th World Scout Jamboree, Asagiri. P 13½.

1265	**707**	15y. multicoloured	50	10

708 Rose Emblem

709 "Tokyo Horse Tram" (Yoshimura)

(Des M. Hisano. Photo)

1971 (1 Oct). 50th Anniv of Family Conciliation System. P 13½.
1266 **708** 15y. multicoloured 40   30

(Des Y. Kikuchi. Photo)

1971 (6 Oct). International Correspondence Week. P 13.
1267 **709** 50y. multicoloured .... 1·10   25

710 Emperor's Standard

711 "Beyond the Sea" (drawing by Empress Nagako)

(Des S. Watanabe (No. 1268), M. Hisano (1269). Photo)

1971 (14 Oct). European Tour by Emperor Hirohito and Empress Nagako. P 13.
1268 **710** 15y. multicoloured 40   30
          a. Pair. Nos. 1268/9 90   70
1269 **711** 15y. multicoloured 40   30
MS1270 141×111 mm. Nos. 1268/9. Imperf .... 2·00   1·60
  Nos. 1268/9 were issued together in vertical and horizontal se-tenant pairs within the sheet.

712 Tennis

713 Child's Face and "100"

(Des T. Yamanouchi. Photo)

1971 (24 Oct). 26th National Athletic Meeting. P 13.
1271 **712** 15y. multicoloured 40   30

(Des M. Hioki. Photo)

1971 (27 Oct). Centenary of National Family Registration System. P 13½.
1272 **713** 15y. multicoloured 40   30

714 "Dragon" (G. Hashimoto)

715 "Tiger" (G. Hashimoto)

(Des K. Maeno. Recess and photo)

1971 (1 Nov). Centenary of Government Printing Works, Tokyo. P 13.
1273 **714** 15y. multicoloured 50   25
          a. Pair. Nos 1273/4 .... 1·10   80

1274 **715** 15y. multicoloured 50   25
  Nos. 1273/4 were issued together in vertical and horizontal se-tenant pairs within the sheet.

716 Mt. Yotei from Lake Toya

717 Mt. Showa-Shinzan

(Des M. Hisano. Photo)

1971 (6 Dec). Shikotsu-Toya National Park. P 13½.
1275 **716** 7y. dp bluish green & lt olive-green..... 30   25
1276 **717** 15y. chalky blue and pale brown 40   25

718 "Treasure Ship"

719 Skiing

720 Bobsleighing

721 Figure Skating

(Des Y. Higashitsunoi. Photo)

1971 (10 Dec)–**72**. New Year's Greetings. P 13×13½.
1277 **718** 7y. multicoloured 30   25
1278   10y. multicoloured (11.1.72) 40   25

(Des H. Otsuka (No. 1280), T. Shimizu (1281), S. Watanabe (1282). Photo)

1972 (3 Feb). Winter Olympic Games, Sapporo (2nd issue). P 13½.
1280 **719** 20y. multicoloured 40   25
          a. Tête-bêche (vert pair) 85   65
1281 **720** 20y. multicoloured 40   25
          a. Tête-bêche (vert pair) 85   65
1282 **721** 50y. multicoloured 90   30
          a. Tête-bêche (vert pair) .... 1·90   1·50
1280/1282 *Set of 3* .... 1·50   70
MS1283 145×94 mm. Nos. 1280/2 .... 2·00   1·60
  Nos. 1280/2 were each issued in horizontal rows of 5, vertically tête-bêche, within the sheets.

722 "Kumagai-jinya"   **723** "Nozaki-mura"

724 "Awa-no-Naruto"

725 High-speed
Electric Train on
Sanyo Line

(Des S. Watanabe (No. 1284), M. Hisano (1285), H. Otsuka (1286).
Recess and litho (50y.) or photo (others))

1972 (1 Mar). Japanese Theatre. "Bunraku" Puppet Theatre. P 13 (No.
1285) or 13½ (others).

1284	**722**	20y. multicoloured	30	25
1285	**723**	20y. multicoloured	30	25
1286	**724**	50y. multicoloured	1·00	40
1284/1286		Set of 3	1·40	80

(Des S. Watanabe. Photo)

1972 (15 Mar). Centenary of Japanese Railways (1st issue), and
Opening of Sanyo Line. P 13½.

1287	**725**	20y. multicoloured	50	10

See also Nos. 1305/6.

726 Hiba Mountains   **727** Fishing,
Taishaku-kyo Valley

(Des S. Watanabe. Photo)

1972 (24 Mar). Hiba-Dogo-Taishaku Quasi-National Park. P 13½.

1288	**726**	20y. multicoloured	40	25
1289	**727**	20y. multicoloured	40	25

728 Adult with Human Heart   **729** "Rising Balloon"
(Gakuryo Nakamura)

(Des M. Hioki. Photo)

1972 (15 Apr). World Heart Month. P 13½.

1290	**728**	20y. multicoloured	40	30

(Des M. Hisano Photo)

1972 (20 Apr). Philatelic Week. P 13½.

1291	**729**	20y. multicoloured	40	30

730 Courtesy Gate,   **731** Japanese
Shuri   Camellia

(Des H. Otsuka. Photo)

1972 (15 May). Return of Ryukyu Islands to Japan. P 13½.

1292	**730**	20y. multicoloured	40	30

(Des H. Otsuka. Photo)

1972 (20 May). National Afforestation Campaign. P 13×13½.

1293	**731**	20y. yellow, ultramarine & It emerald	40	30

732 Mt. Kurikoma and   **733** Naruko-kyo Gorge and
Kokeshi Doll   Kokeshi Doll

(Des M. Hisano Photo)

1972 (20 June). Kurikoma Quasi-National Park. P 13½.

1294	**732**	20y. multicoloured	40	30
1295	**733**	20y. multicoloured	40	30

734 Envelope and   **735** Mail-box and
Code Symbol   Code Symbol

(Des M. Hioki (10y.), K. Takeara (20y.). Photo)

1972 (1 July). Postal Codes Campaign. P 13×13½.
1296 **734** 10y. black, dull purple & new blue.......... 30 10
1297 **735** 20y. light red and bright green 30 10

736 Mt. Hodaka   **737** Mt. Tate

(Des M. Hisano. Photo)

1972 (10 Aug). Chuba Sangaku National Park. P 13½.
1298 **736** 10y. bluish violet and mauve.................. 40 30
1299 **737** 20y. blue and yellow-drab 40 30

738 "Tamura"   **739** "Aoi-no-ue"

740 "Hagoromo"

(Des S. Watanabe (No. 1300), T. Shimizu (1301), H. Otsuka (1302). Recess and litho (No. 1300) or photo (others))

1972 (20 Sept). Japanese Theatre. "Noh". P 13½ (50y.) or 13 (others).
1300 **738** 20y. multicoloured 30 25
1301 **739** 20y. multicoloured 30 25
1302 **740** 50y. multicoloured .... 1·00 40
1300/1302 *Set of 3*... 1·40 80

741 Profiles of   **742** "Eitai Bridge"
School-children   (Hiroshige III)

(Des M. Hioki. Photo)

1972 (5 Oct). Centenary of Japanese Education System. P 13½.
1303 **741** 20y. multicoloured 40 30

(Des Y. Kikuchi. Photo)

1972 (9 Oct). International Correspondence Week. P 13.
1304 **742** 50y. multicoloured .... 1·00 25

743 "Inauguration of   **744** Class "C–62" Steam
Railway Service" (Hiroshige III)   Locomotive

(Des S. Watanabe (No. 1305), H. Otsuka (1305). Photo (1305) or recess and litho (1306))

1972 (14 Oct). Centenary of Japanese Railways (2nd issue). P 13.
1305 **743** 20y. multicoloured 70 10
1306 **744** 20y. multicoloured 70 10

745 Kendo (Japanese   **746** Scout and Cub
Fencing)

(Des T. Yamanouchi. Photo)

1972 (22 Oct). 27th National Athletic Meeting, Kagoshima. P 13.
1307 **745** 10y. multicoloured 40 30

(Des T. Yamanouchi. Photo)

1972 (4 Nov). 50th Anniv of Japanese Boy Scouts. P 13½.
1308 **746** 20y. multicoloured 50 10

747 "Harbour and   **748** "Plum
Bund, Yokohama"   Blossom" Plate
(Hiroshige III)   (K. Ogata)

(Des Y. Kikuchi. Photo)

1972 (28 Nov). Centenary of Japanese Customs Service. P 13½.
1309 **747** 20y. multicoloured 50 10

(Des M. Hisano. Photo)

1972 (11 Dec). New Year's Greetings. P 13×13½.
1310 **748** 10y. multicoloured 40 25

749 Mt. Tsurugi

750 River Yoshino, Oboke Valley

(Des H. Otsuka. Photo)

1973 (20 Feb). Tsurugi-san Quasi-National Park. P 13½.
1312 **749** 20y. multicoloured 40 25
1313 **750** 20y. multicoloured 40 25

751 Mt. Takao

752 Minoo Falls and Japanese Macaques

(Des S. Watanabe. Photo)

1973 (12 Mar). Meiji-no-mori Quasi-National Park. P 13½.
1314 **751** 20y. multicoloured 50 10
1315 **752** 20y. multicoloured 50 10

753 "Dragon" (East Wall)

754 "Male Figures" (East Wall)

755 "Female Figures" (West Wall)

(Des S. Watanabe (50y.). M. Hisano (others). Recess and photo (50y.) or photo (others))

1973 (26 Mar). Asuka Archaeological Conservation Fund. Takamatsuzuka Kofun Tomb Murals. P 13½.
1316 **753** 20y. +5y. multicoloured 40 30
1317 **754** 20y. +5y. multicoloured 40 30
1318 **755** 50y. +10y. multicoloured .... 1·30 1·00
1316/1318 Set of 3 .... 1·90 1·50

756 Phoenix Tree

757 "Sumiyoshi-mode" (R. Kishida)

(Des H. Otsuka. Photo)

1973 (7 Apr). National Afforestation Campaign. P 13×13½.
1319 **756** 20y. multicoloured 40 30

(Des M. Hisano. Photo)

1973 (20 Apr). Philatelic Week. P 13½.
1320 **757** 20y. multicoloured 50 30

758 Mt. Kama

759 Rock Outcrops. Mt. Haguro

(Des H. Otsuka Photo)

1973 (25 May). Suzuka Quasi-National Park. P 13½.
1321 **758** 20y. multicoloured 40 30
1322 **759** 20y. multicoloured 40 30

760 Chichi-jima Island Beach

761 Coral Reef, Minami-jima Island

(Des T. Shimizu Photo)

1973 (26 June). Ogasawara Islands National Park. P 13½.
1323 **760** 10y. deep turquoise-blue 30 10
1324 **761** 20y. plum 40 10

762 Postal Code Symbol and Tree

763 Postman and Symbol

(Des T. Yamanouchi (10y.), M. Hioki (20y.). Photo)

1973 (1 July). Postal Codes Campaign. P 13×13½ (10y.) or P 13½×13 (20y.).
1325 **762** 10y. gold and emerald 30 10
1326 **763** 20y. slate-lilac, red and light blue 40 10

764 Mt. Shinnyu

765 Waterfall, Sandan-kyo Gorge

(Des S. Watanabe. Photo)

1973 (28 Aug). Nishi-Chugoku-Sanchi Quasi-National Park. P 13½.
1327 **764** 20y. multicoloured 40   30
1328 **765** 20y. multicoloured 40   30

766 Valley of River Tenryu

767 Scops Owl and Woodland Path, Mt. Horaiji

768 "Cock" (J. Ito)

(Des T. Shimizu (No. 1329), M. Hisano (1330). Photo)

1973 (18 Sept). Tenryu-Okumikawa Quasi-National Park. P 13½.
1329 **766** 20y. multicoloured 70   10
1330 **767** 20y. blue, dull green and silver 70   10

(Des Y. Kikuchi. Photo)

1973 (6 Oct). International Correspondence Week. P 13.
1331 **768** 50y. multicoloured .... 1·20   10

769 Sprinting

770 Kan-Mon Bridge

(Des T. Yamanouchi. Photo)

1973 (14 Oct). 28th National Athletic Meeting. Chiba. P 13.
1332 **769** 10y. multicoloured 40   30

(Des S. Watanabe. Recess)

1973 (14 Nov). Opening of Kan-Mon Suspension Bridge. P 13.
1333 **770** 20y. multicoloured 50   10

771 Hanasaka-jijii and his Dog

772 Hanasaka-jijii finds the Gold

773 Hanasaka-jijii and Tree in Blossom

(Des K. Sugimoto and S. Watanabe. Photo)

1973 (20 Nov). Japanese Folk Tales (1st series). "Hanasaka-jijii". P 13.
1334 **771** 20y. multicoloured 40   15
1335 **772** 20y. multicoloured 40   15
1336 **773** 20y. multicoloured 40   15
1334/1336 *Set of 3* .... 1·10   40
     See also Nos. 1342/4, 1352/4, 1358/60, 1362/4, 1378/80 and 1387/9.

774 Lantern

(Des T. Shimizu. Photo)

1973 (10 Dec). New Year's Greetings. P 13×13½.
1337 **774** 10y. multicoloured 30   10

775 Niju-bashi Bridge

776 Imperial Palace

(Des S. Watanabe. Photo)

1974 (26 Jan). Imperial Golden Wedding. P 13
1339 **775** 20y. multicoloured 40   30
1340 **776** 20y. multicoloured 40   30
MS1341 145×89 mm. Nos. 1339/40 .... 1·60   1·20

777 "The Crane Damsel"

778 Manchurian Crane "weaving"

783 Iriomote Cat

784 "Finger" (Shinsui Ito)

(Des T. Yamanouchi. Recess and litho)

1974 (25 Mar). Nature Conservation (1st series). P 13.

1348 **783** 20y. multicoloured 50 25

    See also Nos. 1356, 1361, 1372, 1377, 1381, 1405, 1419, 1422, 1430, 1433/4, 1449, 1457, 1469/70, 1475, 1490, 1497 and 1502.

779 Manchurian Cranes in Flight

(Des F. Hori and S. Watanabe. Photo)

1974 (20 Feb). Japanese Folk Tales (2nd series). "Tsuru-Nyobo". P 13.

1342 **777** 20y. multicoloured 40 10
1343 **778** 20y. multicoloured 40 10
1344 **779** 20y. multicoloured 40 10
1342/1344 *Set of 3* .... 1·10 25

(Des H. Otsuka. Photo)

1974 (20 Apr). Philatelic Week. P 13½.

1349 **784** 20y. multicoloured 40 30

785 Nambu Red Pine

786 Supreme Court Building

(Des T. Shimizu Photo)

1974 (18 May). National Afforestation Campaign. P 13×13½.

1350 **785** 20y. multicoloured 40 30

(Des H. Otsuka. Recess)

1974 (23 May). Completion of Supreme Court Building, Tokyo. P 13×13½.

1351 **786** 20y. red-brown.. 40 30

780 "A Reefy Coast" (Hyakusui Hirafuku)

(Des M. Hisano. Photo)

1974 (2 Mar). International Ocean Exposition, Okinawa (1975) (1st issue). P 13½.

1345 **780** 20y. +5y. multicoloured............................. 50 40

    See also Nos. 1401/**MS**1404.

787 "Sailing in a Wooden Bowl"

788 "Conquering the Goblins"

781 Marudu Falls

782 Seascape

(Des Y. Kikuchi. Photo)

1974 (15 Mar). Iriomote National Park. P 13½.

1346 **781** 20y. multicoloured 50 10
1347 **782** 20y. multicoloured 50 10

789 "Wielding the Little Magic Mallet"

(Des J. Takidaira. Photo)

1974 (10 June). Japanese Folk Tales (3rd series). "The Dwarf". P 13.
1352	**787**	20y. multicoloured	40	30
1353	**788**	20y. multicoloured	40	30
1354	**789**	20y. multicoloured	40	30
1352/1354		Set of 3	1·10	80

790 "Uniform Rivalry" (detail after Kunimasa Baido)

791 European Otter

(Des M. Hisano. Photo)

1974 (17 June). Centenary of Japanese Police System. P 13.
1355	**790**	20y. multicoloured	40	30

(Des Y. Higashikadoi. Recess and photo)

1974 (25 June). Nature Conservation (2nd series). P 13.
1356	**791**	20y. multicoloured	50	25

792 "World Blood Donation"

(Des M. Hisano. Photo)

1974 (1 July). International Red Cross Day. P 13.
1357	**792**	20y. multicoloured	50	10

793 "Discovery of Kaguya Hime"

794 "Kaguya Hime as a Young Woman"

795 "The Ascent to Heaven"

(Des K. Morita. Photo)

1974 (29 July). Japanese Folk Tales (4th series). "Kaguya Hime". P 13.
1358	**793**	20y. multicoloured	40	30
1359	**794**	20y. multicoloured	40	30
1360	**795**	20y. multicoloured	40	30
1358/1360		Set of 3	1·10	80

796 Ryukyu Rabbit

(Des W. Emori. Recess and photo)

1974 (30 Aug). Nature Conservation (3rd series). P 13.
1361	**796**	20y. multicoloured	50	25

797 Old Men in front of Yahata Shrine

798 Old Man dancing with Demons

799 Old Man with Two Warts

(Des T. Kataoka. Photo)

1974 (9 Sept). Japanese Folk Tales (5th series). "Kobutori-Jii san". P 13.
1362	**797**	20y. multicoloured	40	30
1363	**798**	20y. multicoloured	40	30
1364	**799**	20y. multicoloured	40	30
1362/1364		Set of 3	1·10	80

800 Map of the World

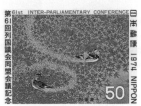

801 "Aizen" (Kawabata)

(Des K. Takeara (20y.), M. Hisano (50y.). Photo)

1974 (1 Oct). 61st Inter-Parliamentary Union Congress, Tokyo.
P 13½.
1365 **800** 20y. multicoloured 30   10
1366 **801** 50y. multicoloured 90   25

802 "Pine and   **803** U.P.U. Emblem
Northern Goshawk"
(detail, Sesson)

804 "Tending a Cow" (Fan-painting,
Sotatsu Tawaraya)

1974 (7 Oct). International Correspondence Week. Photo. P 13.
1367 **802** 50y. blackish brown & dull purple .... 1·00   25

(Des T. Kono (20y.), T. Shimizu (50y.). Photo)

1974 (9 Oct). Centenary of Universal Postal Union. P 13½.
1368 **803** 20y. multicoloured 40   10
1369 **804** 50y. multicoloured 90   25

805 Football   **806** Shii-take Mushrooms

(Des T. Yamanouchi. Photo)

1974 (20 Oct). 29th National Athletic Meeting. P 13.
1370 **805** 10y. multicoloured... 40   30

(Des M. Hioki. Photo)

1974 (2 Nov). Ninth International Scientific Conference on Cultivation
of Edible Fungi. P 13½.
1371 **806** 20y. multicoloured 50   10

807 Bonin Islands Flying Fox

(Des Y. Higashitsunoi. Recess and photo)

1974 (15 Nov). Nature Conservation (4th series). P 13.
1372 **807** 20y. multicoloured 80   30

808 Class "D–51" Locomotive   **809** Class "C–57" Locomotive

(Des S. Watanabe. Photo)

1974 (26 Nov). Steam Locomotives (1st series). P 13.
1373 **808** 20y. multicoloured 65   10
             a. Pair. Nos. 1373/4................................. 1·40   20
1374 **809** 20y. multicoloured 65   10
       Nos. 1373/4 were issued together in *se-tenant* pairs within the
sheet.
       See also Nos. 1382/3, 1385/6, 1395/6 and 1398/9.

810 "Kugikakushi"   **811** Short-tailed
(ornamental   Albatrosses
nail-covering) in
the form of a
Daffodil

(Des S. Watanabe. Photo)

1974 (10 Dec). New Year's Greetings. P 13½ ×13.
1375 **810** 10y. multicoloured 40   25

(Des M. Yabuuchi. Recess and photo)

1975 (16 Jan). Nature Conservation (5th series). P 13.
1377 **811** 20y. multicoloured .... 1·00   10

812 Taro releasing Tortoise   **813** Sea-God's Palace

814 Taro and Pandora's Box

(Des C. Oyamo. Photo)

1975 (28 Jan). Japanese Folk Tales (6th series). "Urashima Taro". P 13.
1378	**812**	20y. multicoloured	40	10
1379	**813**	20y. multicoloured	40	10
1380	**814**	20y. multicoloured	40	10
1378/1380 *Set of 3*			1·10	25

815 Manchurian Cranes

(Des T. Yamanouchi. Recess and photo)

1975 (13 Feb). Nature Conservation (6th series). P 13.
1381	**815**	20y. multicoloured	1·00	25

816 Class "C–58" Locomotive   **817** Class "D–52" Locomotive

(Des S. Watanabe. Photo)

1975 (25 Feb). Steam Locomotives (2nd series). P 13.
1382	**816**	20y. multicoloured	80	25
		a. Pair. Nos. 1382/3	1·70	60
1383	**817**	20y. multicoloured	80	25

Nos 1382/3 were issued together in *se-tenant* pairs within the sheet.

818 "Sight and Hearing" (Shiko Munakata)

(Des M. Hisano. Photo)

1975 (20 Mar). 50th Anniv of Japanese Broadcasting Corporation. P 13.
1384	**818**	20y. multicoloured	40	25

819 Class "8620" Locomotive   **820** Class "C–11" Locomotive

(Des S. Watanabe. Photo)

1975 (3 Apr). Steam Locomotives (3rd series). P 13.
1385	**819**	20y. multicoloured	80	25
		a. Pair. Nos. 1385/6	1·70	60
1386	**820**	20y. multicoloured	80	25

Nos. 1385/6 were issued together in *se-tenant* pairs within the sheet.

821 Old Man feeding Mouse   **822** Old Man holding Mouse's Tail

823 Mice giving Feast to Old Man

(Des G. Kurosaki. Photo)

1975 (15 Apr). Japanese Folk Tales (7th series). "Nezumi No Jodo". P 13.
1387	**821**	20y. multicoloured	40	25
1388	**822**	20y. multicoloured	40	25
1389	**823**	20y. multicoloured	40	25
1387/1389 *Set of 3*			1·10	70

824   Matsuura Screen   **825**

(Des Y. Kikuchi. Photo)

1975 (21 Apr). Philatelic Week. P 13½.
1390	**824**	20y. multicoloured	40	25
		a. Horiz pair. Nos. 1390/1	85	55
1391	**825**	20y. multicoloured	40	25

Nos. 1390/1 were issued together in horizontal *se-tenant* pairs within the sheet, forming the composite design shown.

827 Oil Rigs

(Des H. Hasebe. Photo)

1975 (10 May). Ninth World Petroleum Congress, Tokyo. P 13.
1394 **827** 20y. multicoloured 40 25

828 Class "9600" Locomotive   **829** Class "C–51" Locomotive

(Des S. Watanabe. Photo)

1975 (15 May). Steam Locomotives (4th series). P 13.
1395 **828** 20y. multicoloured 80 25
     a. Pair. Nos. 1395/6................................. 1·70 60
1396 **829** 20y. multicoloured 80 25
Nos. 1395/6 were issued together in *se-tenant* pairs within the sheet.

830 Plantation

(Des T. Amano. Photo)

1975 (24 May). National Land Afforestation Campaign. P 13.
1397 **830** 20y. multicoloured 40 25

831 Class "7100" Locomotive   **832** Class "150" Locomotive

(Des S. Watanabe. Recess and photo)

1975 (10 June). Steam Locomotives (5th series). P 13.
1398 **831** 20y. black and pale buff............................. 80 25
     a. Pair. Nos. 1398/9.................................. 1·70 60
1399 **832** 20y. black and pale greenish yellow 80 25
Nos. 1398/9 were issued together in *se-tenant* pairs within the sheet.

833 Woman's Head
and I.W.Y. Emblem

(Des T. Amano. Photo)

1975 (23 June). International Women's Year. P 13½.
1400 **833** 20y. multicoloured 40 25

834 Okinawa   **835** Bingata Textile
Dance   Pattern

836 "Aquapolis and Globe" Emblem

(Des S. Watanabe (20y.), Y. Kikuchi (30y.), K. Takeara (50y.). Photo)

1975 (19 July). International Ocean Exposition, Okinawa (2nd issue). P 13½.
1401 **834** 20y. multicoloured 40 25
1402 **835** 30y. multicoloured 60 25
1403 **836** 50y. multicoloured 90 30
1401/1403 *Set of 3*.. 1·70 70
MS1404 144×94 mm. Nos. 1401/3................... 2·00 1·60

837 Bonin Island Honeyeater

(Des H. Otsuka. Recess and photo)

1975 (8 Aug). Nature Conservation (7th series). P 13.
1405 **837** 20y. multicoloured .... 1·00 25

838 Kentoshisen (7th–9th   **839** Kenminsen (7th–9th
centuries)   centuries)

(Des Y. Sunagawa, eng Oshikiri (T **838**). Des R. Murayama,
eng S. Aizawa (T **839**). Recess)

1975 (30 Aug). Japanese Ships (1st series). P 13.
1406 **838** 20y. rose-red 70 25
     a. Pair Nos. 1406/7..................................... 1·50 55
1407 **839** 20y. sepia 70 25
Nos. 1406/7 were issued together in *se-tenant* pairs within the sheet.
See also Nos. 1409/10, 1420/1, 1423/4, 1428/9 and 1431/2.

840 Apple

(Des Y. Higashitsunoi. Photo)

1975 (17 Sept). Centenary of Apple Cultivation in Japan. P 13½.
1408 **840** 20y. multicoloured 40 25

841 Goshuin-sen
(16th-century trading
ship)

842 *Tenchi-maru*
(state barge), 1630

(Des Y. Sunagawa, eng M. Orihara (T **841**). Des R. Murayama,
eng T. Kasano (T **842**). Recess)

1975 (25 Sept). Japanese Ships (2nd series). P 13.
1409 **841** 20y. bronze green 70 25
    a. Pair. Nos 1409/10 .... 1·50 55
1410 **842** 20y. blue................................. 70 25
    Nos. 1409/10 were issued together in *se-tenant* pairs within the
sheet.

843 Green Peafowl
(after K. Ogata)

(Des Y. Kikuchi. Photo)

1975 (6 Oct). International Correspondence Week. P 13.
1411 **843** 50y. multicoloured .... 1·20 30

844 United States Flag   **845** Japanese Flag

(Des S. Watanabe. Photo)

1975 (14 Oct). Tour of U.S.A. by Emperor Hirohito and Empress
Nagako. P 13.
1412 **844** 20y. multicoloured 40 25
1413 **845** 20y. multicoloured 40 25
MS1414 146×93 mm. Nos. 1412/3............................. 1·90 1·50

846 Savings Box   **847** Weightlifting

(Des T. Shimizu Photo)

1975 (24 Oct). Centenary of Japanese Post Office Savings Bank.
P 13½.
1415 **846** 20y. multicoloured 40 25

(Des T. Yamanouchi. Photo)

1975 (25 Oct). 30th National Athletic Meeting. P 13.
1416 **847** 10y. multicoloured 40 25

848 "Tatsu-
guruma" (toy)

849 Ryukyu Robin

(Des Y. Kikuchi. Photo)

1975 (13 Dec). New Year's Greetings. P 13×13½.
1417 **848** 10y. multicoloured 60 25

(Des Y. Higashitsunoi. Recess and photo)

1976 (27 Feb). Nature Conservation (8th series). P 13.
1419 **849** 50y. multicoloured .... 1·20 25

850 Sengoku-bune (fishing
boat)

851 *Shohei Maru* (war junk)

(Des R. Murayama, eng T. Kesano (No. 1420). Des Y. Sunagawa, eng
S. Nakada (No. 1421). Recess)

1976 (11 Mar). Japanese Ship (3rd series). P 13.
1420 **850** 50y. chalky blue......................... 1·00 25
    a. Pair. Nos 1420/1 .... 2·10 55
1421 **851** 50y. reddish violet....................... 1·00 25
    Nos. 1420/1 were issued together in *se- tenant* pairs within the
sheet.

852 Tortoise

(Des H. Otsuka. Recess and photo)

1976 (25 Mar). Nature Conservation (9th series). P 13.

1422 **852** 50y. multicoloured .... 1·00   10

853 *Taisei Maru*   **854** *Tenyo Maru* (liner)
(cadet ship)

(Des Y. Sagawa, eng S. Okamura (No. 1423). Des G. Yamataka, eng K. Oshikiri (No. 1424). Recess)

1976 (12 Apr). Japanese Ships (4th series). P 13.

1423 **853** 50y. black .... 1·00   25
     a. Pair. Nos. 1423/4 .... 2·10   55
1424 **854** 50y. deep purple-brown............................ 1·00   25
Nos 1423/4 were issued together in *se-tenant* pairs within the sheet.

855   Sections of Hikone Folding Screen   **856**

(Des M. Hisano. Photo)

1976 (20 Apr). Philatelic Week. P 13.

1425 **855** 50y. multicoloured 70   25
     a. Horiz pair. Nos 1425/6 .... 1·60   55
1426 **856** 50y. multicoloured 70   25
Nos. 1425/6 were issued together in horizontal *se-tenant* pairs within the sheet.

857 Cedar   **858** *Asama Maru* (liner)
Forest, Plum
Blossom and
Mt. Tsukuba

859 *Kinai Maru* (cargo liner)   **860** Green Tree Frog
       (*Rhacophorus*
       arboreus)

(Des T. Yamanouchi. Photo).

1976 (22 May). National Afforestation Campaign. P 13.

1427 **857** 50y. multicoloured 70   10

(Des G. Yamataka. Eng K. Oshikiri (1428), S. Okamura (1429). Recess)

1976 (1 June). Japanese Ships (5th series). P 13.

1428 **858** 50y. yellow-olive.. 1·00   25
     a. Pair. Nos. 1428/9................................ 2·10   55
1429 **859** 50y. olive-brown.. 1·00   25
Nos. 1428/9 were issued in *se-tenant* pairs within the sheet.

(Des W. Emori. Recess and photo)

1976 (20 July). Nature Conservation (10th series). P 13.

1430 **860** 50y. multicoloured .... 1·10   25

861 *Kamakura Maru*   **862** *Nissei Maru* (oil tanker)
(container ship)

(Des K. Hishinuma and S. Watanabe. Eng S. Nakada (1431), S. Yajima (1432). Recess)

1976 (18 Aug). Japanese Ships (6th series). P 13.

1431 **861** 50y. blue... 1·00   25
     a. Pair. Nos. 1431/2............................... 2·10   55
1432 **862** 50y. deep ultramarine .... 1·00   25
Nos. 1431/2 were issued together in *se-tenant* pairs within the sheet.

863 Carp (*Tanakia tanago*)   **864** Three-spined Stickleback
                         (*Gasterosteus aculeatus*)

(Des H. Otsuka (1433), T. Yamanouchi (1434). Recess and photo)

1976 (26 Aug–16 Sept). Nature Conservation (11th and 12th series). P 13.

1433 **863** 50y. multicoloured (Aug) .... 1·10   25
1434 **864** 50y. multicoloured (Sept)......................... 1·10   25

865 "Kite and Rooks"   **866** Gymnastics
(detail Yosa Buson)

(Des Y. Kikuchi. Photo)

1976 (6 Oct). International Correspondence Week. P 13.
1435 **865** 100y. multicoloured .... 1·90   25

(Des Y. Higashitsunoi. Photo)

1976 (23 Oct). 31st National Athletic Meeting. P 13.
1436 **866** 20y. multicoloured 40   25

867 *KDD Maru* (cable ship) laying cable

868 Man-zai-raku (classical dance)

869 Coronation Coach

870 Children at First Kindergarten

(Des K. Takeara. Photo)

1976 (25 Oct). Opening of Sino–Japanese Cable. P 13.
1437 **867** 50y. multicoloured .... 1·00   25

(Des S. Watanabe (1438), Y. Kikuchi (1439). Photo)

1976 (10 Nov). Golden Jubilee of Emperor Hirohito's Accession. P 13.
1438 **868** 50y. multicoloured 70   25
1439 **869** 50y. carmine-lake, gold and black 70   25
MS1440 144×93 mm. Nos. 1438/9 .... 1·90   1·50

(Des M. Hisano. Photo)

1976 (16 Nov). Centenary of First Kindergarten, Tokyo. P 13.
1441 **870** 50y. multicoloured 70   25

871 Family Group

872 Bamboo Snake

(Des T. Shimizu. Photo)

1976 (24 Nov). 50th Anniv (1977) of Health Insurance System. P 13.
1442 **871** 50y. multicoloured 70   25

(Des M. Hisano. Photo)

1977 (1 Dec). New Year's Greetings. P 13.
1443 **872** 20y. multicoloured 50   25

873 East Pagoda, Yakushi Temple

874 Deva King, Todai Temple

(Des S. Watanabe. Photo (50y.), recess (100y.))

1976 (9 Dec). National Treasures (1st series). P 13×13½.
1445 **873** 50y. multicoloured .... 1·20   30
1446 **874** 100y. multicoloured .... 2·20   45
    See also Nos. 1447/8, 1452/3, 1463/4, 1471/2, 1480/1 and 1486/9.

875 Golden Pavilion, Toshodai Temple

876 Illustration from *Heike Nokyo Sutra*

877 Horseshoe Crabs (*Tachypleus tridentatus*)

(Des S. Watanabe. Eng S. Mizutani (50y.). Recess and photo (50y.). photo (100y.))

1977 (20 Jan). National Treasures (2nd series). P 13.
1447 **875** 50y. multicoloured .... 1·20   30
1448 **876** 100y. multicoloured .... 2·40   45

(Des H. Otsuka. Recess and photo)

1977 (18 Feb). Nature Conservation (13th series). P 13.
1449   877   50y. multicoloured .... 1·00   10

878   Figure Skating   **879**

(Des T. Yamanouchi. Photo)

1977 (1 Mar). World Figure Skating Championships, Tokyo. P 13.
1450   878   50y. multicoloured 70   25
1451   879   50y. multicoloured 70   25

880 Detail of Picture Scroll (attr. Toba Sojo Kakuyu)

881 Wood Carving of Buddhist Saint (attr. Jocho), Byodoin Temple, Uji

882 Forest in Sunshine

(Des S. Watanabe. Photo (50y.), recess (100y.))

1977 (25 Mar). National Treasures (3rd series). P 13.
1452   880   50y. multicoloured 80   25
1453   881   100y. blackish-brn, ol-brn & brn-ol .... 2·00   30

(Des T. Amano. Photo)

1977 (16 Apr). National Afforestation Campaign. P 13.
1454   882   50y. multicoloured .... 1·00   10

883   "Woman Weavers"   **884**

(Des Y. Kikuchi. Photo)

1977 (20 Apr). Philatelic Week. P 13½×13.
1455   883   50y. multicoloured 70   25
        a. Horiz pair. Nos 1455/6 .... 1·60   55
1456   884   50y. multicoloured 70   25
    Nos. 1455/6 were issued together in horizontal *se-tenant* pairs within the sheet, each pair forming a composite design.

885 Mikado Swallowtail (*Graphium doson*)   **886** Nurses

(Des W. Emori, Recess and photo)

1977 (18 May). Nature Conservation (14th series). P 13.
1457   885   50y. multicoloured .... 1·00   25

(Des S. Watanabe. Photo)

1977 (30 May). 16th Congress of International Council of Nurses, Tokyo. P 13.
1458   886   50y. multicoloured 70   25

887 Central Part of Nuclear Reactor

(Des H. Otsuka. Photo)

1977 (6 June). Reaching of Critical Mass by Joyo Fast Breeder Reactor, Oarai Town. P 13.
1459   887   50y. multicoloured 70   25

888 Carrier Pigeons and Mail Box with U.P.U. Emblem   **889** U.P.U. Emblem and World Map

(Des M. Hioki (50y.), M. Morita (100y.). Photo)

1977 (20 June). Centenary of Japan's Admission to Universal Postal Union. P 13.

1460	**888**	50y. multicoloured	70	25
1461	**889**	100y. multicoloured	1·80	30
MS1462		144×93 mm. Nos. 1460/1	2·40	1·90

890 Illustration from "Picture Scroll of Lady Murasaki's Diary"

891 Statue of Seitaka-Doji

(Des S. Watanabe. Eng. S. Okamura (100y.). Photo (50y.), recess (100y.))

1977 (27 June). National Treasures (4th series). P 13½×13 (50y.) or 13×13½ (100y.).

1463	**890**	50y. multicoloured	70	25
1464	**891**	100y. red-brn, blackish brn & ol-brn	1·80	30

892 Green Cross (safety emblem) and Workmen

893 Worker and High-rise Building

894 Unloading Freight

895 Machine Worker

896 Firefly (*Luciola cruciata*)

(Des M. Hioki. Photo)

1977 (1 July). National Safety Week. P 13.

1465	**892**	50y. multicoloured	1·10	25
		a. Strip or block of 4. Nos. 1465/8	4·50	1·10
1466	**893**	60y. multicoloured	1·10	25

1467	**894**	50y. multicoloured	1·10	25
1468	**895**	50y. multicoloured	1·10	25
1465/1468		Set of 4	4·00	90

Nos. 1465/8 were issued together *se-tenant* within the sheet, arranged to form both horizontal strips and blocks of four.

(Des M. Kimura. Recess and photo)

1977 (22 July). Nature Conservation (15th series). P 13.

1469	**896**	50y. multicoloured	1·00	10

897 Cicada (*Euterpnosia chibensis*)

898 Drawing of Han Shan by Kao

899 Matsumoto Castle

(Des Y. Kikuchi. Recess and photo)

1977 (15 Aug). Nature Conservation (16th series). P 13.

1470	**897**	50y. multicoloured	1·00	10

(Des S. Watanabe. Photo (50y). Des Y. Kikuchi. Eng S. Yajima. Recess and photo (100y.))

1977 (25 Aug). National Treasures (5th series). P 13.

1471	**898**	50y. multicoloured	70	25
1472	**899**	100y. multicoloured	1·80	30

900 Map and Child on Telephone

901 Surgeon

(Des Y. Higashitsunoi. Photo)

1977 (26 Aug). Opening of Okinawa–Luzon–Hong Kong Submarine Cable. P 13.

1473	**900**	50y. multicoloured	70	10

(Des T. Yamanouchi. Photo)

1977 (3 Sept). 27th Congress of International Society of Surgeons, Kyoto. P 13.

1474	**901**	50y. multicoloured	70	15

902 Dragonfly
(*Boninthemis insularis*)

903 Horn-shaped Speaker and Telegraph Key

(Des M. Morita. Recess and photo)

1977 (14 Sept). Nature Conservation (17th series). P 13.
1475　**902**　50y. multicoloured .... 1·00　25

(Des T. Yamanouchi. Photo)

1977 (24 Sept). 50th Anniv of Amateur Radio League. P 13.
1476　**903**　50y. multicoloured .... 70　10

904 Racing Cyclist and Mt. Iwaki

905 "Kacho-zu" (detail, Nobuharu Hasegawa)

(Des Y. Higashitsunoi. Photo)

1977 (1 Oct). 32nd National Athletic Meeting. P.13.
1477　**904**　20y. multicoloured .... 40　30

(Des Y. Kikuchi. Photo)

1977 (6 Oct). International Correspondence Week. P 13.
1478　**905**　100y. multicoloured .... 2·00　25

906 Long-necked Dinosaur and Museum

(Des M. Hisano. Photo)

1977 (2 Nov). Centenary of National Science Museum. P 13.
1479　**906**　50y. multicoloured .... 2·00　30

907 Detail, Folding Screen, Chishakuin Temple, Kyoto

908 Kiyomizu-dera Temple　　**909** Toy Horse

(Des S. Watanabe. Photo (50y.). Des M. Hisano. Eng T. Suzuki. Recess (100y.))

1977 (16 Nov). National Treasures (6th series). P 13.
1480　**907**　50y. multicoloured .... 70　25
1481　**908**　100y. blackish brown, ol-grn & dp bl .... 1·70　30

(Des M. Hisano. Photo)

1977 (1 Dec). New Year's Greetings. P 13.
1482　**909**　20y. multicoloured .... 50　10

910 Underground Train, 1927　**911** Underground Train, 1977

(Des M. Morita. Photo)

1977 (6 Dec). 50th Anniv of Tokyo Underground Railway. P 13.
1484　**910**　50y. multicoloured .... 1·00　25
　　　　　a. Pair. Nos. 1484/5 .... 2·10　50
1485　**911**　50y. multicoloured .... 1·00　25
　　　Nos. 1484/5 were issued together in *se-tenant* pairs within the sheet.

912 Genji's Carriage at Sumiyoshi Shrine (scene on folding screen (Sotatsu Tawaraya) from *Tale of Genji* by Lady Murasaki)

913 Inkstone Case (Koetsu Honami)

(Des S. Watanabe. Eng M. Orihara (100y.). Photo (50y.), recess and photo (100y.))

1978 (26 Jan). National Treasures (7th series). P 13½.
1486　**912**　50y. multicoloured .... 70　25
1487　**913**　100y. multicoloured .... 1·70　30

914 "Noryozu" (Morikage Kusumi)

915 Yomei Gate, Tosho Shrine, Nikko   **916** *Primula sieboldi*

(Des S. Watanabe. Photo (50y.). Des M. Saito. Eng K. Oshikiri. Recess and photo (100y.))

1978 (3 Mar). National Treasures (8th series). P 13.
1488	**914**	50y. multicoloured	70	25
1489	**915**	100y. multicoloured	1·70	30

(Des W. Emori. Recess and photo)

1978 (12 Apr). Nature Conservation (18th series). P 13.
1490	**916**	50y. multicoloured	90	25

917 Seated Woman with Flower (hanging scroll)   **918** Dancing Woman (hanging scroll)

(Des Y. Kikuchi. Photo)

1978 (20 Apr). Philatelic Week. P 13.
1491	**917**	50y. multicoloured	70	30
		a. Horiz pair. Nos. 1491/2	1·70	1·30
1492	**918**	50y. multicoloured	70	30

Nos. 1491/2 were issued together in horizontal *se-tenant* pairs within the sheet.

919 Rotary Emblem and Mt. Fuji (from "36 Views of Mt. Fuji" by Hokusai Katsushika)   **920** Congress Emblem

(Des M. Morita. Photo)

1978 (13 May). Rotary International Convention, Tokyo. P 13.
1493	**919**	50y. multicoloured	1·00	10

(Des T. Okamoto. Photo)

1978 (15 May). 23rd International Ophthalmological Congress, Kyoto. P 13.
1494	**920**	50y. multicoloured	70	10

921 Passenger Terminal Building   **922** Cape Ashizuri, Rainbow and Cedar Trees

(Des S. Watanabe. Photo)

1978 (20 May). Opening of Narita Airport, Tokyo. P 13.
1495	**921**	50y. multicoloured	80	10

(Des T. Amano. Photo)

1978 (20 May). National Afforestation Campaign. P 13.
1496	**922**	50y. multicoloured	70	10

923 *Pinguicula ramosa*   **924** "Karashishi" (attr. Sotatsu Tawaraya) and Lions Emblem

(Des H. Otsuka. Recess and photo)

1978 (8 June). Nature Conservation (19th series). P 13½×13.
1497	**923**	50y. multicoloured	90	25

(Des S. Watanabe. Recess and photo)

1978 (21 June). 61st Lions International Convention, Tokyo. P 13.
1498	**924**	50y. multicoloured	1·00	10

925   "Grand Champion Raigoyo   **926** Hidenoyama in the Ring" (Toyokuni III)

927 "Drum Tower of Ekoin Temple, Ryogoku" (Hiroshige)

928 *Dicentra peregrina*

(Des S. Watanabe. Recess and photo (1499/1500), photo (1501))

1978 (1 July). Sumo (Japanese Wrestling) Pictures (1st series). P 13.
1499	**925**	50y. multicoloured	70	30
		a. Horiz pair. Nos. 1499/1500	1·70	1·30
1500	**926**	50y. multicoloured	70	30
1501	**927**	50y. multicoloured	70	30
1499/1501		Set of 3	1·90	80

Nos. 1499/1500 were issued together in horizontal *se tenant* pairs within the sheet.
See also Nos. 1505/7, 1513/15, 1519/21 and 1523/5.

(Des M. Morita. Recess and photo)

1978 (25 July). Nature Conservation (20th series). P 12½×13.
1502	**928**	50y. multicoloured	90	25

929 Keep Fit Exercise

930 Chamber of Commerce and Industry Building and Centenary Emblem

(Des K. Tsukuda and Y. Kikuchi. Photo)

1978 (1 Aug). 50th Anniv of Radio Gymnastic Exercises. P 13.
1503	**929**	50y. multicoloured	1·60	10

(Des T. Yamanouchi. Photo)

1978 (28 Aug). Centenary of First Chambers of Commerce, Tokyo and Osaka. P 13.
1504	**930**	50y. multicoloured	70	10

931 "Dohyoiri" (wrestlers Tanikaze and Onogawa) (Shunsho Katsukawa) **932**

933 "Jinmaku versus Raiden" (Shunnei Katsukawa)

934 Statues on Tokyo Securities Exchange Building

(Des S. Watanabe. Recess and photo)

1978 (9 Sept). Sumo Pictures (2nd series). P 12½×13.
1505	**931**	50y. multicoloured	70	30
		a. Horiz pair. Nos. 1505/6	1·70	1·30
1506	**932**	50y. multicoloured	70	30
1507	**933**	50y. multicoloured	70	30
1505/1507		Set of 3	1·90	80

Nos. 1505/6 were issued together in horizontal *se-tenant* pairs within the sheet, each pair forming a composite design.

(Des M. Morita. Recess)

1978 (14 Sept). Centenary of Tokyo and Osaka Stock Exchanges. P 13.
1508	**934**	50y. reddish brown, reddish purple and bronze green	70	10

935 Copper Pheasant (detail of door painting attr. Sanraku Kano)

936 Mt. Yari and Softball Players

(Des Y. Kikuchi. Photo)

1978 (6 Oct). International Correspondence Week. P 12½×13.
1509	**935**	100y. multicoloured	2·50	25

(Des H. Otsuka. Photo)

1978 (14 Oct). 33rd National Athletic Meeting. P 12½×13.
1510	**936**	20y. multicoloured	40	30

937 Artificial Joint

938 Refracting Telescope and Stars

(Des H. Otsuka. Photo)

1978 (16 Oct). 14th Congress of International Society of Orthopaedic and Traumatic Surgeons, Kyoto. P 13.
1511	**937**	50y. lt greenish bl, ultram & silver	70	15

(Des K. Takeara. Photo)

1978 (1 Nov). Centenary of Tokyo Astronomical Observatory. P 13.
1512 **938** 50y. multicoloured 70 10

939 "The then Heroic Champion's **940**
Sumo Wrestling" (detail,
Toyokuni III)

941 "Children's   **942** Sheep Bell   **943** Family and
Charming Sumo   (folk toy)   Human Rights
Play" (Utamaro   Emblem
Kitagawa)

(Des S. Watanabe. Recess and photo)

1978 (11 Nov). Sumo Pictures (3rd series). P 12½×13.
1513 **939** 50y. multicoloured 70 30
        a. Horiz pair. Nos. 1513/14..................... 1·70 1·30
1514 **940** 50y. multicoloured 70 30
1515 **941** 50y. multicoloured 70 30
1513/1515 *Set of 3* .... 1·90 80
    Nos 1513/14 were issued together in horizontal *se-tenant* pairs
within the sheet.

(Des M. Hisano. Photo)

1978 (1 Dec). New Year's Greetings. P 13.
1516 **942** 20y. multicoloured 50 10

(Des T. Shimizu. Photo)

1978 (4 Dec). 30th Anniv of Declaration of Human Rights. P 13.
1518 **943** 50y. multicoloured 70 10

944 "Great Sumo Wrestlers **945**
crossing Ryogoku Bridge"
(Toyokuni III)

946 "Yumitori   **947** Hands protecting
Ceremony at Grand   Children
Fund-raising
Tournament"
(Kunisada II)

(Des S. Watanabe. Recess and photo)

1979 (13 Jan). Sumo Pictures (4th series). P 12½×13.
1519 **944** 50y. multicoloured 70 30
        a. Horiz pair. Nos. 1519/20..................... 1·70 1·30
1520 **945** 50y. multicoloured 70 30
1521 **946** 50y. multicoloured 70 30
1519/1521 *Set of 3* .... 1·90 80
    Nos. 1519/20 were issued together in horizontal *se-tenant* pairs
within the sheet, each pair forming a composite design.

(Des T. Amano. Photo)

1979 (16 Feb). Education for the Handicapped. P 13.
1522 **947** 50y. multicoloured 70 25

948   "Takekuma versus Iwamigata"   **949**
(Kuniyoshi Utagawa)

950 "Daidozan's Dohyoiri"
(Sharaku Toshusai)

(Des S. Watanabe. Recess and photo)

1979 (10 Mar). Sumo Pictures (5th series). P 12½×13.
1523 **948** 50y. multicoloured 70 30
        a. Horiz pair. Nos. 1523/4..................... 1·70 1·30
1523 **949** 50y. multicoloured 70 30
1524 **950** 50y. multicoloured 70 30
1523/1525 *Set of 3* .... 1·90 80
    Nos. 1523/4 were issued together in horizontal *se-tenant* pairs
within the sheet, each pair forming a composite design.

951 Telephone Dial and Push Buttons

952 Drawing by Leonardo da Vinci

956 "Goddess of Maternal Mercy" (Kano Hogai)

957 "The Princess of the Sea God" (Aoki Shigeru)

(Das M. Hisano. Photo)

1979 (14 Mar). Completion of Telephone Automation. P 13.
1526 **951** 50y. multicoloured 70 10

(Des H. Otsuka. Recess and photo)

1979 (7 Apr). Centenary of Western Medicine in Japan. P 13.
1527 **952** 50y. multicoloured 70 10

(Des Y. Kikuchi. Recess and photo (1531), photo (1532))

1979 (30 May). Modern Japanese Art (1st series). P 13.
1531 **956** 50y. multicoloured 90 25
1532 **957** 50y. multicoloured 80 25
See also Nos. 1533/4, 1544/5, 1550/1, 1558/9, 1567/8, 1574/5, 1610/11, 1618/19, 1628/9, 1650/1, 1656/7, 1675/6, 1689/90, 1693/4 and 1697/8.

953 "Standing Beauties" **954** (Kaigetsudo School)

(Des Y. Kikuchi. Photo)

1979 (20 Apr). Philatelic Week. P 13.
1528 **953** 50y. multicoloured.................................. 70 25
    a. Horiz pair. Nos. 1528/9 .... 1·70 1·30
1529 **954** 50y. multicoloured.................................. 70 25
Nos 1528/9 were issued together in horizontal *se-tenant* pairs within the sheet.

958 "Fire Dance" (Gyoshu Hayami)

959 "Leaning Figure" (Tetsugoro Yorozu)

(Des Y. Kikuchi. Photo (1533), recess and photo (1534))

1979 (25 June). Modern Japanese Art (2nd series). P 13.
1533 **958** 50y. multicoloured .... 1·20 25
1534 **959** 50y. multicoloured .... 1·20 25

955 Mt. Horaiji and Maple Leaves

(Des M. Morita. Photo)

1979 (26 May). National Afforestation Campaign. P 13.
1530 **955** 50y. multicoloured 70 10

960 Quarantine Officers

(Des T. Yamanouchi. Photo)

1979 (14 July). Centenary of Quarantine System. P 13.
1535 **960** 50y. multicoloured .... 1·00 10

961 Girl with Letter

962 Hakata Doll

963 Baseball Pitcher and Ball

(Des T. Shimizu (20y.), S. Watanabe (50y.). Photo)

1979 (23 July). Letter Writing Day. P 13.

1536	**961**	20y. multicoloured	40	25
1537	**962**	50y. multicoloured	70	25

(Des M. Hisano. Photo)

1979 (27 July). 50th National Inter-city Amateur Baseball Tournament. P 13½×13.

1538	**963**	50y. multicoloured	70	15

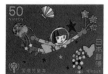

964 Girl collecting Stars

965 Boy catching Toy Insects

(Des H. Manabe and M. Morita. Photo)

1979 (1 Aug). International Year of the Child. P 13×12½.

1539	**964**	50y. multicoloured	1·00	15
1540	**965**	50y. multicoloured	1·00	15
MS1541		144×93 mm. Nos. 1539/40	2·40	1·90

966 *The Moon over the Castle Ruins* (Bansui Doi and Rentaro Taki)

967 *Evening Glow* (Uko Nakamura and Shin Kusakawa)

(Des J. Takidaira (1542), R.Taniuchi (1543). Recess and photo)

1979 (24 Aug). Japanese Songs (1st series). P 12½×13.

1542	**966**	50y. multicoloured	70	25
1543	**967**	50y. multicoloured	70	25

See also Nos. 1552/3, 1556/7, 1561/2, 1565/6, 1572/3, 1580/1, 1616/17 and 1620/1.

968 "The Black Cat" (Shunso Hishida)

969 "Kinyo" (Sotaro Yasui)

(Des Y. Kikuchi. Photo)

1979 (21 Sept). Modern Japanese Art (3rd series). P 13.

1544	**968**	50y. multicoloured	1·10	25
1545	**969**	50y. multicoloured	1·10	25

970 "Steep Mountains and the Dark Dale" (detail) (Okyo Maruyama)

971 Long Distance Runner

(Des Y. Kikuchi Photo)

1979 (8 Oct). International Correspondence Week. P 13.

1546	**970**	100y. multicoloured	2·50	25

(Des T. Shimizu. Photo)

1979 (13 Oct). 34th National Athletic Meeting, Miyazaki. P 13.

1547	**971**	20y. multicoloured	70	10

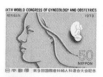

972 "I.T.U." and Globe

973 Woman and Embryo

(Des M. Hisano. Photo)

1979 (13 Oct). Centenary of Admission to International Telecommunications Union. P 13½.

1548	**972**	50y. multicoloured	70	10

(Des M. Hisano. Photo)

1979 (25 Oct) Ninth International Obstetrics and Gynaecology Convention, Tokyo. P 13½.

1549	**973**	50y. multicoloured	70	25

974 "Nude" (Kagaku Murakami)

975 "Harvest" (Asai Chu)

(Des Y. Kikuchi. Recess and photo (1550), photo (1551))

1979 (22 Nov). Modern Japanese Art (4th series). P 13½.
1550 **974** 50y. multicoloured 70 25
1551 **975** 50y. multicoloured 50 10

976 *Maple Leaves* (Tatsuyuki Takano and Teiichi Okano)

977 *Birthplace* (Tatsuyuki Takano and Teiichi Okano)

(Des F. Hori (1552), T. Murakami (1553). Recess and photo)

1979 (26 Nov). Japanese Songs (2nd series). P 13.
1552 **976** 50y. multicoloured 50 10
1553 **977** 50y. multicoloured 50 10

978 Happy Monkeys (folk toy)

(Des M. Morita. Photo)

1979 (1 Dec). New Year's Greetings. P 13×13½.
1554 **978** 20y. multicoloured 50 10

979 *Winter Scene* (anon)   **980** *Mt. Fuji* (anon)

(Des S. Ishikawa (1556), S. Watanabe (1557). Recess and photo)

1980 (28 Jan). Japanese Songs (3rd series). P 13.
1556 **979** 50y. multicoloured .... 1·00 25
1557 **980** 50y. multicoloured .... 1·00 25

981 "Salmon" (Yuichi Takahashi)

982 "Hall of the Supreme Buddha" (Kokei Kobayashi)

(Des Y. Kikuchi. Recess and photo (1558), photo (1559))

1980 (22 Feb). Modern Japanese Art (5th series). P 13½.
1558 **981** 50y. multicoloured .... 1·20 25
1559 **982** 50y. multicoloured .... 1·20 25

983 Scales

(Des K. Takeara. Photo)

1980 (5 Mar). Centenary of Government Auditing Bureau. P 13½.
1560 **983** 50y. multicoloured 70 10

984 *Spring Brook* (Tatsuyuki Takano and Teiichi Okano)

985 *Cherry Blossoms* (anon)

(Des M. Anno (1561), K Morita (1562). Recess and photo)

1980 (21 Mar). Japanese Songs (4th series). P 13.
1561 **984** 50y. multicoloured 70 25
1562 **985** 50y. multicoloured 70 25

986   "Scenes of Outdoor Play in Spring"   **987**
(Sukenobu Nishikawa)

(Des Y. Kikuchi Photo)

1980 (21 Apr). Philatelic Week. P 13½.
1563	**988**	50y. multicoloured	70	25
		a. Horiz pair. Nos. 1563/4	1·70	1·30
1564	**987**	50y. multicoloured	70	25

Nos. 1563/4 were issued together in horizontal *se-tenant* pairs within the sheet.

988 *Sea* (Ryuha Hayashi and Takeshi Inoue)

989 *Misty Moonlight Night* (Tatsuyuki Takano and Teiichi Okano)

(Des R. Taniuchi (1565), F. Hori (1566). Recess and photo)

1980 (28 Apr). Japanese Songs (5th series). P 13.
1565	**988**	50y. multicoloured	70	25
1566	**989**	50y. multicoloured	70	25

990 "Maiko Girls" (Seiki Kuroda)

991 "Mother and Child" (Shoen Uemura)

(Des Y. Kikuchi. Photo)

1980 (12 May). Modern Japanese Art (6th series). P 13½.
1567	**990**	50y. multicoloured	70	25
1568	**991**	50y. multicoloured	70	25

992 *Nippon Maru*   **993** Mt. Gozaisho and Cedars   **994** "Acrobatic Performances on a Ladder at New Year's Parade of Yayosu Fire Brigades" (Hiroshige III)

(Des Y. Kikuchi. Photo)

1980 (17 May). 50th Anniv of Cadet Ships *Nippon Maru* and *Kaio Maru*. P 13½.
1569	**992**	50y. multicoloured	1·20	10

(Des T. Yamanouchi. Photo)

1980 (24 May). National Afforestation Campaign. P 13×13½.
1570	**993**	50y. multicoloured	80	30

(Des S. Watanabe. Recess and photo)

1980 (31 May). Centenary of Fire Fighting System. P 13½.
1571	**994**	50y. multicoloured	80	30

995 *The Sun* (Tatsuyuki Takano and Teiichi Okano)

996 *Memories of Summer* (Shoko Ema and Yoshinao Nakata)

(Des S. Watanabe (1572), M. Anno (1573). Recess and photo)

1980 (16 June). Japanese Songs (6th series). P 13.
1572	**995**	50y. multicoloured	80	25
1573	**996**	50y. multicoloured	80	25

997 "Black Fan" (Takeji Fujishima)

998 "The Dance *Are Yudachi ni*" (Seiho Takeuchi)

(Des Y. Kikuchi. Photo)

1980 (7 July). Modern Japanese Art (7th series). P 13½.
1574	**997**	50y. multicoloured	80	25
1575	**998**	50y. multicoloured	80	25

999 Teddy Bear holding Letter

1000 Knotted Letter

1006 Akita Dog

1007 Adonis

1008 Lily

(Des M. Sato and S. Watanabe (20y.), H. Tamai (50y.). Photo)

1980 (23 July). Letter Writing Day. P 13×13½ (20y.) or 13½×13 (50y.).
1576　**999** 20y. multicoloured .... 50　30
1577　**1000** 50y. multicoloured .... 1·00　25

1001 *Luehdorfia japonica*

1002 Map on Three-dimensional Graph

(Des M. Morita. Photo)

1980 (2 Aug). 16th International Congress of Entomology. P 13½.
1578　**1001** 50y. multicoloured .... 90　30

(Des F. Otani. Photo)

1980 (25 Aug). 24th International Geographical Congress and 10th International Cartographic Conference, Tokyo. P 13½.
1579　**1002** 50y. multicoloured .... 80　30

1003 *Red Dragonfly* (Rofu Miki and Kosaku Yamada)

1004 *Song by the Sea* (Kokei Hayashi and Tamezo Narita)

(Des K. Negishi (1580), S. Hayashi (1581). Recess and photo)

1980 (18 Sept). Japanese Songs (7th series). P 13.
1580　**1003** 50y. multicoloured .... 80　25
1581　**1004** 50y. multicoloured .... 80　25

1005 Integrated Circuit

(Des F. Otani. Photo)

1980 (29 Sept). Eighth World Computer Congress and Third World Conference on Medical Informatics, Tokyo. P 13½.
1582　**1005** 50y. multicoloured .... 80　30

1009 Camellia

1010 Small Cabbage Whites on Rape Blossom

1011 Japanese Babylonia

1012 Noble Scallops

1013 Flowering Cherry

1014 Hanging Bell, Byodoin Temple, Uji

1015 Yoka Star Shell

1016 Precious Wentletrap

1017 Flautist, Horyu Temple

1018 Deer (from lacquer writing box)

1019 Mirror with Figures

1020 Heart-shaped Earthen Figurine

1021 Silver Crane, Kasuga Taisha Shrine, Nara

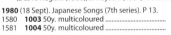

1022 Miroku Bosatsu, Horyu Temple

1023 Dainichi Buddha, Chuson Temple

1024 Keiki Doji, Kongobu Temple

1025 Komoku Ten, Todai Temple, Nara

1026 Lady Maya, Horyu Temple

1027 Tea Jar with Wisteria Decoration (Ninsei Nonomura)

1028 Miroku Bosatsu

1031 "Cranes" (door painting, Motooki Watanabe)

1032 Archer and Mt. Nantai

(Des M. Kimura (T **1006**), Y. Higashitsunoi (**1007**), M. Hisano (**1008**), T. Yamanouchi (**1009**), H. Hasebe (**1010**, **1013**), S. Watanabe (**1017**, **1023**), F. Otani (**1019**, **1022**), Y. Kikuchi (**1020/1**, **1024/6**), M. Morita (others). Eng H. Oura (300y.). Recess (300y.). Photo (others))

1980 (1 Oct)–**89**. P 13×13½.

1582a	**1006**	2y. dp turquoise-blue (1.4.89)	10	10
1583	**1007**	10y. yell, dp grn & lt brn (5.7.82)	20	15
		a. Coil. P 13×imperf (20.10.82)	20	25
1584	**1008**	20y. yell, bl & brt grn (5.7.82)	30	15
1585	**1009**	30y. multicoloured	55	20
1586	**1010**	40y. multicoloured	50	15
		a. Coil. P 13×imperf (1.4.81)	70	35
1587	**1011**	40y. multicoloured (1.4.88)	85	25
		a. Booklet pane. Nos. 1587×5 and 1591×5 (1.4.88)	6·00	
1588	**1012**	41y. multicoloured (24.3.89)	70	20
		a. Booklet pane. Nos. 1588×2 and 1592×4 (1.4.89)	3·50	
		b. Coil. P 13×imperf (3.7.89)	1·00	75
1589	**1013**	50y. multicoloured	80	15
1590	**1014**	60y. yellowish green and black (25.11.80)	70	10
		a. Coil. P 13×imperf (20.1.81)	90	40
		b. Booklet pane. No. 1590×5 (20.2.81)	4·25	
1591	**1015**	60y. multicoloured (1.4.88)	1·00	10
1592	**1016**	62y. multicoloured (24.3.89)	1·10	20
		a. Coil. P 13×imperf (3.7.89)	1·00	55
1593	**1017**	70y. royal blue & yell (25.11.80)	1·30	30
1594	**1018**	70y. orange-yellow, black and royal blue (6.12.82)	80	15
1594a		72y. yell, blk & ultram (1.4.89)	80	15
1595	**1019**	80y. yellowish green and black (10.7.81)	1·50	10
1596	**1020**	90y. bistre-yellow, brownish black & blue-grn (10.7.81)	1·60	10
1597	**1021**	100y. black, azure and ultramarine (10.7.81)	90	10
		a. Coil. P 13×imperf (20.10.82)	1·40	15
1598	**1022**	170y. blackish purple and bistre (20.1.81)	2·00	15
1599		175y. agate, pale turquoise-green and olive-bistre (1.6.89)	1·90	15
1600	**686**	210y. bright orange and reddish lilac (1.6.89)	2·30	15
1601	**1023**	260y. blackish brown and orange-vermilion (20.1.81)	3·00	15
1602	**1024**	300y. chocolate (3.4.84)	3·50	10
1603	**1025**	310y. grey-brn & dp vio (16.3.81)	3·50	10
1604	**689**	360y. dull brn-pur & pk (1.6.89)	4·00	25
1605	**1026**	410y. dull orange and deep turquoise-blue (20.1.81)	6·50	30
1606	**1027**	410y. multicoloured (6.12.82)	6·75	20
1607	**1028**	600y. orange-yellow, maroon and rose-lilac (16.3.81)	7·00	15
1582a/1607		Set of 27	50·00	6·25

The 175, 210 and 360y. differ from the illustrated types in the arrangement of the inscription; the two higher values also have a frame added.

No. 1590b is arranged with a block of four stamps on the right separated by a wide gutter from a single example on the left; the pane is folded along the gutter and attached to the cover on one side of the folded edge so that the halves face each other.

All the panes have their outer edges imperforate.

For 41 and 62y. but self-adhesive see Nos. 1991/2.

(Des Y. Kikuchi. Photo)

1980 (6 Oct). International Correspondence Week. P 13.

1608	**1031**	100y. multicoloured	1·90	30

(Des Y. Higashitsunoi. Photo)

1980 (11 Oct). 35th National Athletic Meeting, Tochigi. P 13.

1609	**1032**	20y. multicoloured	40	25

1033 "Woman" (sculpture, Morie Ogiwara)

1034 "Woman of the Kurofune-ya" (Yumeji Takehisa)

(Des Y. Kikuchi. Photo)

1980 (27 Oct). Modern Japanese Art (8th series). P 13½.

1610	**1033**	50y. multicoloured	80	25
1611	**1034**	50y. multicoloured	80	25

1035 "Energy"

1036 Diet Building and Doves

1037 Toy Rooster

(Des M. Morita. Photo)

1980 (8 Nov). 35th World Congress of Junior Chambers of Commerce, Osaka. P 13.

1612	**1035**	50y. multicoloured	80	30

(Des M. Hisano. Recess and photo)

1980 (29 Nov). 90th Anniv of Japanese Diet. P 13½.

1613	**1036**	50y. multicoloured	1·00	10

(Des M. Morita. Photo)

1980 (1 Dec). New Year's Greetings. P 13×13½.

1614	**1037**	20y. multicoloured	50	10

1038 *Komori-Uta* (nursery song)

1039 *Coconut* (Toson Shimazaki and Toraji Ohaka)

(Des K. Morita (1616), M. Yonekura (1617). Recess and photo)

1981 (9 Feb). Japanese Songs (8th series). P 13
1616 **1038** 60y. multicoloured 80 25
1617 **1039** 60y. multicoloured 80 25

1040 "Power Station in the Snow" (Shikanosuke Oka)

1041 "Nukada-no Okimi of Asuka in Spring" (Yukihiko Yasuda)

(Des Y. Kikuchi. Recess and photo (1618), photo (1619))

1981 (26 Feb). Modern Japanese Art (9th series). P 13½.
1618 **1040** 60y. multicoloured .... 1·10 30
1619 **1041** 60y. multicoloured .... 1·10 30

1042 *Spring has Come* (Tatsuyuki Takano and Teiichi Okano)

1043 *Cherry Blossoms* (Hagoromo Takeshima and Rentaro Taki)

(Des T. Murakami (1620), S. Hayashi (1621). Recess and photo)

1981 (10 Mar). Japanese Songs (9th series). P 13.
1620 **1042** 60y. multicoloured .... 1·10 25
1621 **1043** 60y. multicoloured .... 1·10 25

1044 Port Island and Exposition Emblem

1045 Cereal, Tree and Fish on "100"

(Des K. Takeara. Photo)

1981 (20 Mar). Kobe Port Island Exposition, Kobe City. P 13
1622 **1044** 60y. multicoloured .... 1·00 30

(Des F. Otani. Photo)

1981 (7 Apr). Centenary of Agriculture, Forestry and Fishery Promotion. P 13.
1623 **1045** 60y. multicoloured .... 1·20 10

1046 Yugao (Lady of the Evening Roses)

1047 Genji

(Des Y. Kikuchi. Photo)

1981 (20 Apr). Philatelic Week. Details of Harunobu Suzuki's Illustrations of *Tale of Genji* by Lady Murasaki. P 13½.
1624 **1046** 60y. multicoloured .... 1·00 30
    a. Horiz pair. Nos. 1624/5 .... 2·10 1·60
1625 **1047** 60y. multicoloured .... 1·00 30
Nos. 1624/5 were issued together in horizontal se-tenant pairs within the sheet, each pair forming a composite design.

1048 Pagodas at Nara and Cherry Blossom

1049 Container Ship and Crane

(Des S. Watanabe. Photo)

1981 (23 May). National Afforestation Campaign. P 13×13½.
1626 **1048** 60y. multicoloured .... 1·00 30

(Des F. Otani. Photo)

1981 (25 May). 12th International Port and Harbour Association Conference. P 13.
1627 **1049** 60y. multicoloured .... 1·00 10

1050 "N's Family" (Narashige Koide)

1051 "Bamboo Shoots" (Heihachiro Fukuda)

(Des Y. Kikuchi. Recess and photo (1628), photo (1629))

1981 (18 June). Modern Japanese Art (10th series). P 13½.
1628   **1050** 60y. multicoloured 80   25
1629   **1051** 60y. multicoloured 80   25

1052 Stylized Debris Barriers

1053 Human Figure and Dose Response Chart

(Des K. Takeara. Photo)

1981 (27 June). Centenary of Land Erosion Control. P 13½.
1630   **1052** 60y. multicoloured .... 1·00   25

(Des F. Otani. Photo)

1981 (18 July). Eighth International Congress of Pharmacology, Tokyo. P 13½.
1631   **1053** 60y. multicoloured .... 1·00   30

(Des T. Shimizu (40y.), M. Hisano (60y.). Photo)

1981 (23 July). Letter Writing Day. P 13×13½.
1632   **1054** 40y. multicoloured 70   30
1633   **1055** 60y. multicoloured .... 1·00   25

(Des M. Morita. Litho)

1981 (27 July). 50th Anniv of National Parks. P 13½.
1634   **1056** 60y. multicoloured .... 1·10   30

1057 Electric Plug and dripping Tap

1058 Energy Recycling

(Des S. Maejima and F. Otani (40y.), H. Toyomasu and Y. Kikuchi (60y.). Photo)

1981 (1 Aug). Energy Conservation. P 13×13½ (40y.) or 13½×13 (60y.).
1635   **1057** 40y. indigo, brt lilac & greenish bl.......... 80   30
1636   **1058** 60y. multicoloured .... 1·20   25

1059 Oura Cathedral, Nagasaki

1060 Hyokei Hall, Tokyo

(Des Z. Chikaoka. Recess and photo)

1981 (22 Aug). Modern Western-style Architecture (1st series). P 13.
1637   **1059** 60y. multicoloured .... 1·00   30
1638   **1060** 60y. multicoloured .... 1·00   30
See also Nos 1648/9, 1654/5, 1658/9, 1669/70, 1680/1, 1695/6, 1705/6, 1710/11 and 1732/3.

1054 Girl writing Letter

1055 Boy with Pencil and Stamp

1056 Japanese Crested Ibis

1061 Bluebird and IYDP Emblem

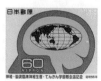
1062 Globe in Brain

(Des M. Morita. Photo and embossed)

1981 (1 Sept). International Year of Disabled Persons. P 13½.
1639 **1061** 60y.+10y. multicoloured .... 1·20   30

(Des F. Otani. Photo)

1981 (12 Sept). International Neurological Conferences, Kyoto. P 13.
1640 **1062** 60y. multicoloured 80   10

(Des Y. Kikuchi. Recess and photo)

1981 (9 Oct). "Philatokyo '81" International Stamp Exhibition, Tokyo. Multicoloured, frame colour of stamp within design given. P 13.
1643 **1065** 60y. reddish brown.................................... 90   30
     a. Block or vert strip of 4.
       Nos. 1643/6 .... 4·00
1644 **1066** 60y. indigo... 90   30
1645 **1067** 60y. vermilion................................... 90   30
1646 **1068** 60y. deep yellow-green 90   30
1643/1646 *Set of 4*.. 3·25   1·10
  Nos. 1643/6 were issued together *se-tenant* in the sheet, arranged to form both vertical strips and blocks of four.

1063 Convention Emblem   **1064** "Two Turtle Doves" (Sanraku Kano)

(Des T. Kono. Photo)

1981 (16 Sept). International Federation of Postal, Telegram and Telephone Workers' Union World Convention, Tokyo. P 13.
1641 **1063** 60y. multicoloured .... 1·00   30

(Des Y. Kikuchi. Photo)

1981 (6 Oct). International Correspondence Week. P 13.
1642 **1064** 130y. multicoloured .... 2·50   30

1069 Badminton and Lake Biwa

(Des M. Hisano. Photo)

1981 (13 Oct). 36th National Athletic Meeting, Shiga. P 13.
1647 **1069** 40y. multicoloured 70   25

1070 Former Kaichi School, Matsumoto   **1071** Doshisha Chapel, Kyoto

(Des Z. Chikaoka. Recess and photo)

1981 (9 Nov). Modern Western-style Architecture (2nd series). P 13.
1648 **1070** 60y. multicoloured .... 1·00   30
1649 **1071** 60y. multicoloured .... 1·00   30

1065 48m. Stamp, 1871   **1066** 100m. Stamp, 1871

1067 200m. Stamp, 1871   **1068** 500m. Stamp, 1871

1072 "Portrait of Reiko" (Ryusei Kishida)   **1073** "Ichiyo" (Kiyokata Kaburagi)

(Des Y. Kikuchi. Recess and photo (1650), photo (1651))

1981 (27 Nov). Modern Japanese Art (11th series). P 13½.
1650   **1072** 60y. multicoloured   80   30
1651   **1073** 60y. multicoloured   80   30

(Des Y. Kikuchi. Recess and photo (1656), photo (1657))

1982 (25 Feb). Modern Japanese Art (12th series). P 13½.
1656   **1077** 60y. multicoloured   80   30
1657   **1078** 60y. multicoloured   80   30

1074 Clay Dog
(folk toy)

(Des M. Morita. Photo)

1981 (1 Dec). New Year's Greetings. P 13×13½.
1652   **1074** 40y. multicoloured   70   10

1079 Bank of Japan, Kyoto
Branch (now museum)

1080 Saiseikan
Hospital, Yamagata

(Des Z. Chikaoka. Recess and photo)

1982 (10 Mar). Modern Western-style Architecture (4th series). P 13.
1658   **1079** 60y. multicoloured ....   1·00   30
1659   **1080** 60y. multicoloured ....   1·00   30

1075 St. John's
Church, Inuyama

1076 Military Exercise Hall,
Sapporo Agricultural School

(Des Z. Chikaoka. Recess and photo)

1982 (29 Jan). Modern Western-style Architecture (3rd series). P 13.
1654   **1075** 60y. multicoloured ....   1·00   30
1655   **1076** 60y. multicoloured ....   1·00   30

1081 Gorilla and
Greater Flamingo

1082 Lion and King
Penguins

1077 "Yoritomo in a Cave" (Seison
Maeda)

1083 Giant Panda
and Indian Elephants

1084 Giraffe and
Common Zebras

(Des M. Morita. Photo)

1982 (20 Mar). Centenary of Ueno Zoo. P 13.
1660   **1081** 60y. multicoloured   90   25
    a. Horiz strip of 4. Nos 1660/3.....   6·00
1661   **1082** 60y. multicoloured   90   25
1662   **1083** 60y. multicoloured   90   25
1663   **1084** 60y. multicoloured   90   25
1660/1663 Set of 4..   3·25   90
    Nos. 1660/3 were issued together in horizontal se-tenant strips of
four within the sheet.

1078 "Posters on a Terrace" (Yuzo Saeki)

1085 "Enjoying Snow Landscape of **1086**
Matsuchi-yama" (Torii Kiyonaga)

(Des Y. Kikuchi. Photo)

1982 (20 Apr). Philatelic Week. P 13½.
1664 **1085** 60y. multicoloured 90 30
   a. Horiz pair. Nos. 1664/5 .... 1·90 1·50
1665 **1086** 60y. multicoloured 90 30
Nos. 1664/5 were issued together in horizontal *se-tenant* pairs within the sheet, each pair forming a composite design.

1087 Lion   **1088** Arbor
Festival
Emblem and
Blue and White
Flycatcher

(Des Y. Higashitsunoi. Photo)

1982 (15 May). Tenth Anniv of Return of Okinawa (Ryukyu Islands). P 13.
1666 **1087** 60y. multicoloured 90 25

(Des T. Amano Photo)

1982 (22 May). National Afforestation Campaign. P 13×13½.
1667 **1088** 60y. multicoloured..................... 1·20 25

1089 Noh Mask

(Des M. Morita. Photo)

1982 (24 May). 16th World Dermatology Congress, Tokyo. P 13.
1668 **1089** 60y. multicoloured 90 25

1090 Divine Gate   **1091** Former Iwasaki Mansion,
of Oyama Shrine,   Taito-ku, Tokyo (now Training
Kanazawa   Institute)

(Des Z. Chikaoka. Recess and photo)

1982 (12 June). Modern Western-style Architecture (5th series). P 13.
1669 **1090** 60y. multicoloured 90 25
1670 **1091** 60y. multicoloured 90 25

1092 "SL 1290" Steam   **1093** Super-express Diesel
Locomotive

(Des F. Otani. Photo)

1982 (23 June). Opening of Tohoku-Shinkansen Railway Line. P 13.
1671 **1092** 60y. multicoloured .... 1·10 25
   a. Pair. Nos. 1671/2..................... 2·30 60
1672 **1093** 60y. multicoloured .... 1·10 25
Nos. 1671/2 were issued together in *se-tenant* pairs within the sheet.

1094 Gull and   **1095** Bird carrying
Balloon with   Letter to Fairy
Letter

(Des T. Shimizu (40y.), Moe Nagata (60y.). Photo)

1982 (23 July). Letter Writing Day. P 13×13½ (40y.) or 13½×13 (60y.).
1673 **1094** 40y. multicoloured 90 30
1674 **1095** 60y. multicoloured .... 1·30 25

1103 16th-century
Portuguese Galleon and
World Map

1104 "T'ien T'an in the
Clouds" (Ryuzaburo Umehara)

(Des F. Otani. Photo)

1982 (20 Sept). 400th Anniv of Christian Boys' Delegation to Europe.
P 13½.
1682   **1103** 60y. multicoloured ....   1·20   25

1096 "Garment
patterned with Irises"
(Saburosuke Okada)

1097 "Buddhisattva
Kannon on Potalaka
Island" (Tessai Tomioka)

(Des Y. Kikuchi. Photo)

1982 (29 Sept). Tenth Anniv of Restoration of Diplomatic Relations
with China. P 13.
1683   **1104** 60y. multicoloured ....   1·00   30

(Des Y. Kikuchi. Photo)

1982 (5 Aug). Modern Japanese Art (13th series). P 13½.
1675   **1096** 60y. multicoloured   90   25
1676   **1097** 60y. multicoloured   90   25

1098 Wreath
(condolences)

1099 Folded
Paper Crane
(congratulations)

1100 Pine,
Plum and
Bamboo
Blossom
(congratulations)

(Des H. Otsuka (1677), T. Yamanouchi (others). Photo)

1982 (23 Aug). Special Correspondence Stamps. P 13×13½.
1677   **1098** 60y. multicoloured ....   1·20   30
1678   **1099** 60y. multicoloured ....   1·20   30
1679   **1100** 70y. multicoloured ....   1·40   30
1677/1679 Set of 3 ....   3·50   80
     For 40y. stamps see Nos. 1722/3, for 41, 62 and 72y. values see Nos.
2013/16 and for 50, 80 and 90y. values see Nos. 2289/92.

1105 Table Tennis
and Monument of
the Meet

1106 "Amusement"
(wooden doll by
Goyo Hirata)

(Des H. Otsuka. Photo)

1982 (2 Oct). 37th National Athletic Meeting, Matsue. P 13.
1684   **1105** 40y. multicoloured   70   30

(Des M. Morita. Photo)

1982 (6 Oct). International Correspondence Week. P 13.
1685   **1106** 130y. multicoloured ....   1·90   30

1101 Hokkaido Prefectural
Building, Sapporo

1102 Saigo Tsugumichi
Mansion, Meguro (now in
Inuyama)

(Des Z. Chikaoka. Recess and photo)

1982 (10 Sept). Modern Western-style Architecture (6th series) P 13.
1680   **1101** 60y. multicoloured ....   1·40   40
1681   **1102** 60y. multicoloured ....   1·40   40

1107 "The Bank of Japan
near Eitaibashi in Snow"
(Yasuji Inoue)

(Des Y. Kikuchi. Recess and photo)

1982 (12 Oct). Centenary of Central Bank System. P 13½.
1686   **1107** 60y. multicoloured .... 1·00   30

1108 Joetsu Express Train   **1109** "ED16" Electric
Locomotive

(Des F. Otani. Photo)

1982 (15 Nov). Opening of Joetsu–Shinkansen Railway Line. P 13½.
1687   **1108** 60y. multicoloured .... 1·10   25
        a. Pair. Nos. 1687/8 .... 2·30   60
1688   **1109** 60y. multicoloured .... 1·10   25
   Nos. 1687/8 were issued together in *se-tenant* pairs within the
sheet.

1110 "Srimahadevi"   **1111** "Saltimbanque"
(Shiko Munakata)   (Seiji Togo)

(Des K. Kikuchi. Photo)

1982 (24 Nov). Modern Japanese Art (14th series). P 13½.
1689   **1110** 60y. multicoloured 90   25
1690   **1111** 60y. multicoloured 90   25

1112 "Kintaro
on a Wild Boar"
(clay Tsutsumi
doll)

(Des M. Morita. Photo)

1982 (1 Dec). New Year's Greetings. P 13×13½.
1691   **1112** 40y. multicoloured 70   25

1113 "Snowstorm"   **1114** "Spiraea and
(Shinsui Ito)   Calla in a Persian Vase"
                     (Zenzaburo Kojima)

(Des Y. Kikuchi. Photo)

1983 (24 Jan). Modern Japanese Art (15th series). P 13½.
1693   **1113** 60y. multicoloured 90   25
1694   **1114** 60y. multicoloured 90   25

1115 Fujimura   **1116** Porch of Sakuranomiya
Memorial Hall, Kofu   Public Hall, Osaka
(formerly Mutsuzawa
School)

(Des Z. Chikaoka. Recess and photo)

1983 (15 Feb). Modern Western-style Architecture (7th series). P 13.
1695   **1115** 60y. multicoloured 90   25
1696   **1116** 60y. multicoloured 90   25

1117 "Selflessness"   **1118** "Aged Monkey"
(Taikan Yokoyama)   (wood carving, Koun
                     Takamura)

(Des Y. Kikuchi. Photo (1697), recess and photo (1698))

1983 (10 Mar). Modern Japanese Art (16th series). P 13½.
1697   **1117** 60y. multicoloured .... 1·00   30
1698   **1118** 60y. multicoloured .... 1·00   30

1119 Museum and Japanese Characters representing History, Folklore and Antiquity

(Des F. Otani. Photo)

1983 (16 Mar). Opening of National Museum of History and Folklore. P 13.

1699	**1119** 60y. multicoloured	....	1·00	30

1123 Colt and Racehorse   **1124** Rabbit and Empty Can

(Des M. Morita. Photo)

1983 (28 May). 50th Nippon Derby. P 13.

1703	**1123** 60y. multicoloured	....	1·20	25

(Des T. Shimizu. Photo)

1983 (13 June). Islands Clean-up Campaign. P 13½.

1704	**1124** 60y. multicoloured	....	1·20	25

1120   "Women working in the Kitchen" (Utamaro Kitagawa)   **1121**

(Des Y. Kikuchi. Photo)

1983 (20 Apr). Philatelic Week. P 13½.

1700	**1120** 60y. multicoloured	....	1·00	30
	a. Horiz pair. Nos. 1700/1	....	2·10	1·60
1701	**1121** 60y. multicoloured	....	1·00	30

Nos. 1700/1 were issued together in horizontal *se-tenant* pairs within the sheet, each pair forming a composite design.

1125 Hohei-kan House (Wedding Hall), Sapporo   **1126** Glover House, Nagasaki

(Des Z. Chikaoka. Recess and photo)

1983 (23 June). Modern Western-style Architecture (8th series). P 13.

1705	**1125** 60y. multicoloured	....	90	25
1706	**1126** 60y. multicoloured	....	90	25

1127 First issue and Nihonbashi Bulletin Board   **1128** Boy with Letter   **1129** Fairy with Letter

(Des Y. Higashitsunoi. Recess and photo)

1983 (2 July). Centenary of *Government Journal*. P 13.

1707	**1127** 60y. multicoloured	....	1·00	30

1122 *Hiba arborvitae,* Japanese Black Fritillary and Hakusan Mountains

(Des M. Hisano. Photo)

1983 (21 May). National Afforestation Campaign. P 13½.

1702	**1122** 60y. multicoloured	....	1·00	30

(Des M. Hisano (40y.), Moe Nagata (60y.). Photo)

1983 (23 July). Letter Writing Day. P 13×13½ (40y.) or 13½×13 (60y.).

1708	**1128** 40y. multicoloured	....	70	30
1709	**1129** 60y. multicoloured	....	1·00	25

1130 59th Bank, Hirosaki

1131 Auditorium of
Gakushuin Elementary
School (now in Narita)

(Des Z. Chikaoka. Recess and photo)

1983 (15 Aug). Modern Western-style Architecture (9th series). P 13.
1710 **1130** 60y. multicoloured 90 25
1711 **1131** 60y. multicoloured 90 25

1132 Theatre and Noh
Player

(Des S. Watanabe. Photo)

1983 (14 Sept). Opening of National Noh Theatre, Tokyo. P 13.
1712 **1132** 60y. multicoloured .... 1·00 30

1133 Okinawa Rail
(*Rallus okinawae*)

1134 Blakiston's Fish Owl
(*Ketupa blakistoni*)

(Des M. Morita. Recess and photo (1713), photo (1714))

1983 (22 Sept). Endangered Birds (1st series). P 13.
1713 **1133** 60y. multicoloured .... 1·50 30
1714 **1134** 60y. multicoloured .... 1·50 30
See also Nos. 1724/5, 1729/30, 1735/6, 1742/3 and **MS**1768.

1135 "Chi-kyu"
(paper doll by Juzo
Kagoshima)

1136 Naginata Player
and Myogi Mountains

(Des M. Morita. Photo)

1983 (6 Oct). International Correspondence Week. P 13.
1715 **1135** 130y. multicoloured .... 1·90 40

(Des T. Yamanouchi. Photo)

1983 (15 Oct). 38th National Athletic Meeting, Gumman. P 13.
1716 **1136** 40y. multicoloured 70 30

1137 Ferris Wheel

1138 Children
supporting Globe

(Des H. Matsuda, K. Kasugai, F. Otani, Y. Kikuchi. Photo)

1983 (17 Oct). World Communications Year. P 13½ (1717) or 13×13½
(1718).
1717 **1137** 60y. multicoloured .... 1·00 30
1718 **1138** 60y. multicoloured .... 1·00 30

1139 Park and Monument

(Des M. Hisano. Photo)

1983 (26 Oct). Opening of Showa Memorial National Park. P 13.
1719 **1139** 60y. multicoloured .... 1·00 25

1140 Congress
Emblem and
Mouth Mirror

1141 *Shirase*

(Des Y. Kikuchi. Photo)

1983 (14 Nov). 71st World Dental Congress, Tokyo. P 13½.
1720 **1140** 60y. multicoloured .... 1·00 30

(Des S. Watanabe. Photo)

1983 (14 Nov). Maiden Voyage of Antarctic Research Ship *Shirase*.
P 13½.
1721 **1141** 60y. multicoloured .... 2·50 25

1983 (22 Nov). Special Correspondence Stamps. P 13×13½.
1722 **1098** 40y. multicoloured 80 30
1723 **1099** 40y. multicoloured 80 30

1142 Pryer's
Woodpecker
(*Sapheopipo noguchii*)

1143 Canada Goose (*Branta
canadensis leucopareia*)

(Des M. Morita. Photo (1724), recess and photo (1725))

1983 (25 Nov). Endangered Birds (2nd series). P 13.
1724	**1142** 60y. multicoloured	1·40	25
1725	**1143** 60y. multicoloured	1·40	25

1144 "Mouse
riding Small
Hammer" (folk
toy)

1145 Human Rights
Emblem

(Des M. Morita. Photo)

1983 (1 Dec). New Year's Greetings. P 13×13½.
1726	**1144** 40y. multicoloured	70	25

(Des M. Hisano. Photo)

1983 (5 Dec). 35th Anniv of Declaration of Human Rights. P 13½.
1728	**1145** 60y. multicoloured	70	25

1146 Japanese Marsh Warbler
(*Megalurus pryeri pryeri*)

1147 Crested Serpent
Eagle *Spilornis* (*cheela
perplexus*)

(Des M. Morita. Recess and photo (1729), photo (1730))

1984 (26 Jan). Endangered Birds (3rd series). P 13.
1729	**1146** 60y. multicoloured	1·00	30
1730	**1147** 60y. multicoloured	1·50	25

For No. 1730 in miniature sheet see No. **MS**1768.

1148 Exhibition Emblem
and Mascot

(Des T. Shimizu. Photo)

1984 (10 Feb). "Expo '85" International Science and Technology
Exhibition, Tsukuba (1985). P 13½.
1731	**1148** 60y.+10y. multicoloured	1·50	25

1149 Bank of Japan Head
Office

1150 Hunter House, Kobe

(Des Z. Chikaoka. Recess and photo)

1984 (16 Feb). Modern Western-style Architecture (10th series). P 13.
1732	**1149** 60y. multicoloured	90	25
1733	**1150** 60y. multicoloured	90	25

1151 Japanese-style Cake
and Bamboo Tea Whisk

(Des M. Kimura. Photo)

1984 (24 Feb). 20th Confectionery Fair, Tokyo. P 13½.
1734	**1151** 60y. multicoloured	1·00	30

1152 Black Wood
Pigeon (*Columba
janthina nitens*)

1153 Spotted Greenshank
(*Tringa guttifer*)

(Des M. Morita. Litho (1735), Photo (1736))

1984 (15 Mar). Endangered Birds (4th series). P 13.
1735	**1152** 60y. multicoloured	1·50	25
1736	**1153** 60y. multicoloured	1·50	25

1154 Bunraku Puppet and Theatre

(Des T. Shimizu. Photo)

1984 (6 Apr). Opening of National Bunraku Theatre, Osaka. P 13½.
1737 **1154** 60y. multicoloured .... 1·40 40

1155 "Otani Oniji as Edobeh" (Toshusai Sharaku)

1156 "Iwai Hanshiro IV as Shigenoi" (Toshusai Sharaku)

(Des Y. Kikuchi. Recess and photo)

1984 (20 Apr). Philatelic Week. P 13½.
1738 **1155** 60y. multicoloured .... 1·00 30
     a. Horiz pair. Nos. 1738/9 .... 2·10 1·60
1739 **1156** 60y. multicoloured .... 1·00 30
Nos. 1738/9 were issued together in horizontal *se-tenant* pairs within the sheet.

1157 Kaikozu Tree and Sakura Volcano

1158 "Himawari" Weather Satellite and Chart

(Des M. Hisano. Photo)

1984 (19 May). National Afforestation Campaign. P 13½.
1740 **1157** 60y. multicoloured .... 1·00 30

(Des F. Otani. Photo)

1984 (1 June). Centenary of National Weather Forecasts. P 13.
1741 **1158** 60y. multicoloured .... 1·00 25

1159 White-backed Woodpecker (*Dencrocopos leucotos owstoni*)

1160 Peregrine Falcon (*Falco peregrinus fruitii*)

(Des M. Morita. Recess and photo (1742), photo (1743))

1984 (22 June). Endangered Birds (5th series). P 13.
1742 **1159** 60y. multicoloured .... 1·50 25
1743 **1160** 60y. multicoloured .... 1·50 25
For No. 1743 in miniature sheet see No. **MS**1768.

1161 Doves

1162 Birds in Tree

1163 Bird and Flowers

(Des K. Takeara. Photo)

1984 (16 July). Federation of U.N.E.S.C.O. Clubs and Associations World Congress, Sendai. P 13.
1744 **1181** 60y. multicoloured .... 1·20 25

(Des T. Amano (40y.), Moe Nagata (60y.). Photo

1984 (23 July). Letter Writing Day. P 13×13½ (40y.) or 13½×13 (60y.).
1745 **1162** 40y. multicoloured 90 30
1746 **1163** 60y. multicoloured .... 1·30 25

1164 "Fire and Wind" (Motomi Hagimoto)

1165 "Bonds' (Noboru Kanda)

(Des Y. Kikuchi (40y.), F. Otani (60y.). Photo)

1984 (23 Aug). Disaster Prevention Week. P 13.
1747 **1164** 40y. multicoloured 70 30
1748 **1165** 60y. black and yellow .... 1·00 25

1166 Leontopodium fauriei

1167 Lagotis glauca

(Des Y. Higashitsunoi. Recess and photo)

1984 (27 Aug). Alpine Plants (1st series). P 13.
1749	**1166**	60y. multicoloured	1·00	30
1750	**1167**	60y. multicoloured	1·00	30

See also Nos. 1752/3, 1769/70, 1775/6, 1802/3, 1813/14 and 1827/8.

1168 Basho's Crossroads, Sendai

(Des F. Otani. Photo)

1984 (1 Sept). Sixth International Virology Congress, Sendai. P 13.
1751 **1168** 60y. multicoloured 90   25

1169 Globe Flower (Trollius riederianus)

1170 Primula cuneifolia

(Des Y. Higashitsunoi. Recess and photo)

1984 (21 Sept). Alpine Plants (2nd series). P 13.
1752 **1169** 60y. multicoloured .... 1·00   30
1753 **1170** 60y. multicoloured .... 1·00   30

1171 Logo

1172 "Serenity" (doll by Ryujo Hori)

(Des T. Shimizu. Photo)

1984 (1 Oct). Electronic Mail. P 13½×13.
1754 **1171** 500y. multicoloured .... 14·50   6·25

(Des M. Morita. Photo)

1984 (6 Oct). International Correspondence Week. P 13.
1755 **1172** 130y. multicoloured .... 1·90   30

1173 Silver Pavilion, Jisho Temple

1174 Hockey and East Pagoda of Yakushi Temple

(Des T. Asada. Photo)

1984 (8 Oct). 17th International Internal Medicine Congress, Kyoto City. P 13.
1756 **1173** 60y. multicoloured 90   25

(Des H. Otsuka. Photo)

1984 (12 Oct). 39th National Athletic Meeting, Nara. P 13.
1757 **1174** 40y. multicoloured 70   30

1175 Birds in Tree

1176 Flowers

1177 Chrysanthemums Design

1178 Leaf and Bird Design

(Des Y. Kikuchi. Photo)

1984 (2 Nov). Traditional Crafts (1st series). Kutani Porcelain Plates and Nishijin Silk Weavings. P 13.
1758	**1175**	60y. multicoloured	90	25
		a. Pair. Nos. 1758/9	1·90	55
1759	**1176**	60y. multicoloured	90	25
1760	**1177**	60y. multicoloured	90	25
		a. Pair. Nos. 1760/1	1·90	55
1761	**1178**	60y. multicoloured	90	25
1758/1761	Set of 4		3·25	90

Nos. 1758/9 and 1760/1 were issued together in se-tenant pairs within their sheets.

See also Nos. 1771/4, 1787/90, 1795/8, 1805/8, 1820/3 and 1829/32.

1179 Eiji Sawamura (pitcher)　**1180** Masaru Kageura (striker)　**1181** Ball, Birds and Matsutaro Shoriki (founder)

(Des K. Takeara (1764), Y. Higashitsunoi (others). Photo)

1984 (15 Nov). 50th Anniv of Japan Tokyo Baseball Club. P 13½.
1762　**1179** 60y. multicoloured .... 90　25
　　　a. Block of 4. Nos 1762/3 and
　　　　1764×2 .... 2·00　60
1763　**1180** 60y. multicoloured .... 90　25
1764　**1181** 60y. multicoloured .... 90　25
1762/1764　*Set of 3* .... 2·40　70
　Nos. 1762/4 were issued together in sheetlets of 20 stamps (4×5), containing six examples each of Nos. 1762/3 and eight examples of No. 1764. The 1st, 3rd and 5th horizontal rows contain *se-tenant* pairs of Nos. 1762 and 1763; the 2nd and 4th rows contain No. 1764.

1182 Workers' Profiles and Symbols　**1183** Bamboo Ox (Sakushu folk toy)

(Des T. Amano. Photo)

1984 (20 Nov). Centenary of Technical Education. P 13.
1765　**1182** 60y. multicoloured .... 1·20　25

(Des M. Morita. Photo)

1984 (1 Dec). New Year's Greetings. P 13½×13.
1766　**1183** 40y. multicoloured .... 1·10　30
　No. 1767 *is vacant.*

(Des M. Morita. Recess and photo)

1984 (10 Dec). Endangered Birds (6th series). Sheet 93×120 mm. P 13.
MS1768 **1134** 60y. slate-blue; **1147** 60y. slate-purple;
　1160 60y. black .... 6·00　4·00

1184 *Rhododendron aureum*　**1185** *Oxytropis nigrescens*

(Des M. Yoshikawa (1769), Y. Higashitsunoi (1770). Recess and photo)

1985 (25 Jan). Alpine Plants (3rd series). P 13.
1769　**1184** 60y. multicoloured .... 1·00　30
1770　**1185** 60y. multicoloured .... 1·00　30

1186 Dolls　**1187** Doll with Cat

1188 Bird and Flower Design　**1189** Birds and Chrysanthemums Design

(Des Y. Kikuchi. Photo)

1985 (15 Feb). Traditional Crafts (2nd series). Edo Kimekomi Dolls and Okinawa Bingata Cloth. P 13.
1771　**1186** 60y. multicoloured .... 1·00　30
　　　a. Pair. Nos. 1771/2 .... 3·00　2·30
1772　**1187** 60y. multicoloured .... 1·00　30
1773　**1188** 60y. multicoloured .... 1·00　30
　　　a. Pair. Nos. 1773/4 .... 3·00　2·30
1774　**1189** 60y. multicoloured .... 1·00　30
1771/1774　*Set of 4* .... 3·50　1·10
　Nos. 1771/2 and 1773/4 were issued together in *se-tenant* pairs within their sheets.

1190 *Dryas octopetala*　**1191** *Draba japonica*

(Des H. Otsuka (1775), S. Watanabe (1776). Recess and photo)

1985 (28 Feb). Alpine Plants (4th series). P 13.
1775　**1190** 60y. multicoloured .... 1·00　30
1776　**1191** 60y. multicoloured .... 1·00　30

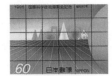

1192 Theme Pavilion and Symbol Tower

1193 Geometric City

(Des T. Shimizu and K. Takeara. Photo)

1985 (16 Mar). "EXPO '85" World's Fair, Tsukuba. P 13.

1777	**1192**	40y. multicoloured	80	30
1778	**1193**	60y. multicoloured	90	30
MS1779	144×93 mm. Nos. 1777/8		3·25	2·50

1194 University Buildings, Chiba City, and Transmitter

1195 Aerial and Communication Lines

(Des M. Morita. Litho)

1985 (1 Apr). Inauguration of University of the Air. P 13½.

1780	**1194**	60y. multicoloured	1·00	25

(Des K. Takeara. Photo)

1985 (1 Apr). Privatisation of Nippon Telegraph and Telephone Corporation. P 13½.

1781	**1195**	60y. multicoloured	1·00	25

1196 Map of Japan (after Teixeira's map in Ortelius's *Atlas*, 1595)

1197 Korekiyo Takahashi (proposer of Patent Laws)

(Des F. Otani. Photo)

1985 (5 Apr). World Import Fair, Nagoya. P 13.

1782	**1196**	60y. multicoloured	1·20	25

(Des H. Otsuka. Photo)

1985 (18 Apr). Centenary of Industrial Patents System. P 13½.

1783	**1197**	60y. multicoloured	90	25

1198 "Winter in the North" (Yumeji Takehisa)

1199 "Toward the Morning Light" (Yumeji Takehisa)

(Des Y. Kikuchi. Photo)

1985 (20 Apr). Philatelic Week. P 13.

1784	**1198**	60y. multicoloured	90	30
		a. Pair. Nos. 1784/5	2·20	1·70
1785	**1199**	60y. multicoloured	90	30

Nos. 1784/5 were issued together in *se-tenant* pairs within the sheet.

1200 Mt. Aso and Gentian

(Des M. Hisano. Photo)

1985 (10 May). National Afforestation Campaign. P 13½.

1786	**1200**	60y. multicoloured	1·20	25

1201 Hawk

1202 Ducks

1203 Bowl

1204 Plate

(Des Y. Kikuchi. Photo)

1985 (23 May). Traditional Crafts (3rd series). Yew Wood Carvings and Arita Porcelain. P 13.

1787	**1201**	60y. multicoloured	1·00	30
		a. Pair. Nos. 1787/8	3·00	2·30
1788	**1202**	60y. multicoloured	1·00	30
1789	**1203**	60y. multicoloured	1·00	30
		a. Pair. Nos. 1789/90	3·00	2·30
1790	**1204**	60y. multicoloured	1·00	30
1787/1790	*Set of 4*		3·50	1·10

Nos. 1787/8 and 1789/90 were issued together in *se-tenant* pairs within their sheets.

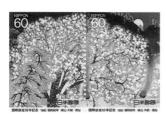

| 1205 | "Cherry Trees at Night" | 1206 |
| | (Taikan Yokoyama) | |

(Des M. Morita. Photo)

1985 (1 June). 50th Anniv of Radio Japan (overseas broadcasting station). P 13.

1791	**1205** 60y. multicoloured	1·00	30
	a. Horiz pair. Nos. 1791/2	2·10	65
1792	**1206** 60y. multicoloured	1·00	30

Nos. 1791/2 were issued together in horizontal se-tenant pairs within the sheet, each pair forming a composite design.

1207 Maeshima and	1208 Bridge
"Tokyo Post Office"	
(Hiroshige III)	

(Des M. Morita. Recess and photo)

1985 (5 June). 150th Birth Anniv of Baron Hisoka Maeshima (first Postmaster-General). P 13.

| 1793 | **1207** 60y. multicoloured | 90 | 25 |

(Des H. Otsuka. Photo)

1985 (7 June). Opening of Great Naruto Bridge. P 13½.

| 1794 | **1208** 60y. multicoloured | 90 | 25 |

| 1209 Weaving | 1210 Weaving |

| 1211 Dish | 1212 Panel |

(Des Y. Kikuchi. Photo)

1985 (24 June). Traditional Crafts (4th series). Ojiya Linen Weavings and Kamakura Lacquered Wood Carvings. P 13.

1795	**1209** 60y. multicoloured	90	30
	a. Pair. Nos. 1795/6	3·50	2·75
1796	**1210** 60y. multicoloured	90	30
1797	**1211** 60y. multicoloured	90	30
	a. Pair. Nos. 1797/8	3·50	2·75
1798	**1212** 60y. multicoloured	90	30
1795/1798	Set of 4	3·25	1·10

Nos. 1795/6 and 1797/8 were issued together in se-tenant pairs within their sheets.

1213 Silhouette of Laurel and Couple

(Des K. Takeara. Photo)

1985 (20 July). International Youth Year. P 13.

| 1799 | **1213** 60y. multicoloured | 90 | 25 |

| 1214 Owl | 1215 Girl holding |
| with Letter | Bird, Letter and Cat |

(Des E. Uchida (40y.), T. Murakami (60y.). Photo)

1985 (23 July). Letter Writing Day. P 13×13½ (40y.) or 13½×13 (60y.).

| 1800 | **1214** 40y. multicoloured | 70 | 30 |
| 1801 | **1215** 60y. multicoloured | 1·00 | 30 |

| 1216 Gentian | 1217 Callianthemum |
| (Gentiana nipponica) | insigne |

(Des Y. Higashitsunoi (1802), M. Morita (1803). Recess and photo)

1985 (31 July). Alpine Plants (5th series). P 13.

| 1802 | **1216** 60y. multicoloured | 1·00 | 30 |
| 1803 | **1217** 60y. multicoloured | 1·00 | 30 |

1218 Logo

(Des F. Otani. Photo)

1985 (1 Aug). Electronic Mail. P 13×13½.
1804 **1218** 500y. multicoloured .... 9·25 95

1219 Noh Theatre Actor   **1220** Mother with Child

1221 Tea Kettle with Fish Design   **1222** Tea Kettle

(Des Y. Kikuchi. Photo (1805/6), recess and photo (1807/8)

1985 (8 Aug). Traditional Crafts (5th series). Hakata Clay Figurines and Nambu Iron Ware. P 13.
1805 **1219** 60y. multicoloured 90 30
    a. Pair. Nos. 1805/6............................. 2·00 1·60
1806 **1220** 60y. multicoloured 90 30
1807 **1221** 60y. multicoloured 90 30
    a. Pair Nos. 1807/8............................. 2·00 1·60
1808 **1222** 60y. multicoloured 90 30
1805/1808 Set of 4 .... 3·25 1·10
Nos. 1805/6 and 1807/8 were issued together in *se-tenant* pairs within their sheets.

1223 Hideki Yukawa (physicist) and Meson Field   **1224** Gymnasts

(Des K. Takeara. Photo)

1985 (15 Aug). 50th Anniv of Yukawa's Meson Theory. P 13.
1809 **1223** 60y. multicoloured 90 25

(Des T. Amano. Photo)

1985 (24 Aug). University Games, Kobe. P 13½.
1810 **1224** 60y. multicoloured 90 25

1225 Competitor filing Test Piece   **1226** *Hibiscus syriacus* (national flower of S. Korea)

(Des K. Takeara. Photo)

1985 (13 Sept). 28th International Vocational Training Competition, Osaka. P 13½.
1811 **1225** 40y. multicoloured 80 30

(Des M. Morita. Photo)

1985 (18 Sept). 20th Anniv of Japan–South Korea Diplomatic Relations. P 13½.
1812 **1226** 60y. multicoloured .... 1·00 30

1227 *Viola crassa*   **1228** *Campanula chamissonis*

(Des H. Otsuka (1813), S. Watanabe (1814). Recess and photo)

1985 (27 Sept). Alpine Plants (6th series). P 13.
1813 **1227** 60y. multicoloured .... 1·00 30
1814 **1228** 60y. multicoloured .... 1·00 30

1229 Tunnels and Section through Mt. Tanigawa   **1230** "Seisen" (doll by Goyo Hirata)

(Des F. Otani. Photo)

1985 (2 Oct). Opening of North-bound Kan-Etsu Tunnel. P 13.
1815 **1229** 60y. multicoloured 90 25

(Des M. Morita. Photo)

1985 (7 Oct). International Correspondence Week. P 13.
1816 **1230** 130y. multicoloured .... 1·90 30

1231 Youth helping
African Farmer

(Des Y. Kikuchi. Litho)

1985 (9 Oct). 20th Anniv of Japanese Overseas Co-operation Volunteers. P 13.

1817	**1231**	60y. multicoloured	90	25

1232 Honey Bee on
Strawberry Blossom

1233 Handball Player
and Mt. Daisen

(Des T. Amano. Photo)

1985 (9 Oct). 30th International Bee Keeping Congress, Nagoya. P 13.

1818	**1232**	60y. multicoloured	1·20	25

(Des T. Yamanouchi. Photo)

1985 (19 Oct). 40th National Athletic Meeting, Tottori. P 13.

1819	**1233**	40y. multicoloured	1·10	40

1234 Table

1235 Bowl

1236 Lantern on
Column

1237 Lantern

(Des Y. Kikuchi. Photo (1820/1), recess and photo (1822/3))

1985 (15 Nov). Traditional Crafts (6th series). Wajima Lacquerware and Izumo Sandstone Lanterns. P 13.

1820	**1234**	60y. multicoloured	90	30
		a. Pair. Nos. 1820/1		
1821	**1235**	60y. multicoloured	90	30
1822	**1236**	60y. multicoloured	90	30
		a. Pair. Nos. 1822/3		
1823	**1237**	60y. multicoloured	90	30
1820/1823		Set of 4	3·25	1·10

Nos. 1820/1 and 1822/3 were issued together in *se-tenant* pairs within their sheets.

1238 Osaka
Papier-mâché
Tiger

1239 Cabinet Emblem and
Official Seal

(Des M. Morita. Photo)

1985 (2 Dec). New Year's Greetings. P 13×13½.

1824	**1238**	40y. multicoloured	70	25

No. 1825 is vacant.

(Des M. Morita. Litho)

1985 (20 Dec). Centenary of Cabinet System of Government. P 13½.

1826	**1239**	60y. multicoloured	90	25

1240 Diapensia
lapponica

1241 Pedicularis
apodochila

(Des M. Yoshikawa (1827), Y. Higashitsunoi (1828). Recess and photo)

1986 (13 Feb). Alpine Plants (7th series). P 13.

1827	**1240**	60y. multicoloured	1·00	30
1828	**1241**	60y. multicoloured	1·00	30

1242 Fan with
Tree Design

1243 Fan with
Flower Design

1244 Flask with   **1245** Tea Caddy
Fish Pattern

(Des Y. Kikuchi. Photo)

1986 (13 Mar). Traditional Crafts (7th series). Kyoto Fans and Tobe
Porcelain. P 13.
1829	**1242**	60y. multicoloured	90	30
		a. Pair. Nos. 1829/30	2·00	1·60
1830	**1243**	60y. multicoloured	90	30
1831	**1244**	60y. multicoloured	90	30
		a. Pair. Nos. 1831/2	2·00	1·60
1832	**1245**	60y. multicoloured	90	30
1829/1832		*Set of 4*	3·25	1·10

Nos. 1829/30 and 1831/2 were issued together in *se-tenant* pairs
within their sheets.

1246 Gothic Style
Finial and
"Golden Norm"

(Des T. Amano. Photo)

1986 (9 Apr). Centenary of Architecture Institute, Shiba, Tokyo. P 13.
1833	**1246**	60y. multicoloured	1·00	30

1247 Standing Lady   **1248** Seated Lady

(Des Y. Kikuchi. Photo)

1986 (15 Apr). Philatelic Week. Details of "South of Hateruma" by
Kaigetsu Kikuchi. P 13.
1834	**1247**	60y. multicoloured	1·00	30
		a. Horiz pair. Nos. 1834/5	2·10	65
1835	**1248**	60y. multicoloured	1·00	30

Nos. 1834/5 were issued together in horizontal *se-tenant* pairs
within the sheet.

1249 Phoenix and   **1250** Imperial Palace Ridge
Enthronement Hall,   Decoration
Kyoto Palace

(Des H. Otsuka (1836), S. Watanabe (1837), Y. Kikuchi (**MS**1838).
Photo)

1986 (28 Apr). 60th Anniv of Emperor Hirohito's Accession. P 13.
1836	**1249**	60y. multicoloured	1·00	30
1837	**1250**	60y. multicoloured	1·00	30
MS1838		144×93 mm. Nos. 1836/7	2·50	1·90

1251 "Mt. Fuji in Early   **1252** Bull-headed
Morning" (Yukihiko Yasuda) Shrike in Reeds

(Des Y. Aoki. Photo)

1986 (2 May). 12th Economic Summit of Industrialised Countries,
Tokyo. P 13.
1839	**1251**	60y. multicoloured	1·00	30

(Des M. Hisano. Photo)

1986 (9 May). National Afforestation Campaign. P 13½.
1840	**1252**	60y. multicoloured	1·20	25

1253 Capsule, Tablets and   **1254** Map and Clock
Structure of Toluene

(Des T. Shimizu. Photo)

1986 (25 June). Centenary of Japanese Pharmacopoeia. P 13½.
1841	**1253**	60y. multicoloured	90	25

(Des K. Takeara Litho)

1986 (11 July). Centenary of Japanese Standard Time. P 13.
1842	**1254**	60y. multicoloured	1·00	30

1255 Bird on
Chair and
Letter on Table

1256 Girl
holding Rabbit
and Letter

(Des E. Uchida (40y.), T. Murakami (60y.). Photo)

1986 (23 July–Aug). Letter Writing Day. P 13×13½.
1843 **1255** 40y. multicoloured 90   25
    a. Booklet pane Nos. 1843×5 and
       1844×5 (23.8) .... 6·00
1844 **1256** 60y. multicoloured .... 1·30   25
  The booklet pane has its outer edges imperforate, giving stamps
with one or two adjacent sides imperforate.
  No. 1845 is vacant.

1257 Yataro Iwasaki, Makoto
Kondo and Cadet Ship
Nippon Maru II

(Des M. Hisano. Photo)

1986 (26 July). 110th Anniv of Merchant Navy Education. P 13.
1846 **1257** 60y. multicoloured .... 1·20   25

1258 Asian Apollo
(*Parnassius
eversmanni*)

1259 Shieldbug
(*Poecilocoris lewisi*)

1260 Longhorn Beetle
(*Rosalia batesi*)

1261 *Epiophlebia
superstes*

(Des M. Morita. Recess and photo)

1986 (30 July). Insects (1st series). P 13.
1847 **1258** 60y. multicoloured .... 1·50   30
    a. Pair. Nos. 1847/8 .... 3·25   2·30
1848 **1259** 60y. multicoloured .... 1·50   30
1849 **1260** 60y. multicoloured .... 1·50   30
    a. Pair. Nos. 1849/50 .... 3·25   2·30
1850 **1261** 60y. multicoloured .... 1·50   30
1847/1850 *Set of 4* .... 5·50   1·10
  Nos. 1847/8 and 1849/50 were issued together in *se-tenant* pairs
within their sheets
  For booklet pane containing No. 1847, see No. 1911a.
  See also Nos. 1854/7, 1861/4, 1869/72, 1878/**MS**1882 and
1911/12.

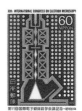

1262 "Folkways in
Twelve Months"
(detail, Shunsho
Katsukawa)

1263 Electron
Microscope

(Des F. Otani. Photo)

1986 (23 Aug) 52nd International Federation of Library Associations
General Conference, Tokyo. P 13.
1851 **1262** 60y. multicoloured .... 1·00   30

(Des F. Otani. Photo)

1986 (30 Aug). 11th International Electron Microscopy Congress,
Kyoto. P 13.
1852 **1263** 60y. multicoloured .... 1·00   30

1264 Couple and
Conference Emblem

(Des N. Takeara. Litho)

1986 (30 Aug). 23rd International Social Welfare Conference, Tokyo.
P 13.
1853 **1264** 60y. multicoloured .... 1·00   30

1265 Dragonflies
(*Sympetrum
pedemontanum*)

1266 Weevil
(*Damaster blaptoides*)

1267 Stag Beetle
(*Dorcus hopei*)

1268 Wonderful
Hairstreak
(*Thermozephyrus
ataxus*)

1272 *Elcysma
westwoodii* (moth)

1273 *Rhyothemis
variegata*

(Des M. Morita. Recess and photo)

1986 (26 Sept). Insects (2nd series). P 13.

1854	**1265**	60y. multicoloured	1·50	30
		a. Pair. Nos. 1854/5	3·25	2·30
1855	**1266**	60y. multicoloured	1·50	30
1856	**1267**	60y. multicoloured	1·50	30
		a. Pair. Nos. 1856/7	3·25	2·30
1857	**1268**	60y. multicoloured	1·50	30
1854/1857	Set of 4		5·50	1·10

Nos. 1854/5 and 1856/7 were issued together in *se-tenant* pairs within their sheets.

1274 Cicada
(*Tibicen japonicus*)

1275 *Chrysochroa
holstii*

(Des M. Morita. Recess and photo)

1986 (21 Nov). Insects (3rd series). P 13.

1861	**1272**	60y. multicoloured	1·50	30
		a. Pair. Nos. 1861/2	3·25	2·30
1862	**1273**	60y. multicoloured	1·50	30
1863	**1274**	60y. multicoloured	1·50	30
		a. Pair. Nos. 1863/4	3·25	2·30
1864	**1275**	60y. multicoloured	1·50	30
1861/1864	Set of 4		5·50	1·10

Nos. 1861/2 and 1863/4 were issued together in *se-tenant* pairs within their sheets.

1269 "Ohmori
miyage" (shiso doll,
Juzoh Kagoshima)

1270 Gymnast and
Mt. Fuji

(Des M. Morita. Photo)

1986 (6 Oct). International Correspondence Week. P 13.

1858	**1269**	130y. multicoloured	2·00	30

(Des T. Yamanouchi. Photo)

1986 (9 Oct). 41st National Athletic Meeting, Yamanashi. P 13.

1859	**1270**	40y. multicoloured	70	25

1276 Stylized Dove

1277 Circle of Children

(Des A. Kawabata; litho (40y.). Des M. Tsujii; photo (60y.))

1986 (28 Nov). International Peace Year. P 13.

1865	**1276**	40y. multicoloured	70	30
1866	**1277**	60y. multicoloured	1·00	30

1271 "Flowers in Autumn
and Girl in Rakuhoku"

(Des K. Morita. Photo)

1986 (17 Oct). Fifth World Ikebana Convention, Kyoto. P 13.

1860	**1271**	60y. multicoloured	1·00	30

1278 "Rabbits
making Rice
Cake" (Nagoya
clay model)

(Des M. Morita. Photo)

1986 (1 Dec). New Years Greetings. P 13×13½.

1867	**1278**	40y. multicoloured	1·10	40

No. 1868 *is vacant.*

1279 *Cheirotonus jambar*

1280 Chestnut Tiger (*Parantica sita*)

1286 Kegon Falls

1287 "Sunlight" (Toshu Shrine)

(Des G. Aoki (1874/5), T. Asada (1876/7); calligraphy (1875, 1877) S. Aoyama. Photo)

1987 (26 Feb). *Narrow Road to a Far Province* (travel diary) by Basho Matsuo (1st series). P 13.

1874	**1284** 60y. multicoloured	1·00	30
	a. Pair. Nos. 1874/5	2·10	1·60
1875	**1285** 60y. multicoloured	1·00	30
1876	**1286** 60y. multicoloured	1·00	30
	a. Pair. Nos. 1876/7	2·10	1·60
1877	**1287** 60y. multicoloured	1·00	30
1874/1877	Set of 4	4·50	1·10

Nos. 1874/5 and 1876/7 were issued together in *se-tenant* pairs within their sheets.

In this series each pair of stamps (except Nos. 1874/5) illustrates one *haiku* (17-syllable poem) from the diary. The full text of the *haiku* is printed on one stamp and given in calligraphy on the other with appropriate illustrations. Each *haiku* was written at a particular point in the journey (given in brackets in the caption to the second stamp of each pair).

See also Nos. 1896/9, 1906/9, 1925/8, 1932/5, 1945/8, 1962/5, 1973/6, 1982/5, **MS**1988, 2000/3 and **MS**2012.

1281 *Anotogaster sieboldii*

1282 Stag Beetle (*Lucanus maculifemoratus*)

(Des M. Yoshikawa (1871), M. Kimura (1872), M. Morita (others). Recess and photo)

1987 (23 Jan). Insects (4th series). P 13.

1869	**1279** 60y. multicoloured	1·50	30
	a. Pair. Nos. 1869/70	3·25	2·30
1870	**1280** 60y. multicoloured	1·50	30
1871	**1281** 60y. multicoloured	1·50	30
	a. Pair. Nos. 1871/2	3·25	2·30
1872	**1282** 60y. multicoloured	1·50	30
1869/1872	Set of 4	5·50	1·10

Nos. 1869/70 and 1871/2 were issued together in *se-tenant* pairs within their sheets.

For No. 1870 in miniature sheet see No. **MS**1882 and in booklet pane see No. 1912a.

1288 Owl-fly (*Ascaraphus ramburi*)

1289 Cockchafer (*Polyphylla laticollis*)

1283 Characters for "Toki" (Registry) and Map

(Des F. Otani. Photo)

1987 (30 Jan). Centenary of Land Registration. P 13½.

1873	**1283** 60y. multicoloured	1·00	30

1284 Basho Matsuo (after Haritsu Ogawa)

1285 "Departing Spring" (Senju)

1290 Leaf Butterfly (*Kallima inachus*)

1291 *Calopteryx cornelia*

1292 Orange-tip
(*Anthocaris
cardamines*)

1293 Great Purple
(*Sasakia charonda*)

(Des M. Morita. Recess and photo)

1987 (12 Mar). Insects (5th series). P 13.

1878	**1288**	60y. multicoloured	1·50	30
		a. Pair. Nos. 1878/9	3·25	2·50
1879	**1289**	60y. multicoloured	1·50	30
1880	**1290**	60y. multicoloured	1·50	30
		a. Pair. Nos. 1880/1	3·25	2·50
1881	**1291**	80y. multicoloured	1·50	30
1878/1881		*Set of 4*	5·50	1·10

MS1882 143×93 mm. multicoloured. 40y.
Type **1292**; 40y. Type **1293**; 60y. Type **1258**;
60y. Type **1280** .... 5·50 4·25
Nos. 1878/9 and 1880/1 were issued together in *se-tenant* pairs
within their sheets.
For 40y. in Types **1292/3** see Nos. 1911/12.

1294 Wind Orchid

1295 Lobster-root

(Des Y. Higashitsunoi (1883), S. Watanabe (1884). Photo)

1987 (19 Mar). 12th International Orchid Conference, Tokyo. P 13.

1883	**1294**	60y. multicoloured	1·00	30
1884	**1295**	60y. multicoloured	1·00	30

1296 Early Mail Sorting
Carriage

1297 Loading Mail Sacks
(detail of scroll painting by
Beisen Kubota)

(Des T. Shimizu (1885), F. Otani (1886). Litho)

1987 (26 Mar). Ending of Railway Mail Carriage Contracts. P 13½.

1885	**1296**	60y. multicoloured	1·20	30
		a. Pair. Nos. 1885/6	2·50	1·90
1886	**1297**	60y. multicoloured	1·20	30

Nos. 1885/6 were issued together in *se-tenant* pairs within the
sheet.

1298 Steam Tank
Locomotive No. 137

1299 High-speed Train
No. 002

(Des T. Shimizu (1887), Y. Higashitsunoi (1888). Photo)

1987 (1 Apr). Privatisation of Japan Railways. P 13½.

1887	**1298**	60y. multicoloured	1·10	25
1888	**1299**	60y. multicoloured	1·10	25

1300 Nudibranchs

(Des T. Amano. Photo)

1987 (2 Apr). Centenary of Marine Biology Studies in Japan. P 13.

1889	**1300**	60y. multicoloured	1·00	30

1301 "Woman with
a Comb"

1302 "Woman
putting on Make-up"

(Des Y. Kikuchi. Photo)

1987 (14 Apr). Philatelic Week. Paintings by Goyo Hashiguchi. P 13.

1890	**1301**	60y. multicoloured	1·00	30
		a. Pair. Nos. 1890/1	2·10	1·60
1891	**1302**	60y. multicoloured	1·00	30

Nos. 1890/1 were issued together in *se-tenant* pairs within the
sheet.

1303 Map and Emblem

1304 Magpie and
Forested Coastline

(Des F. Otani. Photo)

1987 (27 Apr). 20th Annual General Meeting of Asian Development
Bank. P 13½.

1892	**1303**	60y. multicoloured	1·00	30

(Des M. Hisano. Photo)

1987 (23 May). National Afforestation Campaign. P 13½.

1893 **1304** 60y. multicoloured .... 1·00   30

1305 Yatsuhashi Gold   **1306** Hikone Castle
Lacquer and Nacre Inkstone
Case (Kohrin Ogata)

(Des M. Morita; photo (60y.). Des S. Asaga and M. Morita; recess and photo (110y.))

1987 (26 May). National Treasures (1st series). P 13 (60y.) or 13½ (110y.).

1894 **1305** 60y. multicoloured .... 1·00   40
1895 **1306** 110y. multicoloured .... 1·80   55
    See also Nos. 1900/1, 1929/30, 1949/50, 1968/9, 1980/1, 2006/7 and 2017/18.

1307 European   **1308** Horse and
Cuckoo   River (Nasu)

1309 "In the Shade   **1310** Paddy Field
of the Willow"   (Ashino)

(Des W. Emori (1896/7), T. Tabuchi (1898/9); calligraphy (1897, 1899) S. Kamijo. Photo)

1987 (23 June). *Narrow Road to a Far Province* by Basho Matsuo (2nd series). P 13.

1896 **1307** 60y. multicoloured .... 1·50   30
     a. Pair. Nos. 1896/7 .... 3·25   2·30
1897 **1308** 60y. multicoloured .... 1·50   30
1898 **1309** 60y. multicoloured .... 1·50   30
     a. Pair. Nos. 1898/9 .... 3·25   2·30
1899 **1310** 60y. multicoloured .... 1·50   30
1896/1899 *Set of 4* .... 5·50   1·10
    Nos. 1896/7 and 1898/9 were issued together in *se-tenant* pairs within their sheets.

1311 Golden Turtle   **1312** Inuyama Castle
Reliquary for Buddha's
Ashes (Toshodai
Temple)

(Des M. Morita. Photo (60y.), recess and photo (110y.))

1987 (17 July). National Treasures (2nd series). P 13 (60y.) or 13½ (110y.).

1900 **1311** 60y. multicoloured .... 1·00   40
1901 **1312** 110y. multicoloured .... 1·80   55

1313 Flowers   **1314** Elephant
in Envelope   holding Letter

(Des Etsuyo Uchida (40y.), T. Murakami (60y.). Photo)

1987 (23 July). Letter Writing Day. P 13×13½.

1902 **1313** 40y. multicoloured 90   30
     a. Booklet pane. Nos. 1902×5 and
         1903×5 .... 6·00
1903 **1314** 60y. multicoloured .... 1·30   45
    The booklet pane has its outer edges imperforate, giving stamps with one or two adjacent sides imperforate.
    No. 1904 is vacant.

1315 Flood Barrier across
Rivers

(Des S. Watanabe. Litho)

1987 (7 Aug). Centenary of Modern Flood Control of Rivers Kiso, Nagara and Ibi. P 13½×13.

1905 **1315** 60y. multicoloured .... 1·00   25

1316 Chestnut   **1317** Chestnut
Blossoms   Leaves (Sukagawa)

1318 Transplanting Rice

1319 Fern Leaves ("Dyeing Stone", Shinobu)

(Des G. Aoki (1906/7), K. Morita (1908), A. Kikuchi (1909); calligraphy (1907, 1909) R. Tonomura. Photo)

1987 (25 Aug). *Narrow Road to a Far Province* by Basho Matsuo (3rd series). P 13.

1906	**1316**	60y. multicoloured	1·00	30
	a. Pair. Nos. 1906/7		2·10	1·60
1907	**1317**	60y. multicoloured	1·00	30
1908	**1318**	60y. multicoloured	1·00	30
	a. Pair. Nos. 1908/9		2·10	1·60
1909	**1319**	60y. multicoloured	1·00	30
1906/1909	Set of 4		3·50	1·10

Nos. 1906/7 and 1908/9 were issued together in *se-tenant* pairs within their sheets.

1320 Temple of Emerald Buddha and Cherry Blossom

(Des M. Hisano. Photo)

1987 (26 Sept). Centenary of Japan–Thailand Friendship Treaty. P 13.

1910	**1320**	60y. multicoloured	1·00	30

1987 (30 Sept). Insects (6th series). Booklet stamps. P 13.

1911	**1292**	40y. multicoloured	2·00	1·60
	a. Booklet pane. Nos. 1911×5 and 1847×5		10·50	
1912	**1293**	40y. multicoloured	2·00	1·60
	a. Booklet pane. Nos. 1912×5 and 1870×5		10·50	

The booklet pane has its outer edges imperforate, giving stamps with one or two adjacent edges imperforate.

1321 "Gensho Kanto" (Ryujo Hori)

1322 "Utage-no-Hana" (Goyo Hirata)

(Des M. Morita. Photo)

1987 (6 Oct). International Correspondence Week. P 13.

1913	**1321**	130y. multicoloured	2·00	40
1914	**1322**	150y. multicoloured	2·20	45

1323 "Three Beauties" (detail, Toyokuni Utagawa)

1324 Lions Head Public Water Tap

(Des M. Morita. Photo)

1987 (9 Oct). 13th International Certified Public Accountants Congress, Tokyo. P 13.

1916	**1323**	60y. multicoloured	1·00	30

(Des M. Morita. Litho)

1987 (16 Oct). Centenary of Yokohama Waterworks. P 13.

1916	**1324**	60y. multicoloured	1·00	30

1325 Basketball Players and Shuri Gate, Naha

1326 Playing Card with Queen holding Bird and King smoking

(Des T. Yamanouchi. Photo)

1987 (24 Oct). 42nd National Athletic Meeting, Okinawa. P 13.

1917	**1325**	40y. multicoloured	30	25

(Des S. Watanabe. Photo)

1987 (9 Nov). Sixth International Smoking and Health Conference, Tokyo. P 13.

1918	**1326**	60y. multicoloured	1·00	30

1327 Dish Aerial, Kashima Station

1328 Nijo Castle

(Des K. Takeara. Photo)

1987 (13 Nov). International Telecommunications Conference, Tokyo. P 13½.

1919	**1327**	60y. multicoloured	1·00	25

(Des G. Aoki. Photo)

1987 (18 Nov). World Historic Cities Conference, Kyoto. P 13.

1920	**1328**	60y. multicoloured	1·00	30

1329 Family in Tree   **1330** Houses (Yoko Sasaki)
(Takahiro Nagahama)

(Des M. Morita. Photo)

1987 (25 Nov). International Year of Shelter for the Homeless. P 13.
1921 **1329** 40y. multicoloured 90   30
1922 **1330** 60y. multicoloured .... 1·30   25

1331 Kurashiki
Papier-mâché
Dragon

(Des M. Morita. Photo)

1987 (1 Dec). New Year's Greetings. P 13×13½.
1923 **1331** 40y. multicoloured 70   25
No. 1924 is vacant.

1332 Sweet Flags   **1333** Sweet Flags
and Birds (Sendai)

1334 "Recollecting   **1335** "Summer
the Past"   Grasses" (Hiraizumi)

(Des W. Emori (1925/6), K. Morita (1927), G. Aoki (1928); calligraphy
(1926, 1928) K. Sugioka. Photo)

1988 (23 Jan). Narrow Road to a Far Province by Basho Matsuo (4th
series). P 13.
1925 **1332** 60y. multicoloured .... 1·00   30
     a. Pair. Nos. 1925/6 .... 2·10   1·60
1926 **1333** 60y. multicoloured .... 1·00   30
1927 **1334** 60y. multicoloured .... 1·00   30
     a. Pair. Nos. 1927/8 .... 2·10   1·60
1928 **1335** 60y. multicoloured .... 1·00   30
1925/1928 Set of 4 .... 3·50   1·10
Nos. 1925/6 and 1927/8 were issued together in se-tenant pairs
within their sheets.

1336 Kongo   **1337** Ekoh-Doji,
Samma-in Pagoda,   Kongobu Temple
Mt. Koya

(Des M. Morita. Photo (60y.), recess and photo (110y.))

1988 (12 Feb). National Treasures (3rd series). P 13 (60y.) or 13½
(110y.).
1929 **1336** 60y. multicoloured .... 1·00   40
1930 **1337** 110y. multicoloured .... 1·80   55

1338 Class "ED791"
Locomotive Sea of Japan
leaving Tunnel and Map

(Des T. Shimizu. Litho)

1988 (11 Mar). Opening of Seikan (Aomori-Hakodate) Railway
Tunnel. P 13½.
1931 **1338** 60y. multicoloured .... 1·20   25
No. 1931 was issued both in sheets of 20 stamps and in sheetlets of
10 stamps (5×2) imperforate at the outer edges. Although the latter
resembles a booklet pane the postal authority issued no booklet.

1339 Safflower   **1340** Willow Trees
(Obanazawa)

1341 Risshaku (or   **1342** Pine Trees
Mountain) Temple   (Risshaku Temple)

(Des T. Matsuo (1932/3), S. Gotoh (1934/5); calligraphy C. Miyamoto (1933), R. Tonomura (1935). Photo)

1988 (26 Mar). *Narrow Road to a Far Province* by Basho Matsuo (5th series). P 13.

1932	**1339** 60y. multicoloured	1·00	40
	a. Pair. Nos. 1932/3	2·10	1·60
1933	**1340** 60y. multicoloured	1·00	40
1934	**1341** 60y. multicoloured	1·00	40
	a. Pair. Nos. 1934/5	2·10	1·60
1935	**1342** 60y. multicoloured	1·00	40
1932/1935	*Set of 4*	3·50	1·40

Nos. 1932/3 and 1934/5 were issued together in *se-tenant* pairs within their sheets.

1343 South Bisan Section from Kagawa Side **1344**

1345 Shimotsui Section from Okayama Side **1346**

(Des S. Watanabe. Litho)

1988 (8 Apr). Opening of Seto Great Road and Rail Bridge. P 13½.

1936	**1343** 60y. multicoloured	1·40	40
	a. Strip or block of 4. Nos. 1936/9	6·75	
1937	**1344** 60y. multicoloured	1·40	40
1938	**1346** 60y. multicoloured	1·40	40
1939	**1346** 60y. multicoloured	1·40	40
1936/1939	*Set of 4*	5·25	1·40

Nos. 1936/9 were issued together in *se-tenant* strips and blocks of four, each pair forming composite designs as illustrated.

1347 "Long Undergarment" (Kotondo Torii)

1348 "Kimono Sash" (Kotondo Torii)

(Des G. Aoki. Photo)

1988 (19 Apr). Philatelic Week. P 13.

1940	**1347** 60y. multicoloured	1·40	40
	a. Pair. Nos. 1940/1	3·50	2·75
1941	**1348** 60y. multicoloured	1·40	40

Nos. 1940/1 were issued together in *se-tenant* pairs within sheets of 10 or 20 stamps, the latter arranged in two panes divided by a vertical gutter

No. 1942 is vacant.

1349 Detail of Biwa Plectrum Guard

1350 Yashima, Little Cuckoo and Olive Tree

(Des M. Morita. Recess and photo)

1988 (23 Apr). "Silk Road" Exhibition, Nara. P 13.

1943	**1349** 60y. multicoloured	1·40	45

(Des. M Hisano. Photo)

1988 (20 May). National Afforestation Campaign. P 13½.

1944	**1350** 60y. multicoloured	1·50	45

1351 River Mogami

1352 Irises in the Rain (Oishida)

1353 Moon Mountain

1354 Moon Mountain (Gassan)

(Des F. Hori (1945/6), C. Konno (1947/8); calligraphy (1946, 1948) C. Miyamoto. Photo)

1988 (30 May). *Narrow Road to a Far Province* by Basho Matsuo (6th series). P 13.

1945	**1351** 60y. multicoloured	1·00	30
	a. Pair. Nos. 1945/6	2·10	1·60
1946	**1352** 60y. multicoloured	1·00	30

1947 **1353** 60y. multicoloured .... 1·00   30
         a. Pair. Nos. 1947/8................................. 2·10   1·60
1948 **1354** 60y. multicoloured .... 1·00   30
1945/1948 Set of 4.. 3·50   1·10
    Nos. 1945/6 and 1947/8 were issued together in se-tenant pairs
within their sheets.

1355 Morodo Shrine,   **1356** Kozakura-gawa
Itsukushima   Braided Armour

(Des M. Morita. Photo (60y.), recess and photo (100y.))
1988 (23 June). National Treasures (4th series). P 13 (60y.) or 13½
(100y.)
1949 **1355** 60y. multicoloured .... 1·00   30
1950 **1356** 100y. multicoloured .... 1·70   40

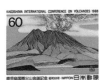

1357 Mt. Sakura

(Des G. Aoki. Photo)
1988 (19 July). International Conference on Volcanoes, Kagoshima.
    P 13.
1951 **1357** 60y. multicoloured .... 1·00   30

1358 Cat with   **1359** Crab with Letter
Letter

1360 Fairy with   **1361** Girl and Letter
Letter

(Des T. Murakami (1952), K. Yamada (1953), Moe Nagata (1954),
    T. Ukai (1955). Photo (1952, 1954), litho (others))
1988 (23 July). Letter Writing Day (1st issue). P 13×13½ (1952, 1954)
or 13 (others).
1952 **1358** 40y. multicoloured 90   30
         a. Booklet pane. Nos. 1952×5 and
            1954 ×5.. 5·50
1953 **1359** 40y. multicoloured .... 1·20   40
1954 **1360** 60y. multicoloured .... 1·40   40
1955 **1361** 60y. multicoloured 90   30
1952/1955 Set of 4.. 4·00   1·30
    The booklet pane has its outer edges imperforate, giving stamps
with one or two adjacent sides imperforate.
    For Types **1358** and **1360** but self-adhesive see Nos. 1986/7.

1362 Ohana   **1363** Stick Puppet
(Kinosuke puppet,   (Czechoslovakia)
Japan)

1364 Shadow   **1365** Knight (Italy)
Puppet (China)

(Des E. Uchida. Photo)
1988 (27 July). International Puppetry Festival, Nagoya, Iida and
    Tokyo. P 13.
1956 **1382** 60y. multicoloured 90   25
         a. Strip or block of 4. Nos. 1956/9........ 3·75
1957 **1363** 60y. multicoloured 90   25
1958 **1364** 60y. multicoloured 90   25
1959 **1365** 60y. multicoloured 90   25
1956/1959 Set of 4.. 3·25   90
    Nos. 1956/9 were issued together in se-tenant blocks and strips of
four within the sheet.

1366 Peonies   **1367** Ton-ton
                              (giant panda)

(Des M. Morita. Photo)

1988 (12 Aug). Tenth Anniv of Japanese–Chinese Treaty of Peace and Friendship. P 13.

1960 **1366** 60y. multicoloured .... 1·50   25
     a. Pair. Nos. 1960/1 .... 3·25   1·60
1961 **1367** 60y. multicoloured .... 1·50   25

Nos. 1960/1 were issued together in *se-tenant* pairs within the sheet.

1368 Mimosa Flowers

1369 Lagoon and Grass (Kisagata)

1370 Rough Sea

1371 Waves (Ichiburi)

(Des T. Matsuo (1962/3), G. Aoki (1964/5); calligraphy (1963, 1965) S. Murakami. Photo)

1988 (23 Aug). Narrow Road to a Far Province by Basho Matsuo (7th series). P 13.

1962 **1368** 60y. multicoloured .... 1·00   30
     a. Pair. Nos. 1962/3 ....
1963 **1369** 60y. multicoloured .... 1·00   30
1964 **1370** 60y. multicoloured .... 1·00   30
     a. Pair. Nos. 1964/5 ....
1965 **1371** 60y. multicoloured .... 1·00   30
1962/1965 *Set of 4* .... 3·50   1·10

Nos. 1962/3 and 1964/5 were issued together in *se-tenant* pairs within their sheets.

1372 Nagoya and Egg

1373 Globe and "Rehabilitation" in Braille

(Des Y. Higashitsunoi. Photo)

1988 (3 Sept). 18th International Poultry Congress. Nagoya. P 13½.
1966 **1372** 60y. multicoloured .... 1·00   30

(Des F. Otani. Embossed and photo)

1988 (5 Sept). 16th Rehabilitation International World Congress, Tokyo. P 13.
1967 **1373** 60y. multicoloured 90   25

1374 Nakatsuhime-no-mikoto, Yakushi Temple

1375 Muroh Temple

(Des M. Morita. Photo (60y.), recess and photo (100y.))

1988 (26 Sept). National Treasures (5th series). P 13 (60y.) or 13½ (100y.).
1968 **1374** 60y. multicoloured .... 1·00   30
1969 **1375** 100y. multicoloured .... 1·70   40

1376 "Kimesaburo Iwai as Chiyo" (Kunimasa Utagawa)

1377 "Komazo Ichikawa III as Ganryu Sasaki" (Toyokuni Utagawa)

(Des M. Morita. Photo)

1988 (6 Oct). International Correspondence Week. P 13.
1970 **1376** 80y. multicoloured .... 1·10   40
1971 **1377** 120y. multicoloured .... 1·80   40

1378 Gymnast and Temple of the Golden Pavilion

(Des T. Shimizu. Photo)

1988 (14 Oct). 43rd National Athletic Meeting, Kyoto. P 13.
1972 **1378** 40y. multicoloured 60   25

1379 Rice

1380 Ariso Sea
(Kurikara Pass)

1385 Figures and
Globe

(Des M. Saito and A. Kikuchi. Litho)

1988 (5 Dec). 40th Anniv of Declaration of Human Rights. P 13½.
1979 **1385** 60y. multicoloured 90   25

Emperor Akihito, 7 January 1989

1381 Sun

1382 "Autumn Wind
and Sun" (Kanazawa)

(Des H. Ohno (1973/4), Y. Nakaji (1975/6); calligraphy S. Kamijo
(1974), K. Sugioka (1976). Photo)

1988 (11 Nov). *Narrow Road to a Far Province* by Basho Matsuo (8th
series). P 13.
1973 **1379** 60y. multicoloured .... 1·00   30
     a. Pair. Nos. 1973/4 ....
1974 **1380** 60y. multicoloured .... 1·00   30
1975 **1381** 60y. multicoloured .... 1·00   30
     a. Pair. Nos. 1975/6 ....
1976 **1382** 60y. multicoloured .... 1·00   30
1973/1976 *Set of 4* .... 3·50   1·10
   Nos. 1973/4 and 1975/6 were issued together in *se-tenant* pairs
within their sheets.

1386 Gold-plated Silver Pot
with Hunting Design, Todai
Temple

1387 Bronze Figure of
Yakushi (Buddha of
Medicine), Horyu
Temple

(Des M. Morita. Photo (60y.), recess and photo (100y.))

1989 (20 Jan). National Treasures (6th series). P 13 (60y.) or 13½
(100y.).
1980 **1386**   60y. multicoloured .... 1·00   30
1981 **1387** 100y. multicoloured .... 1·70   40

1383 Mexican State
Arms

1384 Snake
(Shimotsuke
clay bell)

(Des M. Morita. Photo)

1988 (30 Nov). Centenary of Japan–Mexico Friendship and Trade
Treaty. P 13.
1977 **1383** 60y. multicoloured .... 1·00   40

(Des I. Harada. Photo)

1988 (1 Dec). New Year's Greetings. P 13×13½.
1978 **1384** 40y. multicoloured .... 1·00   25

1388 Nata Temple

1389 Pampas
Grass (Natadera)

1390 Moonlight,
Kehi Shrine

1391 Moon and Pine
Trees (Tsuruga)

(Des C. Konno (1982/3), S. Goto (1984/5); calligraphy S. Aoyama (1983), S. Murakami (1985). Photo)

1989 (13 Feb). *Narrow Road to a Far Province* by Basho Matsuo (9th series). P 13.

1982	**1388** 60y. multicoloured	1·00	30
	a. Pair. Nos. 1982/3		
1983	**1389** 60y. multicoloured	1·00	30
1984	**1390** 60y. multicoloured	1·00	30
	a. Pair. Nos. 1984/5		
1985	**1391** 60y. multicoloured	1·00	30
1982/1985	*Set of 4*	3·50	1·10

Nos. 1982/3 and 1984/5 were issued together in *se-tenant* pairs within their sheets.

1989 (1 Mar). Letter Writing Day (1988) (2nd issue). Booklet stamps. Self-adhesive. Die-cut.

1986	**1358** 40y. multicoloured	1·10	85
1987	**1360** 60y. multicoloured	1·40	1·10

The individual stamps are peeled directly from the booklet cover. It is not therefore possible to collect these as booklet panes.

(Des A. Kikuchi. Photo)

1989 (10 Mar). *Narrow Road to a Far Province* by Basho Matsuo (10th series). Ten sheets, each 112×72 mm. Imperf.

MS1988 10 sheets. (a) Nos. 1874/5; (b) Nos. 1876/7; (c) Nos. 1896/7; (d) Nos. 1898/9; (e) Nos. 1906/7; (f) Nos. 1908/9; (g) Nos. 1925/6; (h) Nos. 1927/8; (i) Nos. 1932/3; (j) Nos. 1934/5 .... 29·00   23·00

1392 Globe and Exhibition Site

1393 "Russian Ladies sight-seeing at Port" (detail, Yoshitora) and Art Gallery

(Des M. Hisano. Photo)

1989 (16 Mar). "Fukuoka '89" Asian–Pacific Exhibition, Fukuoka. P 13.

1989	**1392** 60y. multicoloured	1·00	25

For 62y. value see No. 1996.

(Des M. Morita. Litho)

1989 (24 Mar). "Space and Children" Exhibition, Yokohama. P 13.

1990	**1393** 60y. multicoloured	90	25

For 62y. value see No. 1997.

1989 (1 Apr). Booklet stamps. As Nos. 1588 and 1592 but self-adhesive. Die-cut.

1991	**1012** 41y. multicoloured	1·00	30
1992	**1016** 62y. multicoloured	1·50	30

Nos. 1991/2 are peeled directly from the cover of the booklet. It is not therefore possible to collect these as booklet panes.

1394 Bonsai Japanese White Pine

(Des M. Morita. Photo)

1989 (6 Apr). World Bonsai Convention, Omiya. P 13.

1993	**1394** 62y. multicoloured	90	25

1395 Lute-player   **1396** Dancer

(Des G. Aoki. Photo)

1989 (18 Apr). Philatelic Week. Details of "Awa Dance" (painting) by Tsunetomi Kitano. P 13.

1994	**1395** 62y. multicoloured	90	25
	a. Pair. Nos. 1994/5	90	25
1995	**1396** 62y. multicoloured	90	25

Nos. 1994/5 were issued together in *se-tenant* pairs within sheets of 10 stamps or 20 stamps and five labels showing "Phila Nippon '91" stamp exhibition label.

1989 (18 Apr). As Nos. 1989/90 but new value. P 13.

1996	**1392** 62y. multicoloured	1·00	45
1997	**1393** 62y. multicoloured	90	45

1397 "Dutch East Indiaman entering Harbour" (Nagasaki woodblock print)

1398 Chikura Communication Tower and Cable Route

(Des F. Otani. Photo)

1989 (19 Apr). "Holland Festival '89". P 13×13½.

1998	**1397** 62y. multicoloured	1·00	25

(Des T. Amano. Photo)

1989 (10 May). Opening of Third Trans-Pacific Submarine Telephone Cable (Japan–Hawaii). P 13.

1999	**1398** 62y. multicoloured	1·40	30

1399 Beach in Autumn

1400 Bush Clover (Ironohama)

1405 Saddle Fitting from Burial Mound, Konda

1406 "Beetle Wings" Zushi, Horyu Temple

(Des M. Morita. Photo (62y.), recess and photo (100y.))

1989 (30 June). National Treasures (7th series). P 13 (62y.) or 13½ (100y.).

2006	**1405**	62y. multicoloured	90	25
2007	**1406**	100y. multicoloured	1·60	30

1401 Poker-drop Venuses

1402 Wedded Rocks, Futami Bay (Ohgaki)

(Des T. Tabushi (2000/1), H. Ohno (2002/3); calligraphy C. Miyamoto (2001), S. Aoyama (2003). Photo)

1989 (12 May). Narrow Road to a Far Province by Basho Matsuo (11th series). P 13.

2000	**1399**	62y. multicoloured	1·00	30
		a. Pair. Nos. 2000/2001		
2001	**1400**	62y. multicoloured	1·00	30
2002	**1401**	62y. multicoloured	1·00	30
		a. Pair. Nos. 2002/3		
2003	**1402**	62y. multicoloured	1·00	30
2000/2003		Set of 4	3·50	1·10

Nos. 2000/1 and 2002/3 were issued together in se-tenant pairs within their sheets.

1407 "Crystal of Light and Auspicious Clouds"

1408 "design"

(Des K. Sugiura, F. Watanabe and A. Tanimura (41y.), H. Isoda (62y.). Photo)

1989 (14 July). World Design Exposition, Nagoya. P 13.

2008	**1407**	41y. multicoloured	60	25
2009	**1408**	62y. multicoloured	90	25

1403 Mt. Tsurugi, Lime and Bay Trees

1404 Children in Bird and Flower "Balloon"

(Des A. Kikuchi. Photo)

1989 (19 May). National Afforestation Campaign. P 13½.

2004	**1403**	62y. multicoloured	90	25

(Des Moe Nagata. Photo)

1989 (1 June). International Garden and Greenery Exposition, Osaka (1990) (1st issue). P 13.

2005	**1404**	62y.+10y. multicoloured	1·50	30

The premium was for the exposition funds.
See also Nos. 2035/6.

1409 Bird as Vase holding Envelope

1410 Mother Rabbit reading Letter

(Des E. Uchida (41y.), K. Kuroi (62y.). Photo)

1989 (21 July). Letter Writing Day. P 13×13½.

2010	**1409**	41y. multicoloured	70	45
		a. Booklet pane. Nos. 2010×5 and 2011×5	5·50	
2011	**1410**	62y. multicoloured	1·90	1·50

The booklet pane has its outer edges imperforate, giving stamps with one or two adjacent sides imperf.

(Des A. Kikuchi. Photo)

1989 (1 Aug). Narrow Road to a Far Province by Basho Matsuo (12th series). Ten sheets, each 112×72 mm. Imperf.

MS2012	10 sheets. (a) Nos. 1945/6; (b) Nos. 1947/8; (c) Nos. 1963/4; (d) Nos. 1965/6; (e) Nos. 1973/4; (f) Nos. 1975/6; (g) Nos. 1982/3; (h) Nos. 1984/5; (i) Nos. 2000/2001; (j) Nos. 2002/3	29·00	23·00

1989 (10 Aug). Special Correspondence Stamps. As Nos. 1677/9 but new values. P 13×13½.

2013	**1098**	41y. multicoloured	60	30
2014	**1099**	41y. multicoloured	90	30
2015		62y. multicoloured	1·00	30
2016	**1100**	72y. multicoloured	1·20	30
2013/2016		*Set of 4*	3·25	1·10

1411 Gold Stamp   **1412** Bronze Mirror

(Des M. Morita. Photo (62y.), recess and photo (100y.))

1989 (15 Aug). National Treasures (8th series). P 13 (62y.) or 13½ (100y.).

2017	**1411**	62y. multicoloured	90	25
2018	**1412**	100y. multicoloured	1·60	30

1413 Bouquet of Orchids and Stephanotis   **1414** Wheelchair Race

(Des I. Harada. Photo)

1989 (25 Aug). Sixth Interflora World Congress, Tokyo. P 13½.

2019	**1413**	62y. multicoloured	90	60

(Des T. Shimizu. Photo)

1989 (14 Sept). Far East and South Pacific Games for the Disabled, Kobe. P 13½.

2020	**1414**	62y. multicoloured	90	60

1415 Narrators and Drummers   **1416** Okuni (actress)

(Des M. Morita. Photo)

1989 (18 Sept). "Europalia 89 Japan" Festival, Belgium. Details of "Okuni Theatre" (painting on folding screen). P 13.

2021	**1415**	62y. multicoloured	90	25
2022	**1416**	70y. multicoloured	1·00	30

1417 New Emperor and Kaoru playing Go ("Yadorigi" scroll)

1418 Yugao's Granddaughters playing Go ("Takekawa" scroll)

(Des M. Morita. Photo)

1989 (6 Oct). International Correspondence Week. Details of Takayoshi Picture Scrolls illustrating *Tale of Genji* by Lady Murasaki. P 13½.

2023	**1417**	80y. multicoloured	1·00	30
2024	**1418**	120y. multicoloured	1·80	45

1419 Ear of Rice and Paddy Field   **1420** Shinzan (first winner of all five major races)

(Des E. Uchida. Photo)

1989 (13 Oct). Seventh Asian/African Conference of International Irrigation and Drainage Commission. P 13½.

2025	**1419**	62y. multicoloured	90	25

(Des M. Morita. Photo)

1989 (2 7 Oct). 100th Tenno Sho Horse Race. P 13.

2026	**1420**	62y. multicoloured	1·00	30

1421 Balloons   **1422** Conductor

(Des T. Shimizu. Photo)

1989 (17 Nov). Ninth Hot Air Balloon World Championship, Saga City. P 13.
2027 **1421** 62y. multicoloured .... 1·00   25

(Des M. Morita. Photo)

1989 (17 Nov). 50th Anniv of Japanese Copyright Control Act. P 13.
2028 **1422** 62y. multicoloured 90   25

1429 Fairies on Flower   **1430** Bicycle under Tree

(Des Moe Nagata (41y.), K. Kuroi (62y.). Photo)

1990 (30 Mar). "Expo 90" International Garden and Greenery Exposition, Osaka (2nd issue). P 13.
2035 **1429** 41y. +4y. multicoloured........................... 70   55
2036 **1430** 62y. multicoloured .... 1·00   30
The premium was for the exposition funds.

1423 Yawata Wooden Horse   **1424** Hamamatsu Papier-mâché Horse

(Des I. Harada. Photo)

1989 (1 Dec). New Year's Greetings. P 13×13½.
2029 **1423** 41y. multicoloured .... 1·00   25

(Des M. Hisano. Photo and typo)

1989 (1 Dec). New Year Lottery Stamp. P 13½
2030 **1424** 62y. multicoloured .... 1·00   60
Each stamp carries a lottery number.

1431 "Women gazing at the Stars" (Chou Ohta)

(Des G. Aoki. Photo)

1990 (20 Apr). Philatelic Week. P 13.
2037 **1431** 62y. multicoloured 80   30
MS2038 60×77 mm. No. 2037 .... 2·00   1·60
No. 2037 was issued in sheets of 10 or 20 stamps, the latter arranged in two panes divided by a vertical gutter bearing "Phila Nippon '91" stamp exhibition emblems.

1425 Type "10000"   **1426** Type "EF 58"

(Des M. Morita. Recess and photo (2031), photo (2032))

1990 (31 Jan). Electric Railway Locomotives (1st series). P 13.
2031 **1425** 62y. slate-purple, reddish lilac and pale yellow-olive........................... 1·10   25
2032 **1426** 62y. multicoloured .... 1·10   25
See also Nos. 2033/4, 2039/40, 2089/90 and 2101/2.

1432 Type "EF53"   **1433** Type "ED70"

(Des M. Morita. Recess and photo (2039), photo (2040))

1990 (23 Apr) Electric Railway Locomotives (3rd series). P 13.
2039 **1432** 62y. multicoloured .... 1·10   25
2040 **1433** 62y. multicoloured .... 1·10   25

1427 Type "ED40"   **1428** Type "EH10"

(Des M. Morita. Recess and photo (2032), photo (2033))

1990 (28 Feb). Electric Railway Locomotives (2nd series). P 13.
2033 **1427** 62y. multicoloured .... 1·10   25
2034 **1428** 62y. multicoloured .... 1·10   25

1434 Sweet Briar (Hokkaido)   **1435** Apple Blossom (Aomori)   **1436** *Paulownia tomentosa* (Iwate)

1437 Japanese Bush Clover (Miyagi)

1438 Butterbur Flower (Akita)

1439 Safflower (Yamagata)

1452 Fritillaria (Ishikawa)

1453 Narcissi (Fukui)

1454 Chinese Milk Vetch (Gifu)

1440 Rhododendron (Fukushima)

1441 Rose (Ibaraki)

1442 Yashio Azalea (Tochigi)

1455 Azalea (Shizuoka)

1456 Rabbit-ear Iris (Aichi)

1457 Iris (Mie)

1443 Japanese Azalea (Gunma)

1444 Primrose (Saitama)

1445 Rape (Chiba)

1458 Rhododendron (Shiga)

1459 Weeping Cherry Blossom (Kyoto)

1460 Japanese Apricot and Primrose (Osaka)

1446 Gold-banded Lily (Kanagawa)

1447 Cherry Blossom (Tokyo)

1448 Cherry Blossom (Yamanashi)

1461 Marguerites (Hyogo)

1462 Double Cherry Blossom (Nara)

1463 Japanese Apricot (Wakayama)

1449 Gentian (Nagano)

1450 Tulip (Niigata)

1451 Tulip (Toyama)

1464 Pear Blossom (Tottori)

1465 Peony (Shimane)

1466 Peach Blossom (Okayama)

1467 Japanese Maple (Hiroshima)

1468 Summer Orange Blossom (Yamaguchi)

1469 Sudachi Orange Blossom (Tokushima)

1470 Olive Blossom (Kagawa)

1471 Mandarin Orange Blossom (Ehime)

1472 *Myrica rubra* (Kochi)

1473 Japanese Apricot (Fukuoka)

1474 Laurel (Saga)

1475 Unzen Azalea (Nagasaki)

1476 Gentian (Kumamoto)

1477 Japanese Apricot (Oita)

1478 Crinum (Miyazaki)

1479 Rhododendron (Kagoshima)

1480 Coral Tree (Okinawa)

1990 (27 Apr). Prefecture Flowers. Litho. P 13½.

2041	**1434**	62y. multicoloured	2·50	1·90
		a. Sheet of 47 stamps (Nos. 2041/87) and 3 labels	49·00	
2042	**1435**	62y. multicoloured	80	60
2043	**1436**	62y. multicoloured	80	60
2044	**1437**	62y. multicoloured	80	60
2045	**1438**	62y. multicoloured	80	60
2046	**1439**	62y. multicoloured	80	60
2047	**1440**	62y. multicoloured	80	60
2048	**1441**	62y. multicoloured	80	60
2049	**1442**	62y. multicoloured	80	60
2050	**1443**	62y. multicoloured	80	60
2051	**1444**	62y. multicoloured	80	60
2052	**1445**	62y. multicoloured	80	60
2053	**1446**	62y. multicoloured	80	60
2054	**1447**	62y. multicoloured	80	60
2055	**1448**	62y. multicoloured	80	60
2056	**1449**	62y. multicoloured	2·50	1·90
2057	**1450**	62y. multicoloured	80	60
2058	**1451**	62y. multicoloured	80	60
2059	**1452**	62y. multicoloured	80	60
2060	**1453**	62y. multicoloured	80	60
2061	**1454**	62y. multicoloured	1·00	80
2062	**1455**	62y. multicoloured	1·30	1·00
2063	**1456**	62y. multicoloured	80	60
2064	**1457**	62y. multicoloured	80	60
2065	**1458**	62y. multicoloured	2·00	1·60
2066	**1459**	62y. multicoloured	2·00	1·60
2067	**1460**	62y. multicoloured	80	60
2068	**1461**	62y. multicoloured	80	60
2069	**1462**	62y. multicoloured	1·30	1·00
2070	**1463**	62y. multicoloured	1·00	80
2071	**1464**	62y. multicoloured	80	60
2072	**1465**	62y. multicoloured	80	60
2073	**1466**	62y. multicoloured	80	60
2074	**1467**	62y. multicoloured	80	60
2075	**1468**	62y. multicoloured	80	60
2076	**1469**	62y. multicoloured	1·00	80
2077	**1470**	62y. multicoloured	3·25	2·50
2078	**1471**	62y. multicoloured	1·60	1·20
2079	**1472**	62y. multicoloured	1·30	1·00
2080	**1473**	62y. multicoloured	80	60
2081	**1474**	62y. multicoloured	80	60
2082	**1475**	62y. multicoloured	80	60
2083	**1476**	62y. multicoloured	80	60
2084	**1477**	62y. multicoloured	80	60
2085	**1478**	62y. multicoloured	80	60
2086	**1479**	62y. multicoloured	80	60
2087	**1480**	62y. multicoloured	80	60
2041/2087		*Set of 47*	44·00	33·00

Nos. 2041/87 were issued both together in *se-tenant* sheets of 47 stamps and three labels showing the "Phila Nippon '91" stamp exhibition emblem (these sheets being sold in all post offices), and in separate sheets of 20 stamps which were only on sale in the appropriate region and at the central Tokyo and Osaka post offices.

1481 Mt. Unzen and Unzen Azalea

(Des A. Kikuchi. Photo)

1990 (18 May). National Afforestation Campaign. P 13½.

2088	**1481**	62y. multicoloured	80	30

1482 Type "EF55"

1483 Type "ED61"

(Des M. Morita. Recess and photo (2089), photo (2090))

1990 (23 May). Electric Railway Locomotives (4th series). P 13.
2089   **1482** 62y. multicoloured .... 1·10   25
2090   **1483** 62y. multicoloured .... 1·10   25

1484 Fritillary *(Fabriciana nerippe)* on Thistle   **1485** "Communication"

(Des K. Yoshikawa (62y.), Angelika Winkhaus (70y.). Photo)

1990 (1 June). Winning Entries in Postage Stamp Design Contest. P 13.
2091   **1484** 62y. multicoloured .... 1·40   25
2092   **1485** 70y. multicoloured .... 1·60   30

1486 17th-century Ottoman Tile

(Des A. Kikuchi. Photo)

1990 (13 June). Century of Japan–Turkey Friendship. P 13.
2093   **1486** 62y. multicoloured 80   30

1487/1491 Folding Screen (½-size illustration)

1492 "Ponies" (Kayo Yamaguchi)   **1493** Emblem and Landscape

(Des M. Morita. Photo (2099), recess and photo (others))

1990 (20 June). The Horse in Culture (1st series). P 13 (2099) or 13×13½ (others).
2094   **1487** 62y. multicoloured .... 1·50   25
     a. Horiz strip of 5. Nos. 2094/8............ 9·25
2095   **1488** 62y. multicoloured .... 1·50   25
2096   **1489** 62y. multicoloured .... 1·50   25
2097   **1490** 62y. multicoloured .... 1·50   25
2098   **1491** 62y. multicoloured .... 1·50   25
2099   **1492** 62y. multicoloured .... 1·50   25
2094/2099   *Set of 6*.................................... 8·00   1·40

Nos. 2094/8 were issued together in horizontal *se-tenant* strips of five stamps forming the composite design shown.
See also Nos. 2106/8, 2113/14, 2132/4 and 2135/6.

(Des N. Takeara. Photo)

1990 (25 June). 38th International Youth Hostel Federation Congress, Muikamachi and Kashiwazaki. P 13.
2100   **1493** 62y. multicoloured 90   30

1494 Type "EF57"   **1495** Type "EF30"

(Des M. Morita. Recess and photo (2101), photo (2102))

1990 (18 July). Electric Railway Locomotives (5th series). P 13.
2101   **1494** 62y. multicoloured .... 1·10   25
2102   **1495** 62y. multicoloured .... 1·10   25

1496 Bluebird and Heart   **1497** Fairy on Horse

(Des Moe Nagata. Photo)

1990 (23 July). Letter Writing Day. P 13×13½ (41y.) or 13½ (62y.).
2103   **1496** 41y. multicoloured 70   30
     a. Booklet pane. Nos. 2103×5 and
         2104×5.. 8·75
2104   **1497** 62y. multicoloured .... 1·00   25
MS2105   72×93 mm. No 2104 .... 1·50   1·20

The booklet pane has its horizontal outer edges imperforate, giving stamps with one edge imperf.
For similar design to Type **1497** but with central motif drawn smaller, see No. 2157.

1498 16th-century Lacquered Saddle   **1499** 16th-century Lacquered Stirrups

1500 "A Horse" (Suisho Nishiyama)

1505 "Kurabeuma Race" (detail of kimono)

1506 "Kettei" (Shodo Sasaki)

(Des M. Morita. Photo (2108), recess and photo (others))

1990 (31 July). The Horse in Culture (2nd series). P 13.

2106	**1498** 62y. multicoloured		1·50	25
	a. Pair. Nos. 2106/7		4·75	
2107	**1499** 62y. multicoloured		1·50	25
2108	**1500** 62y. multicoloured		1·50	25
2106/2107	Set of 4		4·00	70

Nos. 2106/7 were issued together in *se-tenant* pairs within the sheet.

(Des M. Morita. Photo)

1990 (27 Sept). The Horse in Culture (3rd series). P 13.

2113	**1505** 62y. multicoloured		80	30
2114	**1506** 62y. multicoloured		80	30

1501 Origami Polyhedron

1502 Track Race

(Des M. Hisano. Photo)

1990 (17 Aug). International Mathematicians Congress, Kyoto. P 13.

2109	**1501** 62y. multicoloured		80	30

(Des T. Shimizu. Litho)

1990 (20 Aug). World Cycling Championships, Maebashi and Tochigi Prefecture. P 13½.

2110	**1502** 62y. multicoloured		80	30

1507 Peaceful Landscape

(Des K. Kuroi. Photo)

1990 (27 Sept). International Decade for Natural Disaster Reduction Conference, Yokohama. P 13.

2115	**1507** 62y. multicoloured		80	30

1508 Animals at Dance

1503 Ogai Mori (translator) and Passage from Goethe's *Faust*

1504 "Ji" (character) and Rosetta Stone

(Des S. Watanabe. Photo)

1990 (27 Aug). Eighth International Association for Germanic Studies Congress, Tokyo. P 13½.

2111	**1503** 62y. greenish blue, yellow and sepia		80	30

1509 Dancing Frogs

(Des M. Morita. Photo and typo)

(Des H. Isoda. Photo)

1990 (7 Sept). International Literacy Year. P 13.

2112	**1504** 62y. multicoloured		80	30

1990 (5 Oct). International Correspondence Week. Details from "Choju-jinbutsu-giga" Picture Scroll. P 13½.

2116	**1508** 80y. multicoloured		1·20	40
2117	**1509** 120y. multicoloured		1·80	40

1510 Midwife, Mother and Baby

1511 "Letter Bearer" (detail, Harunobu Suiendo)

(Des S. Watanabe. Photo)

1990 (5 Oct). 22nd International Confederation of Midwives Congress, Kobe City. P 13.

| 2118 | **1510** 62y. multicoloured | 80 | 40 |

(Des G. Aoki. Photo)

1990 (16 Oct). "Phila Nippon '91" International Stamp Exhibition, Tokyo (1st issue). P 13½.

| 2119 | **1511** 100y. multicoloured | 1·40 | 45 |
| MS2120 | 94×90 mm. No. 2119 | 2·00 | 1·60 |

No. **MS**2120 additionally overprinted with the exhibition emblem at the top and a three-line inscription and a number at the bottom was a private production made by the exhibition organizers to act as an entrance ticket.

See also Nos. 2170/**MS**2171.

1512 Hand reading Braille

1513 "Justice" (Supreme Court bronze statue, Katsuzo Entsuba)

(Des T. Shimizu. Embossed and photo)

1990 (1 Nov). Centenary of Japanese Braille. P 13½.

| 2121 | **1512** 62y. multicoloured | 80 | 30 |

(Des M. Morita. Photo)

1990 (1 Nov). Centenary of Modern Judiciary System. P 13×13½.

| 2122 | **1513** 62y. multicoloured | 80 | 30 |

1514 Chinese Phoenix (detail from dais of Emperor's enthronement seat)

1515 Pattern from Robes of Manzai Raku Dancers

(Des G. Aoki. Photo)

1990 (9 Nov). Enthronement of Emperor. P 13.

2123	**1514** 62y. multicoloured	1·00	30
2124	**1515** 62y. multicoloured	1·00	30
MS2125	144×93 mm. Nos. 2123/4	3·00	2·30

1516 Stained Glass Window (Diet building)

1517 Sheep (Nogomi ceramic bell)

(Des M. Morita. Litho)

1990 (29 Nov). Centenary of Diet. P 13.

| 2126 | **1516** 62y. multicoloured | 80 | 30 |

(Des M. Hisano. Photo)

1990 (3 Dec). New Year's Greetings. P 13×13½.

| 2127 | **1517** 41y. multicoloured | 1·00 | 25 |

1518 Sheep (Tosa ceramic bell)

1519 Tsuneishi-Hariko Papier-mâché Ram

(Des Y. Higashitsunoi (41y.), H. Otsuka (62y.). Photo and typo)

1990 (3 Dec). New Year Lottery Stamps. P 13½.

| 2128 | **1518** 41y. multicoloured | 70 | 55 |
| 2129 | **1519** 62y. multicoloured | 1·00 | 80 |

Each stamp carries a lottery number.

1520 Dr. Nishina and Radio Isotope

1521 "Lady using Telephone" (Senseki Nakamura)

(Des A. Kikuchi. Photo)

1990 (6 Dec). Birth Centenary of Dr. Yoshio Nishina (physicist) and 50th Anniv of First Japanese Cyclotron (radio isotope generator). P 13.

2130 **1520** 62y. multicoloured 80 30

(Des M. Morita. Photo)

1990 (14 Dec). Centenary of Telephone Service in Japan. P 13.

2131 **1521** 62y. multicoloured 80 30

1522 Horse-drawn Post Carriages **1523** (detail of scroll painting by Beisen Kubota)

1524 Inkstone Case (Korin Ogata)

(Des M. Morita. Photo (2134), recess and photo (others))

1991 (31 Jan). The Horse in Culture (4th series). P 13.

2132	**1522** 62y. multicoloured	1·00	30
	a. Horiz pair. Nos. 2132/3	2·10	65
2133	**1523** 62y. multicoloured	1·00	30
2134	**1524** 62y. multicoloured	1·00	30
2132/2134	Set of 3	2·75	80

Nos. 2132/3 were issued together in horizontal *se-tenant* pairs within the sheet, each pair forming the composite design shown.

1525 "Spring Warmth" (Kogetsu Saigo)

1526 "Senju in Musashi Province" (from "36 Views of Mt. Fuji" by Hokusai Katsushika)

(Des M. Morita. Photo (2135), recess and photo (2136))

1991 (28 Feb). The Horse in Culture (5th series). P 13.

2135 **1525** 62y. multicoloured 80 30
2136 **1526** 62y. multicoloured 80 30

1527 Figure Skating

1528 Short-track Speed Skating

(Des I. Harada (41y.), S. Watanabe (62y.). Photo)

1991 (1 Mar). Winter Universiade, Sapporo and Furano. P 13½ (41y.) or 13 (62y.).

2137 **1527** 41y. multicoloured 80 40
2138 **1528** 62y. multicoloured 90 40

1529 Bouquet

1530 "Glory of the Earth" (Komei Bekki)

(Des I. Harada. Photo)

1991 (1 Apr). New Postal Life Insurance System. P 13.

2139 **1529** 62y. multicoloured 80 60

(Des M. Morita. Photo)

1991 (19 Apr). "Ceramic World Shigaraki '91" Exhibition. P 13½.

2140 **1530** 62y. multicoloured 80 30

1531 "Beauty looking Back" (Moronobu Hishikawa)

1532 "The Prelude" (Shuho Yamakawa)

(Des G. Aoki. Photo)

1991 (19 Apr). Philatelic Week. 120th Anniv of first Japanese Stamps. P 13.

2141 **1531** 62y. multicoloured 90 30
2142 **1532** 62y. multicoloured 90 30
MS2143 93×77 mm. Nos. 2141/2 .... 2·50 2·00

Nos. 2141/2 were issued in separate sheets of 10 stamps and also together in sheets of 20 stamps containing the two values in separate panes divided by five inscribed labels in a vertical gutter.

1533 Weeping Cherry Blossom and Phoenix Hall, Byodoin Temple

1534 Early Leveller and Standard Datum Repository, Tokyo

1539 Japanese Snipe (*Gallinago hardwickii*)

1540 Brown Booby (*Sula leucogaster*)

(Des M. Morita. Photo)

(Des E. Uchida. Photo)

1991 (24 May). National Afforestation Campaign. P 13½.

2144 **1533** 41y. multicoloured 60   30

1991 (28 June). Water Birds (1st series). P 13½.

2150 **1539** 62y. multicoloured .... 1·50   80
2151 **1540** 62y. multicoloured .... 1·50   80

Nos. 2150/1 were issued together in sheets of 20 stamps arranged in separate panes of each value, the panes divided by a vertical gutter.

See also Nos. 2162/3, 2179/80, 2184/5, 2198/9, 2241/2, 2247/8 and 2251/2.

(Des S. Watanabe. Photo)

1991 (30 May). Centenary of Standard Datum of Levelling. P 13.

2145 **1534** 62y. multicoloured 80   30

1535 Flowers

1536 Couple in Traditional Dress

1541 Kikugoro Onoe VI in Title Role of *Spirit of the Lion*

1542 Utaemon Nakamura VI as Princess Yaegaki in *24 Examples of Filial Piety*

(Des G. Aoki. Photo)

1991 (28 June). Kabuki Theatre (1st series). P 13 (62y.) or 13½ (100y.).

2152 **1541** 62y. dp grey-green, gold & black........... 1·00   30
2153 **1542** 100y. multicoloured..................... 1·70   40

See also Nos. 2164/5, 2172/3, 2181/2, 2186/7 and 2190/1.

1537 "World Peace"

1538 Butterfly

1543 "Solidarity" in Sign Language and Congress Emblem

1544 Crystal Structure

(Des M. Kodama (41y.), Z. Horváth (62y.), Eva Suto (70y.), K. Sashida (100y.). Photo)

(Des H. Sato and A. Kikuchi. Photo)

1991 (31 May). Winning Entries in Postage Stamp Design Contest. P 13.

2146 **1535** 41y. multicoloured 60   30
2147 **1536** 62y. multicoloured 80   30
2148 **1537** 70y. yellow-brown, ultram & blk............. 1·10   30
2149 **1538** 100y. multicoloured..................... 1·60   40
2146/2149 *Set of 4*.................................. 3·75   1·20

1991 (5 July). 11th World Federation of the Deaf International Congress, Tokyo. P 13.

2154 **1543** 62y.+10y. multicoloured .... 1·00   30

The premium was assigned to programmes for helping the deaf.

(Des S. Watanabe. Litho)

1991 (19 July). International Conference on Materials and Mechanism of Superconductivity, Kanazawa. P 13½.

2155 **1544** 62y. multicoloured 80   30

1545 Girl sitting on Morning Glory

1546 Fairy on Horse

(Des Moe Nagata. Photo)

1991 (23 July). Letter Writing Day. P 13×13½ (41y.) or 13½ (62y.).
2156 **1545** 41y. multicoloured 70 30
   a. Booklet pane. Nos. 2156×5
   and 2157×5.............................. 8·75
2157 **1546** 62y. multicoloured .... 1·00 30
MS2158 72×93 mm. No. 2157 .... 1·10 85
  The booklet pane has its horizontal edges imperforate, giving stamps with one edge imperf.
  For design similar to Type **1546** but with centre motif drawn larger, see No. 2104.

1547 High Jumping

1548 Putting the Shot

(Des T. Shimizu. Photo)

1991 (23 Aug). Third World Athletics Championships, Tokyo. P 13.
2159 **1547** 41y. multicoloured 60 30
2160 **1548** 62y. multicoloured 80 30

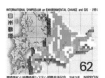

1549 Map and Computer Image of Hokkaido

(Des M. Hisano. Photo)

1991 (23 Aug). International Symposium on Environmental Change and Geographic Information Systems, Asahikawa, Hokkaido. P 13.
2161 **1549** 62y. multicoloured 80 30

1550 Japanese Gull (*Larus crassirostris*)

1551 Little Grebe (*Podiceps ruficollis*)

(Des M. Morita. Photo)

1991 (27 Sept). Water Birds (2nd series). P 13½.
2162 **1550** 62y. multicoloured .... 1·50 80
2163 **1551** 62y. multicoloured .... 1·50 80
  Nos. 2162/3 were issued together in sheets of 20 stamps arranged in separate panes of each value, the panes divided by a vertical gutter.

1552 Koshiro Matsumoto VII as Benkei in *The Subscription List*

1553 Danjuro Ichikawa XI as Danjo in *Tweezers*

(Des G. Aoki. Photo)

1991 (27 Sept). Kabuki Theatre (2nd series). P 13 (62y.) or 13½ (100y.).
2164 **1552** 62y. black, lavender-grey and gold .... 1·00 30
2165 **1553** 100y. multicoloured .... 1·70 40

1554 Nobles watching burning Oten Gate

1555 Arrest of Yoshio Tomo (arsonist)

(Des M. Morita. Recess and photo)

1991 (7 Oct). International Correspondence Week. Details from Ban Dainagon Picture Scrolls by Mitsunaga Tokiwa. P 13½.
2166 **1554** 80y. multicoloured .... 1·00 30
2167 **1555** 120y. multicoloured .... 1·60 45

1556 "Clear Day with Southern Breeze" (from "36 Views of Mt. Fuji" by Hokusai Katsushika) and Seismographic Wave	**1557** Tea Utensils and Flower

(Des M. Morita. Photo)

1991 (8 Oct). Earthquake and Natural Disaster Countermeasures Conference, Tokyo. P 13.
2168 **1556** 62y. multicoloured 85   30

(Des S. Watanabe. Litho)

1991 (31 Oct). 800th Anniv of Introduction of Green Tea into Japan. P 13.
2169 **1557** 62y. multicoloured 85   30

1558 "Saucy Girl" (from "A Selection of Beautiful Women" by Kunisada Utagawa)

(Des G. Aoki. Recess and litho)

1991 (15 Nov). "Phila Nippon '91" International Stamp Exhibition, Tokyo (2nd issue). Phosphorescent paper (No. 2170). P 13.
2170 **1558** 62y. multicoloured 95   30
MS2171 93×77 mm. No. 2170×2 .... 2·00   2·00

1559 Baigyoku Nakamura III as the Ogiya Courtesan Yugiri in *Yoshida-ya*	**1560** Ganjiro Nakamura III as Jihei Kamiya in *Shinju-Ten no Amijima*

(Des G. Aoki. Photo)

1991 (20 Nov). Kabuki Theatre (3rd series). Works by Chikamatsu Monzaemon. Phosphorescent paper (62y.). P 13 (62y.) or 13½ (100y.).
2172 **1559** 62y. black, dull mauve and gold............. 1·00   30
2173 **1560** 100y. multicoloured .... 1·80   40

1561 Boy building Toy Town	**1562** Ishikawa Papier-mâché Monkey	**1563** Obata Monkey

(Des M. Morita. Photo)

1991 (20 Nov). 30th Anniv of Administrative Counsellors System. Phosphorescent paper. P 13.
2174 **1561** 62y. multicoloured 85   25

(Des I. Harada (41y.), Etsuyo Uchida (62y.). Photo)

1991 (2 Dec). New Year's Greetings. P 13×13½ (41y.) or 13 (62y.).
2175 **1562** 41y. multicoloured 65   30
2176 **1563** 62y. multicoloured 85   30

1564 Ishikawa Pâpier-maché Monkey	**1565** Obata Monkey

(Des I. Harada (41y.), Etsuyo Uchida (62y.). Photo and typo)

1991 (2 Dec). New Year Lottery Stamps. P 13½.
2177 **1564** 41y. +3y. multicoloured 85   60
2178 **1565** 62y. +3y. multicoloured .... 1·20   85
Each stamp carries a lottery number.

1566 Tufted Puffin (*Lunda cirrhata*)	**1567** Hooded Cranes (*Grus monacha*)

(Des M. Morita. Photo)

1992 (30 Jan). Water Birds (3rd series). P 13½.
2179 **1566** 62y. multicoloured .... 1·60   70
2180 **1567** 62y. multicoloured .... 1·60   70
Nos. 2179/80 were issued together in sheets of 20 stamps arranged in separate panes of each value, the panes divided by a vertical gutter.

1568 Kichiemon Nakamura I as Jiro Naozane Kumagai in *Chronicle of Two Boys at Battle of Ichinotani* by Munesuke Namiki

1569 Nizaemon Kataoka XIII as Old Man in *Kotobuki Shiki Sambaso*

1573 Enjaku Jitsukawa II as Ishikawa-Goemon in *Two-Storey Gate—Pawlonia* by Gohei Namiki

1574 Hakuo Matsumoto I as Oishi-Kuranosuke in *Loyal Retainers in Genroku* by Seika Mayama

(Des G. Aoki. Photo)

1992 (20 Feb). Kabuki Theatre (4th series). Phosphorescent paper (62y.). P 13 (62y.) or 13½ (100y.).

2181	**1568**	62y. multicoloured	1·00	30
2182	**1569**	100y. multicoloured	1·80	40

(Des G. Aoki. Photo)

1992 (10 Apr). Kabuki Theatre (5th series). Phosphorescent paper (62y.). P 13 (62y.) or 13½ (100y.).

2186	**1573**	62y. multicoloured	1·00	35
2187	**1574**	100y. multicoloured	1·80	40

1575 "Flowers on Chair" (Hoshun Yamaguchi)

1576 Shuri Castle

1570 Orchid and Chimpanzees

(Des G. Aoki. Photo)

(Des S. Watanabe. Photo)

1992 (20 Apr). Philatelic Week. Phosphorescent paper. P 13.

2188	**1575**	62y. multicoloured	85	35

1992 (2 Mar). Eighth Conference of Parties to Convention on International Trade in Endangered Species, Kyoto City. Phosphorescent paper. P 13.

2183	**1570**	62y. multicoloured	1·30	40

(Des M. Hisano. Photo)

1992 (15 May). 20th Anniv of Return of Okinawa (Ryukyu Islands). Phosphorescent paper. P 13.

2189	**1576**	62y. multicoloured	1·30	25

1571 Whooper Swan (*Cygnus cygnus*)

1572 Painted Snipe (*Rostratula benghalensis*)

1577 Baiko Onoe VII as the Wisteria Maiden

1578 Shoroku Onoe II as Goro Soga and Kanzaburo Nakamura XVII as Juro Soga in *Kotobuki-Soga-taimen*

(Des M. Morita. Photo)

1992 (25 Mar). Water Birds (4th series). P 13½.

2184	**1571**	62y. multicoloured	1·60	35
2185	**1572**	62y. multicoloured	1·50	35

Nos. 2184/5 were issued together in sheets of 20 stamps arranged in separate panes of each value, the panes divided by a vertical gutter.

(Des G. Aoki. Photo)

1992 (30 June). Kabuki Theatre (6th series). Phosphorescent paper (62y.). P 13 (62y.) or 13½ (100y.*).

2190	**1577**	62y. multicoloured	1·00	35
2191	**1578**	100y. multicoloured	1·80	40

1579 "ADEOS"
Observation
Satellite

1580 "BS-3"
Broadcasting Satellite
and Space Station

(Des S. Watanabe. Photo)

1992 (7 July). International Space Year. Phosphorescent paper. P 13.
2192 **1579** 62y. multicoloured 85   25
    a. Horiz pair. Nos. 2192/3 .... 1·80   55
2193 **1580** 62y. multicoloured 85   25
    Nos. 2192/3 were issued together in horizontal *se-tenant* pairs
within the sheet, forming the composite design illustrated.

1581 Bird
delivering Letter
to Flower

1582 Bird
delivering Letter
to Dog

(Des Etsuyo Uchida (41y.), S. Yoh (62y.). Photo)

1992 (23 July). Letter Writing Day. P 13×13½ (41y.) or 13½ (62y.).
2194 **1581** 41y. multicoloured 75   25
    a. Booklet pane. Nos. 2194×5
    and 2195×5 .... 9·00
2195 **1582** 62y. multicoloured .... 1·00   60
MS2196 72×93 mm. No. 2195 .... 3·25   2·75
    The booklet pane has its horizontal outer edges imperforate giving
stamps with one edge imperf.

1583 Ammonite, Map and
Stratigraphic Plan

(Des K. Takeara. Photo)

1992 (24 Aug). 29th International Geological Congress, Kyoto.
Phosphorescent paper. P 13.
2197 **1583** 62y. multicoloured 85   40

1584 White-faced Shearwater
(*Calonectris leucomelas*)

1585 Ruddy Kingfisher
(*Halcyon coromanda*)

(Des M. Morita. Photo)

1992 (31 Aug). Water Birds (5th series). P 13½.
2198 **1584** 62y. multicoloured .... 1·60   60
2199 **1585** 62y. multicoloured .... 1·60   60
    Nos. 2198/9 were issued together in sheets of 20 stamps arranged
in separate panes of each value, the panes divided by a gutter.

1586 Canoeing

(Des A. Kikuchi. Photo)

1992 (4 Sept). 47th National Athletic Meeting, Yamagata.
Phosphorescent paper. P 13½.
2200 **1586** 41y. multicoloured 75   25

1587 Japanese Jar
(Ninsei Nonomura)

1588 Chinese Vase
(Tang dynasty)

(Des M. Morita. Recess and photo)

1992 (29 Sept). 20th Anniv of Restoration of Diplomatic Relations
with China. Phosphorescent paper. P 13.
2201 **1587** 62y. multicoloured 85   35
    a. Pair. Nos. 2201/2 .... 1·80   75
2202 **1588** 62y. multicoloured 85   35
    Nos. 2201/2 were issued together in *se-tenant* pairs within the
sheet.

1589 Nobles arriving at Taiken Gate

1590 Fujiwara no Nobuyori giving
Audience

(Des M. Morita. Litho)

1992 (6 Oct). International Correspondence Week. Details from "Tale of Heiji" Shinzei Picture Scroll. P 13½.

2203	**1589**	80y. multicoloured	1·20	35
2204	**1590**	120y. multicoloured	1·90	35

1591 "Friends" (Tomoko Komoto)

1592 "Gaiety on Christmas Night" (Brat Anca)

(Des M. Morita. Photo)

1992 (9 Oct). Third Stamp Design Competition Winners. Phosphorescent paper (62y.). P 13.

2205	**1591**	62y. multicoloured	85	35
2206	**1592**	70y. multicoloured	95	35

1593 "Kyo" Ideograph, Mt. Fuji, Sun and Waves

(Des N. Takeara. Photo)

1992 (27 Oct). 30th International Co-operative Alliance Congress, Tokyo. Phosphorescent paper. P 13.

2207	**1593**	62y. multicoloured	85	35

1594 Takakazu Seki (mathematician, 350th birth)

1595 Akiko Yosano (poet, 50th death)

(Des G. Aoki. Recess and photo)

1992 (4 Nov). Anniversaries. Phosphorescent paper. P 13.

2208	**1594**	62y. multicoloured	1·10	35
2209	**1595**	62y. multicoloured	1·10	35

1596 Certified Public Tax Accountants' Association Emblem

1597 Papier-mâché and Clay Cock

1598 Tsuyazaki Clay Cock on Drum

(Des A. Kikuchi. Photo)

1992 (9 Nov). 50th Anniv of Tax Accountants Law. Phosphorescent paper. P 13.

2210	**1596**	62y. multicoloured	85	35

(Des Etsuyo Uchida (41y.), I. Harada (62y.). Photo)

1992 (16 Nov). New Year's Greetings. P 13×13½.

2211	**1597**	41y. multicoloured	75	35
2212	**1598**	62y. multicoloured	1·10	35

1599 Papier-mâché and Clay Cock

1600 Tsuyazaki Clay Cock on Drum

(Des Etsuyo Uchida (41y.), I. Harada (62y.). Photo)

1992 (16 Nov). New Year Lottery Stamps. P 13½.

2213	**1599**	41y. +3y. multicoloured	85	70
2214	**1600**	62y. +3y. multicoloured	1·20	95

Each stamp carries a lottery number.

1601 *Orthetrum albistylum* (dragonfly)

1601a *Oxycetonia jucunda* (beetle)

1602 Mikado Swallowtail

1603 Ladybirds

1603a Honey Bee

1603b *Lycaena* (copper butterfly)

1604 Mandarin

1605 Japanese White Eye

1606 Eastern Turtle Dove

1617 Praying Mantis, Chrysanthemums and Hibiscus (after Hoitsu Sakai)

1618 "Pine and Hawk" (Sesson Shukei)

1606a Great Tit

1607 Varied Tit

1608 Greater Pied Kingfisher

(Des Y. Higashitsunoi (15y.), M. Hisano (9, 18y.), M. Morita (others). Recess and photo (1000y.), photo (others))

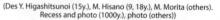

1992 (30 Nov)–**02**. (a) Ordinary gum. Ordinary paper (9, 15, 18, 41, 62, 72, 420y.) or phosphorescent paper (others). P 13×13½.

2215	**1601**	9y. olive-yellow, black and greenish blue (13.1.94)	20	20
2215a	**1601a**	10y. multicoloured (28.11.97)	20	20
		a. Coil. P 13×imperf (11.9.98)	20	20
2216	**1602**	15y. blackish brown, apple green and yellow-green (25.4.94)	30	25
2217	**1603**	18y. yellow-green, violet-grey and vermilion (13.1.94)	65	55
2217a	**1603a**	20y. multicoloured (28.11.97)	45	20
2217b	**1603b**	30y. multicoloured (28.11.97)	75	35
2218	**1604**	41y. orange, dp blue & new blue	95	25
		a. Booklet pane. Nos. 2218×5 and 2220×5 (26.2.93)	21·00	
2219	**1605**	50y. olive-yellow, greenish blue and black (13.1.94)	1·60	55
		a. Sheetlet. Nos. 2219×5, 2222×10 plus labels (29.3.94)	42·00	
		b. Coil. P 13×imperf (24.1.94)	1·60	55
2220	**1606**	62y. pale orge, dp bl & greenish bl....	1·10	45
2220a	**1606a**	70y. multicoloured (22.7.97)	1·20	45
2221	**1607**	72y. orange, deep blue & lt green	2·40	95
2222	**1608**	80y. dp violet-blue, yellow-ochre & brt yellowish gm (13.1.94)	2·50	55
		a. Coil. P 13×imperf (24.1.94)	2·50	1·10
2223	**1609**	90y. brn, yell & new bl (13.1.94)	3·00	60
2223a	**1609a**	110y. multicoloured (22.7.97)	2·20	70
2223b	**1609b**	120y. multicoloured (16.2.98)	2·75	95
2224	**1610**	130y. multicoloured (25.4.94)	2·40	45
2224a	**1610a**	140y. multicoloured (16.2.98)	3·25	1·10
2224b	**1610b**	160y. multicoloured (16.2.98)	3·75	1·10
2225	**1611**	190y. multicoloured (25.4.94)	3·50	70
2226	**1612**	270y. multicoloured (24.1.94)	5·50	90
2227	**1613**	350y. magenta, lavender and pale green (24.1.94)	7·00	1·20
2228	**1614**	390y. multicoloured (28.3.96)	7·50	80
2229	**1615**	420y. bright violet, apple green and deep green (24.1.94)	8·75	1·40
2230	**1616**	430y. multicoloured (25.4.94)	8·00	1·60
2231	**1617**	700y. multicoloured (4.7.95)	13·00	5·25
2232	**1618**	1000y. multicoloured (28.3.96)	15·00	5·25
2215/2232		*Set of 26*	90·00	24·00

(b) Booklet stamps. Self-adhesive gum. Ordinary paper. Die-cut

2235	**1604**	41y. orange, dp blue & new blue	1·30	95
2236	**1605**	50y. olive-yellow, greenish blue and black (24.1.94)	1·40	1·10
		a. Die-cut perf 12 (25.2.02)	1·40	1·10
2237	**1606**	62y. pale orge, dp bl & greenish bl	1·70	95
2238	**1608**	80y. dp violet-blue, yellow-ochre & brt yellowish grn (24.1.94)	2·50	2·10
		a. Die-cut perf 12 (25.2.02)	2·50	2·10

No. 2218a has its outer edges imperforate, giving stamps with one or two adjacent sides imperf.

No. 2219a exists in two versions, differing in the design of the labels.

No. 2220 was issued both in sheets of 100 and in sheetlets of 10 stamps (5×2) imperforate at the outer edges. Although the latter resembles a booklet pane the postal authority issued no booklet.

Nos. 2235/8 are peeled directly from the booklet covers. It is not therefore possible to collect them as booklet panes.

1606a Great Tit

1607 Varied Tit

1608 Greater Pied Kingfisher

1609 Spotbill Duck

1609a Little Ringed Plover

1609b Bull-headed Shrike

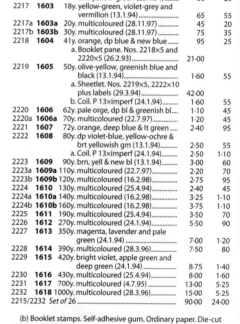

1610 Bullfinch

1610a Japanese Grosbeak

1610b Jay

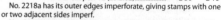

1611 Orchids

1612 Wild Pinks

1613 Adder's Tongue Lily

1614 Dayflowers

1615 Iris

1616 Violets

1621 Common Kingfisher (*Alcedo atthis*) **1622** Cattle Egret (*Bubulcus ibis*)

(Des M. Morita. Photo)

1993 (29 Jan). Water Birds (6th series). P 13½.
2241 **1621** 62y. multicoloured .... 1·80   45
2242 **1622** 62y. multicoloured .... 1·80   45
Nos. 2241/2 were issued together in sheets of 20 stamps arranged in separate panes of each value, the panes divided by a vertical gutter.

1623 Super Giant Slalom   **1624** Downhill

(Des S. Watanabe (41y.), T. Shimizu (62y.). Photo)

1993 (3 Feb). World Alpine Skiing Championships, Shizukuishi (nr. Morioka). Phosphorescent paper. P 13.
2243 **1623** 41y. multicoloured 75   35
2244 **1624** 62y. multicoloured .... 1·10   35

1625 Poppies (after Hochu Nakamura)   **1626** Cherry Blossoms (after Hoitsu Sakai)

(Des G. Aoki. Photo)

1993 (12 Mar). Seasonal Flowers (1st series). Phosphorescent paper. P 13.
2245 **1625** 41y. multicoloured .... 1·10   45
2246 **1626** 62y. multicoloured .... 1·70   45
See also Nos. 2258/9, 2269/70 and 2287/8.

1627 White-fronted Geese (*Anser albifrons*)   **1628** Japanese White-necked Cranes (*Grus vipio*)

(Des M. Morita. Photo)

1993 (31 Mar). Water Birds (7th series). P 13½.
2247 **1627** 62y. multicoloured .... 1·80   45
2248 **1628** 62y. multicoloured .... 1·80   45
Nos. 2247/8 were issued together in sheets of 20 stamps arranged in separate panes of each value, the panes divided by a vertical gutter.
No. 2247 is wrongly inscribed "Ansner".

1629 "In the Studio" (Nanpu Katayama)   **1630** Coral Trees and Reef, Minnajima Island

(Des G. Aoki. Photo)

1993 (20 Apr). Philatelic Week. Phosphorescent paper. P 13.
2249 **1629** 62y. multicoloured 95   35

(Des Etsuyo Uchida. Photo)

1993 (23 Apr). National Afforestation Campaign. Phosphorescent paper. P 13½.
2250 **1630** 41y. multicoloured .... 1·20   45

1631 Baikal Teal (*Anas formosa*)   **1632** White-tailed Sea Eagle (*Haliaeetus albicilla*)

(Des M. Morita. Photo)

1993 (25 May). Water Birds (8th series). P 13½.
2251 **1631** 62y. multicoloured .... 1·30   1·10
2252 **1632** 62y. multicoloured .... 1·30   1·10
Nos. 2251/2 were issued together in sheets of 20 stamps arranged in separate panes of each value, the panes divided by a vertical gutter.

1633 "Mandarin Duck in Nest" (pattern of groom's jacket)   **1634** "Gardenia in Nest" (pattern of bride's robe)

1635 "Mandarin Duck in Nest" and "Gardenia in Nest"

(Des M. Morita. Photo)

1993 (8 June). Wedding of Crown Prince Naruhito and Masako Owada (1st issue). Phosphorescent paper (62y.). P 13.
2253 **1633** 62y. multicoloured .... 1·10 45
    a. Pair. Nos. 2253/4.................... 2·30 95
2254 **1634** 62y. multicoloured .... 1·10 45
2255 **1635** 70y. multicoloured .... 1·20 45
2253/2255 *Set of 3* .... 3·00 1·20
Nos. 2253/4 were issued together in *se-tenant* pairs within the sheet.
See also No. **MS**2276.

1636 Manchurian Crane with Chicks   **1637** Manchurian Crane

(Des M. Morita. Photo)

1993 (10 June). Fifth Meeting of Ramsar Convention for the Preservation of Wetlands, Kushiro (Hokkaido). Phosphorescent paper. P 13½.
2256 **1636** 62y. multicoloured .... 1·10 45
    a. Pair. Nos. 2256/7.................... 2·30 95
2257 **1637** 62y. multicoloured .... 1·10 45
Nos. 2256/7 were issued together in *se-tenant* pairs within the sheet.

1638 Lily (after Kiitsu Suzuki)   **1639** Thistle (after Shiko Watanabe)

(Des G. Aoki. Photo)

1993 (18 June). Seasonal Flowers (2nd series). Phosphorescent paper. P 13½ (41y.) or 13 (62y.).
2258 **1638** 41y. multicoloured 75 25
2259 **1639** 62y. multicoloured .... 1·10 45

1640 Stylized Ideographs for "Commercial Registration" **1641** Puppy reading Letter under Tree **1642** Man pointing at Flying Letter

(Des N. Takeara. Photo)

1993 (1 July). Centenary of Commercial Registration System. Phosphorescent paper. P 13.
2260 **1640** 62y. multicoloured .... 1·10 45

(Des S. Yo (41y.), T. Yanase (62y.). Photo)

1993 (23 July). Letter Writing Day. Phosphorescent paper. P 13×13½ (41y.) or 13½ (62y.).
2261 **1641** 41y. multicoloured 95 35
    a. Booklet pane. Nos. 2261×5 and 2262×5.................... 11·50
2262 **1642** 62y. multicoloured .... 1·30 45
MS2263 72×93 mm. No. 2262 .... 1·40 1·10
The booklet pane has its horizontal outer edges imperforate, giving stamps with one side imperf.

1643 Heart, Clouds and Flowers

(Des Etsuyo Uchida. Photo)

1993 (23 Aug). World Federation for Mental Health Congress, Chiba City. Phosphorescent paper. P 13.
2264 **1643** 62y. multicoloured .... 1·10 45

1644 *Glaucidium palmatum*   **1645** *Sciadopitys verticillata*

(Des M. Hisano. Photo)

1993 (23 Aug). 15th International Botanical Congress, Yokohama. Phosphorescent paper. P 13.
2265 **1644** 62y. multicoloured .... 1·10 45
    a. Pair. Nos. 2265/6.................... 2·30 95
2266 **1645** 62y. multicoloured .... 1·10 45
Nos. 2265/6 were issued together in *se-tenant* pairs within the sheet.

1646 Swimming   **1647** Karate

(Des A. Kikuchi. Photo)

1993 (3 Sept). 48th National Athletic Meeting, Kagawa Prefecture. Phosphorescent paper. P 13½.

2267	**1646**	41y. multicoloured	85	35
	a.	Pair. Nos. 2267/8	1·80	75
2268	**1647**	41y. multicoloured	85	35

Nos. 2267/8 were issued together in *se-tenant* pairs within the sheet.

1648 "Chinese Bellflowers" (Korin Ogata)

1649 Chrysanthemums (detail of "Cranes and Plants in Spring and Autumn", Kiitsu Suzuki)

(Des G. Aoki. Photo)

1993 (16 Sept). Seasonal Flowers (3rd series). Phosphorescent paper. P 13½ (41y.) or 13 (62y.).

2269	**1648**	41y. multicoloured	75	25
2270	**1649**	62y. multicoloured	1·20	45

1650 "Arrival of Portuguese" (folding screen)

1651 Jesuit Mother-of-Pearl Inlaid Host Box

(Des M. Morita. Photo)

1993 (22 Sept). 450th Anniv of First Portuguese Visit to Japan. Phosphorescent paper. P 13.

2271	**1650**	62y. multicoloured	1·10	45
	a.	Pair. Nos. 2271/8	2·30	95
2272	**1651**	62y. multicoloured	1·10	45

Nos. 2271/2 were issued together in *se-tenant* pairs within the sheet.

1652 Ki no Tsurayuki (Agetatami Scrolls)

1653 Kodai no Kimi (Satake Scrolls)

(Des M. Morita. Photo)

1993 (6 Oct). International Correspondence Week. Picture Scrolls of the Thirty-six Immortal Poets. P 13½.

2273	**1652**	80y. multicoloured	1·40	55
2274	**1653**	120y. multicoloured	2·10	80

1654 Sprinter

1655 Prince Naruhito and Princess Masako

(Des M. Hisano. Photo)

1993 (7 Oct). Tenth International Veterans' Athletic Championships, Miyazaki. Phosphorescent paper. P 13.

2275	**1654**	62y. multicoloured	1·10	45

(Des S. Watanabe. Photo)

1993 (13 Oct). Wedding of Crown Prince Naruhito and Masako Owada (2nd issue). Sheet 90×93 mm. P 13½.

MS2276	**1655**	62y. multicoloured	2·40	1·90

Price quoted is for the miniature sheet alone. A commemorative folder for the sheet was sold separately.

1656 Toson Shimazaki (writer, 50th death)

1657 Umetaro Suzuki (scientist, 50th death)

1658 Kazan Watanabe (after Chinzan Tsubaki) (artist, birth bicentenary)

1659 Shibahara Clay Chin Dog

1660 Kosen Clay Tosa Dog

(Des G. Aoki. Litho (2279), recess and photo (others))

1993 (4 Nov). Anniversaries. Phosphorescent paper. P 13.
2277 **1656** 62y. multicoloured .... 1·10   45
2278 **1657** 62y. multicoloured .... 1·10   45
2279 **1658** 62y. multicoloured .... 1·10   45
2277/2279 Set of 3 .... 3·00   1·20

(Des I. Harada (41y.), A. Kikuchi (62y.). Photo)

1993 (15 Nov). New Year's Greetings. P 13×13½.
2280 **1659** 41y. multicoloured   95   35
2281 **1660** 62y. multicoloured .... 1·10   45

1661 Shibahara
Clay Chin Dog

1662 Kosen Clay
Tosa Dog

1663 Rice Flowers

(Des I. Harada (41y.), A Kikuchi (62y.). Photo and typo)

1993 (15 Nov). New Year Lottery Stamps. P 13½.
2282 **1661** 41y.+3y. multicoloured.............................. 1·10   90
2283 **1662** 62y.+3y. multicoloured.............................. 1·20   95
Each stamp carries a lottery number.

(Des A. Tamaki. Photo)

1993 (17 Nov). Centenary of Agricultural Research Centre, Nishigahara. Phosphorescent paper. P 13½.
2284 **1663** 62y. multicoloured .... 1·10   45

1664 Man and Bird
(Soichiro Asaba)

1665 Symbols
(Armand Clotagatilde)

(Des M. Morita. Photo)

1993 (10 Dec). 45th Anniv of Declaration of Human Rights. Stamp design contest winning entries. Phosphorescent paper (62y.). P 13.
2285 **1664** 62y. multicoloured .... 1·10   45
2286 **166S** 70y. multicoloured .... 1·20   45

1666 Plum Blossom
(after Korin Ogata)

1667 Winter Camellia
(after Hoitsu Sakai)

(Des G. Aoki. Photo)

1994 (28 Jan). Seasonal Flowers (4th series). Phosphorescent paper. P 13½ (50y.) or 13 (80y.).
2287 **1666** 50y. multicoloured   85   35
2288 **1667** 80y. multicoloured .... 1·40   60

1994 (10 Mar). Special Correspondence Stamps. As Nos. 1677/9 but values changed. Phosphorescent paper. P 13×13½.
2289 **1098** 50y. multicoloured .... 1·50   45
2290 **1099** 50y. multicoloured   85   35
2291   80y. multicoloured .... 1·40   60
2292 **1100** 90y. multicoloured .... 1·60   60
2289/2292 Set of 4.. 4·75   1·80

1668 Ladies' Figure Skating

1669 Ice Dancing

1670 Men's Figure
Skating

1671 Pairs Figure
Skating

(Des M. Hisano (2293), S. Watanabe (2294), A. Kikuchi (others). Photo)

1994 (17 Mar). World Figure Skating Championships, Chiba City. Phosphorescent paper. P 13.
2293 **1668** 50y. multicoloured   85   35
            a. Pair. Nos. 2293/4..................... 1·80   75
2294 **1669** 50y. multicoloured   85   35
2295 **1670** 80y. multicoloured .... 1·40   60
            a. Pair. Nos. 2295/6..................... 3·00   1·30
2296 **1671** 80y. multicoloured .... 1·40   60
2293/2296 Set of 4.. 4·00   1·70
Stamps of the same value were issued together in se-tenant pairs within their sheets.

1672 "Irises"
(Heihachiro Fukuda)

(Des G. Aoki. Photo)

1994 (20 Apr). Philatelic Week. Phosphorescent paper. P 13.
2297 **1672** 80y. multicoloured .... 2·40   60

1673 "Love" (Chieko Kitajima)

1674 "Happiness Flower" (Shigenobu Nagaishi)

1675 "Family flowering at Home" (Junichi Mineta)

1676 "Family in Flight" (Soichiro Asaba)

1994 (13 May). International Year of the Family. Winning Entries in Stamp Design Contest. Phosphorescent paper. Photo. P 13.

2298	**1673** 50y. multicoloured	1·20	35
	a. Pair. Nos. 2298 and 2300	2·50	75
2299	**1674** 50y. multicoloured	1·20	35
	a. Pair. Nos. 2299 and 2301	1·70	60
2300	**1675** 80y. multicoloured	3·75	1·30
2301	**1676** 80y. multicoloured	1·70	60
2298/2301	Set of 4	5·25	1·70

Nos. 2298 and 2300 and Nos. 2299 and 2301 respectively were issued together in se-tenant pairs within their sheets.

1677 White Stork, Marguerites and Camphor Tree

1678 Houses by the Waterside

(Des Etsuyo Uchida. Photo)

1994 (20 May). National Afforestation Campaign. Phosphorescent paper. P 13½.
2302 **1677** 50y. multicoloured .... 1·50   60

(Des K. Kuroi. Photo)

1994 (23 May). International Conference on Reduction of Natural Disasters, Yokohama. Phosphorescent paper. P 13.
2303 **1678** 80y. multicoloured .... 1·40   60
No. 2303 was issued in sheets of 16 stamps and four labels bearing the conference emblem.

1679 Pylon and Monju Building

1680 Wildlife

(Des K. Takeara. Photo)

1994 (24 May). Achievement of Initial Criticality (self-sustaining reaction) in Monju Nuclear Fast Breeder Reactor, Tsuruga. Phosphorescent paper. P 13.
2304 **1679** 80y. multicoloured .... 2·40   60

(Des T. Murakami. Photo)

1994 (3 June). Environment Day. Phosphorescent paper. P 13.
2305 **1680** 80y. multicoloured .... 2·40   60

1681 Envelope "Ship" and Man

1682 Giraffe carrying Envelope

(Des T. Yanase (50y.), Y. Sugita (80y.). Photo)

1994 (22 July). Letter Writing Day. Non-phosphorescent paper. (**MS**2308) or phosphorescent paper (others). P 13½.

2306	**1681** 50y. multicoloured	1·10	35
	a. Booklet pane. Nos. 2306×5 and 2307×5	26·00	
2307	**1682** 80y. multicoloured	1·40	60
MS2308	72×93 mm. No. 2307	1·50	1·20

The booklet pane has its outer edges imperforate, giving stamps with one or two sides imperf.

1683 Emblem in Eye

1684 Baron Maeshima (Postal Minister) and 1871 48 mon "Dragon" Stamp

(Des M. Hisano. Photo)

1994 (5 Aug). Tenth International AIDS Conference, Yokohama. Phosphorescent paper. P 13½.
2309 **1683** 80y. multicoloured .... 1·40   60

(Des M. Morita. Recess and photo)

1994 (10 Aug). History of Stamps (1st series). First Japanese Issue. Multicoloured, frame colour of "Dragon" stamp given. Phosphorescent paper. P 13½.

2310	**1684** 80y. brown	1·40	60
	a. Horiz strip of 4. Nos. 2310/13	5·75	
2311	– 80y. indigo	1·40	60
2312	– 80y. red	1·40	60
2313	– 80y. bronze green	1·40	60
2310/2313	Set of 4	5·00	2·20

Designs:—No. 2311, 100mon "Dragon" stamp; 2312, 200mon "Dragon" stamp; 2313, 500mon "Dragon" stamp. The central portion of the stamp portrayed varies according to value.
Nos. 2310/13 were issued together in horizontal se-tenant strips of four stamps within the sheet.
See also Nos. 2339/42, 2345/6, 2363/4, 2382/5 and 2416/19.

1685/1686 Airport and Airplane bearing Airport Code

1687 Airplane approaching Airport

(Des A. Tamaki. Photo)

1994 (2 Sept). Opening of Kansai International Airport, Osaka. Phosphorescent paper. P 13.

2314	**1685** 80y. multicoloured	1·40	60
	a. Vert strip of 3. Nos. 2314/16	4·50	
2315	**1686** 80y. multicoloured	1·40	60
2316	**1687** 80y. multicoloured	1·40	60
2314/2316	*Set of 3*	3·75	1·60

Nos. 2314/16 were issued together in vertical *se-tenant* strips of three within sheets of 20 stamps containing eight examples each of Nos. 2314/15 and four examples of No. 2316. Nos. 2314/15 form the composite design shown.

1688 Dish Aerial and Satellite

1689 Kickball

1690 Steeplechase

1691 Synchronized Swimming

(Des I. Harado. Photo)

1994 (19 Sept). International Telecommunications Union Plenipotentiary Conference, Kyoto. Phosphorescent paper. P 13.

2317	**1688** 80y. multicoloured	1·40	55

(Des I. Harada (50y.), T. Shimizu (others). Photo)

1994 (30 Sept). 12th Asian Games, Hiroshima. Phosphorescent paper. P 13.

2318	**1689** 50y. multicoloured	85	35
2319	**1690** 80y. multicoloured	1·40	55
	a. Pair. Nos. 2319/20.	3·00	1·20
2320	**1691** 80y. multicoloured	1·40	55
2318/2320	*Set of 3*	3·25	1·30

Nos. 2319/20 were issued together in *se-tenant* pairs within the sheet.

1692 Sugoroku

1693 Shogi

1694 Go

(Des M. Morita. Photo)

1994 (6 Oct). International Correspondence Week. Details of "House of Entertainment" (folding screen). Phosphorescent paper. P 13½.

2321	**1692** 90y. multicoloured	1·60	60
2322	**1693** 110y. multicoloured	1·90	80
2323	**1694** 130y. multicoloured	2·20	90
2321/2323	*Set of 3*	5·25	2·10

1695 Handball

(Des A. Kikuchi. Photo)

1994 (28 Oct). 49th National Athletic Meeting, Aichi. Phosphorescent paper. P 13½.

2324	**1695** 50y. multicoloured	85	35

1696 Michio Miyagi (composer)

1697 Gyoshu Hayami (painter) and "Moths"

(Des G. Aoki. Recess and photo)

1994 (4 Nov). Birth Centenaries. Phosphorescent paper. P 13.
2325 **1696** 80y. multicoloured .... 1·40   55
2326 **1897** 80y. multicoloured .... 1·40   55

1698 Fujiwara no Michinaga and Insulin Crystals

(Des K. Takeara. Photo)

1994 (4 Nov). 15th International Diabetes Federation Congress, Kobe. Phosphorescent paper. P 13.
2327 **1698** 80y. multicoloured .... 1·40   55
Fujiwara no Michinaga (966–1028) was the earliest known Japanese diabetic.

1699/1703 "Viewing Maple Leaves at Takao" (folding screen, Hideyori Kano) (½-size illustration)

1704 "Yokuryuchi Pool, Shugakuin Imperial Villa" (Kenji Kawai)

1705 "Rock Garden, Ryoan Temple" (Eizo Kato)

(Des G. Aoki (2333/4), M. Morita (others). Photo)

1994 (8 Nov). 1200th Anniv of Kyoto. Paintings. Phosphorescent paper. P 13½ (2333/4) or 13×13½ (others).
2328 **1699** 80y. multicoloured .... 1·40   55
     a. Horiz strip of 5. Nos. 2328/32 .... 7·25

2329 **1700** 80y. multicoloured .... 1·40   55
2330 **1701** 80y. multicoloured .... 1·40   55
2331 **1702** 80y. multicoloured .... 1·40   55
2332 **1703** 80y. multicoloured .... 1·40   55
2333 **1704** 80y. multicoloured .... 1·40   55
2334 **1705** 80y. multicoloured .... 1·40   55
2328/2334 *Set of 7* .... 8·75   3·50
     Nos. 2328/32 were issued together in horizontal *se-tenant* strips of five stamps within the sheet, forming the composite design illustrated.

1706 Izumo Papier-mâché Boar

1707 Boar (Takayama soft toy)

(Des H. Otsuka (50y.), Y. Higashitsunoi (80y.). Photo)

1994 (15 Nov). New Year's Greetings. Phosphorescent paper. P 13×13½.
2335 **1706** 50y. multicoloured 85   35
2336 **1707** 80y. multicoloured .... 1·40   55

1708 Izumo Papier-mâché Boar

1709 Boar (Takayama soft toy)

1710 5r. Stamp and Edoardo Chiossone (designer)

(Des H. Otsuka (50y.), Y. Higashitsunoi (80y.). Photo and typo)

1994 (15 Nov). New Year Lottery Stamps. Phosphorescent paper. P 13½.
2337 **1708** 50y.+3y. multicoloured.............................. 95   35
2338 **1709** 80y.+3y. multicoloured.............................. 1·50   60
     Each stamp carries a lottery number.

(Des M. Morita. Recess and photo)

1994 (18 Nov). History of Stamps (2nd series). "Koban" issue of 1876–88. Vert designs as T **1710**. Multicoloured, colour of featured stamp given. Phosphorescent paper. P 13½.
2339 **1710** 80y. green-slate .... 1·40   55
     a. Horiz strip of 4. Nos. 2339/42 .... 5·75
2340   – 80y. blackish brown........................... 1·40   55
2341   – 80y. carmine...................................... 1·40   55
2342   – 80y. deep blue................................... 1·40   55
2339/2342 *Set of 4* .... 5·00   2·00
     Featured stamps:—No. 2340, 1s. stamp (Type **20**); 2341, 12s. stamp (Type **21**); 2342, 20s. stamp (Type **22**).
     Nos. 2339/42 were issued together in horizontal *se-tenant* strips of four stamps within the sheet.

1711 Himeji Castle Tower

1712 "Himeji Castle" (Masami Takahashi)

1717 Emblem and National Flowers

1718 Emblem and Sports

(Des M. Morita. Photo)

1994 (14 Dec). World Heritage Sites (1st series). Phosphorescent paper. P 13.

2343	**1711** 80y. multicoloured	1·40	55
2344	**1712** 80y. multicoloured	1·40	55

See also Nos. 2347/8, 2373/4 and 2400/1.

(Des M. Morita (2349), A. Kikuchi (2350). Photo)

1995 (3 Mar). Centenary of Japan–Brazil Treaty of Friendship. Phosphorescent paper. P 13½.

2349	**1717** 80y. multicoloured	1·40	55
2350	**1718** 80y. multicoloured	1·40	55

Nos. 2349/50 were issued together in sheets of 20 stamps arranged in separate panes of each design, the panes divided by a vertical gutter.

1713 2s. Stamp and Postal Delivery by Hand-drawn Cart

1714 5s. Stamp and Postal Delivery by Horse-drawn Carriage

1719 Unebi and Nijo Mountains and Tile from Palace

1720 "Remembering Times Past" (Saburosuke Okada)

(Des M. Morita. Recess and photo)

1995 (25 Jan). History of Stamps (3rd series). 1894 Emperor's Silver Wedding issue and paintings by Shinsai Shibata. Phosphorescent paper. P 13½.

2345	**1713** 80y. multicoloured	1·40	55
2346	**1714** 80y. multicoloured	1·40	55

Nos. 2345/6 were issued together in sheets of 20 stamps arranged in separate panes of each design, the panes divided by a vertical gutter.

(Des M. Morita. Photo)

1995 (28 Mar). 1300th Anniv of Fujiwara Palace, Kashihara. Phosphorescent paper. P 13½.

2351	**1719** 50y. multicoloured	85	35
2352	**1720** 80y. multicoloured	1·40	55

1721 "Dissection" (Seison Maeda)

1722 "National Census" and "16"

(Des M. Morita. Photo)

1995 (31 Mar). Modern Anatomy Education. Phosphorescent paper. P 13.

2353	**1721** 80y. multicoloured	1·40	55

1715 "Kannon Bosatsu" (wall painting, Kondo Hall)

1716 Kondo Hall, Horyu Temple

(Des M. Morita. Photo)

1995 (22 Feb). World Heritage Sites (2nd series). Phosphorescent paper. P 13 (80y.) or 13½ (110y.).

2347	**1715** 80y. multicoloured	1·40	55
2348	**1716** 110y. multicoloured	1·90	80

(Des N. Takeara. Photo)

1995 (12 Apr). 16th National Census. Phosphorescent paper. P 13.

2354	**1722** 80y. multicoloured	1·40	55

1723 Volunteer teaching Bangladeshi Woman to Read

1724 "Visitor to Art Studio" (Keika Kanashima)

(Des H. Otsuka. Photo)

1995 (20 Apr). 30th Anniv of Japanese Overseas Co-operation Volunteers Service. Phosphorescent paper. P 13½.
2355 **1723** 80y. multicoloured .... 1·40   55

(Des G. Aoki. Photo)

1995 (20 Apr). Philatelic Week. Phosphorescent paper. P 13.
2356 **1724** 80y.+20y. multicoloured .... 1·80   1·50
The premium was for the Osaka/Kobe and Awaji earthquake victims' fund.

1725 Auspicious Clouds

1726 Reeds (mourning)

1727 Water Lily (mourning)

1728 Cloud, "Wind" and Pine Bark Pattern

1729 *Daphniphyllum macropodum*

(Des H. Isoda. Photo)

1995 (25 Apr). Special Correspondence Stamps. Phosphorescent paper. P 13×13½ (2357/8) or13½ (others).
2357 **1725** 50y. multicoloured 85   35
2358 **1726** 50y. multicoloured .... 1·20   35
2359 **1727** 80y. multicoloured .... 1·70   55
2360 **1728** 80y. multicoloured .... 1·40   55
2361 **1729** 90y. multicoloured .... 1·60   60
2357/2361 *Set of 5*... 6·00   2·20

1730 Maple and Shrine Island, Aki

(Des I. Harada. Photo)

1995 (19 May). National Afforestation Campaign. Phosphorescent paper. P 13½.
2362 **1730** 50y. multicoloured 85   35

1731 8½s. Stamp and First Airmail Flight from Osaka to Tokyo

1732 18s. Stamp and loading Freight onto Airplane

(Des M. Morita. Recess and photo)

1995 (25 May). History of Stamps (4th series). 1929 First Airmail issue. Phosphorescent paper. P 13½.
2363 **1731** 110y. multicoloured .... 1·90   80
2364 **1732** 110y. multicoloured .... 1·90   80
Nos. 2363/4 were issued together in sheets of 20 stamps arranged in separate panes of each design, the panes divided by a horizontal gutter.

1733 Hearts forming Flower

1734 Child with Balloon

1735 Flower and Pencil

1736 Star, Sun and Moon

1737 Child with Dog

1995 (1 June). Greetings Stamps. Phosphorescent paper. Self-adhesive. Photo. Die-cut perf 13½.
2365 **1733** 80y. multicoloured .... 1·40   55
    a. Pane. Nos. 2365/9 plus 5 labels....... 7·25
2366 **1734** 80y. multicoloured .... 1·40   55
2367 **1735** 80y. multicoloured .... 1·40   55
2368 **1736** 80y. multicoloured .... 1·40   55
2369 **1737** 80y. multicoloured .... 1·40   55
2365/2369 *Set of 5*... 6·25   2·50
Nos. 2365/9 were issued in self-adhesive panes of five stamps and five greetings labels.

1738 Postman

1739 Ostrich

(Des T. Yanase (50y.), Y. Sugita (80y.). Photo)

1995 (21 July). Letter Writing Day. Phosphorescent paper. P 13½.
2370 **1738** 50y. multicoloured 85   35
    a. Booklet pane. Nos. 2370×5 and 2371×5 .... 11·50
2371 **1739** 80y. multicoloured .... 1·40   55

MS2372 72×93 mm. No. 2371 .... 1·50   1·20
  The booklet pane has its outer edges imperforate, giving stamps with one or two sides imperf.

1740 Cedar
(*Cryptomeria japonica*)

1741 Sika Deer
(*Cervus nippon*)

(Des M. Morita. Photo)

1995 (28 July). World Heritage Sites (3rd series). Yaku Island. Phosphorescent paper. P 13.
2373 **1740** 80y. multicoloured .... 1·40   55
2374 **1741** 80y. multicoloured .... 1·40   55

1742 "Friends, One and All" (Yuki Ogawa)

1743 Atomic Bomb Dome, Hiroshima (Nobuya Nagata)

1744 "Light of Peace" (Nobuo Suenaga)

1745 Marathon Runners

1995 (1 Aug). 50th Anniv of End of Second World War. Stamp Design Contest Winners. Phosphorescent paper. Photo. P 13.
2375 **1742** 50y. multicoloured 85   35
2376 **1743** 80y. multicoloured .... 1·40   55
2377 **1744** 80y. multicoloured .... 1·40   55
2375/2377 *Set of 3* .... 3·25   1·30

(Des A. Kikuchi. Photo)

1995 (23 Aug). 18th International University Games, Fukuoka. Phosphorescent paper. P 13.
2378 **1745** 80y. multicoloured .... 1·40   55

1746 Radio-controlled Plane

1747 Radio-controlled Helicopter

(Des A. Tamaki. Photo)

1995 (25 Aug). World Aeromodel Championships, Kasaoka. Phosphorescent paper. P 13.
2379 **1746** 50y. multicoloured 85   35
2380 **1747** 80y. multicoloured .... 1·40   55

1748 Horse, Cow and Labrador

(Des M. Morita. Photo)

1995 (1 Sept). World Veterinary Congress, Yokohama. Phosphorescent paper. P 13.
2381 **1748** 80y. multicoloured .... 1·40   1·10

1749 5y. Stamp and Cherub on Tokyo Mailbox

1750 500y. Stamp and Mail Van

1751 20y. Stamp and Mail Van

1752 100y. Stamp and Cherub on Tokyo Mailbox

(Des M. Morita. Recess and photo)

1995 (19 Sept). History of Stamps (5th series). Industries issue of 1948–49. Phosphorescent paper. P 13½.
2382 **1749** 80y. multicoloured .... 1·30   55
  a. Block or vert strip of 4.
    Nos. 2382/5 .... 5·50
2383 **1750** 80y. multicoloured .... 1·30   55
2384 **1751** 80y. multicoloured .... 1·30   55
2385 **1752** 80y. multicoloured .... 1·30   55
2382/2385 *Set of 4* .... 4·75   2·00
  Nos. 2382/5 were issued together in blocks and vertical strips of four stamps within the sheet.

1753 Judo (Makuhari, Chiba)

1754 Gymnastics (Sabae, Fukui)

(Des A. Kikuchi. Photo)

1995 (28 Sept). World Sports Championships. Phosphorescent paper. P 13.
2386	**1753** 80y. multicoloured	1·30	55
2387	**1754** 80y. multicoloured	1·30	55

1755 Shell Matching Game (from "New Year's Amusements")

1756 Battledore and Shuttlecock (from "Twelve Months")

1757 Playing Cards (from "Matsuura Folding Screen")

(Des M. Morita. Photo)

1995 (6 Oct). International Correspondence Week. Details of paintings on folding screens. Phosphorescent paper. P 13½.
2388	**1755** 90y. multicoloured	1·40	1·10
2389	**1756** 110y. multicoloured	1·70	1·40
2390	**1757** 130y. multicoloured	2·10	1·70
2388/2390	Set of 3	4·75	3·75

1758 Cyclists

(Des A. Kikuchi. Photo)

1995 (13 Oct). 50th National Athletic Meeting, Fukushima. P 13½.
2391	**1758** 50y. multicoloured	95	45

1759 Patchwork Hearts (Tomoko Suzuki)

1760 Children with Heart Balloon (Yukino Ikeda)

(Des M. Morita. Photo)

1995 (24 Oct). 50th Anniversaries of United Nations Organization (2392) and United Nations Educational, Scientific and Cultural Organization (2393). Phosphorescent paper. P 13.
2392	**1759** 80y. multicoloured	1·30	1·10
2393	**1760** 80y. multicoloured	1·30	1·10

1761 Tadataka Ino (cartographer, 250th birth)

1762 Kitaro Nishida (philosopher, 50th death)

(Des G. Aoki. Photo)

1995 (6 Nov). Anniversaries. Phosphorescent paper. P 13.
2394	**1761** 80y. multicoloured	1·30	55
2395	**1762** 80y. multicoloured	1·30	55

1763 Tsutsumi Clay Rat on Cayenne Pepper

1764 Satsuma Papier-mâché Rat in Rice Store

(Des T. Oya (2396), Etsuyo Uchida (2397). Photo)

1995 (15 Nov). New Year's Greetings. P 13×13½.
2396 **1763** 50y. multicoloured 75   25
2397 **1764** 80y. multicoloured .... 1·30   55

1765 Tsutsumi
Clay Rat on Turnip

1766 Satsuma
Papier-mâché Rat
in Rice Store

(Des I. Harada (2398), A. Tamaki (2399). Photo and typo)

1995 (15 Nov). New Year's Lottery Stamps. P 13½.
2398 **1765** 50y.+3y. multicoloured.............................. 1·10   90
2399 **1766** 80y.+3y. multicoloured.............................. 1·50   1·20
Each stamp carries a lottery number.

1767 Beech Forest

1768 Black
Woodpecker
(*Dryocopus martius*)

(Des M. Morita. Photo)

1995 (21 Nov). World Heritage Sites (4th series). Shirakami Mountains.
Phosphorescent paper. P 13.
2400 **1767** 80y. multicoloured .... 1·30   55
2401 **1768** 80y. multicoloured .... 1·30   55

1769 Obi Material
showing Choson
Dynasty Boxes
(Keisuke Serizawa)

1770 Siebold

(Des M. Morita. Photo)

1995 (18 Dec). 30th Anniv of Resumption of Japan–Korea Diplomatic
Relations. Phosphorescent paper. P 13.
2402 **1769** 80y. multicoloured .... 1·30   55

(Des M. Morita. Photo)

1996 (16 Feb). Birth Bicentenary of Philipp Franz von Siebold
(physician and Japanologist). Phosphorescent paper. P 13.
2403 **1770** 80y. multicoloured .... 1·40   55

1771 Twined Ropes

1772 Turtle and
Crane

(Des A. Kikuchi. Photo)

1996 (1 Mar). 50th Anniv of Labour Relations Commissions.
Phosphorescent paper. P 13.
2404 **1771** 80y. multicoloured .... 1·20   45

(Des Y. Sugita. Photo)

1996 (21 Mar). Senior Citizens. Phosphorescent paper. P 13½.
2405 **1772** 80y. multicoloured .... 1·20   45
No. 2405 was issued in sheetlets of five stamps. Each citizen over
70 was entitled to one sheetlet free.

1773 Driving to Diet
for Promulgation of
Constitution, 1946

1774 Signing San
Francisco Peace
Treaty, 1951

1775 Return of
Okinawa, 1972

(Des M. Morita. Photo)

1996 (5 Apr). 50 Post-war Years (1st series). Phosphorescent paper.
P 13.
2406 **1773** 80y. maroon, rose-lilac and gold............ 2·20   1·10
         a. Pair. Nos. 2406/7 .... 4·75
2407 **1774** 80y. blackish grn, dull bl-grn & gold ...... 2·20   1·10
2408 **1775** 80y. indigo, pale blue and gold .... 2·20   1·10
2406/2408 *Set of 3*... 6·00   3·00
No. 2406/7 were issued together in *se-tenant* pairs within the
sheet.
See also Nos. 2420/1, 2429/30, 2443/4 and 2449/54.

1776 Woman and Diet Building

1777 "Window" (Yukihiko Yasuda)

(Des A. Tamaki. Photo)

1996 (10 Apr). 50th Anniv of Women's Suffrage. Phosphorescent paper. P 13½.

2409 **1776** 80y. multicoloured .... 1·20   45

(Des G. Aoki. Photo)

1996 (19 Apr). Philatelic Week. P 13.

2410 **1777** 80y. multicoloured .... 1·20   45

1778 Mother and Child

1779 Children and Sun

(Des A. Kikuchi. Photo)

1996 (1 May). 50th Anniv of United Nations Children's Fund. Phosphorescent paper. P 13.

2411 **1778** 80y. multicoloured .... 1·50   55

(Des T. Yanase. Photo)

1996 (1 May). Child Welfare Week. Phosphorescent paper. P 13.

2412 **1779** 80y. multicoloured .... 1·50   55

1780 Narcissus Flycatcher

1781 Binoculars and Bird feeding Nestlings

(Des M. Morita. Photo)

1996 (10 May). Bird Week. Phosphorescent paper. P 13.

2413 **1780** 80y. multicoloured .... 1·30   55
   a. Pair. Nos. 2413/14. .... 2·75   1·20
2414 **1781** 80y. multicoloured .... 1·30   55

Nos. 2413/14 were issued together in *se-tenant* pairs within the sheet.

1782 Cherry Blossom and Tokyo Buildings

1783 1991 Design

1784 1949 Design

(Des I. Harada. Photo)

1996 (17 May). National Afforestation Campaign. Phosphorescent paper. P 13½.

2415 **1782** 50y. multicoloured 95   45

(Des M. Morita. Photo and recess)

1996 (3 June). History of Stamps (6th series). Philatelic Week Issues. Phosphorescent paper. P 13.

2416 **1783** 80y. sepia, ochre and lilac .... 1·20   45
   a. Horiz strip of 4. Nos. 2416/19 .... 5·00
2417   80y. multicoloured .... 1·20   45
2418 **1784** 80y. deep lilac and lilac .... 1·20   45
2419   80y. multicoloured .... 1·20   45
2416/2419 *Set of* 4 .... 4·25   1·60

Nos. 2416/19 were issued together in horizontal *se-tenant* strips of four stamps within the sheet.

1785 Olympic Flame (Olympic Games, Tokyo, 1964)

1786 Sun Tower ("Expo 70" World Fair, Osaka)

(Des M. Morita. Photo)

1996 (24 June). 50 Post-war Years (2nd series). Phosphorescent paper. P 13.

2420 **1785** 80y. multicoloured .... 1·50   45
2421 **1786** 80y. multicoloured .... 1·50   45

1787/1788 "Oirase no Keiryu" (Chikkyo Ono)

(Des M. Morita. Photo)

1996 (5 July). Centenary of Modern River Control Systems. Phosphorescent paper. P 13½.
2422 **1787** 80y. multicoloured .... 1·30   1·10
     a. Horiz pair. Nos. 2422/3 .... 2·75   2·30
2423 **1788** 80y. multicoloured .... 1·30   1·10
Nos. 2422/3 were issued together in horizontal *se-tenant* pairs within the sheet, each pair forming the composite design illustrated.

1789 Emblem

1790 *Nippon Maru II* (cadet ship)

(Des A. Tamaki. Photo)

1996 (19 July). Marine Day. Phosphorescent paper. P 13½.
2424 **1789** 50y. multicoloured 95   45
2425 **1790** 80y. multicoloured .... 1·30   45

1791 Cat   **1792** Toy Horse

(Des Y. Ryuichi (50y.), S. Yutaka (80y.). Photo)

1996 (23 July). Letter Writing Day. Phosphorescent paper. P 13½.
2426 **1791** 50y. multicoloured 95   80
     a. Booklet pane. Nos. 2426×5 and
         2427×5 .... 11·50
2427 **1792** 80y. multicoloured .... 1·30   1·10
MS2428 72×93 mm. No. 2427 .... 1·50   1·20

1793 Shinkansen Express Train and Motorway   **1794** Woman and Modern Appliances

(Des M. Morita. Photo)

1996 (27 Aug). 50 Post-war Years (3rd series). Modern Life. Phosphorescent paper. P 13.
2429 **1793** 80y. multicoloured .... 1·50   1·20
2430 **1794** 80y. multicoloured .... 1·50   1·20

1795 Kenji Miyazawa (writer, centenary)   **1796** Hokiichi Hanawa (scholar and editor, 250th)

(Des G. Aoki. Recess and photo)

1996 (27 Aug). Birth Anniversaries. Phosphorescent paper. P 13.
2431 **1795** 80y. multicoloured .... 1·50   1·20
2432 **1796** 80y. multicoloured .... 1·50   1·20

1797 Archer   **1798** Paper-chain People around Red Feather (donor pin)

(Des A. Kikuchi. Photo)

1996 (6 Sept). 51st National Athletic Meeting, Hiroshima. Phosphorescent paper. P 13½.
2433 **1797** 50y. multicoloured 85   70

(Des K. Takeara. Photo)

1996 (30 Sept). 50th Anniv of Community Chest. P 13½.
2434 **1798** 80y. multicoloured .... 1·50   1·20

1799 Piano Keys and Double Clef

(Des E. Uchida. Photo)

1996 (1 Oct). International Music Day. P 13.
2435 **1799** 80y. multicoloured .... 1·50   1·20

1800 "Water Mill in Onden"

1801 Flowers

1802 "Fine Day with a South Wind"

1803 Flowers

1804 "Lake in Sosyu Hakone"

1805 Flowers

(Des M. Morita. Photo)

1996 (7 Oct). International Correspondence Week. Paintings from "36 Views of Mt. Fuji" by Hokusai Katsushika (2436, 2438, 2440) and details of paintings of folding screen by Kohrin Ogata (others). Phosphorescent paper. P 13½.

2436	**1800**	90y. multicoloured	1·30	1·10
		a. Pair. Nos. 2436/7	2·75	2·30
2437	**1801**	90y. multicoloured	1·30	1·10

2438	**1802**	110y. multicoloured	1·80	1·50
		a. Pair. Nos. 2438/9	3·75	3·25
2439	**1803**	110y. multicoloured	1·80	1·50
2440	**1804**	130y. multicoloured	2·10	1·70
		a. Pair. Nos. 2440/1	4·50	3·75
2441	**1805**	130y. multicoloured	2·10	1·70
2436/2441		*Set of 6*	9·25	7·75

Stamps of the same value were issued together in *se-tenant* pairs within their sheets.

1806 Congress Emblem and Squirrel

(Des A. Kikuchi. Photo)

1996 (23 Oct). 18th International Savings Banks Congress, Tokyo. Phosphorescent paper. P 13.

2442	**1806**	80y. multicoloured	1·50	1·20

1807 Mobile Telephone, Fibre-optic Cable and Communications Satellite

1808 Satellite Photograph of Earth

(Des M. Morita. Photo)

1996 (8 Nov). 50 Post-war Years (4th series). Telecommunications and Environmental Protection. Phosphorescent paper. P 13.

2443	**1807**	80y. multicoloured	1·50	1·20
2444	**1808**	80y. multicoloured	1·50	1·20

1809 Okinawa Papier-mâché Fighting Bull

1810 Child on Bull (Takamatsu Wedding Doll)

(Des I. Harada (50y.), T. Oya (80y.). Photo)

1996 (15 Nov). New Year's Greetings. P 13×13½.

2445	**1809**	50y. multicoloured	95	80
2446	**1810**	80y. multicoloured	1·40	1·10

1811 Okinawa
Papier-mâché
Fighting Bull

1812 Child on Bull
(Takamatsu
Wedding Doll)

(Des A. Tamaki (50y.), Eiko Nakano (80y.). Photo)

1996 (15 Nov). New Year Lottery Stamps. P 13½.
2447 **1811** 50y. +3y. multicoloured .... 1·10 90
2448 **1812** 80y. +3y. multicoloured .... 1·50 1·20
Each stamp carries a lottery number.

1813 Yujiro Ishihara
(actor) as Youth

1814 Ishihara
smoking Pipe

1815 Hibaré Misorá
(actress and singer)
iï Kanashiké
Kuchibue

1816 Misora singing

1817 Osamu Tezuka
(cartoonist) and
Cartoon Characters

1818 Self-portrait
and Astroboy

(Des M. Morita. Photo)

1997 (28 Jan). 50 Post-war Years (5th series). Entertainers.
Phosphorescent paper. P 13.
2449 **1813** 80y. black, purple-brown and gold .... 1·20 45
    a. Pair. Nos. 2449/50 .... 2·50 95

2450 **1814** 80y. multicoloured .... 1·20 45
2451 **1815** 80y. black, dull violet-blue and gold...... 1·20 45
    a. Pair. Nos. 2451/2 .... 2·50 95
2452 **1816** 80y. multicoloured .... 1·20 45
2453 **1817** 80y. multicoloured .... 1·20 45
    a. Pair. Nos. 2453/4 .... 2·50 95
2454 **1818** 80y. multicoloured .... 1·20 45
2449/2454 *Set of 6* .... 6·50 2·50
  Nos. 2449/50, 2451/2 and 2453/4 were issued together in *se-tenant*
pairs within their sheets.

1819 Emblem

1820 Snowlets
(mascots)

(Des A. Kikuchi and A. Tamaki. Photo)

1997 (7 Feb). Winter Olympic Games, Nagano (1998). Phosphorescent
paper. P 13.
2455 **1819** 80y. +10y. multicoloured.......................... 1·60 1·30
    a. Pair. Nos. 2455/6 .... 3·50 2·75
2456 **1820** 80y. +10y. multicoloured.......................... 1·60 1·30
  Nos. 2455/6 were issued together in *se-tenant* pairs within the
sheet.

1821 "Daigo" (Togyu
Okumura)

1822 Main Court
Room

(Des G. Aoki. Photo)

1997 (18 Apr). Philatelic Week. Phosphorescent paper. P 13½.
2457 **1821** 80y. multicoloured .... 1·50 60

(Des F. Kanematsu. Photo)

1997 (2 May). 50th Anniv of Supreme Court. Phosphorescent paper.
P 13.
2458 **1822** 80y. multicoloured .... 1·50 60

1823 Parachutist

1824 Waving to
Mechanical Doll

1825 Stamp Lover   **1826** Helicopter
                           Postman

1827 With Love Letter

(Des H. Fujimoto and A. Tamaki. Photo)

1997 (2 May). Greetings Stamps. Doraemon (cartoon character).
Phosphorescent paper. Die-cut perf 13½.
2459   **1823** 80y. multicoloured ....   1·30   90
     a. Pane. Nos. 2459/63 plus 5 labels ....   6·75
2460   **1824** 80y. multicoloured ....   1·30   90
2461   **1825** 80y. multicoloured ....   1·30   90
2462   **1826** 80y. multicoloured ....   1·30   90
2463   **1827** 80y. multicoloured ....   1·30   90
2459/2463   *Set of 5* ....   5·75   4·00
     Nos. 2459/63 were issued in self-adhesive panes of five stamps and
five greetings labels.

1828 Mexican   **1829** Zao Crater
Mythological Figures   Lake and Bush
(Luis Nishizawa)   Clover

(Des M. Morita. Photo)

1997 (12 May). Centenary of Japanese Emigration to Mexico.
Phosphorescent paper. P 13.
2464   **1828** 80y. multicoloured ....   1·50   60

(Des I. Harada. Photo)

1997 (16 May). National Afforestation Campaign. Phosphorescent
paper. P 13½.
2465   **1829** 50y. multicoloured   85   35

1830 House's Seal
and Diet Building

(Des S. Watanabe. Photo)

1997 (20 May). 50th Anniv of House of Councillors. Phosphorescent
paper. P 13.
2466   **1830** 80y. multicoloured ....   1·50   60

1831 "Happy Balloon"   **1832** "Bird Friends"
(Orville Isaac)   (Haruka Kumiya)

1833 "Message from   **1834** "Greetings"
Rainbow Forest"   (Yumi Kiryu)
(Anna Romanovskaya)

1997 (23 July). Letter Writing Day. Photo. Phosphorescent paper.
Photo. P 13.
2467   **1831** 50y. multicoloured   95   80
     a. Booklet pane. Nos. 2467×5 and
       2469×5 ....   24·00
2468   **1832** 70y. multicoloured ....   1·20   95
2469   **1833** 80y. multicoloured ....   1·40   1·10
2470   **1834** 90y. multicoloured ....   1·50   1·20
2467/2470   *Set of 4* ....   4·50   3·75
MS2471   72×93 mm. No. 2469 ....   1·80   1·30
     The booklet pane has its outer edges imperforate, giving stamps
with one or two adjacent sides imperf.

1835 Bird with Letter   **1836** Stylized Worker
and Owl on Blackboard

(Des A. Tamaki. Photo)

1997 (11 Aug). 50th Anniv of High School Part-time and
Correspondence Courses. Phosphorescent paper. P 13.
2472   **1835** 50y. multicoloured   85   35

(Des A. Kikuchi. Photo)

1997 (1 Sept). 50th Anniv of Labour Standards Law. Phosphorescent
paper. P 13.
2473   **1836** 80y. multicoloured ....   1·50   60

1837 Pacific Ocean
and Mt. Osorno
(after Hokusai
Katsushika)

1838 Mopi (mascot)
and Synchronized
Swimmers

(Des M. Morita. Photo)

1997 (1 Sept). Centenary of Japan–Child Relations. Phosphorescent paper. P 13½.

2474 **1837** 80y. multicoloured .... 1·50 60

(Des A. Kikuchi. Photo)

1997 (12 Sept). 52nd National Athletic Meeting, Osaká. Phosphorescent paper. P 13½.

2475 **1838** 50y. multicoloured 85 35

1839 "Hodogaya" (from "53 Stations of Tokaido")

1840 Woodpecker and Flowers

1841 "Kameyama" (from "53 Stations of Tokaido")

1842 Foliage

1843 "Snow View from Sumida River Revetment" (from "Edo Scenic Sites: Snow, Moon and Flower")

1844 Snow-covered Tree

(Des M. Morita. Photo)

1997 (6 Oct). International Correspondence Week. Paintings by Hiroshige Ando (2476, 2478, 2480) and details from "The Four Seasons" by Hoitsu Sakai (others). Phosphorescent paper. P 13½.

2476 **1839** 90y. multicoloured .... 1·40 60
        a. Pair. Nos. 2476/7 .... 3·00 1·30
2477 **1840** 90y. multicoloured .... 1·40 60
2478 **1841** 110y. multicoloured .... 1·70 70
        a. Pair. Nos. 2478/9 .... 3·50 1·50
2479 **1842** 110y. multicoloured .... 1·70 70
2480 **1843** 130y. multicoloured .... 2·10 90
        a. Pair. Nos. 2480/1 .... 4·50 1·90
2481 **1844** 130y. multicoloured .... 2·10 90
2476/2481 Set of 6.. 9·25 4·00

Stamps of the same value were issued together in *se-tenant* pairs within their sheets.

1845 Auditorium, Takeru (opera character) and Ballerina

(Des A. Kikuchi. Photo)

1997 (9 Oct). Inauguration of New National Theatre, Tokyo. Phosphorescent paper. P 13.

2482 **1845** 80y. multicoloured .... 1·50   60

1852 Miharu   **1853** Hakata
Hariko Paper Tiger   Hariko Paper Tiger

(Des M. Mimata (50y.), J. Kaifuchi (80y.). Photo)

1997 (14 Nov). New Year Lottery Stamps. P 13½.

2489 **1852** 50y. +3y. multicoloured .... 1·10   90
2490 **1853** 80y. +3y. multicoloured .... 1·50   1·20
Each stamp carries a lottery number.

1846 Iihi Tabidachi   **1847** Tsuki No. Sabaku
(Shinji Tanimura)   (Masao Kato and
                    Suguru Sasaki)

(Des K. Kuroi (50y.), M. Kato (80y.). Photo)

1997 (24 Oct). Favourite Songs (1st series). Phosphorescent paper. P 13.

2483 **1846** 50y. multicoloured 95   45
2484 **1847** 80y. multicoloured .... 1·40   60
     See also Nos. 2497/8, 2499/500, 2522/3, 2527/8, 2531/2, 2558/9, 2568/9 and 2578/9.

1854 "Yotsutake,
Ryukyu Dance"
(Taiji Hamada)

(Des M. Morita. Photo)

1997 (21 Nov). 25th Anniv of Return of Okinawa (Ryukyu Islands). P 13.

2491 **1854** 80y. multicoloured .... 1·50   60

1848 Rohan Kouda   **1849** Hiroshige Ando
(writer, 130th anniv)   (after Toyo Kuni III)
                        (painter, bicentenary)

(Des H. Yamamoto (2485), G. Aoki (2486). Recess and photo)

1997 (4 Nov). Birth Anniversaries. Phosphorescent paper. P 13.

2485 **1848** 80y. multicoloured .... 1·50   60
2486 **1849** 80y. multicoloured .... 1·50   60

1855 Former Shibuya House,   **1856** Tomizawa House
Yamagata

(Eng H. Sasaké (2492), K. Uematsu (2493). Recess and photo)

1997 (28 Nov). Traditional Houses (1st series). Phosphorescent paper. P 13½.

2492 **1855** 80y. multicoloured .... 1·50   60
2493 **1856** 80y. multicoloured .... 1·50   60
     Nos. 2492/3 were issued together in sheets of 20 stamps arranged in separate panes of each design, the panes divided by a vertical gutter.
     See also Nos. 2513/14, 2529/30, 2539/40 and 2570/2.

1850 Miharu   **1851** Hakata
Hariko Paper   Hariko Paper
Tiger   Tiger

(Des I. Harada (50y.), T. Oya (80y.). Photo)

1997 (14 Nov). New Year's Greetings. P 13×13½.

2487 **1850** 50y. multicoloured 95   80
2488 **1851** 80y. multicoloured .... 1·40   1·10

1857 "Mother Sea"
(Bokunen Naka)

1858 "Mother Earth"
(Bokunen Naka)

(Des M. Morita. Photo)

1997 (1 Dec). United Nations Framework Convention on Climate Change, Kyoto. Phosphorescent paper. P 13.

2494	**1857** 80y. multicoloured	1·50	60
	a. Horiz pair. Nos. 2494/5	3·25	1·30
2495	**1858** 80y. multicoloured	1·50	60

Nos. 2494/5 were issued together in horizontal *se-tenant* pairs within the sheet.

1859 Drying
Harvested Rice

(Des A. Tamaki. Photo)

1997 (2 Dec). 50th Anniv of Agricultural Insurance System. Phosphorescent paper. P 13.

| 2496 | **1859** 80y. multicoloured | 1·50 | 60 |

1860 Sunayama
(Hakushu Kitahara
and Shinpei
Nakayama)

1861 Jingle Bells
(Shoji Miyazawa and
J. Pierpont)

(Des T. Kokuryo (2497), S. Fujishiro (2498). Photo)

1997 (8 Dec). Favourite Songs (2nd series). Phosphorescent paper. P 13.

| 2497 | **1860** 50y. multicoloured | 95 | 45 |
| 2498 | **1861** 80y. multicoloured | 1·40 | 60 |

1862 Shabondama
(Ujo Noguchi and
Shinpei Nakayama)

1863 Kitaguni no
Haru (Haku Ide and
Minoru Endo)

(Des C. Iwasaki (50y.), F. Hori (80y.). Photo)

1998 (26 Jan). Favourite Songs (3rd series). Phosphorescent paper. P 13.

| 2499 | **1862** 50y. multicoloured | 95 | 45 |
| 2500 | **1863** 80y. multicoloured | 1·40 | 60 |

1864 Hollyhock

1865 Ice Sledge
Hockey

(Des F. Kanematsu (50y.), A. Kikuchi (80y.). Photo)

1998 (5 Feb). Winter Paralympics, Nagano. Phosphorescent paper. P 13.

2501	**1864** 50y. multicoloured	1·40	60
	a. Pair. Nos. 2501/2	3·25	1·40
2502	**1865** 80y. multicoloured	1·70	70

Nos. 2501/2 were issued together in *se-tenant* pairs within the sheet.

1866 Miyama
Gentian (*Gentiana
nipponica*)

1867 Marsh Marigold
(*Caltha palustris*)

1868 Black Lily
(*Fritillaria
camtschaensis*

1869 Peony (*Paeonia
japonica*)

1870 Adder's Tongue
Lily (*Erythronium
japonicum*)

1871 Snowboarding

1872 Curling

1873 Speed Skating

1874 Cross-country
Skiing

1875 Alpine Skiing

(Des A. Tamaki (2503/7), A. Kikuchi (2508/12). Photo)

1998 (5 Feb). Winter Olympic Games, Nagano. Phosphorescent
paper. P 13.

2503	**1866**	50y. multicoloured	95	80
		a. Sheetlet of 10. Nos. 2502/12	11·50	
2504	**1867**	50y. multicoloured	95	80
2505	**1868**	50y. multicoloured	95	80
2506	**1869**	50y. multicoloured	95	80
2507	**1870**	50y. multicoloured	95	80
2508	**1871**	80y. multicoloured	1·30	1·10
2509	**1872**	80y. multicoloured	1·30	1·10
2510	**1873**	80y. multicoloured	1·30	1·10
2511	**1874**	80y. multicoloured	1·30	1·10
2512	**1875**	80y. multicoloured	1·30	1·10
2503/2512		*Set of* 10	10·25	9·00

Nos. 2502/12 were issued together in *se-tenant* sheetlets of 10
stamps, with enlarged illustrated right-hand margin.

1876 Former Baba House,
Nagano

1877 Naka House

(Eng K. Uematsu (2513), H. Sasaki (2514). Recess and photo)

1998 (23 Feb). Traditional Houses (2nd series). Phosphorescent
paper. P 13½.

2513	**1876**	80y. multicoloured	1·50	60
2514	**1877**	80y. multicoloured	1·50	60

Nos. 2513/14 were issued together in sheets of 20 stamps
arranged in separate panes of each design, the panes divided by a
vertical gutter.

1878 Fireman and
Ambulance

1879 Fireman and
Fire Engine

(Des F. Kanematsu. Photo)

1998 (6 Mar). 50th Anniv of Japanese Fire Service. Phosphorescent
paper. P 13.

2515	**1878**	80y. multicoloured	1·50	60
		a. Pair. Nos. 2515/16	3·25	1·30
2516	**1879**	80y. multicoloured	1·50	60

The firemen in the designs are taken from paintings of actors by
Kunichika Toyohara.

Nos. 2515/16 were issued together in *se-tenant* pairs within the
sheet.

1880 Puppy

1881 Kitten

1882 Budgerigars

1883 Pansies

1884 Rabbit

1998 (13 Mar). Greetings Stamps. Self-adhesive. Phosphorescent paper. Die-cut.

2517	**1880** 80y. multicoloured		1·20	95
	a. Sheetlet of 5. Nos. 2517/21		6·25	
2518	**1881** 80y. multicoloured		1·20	95
2519	**1882** 80y. multicoloured		1·20	95
2520	**1883** 80y. multicoloured		1·20	95
2521	**1884** 80y. multicoloured		1·20	95
2517/2521	*Set of 5*		5·50	4·25

Nos. 2517/21 were issued together in sheetlets of five stamps. The stamps are die-cut Perf 13 around the edges of the rectangle and straight-cut to shape around the outline of the motif.

1885 Medaka-no-Gakko (Shigeru Chaki and Yoshinao Nakada)

1886 Aoi Sanmyaku (Yaso Saijo and Ryoichi Hattori)

(Des R. Saigan (50y.), M. Anno (80y.). Photo)

1998 (16–23 Mar). Favourite Songs (4th series). Phosphorescent paper. P 13.

2522	**1885** 50y. multicoloured (23.3)		95	45
2523	**1886** 80y. multicoloured		1·40	60

1887 "Poppies" (Kokei Kobayashi)

1888 "Liberty Leading the People" (Eugéne Delacroix)

(Des G. Aoki. Photo)

1998 (17 Apr). Philatelic Week. Phosphorescent paper. P 13×13½.

2524	**1887** 80y. multicoloured		1·50	60

(Des M. Morita. Photo)

1998 (28 Apr). Year of France in Japan. Phosphorescent paper. P 13½.

2525	**1888** 110y. multicoloured		1·80	1·10

1889 Trout and Japanese Azalea

(Des T. Ooya. Photo)

1998 (8 May). National Afforestation Campaign. Phosphorescent paper. P 13.

2526	**1889** 50y. multicoloured		85	35

1890 Wild Roses (Sakufu Kondo and Franz Schubert)

1891 Hill abloom with Tangerine Flowers (Minoru Uminuma and Shogo Kato)

(Des Y. Hayakawa (50y.), Y. Yomogida (80y.). Photo)

1998 (25 May). Favourite Songs (5th series). Phosphorescent paper. P 13.

2527	**1890** 50y. multicoloured		95	45
2528	**1891** 80y. multicoloured		1·40	60

1892 Kowata Residence, Shinji

1893 Kamihaga Residence, Uchiko

(Des H. Sasaki (2529), K. Uematsu (2530). Recess and photo)

1998 (22 June). Traditional Houses (3rd series). Phosphorescent paper. P 13.

2529	**1892** 80y. multicoloured		1·50	60
2530	**1893** 80y. multicoloured		1·50	60

Nos. 2529/30 were issued together in sheets of 20 stamps arranged in separate panes of each design, the panes divided by a vertical gutter.

1894 This Road
(Hakusyu Kitahara
and Kousaku Yamada)

1895 I'm a Boy of the
Sea (anon)

(Des S. Yo (2531), T. Murakami (2532). Photo)

1998 (6 July). Favourite Songs (6th series). Phosphorescent paper.
P 13.
2531 **1894** 50y. multicoloured 95   45
2532 **1895** 80y. multicoloured .... 1·40 60

1896 Boy writing

1897 Girl with Letter

1898 Girl holding
Pen

1899 Boy holding
Pen

1900 Boy and Girl reading
Letters

(Des D. Bruna and M. Morita. Photo)

1998 (23 July). Letter Writing Day. Phosphorescent paper. P 13.
2533 **1896** 50y. multicoloured 95   45
   a. Pair. Nos. 2533/4................................. 2·00 95
   b. Booklet pane. Nos. 2533/7,
      each×2....................................... 13·50
2534 **1897** 50y. multicoloured 95   45
2535 **1898** 80y. multicoloured .... 1·50 60
   a. Vert strip of 5. Nos. 2535×2,
      2536×2 and 2537 .... 7·75

2536 **1899** 80y. multicoloured .... 1·50   60
2537 **1900** 80y. multicoloured .... 1·50   60
2533/2537 *Set of 5*... 5·75   2·40
MS2538 93×72 mm. No. 2537 .... 1·80   1·50
   Nos. 2533/4 were issued together in *se-tenant* pairs within the
sheet. Nos. 2535/7 were issued together in sheets containing two
strips of No. 2535a with an enlarged illustrated right-hand margin.
   The booklet pane has its outer edge imperforate, giving stamps
with one or two adjacent sides imperforate.

1901 Kamio Residence, Oita

1902 Nakamura Residence,
Okinawa

(Des K. Uematsu (2539), H. Sasaki (2540). Recess and photo)

1998 (24 Aug). Traditional Houses (4th series). Phosphorescent
paper. P 13.
2539 **1901** 80y. multicoloured .... 1·50 60
2540 **1902** 80y. multicoloured .... 1·50 60

1903 FJ Class Dinghy
Racing

(Des I. Harada. Photo)

1998 (11 Sept). 53rd National Athletic Meeting, Kanagawa.
Phosphorescent paper. P 13.
2541 **1903** 50y. multicoloured 85   35

1904 "Sketch of Maple Leaf" (detail)

1905 "Parakeet in Oak Tree"

1906 "Drake and Duck in Snow" (detail)

1907 "Coloured Chicken in Snow-laden Bamboo"

1908 "Butterfly in the Peonies" (detail)

1909 "Parakeet in Rose Bush"

(Des M. Morita. Photo)

1998 (6 Oct). International Correspondence Week. Paintings by Shakuchu Ito. Phosphorescent paper. P 13.

2542	**1904**	90y. multicoloured	1·50	1·20
		a. Pair. Nos. 2542/3	3·25	2·50
2543	**1905**	90y. multicoloured	1·50	1·20
2544	**1906**	110y. multicoloured	1·80	1·50
		a. Pair. Nos. 2544/5	3·75	3·25
2545	**1907**	110y. multicoloured	1·80	1·50
2546	**1908**	130y. multicoloured	2·10	1·70
		a. Pair. Nos. 2546/7	4·50	3·75
2547	**1909**	130y. multicoloured	2·10	1·70
2542/2547		Set of 6	9·75	8·00

Stamps of the same value were issued together in *se-tenant* pairs within their sheets.

1910 Serving

1911 Receiving

1912 Set and Attack

1913 Blocking

(Des A. Tamaki. Photo)

1998 (2 Nov). World Volleyball Championships, Japan. Phosphorescent paper. P 13.

2548	**1910**	80y. multicoloured	1·50	60
		a. Horiz strip of 4. Nos. 2548/51	6·25	
2549	**1911**	80y. multicoloured	1·50	60
2550	**1912**	80y. multicoloured	1·50	60
2551	**1913**	80y. multicoloured	1·50	60
2548/2551		Set of 4	5·50	2·20

1914 Bakin Takizawa (writer, 150th death anniv)

1915 Yoshie Fujiwara (opera singer, birth centenary)

(Des G. Aoki (2552), S. Oikawa (2553). Recess and photo)

1998 (4 Nov). Anniversaries. Phosphorescent paper. P 13.

2552	**1914**	80y. multicoloured	1·50	60
2553	**1915**	80y. multicoloured	1·50	60

1916 Sahara Papier-mâché Rabbit making Rice Cake

1917 Yamagata Papier-mâché Rabbit on Ball

(Des T. Ooya. Photo)

1998 (13 Nov). New Year's Greetings. P 13×13½.
2554 **1916** 50y. multicoloured 95 45
2555 **1917** 80y. multicoloured .... 1·40 60
No. 2554 was issued both in separate sheets of 10 and in sheets
se-tenant with previous New Year rabbit designs (see No. 2565a).

1918 Sahara Papier-
mâché Rabbit
making Rice Cake

1919 Yamagata
Papier-mâché
Rabbit on Ball

(Des I. Harada (2556), A. Hoshiyama (2557). Photo)

1998 (13 Nov). New Year's Lottery Stamps. P 13½.
2556 **1918** 50y. +3y. multicoloured .... 1·10 90
2557 **1919** 50y. +3y. multicoloured .... 1·50 1·20
Each stamp carries a lottery number.

1920 The Apple Song
(Hachiro Sato and
Tadashi Manjome)

1921 The Toy Cha-
Cha-Cha (Akiyuki
Nasaka and Osamu
Yoshioka)

(Des T. Nadamoto (2558), H. Yamagata (2559). Photo)

1998 (24 Nov). Favourite Songs (7th series). Phosphorescent paper.
P 13.
2558 **1920** 50y. multicoloured 95 45
2559 **1921** 80y. multicoloured .... 1·40 60

1922 Tango Dancers
(Goro Sasaki)

(Des A. Tamaki. Photo)

1998 (2 Dec). Centenary of Friendship Treaty between Japan and
Argentina. Phosphorescent paper. P 13.
2560 **1922** 80y. multicoloured .... 1·50 60

1923 "Family"
(Chakou Wiam)

1924 "Heart Tree"
(Atsuko Niizato)

1925 "Hito" (Shozo
Somekawa)

1926 "Happiness"
(Mary Carmel
Mulloor)

(Des M. Morita. Photo)

1998 (10 Dec). 50th Anniv of Universal Declaration of Human Rights.
Phosphorescent paper. P 13.
2561 **1923** 50y. multicoloured 95 45
2562 **1924** 70y. multicoloured .... 1·30 55
2563 **1925** 80y. multicoloured .... 1·40 60
2564 **1926** 90y. multicoloured .... 1·70 70
2561/2564 *Set of 4* .... 4·75 2·10

(Des M. Morita. Photo)

1998 (15 Dec). 50th Anniv of New Year's Greetings Stamps.
P 13×13½.
2565 **241** 50y. bright magenta 95 45
a. Block or vert strip of 4. Nos. 2554
and 2565/7 .... 4·00
2566 **445** 50y. multicoloured 95 45
2567 **1278** 50y. multicoloured 95 45
2554, 2565/2567 *Set of 4* .... 3·50 1·60
Nos. 2565/7 were issued together with No. 2554 in vertical
se-tenant strips of four within sheets of eight stamps.

1927 Flowing like a
River (Yasushi
Akimoto and Akira
Mitake)

1928 Song of the
Four Seasons
(Toyohisa Araki)

(Des M. Kayama (50y.), Moe Nagata (80y.). Photo)

1999 (26 Jan). Favourite Songs (8th series). Phosphorescent paper.
P 13.

2568	**1927**	50y. multicoloured	1·20	55
2569	**1928**	80y. multicoloured	1·80	80

1929 Iwase Residence,
Nishi-Akao

1930/1 Ogimachi Houses, Shirakawa

(Des H. Sasaki (2570), K. Uematsu (2571/2). Recess and photo)

1999 (16 Feb). Traditional Houses (5th series). Phosphorescent paper.
P 13½.

2570	**1929**	80y. multicoloured	1·50	60
2571	**1930**	80y. multicoloured	1·50	60
	a. Horiz pair. Nos. 2571/2		3·25	1·30
2572	**1931**	80y. multicoloured	1·50	60
2570/2572	*Set of 3*		4·00	1·60

Nos. 2571/2 were issued together in horizontal *se-tenant* pairs within the sheet, each pair forming the composite design illustrated.

1932 "The Kaen-　　　**1933** "Toku the
daiko Drum"　　　　　Boatman" (Bunraku
(Shinsho Kokontei V)　Katsura VIII)

1934 "Mr. Kobee, the　**1935** "Time Noodles"
Faultfinder" (Ensho　　(Kosan Yanagiya V)
Sanyutei VI)

1936 "Once in a
Hundred Years"
(Beicho Katsura III)

(Des S. Yamafugi. Photo)

1999 (12 Mar). Comic Stories. Phosphorescent paper. P 13.

2573	**1932**	80y. multicoloured	1·30	90
	a. Vert strip of 5. Nos. 2573/7		7·00	
2574	**1933**	80y. multicoloured	1·30	90
2575	**1934**	80y. multicoloured	1·30	90
2576	**1935**	80y. multicoloured	1·30	90
2577	**1936**	80y. multicoloured	1·30	90
2573/2577	*Set of 5*		5·75	4·00

Nos. 2573/7 were issued together in *se-tenant* sheetlets of ten stamps, with enlarged right-hand margin giving the outlines of the stories (in Japanese characters).

1937 Sukiyaki　　　　**1938** "Early Spring"
(Rokusuke Ei and　　　(Kazumasa Yoshimaru
Hachidai Nakamura)　　and Akira Nakada)

(Des M. Wada (50y.), I. Hirayama (80y.). Photo)

1999 (16 Mar). Favourite Songs (9th series). Phosphorescent paper.
P 13.

2578	**1937**	50y. multicoloured	95	45
2579	**1938**	80y. multicoloured	1·50	60

1939 Kitten

1940 Roses

1941 Puppy

1942 Brown Rabbit

1943 Grey and White Rabbit

1999 (23 Mar). Greetings Stamps. Self-adhesive. Phosphorescent paper. Die-cut.

2580	**1939** 80y. multicoloured	1·50	90
	a. Sheetlet of 5. Nos. 2580/4	7·75	
2581	**1940** 80y. multicoloured	1·50	90
2582	**1941** 80y. multicoloured	1·50	90
2583	**1942** 80y. multicoloured	1·50	90
2584	**1943** 80y. multicoloured	1·50	90
2580/2584	Set of 5	6·75	4·00

Nos. 2580/4 were issued together in sheetlets of five stamps. The stamps are die-cut perf 13 around the edges of the rectangle and straight-cut to shape around the outline of the motif.

1944 Body Parts and Staff of Asclepius

(Des A. Tamaki. Photo)

1999 (2 Apr). 25th General Assembly of Japan Medical Congress. Phosphorescent paper. P 13.

2585	**1944** 80y. multicoloured	1·70	60

1945/6 "Hare playing on the field in Spring" (Insho Domoto) (½-size illustration)

(Des M. Morita. Photo)

1999 (20 Apr). Philatelic Week. Phosphorescent paper. P 13½.

2586	**1945** 80y. multicoloured	1·50	60
	a. Horiz pair. Nos. 2586/7	3·25	1·30
2587	**1946** 80y. multicoloured	1·50	60

Nos. 2586/7 were issued together in horizontal se-tenant pairs within the sheet, each pair forming the composite design illustrated.

1947 Nazca Lines, Llama and Machu Picchu Ruins

1948 Amagi Alpine Rose and Mount Fuji

(Des K. Shimoda. Photo)

1999 (18 May). 100 Years of Japanese Emigration to Peru. P 13.

2588	**1947** 80y. multicoloured	1·50	60

(Des M. Mimata. Photo)

1999 (28 May). National Afforestation Campaign. Phosphorescent paper. P 13½.

2589	**1948** 50y. multicoloured	1·10	70

1949 Tholos, Delphi

1950 Demon Dancer (Ouro Carnival), Lake Titicaca and Andean Condor

(Des M. Murai. Photo)

1999 (1 June). Centenary of Japan–Greece Treaty of Commerce and Navigation. Phosphorescent paper. P 13.

2590	**1949** 80y. multicoloured	1·50	60

(Des K. Shimoda. Photo)

1999 (3 June). 100 Years of Japanese Emigration to Bolivia. Phosphorescent paper. P 13.

2591	**1950** 80y. multicoloured	1·50	60

1951 Houses and Paddy Fields

1952 "Hill where Camellias Bloom" (detail of statue, Naoki Tominaga) and "Hope" (detail of stained glass window, Louis Fransen)

(Des K. Kuroi. Photo)

1999 (4 June). 50th Anniv of Land Improvement Law. Phosphorescent paper. P 13.
2592 **1951** 80y. multicoloured .... 1·50 60

(Des M. Morita. Photo)

1999 (16 June). 50th Anniv of Family Court. Phosphorescent paper. P 13.
2593 **1952** 80y. multicoloured .... 1·50 60

1953 Primroses

1954 Rickshaw, 1899

(Des M. Mimata. Photo)

1999 (1 July). 50th Anniv of Rehabilitation Support Programme. Phosphorescent paper. P 13.
2594 **1953** 80y. multicoloured .... 1·50 60

(Des A. Tamaki. Photo)

1999 (1 July). Centenary of Patent Attorney System. Phosphorescent paper. P 13.
2595 **1954** 80y. multicoloured .... 1·50 60

1955 Masaakira Tomii, Kenjiro Ume and Nobushige Hozumi (drafters)

1956 Sayo-chan, Saku-chan and Ken-chan (originator, developer and inspector) (Takashi Yanase)

(Des S. Oikawa and O. Makoto. Photo)

1999 (19 July). Centenaries of Civil (1998) and Commercial (1999) Laws. Phosphorescent paper. P 13.
2596 **1955** 80y. multicoloured .... 1·50 60

(Des A. Tamaki. Photo)

1999 (22 July). Centenary of Japanese Copyright System. Phosphorescent paper. P 13.
2597 **1956** 80y. multicoloured .... 1·50 60

1957 Children and Envelope

1958 Bear and Crayon

1959 Girl with Pen

1960 Clown jumping from Envelope

1961 Giraffes

1962 Kite

1963 Boy and Star

1964 Girl with Pencil

1965 Miffie and Barbara

1966 Boy playing Trumpet

1967 Girl playing Cello

1968 Girl

1969 Girl with Letter

1970 Ducklings

(Des D. Bruna and M. Morita. Photo Questa (2602/11) or Govt Ptg Wks (others))

1999 (23 July). Letter Writing Day. 50th Anniv of Japanese Association of Pen Friend Clubs. Phosphorescent paper. P 13.

2598	**1957**	50y. multicoloured	1·10	70
		a. Horiz strip of 4. Nos. 2598/2601	4·75	
		b. Booklet pane. Nos. 2598/2601, 2604×2, 2608×2 and 2610×2	14·00	
2599	**1958**	50y. multicoloured	1·10	70
2600	**1959**	50y. multicoloured	1·10	70
2601	**1960**	50y. multicoloured	1·10	70
2602	**1961**	80y. blue, black and bright lemon	1·50	95
		a. Sheetlet of 10. Nos. 2602/11	16·00	
2603	**1962**	80y. multicoloured	1·50	95
2604	**1963**	80y. black, blue and bright lemon	1·50	95
2605	**1964**	80y. black, orange-vermilion and bright lemon	1·50	95
2606	**1965**	80y. multicoloured	1·50	95
2607	**1966**	80y. black, bright lemon and blue	1·50	95
2608	**1967**	80y. multicoloured	1·50	95
2609	**1968**	80y. black and orange-vermilion	1·50	95
2610	**1969**	80y. black, bright lemon and deep green	1·50	95
2611	**1970**	80y. deep green, black and bright lemon	1·50	95
2598/2611		Set of 14	17·00	11·00
MS2612		72×94 mm. Nos. 2598 and 2608	2·75	2·20

Nos. 2598/2601 were issued in horizontal *se-tenant* strips of four stamps within the sheet. Nos. 2602/11 were issued in sheetlets of ten stamps.

The booklet pane has its outer edges imperforate, giving stamps with one or two adjacent sides imperforate.

1971 Doves and Hearts

1972 Japanese Character

1973 Crane and Leaves

1999 (16 Aug). Greetings Stamps. Phosphorescent paper. Photo. P 13½.

2613	**1971**	50y. multicoloured	95	60
2614	**1972**	80y. multicoloured	1·50	1·10
2615	**1973**	90y. multicoloured	1·70	1·30
2613/2615		Set of 3	3·75	2·75

1974 Wagahai wa Neko de Aru (novel by Natsume Soseki)

1975 Bochan (novel by Natsume Soseki)

1976 Yosano Akiko (poet)

1977 Denkikan Cinema, Asakusa

1978 Tram, Tokyo, 1903

1979 Kawakami Otojirou and Sadayakko (actor couple)

1980 "Haikara" (western-style fashion)

1981 Sumo Wrestlers (opening of Sumo Ring, Ryogoku, Tokyo, 1909)

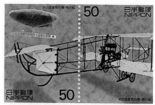

1985/6 Biplane "Kaishiki No. 1" and Airship "Yamadashiki No. 1" (first Japanese-built aircraft)

1982 Moving Casualties, Russo–Japanese War, 1904

1983 Military Hospital, Russo–Japanese War

1987 Children singing (School Song Book, 1910)

1988 Explorer and Dog (Shirase Antarctic Expedition, 1910)

(Des M. Morita. Photo)

1999 (23 Aug). The Twentieth Century (1st series). The 1900s. Phosphorescent paper. P 13.

2616	**1974** 50y. multicoloured	1·30	95
	a. Sheetlet of 10. Nos. 2616/25	15·00	
2617	**1975** 50y. multicoloured	1·30	95
2618	**1976** 80y. multicoloured	1·50	1·10
2619	**1977** 80y. multicoloured	1·50	1·10
2620	**1978** 80y. multicoloured	1·50	1·10
2621	**1979** 80y. multicoloured	1·50	1·10
2622	**1980** 80y. multicoloured	1·50	1·10
2623	**1981** 80y. multicoloured	1·50	1·10
2624	**1982** 80y. multicoloured	1·50	1·10
2625	**1983** 80y. multicoloured	1·50	1·10
2616/2625	*Set of* 10	13·00	9·75

Nos. 2616/25 were issued together in *se-tenant* sheetlets of ten stamps with a description of each stamp in Japanese in the margin.

See also Nos. 2627/36, 2644/53, 2677/86, 2687/96, 2697/706, 2707/16, 2717/26, 2739/48, 2759/68, 2771/80, 2798/807, 2808/17, 2819/28, 2832/41, 2850/9 and 2861/70.

1989 Dr. Noguchi Hideyo (discovery of Oroya Fever germ, 1926)

1990 Wolf (extinction of indigenous wolves, 1905)

1991 Kanaguri Shizo and Mishima Yahiko at Opening Parade, Olympic Games, Stockholm, 1912

1992 Dancers (formation of Takarazuka Musical Company, 1913)

1984 Golfer and Gentian

(Des M. Mimata. Photo)

1999 (10 Sept). 54th National Sports Festival, Kumamoto. Phosphorescent paper. P 13½.

2626	**1984** 50y. multicoloured	1·10	60

1993 Matsui Sumako as Kachucha in Resurrection (play by Shimamura Hogetsu), 1914

1994 Mother and Children (first sale of milk caramel in Japan, 1913)

(Des M. Morita. Photo)

1999 (22 Sept). The Twentieth Century (2nd series). Phosphorescent paper. P 13.

2627	**1985**	50y. multicoloured	1·30	95
	a.	Horiz pair. Nos. 2627/8	2·75	2·00
	b.	Sheetlet of 10. Nos. 2627/36	15·00	
2628	**1986**	50y. Type **1965**	1·30	95
2629	**1987**	80y. multicoloured	1·50	1·10
2630	**1988**	80y. multicoloured	1·50	1·10
2631	**1989**	80y. multicoloured	1·50	1·10
2632	**1990**	80y. multicoloured	1·50	1·10
2633	**1991**	80y. multicoloured	1·50	1·10
2634	**1992**	80y. multicoloured	1·50	1·10
2635	**1993**	80y. multicoloured	1·50	1·10
2636	**1994**	80y. multicoloured	1·50	1·10
2627/2636	*Set of* 10		13·00	9·75

Nos. 2627/36 were issued together in *se-tenant* sheetlets of ten stamps, Nos. 2627/8 forming the composite design illustrated, with a description of each stamp in Japanese in the margin.

1995 Stork on Elephant

(Des Y. Sugita. Photo)

1999 (1 Oct). International Year of the Elderly. Phosphorescent paper. P 13.

2637	**1995**	80y. multicoloured	1·50	80

1996 "Sea Route in Kazusa Area" (from "36 Views of Mt. Fuji" by Hokusai Katsushika)

1997 "Confederate Roses and a Sparrow"

1998 "Rain beneath the Mountain Top" (from "36 Views of Mt. Fuji")

1999 "Chrysanthemums and a Horsefly"

2000 "Under the Fukagawa Mannen Bridge" (from "36 Views of Mt. Fuji")

2001 "Peonies and a Butterfly"

(Des A. Tamaki. Photo)

1999 (6 Oct). International Correspondence Week. 125th Anniv of Universal Postal Union. Phosphorescent paper. P 13½.

2638	**1996**	90y. multicoloured	1·60	95
	a.	Pair. Nos. 2638/9	3·50	2·00
2639	**1997**	90y. multicoloured	1·60	95
2640	**1998**	110y. multicoloured	2·20	1·10
	a.	Pair. Nos. 2640/1	4·75	2·30
2641	**1999**	110y. multicoloured	2·20	1·10
2642	**2000**	130y. multicoloured	2·40	1·30
	a.	Pair. Nos. 2642/3	5·00	2·75
2643	**2001**	130y. multicoloured	2·40	1·30
2638/2643	*Set of* 6		11·00	6·00

Stamps of the same value were issued together in *se-tenant* pairs within their sheets.

2002 Couple in Junk (Takehisa Yumeji)

2003 Takehisa Yumeji (artist)

2004/5 Inauguration of Tokyo Railway Station, 1914

2647	**2005** 80y. multicoloured	1·50	1·10
2648	**2006** 80y. multicoloured	1·50	1·10
2649	**2007** 80y. multicoloured	1·50	1·10
2650	**2008** 80y. multicoloured	1·50	1·10
2651	**2009** 80y. multicoloured	1·50	1·10
2652	**2010** 80y. multicoloured	1·50	1·10
2653	**2011** 80y. multicoloured	1·50	1·10
2644/2653	*Set of* 10	13·00	9·75

Nos. 2644/53 were issued together in *se-tenant* sheetlets of ten stamps, Nos. 2646/7 forming the composite design illustrated, with a description of each stamp in Japanese in the margin.

2006 Navy Cadets (Start of First World War, 1914)

2007 "Yohatsu" (western-style hair)

2012 Yokohama Bay Stars Mascot (Central League)

2013 Chunichi Dragon Mascot (Central League)

2008 Akutagawa Ryunosuke and Title Page of *Rashomon* (first book of poetry, published 1915)

2009 Princess and Clouds (postal life assurance, 1916)

2014 Seibu Lions Mascot (Pacific League)

2015 Nippon Ham Fighters Mascot (Pacific League)

2010 Yoshino Sakuzo (political scientist) (Taisho Democracy)

2011 Farmers (rice riots, 1918)

2016 Yomiuri Giants Mascot (Central League)

2017 Yakult Swallows Mascot (Central League)

(Des M. Morita. Photo)

1999 (22 Oct). The Twentieth Century (3rd series). Phosphorescent paper. P 13.

2644	**2002** 50y. multicoloured	1·30	95
	a. Sheetlet of 10. Nos. 2644/53	15·00	
2645	**2003** 50y. multicoloured	1·30	95
2646	**2004** 80y. multicoloured	1·50	1·10
	a. Horiz pair. Nos. 2646/7	2·75	2·00

2018 Orix Blue Wave Mascot (Pacific League)

2019 Fukuoka Daiei Hawks Mascot (Pacific League)

2020 Hiroshima Toyo Carp Mascot (Central League)

2021 Hanshin Tigers Mascot (Central League)

2025 Katsushika Hokusai (artist, 150th death anniv)

2022 Kintetsu Buffaloes Mascot (Pacific League)

2023 Chiba Lotte Marines Mascot (Pacific League)

(Des M. Morita. Photo)

1999 (22 Oct). Professional Japanese Baseball Clubs. Self-adhesive. Phosphorescent paper. Die-cut.

2654	**2012**	80y. multicoloured	1·50	1·10
		a. Sheetlet of 12. Nos. 2654/65	19·00	
2655	**2013**	80y. multicoloured	1·50	1·10
2656	**2014**	80y. multicoloured	1·50	1·10
2657	**2015**	80y. multicoloured	1·50	1·10
2658	**2016**	80y. multicoloured	1·50	1·10
2659	**2017**	80y. multicoloured	1·50	1·10
2660	**2018**	80y. multicoloured	1·50	1·10
2661	**2019**	80y. multicoloured	1·50	1·10
2662	**2020**	80y. multicoloured	1·50	1·10
2663	**2021**	80y. multicoloured	1·50	1·10
2664	**2022**	80y. multicoloured	1·50	1·10
2665	**2023**	80y. multicoloured	1·50	1·10
2654/2665		Set of 12	16·00	12·00

Nos. 2654/65 were issued together in sheetlets of 12 stamps. The stamps are die-cut Perf 13 around the edges of the rectangle and straight-cut to shape around the outline of the motif.

2026 Uemera Shoen (artist, 50th death anniv)

2027 Kawabata Yasunari (author, birth centenary)

(Des G. Aoki (2667), S. Oikawa (2668), H. Yamamoto (2669). Photo)

1999 (4 Nov). Anniversaries. Phosphorescent paper. P 13.

2667	**2025**	80y. multicoloured	1·50	95
2668	**2026**	80y. multicoloured	1·50	95
2669	**2027**	80y. multicoloured	1·50	95
2667/2669		Set of 3	4·00	2·50

2028 Paulownia and Bamboo Embroidery (Manzairaku costume)

2024 Rainbow, Buildings and Mt. Fuji

(Des A. Tamaki. Photo)

1999 (28 Oct). 50th Anniv of Japanese Science Council. Phosphorescent paper. P 13.

2666	**2024**	80y. multicoloured	1·50	95

2029 Chinese Phoenix Embroidery (Engiraku costume)

(Des M. Morita. Photo)

1999 (12 Nov). Tenth Anniv of Accession of Emperor Akihito. Phosphorescent paper. P 12½.

2670	**2028**	80y. multicoloured	1·60	1·10
2671	**2029**	80y. multicoloured	1·60	1·10
MS2672		144×93 mm. Nos. 2670/1	3·50	3·00

2030
Karatsuyama
ningyo Folk Toy

2031
Tsuneishihariko
Doll

(Des T. Oya (2673), A. Hoshiyama (2674). Photo)

1999 (15 Nov). New Year's Greetings. P 13×13½.
2673 **2030** 50y. multicoloured .... 1·30 80
2674 **2031** 80y. multicoloured .... 2·10 1·10

2038 Ruined Building
(Great Kanto
earthquake, 1923)

2039 Easygoing Dad
(comic strip character
by Yutaka Aso, 1923)

2032 Karatsuyama
ningyo Folk Toy

2033
Tsuneishihariko
Doll

(Des M. Mimata (2675), J. Kaifuchi (2676). Photo)

1999 (15 Nov). New Year's Lottery Stamps. P 13½.
2675 **2032** 50y. +3y. multicoloured .... 1·20 95
2676 **2033** 80y. +3y. multicoloured .... 1·80 1·50
Each stamp carries a lottery number.

2040 Adventures of
Sho-chan (comic strip
illustrated by Katsuichi
Kabashima, 1923)

2041 Japanese Crane
(protected species,
1924)

2034 Onoe
Matsunosuke (silent
film star, 1925)

2035 Bandoh
Tsumasaburo (silent
film star, 1925)

2042 Baseball Players
(opening of Koshien
Stadium, 1924)

2043 Couple wearing
Western-style Clothes

(Des M. Morita. Photo)

1999 (22 Dec). The Twentieth Century (4th series). Phosphorescent
paper. P 13.
2677 **2034** 50y. multicoloured .... 1·30 95
    a. Sheetlet of 10. Nos. 2677/86............ 15·00
2678 **2035** 50y. multicoloured .... 1·30 95
2679 **2036** 80y. multicoloured .... 1·50 1·10
2680 **2037** 80y. multicoloured .... 1·50 1·10
2681 **2038** 80y. multicoloured .... 1·50 1·10
2682 **2039** 80y. multicoloured .... 1·50 1·10
2683 **2040** 80y. multicoloured .... 1·50 1·10
2684 **2041** 80y. multicoloured .... 1·50 1·10
2685 **2042** 80y. multicoloured .... 1·50 1·10
2686 **2043** 80y. multicoloured .... 1·50 1·10
2677/2686 *Set of* 10 .... 13·00 9·75
   Nos. 2677/86 were issued together in *se-tenant* sheetlets of ten
stamps with a description of each stamp in Japanese in the margin.

2036 Runners (first
Hakone relay
marathon, 1920)

2037 Gramophone
(Gondola Song, 1920)

2044 Underground Train (opening of Tokyo Underground, 1927)

2045 Platform (opening of Tokyo Underground)

2052 Man (emergence of cafés for social gatherings)

2053 Cover of *Horoki* (novel by Hayashi Fumiko)

(Des M. Morita. Photo)

2000 (21 Jan). The Twentieth Century (5th series). Phosphorescent paper. P 13.

2687	**2044**	50y. multicoloured	1·30	95
		a. Sheetlet of 10. Nos. 2687/96	15·00	
2688	**2045**	50y. multicoloured	1·30	95
2689	**2046**	80y. multicoloured	1·50	1·10
2690	**2047**	80y. multicoloured	1·50	1·10
2691	**2048**	80y. multicoloured	1·50	1·10
2692	**2049**	80y. multicoloured	1·50	1·10
2693	**2050**	80y. multicoloured	1·50	1·10
2694	**2051**	80y. multicoloured	1·50	1·10
2695	**2052**	80y. multicoloured	1·50	1·10
2696	**2053**	80y. multicoloured	1·50	1·10
2687/2696		*Set of 10*	13·00	9·75

Nos. 2687/96 were issued together in *se-tenant* sheetlets of ten stamps with a description of each stamp in Japanese in the margin.

2046 Arashi Chozaburo in Title Role (*Kurama Tengu* (film), 1927)

2047 Man doing Gymnastics (first radio broadcast of gymnastic exercises, 1928)

2054/5 Datsun Model 10, 1932 and Toyota Model AA, 1936 (mass production of domestic cars)

2048 Tsuruta Yoshiyuki (swimmer) (Gold Medal winner, Olympic Games, Amsterdam, 1928)

2049 Oda Mikio (athlete) (Gold Medal winner, Olympic Games, Amsterdam)

2050 2nd August Track and Field Programme (Olympic Games, Amsterdam)

2051 Hitomi Kinue (athlete) (Silver Medal winner, Olympic Games, Amsterdam)

2056 Eruption of Mt. Asama, 1929

2057 Kobayashi Takiji (author) (Crab Cannery Ship published in War Banner (paper))

2058 Couple wearing Western Clothes (importing of western fashion)

2059 Kuro (comic strip character by Tagawa Suiha, 1931)

2064/5 D51 Steam Locomotive, 1936

2060 Kabutoyama (winner of first Japanese Derby, 1932)

2061 Matsumidori (winner of 14th Derby)

2066 Otsuki Fumihiko (first edition of *Daigenkai* (dictionary compiled by Otsuki Fumihiko and Otsuki Joden), 1932)

2067 Woman (release of Tokyo Ondo (song by Nakayama Shimpei), 1933)

2068 Enomoto Kenichi (actor)

2062 Woman (release of Longing for Your Shadow (song by Koga Masao), 1931)

2063 Prime Minister's Residence (assassinations of Prime Minister Tsuyoshi Inukai, 1932, and of Finance Minister Takahashi Korekiyo and Lord Keeper of the Privy Seal Saito Makoto, 1936)

2069/70 Players (formation of Tokyo Baseball Club, 1934)

(Des M. Morita. Photo)

2000 (9 Feb). The Twentieth Century (6th series). Phosphorescent paper. P 13.

2697	**2054**	50y. multicoloured	1·30	95
		a. Sheetlet of 10. Nos. 2697/2706	15·00	
2698	**2055**	50y. multicoloured	1·30	95
2699	**2056**	80y. multicoloured	1·50	1·10
2700	**2057**	80y. multicoloured	1·50	1·10
2701	**2058**	80y. multicoloured	1·50	1·10
2702	**2059**	80y. multicoloured	1·50	1·10
2703	**2060**	80y. multicoloured	1·50	1·10
2704	**2061**	80y. multicoloured	1·50	1·10
2705	**2062**	80y. multicoloured	1·50	1·10
2706	**2063**	80y. multicoloured	1·50	1·10
2697/2706	*Set of 10*		13·00	9·75

Nos. 2697/2706 were issued together in *se-tenant* sheetlets of ten stamps with a description of each stamp in Japanese in the margin.

2071 Chuken Hachiko and Statue (erection of statue of Chuken Hachiko, Shikuya Station, Tokyo, 1934)

2072 Yoshikawa Eiji (author) (*Miyamoto* (story) first published in 1935)

2073 Silver-banded
Black Pigeon (declared
extinct, 1936)

(Des M. Morita. Photo)

2078 Yamamoto
Yuzo (author) (*Robo
No Ishi* (novel) first
published in 1937)

2079 Tanaka Kinuyo
and Uehara Ken
(actors) in
Aizenkatsura (film),
1938

2000 (23 Feb). The Twentieth Century (7th series). Phosphorescent
paper. P 13.

2707	**2064**	50y. multicoloured	1·30	95
		a. Horiz pair. Nos. 2707/8	2·75	2·00
		b. Sheetlet of 10. Nos. 2707/16	15·00	
2708	**2065**	50y. multicoloured	1·30	95
2709	**2066**	80y. multicoloured	1·50	1·10
2710	**2067**	80y. multicoloured	1·50	1·10
2711	**2068**	80y. multicoloured	1·50	1·10
2712	**2069**	80y. multicoloured	1·50	1·10
		a. Horiz. pair. Nos. 2712/13	2·75	2·00
2713	**2070**	80y. multicoloured	1·50	1·10
2714	**2071**	80y. multicoloured	1·50	1·10
2715	**2072**	80y. multicoloured	1·50	1·10
2716	**2073**	80y. multicoloured	1·50	1·10
2707/2716		*Set of 10*	13·00	9·75

Nos. 2707/16 were issued together in *se-tenant* sheetlets of ten
stamps, Nos. 2707/8 and 2712/13 respectively forming the composite
design illustrated, with a description of each stamp in Japanese in
the margin.

2080 Yokozuna
Futabayama (sumo
wrestler) (victory in
69 consecutive
matches, 1936–1939)

2081 Sawamura Eiji
(baseball player)

2074/5 Mitsubishi Twin-engined Transport
and Ki-15 Prototype Type 97 Kamikaze
Airplanes

2082 Birds (release
of Dareka Kokyo wo
Omowazaru (song
by Koga Masao))

2083 Woodblock
Carving (Munakata
Shiko)

(Des M. Morita. Photo)

2000 (23 Mar). The Twentieth Century (8th series). Phosphorescent
paper. P 13.

2717	**2074**	50y. multicoloured	1·30	95
		a. Horiz pair. Nos. 2717/18	2·75	2·00
		b. Sheetlet of 10. Nos. 2717/26	15·00	
2718	**2075**	50y. multicoloured	1·30	95
2719	**2076**	80y. multicoloured	1·50	1·10
2720	**2077**	80y. multicoloured	1·50	1·10
2721	**2078**	80y. multicoloured	1·50	1·10
2722	**2079**	80y. multicoloured	1·50	1·10
2723	**2080**	80y. multicoloured	1·50	1·10
2724	**2081**	80y. multicoloured	1·50	1·10
2725	**2082**	80y. multicoloured	1·50	1·10
2726	**2083**	80y. multicoloured	1·50	1·10
2717/2726		*Set of 10*	13·00	9·75

2076 Helen Keller's
First Visit to Japan,
1937

2077 Woman with
Bag and Civilian in
National Uniform
(wartime clothing,
1937–40)

Nos. 2717/26 were issued together in *se-tenant* sheetlets of ten
stamps, Nos. 2717/19 forming the composite design illustrated, with
a description of each stamp in Japanese in the margin.

2084/5 Children and Flowers

2086/7 Faces and Building

2088 Girl as Butterfly with Book   **2089** Two Faces and Building

(Des T. Akira. Photo)

2000 (31 Mar). Children's Book Day. Phosphorescent paper. P 13.

2727	**2084** 80y. multicoloured		1·60	1·10
	a. Sheetlet of 10. Nos. 2727/30,			
	each×2, and 2731/2		17·00	
2728	**2085** 80y. multicoloured		1·60	1·10
2729	**2086** 80y. multicoloured		1·60	1·10
2730	**2087** 80y. multicoloured		1·60	1·10
2731	**2088** 80y. multicoloured		1·60	1·10
2732	**2089** 80y. multicoloured		1·60	1·10
2727/2732	Set of 6		8·75	6·00

Nos. 2727/32 were issued together in *se-tenant* sheetlets of ten stamps, Nos. 2727/8 and 2929/30 respectively forming the composite designs illustrated.

2090 Hanaoka Seisyu (surgeon) and Korean Morning Glory

(Des T. Akira. Photo)

2000 (11 Apr). Centenary of Japanese Surgical Society Congress. Phosphorescent paper. P 13.

2733	**2090** 80y. multicoloured		1·80	1·10

2091 *Liefde* (17th-century merchant ship)   **2092** Dutchman and Nagasaki

(Des M. Morita. Photo)

2000 (19 Apr). 400th Anniv of Japan–Netherlands Cultural Relations. Phosphorescent paper. P 13.

2734	**2091** 80y. multicoloured		1·80	1·10
	a. Horiz pair. Nos. 2734/5		3·75	2·30
2735	**2092** 80y. multicoloured		1·80	1·10

Nos. 2734/5 were issued together in horizontal *se-tenant* pairs within the sheet, each pair forming a composite design.

2093/4 "Ryukozu" (Hashimoto Gaho) ½-size illustration)

(Des M. Morita. Photo)

2000 (20 Apr). Philatelic Week. Phosphorescent paper. P 13½.

2736	**2093** 80y. multicoloured		1·80	1·10
	a. Horiz pair. Nos. 2736/7		3·75	2·30
2737	**2094** 80y. multicoloured		1·80	1·10

Nos. 2736/7 were issued together in horizontal *se-tenant* pairs within the sheet, each pair forming the composite design illustrated.

2095 Bird, Plum Tree and Kuju Mountain Range

(Des M. Mie. Photo)

2000 (21 Apr). National Afforestation Campaign. Phosphorescent paper. P 13½.

2738	**2095** 50y. multicoloured		1·10	60

2096 Golden Bat (comic strip character by Suzuki Ichiro)

2097 Golden Bat

2104 Statue (atomic bomb on Nagasaki, 9 August 1945)

2105 Lieut-General Umezu, Chief of the Imperial Staff signing Surrender (end of Second World War, 1945)

2098 Vice-Consul Sugihara Chiune (issued visas to Jews from Consulate in Lithuania), 1940

2099 Children (Kokumin Gakko school system, 1941)

(Des M. Morita. Photo)

2000 (21 Apr). The Twentieth Century (9th series). Phosphorescent paper. P 13.

2739	**2096** 50y. multicoloured	1·60	1·10
	a. Sheetlet of 10. Nos. 2739/48	19·00	
2740	**2097** 50y. multicoloured	1·60	1·10
2741	**2098** 80y. multicoloured	1·80	1·30
2742	**2099** 80y. multicoloured	1·80	1·30
2743	**2100** 80y. multicoloured	1·80	1·30
2744	**2101** 80y. multicoloured	1·80	1·30
2745	**2102** 80y. multicoloured	1·80	1·30
2746	**2103** 80y. multicoloured	1·80	1·30
2747	**2104** 80y. multicoloured	1·80	1·30
2748	**2105** 80y. multicoloured	1·80	1·30
2739/2748	*Set of 10*	16·00	11·50

Nos. 2739/48 were issued together in *se-tenant* sheetlets of ten stamps, with a description of each stamp in Japanese in the margin.

2100 Airplane over Pearl Harbor (outbreak of Second World War in the Pacific, 1941)

2101 Takamura Kotaro (poet) (Dotei (collected poems) awarded First Imperial Art Academy Prize, 1942)

2106 Wild Goose

2107 Wagtail

2102 Mt. Showashin-zan (formed by volcanic activity of Mt. Usu, 1944)

2103 Damaged Buildings (atomic bomb on Hiroshima, 6 August 1945)

2108 Goshawk

2109 "Girl Blowing Glass Whistle" (Kitagawa Utamaro)

2110 Ichikawa Ebizo (actor) (Toshusai Sharaku)

2111 Roses and Pansies

2116 Astro Boy (comic strip character by Tezuka Osamu, 1951) on cover of Shonen (magazine), July, 1951.

2117 Astro Boy from Cover of Shonen, August, 1961

2112 Puppy and Kitten

2113 Girl with Pen and Boy with Letter

2118 Cover of Music Score and Apples (release of Song of Apples (song by Sato Hachiro and Manjoume Tadashi), 1945)

2119 Sazae San (comic strip by Hasegawa Machiko)

2114 Children and Letter

2115 Girl with Letter and Boy with Pen

(Des M. Morita. Photo)

2120 Mother and Child (promulgation of new constitution, 1947)

2121 Trophy (new world records set by Furuhashi Hironoshin (swimmer), 1949)

2000 (19 May). Phila Nippon '01 International Stamp Exhibition, Tokyo. Self-adhesive. Die-cut.

2749	**2106**	80y. multicoloured	1·80	1·30
		a. Sheetlet of 10. Nos. 2749/58	19·00	
2750	**2107**	80y. multicoloured	1·80	1·30
2751	**2108**	80y. multicoloured	1·80	1·30
2752	**2109**	80y. multicoloured	1·80	1·30
2753	**2110**	80y. multicoloured	1·80	1·30
2754	**2111**	80y. multicoloured	1·80	1·30
2755	**2112**	80y. multicoloured	1·80	1·30
2756	**2113**	80y. multicoloured	1·80	1·30
2757	**2114**	80y. multicoloured	1·80	1·30
2758	**2115**	80y. multicoloured	1·80	1·30
2749/2758		Set of 10	16·00	11·50

Nos. 2749/58 were issued together in *se-tenant* sheetlets of ten stamps.

Nos. 2749/51 are die-cut perf 13½ around the edges of the rectangle and perf 11½ around the circular part of the design, and Nos. 2752/8 die-cut perf 13½ around the edges of the rectangle but straight-cut to shape around the outline of the motif.

2122 Dr. Yukawa Hideki and Atoms (winner of Nobel Prize for Physics, 1949)

2123 Championship Flag (first radio broadcast of Kohaku Uta Gassen (singing competition), 1951)

2124 Kishi Keiko and Sata Keiji (actors) in Kimino Na Wa (film), 1953

2125 Tsuboi Sakae (author) and Cover Illustration by Morita Motoko from First Edition of Nijyu-Yon No Hitomi (novel)

2130 Early Radio and Television Sets (regular television broadcasts, 1953)

(Des M. Morita. Photo)

2000 (23 May). The Twentieth Century (10th series). P 13.

2759	**2116** 50y. multicoloured		1·60	1·10
	a. Sheetlet of 10. Nos. 2759/68		19·00	
2760	**2117** 50y. multicoloured		1·60	1·10
2761	**2118** 80y. multicoloured		1·80	1·30
2762	**2119** 80y. multicoloured		1·80	1·30
2763	**2120** 80y. multicoloured		1·80	1·30
2764	**2121** 80y. multicoloured		1·80	1·30
2765	**2122** 80y. multicoloured		1·80	1·30
2766	**2123** 80y. multicoloured		1·80	1·30
2767	**2124** 80y. multicoloured		1·80	1·30
2768	**2125** 80y. multicoloured		1·80	1·30
2759/2768	*Set of 10*		16·00	11·00

Nos. 2759/68 were issued together in *se-tenant* sheetlets of ten stamps, with a description of each stamp in Japanese in the margin.

2131/2 Kurosawa Akira (film director) and Scene from *Seven Samurai*, 1954

2126 Flowers

2127 Flowers and Sea

(Des S. Arai. Photo)

2000 (21 June). Kyushu–Okinawa Summit. Phosphorescent paper. P 13.

2769	**2126** 80y. multicoloured		1·80	1·30
	a. Pair. Nos. 2769/70		3·75	2·75
2770	**2127** 80y. multicoloured		1·80	1·30

Nos. 2769/70 were issued together in *se-tenant* pairs within the sheet.

2133 Rikidozan (wrestler) and Championship Belt

2134 Rikidozan

2128 Tokyo Tower Entrance Ticket, 1958

2129 Tokyo Tower (construction completed in 1958)

2135 *Godzilla* (release of film, 1954)

2136 Prince Shotoku (issue of 10,000 yen banknote, 1958)

2137 Influence of
Taiyozoku Fashion on
Youth Culture
(release of *Taiyo No
Kisetsu* (film), 1956)

(Des M. Morita. Photo)

2000 (23 June). The Twentieth Century (11th series). Phosphorescent
paper. P 11 (2779) or 13 (others).

2771	**2128**	50y. multicoloured	1·60	1·10
		b. Sheetlet of 10. Nos. 2771/80	19·00	
2772	**2129**	50y. multicoloured	1·60	1·10
2773	**2130**	80y. multicoloured	1·80	1·30
2774	**2131**	80y. multicoloured	1·80	1·30
		a. Horiz pair. Nos. 2774/5	3·75	2·75
2775	**2132**	80y. multicoloured	1·80	1·30
2776	**2133**	80y. multicoloured	1·80	1·30
2777	**2134**	80y. multicoloured	1·80	1·30
2778	**2135**	80y. multicoloured	1·80	1·30
2779	**2136**	80y. multicoloured	1·80	1·30
2780	**2137**	80y. blackish brown and stone	1·80	1·30
2771/2780		*Set of* 10	16·00	11·50

Nos. 2771/80 were issued together in *se-tenant* sheetlets of ten
stamps, Nos. 2774/5 forming the composite design illustrated, with
a description of each stamp in Japanese in the margin.

2138/9 Sunflowers

(Des S. Ozaki. Photo)

2000 (30 June). 50th Anniv of Crime Prevention Campaign.
Phosphorescent paper. P 13.

2781	**2138**	80y. multicoloured	1·80	1·30
		a. Horiz pair. Nos. 2781/2	3·75	2·75
2782	**2139**	80y. multicoloured	1·80	1·30

Nos. 2781/2 were issued together in *se-tenant* horizontal pairs
within the sheet, each pair forming a composite design.

2140 Girl with Pen

2141 House and Birds

2142 Clown and
Envelope

2143 Boy with Dog

2144 Girl and Dog in
Balloon Basket

2145 Apple Tree

2146 Parrots
holding Letter

2147 Bicycle

2148 Girl and Boy
holding Dove

2149 Girl, Letter and
Hedgehog

2150 Girl playing Harp

2151 Boy playing
Recorder

2152 Boy playing Cello

2153 Boy carrying Pen

(Des D. Bruna. Photo)

2000 (21 July). Letter Writing Day. Phosphorescent paper. P 12 (2795), 11 (2788/90, 2792) or 13 (others).

2783	2140	50y. multicoloured	1·70	1·20
		a. Horiz. strip of 4. Nos. 2783/6	7·00	
		b. Booklet pane. Nos. 2783/6, 2791×2, 2793, 2794 and 2796 ×2	20·00	
2784	2141	50y. multicoloured	1·70	1·20
2785	2142	50y. multicoloured	1·70	1·20
2786	2143	50y. multicoloured	1·70	1·20
2787	2144	80y. multicoloured	2·10	1·50
		a. Sheetlet of 10. Nos. 2787/96	22·00	
2788	2145	80y. multicoloured	2·10	1·50
2789	2146	80y. multicoloured	2·10	1·50
2790	2147	80y. multicoloured	2·10	1·50
2791	2148	80y. multicoloured	2·10	1·50
2792	2149	80y. multicoloured	2·10	1·50
2793	2150	80y. multicoloured	2·10	1·50
2794	2151	80y. multicoloured	2·10	1·50
2795	2152	80y. multicoloured	2·10	1·50
2796	2153	80y. multicoloured	2·10	1·50
2783/2796		*Set of 14*	25·00	18·00
MS2797		72×93 mm. Nos. 2784 and 2791	3·25	2·75

Nos. 2783/6 were issued together in horizontal *se-tenant* strips of four stamps within the sheet. Nos. 2787/96 were issued in sheetlets of ten stamps.

The booklet pane has its outer edges imperforate, giving stamps with one or two adjacent sides imperforate.

2154/5 Taro and Giro (left at Showa Base, 1958)

2156 Commemorative Cake Box (marriage of Prince Akihito, 1959)

2157 Meteorological Chart showing the Isewan Typhoon, 1959

2158 Stars and Music Score (release of Sukiyaki (song by Ei Rokusuke and Nakamura Hachidai)), 1960

2159 Shiba Ryotaro (author) (serialization of *Ryomaga Yuku* (novel)), 1962

2160 Doll and Music Score (release of Hello, My Baby (song by Ei Rokusuke and Nakamura Hachidai)), 1963

2161 Tokyo–Osaka High Speed Bullet Train Service, 1964

2162 Official Poster of Olympic Games, Tokyo, 1964

2163 Official Poster of Olympic Games, Tokyo

(Des M. Morita. Photo)

2000 (21 July). The Twentieth Century (12th series). Phosphorescent paper. P 13.

2798	2154	50y. multicoloured	1·80	1·30
		a. Horiz pair. Nos. 2798/9	3·75	2·75
		b. Sheetlet of 10. Nos. 2798/2807	21·00	
2799	2155	50y. multicoloured	1·80	1·30
2800	2156	80y. multicoloured	2·10	1·50
2801	2157	80y. multicoloured	2·10	1·50
2802	2158	80y. multicoloured	2·10	1·50
2803	2159	80y. multicoloured	2·10	1·50
2804	2160	80y. multicoloured	2·10	1·50
2805	2161	80y. multicoloured	2·10	1·50
2806	2162	80y. multicoloured	2·10	1·50
2807	2163	80y. multicoloured	2·10	1·50
2798/2807		*Set of 10*	18·00	13·00

Nos. 2798/2807 were issued together in *se-tenant* sheetlets of ten stamps, Nos. 2798/9 forming the composite design illustrated with a description of each stamp in Japanese in the margin.

2164/5 Characters from Hyokkori Hyotan-jima (launch of children's television programme, 1964)

2166 Television, Car and Air Conditioning Unit, 1960

2167 Ultraman (launch of Ultraman (television series), 1966)

2168 Baltan (character from Ultraman)

2169 Guitars (formation of pop bands following 1966 tour by The Beatles)

2170 Kawabata Yasunari and Oe Kenzaburo (winners of the Nobel Prize for Literature)

2171 Atsumi Taro (actor) in *Otokowa Tsuraiyo* (film)

2172 Tower of the Sun (sculpture, Okamoto Taro) (World's Fair, Osaka, 1970)

2173 Youths and Music Score (release of Children Who Didn't Know the War (song), by Kitayama Osamu and Sugita Jiro, 1971)

(Des M. Morita. Photo)

2000 (23 Aug). The Twentieth Century (13th series). Phosphorescent paper. P 11×12½ (2808/9) or 13 (others).

2808	**2164**	50y. multicoloured	1·80	1·30
		a. Horiz pair. Nos. 2808/9	3·75	2·75
		b. Sheetlet of 10. Nos. 2808/17	21·00	
2809	**2165**	50y. multicoloured	1·80	1·30
2810	**2166**	80y. multicoloured	2·10	1·50
2811	**2167**	80y. multicoloured	2·10	1·50
2812	**2168**	80y. multicoloured	2·10	1·50
2813	**2169**	80y. multicoloured	2·10	1·50
2814	**2170**	80y. multicoloured	2·10	1·50
2815	**2171**	80y. multicoloured	2·10	1·50
2816	**2172**	80y. multicoloured	2·10	1·50
2817	**2173**	80y. multicoloured	2·10	1·50
2808/2817		*Set of 10*	18·00	13·00

Nos. 2808/9 were perforated 11 around the circular part of the stamp and perf 12½ between.

Nos. 2808/17 were issued together in *se-tenant* sheetlets of ten stamps, Nos. 2808/9 forming the composite design illustrated with a description of each stamp in Japanese in the margin.

2174 Naruse Jinzo (founder of Women's University), Yoshioka Yayoi (founder of Women's Medical College, Tokyo) and Tsuda Umeko (founder of Tsuda College)

(Des Y. Yasuhiro. Photo)

2000 (22 Sept). Centenary of Private Higher Education for Women. Phosphorescent paper. P 13.

2818	**2174**	80y. multicoloured	2·10	1·30

2175 Oh Sadaharu (baseball player) swinging Bat, 1964

2176 Nagashima Shigeo (baseball player) running, 1962

2177 Wall Painting (discovery of wall paintings at Takamatsu Zuka, 1972)

2178 Wall Painting (from Takamatsu Zuka)

2179 Pandas (gift from China to Japan, 1972)

2180 Shureimon Gate (return to Japan of administrative rights over Okinawa, 1972)

2185 "Okabe"

2181 Lady Oscar (character from Belubara, 1972) (cartoon by Ikeda Riyoko)

2182 Ozawa Seiji (conductor)

2186 "Maisaka"

2183 Cliffs and Music Score (release of Erimo Misaki (song) by Okamoto Osami and Yoshida Takuro, 1974)

2184 Futuristic Space Shuttle (cartoon series Uchu Senkan Yamato by Matsumoto Reiji, 1974)

2187 "Okazaki"

(Des T. Akira. Photo)

2000 (6 Oct). International Correspondence Week. Paintings from "53 Stations of the Tokaido" by Ando Hiroshige. Phosphorescent paper. P 13½.

2829	**2185**	90y. multicoloured	2·20	1·60
2830	**2186**	110y. multicoloured	2·75	2·20
2831	**2187**	130y. multicoloured	3·25	2·50
2829/2831	*Set of 3*		7·50	5·75

(Des M. Morita. Photo)

2000 (22 Sept). The Twentieth Century (14th series). Phosphorescent paper. P 13.

2819	**2175**	50y. multicoloured	1·80	1·30
		a. Sheetlet of 10. Nos. 2819/28	21·00	
2820	**2176**	50y. multicoloured	1·80	1·30
2821	**2177**	80y. multicoloured	2·10	1·50
2822	**2178**	80y. multicoloured	2·10	1·50
2823	**2179**	80y. multicoloured	2·10	1·50
2824	**2180**	80y. multicoloured	2·10	1·50
2825	**2181**	80y. multicoloured	2·10	1·50
2826	**2182**	80y. multicoloured	2·10	1·50
2827	**2183**	80y. multicoloured	2·10	1·50
2828	**2184**	80y. multicoloured	2·10	1·50
2819/2828	*Set of 10*		18·00	13·00

Nos. 2819/28 were issued together in *se-tenant* sheetlets of ten stamps with a description of each stamp in Japanese in the margin.

2188 Gundam (cartoon character) (launch of Kidosenshi Gundam, television programme, 1979)

2189 Amuro (cartoon character from Kidosenshi Gundam)

2190 Guitar and Music Score (release of Jidai (song by Nakajima Miyuki), 1975)

2191 Fish and Music Score (release of Oyoge! Taiyaki-kun (song by Takada Hiroo and Sase Juichi), 1975)

(Des M. Morita. Photo)

2000 (23 Oct). The Twentieth Century (15th series). Phosphorescent paper. P 13.

2832	2188	50y. multicoloured	1·80	1·30
		a. Sheetlet of 10. Nos. 2832/41	21·00	
2833	2189	50y. multicoloured	1·80	1·30
2834	2190	80y. multicoloured	2·10	1·50
2835	2191	80y. multicoloured	2·10	1·50
2836	2192	80y. multicoloured	2·10	1·50
2837	2193	80y. multicoloured	2·10	1·50
2838	2194	80y. multicoloured	2·10	1·50
2839	2195	80y. multicoloured	2·10	1·50
2840	2196	80y. multicoloured	2·10	1·50
2841	2197	80y. multicoloured	2·10	1·50
2832/2841		Set of 10	18·00	13·00

Nos. 2832/41 were issued together in se-tenant sheetlets of ten stamps with a description of each stamp in Japanese in the margin.

2192 Microphones and Musical Notes (introduction of Karaoke, 1977)

2193 Flowers and Music Score (release of Cosmos (song, by Sada Masashi), 1977)

2198 Nagaoka Hantaro (physicist, 50th death anniv) and Atomic Models

2199 Nakaya Ukichiro (physicist, birth centenary) and Snow Crystal

2194 Alien Space Ship and Music Score (release of UFO (song by Aku Yu and Tokura Shunichi), 1979)

2195 People crossing Field (launch of San Nen B Gumi Kinpachi Sensi (television series), 1979)

2200 Nakamura Teijo (haiku poet, birth centenary) and Text

(Des O. Shigeru (2842), M. Mie (2843) and Y. Hideo (2844). Photo)

2000 (6 Nov). Anniversaries. Phosphorescent paper. P 13.

2842	2198	80y. multicoloured	2·10	1·50
2843	2199	80y. multicoloured	2·10	1·50
2844	2200	80y. multicoloured	2·10	1·50
2842/2844		Set of 3	5·75	4·00

2196 Keyboard and Musical Notes (popularity of synthesizer music, 1970's)

2197 Woman and Snow-covered House (launch of Oshin (television drama), 1983)

2201 Jindaiji (snake-shaped clay bell)

2202 Sasano (carved wooden toy snake)

(Des S. Maruyama (2845), M. Mimata (2846). Photo)

2000 (15 Nov). New Year's Greetings. P 13×13½.
2845 **2201** 50y. multicoloured .... 1·30 90
2846 **2202** 80y. multicoloured .... 2·10 1·50

2209 Rebuilt Watchtower (excavation of ruins at Yoshinogari Iseki, 1989)

2210 Misora Hibari (singer) (recipient of National Medal of Honor, 1989)

2203 Jindaiji (snake-shaped clay bell)

2204 Sasano (carved wooden toy snake)

(Des S. Maruyama (2847), J. Kaifuchi (2848). Photo)

2000 (15 Nov). New Year's Lottery Stamps. Phosphorescent paper. P 13½.
2847 **2203** 50y. + 3y. multicoloured............................ 1·40 1·20
2848 **2204** 80y. + 3y. multicoloured............................ 2·20 1·80
Each stamp carries a lottery number.

2211/12 "J-Boy" (mascot) and Football (Inception of J-League Football, 1993)

2213 "Tonkomeisya" (detail of painting, Hirayama Ikuo) (World Heritage site, 1987)

2205/6 Chararcters from "Go! Anpanman" (launch of children's television programme, 1988)

2214 "Ikarugano Sato Cyoyo Horyuji" (detail of painting, Hirayama Ikuo) (World Heritage site, 1998)

(Des M. Morita. Photo)

2000 (22 Nov). The Twentieth Century (16th series). Phosphorescent paper. P 13 (2849/54, 2857/8) 12-13½ (curved)×13 (straight edge) (2855/6).
2849 **2205** 50y. multicoloured .... 1·80 1·30
  a. Horiz pair. Nos. 2849/50.................... 3·75 2·75
  b. Sheetlet of 10. Nos. 2849/58............ 21·00
2850 **2206** 50y. multicoloured .... 1·80 1·30
2851 **2207** 80y. multicoloured .... 2·10 1·50
2852 **2208** 80y. multicoloured .... 2·10 1·50
2853 **2209** 80y. multicoloured .... 2·10 1·50
2854 **2210** 80y. multicoloured .... 2·10 1·50
2855 **2211** 80y. multicoloured .... 2·10 1·50
  a. Horiz pair. Nos. 2855/6 .... 4·50 3·25
2856 **2212** 80y. multicoloured .... 2·10 1·50
2857 **2213** 80y. multicoloured .... 2·10 1·50

2207 Trains on Trial and Inaugural Runs (opening of Seikan Tunnel, 1988)

2208 Halley's Comet (first appearance for 76 years, 1986)

2858 **2214** 80y. multicoloured .... 2·10   1·50
2849/2858 *Set of* 10 .... 18·00   13·00
Nos. 2849/58 were issued together in *se-tenant* sheetlets of ten stamps, Nos. 2849/50 and 2855/6 respectively forming the composite designs illustrated with a description of each stamp in Japanese in the margin.

2215 Central Tower and Mosaic Marble Floors (detail)

(Des A. Tamaki. Photo)

2000 (29 Nov). 110th Anniv of Diet (Japanese Parliament). Phosphorescent paper. P 13.
2859 **2215** 80y. multicoloured .... 2·10   1·50

2216 Emblem, Nagano Olympic Games, 1998

2217 "Snowlets" (Nagano Olympic mascots)

2218 Crown Prince Noruhito and Princess Masako (wedding, 1993)

2219 Phoenix, Map of Hanshin-Awaji and Collapsed Bridge (Hanshin-Awaji earthquake, 1995)

2220 Lap-top Computer and Mobile Phone (increased use of wireless telecommunications)

2221 Launch of Space Shuttle *Endeavor* (inclusion of first Japanese astronaut on NASA mission, 1992)

2222 Doi Takao (Japanese astronaut) outside Spaceship

2223 Footballer (Japanese participation in World Cup Football Championship, France, 1998)

2224 "Mother Earth" (Bokunan Naka) (United Nations Framework Convention on Climate Change, Kyoto, 1997)

2225 Official Poster of Nagano Olympic Games

(Des M. Morita. Photo)

2000 (22 Dec). The Twentieth Century (17th series). Phosphorescent paper. P 12 (2868) or 13 (others).
2860 **2216** 50y. multicoloured .... 1·80   1·30
 a. Sheetlet of 10. Nos. 2860/9 .... 21·00
2861 **2217** 50y. multicoloured .... 1·80   1·30
2862 **2218** 80y. multicoloured .... 2·10   1·50
2863 **2219** 80y. multicoloured .... 2·10   1·50
2864 **2220** 80y. multicoloured .... 2·10   1·50
2865 **2221** 80y. multicoloured .... 2·10   1·50
2866 **2222** 80y. multicoloured .... 2·10   1·50
2867 **2223** 80y. multicoloured .... 2·10   1·50
2868 **2224** 80y. multicoloured .... 2·10   1·50
2869 **2225** 80y. multicoloured .... 2·10   1·50
2860/2869 *Set of* 10 .... 18·00   13·00
Nos. 2860/9 were issued together in *se-tenant* sheetlets of ten stamps with a description of each stamp in Japanese in the margin.

2226/7 Red-crested White Cranes ("Grus japonensis" Matazo Kayama)

(Des M. Morita. Photo)

2001 (5 Jan). "Internet Expo 2001 Japan" (virtual Internet fair). Phosphorescent paper. P 13.
2870 **2226** 80y. multicoloured .... 1·70 1·40
　　　a. Sheetlet of 10. Nos. 2870/1 .... 3·75 3·00
2871 **2227** 80y. multicoloured .... 1·70 1·40
Nos. 2870/1 were issued together in horizontal *se-tenant* pairs within the sheet, each pair forming a composite design.

2234 Wind God (statue), Rinnoji Temple　　**2235** Thunder God (statue), Rinnoji Temple

2228 Heliotrope, Flax and Emblem　　**2229** "Gyoseishoshi" (Japanese calligraphy), Computer and Emblem

2236 Peacock, Toshugu Shrine　　**2237** Sleeping Cat, Toshugu Shrine

(Des M. Mimata. Photo)

2001 (17 Jan). United Nations Year of Volunteers. Phosphorescent paper. P 13½.
2872 **2228** 80y. multicoloured .... 1·70 1·40

(Des A. Tamaki. Photo)

2001 (22 Feb). 50th Anniv of Gyoseishoshi Lawyer System (specialist administrative lawyers). Phosphorescent paper. P 13.
2873 **2229** 80y. multicoloured .... 1·70 1·40

2238/9 Rinnoji Temple

(Des M. Morita. Photo)

2001 (23 Feb). World Heritage Sites (1st series). Shrines and Temples, Nikko. Phosphorescent paper. P 13.
2874 **2230** 80y. multicoloured .... 1·70 1·40
　　　a. Sheetlet of 10. Nos. 2874/83 .... 18·00
2875 **2231** 80y. multicoloured .... 1·70 1·40
2876 **2232** 80y. multicoloured .... 1·70 1·40
2877 **2233** 80y. multicoloured .... 1·70 1·40
2878 **2234** 80y. multicoloured .... 1·70 1·40
2879 **2235** 80y. multicoloured .... 1·70 1·40
2880 **2236** 80y. multicoloured .... 1·70 1·40
2881 **2237** 80y. multicoloured .... 1·70 1·40
2882 **2238** 80y. multicoloured .... 1·70 1·40
　　　a. Horiz pair. Nos. 2882/3 .... 3·50 3·00
2883 **2239** 80y. multicoloured .... 1·70 1·40
2874/2883 *Set of* 10 .... 15·00 12·50
Nos. 2874/83 were issued together *se-tenant* in sheetlets of ten stamps, Nos. 2882/3 forming the composite design illustrated, with a description of each stamp in Japanese in the illustrated margin.
See also Nos. 2887/96, 2906/15, 2960/9, 2985/94, 2997/3006, 3020/9, 3045/54, 3060/9, 3083/92 and 3107/16.

2230 Shinkyo Bridge, Futarasan Shrine　　**2231** Main Sanctuary, Futarasan Shrine

2232 Karamon Gate, Toshugu Shrine　　**2233** Kirin (mythical winged horse) (painting), Toshugu Shrine

2240 Emblem

2241 "The Annunciation"
(detail, Botticelli)

2242 "The Annunciation"
(detail, Botticelli)

(Des M. Morita. Photo)

2001 (19 Mar). "Italy in Japan 2001" (cultural and scientific event).
Phosphorescent paper. P 13 (2884) or 13½ (others)

2884	**2240**	80y. multicoloured	1·70	1·40
2885	**2241**	110y. multicoloured	2·40	1·90
		a. Horiz pair. Nos. 2885/6	5·00	4·00
2886	**2242**	110y. multicoloured	2·40	1·90
2884/2886		Set of 3	5·75	4·75

Nos. 2884/6 were issued together in horizontal *se-tenant* pairs
featuring two separate panels of the painting.

2243/4 Marodo Shrine

2245 Main Sanctuary

2246 Lion Dog (statue)

2247 Marodo Shrine
and Pagoda

2248 Traditional
Dance Mask

2249 Horse (statue)

2250 Buildings

2251 Treasure
Pagoda

2252 Oomoto Shrine

(Des M. Morita. Photo)

2001 (23 Mar). World Heritage Sites (2nd series). Itsukushima Shrine.
Phosphorescent paper. P 13.

2887	**2243**	80y. multicoloured	1·70	1·40
		a. Horiz pair. Nos. 2887/8	3·75	3·00
		b. Sheetlet of 10. Nos. 2887/96	18·00	
2888	**2244**	80y. multicoloured	1·70	1·40
2889	**2245**	80y. multicoloured	1·70	1·40
2890	**2246**	80y. multicoloured	1·70	1·40
2891	**2247**	80y. multicoloured	1·70	1·40
2892	**2248**	80y. multicoloured	1·70	1·40
2893	**2249**	80y. multicoloured	1·70	1·40
2894	**2250**	80y. multicoloured	1·70	1·40
2895	**2251**	80y. multicoloured	1·70	1·40
2896	**2252**	80y. multicoloured	1·70	1·40
2887/2896		Set of 10	15·00	12·50

Nos. 2887/96 were issued together in sheetlets of ten stamps, Nos.
2287/8 forming the composite design illustrated, with a description
of each stamp in Japanese illustrated in the margin.

2253 Emblem

2254 Woman
posting Letter
(Nakamura Senseki)

(Des A. Hoshiyama. Photo)

2001 (6 Apr). Centenary of Japanese Dermatological Association. Phosphorescent paper. Multicoloured, colour of triangle beneath face value given. P 13½.

2897	2253	80y. rose-pink	1·70	1·40
		a. Vert strip of 5. Nos. 2897/2901	9·00	
2898		80y. flesh	1·70	1·40
2899		80y. greenish yellow	1·70	1·40
2900		80y. light green	1·70	1·40
2901		80y. dull violet blue	1·70	1·40
2897/2901		Set of 5	7·75	6·25

Nos. 2897/2901 were issued together in vertical *se-tenant* strips of five stamps within the sheet.

(Des M. Morita. Photo)

2001 (20 Apr). Philatelic Week. Centenary of Red Cylindrical Letter Boxes (designed by Taraya Takashhichi and Nakamura Koji). Phosphorescent paper. P 13.

2902	2254	80y. multicoloured	1·70	1·40

No. 2902 was issued in vertical strips of five stamps within the sheetlet with an enlarged illustrated central margin.

2255 "Ato, Nik and Kaz"(mascots) **2256** "Kaz"

2257 "Nik"

(Des M. Morita. Photo)

2001 (31 May). World Cup Football Championship, Japan and South Korea (2002). Phosphorescent paper. P 13.

2903	2255	80y. +10y. multicoloured	2·20	1·80
2904	2256	80y. +10y. multicoloured	2·20	1·80
		a. Horiz pair. Nos. 2904/5	4·75	3·75
2905	2257	80y. +10y. multicoloured	2·20	1·80
2903/2905		Set of 3	6·00	4·75

No. 2904/5 were issued together in horizontal *se-tenant* pairs within the sheet.

2258 Hosodono, Maidono and Tsuchinoya Halls, Kamowakeikazuchi Shrine

2259 Romon Gate, Kamowakeikazuchi Shrine

2260 East Main Hall, Kamomioya Shrine

2261 Guardian Dog (statue), Kamomioya Shrine

2262 Pagoda and South Great Gate, Toji Temple

2263 Fukuu Joju Nyorai (statue), Toji Temple

2264 Pagoda and West Gate, Kiyomizudera Temple

2265 Main Hall, Kiyomizudera Temple

2266 "Nyorin Kannon" (painting), Toji Temple

2267 Daiitoku Myoo (statue), Toji Temple

(Des M. Morita. Photo)

2001 (22 June). World Heritage (3rd series). Temples and Shrines, Kyoto. Phosphorescent paper. P 13.

2906	2258	80y. multicoloured	1·70	1·40
		a. Sheetlet of 10. Nos. 2906/15	18·00	
2907	2259	80y. multicoloured	1·70	1·40
2908	2260	80y. multicoloured	1·70	1·40
2909	2261	80y. multicoloured	1·70	1·40
2910	2262	80y. multicoloured	1·70	1·40

2911	**2263**	80y. multicoloured		1·70	1·40
2912	**2264**	80y. multicoloured		1·70	1·40
2913	**2265**	80y. multicoloured		1·70	1·40
2914	**2266**	80y. multicoloured		1·70	1·40
2915	**2267**	80y. multicoloured		1·70	1·40
2906/2915		*Set of* 10		15·00	12·50

Nos. 2906/15 were issued together in sheetlets of ten stamps with a description of each stamp in Japanese in the margin.

2268 Flowers and Pigeons

(Des S. Arai and A. Hoshiyama. Photo)

2001 (2 July). 50th Anniv of Membership of United Nations Educational, Scientific and Cultural Organisation. Phosphorescent paper. P 13½.

2916	**2268**	80y. multicoloured		1·70	1·40

2269 Swimming

2270 Synchronized Swimming

2271 Diving

2272 Water Polo

(Des M. Mimata. Photo)

2001 (16 July). Ninth International Swimming Federation Championships, Fukuoka. Phosphorescent paper. P 13.

2917	**2269**	80y. multicoloured		1·70	1·40
		a. Horiz strip of 4. Nos. 2917/20		7·00	
2918	**2270**	80y. multicoloured		1·70	1·40
2919	**2271**	80y. multicoloured		1·70	1·40
2920	**2272**	80y. multicoloured		1·70	1·40
2917/2920		*Set of* 4		6·00	5·00

Nos. 2917/20 were issued together in horizontal *se-tenant* strips of four stamps, the backgrounds forming a composite design.

2273 Rabbits

2274 Girl and Pencil

2275 Boy holding Envelope

2276 Girl with Ribbons

2277 Bird in Tree

2278 Girl holding Rabbit

2279 Boy holding Pen

2280 Girl with Envelope and Dog

2281 Girl and Flowers

2282 Flowers and Bird with Envelope

2283 Birds and Roof

2284 Rabbit and Flowers

2289 "Sakata Hangoro as Fujikwa Mizuemon" (Toshusai Shakuru)

2290 "Segawa Kikunojo as Oshizu, Tanabe Bunzo's Wife" (Toshusai Shakuru)

2285 Boy and Rabbit

2286 Chicks, Hen and Pig

(Des D. Bruna and M. Morita. Photo)

2001 (23 July). Letter Writing Day. Phosphorescent paper. P 11 (2932), 12 (2925, 2930) or 13 (others).

2921	**2273**	50y. multicoloured	1·30	1·10
		a. Horiz strip of 4. Nos. 2921/4	5·50	
		b. Booklet pane. Nos. 2921/4,		
		2927/8, each×2 and 2931×2	14·50	
2922	**2274**	50y. multicoloured	1·30	1·10
2923	**2275**	50y. multicoloured	1·30	1·10
2924	**2276**	50y. multicoloured	1·30	1·10
2925	**2277**	80y. multicoloured	1·70	1·40
		a. Sheetlet of 10. Nos. 2925/34	18·00	
2926	**2278**	80y. multicoloured	1·70	1·40
2927	**2279**	80y. multicoloured	1·70	1·40
2928	**2280**	80y. multicoloured	1·70	1·40
2929	**2281**	80y. multicoloured	1·70	1·40
2930	**2282**	80y. multicoloured	1·70	1·40
2931	**2283**	80y. multicoloured	1·70	1·40
2932	**2284**	80y. multicoloured	1·70	1·40
2933	**2285**	80y. multicoloured	1·70	1·40
2934	**2286**	80y. multicoloured	1·70	1·40
2921/2934		Set of 14	20·00	17·00
MS2935		72×93 mm. Nos. 2922 and 2931	3·25	3·00

Nos. 2921/4 were issued together in horizontal *se-tenant* strips of four stamps within the sheet. Nos. 2925/34 were issued in sheetlets of ten stamps.

The booklet pane has its outer edge imperforate, giving stamps with one or two adjacent sides imperforate.

2291 "Ichikawa Omezo as Yakko Ippei" (Toshusai Sakuru)

2292 "Beauty looking Back" (Hishikawa Moronobu)

2293 "Girl playing Glass Flute" (Kitagawa Utamaro)

2294 "Fuzoku Higashino Nishiki, returning from the Bath-house in the Rain" (Torii Kiyonaga)

2287 "Ootani Oniji as Edobei" (Toshusai Sharaku)

2288 "Iwai Hanshiro IV as Shigenoi" (Toshusai Shakuru)

2295 "Iwai Kumesaburo as Chiyo" (Utagawa Kunimasa)

2296 "Ichikawa Komazo III as Sasaski Ganryu" (Utagawa Toyokuni)

2297 "Iwai Hanshiro IV as Shigenoi" (Toshusai Shakuru)

2298 "Ootani Oniji as Edobei" (Toshusai Shakuru)

2299 Mandarin Duck

2300 Japanese White-Eye

2301 Girl and Boy holding Envelopes

2302 "Iwai Kumesaburo as Chiyo" (Utagawa Kunimasa)

2303 "Ichikawa Komazo III as Sasaki Ganryu" (Utagawa Toyokuni)

2304 Eastern Turtle Dove

2305 Greater Pied Kingfisher

2306 1871 48m. Stamp

(Des M. Morita. Photo)

2001 (1 Aug). PHILA NIPPON '01 International Stamp Exhibition, Tokyo.

(a) Ordinary gum. Phosphorescent frame. P 13.

2936	**2287**	50y. multicoloured	1·40	1·10
		a. Sheetlet of 10. Nos. 2936/45	16·00	
2937	**2288**	50y. multicoloured	1·40	1·10
2938	**2289**	50y. multicoloured	1·40	1·10
2939	**2290**	50y. multicoloured	1·40	1·10
2940	**2291**	50y. multicoloured	1·40	1·10
2941	**2292**	80y. multicoloured	1·70	1·40
2942	**2293**	80y. multicoloured	1·70	1·40
2943	**2294**	80y. multicoloured	1·70	1·40
2944	**2295**	80y. multicoloured	1·70	1·40
2945	**2296**	80y. multicoloured	1·70	1·40

(b) Self-adhesive gum. Phosphorescent paper. Die-cut perf 12 (curve)×13 (straight edge) (2950, 2955) or 13 (others).

2946	**2297**	50y. multicoloured	1·50	1·20
		a. Sheetlet of 10. Nos. 2946/55	17·00	
2947	**2298**	50y. multicoloured	1·50	1·20
2948	**2299**	50y. multicoloured	1·50	1·20
2949	**2300**	50y. multicoloured	1·50	1·20
2950	**2301**	50y. multicoloured	1·50	1·20
2951	**2302**	80y. multicoloured	1·80	1·50
2952	**2303**	80y. multicoloured	1·80	1·50
2953	**2304**	80y. multicoloured	1·80	1·50
2954	**2305**	80y. multicoloured	1·80	1·50
2955	**2306**	80y. multicoloured	1·80	1·50
2936/2955		*Set of 20*	29·00	23·00

Nos. 2936/45 were issued *se-tenant* with labels bearing the "PHILA NIPPON '01" logo, in sheetlets of ten stamps and ten labels with an enlarged illustrated margin. Nos. 2946/55 were issued together in sheetlets of ten stamps with an enlarged illustrated margin, Nos. 2946/9 and 2951/4 die-cut perf 13 around the edges of the rectangle and straight-cut to shape around the outline of the motif.

2307 Fly Casting and Discus

2308 Aerobics and Billiards

2309 Water Skiing and Life Saving

2310 Tug of War and Body Building

(Des T. Harada and A. Tamaki. Photo)

2001 (16 Aug). Sixth World Games, Akita. Phosphorescent paper.
P 13.

2956	**2307**	50y. multicoloured	1·30	1·10
		a. Horiz pair. Nos. 2956/7	2·75	2·30
2957	**2308**	50y. multicoloured	1·30	1·10
2958	**2309**	80y. multicoloured	1·70	1·40
		a. Horiz pair. Nos. 2958/9	3·75	3·00
2959	**2310**	80y. multicoloured	1·70	1·40
2956/2959		Set of 4	5·50	4·50

Nos. 2956/7 and Nos. 2958/9 respectively were issued in horizontal se-tenant pairs within the sheet.

2318 Pagoda, Ninnaji Temple

2319 Phoenix Hall, Byodoin Temple

2311 Konpon Chudo Hall, Enryakuji Temple

2312 Eternal Flame, Enryakuji Temple

2320 Bodhisattva floating on Clouds (statue), Byodoin Temple

(Des M. Morita. Photo)

2001 (23 Aug). World Heritage (4th series). Temples, Kyoto.

2960	**2311**	80y. multicoloured	1·70	1·40
		a. Sheetlet of 10. Nos. 2960/9	18·00	
2961	**2312**	80y. multicoloured	1·70	1·40
2962	**2313**	80y. multicoloured	1·70	1·40
2963	**2314**	80y. multicoloured	1·70	1·40
		a. Horiz pair. Nos. 2963/4	3·75	3·00
2964	**2315**	80y. multicoloured	1·70	1·40
2965	**2316**	80y. multicoloured	1·70	1·40
2966	**2317**	80y. multicoloured	1·70	1·40
2967	**2318**	80y. multicoloured	1·70	1·40
2968	**2319**	80y. multicoloured	1·70	1·40
2969	**2320**	80y. multicoloured	1·70	1·40
2960/2969		Set of 10	15·00	12·50

Nos. 2960/9 were issued together in sheetlets of ten stamps, Nos. 2963/4 forming a composite design, with descriptions of each stamp in Japanese in the margin.

2313 Ninai-do Hall, Enryakuji Temple

2314/15 Sanbo-in Temple Garden, Daigoji Temple

2321 War Memorial Opera House and Flowers

(Des M. Mimata. Photo)

2001 (7 Sept). 50th Anniv of San Francisco Peace Treaty. P 13.

2970	**2321**	80y. multicoloured	2·20	1·80

2316 Pagoda, Daigoji Temple

2317 Palace, Ninnaji Temple

2322 "Hara"

2327 Man catching Disc

2328 Wheelchair Race

(Des F. Kanesmatsu. Photo)

2001 (26 Oct). First National Sports Games for the Disabled, Sendai City and Miyagi-gun. P 13.
2976	**2327**	80y. multicoloured	1·80	1·50
		a. Horiz pair. Nos. 2976/7	4·00	3·25
2977	**2328**	80y. multicoloured	1·80	1·50

2323 "Oiso"

2329 Noringa Motoori (writer and scholar, death bicentenary)

2330 Gidayu Takemoto (jojuri chanter and puppeteer, 350th birth) and Illustration from Sonezaki Shinju

(Des M. Mimata (2978) and S. Oikawa (2979). Photo)

2001 (5 Nov). Anniversaries. P 13.
2978	**2329**	80y. multicoloured	1·80	1·50
2979	**2330**	80y. multicoloured	1·80	1·50

2324 "Sakanoshita"

(Des A. Tamaki. Photo)

2001 (5 Oct). International Correspondence Week. Paintings from "53 Stations of Tokaido" by Ando Hiroshige. P 13½.
2971	**2322**	90y. multicoloured	2·50	2·00
2972	**2323**	110y. multicoloured	3·00	2·40
2973	**2324**	130y. multicoloured	3·25	2·75
2971/2973		Set of 3	7·75	6·50

2325 Boy with Birds and Insects

2326 Girl with Birds and Animals

(Des T. Murakami and M. Morita. Photo)

2001 (11 Oct). "Let's Keep our Towns Safe" (national community safety campaign). P 13.
2974	**2325**	80y. multicoloured	1·80	1·50
		a. Horiz pair. Nos. 2974/5	4·00	3·25
2975	**2326**	80y. multicoloured	1·80	1·50

2331 Horse carrying Rice (sedge handicraft)

2332 Red Horse of Kira

(Des J. Kaibuchi (2980) and E. Uchida (2981). Photo)

2001 (15 Nov). New Year's Greetings. P 13×13½.
2980	**2331**	50y. multicoloured	1·30	1·10
2981	**2332**	80y. multicoloured	1·70	1·40

2333 Horse
carrying Rice

2334 Red Horse of
Kira

(Des A. Hoshiyama (2982) and E. Uchida (2983). Photo)
2001 (15 Nov). New Year's Lottery Stamps. P 13½.
2982 2333 50y. + 3y. multicoloured .... 1·40 1·10
2983 2334 80y. + 3y. multicoloured........................... 1·80 1·50
Each stamp carries a lottery number.

2335 Television
Camera, Television
Set and Radio
Microphone

(Des A. Tamaki. Photo)
2001 (15 Nov). 50th Anniv of Commercial Broadcasting. P 13.
2984 2335 80y. multicoloured .... 1·70 1·40

2336 Ujikami Shrine

2337 Kaeru Mata
(main shrine), Ujikami
Shrine

2338 Path to Kozanji
Temple

2339 Sekisuiin,
Kozanji Temple

2340 Kasumijima
Garden, Saihoji Temple

2341 Kojokan Garden,
Saihoji Temple

2342/3 Garden, Tenryuji Temple

2344 Golden Temple,
Rokuonji Temple

2345 Golden Temple
in Winter

2001 (21 Dec). World Heritage (5th series). Temples and Shrines,
Kyoto. Phosphorescent paper. P 13.
2985 2336 80y. multicoloured .... 1·70 1·40
    a. Sheetlet of 10. Nos. 2985/94............ 18·00
2986 2337 80y. multicoloured .... 1·70 1·40
2987 2338 80y. multicoloured .... 1·70 1·40
2988 2339 80y. multicoloured .... 1·70 1·40
2989 2340 80y. multicoloured .... 1·70 1·40
2990 2341 80y. multicoloured .... 1·70 1·40
2991 2342 80y. multicoloured .... 1·70 1·40
    a. Horiz pair. Nos. 2991/2..................... 3·75 3·00
2992 2343 80y. multicoloured .... 1·70 1·40
2993 2344 80y. multicoloured .... 1·70 1·40
2994 2345 80y. multicoloured .... 1·70 1·40
2985/2994 Set of 10 .... 15·00 12·50
    Nos. 2985/94 were issued together in sheetlets of ten stamps, Nos.
2991/2 forming the composite design illustrated, with descriptions
of each stamp in Japanese in the illustrated margin.
    Initially scheduled for release on 22 November 2001, the sheetlets
were withdrawn two days before that date, after it was discovered
that the stamp depicting the path to Kozanji Temple was shown as a
mirror image. Prior to the withdrawal, eight sheetlets were sold from
Tochigi Post Office. Sheetlets containing the corrected image were
finally issued on 21 December 2001.

2346 Upraised Hand

2347 Horse-shaped
Fiddle Head

(Des H. Isoda and M. Morita. Litho)

2002 (24 Jan). 50th Anniv of Legal Aid System. Phosphorescent paper. P 13.
2995 **2346** 80y. multicoloured .... 1·70 1·40

(Des E. Uchida and M. Morita. Litho)

2002 (15 Feb). 30th Anniv of Japan–Mongolia Diplomatic Relations. Phosphorescent paper. P 13.
2996 **2347** 80y. multicoloured .... 1·70 1·40

2348 Silver Pavilion in Snow, Jishoji Temple

2349 Silver Pavilion

2350 Hojo Garden, Ryoanji Temple

2351 Hojo Garden in Winter

2352 Karamon Gate, Honganji Temple

2353 Hiunkaku, Honganji Temple

2354 Shoin, Honganji Temple

2355 Ninomaru Palace, Nijo Castle

2356 Hawk on Pine (detail, painting), Nijo Castle

2357 Hawk on Pine (detail)

2002 (22 Feb). World Heritage (6th series). Temples, Kyoto. Phosphorescent paper. P 13.
2997 **2348** 80y. multicoloured .... 1·70 1·40
    a. Sheetlet of 10. Nos. 2997/3006....... 18·00
2998 **2349** 80y. multicoloured .... 1·70 1·40
2999 **2350** 80y. multicoloured .... 1·70 1·40
3000 **2351** 80y. multicoloured .... 1·70 1·40
3001 **2352** 80y. multicoloured .... 1·70 1·40
3002 **2353** 80y. multicoloured .... 1·70 1·40
3003 **2354** 80y. multicoloured .... 1·70 1·40
3004 **2355** 80y. multicoloured .... 1·70 1·40
3005 **2356** 80y. multicoloured .... 1·70 1·40
3006 **2357** 80y. multicoloured .... 1·70 1·40
2997/3006 *Set of* 10 .... 15·00 12·50
    Nos. 2997/3006 were issued together in sheetlets of ten stamps, with descriptions of each stamp in Japanese in the illustrated margin.

2358 Bell and Mythical Lion-dog

(Des M. Morita. Photo)

2002 (1 Mar). 50th Anniv of Japan Lions (charitable organization). P 13.
3007 **2358** 80y. multicoloured .... 1·60 1·30

2359 Men's Singles Skater

2360 Pairs Skaters

(Des F. Kanematsu. Photo)

2002 (8 Mar). World Figure Skating Championships, Nagano. P 13.
3008 **2359** 80y. multicoloured .... 1·60 1·30
    a. Pair. Nos. 3008/9 .... 3·50 2·75
3009 **2360** 80y. multicoloured .... 1·60 1·30
    Nos. 3008/9 were issued in *se-tenant* pairs in sheets of ten stamps.

2361 Taj Mahal, India

2362 Artefact and Ruins, Moenjodaro, Pakistan

2367 *Hikawa-Maru* (passenger ship)

2368 Ship and Irises

(Des M. Mimata. Photo)

2002 (8 May). 50th Anniv of Japan–USA Fulbright Exchange Programme. P 13.

3016 **2367** 80y. multicoloured .... 1·60   1·30

(Des M. Morita. Photo)

2002 (15 May). 30th Anniv of Return of Okinawa. P 13.

3017 **2368** 80y. multicoloured .... 1·60   1·30

2363 Sigiriya, Sri Lanka

2364 Terracotta Panel and Ruins, Paharpur, Bangladesh

2369 Stylized Football Pitch

2370 FIFA World Cup Trophy

(Des M. Morita. Photo)

2002 (12 Apr). 50th Anniv of Japan–South East Asia Diplomatic Relations. P 13.

3010	**2361** 80y. multicoloured	1·60	1·30
3011	**2362** 80y. multicoloured	1·60	1·30
3012	**2363** 80y. multicoloured	1·60	1·30
3013	**2364** 80y. multicoloured	1·60	1·30
3010/3013	*Set of 4*	5·75	4·75

(Des M. Morita. Photo)

2002 (24 May). World Cup Football Championship, Japan and South Korea. P 13.

3018	**2369** 80y. multicoloured	1·60	1·30
	a. Pair. Nos. 3018/19	3·50	2·75
3019	**2370** 80y. multicoloured	1·60	1·30

Nos. 3018/19 were issued in *se-tenant* pairs within the sheet.

2371 Great Buddha Hall, Todaiji Temple

2372 Southern Gate, Todaiji Temple

2365 Two Horsemen (Kamo folding screen)

2366 Horseman and Spectator (Kamo folding screen)

(Des M. Morita. Photo)

2002 (19 Apr). Philately Week. P 13×13½.

3014	**2365** 80y. multicoloured	1·60	1·30
	a. Pair. Nos. 3014/15	3·50	2·75
3015	**2366** 80y. multicoloured	1·60	1·30

Nos. 3014/15 were issued in *se-tenant* pairs within the sheet.

2373 Great Buddha (detail), Todaiji Temple

2374 Virupaksu (statue), Todaiji Temple

2375 Lotus Hall, Todaiji Temple

2376 Five-storied Pagoda, Kofukuji Temple

2383 House and Flowers

2384 Young Boy and Fence

2377 Northern Octagonal Hall, Kofukuji Temple

2378 Ashura (statue), Kofukuji Temple

2385 Ladybird and Caterpillar

2386 Farmer and Sheep

2379 Buddha Head, Kofukuji Temple

2380 Ryutoki Demon (statue), Kofukuji Temple

2387 Cow

2388 Girl and Flowers

(Des M. Morita. Photo)

2002 (21 June). World Heritage (7th series). Temples, Nara. P 13.

3020	**2371** 80y. multicoloured	1·60	1·30
	a. Sheetlet of 10. Nos. 3020/9	17·00	
3021	**2372** 80y. multicoloured	1·60	1·30
3022	**2373** 80y. multicoloured	1·60	1·30
3023	**2374** 80y. multicoloured	1·60	1·30
3024	**2375** 80y. multicoloured	1·60	1·30
3025	**2376** 80y. multicoloured	1·60	1·30
3026	**2377** 80y. multicoloured	1·60	1·30
3027	**2378** 80y. multicoloured	1·60	1·30
3028	**2379** 80y. multicoloured	1·60	1·30
3029	**2380** 80y. multicoloured	1·60	1·30
3020/3029	Set of 10	14·50	11·50

Nos. 3020/9 were issued in sheetlets of ten stamps, with descriptions of each stamp in Japanese in the illustrated margin.

2389 Boy with Football

2390 Girl carrying Tennis Racquet

2381 Girl carrying Envelope

2382 Monkey hanging from Tree

2391 Mother and Child

2392 Man riding Bicycle

2393 Girl and Vase   **2394** Van and Car

(Des M. Morita. Photo)
2002 (23 July). National Letter Writing Day. P 13.
3030	**2381**	50y. multicoloured	1·20	95
		a. Strip of 4. Nos. 3030/3	5·00	
		b. Booklet pane. Nos. 3030/3 and		
		Nos. 3040/1 each x3	15·00	
3031	**2382**	50y. multicoloured	1·20	95
3032	**2383**	50y. multicoloured	1·20	95
3033	**2384**	50y. multicoloured	1·20	95
3034	**2385**	80y. multicoloured	1·60	1·30
		a. Sheetlet of 10. Nos. 3034/43	17·00	
3035	**2386**	80y. lemon, black and blue	1·60	1·30
3036	**2387**	80y. multicoloured	1·60	1·30
3037	**2388**	80y. multicoloured	1·60	1·30
3038	**2389**	80y. multicoloured	1·60	1·30
3039	**2390**	80y. multicoloured	1·60	1·30
3040	**2391**	80y. multicoloured	1·60	1·30
3041	**2392**	80y. multicoloured	1·60	1·30
3042	**2393**	80y. multicoloured	1·60	1·30
3043	**2394**	80y. multicoloured	1·60	1·30
3030/3043		*Set of* 14	19·00	15·00
MS3044		72x94 mm. Nos. 3031 and 3040	3·25	3·00

Nos. 3030/3 were issued in *se-tenant* strips of four stamps within the sheet.
Nos. 3034/43 were issued in sheetlets of ten stamps.
The booklet pane has its outer edge imperforate, giving stamps with one or two adjacent sides imperforate.

2395 Covered Passageway, Kasuga Taisha Shrine   **2396** Middle Gate, Kasuga Taisha Shrine

2397 Deer, Kasuga-yama Forest   **2398** Zen Meditation Hall, Gango-ji Temple

2399 Pagoda, Gango-ji Temple   **2400** East and West Pagodas, Yakushi-ji Temple

2401 Buddha of Healing, Yakushi-ji Temple   **2402** Golden Hall, Toshodai-ji Temple

2403 Standing Image of the Thousand Handed Goddess of Mercy, Toshodai-ji Temple   **2404** Suzakumon Gate, Heijo Imperial Palace

(Des M. Morita. Photo)
2002 (23 July). World Heritage (8th series). Temples. Phosphorised paper. P 13.
3045	**2395**	80y. multicoloured	1·60	1·30
		a. Sheetlet of 10. Nos. 3045/54	17·00	
3046	**2396**	80y. multicoloured	1·60	1·30
3047	**2397**	80y. multicoloured	1·60	1·30
3048	**2398**	80y. multicoloured	1·60	1·30
3049	**2399**	80y. multicoloured	1·60	1·30
3050	**2400**	80y. multicoloured	1·60	1·30
3051	**2401**	80y. multicoloured	1·60	1·30
3052	**2402**	80y. multicoloured	1·60	1·30
3053	**2403**	80y. multicoloured	1·60	1·30
3054	**2404**	80y. multicoloured	1·60	1·30
3045/3054		*Set of* 10	14·50	11·50

Nos. 3045/54 were issued in sheetlets of ten stamps, with descriptions of each stamp in Japanese in the illustrated margin.

2405 Stylized Human and Flowers   **2406** Basketball Players

(Des A. Sonoko. Photo)

2002 (1 Aug). 12th World Psychiatry Congress. P 13.
3055 **2405** 80y. multicoloured .... 1·60   1·30

(Des G. Sasaki. Photo)

2002 (9 Aug). World Wheelchair Basketball Championship, Japan. P 13.
3056 **2406** 80y. multicoloured .... 1·60   1·30

2407 Twin-engined and Four-propeller Aircrafts

(Des K. Kuroi. Photo)

2002 (6 Sept). 50th Anniv of Japanese Civil Aviation. P 13.
3057 **2407** 80y. multicoloured .... 1·60   1·30

2408 "Shitoka" (Denj Lin)

2409 "Generyucho" (Wang Chuan Feng)

(Des M. Morita. Photo)

2002 (13 Sept). 30th Anniv of Japan–China Diplomatic Relations. P 13.
3058 **2408** 80y. multicoloured .... 1·60   1·30
         a. Pair. Nos. 3058/9.................................. 3·50   2·75
3059 **2409** 80y. multicoloured .... 1·60   1·30
   Nos. 3058/9 were issued in *se-tenant* pairs in sheets of ten stamps.

2410/11 Houses, Ogimachi, Shirakawa-Mura

2412 House and Flowers, Ogimachi

2413 Houses, Ogimachi

2414 Houses covered in Snow, Ogimachi

2415 Aerial View, Ainokura, Taira-Mura

2416 House, Ainokura

2417 Houses, Ainokura

2418 House, Ainokura

2419 House covered in Snow, Ainokura

(Des M. Morita. Photo)

2002 (20 Sept). World Heritage (9th series). Ogimachi and Ainokura Communitites. Phosphorised paper. P 13.
3060 **2410** 80y. multicoloured .... 1·60   1·30
         a. Horiz pair. Nos. 3060/1 .... 3·50   2·75
         b. Sheetlet of 10. Nos. 3060/9 .... 17·00
3061 **2411** 80y. multicoloured .... 1·60   1·30
3062 **2412** 80y. multicoloured .... 1·60   1·30
3063 **2413** 80y. multicoloured .... 1·60   1·30
3064 **2414** 80y. multicoloured .... 1·60   1·30
3065 **2415** 80y. multicoloured .... 1·60   1·30
3066 **2416** 80y. multicoloured .... 1·60   1·30
3067 **2417** 80y. multicoloured .... 1·60   1·30
3068 **2418** 80y. multicoloured .... 1·60   1·30
3069 **2419** 80y. multicoloured .... 1·60   1·30
3060/3069 Set of 10 .... 14·50   11·50
   Nos. 3060/9 were issued in sheetlets of ten stamps. Nos. 3060/1 forming the composite design illustrated, with descriptions of each stamp in Japanese in the illustrated margin.

2420 Naval Ships and Flags

2002 (1 Oct). Fleet Review. Phosphorised paper. Photo. P 13.
3070 **2420** 80y. multicoloured .... 1·60   1·30

2421 "Yui"

2422 "Shono"

2423 "Tozuka"

(Des A. Tamaki. Photo)

2002 (7 Oct). International Correspondence Week. Paintings from "53 Stations of Tokaido" by Ando Hiroshige. P 13½.
3071 **2421** 90y. multicoloured .... 1·80   1·50
3072 **2422** 110y. multicoloured .... 2·40   2·00
3073 **2423** 130y. multicoloured .... 2·75   2·40
3071/3073 *Set of* 3 .... 6·25   5·25

2424 Stylized People

(Des C. Satonaka and M. Mimata. Photo)

2002 (10 Oct). Asian and Pacific Decade of Disabled Persons Conference. Phosphorised paper. P 13.
3074 **2424** 80y. multicoloured .... 1·60   1·30

2425 Masaoka Shiki (writer, death centenary)   **2426** "Three Women" (Torii Kiyonaga (artist, 250th birth))

2427 Tanakadate Aikitu (geophysicist, 50th death)

(Des N. Takeda (3075), M. Nakai (3076) and M. Mimata (3077). Photo)

2002 (7 Nov). Anniversaries. P 13.
3075 **2425** 80y. multicoloured .... 1·60   1·30
3076 **2426** 80y. multicoloured .... 1·60   1·30
3077 **2427** 80y. multicoloured .... 1·60   1·30
3075/3077 *Set of* 3 .... 4·25   3·50

2428 Sheep (earthenware Dorei figure)   **2429** Sheep with Gem (Edo folk toy)

(Des J. Kaifuchi (3078) and E. Uchida (3079). Photo)

2002 (15 Nov). New Year's Greetings. P 13×13½.
3078 **2428** 50y. multicoloured .... 1·30   1·10
3079 **2429** 80y. multicoloured .... 1·60   1·30
    No. 3080 *is vacant.*

2430 Sheep holding Fan (Aizunakayugawa doll)

2431 Sheep (Oku Hariko doll)

(Des E. Uchida (3081) and A. Hoshiyama (3082). Photo)
2002 (15 Nov). New Year Lottery Stamps. Phosphorised paper. P 13½.
3081 **2430** 50y. +3y. multicoloured .... 1·40 1·10
3082 **2431** 80y. +3y. multicoloured .... 1·70 1·40
Each stamp carries a lottery number.

2432 Stone Lion, Shou Dynasty Royal Mausoleum

2433 Stone Gate, Sonohyan'utaki Sanctuary

2434 Cherry Blossom, Nakijinjou Castle

2435 Stone Gate, Zakimijou Castle

2436 Katsurenjou Castle Walls

2437 Second Citadel, Nakagusukujou Castle

2438 "Kankaimon", Shurijou Castle Gate

2439 Main Hall, Shurijou Castle

2440 "Shikina'en" (royal garden)

2441 Seifautaki Sanctuary

(Des M. Morita. Photo)
2002 (20 Dec). World Heritage (10th series). Phosphorised paper. P 13.
3083 **2432** 80y. multicoloured .... 1·60 1·30
    a. Sheetlet of 10. Nos. 3083/92........... 17·00
3084 **2433** 80y. multicoloured .... 1·60 1·30
3085 **2434** 80y. multicoloured .... 1·60 1·30
3086 **2435** 80y. multicoloured .... 1·60 1·30
3087 **2436** 80y. multicoloured .... 1·60 1·30
3088 **2437** 80y. multicoloured .... 1·60 1·30
3089 **2438** 80y. multicoloured .... 1·60 1·30
3090 **2439** 80y. multicoloured .... 1·60 1·30
3091 **2440** 80y. multicoloured .... 1·60 1·30
3092 **2441** 80y. multicoloured .... 1·60 1·30
3083/3092 Set of 10 .... 14·50 11·50
Nos. 3083/92 were issued in sheetlets of ten stamps, with descriptions of each stamp in Japanese in the illustrated margin.

2442 Kabuki Screen showing Izumo no Okuni in Costume

2443 Actors from "Shibaraku" and "Tsuchigumo"

(Des F. Kanematsu. Photo)
2003 (15 Jan). 400th Anniv of First Kabuki Theatre Performance. Phosphorised paper. P 13.
3093 **2442** 80y. multicoloured .... 1·70 1·40
    a. Pair. Nos. 3093/4................... 3·75 3·00
3094 **2443** 80y. multicoloured .... 1·70 1·40
Nos. 3093/4 were issued in se-tenant pairs within the sheet.

2444 Television
Company Emblem
and Street
Television Set

2445 "Hyokkori
Hyotan-Jima" (puppet)
and Early Television
Set

(Des M. Morita. Photo)

2003 (31 Jan). 50th Anniv of Japanese Television. Phosphorised
paper. P 13.
3095 **2444** 80y. multicoloured .... 1·70 1·40
3096 **2445** 80y. multicoloured .... 1·70 1·40

2446 Heart

2447 Dog wearing
Party Clothes

2448 Snowman

2449 Bird on Cake

2450 Cranes and
Turtle

2451 Roses

2452 Reindeer

2453 Cat

2454 Cats in Car

2455 Cherry Blossom

2003 (10 Feb). Greetings Stamps. Self-adhesive. Phosphorised paper.
Die-cut Perf 13.
3097 **2446** 80y. multicoloured .... 1·70 1·40
    a. Sheetlet of 5. Nos. 3097/101
    plus 5 labels .... 8·75
3098 **2447** 80y. multicoloured .... 1·70 1·40
3099 **2448** 80y. multicoloured .... 1·70 1·40
3100 **2449** 80y. multicoloured .... 1·70 1·40
3101 **2450** 80y. multicoloured .... 1·70 1·40
3102 **2451** 80y. multicoloured .... 1·70 1·40
    a. Sheetlet of 5. Nos. 3102/6
    plus 5 labels .... 8·75
3103 **2452** 80y. multicoloured .... 1·70 1·40
3104 **2453** 80y. multicoloured .... 1·70 1·40
3105 **2454** 80y. multicoloured .... 1·70 1·40
3106 **2455** 80y. multicoloured .... 1·70 1·40
3097/3106 *Set of* 10 .... 15·00 12·50
   Nos. 3097/101 and 3102/5, respectively were issued in sheetlets
of five stamps and five circular labels. The labels are die-cut around
the circle.

2456 Genbaku
Dome (atomic bomb
memorial)

2457 Hiroshima
Prefectural Hall

2458 "La Paix"
(Jean-Paul Veret
LeMarinier)

2459 "Taika" (peace)
(Pakalkaite Joskaude)

2460 "Universal Shrine of Peace" (Issac M. Oriville)

2461 "A Prayer for Peace" (Keiji Sugita)

2473a Posuton

2473b Yuchan

2462 "The Radiance of Life" (Shigenobu Nagaishi)

2463 "An Encounter" (Natsuki Nakatani)

2474 Kanchan Girl

2475 Posuton

2464 "Rainbow-coloured Dove" (Makoto Oooka)

2465 "Rabbit" (Shiho Kobayashi)

2466 Posuton

2467 Aichan

2468 Kanchan Girl

2469 Posuton

2003 (20 Mar). World Heritage (11th series). Peace Stamp Design Competition Winners. Phosphorised paper. P 13.

3107	**2456**	80y. multicoloured	1·70	1·40
		a. Sheetlet of 10. Nos. 3107/16	18·00	
3108	**2457**	80y. multicoloured	1·70	1·40
3109	**2458**	80y. multicoloured	1·70	1·40
3110	**2459**	80y. multicoloured	1·70	1·40
3111	**2460**	80y. multicoloured	1·70	1·40
3112	**2461**	80y. multicoloured	1·70	1·40
3113	**2462**	80y. multicoloured	1·70	1·40
3114	**2463**	80y. multicoloured	1·70	1·40
3115	**2464**	80y. multicoloured	1·70	1·40
3116	**2465**	80y. multicoloured	1·70	1·40
3107/3116		Set of 10	15·00	12·50

Nos. 3107/16 were issued in sheetlets of ten stamps, with descriptions of each stamp in Japanese and the Children's Peace Monument by Kazuo Kikuchi in the margin.

2470 Yuchan

2471 Kanchan Boy

(Des A. Hoshiyama. Photo)

2003 (1 Apr). Postal Services Mascots. Self-adhesive. Phosphorised paper. Die-cut Perf 13.

3117	**2472**	50y. multicoloured	1·30	1·10
		a. Sheetlet of 12. Nos. 3117/26	18·00	
3118	**2473**	50y. multicoloured	1·30	1·10
3118a	**2473a**	50y. multicoloured	1·30	1·10
3118b	**2473b**	50y. multicoloured	1·30	1·10
3119	**2474**	50y. multicoloured	1·30	1·10
3120	**2475**	50y. multicoloured	1·30	1·10
3121	**2466**	80y. multicoloured	1·60	1·30
3122	**2467**	80y. multicoloured	1·60	1·30
3123	**2468**	80y. multicoloured	1·60	1·30
3124	**2469**	80y. multicoloured	1·60	1·30
3125	**2470**	80y. multicoloured	1·60	1·30
3126	**2471**	80y. multicoloured	1·60	1·30
3117/3126		Set of 12	15·50	13·00

Nos. 3117/26 were issued in sheetlets of 12 stamps.

2472 Aichan

2473 Kanchan Boy

Japan

2476 Yellow Flower

2477 Primula

(Des M. Morita. Photo)

2003 (1 Apr). Inauguration of Japan Post (public postal corporation). Designs from "Birds and Flowers of the Four Seasons" (folding screen by Sakai Hoitsu). Self-adhesive. Phosphorised paper. Die-cut Perf 13.

3127	2476	80y. multicoloured	1·70	1·40
		a. Sheetlet of 10. Nos. 3127/36	18·00	
3128	2477	80y. multicoloured	1·70	1·40
3129	2478	80y. multicoloured	1·70	1·40
3130	2479	80y. multicoloured	1·70	1·40
3131	2480	80y. multicoloured	1·70	1·40
3132	2481	80y. multicoloured	1·70	1·40
3133	2482	80y. multicoloured	1·70	1·40
3134	2483	80y. multicoloured	1·70	1·40
3135	2484	80y. multicoloured	1·70	1·40
3136	2485	80y. multicoloured	1·70	1·40
3127/3136		Set of 10	15·00	12·50

Nos. 3127/36 were issued in sheetlets of ten stamps.

2478 Violets and Quince

2479 Horsetail

2480 White Wisteria

2481 Flowering Cherry and Swallow

2482 Hydrangea

2483 Magnolia

2484 Water Lily and Moorhen

2485 Peonies and Butterfly

2486 Tree and Sheep

(Des M. Morita. Photo)

2003 (18 Apr). Philately Week. (Batik folding screen). P 13½ ×13.

3137	2486	80y. multicoloured	1·70	1·40

2487 Map of Edo (folding screen)

2488 Hon-maru (fresco, Edo Castle)

2489 Domarugusoku Helmet and Armour

2490 Hatsune maki-e Lacquer Box (detail)

2491 "Chujo" (Noh mask)

(Des M. Morita. Photo)

2003 (23 May). 400th Anniv of Edo Shogunate (1st issue). Phosphorised paper. P 13.

3138	**2487**	80y. multicoloured	1·70	1·40
		a. Sheetlet of 10. Nos. 3138/42,		
		each×2	18·00	
3139	**2488**	80y. multicoloured	1·70	1·40
3140	**2489**	80y. multicoloured	1·70	1·40
3141	**2490**	80y. multicoloured	1·70	1·40
3142	**2491**	80y. multicoloured	1·70	1·40
3138/3142		*Set of 5*	7·75	6·25

Nos. 3138/42, each×2 were issued in sheetlets of ten stamps, with descriptions of each stamp in Japanese in the illustrated margin.

See also Nos. 3143/8 and 3159/64.

2492 "Nihonbashi Bridge" ("53 Stations of Tokaido")

2493 Fireman's Haori (coat)

2494 "Beauty Spots in Edo" (folding screen)

2495 Kyoho-Bina Girl Doll

2496 Kyoho-Bina Boy Doll

2497 Danjuro Ichikawa (actor) as Goro Takenuki

(Des F. Kanematsu. Photo)

2003 (12 June). 400th Anniv of Edo Shogunate (2nd issue). Phosphorised paper. P 13.

3143	**2492**	80y. multicoloured	1·50	1·20
		a. Sheetlet of 10. Nos. 3143/6 and		
		3148 each×2 and 3147	16·00	
3144	**2493**	80y. multicoloured	1·50	1·20
3145	**2494**	80y. multicoloured	1·50	1·20
3146	**2495**	80y. multicoloured	1·50	1·20
3147	**2496**	80y. multicoloured	1·50	1·20
3148	**2497**	80y. multicoloured	1·50	1·20
3143/3148		*Set of 6*	8·00	6·50

Nos. 3143/6 and 3148, each×2 and 3147 were issued in sheetlets of ten stamps, with descriptions of each stamp in Japanese in the illustrated margin.

2498 Omar Ali Saifuddien Mosque, Brunei Darussalam

2499 Angkor Wat, Cambodia

2500 Borobudur Temple, Indonesia

2501 That Luang, Laos

2502 Sultan Abdul Samad Building, Malaysia

2503 Shwedagon Pagoda, Myanmar

2504 Rice Terraces, Cordilleras, Philippines

2505 Merlion (legendary beast), Singapore

2506 Wat Phra Kaeo,　　**2507** Van Mieu,
Thailand　　　　　　　　　Vietnam

(Des A. Hoshiyama. Photo)

2003 (16 June). ASEAN—Japan Exchange Year (Association of Southeast Asian Nations and Japan co-operation). Phosphorised paper. P 13.

3149	**2498**	80y. multicoloured	1·70	1·40
		a. Sheetlet of 10. Nos. 3149/58	18·00	
3150	**2499**	80y. multicoloured	1·70	1·40
3151	**2500**	80y. multicoloured	1·70	1·40
3152	**2501**	80y. multicoloured	1·70	1·40
3153	**2502**	80y. multicoloured	1·70	1·40
3154	**2503**	80y. multicoloured	1·70	1·40
3155	**2504**	80y. multicoloured	1·70	1·40
3156	**2505**	80y. multicoloured	1·70	1·40
3157	**2506**	80y. multicoloured	1·70	1·40
3158	**2507**	80y. multicoloured	1·70	1·40
3149/3158		*Set of* 10	15·00	12·50

Nos. 3149/58 were issued in sheetlets of ten stamps, with descriptions of each stamp and ASEAN in the illustrated margin.

2508 Powhatan　　　**2509** Powhatan

2510 Bakumatsu　　　**2511** Dutch East India
Fusoku Zukan (detail,　　Company Plate
screen)

2512 European　　　**2513** Wind-up Clock
Woman (detail,　　　（Hisahige Tanaka)
painting)

(Des M. Morita. Photo)

2003 (1 July). 400th Anniv of Edo Shogunate (3rd issue). Phosphorised paper. P 13.

3159	**2508**	80y. multicoloured	1·70	1·40
		a. Pair. Nos. 3159/60	3·75	3·00
		b. Sheetlet of 10. Nos. 3159/60 and		
		3161/4, each×2	18·00	
3160	**2509**	80y. multicoloured	1·70	1·40
3161	**2510**	80y. multicoloured	1·70	1·40
3162	**2511**	80y. multicoloured	1·70	1·40
3163	**2512**	80y. multicoloured	1·70	1·40
3164	**2513**	80y. multicoloured	1·70	1·40
3159/3164		*Set of* 6	9·25	7·50

Nos. 3161/4, each×2 and 3159/60 were issued in sheetlets of ten stamps, with descriptions of each stamp in Japanese in the illustrated margin.

2514 Bear playing　　**2515** Monkey
Guitar

2516 Crocodile　　　**2517** Cat holding
playing Accordion　　　Camera and Envelope

2518 Hippo holding　　**2519** Parrot
Flowers

2520 Owl

2521 Seated Bear holding Envelope

2522 Elephant

2523 Giraffe

2524 Rabbit holding Envelope and Flowers

2525 Lion carrying Lantern

2526 Goat holding Envelope

2527 Gorilla

(Des Tsutomu Murakami and M. Morita. Photo)

2003 (23 July). Letter Writing Day. Phosphorised paper. P 13.

3165	**2514**	50y. multicoloured	1·40	1·10
		a. Horiz strip of 4. Nos. 3165/8	5·75	
		b. Booklet pane. Nos. 3165/8 and 3170, 3177/8 each×2	14·50	
3166	**2515**	50y. multicoloured	1·40	1·10
3167	**2516**	50y. multicoloured	1·40	1·10
3168	**2517**	50y. multicoloured	1·40	1·10
3169	**2518**	80y. multicoloured	1·70	1·40
		a. Sheetlet of 10. Nos. 3169/78	18·00	
3170	**2519**	80y. multicoloured	1·70	1·40
3171	**2520**	80y. multicoloured	1·70	1·40
3172	**2521**	80y. multicoloured	1·70	1·40

3173	**2522**	80y. multicoloured	1·70	1·40
3174	**2523**	80y. multicoloured	1·70	1·40
3175	**2524**	80y. multicoloured	1·70	1·40
3176	**2525**	80y. multicoloured	1·70	1·40
3177	**2526**	80y. multicoloured	1·70	1·40
3178	**2527**	80y. multicoloured	1·70	1·40
3165/3178		*Set of 14*	20·00	17·00
MS3179		72×94 mm. Nos. 3170 and 3165	4·25	4·00

Nos. 3165/8 were issued together in horizontal *se-tenant* strips of four stamps within the sheet. Nos. 3169/78 were issued in sheetlets of ten stamps.

The booklet pane has its outer edge imperforate, giving stamps with one or two adjacent sides imperforate.

2528 "Kawaski"

2529 "Miya"

2530 "Otsu"

(Des A. Tamaki. Photo)

2003 (7 Oct). International Correspondence Week. Paintings from "53 Stations of Tokaido" by Ando Hiroshige. P 13½.

3180	**2528**	90y. multicoloured	2·10	1·80
3181	**2529**	110y. multicoloured	2·40	2·00
3182	**2530**	130y. multicoloured	2·75	2·40
3180/3182		*Set of 3*	6·50	5·50

2531 Byakko (White Tiger of the West)

2532 Suzaku (Red Bird of the South)

(Des M. Morita. Photo)

2003 (15 Oct). Cultural Heritage. Wall Paintings, Kitora Tumulus, Nara Prefecture. Phosphorised paper. P 13.

3183	**2531** 80y. +10y. multicoloured	1·60	1·30
	a. Pair. Nos. 3183/4	3·50	2·75
3184	**2532** 80y. +10y. multicoloured	1·60	1·30

Nos. 3183/4 were issued in *se-tenant* pairs within the sheet.

2538 Monkey (Iyo Ittobori wood carving)　　**2539** The Successful Monkey (Edo folk toy)

(Des Kaifuchi and A. Kikuchi. Photo)

2003 (14 Nov). New Year Lottery Stamps. Phosphorised paper. P 13½.

3191	**2538** 50y. +3y. multicoloured	1·40	1·10
3192	**2539** 80y. +3y. multicoloured	1·70	1·40

Each stamp carries a lottery number.

2533 Mokichi Saito (writer, 150th death)　　**2534** Shibasaburo Kitasato (scientist, 150th birth)

(Des N. Sato and S. Oikawa. Photo and litho)

2003 (4 Nov). Anniversaries. P 13.

3185	**2533** 80y. multicoloured	1·70	1·40
3186	**2534** 80y. multicoloured	1·70	1·40

2540 Tetsuwan Atom (flying down)　　**2541** Tetsuwan Atom (with raised arm)

2535 Flowers and Butterflies, Amami Forest (painting, Isson Tanaka)

(Des A. Tamaki. Photo)

2003 (7 Nov). 50th Anniv of Return of Amami Islands to Japan. P 13.
3187 **2535** 80y. multicoloured .... 1·70 1·40

2542 Tetsuwan Atom (upside down)　　**2543** Yumihiki Doji (Edo mechanical doll)

2536 Monkey (Iyo Ittobori wood carving)　　**2537** The Successful Monkey (Edo folk toy)

(Des J. Kaifuchi and A. Hoshiyama. Photo)

2003 (14 Nov). New Year's Greetings. P 13×13½.

3188	**2536** 50y. multicoloured	1·30	1·10
3189	**2537** 80y. multicoloured	1·60	1·30

No. 3190 is vacant.

2544 Nagaoka Hantaro (physicist)　　**2545** H-II Rocket

2546 Morph 3 Robot

2547 Tetsuwan Atom (flying up)

2554 Super Jetter 3

2555 Super Jetter 4

(Des M. Morita. Photo)

2003 (16 Dec). Science, Technology and Animation (1st issue). Phosphorised paper. P 13.

3193	**2540**	80y. multicoloured	1·80	1·50
		a. Sheetlet of 10. Nos. 3193/5, each×2 and 3196/9	19·00	
3194	**2541**	80y. multicoloured	1·80	1·50
3195	**2542**	80y. multicoloured	1·80	1·50
3196	**2543**	80y. multicoloured	1·80	1·50
		a. Sheetlet of 10. Nos. 3196/200, each×2	19·00	
3197	**2544**	80y. multicoloured	1·80	1·50
3198	**2545**	80y. multicoloured	1·80	1·50
3199	**2546**	80y. multicoloured	1·80	1·50
3200	**2547**	80y. multicoloured	1·80	1·50
3193/3200		*Set* of 8	13·00	11·00

Nos. 3193/5, each×2; 3196/9 and 3196/200, each×2, respectively were issued in *se-tenant* sheetlets of 10 stamps, with a description of the stamps in Japanese in the illustrated margin.

See also Nos. 3201/8, 3224/31, 3232/9, 3264/71, 3286/93 and 3305/13.

(Des M. Morita. Photo)

2004 (23 Jan). Science, Technology and Animation (2nd issue). Phosphorised paper. P 13.

3201	**2548**	80y. multicoloured	1·80	1·50
		a. Sheetlet of 10. Nos. 3201/5, each×2	19·00	
3202	**2549**	80y. multicoloured	1·80	1·50
3203	**2550**	80y. multicoloured	1·80	1·50
3204	**2551**	80y. multicoloured	1·80	1·50
3205	**2552**	80y. multicoloured	1·80	1·50
3206	**2553**	80y. multicoloured	1·80	1·50
		a. Sheetlet of 10. Nos. 3206/8, each×2 and 3202/5	19·00	
3207	**2554**	80y. multicoloured	1·80	1·50
3208	**2555**	80y. multicoloured	1·80	1·50
3201/3208		*Set* of 8	13·00	11·00

Nos. 3201/5, each×2 and Nos. 3206/8, each×2 and Nos. 3202/5, respectively were issued in *se-tenant* sheetlets of 10 stamps, with a description of the stamps in Japanese in the illustrated margin.

2548 Super Jetter 1

2549 Wadokei (clock)

2556 Hello Kitty

2557 Hello Kitty

2550 Otomo-go (vintage car)

2551 KAZ (modern car)

2558 Hello Kitty

2559 Hello Kitty

2560 Hello Kitty

2561 Hello Kitty

2552 Stratospheric Balloon

2553 Super Jetter 2

2562 Hello Kitty

2563 Hello Kitty

2564 Hello Kitty

2565 Hello Kitty

2566 Hello Kitty

2567 Hello Kitty

2568 Hello Kitty

2569 Hello Kitty

2570 Hello Kitty

(Des Yamaguchi Yuko. Litho)

2004 (6 Feb). Greetings Stamps. Hello Kitty. Self-adhesive booklet stamps. Die-cut Perf 13½×straight edge (3219/3) or die-cut 13½ (others).

3209	**2556**	50y. multicoloured	1·30	1·10
3210	**2557**	50y. multicoloured	1·30	1·10
3211	**2558**	50y. multicoloured	1·30	1·10
3212	**2559**	50y. multicoloured	1·30	1·10
3213	**2560**	50y. multicoloured	1·30	1·10
3214	**2561**	50y. multicoloured	1·30	1·10
3215	**2562**	50y. multicoloured	1·30	1·10
3216	**2563**	50y. multicoloured	1·30	1·10
3217	**2564**	50y. multicoloured	1·30	1·10
3218	**2565**	50y. multicoloured	1·30	1·10
3219	**2566**	80y. multicoloured	1·80	1·50
3220	**2567**	80y. multicoloured	1·80	1·50
3221	**2568**	80y. multicoloured	1·80	1·50
3222	**2569**	80y. multicoloured	1·80	1·50
3223	**2570**	80y. multicoloured	1·80	1·50
3209/3223		Set of 15	20·00	17·00

Nos. 3209/18 were issued in sheetlets of 10 stamps and Nos. 3219/23 in sheets of 5.

2573 Wooden Microscope

2574 Takamine Jokichi

2575 Drug Delivery System

2576 Marvellous Melmo 2

2577 Marvellous Melmo 3

2578 Marvellous Melmo 4

(Des M. Morita. Photo)

2004 (23 Feb). Science, Technology and Animation (3rd issue). Phosphorised paper. P 13.

3224	**2571**	80y. multicoloured	1·80	1·50
		a. Sheetlet of 10. Nos. 3224/8,		
		each×2	19·00	
3225	**2572**	80y. multicoloured	1·80	1·50
3226	**2573**	80y. multicoloured	1·80	1·50
3227	**2574**	80y. multicoloured	1·80	1·50
3228	**2575**	80y. multicoloured	1·80	1·50
3229	**2576**	80y. multicoloured	1·80	1·50
		a. Sheetlet of 10. Nos. 3229/31,		
		each×2 and 3225/8	19·00	
3230	**2577**	80y. multicoloured	1·80	1·50
3231	**2578**	80y. multicoloured	1·80	1·50
3224/3231		Set of 8	13·00	11·00

Nos. 3224/8, each×2 and Nos. 3229/31, each×2 and Nos. 3225/8, respectively were issued in se-tenant sheetlets of 10 stamps, with a description of the stamps in Japanese in the illustrated margin.

2571 Marvellous Melmo 1

2572 Hanaoka Seishu

2579 Kagaku Ninja-Tai Gatchman 1

2580 Perpetual Motion Machine

2581 OHSUMI (satellite)

2582 Conducting Polymer

2583 Eye (Tissue/ Organ Reproductive Medicine)

2584 Kagaku Ninja-Tai Gatchman 2

2585 Kagaku Ninja-Tai Gatchman 3

2586 Kagaku Ninja-Tai Gatchman 4

(Des M. Morita. Photo)

2004 (23 Mar). Science, Technology and Animation (4th issue). Phosphorised paper. P 13.

3232	**2579**	80y. multicoloured	1·80	1·50
		a. Sheetlet of 10. Nos. 3232/6 each×2	19·00	
3233	**2580**	80y. multicoloured	1·80	1·50
3234	**2581**	80y. multicoloured	1·80	1·50
3235	**2582**	80y. multicoloured	1·80	1·50
3236	**2583**	80y. multicoloured	1·80	1·50
3237	**2584**	80y. multicoloured	1·80	1·50
		a. Sheetlet of 10. Nos. 3237/9, each×2 and 3233/6	19·00	
3238	**2585**	80y. multicoloured	1·80	1·50
3239	**2586**	80y. multicoloured	1·80	1·50
3232/3239		Set of 8	13·00	11·00

Nos. 3232/6 each×2 and Nos. 3237/9, each×2 and Nos. 3233/6, respectively were issued in *se-tenant* sheetlets of 10 stamps, with a description of the stamps in Japanese in the illustrated margin.

2587 Morizo and Kiccoro (official mascots) in Orbit

2588 Morizo and Kiccoro holding Hands

(Des K. Fumiaki. Photo)

2004 (25 Mar). EXPO 2005 World Exhibition, Aichi, Japan. P 13×13½.

3240	**2587**	80y. +10y. multicoloured	1·90	1·60
		a. Pair. Nos. 3240/1	4·00	3·50
3241	**2588**	80y. +10y. multicoloured	1·90	1·60

Nos. 3240/1 were issued in horizontal *se-tenant* pairs within nine different sheets showing pavilions and one sheet showing the entire EXPO 2005 site.

2589 "Uchuno sakura gohiki no saru zu" (Mori Sosen)

(Des A. Tamaki. Photo)

2004 (20 Apr). Philately Week. P 13 (with one elliptical perf on each side).

3242	**2589**	80y. multicoloured	1·80	1·50

2590 Ten Point and Tosho Boy (22nd Arima Memorial Stakes)

2591 Narita Brian (61st Tokyo Yushun (Japanese Derby))

(Des K. Fumiaki. Photo)

2004 (28 May). 50th Anniv of Japan Racing Association. P 13.

3243	**2590**	80y. multicoloured	1·80	1·50
		a. Pair. Nos. 3243/4	3·75	3·25
3244	**2591**	80y. multicoloured	1·80	1·50

Nos. 3243/4 were issued in horizontal *se-tenant* pairs within the sheet.

2592 Police Car

2593 Police Motorcyclist

(Des T. Akira. Photo)

2004 (1 July). 50th Anniv of Police Law. P 13×13½.

3245	**2592**	80y. multicoloured	1·80	1·50
		a. Pair. Nos. 3245/6..	3·75	3·25
3246	**2593**	80y. multicoloured	1·80	1·50

Nos. 3245/6 were issued in horizontal *se-tenant* pairs within the sheet, each pair forming a composite design.

2602 Donkichi

2603 Kuriko

2594 Donkichi holding Pencil

2595 Hime

2604 Goddess

2605 Shochan with Wings

2596 Shochan

2597 Owl

2606 Squirrel holding Envelope and Flowers

2607 Rabbit

2598 Pigeon carrying Envelope

2599 Squirrel with Wings

(Des K. Katsuichi and M. Morita. Photo)

2004 (23 July). Letter Writing Day. Phosphorised paper. P 13.

3247	**2594**	50y. multicoloured	1·30	1·10
		a. Horiz strip of 4. Nos. 3247/50	5·50	
		b. Booklet pane. Nos. 3248/50,		
		3252×2 and 3255/6	13·00	
3248	**2595**	50y. multicoloured	1·30	1·10
3249	**2596**	50y. multicoloured	1·30	1·10
3250	**2597**	50y. multicoloured	1·30	1·10
3251	**2598**	80y. multicoloured	1·80	1·50
		a. Sheetlet of 10. Nos. 3251/60	19·00	
3252	**2599**	80y. multicoloured	1·80	1·50
3253	**2600**	80y. multicoloured	1·80	1·50
3254	**2601**	80y. multicoloured	1·80	1·50
3255	**2602**	80y. multicoloured	1·80	1·50
3256	**2603**	80y. multicoloured	1·80	1·50
3257	**2604**	80y. multicoloured	1·80	1·50
3258	**2605**	80y. multicoloured	1·80	1·50
3259	**2606**	80y. multicoloured	1·80	1·50
3260	**2607**	80y. multicoloured	1·80	1·50
3247/3260		*Set of 14*	21·00	17·00
MS3261		72×94 mm. Nos. 3247 and 3256.................	3·25	3·00

Nos. 3247/50 were issued together in horizontal *se-tenant* strips of four stamps within the sheet. Nos. 3251/60 were issued in sheetlets of ten stamps.

The booklet pane has its outer edge imperforate, giving stamps with one or two adjacent sides imperforate.

2600 Stork

2601 Hime with Wings

2608 Athens, 2004 Emblem

2609 Olympic Rings, Flame and Olympia Ruins

(Des M. Morita. Photo)

2004 (6 Aug). Olympic Games, Athens. P 13.

3262	**2608**	80y. multicoloured	1·60	1·30
	a.	Pair. Nos. 3262/3	3·50	2·75
3263	**2609**	80y. multicoloured	1·60	1·30

Nos. 3262/3 were issued in horizontal *se-tenant* pairs within the sheet.

2610 Majinga Z 4

2611 Model Steam Engine

2612 KS Steel

2613 Shinkai 6500

2614 Fuel Cell

2615 Majinga Z 1

2616 Majinga Z 2

2617 Majinga Z 3

(Des M. Morita. Photo)

2004 (23 Aug). Science, Technology and Animation (5th issue). Phosphorised paper. P 13.

3264	**2610**	80y. multicoloured	1·70	1·40
	a.	Sheetlet of 10. Nos. 3264/8 each×2	18·00	
3265	**2611**	80y. multicoloured	1·70	1·40
3266	**2612**	80y. multicoloured	1·70	1·40
3267	**2613**	80y. multicoloured	1·70	1·40
3268	**2614**	80y. multicoloured	1·70	1·40
3269	**2615**	80y. multicoloured	1·70	1·40
	a.	Sheetlet of 10. Nos. 3269/71 each×2 and 3265/8	18·00	
3270	**2616**	80y. multicoloured	1·70	1·40
3271	**2617**	80y. multicoloured	1·70	1·40
3264/3271		*Set of* 8	12·00	10·00

Nos. 3264/8 each×2 and Nos. 3269/71 each×2 and Nos. 3265/8, respectively were issued in *se-tenant* sheetlets of 10 stamps, with a description of the stamps in Japanese in the illustrated margin.

2618 *Mount Fuji* (Frederic Harris)

2619 *Café* (Yasuo Kuniyoshi)

(Des M. Morita. Photo)

2004 (22 Sept). 150th Anniv of America–Japan Relations. P 13.

3272	**2618**	80y. multicoloured	1·70	1·40
3273	**2619**	80y. multicoloured	1·70	1·40

2620 Medical Symbols as Figure

(Des A. Tamaki. Photo)

2004 (6 Oct). World Medical Association (WMA) General Assembly, Tokyo. P 13

3274	**2620**	80y. multicoloured	1·70	1·40

2621 "Hirarsukai"

2622 "Yokkaichi"

2623 "Tsuchiyama"

(Des A. Tamaki. Photo)

2004 (8 Oct). International Correspondence Week. Paintings from "53 Stations of Tokaido" by Utagawa Hiroshige. P 13½.

3275	2621	90y. multicoloured	1·90	1·60
3276	2622	110y. multicoloured	2·50	2·10
3277	2623	130y. multicoloured	3·00	2·50
3275/3277		Set of 3	6·75	5·50

2624 Lafcadio Hearn (Koizumi Yakumo) (writer) (death centenary)

2625 Isamu Noguchi (sculptor) (birth centenary)

2626 Koga Masao (composer) (birth centenary)

(Des S. Oikawa, K. Doki and H. Yamamoto. Recess and litho)

2004 (4 Nov). Anniversaries. P 13.

3278	2624	80y. multicoloured	1·60	1·30
3279	2625	80y. multicoloured	1·60	1·30
3280	2626	80y. multicoloured	1·60	1·30
3278/3280		Set of 3	4·25	3·50

2627 Rooster (Hita-Dorei (clay bell))

2628 Rooster (Shimotsuke-Dorei (clay bell))

(Des T. Ohya and S. Asaga. Photo)

2004 (15 Nov). New Year's Greetings. P 13×13½.

3281	2627	50y. multicoloured	1·10	90
3282	2628	80y. multicoloured	1·60	1·30

No. 3283 is vacant.

2629 Rooster (Hita-Dorei (clay bell))

2630 Rooster (Shimotsuke-Dorei (clay bell))

(Des T. Ohya and S. Asaga. Photo)

2004 (15 Nov). New Year Lottery Stamps. Phosphorised paper. P 13½.

3284	2629	50y.+3y. multicoloured	1·20	95
3285	2630	80y.+3y. multicoloured	1·70	1·40

Each stamp carries a lottery number.

2631 Doraemon 4

2632 Hiraga Gennai

2633 Mechanical "netsuke"

2634 Television Set

2641 "tori" (Kinbun style) (Onchi Shunyou)

2642 "tori" (Tensho style) (Funamoto Hou'un)

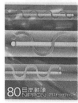

2635 Plastic Optical Fibre (POF)

2636 Doraemon 1

2643 "tori" (Kana style) (Koyama Yasuko)

2644 "tori" (Sousho style) (Watanabe Kan'ou)

2637 Doraemon 2

2638 Doraemon 3

2645 "tori" (Kobun style) (Inamuru un'dou)

2646 "tori" (Reisho style) (Oono Kouken)

(Des M. Morita. Photo)

2004 (22 Nov). Science, Technology and Animation (6th issue). Phosphorised paper. P 13.

3286	**2631**	80y. multicoloured	1·60	1·30
		a. Sheetlet of 10. Nos. 3286/90, each×2	17·00	
3287	**2632**	80y. multicoloured	1·60	1·30
3288	**2633**	80y. multicoloured	1·60	1·30
3289	**2634**	80y. multicoloured	1·60	1·30
3290	**2635**	80y. multicoloured	1·60	1·30
3291	**2636**	80y. multicoloured	1·60	1·30
		a. Sheetlet of 10. Nos. 3291/3, each×2 and 3287/90	17·00	
3292	**2637**	80y. multicoloured	1·60	1·30
3293	**2638**	80y. multicoloured	1·60	1·30
3286/3293		Set of 8	13·00	10·50

Nos. 3286/90 each×2 and Nos. 3291/3, each×2 and Nos. 3287/90, respectively were issued in *se-tenant* sheetlets of 10 stamps, with a description of the stamps in Japanese in the illustrated margin.

2647 "tori" (Kokotsumoji style) (Oohira Santou)

2648 "tori" (Kobun style) (Noguchi Hakutei)

(Des M. Morita. Photo and embossed)

2004 (1 Dec). Greetings Stamps. Eto Calligraphy. Phosphorised paper. P 13.

3294	**2639**	80y. multicoloured	1·60	1·30
		a. Sheetlet of 10. Nos. 3294/303	17·00	
3295	**2640**	80y. multicoloured	1·60	1·30
3296	**2641**	80y. multicoloured	1·60	1·30
3297	**2642**	80y. multicoloured	1·60	1·30
3298	**2643**	80y. multicoloured	1·60	1·30
3299	**2644**	80y. multicoloured	1·60	1·30
3300	**2645**	80y. multicoloured	1·60	1·30
3301	**2646**	80y. multicoloured	1·60	1·30
3302	**2647**	80y. multicoloured	1·60	1·30
3303	**2648**	80y. multicoloured	1·60	1·30
3294/3303		Set of 10	14·50	11·50

2639 "tori" (Tensho style) (Toda Teizan)

2640 "tori" (Kinbun style) (Seki Masato)

Nos. 3294/303 were issued in *se-tenant* sheetlets of 10 stamps, with an illustrated margin.

2657 Time Bokan 3   **2658** Time Bokan 4

(Des M. Morita. Photo)

2649 "Nangicho" (bird of suffering)   **2650** Aircraft and Flowers

(Des A. Tamaki. Litho)

2005 (11 Jan). International Conference on Disaster Reduction. Phosphorised paper. P 13.
3304 **2649** 80y. multicoloured .... 1·60   1·30

(Des A. Hoshiyama. Litho)

2005 (1 Feb). Opening of Chubu International Airport. Phosphorised paper. P 13.
3304a **2650** 80y. multicoloured .... 1·60   1·30

2005 (23 Mar). Science, Technology and Animation (7th issue). Phosphorised paper. P 13.

3305	**2651**	80y. multicoloured	1·60	1·30
		a. Sheetlet of 10. Nos. 3305/9, each×2	17·00	
3306	**2652**	80y. multicoloured	1·60	1·30
3307	**2653**	80y. multicoloured	1·60	1·30
3308	**2654**	80y. multicoloured	1·60	1·30
3309	**2655**	80y. multicoloured	1·60	1·30
3310	**2656**	80y. multicoloured	1·60	1·30
		a. Sheetlet of 10. Nos. 3310/12, each×2 and 3306/9	17·00	
3311	**2657**	80y. multicoloured	1·60	1·30
3312	**2658**	80y. multicoloured	1·60	1·30
3305/3312		Set of 8	11·50	9·25

Nos. 3305/9 each×2, Nos. 3310/12 each×2 and Nos. 3306/9, respectively were issued in *se-tenant* sheetlets of ten stamps, with a description of the stamps in Japanese in the enlarged illustrated left margin.

2651 Time Bokan 1   **2652** Circular Loom (invented by Toyoda Sakichi)

2659/60 Mammoth and Globe

(Des M. Morita. Photo)

2005 (25 Mar). EXPO 2005, World Exposition, Aichi. Phosphorised paper. P 13.
3313 **2659** 80y. multicoloured .... 1·60   1·30
          a. Horiz pair. Nos. 3313/14.................... 3·50   2·75
3314 **2660** 80y. multicoloured .... 1·60   1·30
Nos. 3313/14 were issued in horizontal *se-tenant* pairs within the sheet, each pair forming a composite design.

2653 Shinkansen (bullet train)   **2654** Micro-machine

2661 Daikei-shiyu-zu (giant hen and rooster)   **2662** Children

(Des K. Fumiaki. Photo)

2005 (20 Apr). Philately Week. Phosphorised paper. P 13 (with one elliptical hole on each side).
3315 **2661** 80y. multicoloured .... 1·60   1·30

2655 International Space Station   **2656** Time Bokan 2

(Des M. Morita. Litho)

2005 (28 Apr). Centenary of Rotary International. Phosphorised paper. P 13.
3316 **2662** 80y. multicoloured .... 1·60   1·30

2663 Mt. Hodakadake

2664 Anemone narcissiflora

2665 Mt. Yarigatake

2666 Aquilegia flabellate

(Des M. Morita. Litho)

2005 (2 May). Centenary of Japanese Alpine Club. Phosphorised paper. P 13½.
3317 **2663** 50y. multicoloured .... 1·30   1·10
         a. Horiz strip of 4. Nos. 3317/20 .... 5·50
3318 **2664** 50y. multicoloured .... 1·30   1·10
3319 **2665** 50y. multicoloured .... 1·30   1·10
3320 **2666** 50y. multicoloured .... 1·30   1·10
3317/3320 *Set of 4* .... 4·75   4·00
    Nos. 3317/20 were issued in horizontal *se-tenant* strips of four stamps within the sheet.

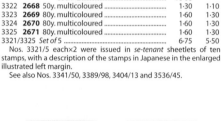

2671 Mew

2005 (23 June). Heroes and Heroines of Animation (1st issue). Pocket Monsters. Phosphorised paper. P 13.
3321 **2667** 50y. multicoloured .... 1·30   1·10
         a. Sheetlet of 10. Nos. 3321/5,
            each×2 .... 16·00
3322 **2668** 50y. multicoloured .... 1·30   1·10
3323 **2669** 80y. multicoloured .... 1·60   1·30
3324 **2670** 80y. multicoloured .... 1·60   1·30
3325 **2671** 80y. multicoloured .... 1·60   1·30
3321/3325 *Set of 5* .... 6·75   5·50
    Nos. 3321/5 each×2 were issued in *se-tenant* sheetlets of ten stamps, with a description of the stamps in Japanese in the enlarged illustrated left margin.
    See also Nos. 3341/50, 3389/98, 3404/13 and 3536/45.

2672 Squirrel holding Nut

2673 Rabbit

2667 Rayquaza

2668 Gonbe

2674 Owl

2675 Kuriko carrying Envelope

2669 Pikachu

2670 Rizadon

2676 Pigeon carrying Envelope

2677 Donkichi

2678 Castle

2679 Shochan

2680 White Rabbit

2681 Kuriko

2682 Hime

2683 Violet

2684 Squirrel

2685 Fox

(Des K. Kabasima and M. Morita. Photo)

2005 (22 July). Letter Writing Day. Phosphorised paper. P 13.

3326	**2672**	50y. multicoloured	1·30	1·10
		a. Horiz strip of 4. Nos. 3326/9	5·50	
		b. Booklet pane. Nos. 3326, 3329,		
		3333×2 and 3336×2	12·00	
3327	**2673**	50y. multicoloured	1·30	1·10
3328	**2674**	50y. multicoloured	1·30	1·10
3329	**2675**	50y. multicoloured	1·30	1·10
3330	**2676**	80y. multicoloured	1·60	1·30
		a. Sheetlet of 10. Nos. 3330/9	17·00	
3331	**2677**	80y. multicoloured	1·60	1·30
3332	**2678**	80y. multicoloured	1·60	1·30
3333	**2679**	80y. multicoloured	1·60	1·30
3334	**2680**	80y. multicoloured	1·60	1·30
3335	**2681**	80y. multicoloured	1·60	1·30
3336	**2682**	80y. multicoloured	1·60	1·30
3337	**2683**	80y. multicoloured	1·60	1·30
3338	**2684**	80y. multicoloured	1·60	1·30

3339	**2685**	80y. multicoloured	1·60	1·30
3326/3339		Set of 14	19·00	16·00
MS3340		72×94 mm. Nos. 3327 and 3333	3·00	2·75

Nos. 3326/9 were issued together in horizontal *se-tenant* strips of four stamps within the sheet. Nos. 3330/9 were issued in sheetlets of ten stamps.

The booklet pane has its outer edge imperforate, giving stamps with one or two adjacent sides imperforate.

2692 Zaku   **2693** Char Aznable

2694 Kamille   **2695** Z Gundum

2690 Amuro Ray   **2691** Gundum

2686 Gundum W   **2687** Hiiro

2688 Freedom
Gundum and Kira
Yamato

2689 Justice Gundum
and Arthrun Zala

2005 (1 Aug). Heroes and Heroines of Animation (2nd issue). Mobile Suit Gundum. Phosphorised paper. P 13.

3341	**2686**	50y. multicoloured	1·20	95
		a. Horiz pair. Nos. 3341/2	2·50	2·00
		b. Sheetlet of 10. Nos. 3341/50	14·00	
3342	**2687**	50y. multicoloured	1·20	95
3343	**2688**	50y. multicoloured	1·60	1·30
		a. Horiz pair. Nos. 3343/4	3·50	2·75
3344	**2689**	50y. multicoloured	1·60	1·30
3345	**2690**	80y. multicoloured	1·60	1·30
		a. Horiz pair. Nos. 3345/6	3·50	2·75
3346	**2691**	80y. multicoloured	1·60	1·30
3347	**2692**	80y. multicoloured	1·60	1·30
		a. Horiz pair. Nos. 3347/8	3·50	2·75
3348	**2693**	80y. multicoloured	1·60	1·30
3349	**2694**	80y. multicoloured	1·60	1·30
		a. Horiz pair. Nos. 3349/50	3·50	2·75
3350	**2695**	80y. multicoloured	1·60	1·30
3341/3350		*Set of* 10	13·50	11·00

Nos. 3341/2, 3343/4, 3345/6, 3347/8 and 3349/50, respectively, were issued in horizontal *se-tenant* pairs within sheetlets of ten stamps, each pair forming a composite design. The sheetlets had a description of the stamps in Japanese in the enlarged illustrated left margin.

2696 Ono no Komachi (poet) (painting) (Tosa Mitsuoki)

2697 Fujiwara no Teika (poet) (painting) (Kano Tanyu)

(Des A. Hoshiyama. Litho)

2005 (1 Sept). Literary Anniversaries. Phosphorised paper. P 13.

3351	**2696**	80y. multicoloured (1100th anniv of Kokinshu)	1·60	1·30
		a. Horiz pair. Nos. 3351/2	3·50	2·75
3352	**2697**	80y. multicoloured (800th anniv of Shinkokinshu)	1·60	1·30

Nos. 3351/2 were issued in horizontal *se-tenant* pairs within the sheet.

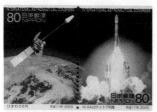

2698/9 Globe, Satellite and Rocket

(Des F. Kanematsu. Litho)

2005 (3 Oct). International Astronautical Congress, Fukuoka. Phosphorised paper. P 13.

3353	**2698**	80y. multicoloured	1·60	1·30
		a. Horiz pair. Nos. 3353/4	3·50	2·75
3354	**2699**	80y. multicoloured	1·60	1·30

Nos. 3353/4 were issued in horizontal *se-tenant* pairs within the sheet, each pair forming a composite design.

2700 "Mariko"

2701 "Minakuchi"

2702 "Shinagawa"

(Des A. Tamaki. Photo)

2005 (7 Oct). International Correspondence Week. Paintings from "53 Stations of Tokaido" by Utagawa Hiroshige. P 13½.

3355	**2700**	90y. multicoloured	1·70	1·40
3356	**2701**	110y. multicoloured	1·90	1·60
3357	**2702**	130y. multicoloured	2·20	1·80
3355/3357		*Set of* 3	5·25	4·25

2703 Cyclamen (Arai Sonoko)

2704 Flower Fairy (Nagata Moe)

2705 Bear (Sugita Yutaka)

2706 Gorilla (Murakami Tsutomu)

2707 Snowman
(Koide Masaki)

2708 Father Christmas
(Koide Masaki)

2709 Poinsettias and
Candle (Arai Sonoko)

2710 Angel, Presents
and Tree (Nagata Moe)

2711 Hamster
(Sugita Yutaka)

2712 Cat (Murakami
Tsutomu)

(Litho Cartor)

2005 (21 Oct). Greetings Stamps. Phosphor borders. Self-adhesive.
Die-cut perf 14.
3358	**2703** 50y. multicoloured	....	1·20	95
	a. Sheetlet of 5. Nos. 3358/62	....	6·25	
3359	**2704** 50y. multicoloured	....	1·20	95
3360	**2705** 50y. multicoloured	....	1·20	95
3361	**2706** 50y. multicoloured	....	1·20	95
3362	**2707** 50y. multicoloured	....	1·20	95
3363	**2708** 80y. multicoloured (27×38 mm)	....	1·60	1·30
	a. Sheetlet of 5. Nos. 3363/7	....	8·25	
3364	**2709** 80y. multicoloured (27×38 mm)	....	1·60	1·30
3365	**2710** 80y. multicoloured (27×38 mm)	....	1·60	1·30
3366	**2711** 80y. multicoloured (27×38 mm)	....	1·60	1·30
3367	**2712** 80y. multicoloured (27×38 mm)	....	1·60	1·30
3358/3367	*Set* of 10	....	12·50	10·00

Nos. 3358/62 and 3363/7, respectively were issued in *se-tenant*
sheetlets of five stamps, with an illustrated lower margin containing
labels for use on mail.

2713 Akita Dog

2714 Dog
(Sadowara (clay))

(Des A. Hishiyama and J. Kaifuchi. Photo)

2005 (15 Nov)–**06**. New Year's Greetings. P 13×13½.
3368	**2713** 50y. multicoloured	.... 1·20	95
3369	**2714** 80y. multicoloured	.... 1·60	1·30

No. 3370 *is vacant.*

2715 Akita Dog   **2716** Dog
(Sadowara (clay))

(Des A. Hishiyama and J. Kaifuchi. Photo)

2005 (15 Nov). New Year Lottery Stamps. Phosphorised paper.
P 13½.
3371	**2715** 50y. +3y. multicoloured	.... 1·30	1·10
3372	**2716** 80y. +3y. multicoloured	.... 1·70	1·40

Each stamp carries a lottery number.

2717 "inu" (Tensho
style) (Ooi Kintei)

2718 "inu" (Kinbun
style) (Takagiwa
Suihou)

2719 "inu"
(pictograph) (Kaneko
Takyoshi)

2720 "inu" (phonetic
letters) (Yonemoto
Ikkou)

2721 "inu" (Tensho
style) (Kishimoto
Tarou)

2722 "inu" (Tensho
style in half moon)
(Tsujimoto Daiwun)

2723 "inu" (symbolic characters) (Seki Masato)

2724 "inu" (semi-cursive style) (Tanaka Touwun)

2731 Equestrian Acrobat (Meissen)

2732 Harlequin (Meissen)

(Des M. Morita. Photo)

2725 "inu" (semi-cursive style) (Katou Shoudou)

2726 "inu" (Koukotsumoji style) (Kobayashi Hougyu)

(Des M. Morita. Photo and embossed)

2005 (1 Dec). Greetings Stamps. Eto Calligraphy. Phosphorised paper. P 13.

3373	**2717**	80y. multicoloured	1·60	1·30
		a. Sheetlet of 10. Nos. 3373/82	17·00	
3374	**2718**	80y. multicoloured	1·60	1·30
3375	**2719**	80y. multicoloured	1·60	1·30
3376	**2720**	80y. multicoloured	1·60	1·30
3377	**2721**	80y. multicoloured	1·60	1·30
3378	**2722**	80y. multicoloured	1·60	1·30
3379	**2723**	80y. multicoloured	1·60	1·30
3380	**2724**	80y. multicoloured	1·60	1·30
3381	**2725**	80y. multicoloured	1·60	1·30
3382	**2726**	80y. multicoloured	1·60	1·30
3373/3382		Set of 10	14·50	11·50

Nos. 3373/82 were issued in *se-tenant* sheetlets of ten stamps, with enlarged illustrated margins.

2005 (1 Dec). Germany in Japan. Phosphorised paper. P 13.

3383	**2727**	80y. multicoloured	1·60	1·30
		a. Sheetlet of 10. Nos. 3383/4 and 3385/8, each×2	17·00	
3384	**2728**	80y. multicoloured	1·60	1·30
3385	**2729**	80y. multicoloured	1·60	1·30
3386	**2730**	80y. multicoloured	1·60	1·30
3387	**2731**	80y. multicoloured	1·60	1·30
3388	**2732**	80y. multicoloured	1·60	1·30
3383/3388		Set of 6	8·75	7·00

Nos. 3383/4 and 3385/8, each×2 were issued in *se-tenant* sheetlets of ten stamps, with enlarged illustrated margins.

2733 Tetsuro   **2734** Maetel

2727 Beethoven

2728 Karl Benz driving Benz Patent Motorwagen, 1886

2735 Claire   **2736** The Conductor

2737 Freija and Maetel   **2738** Tetsuro and Moriki Yutaka

2729 Japanese Musician (Meissen)

2730 Japanese Musician (Meissen)

2739 Emeraldas and Count Mecha   **2740** Herlock

2741 Maetel   **2742** Galaxy Express 999

2006 (1 Feb). Heroes and Heroines of Animation (3rd issue). Galaxy Express 999. Phosphorised paper. Litho. P 13.

3389	**2733**	80y. multicoloured	1·60	1·30
		a. Horiz pair. Nos. 3389/90	3·50	2·75
		b. Sheetlet of 10. Nos. 3389/98	17·00	
3390	**2734**	80y. multicoloured	1·60	1·30
3391	**2735**	80y. multicoloured	1·60	1·30
		a. Horiz pair. Nos. 3391/2	3·50	2·75
3392	**2736**	80y. multicoloured	1·60	1·30
3393	**2737**	80y. multicoloured	1·60	1·30
		a. Horiz pair. Nos. 3393/4	3·50	2·75
3394	**2738**	80y. multicoloured	1·60	1·30
3395	**2739**	80y. multicoloured	1·60	1·30
		a. Horiz pair. Nos. 3395/6	3·50	2·75
3396	**2740**	80y. multicoloured	1·60	1·30
3397	**2741**	80y. multicoloured	1·60	1·30
		a. Horiz pair. Nos. 3397/8	3·50	2·75
3398	**2742**	80y. multicoloured	1·60	1·30
3389/3398		Set of 10	14·50	11·50

Nos. 3389/90, 3391/2, 3393/4, 3395/6 and 3397/8, respectively, were issued in horizontal *se-tenant* pairs within sheetlets of ten stamps, each pair forming a composite design.

2743 Rabbit and Bird (Hirosawa Yo)

2744 Children kissing (Ogasawara Maki)

2745 Bears exchanging Fish (Mori Kiyotaka)

2746 Dog and Bear (Kobayashi Ryota)

2747 Animals on Globe (Takanami Suzuka)

(Des J. Kaifuchi. Photo)

2006 (1 Mar). International Exchanges and Friendship. Winning Entries in Design a Stamp Competition. Phosphorised paper. P 13.

3399	**2743**	80y. multicoloured	1·60	1·30
		a. Vert strip of 5. Nos. 3399/403	8·25	
		b. Sheetlet of 10. Nos. 3399/403, each×2	17·00	
3400	**2744**	80y. multicoloured	1·60	1·30
3401	**2745**	80y. multicoloured	1·60	1·30
3402	**2746**	80y. multicoloured	1·60	1·30
3403	**2747**	80y. multicoloured	1·60	1·30
3399/3403		Set of 5	7·25	5·75

Nos. 3399/403 were issued in vertical *se-tenant* strips of five within sheetlets of ten stamps.

2748 Shrunken Detective   **2749** Detective Conan

2750 Shin'ichi and Conan   **2751** Ran

2752 Doctor Agasa and Ayumi   **2753** Mitsuhiko and Genta

2754 Haibara Ai   **2755** Conan

2756 Mysterious Thief Kid
2757 Shin'ichi and Conan

(Litho Cartor)

2006 (3 Apr). Heroes and Heroines of Animation (4th issue). Detective Conan. Phosphorised paper. P 13.

3404	**2748** 80y. multicoloured	1·60	1·30
	a. Horiz pair. Nos. 3404/5	3·50	2·75
	b. Sheetlet of 10. Nos. 3404/13	17·00	
3405	**2749** 80y. multicoloured	1·60	1·30
3406	**2750** 80y. multicoloured	1·60	1·30
	a. Horiz pair. Nos. 3406/7	3·50	2·75
3407	**2751** 80y. multicoloured	1·60	1·30
3408	**2752** 80y. multicoloured	1·60	1·30
	a. Horiz pair. Nos. 3408/9	3·50	2·75
3409	**2753** 80y. multicoloured	1·60	1·30
3410	**2754** 80y. multicoloured	1·60	1·30
	a. Horiz pair. Nos. 3410/11	3·50	2·75
3411	**2755** 80y. multicoloured	1·60	1·30
3412	**2756** 80y. multicoloured	1·60	1·30
	a. Horiz pair. Nos. 3412/13	3·50	2·75
3413	**2757** 80y. multicoloured	1·60	1·30
3404/3413	*Set of* 10	14·50	11·50

Nos. 3404/5, 3406/7, 3408/9, 3410/11 and 3412/13 respectively, were issued in horizontal *se-tenant* pairs within sheetlets of ten stamps, each pair forming a composite design.

2758 Morning Glory
2759 Puppies

(Des F. Kanematsu. Photo)

2006 (20 Apr). Philatelic Week. Paintings by Maruyama Oukyo. Phosphorised paper. P 13 (with one elliptical hole on each side).

3414	**2758** 80y. multicoloured	1·50	1·20
	a. Horiz pair. Nos. 3414/15	3·25	2·50
3415	**2759** 80y. multicoloured	1·50	1·20

Nos. 3414/15 were issued in horizontal *se-tenant* pairs.

2760 Australian Flag and Uluru (Ayers Rock)
2761 Kangaroo

2762 Sydney Opera House
2763 Flag and Sydney Opera House

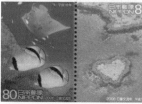

2764 Fish (Great Barrier Reef)
2765 Heart Reef

2766 Golden Wattle
2767 Bottle Bush

2768 Koalas
2769 Kookabura

(Des M. Morita. Photo)

2006 (23 May). Japan–Australia Exchange Year–2006. Phosphorised paper. P 13.

3416	**2760** 80y. multicoloured	1·50	1·20
	a. Horiz pair. Nos. 3416/17	3·25	2·50
	b. Sheetlet of 10. Nos. 3416/25	16·00	
3417	**2761** 80y. multicoloured	1·50	1·20
3418	**2762** 80y. multicoloured	1·50	1·20
	a. Horiz pair. Nos. 3418/19	3·25	2·50
3419	**2763** 80y. multicoloured	1·50	1·20
3420	**2764** 80y. multicoloured	1·50	1·20
	a. Horiz pair. Nos. 3420/1	3·25	2·50
3421	**2765** 80y. multicoloured	1·50	1·20
3422	**2766** 80y. multicoloured	1·50	1·20
	a. Horiz pair. Nos. 3422/3	3·25	2·50
3423	**2767** 80y. multicoloured	1·50	1·20
3424	**2768** 80y. multicoloured	1·50	1·20
	a. Horiz pair. Nos. 3424/5	3·25	2·50

3425 **2769** 80y. multicoloured .... 1·50 1·20
3416/3425 *Set of* 13·50 .... 13·50 11·50
Nos. 3416/17, 3418/19, 3420/1, 3422/3 and 3424/5 respectively,
were issued in horizontal *se-tenant* pairs within sheetlets of ten
stamps. Nos. 3416/17 3418/19 and 3424/5 respectively forming
composite designs.

(Des F. Kanematsu. Photo)

2006 (23 June). World Heritage. Phosphorised paper. P 13.
3426 **2770** 80y. multicoloured .... 1·50 1·20
     a. Horiz. pair. Nos. 3426/7 .... 3·25 2·50
     a. Sheetlet of 10. Nos. 3426/35 .... 16·00
3427 **2771** 80y. multicoloured .... 1·50 1·20
3428 **2772** 80y. multicoloured .... 1·50 1·20
3429 **2773** 80y. multicoloured .... 1·50 1·20
3430 **2774** 80y. multicoloured .... 1·50 1·20
3431 **2775** 80y. multicoloured .... 1·50 1·20
3432 **2776** 80y. multicoloured .... 1·50 1·20
3433 **2777** 80y. multicoloured .... 1·50 1·20
3434 **2778** 80y. multicoloured .... 1·50 1·20
3435 **2779** 80y. multicoloured .... 1·50 1·20
3426/3435 *Set of* 10 .... 13·50 11·00
Nos. 3426/35 were issued in sheetlets of ten stamps.

2770 Kumano
Hongu-taisha Shrine

2771 Kumano
Hongu-taisha Shrine

2772 Nachinoootaki
Waterfall

2773 Kumano
Hongu-taisha Shrine

2774 Fire Festival,
Nachi

2775 Nyoirin-dou
Main Hall, Seigantoji
Temple

2776 Kongobuji
Temple Gate

2777 Kongaradouji
(wooden statue),
Kongobuji Temple

2778 Zaou-dou Main
Hall, Kinpusenji Temple

2779 Zaou-gongen
(wooden statue),
Kinpusenji Temple

2780 Fairy on Flower

2781 Church Bell

2782 Bouquet

2783 Dolphin

2784 Humming Bird

2785 Pink Orchid

2786 Fairy and
Flowers

2787 Oranges and
Blossom

2788 Parrot

2789 Orange Flowers

2006 (30 June). Greetings Stamps. Phosphor borders. Self-adhesive. Litho. Die-cut Perf 14.

3436	**2780**	50y. multicoloured	1·10	90
	a. Sheetlet of 5. Nos. 3436/40		5·75	
3437	**2781**	50y. multicoloured	1·10	90
3438	**2782**	50y. multicoloured	1·10	90
3439	**2783**	50y. multicoloured	1·10	90
3440	**2784**	50y. multicoloured	1·10	90
3441	**2785**	80y. multicoloured	1·50	1·20
	a. Sheetlet of 5. Nos. 3441/5		7·75	
3442	**2786**	80y. multicoloured	1·50	1·20
3443	**2787**	80y. multicoloured	1·50	1·20
3444	**2788**	80y. multicoloured	1·50	1·20
3445	**2789**	80y. multicoloured	1·50	1·20
3436/3445	*Set of* 10		11·50	9·50

Nos. 3436/40 and 3441/5, respectively, were issued in *se-tenant* sheetlets of five stamps, with an illustrated lower margin containing labels for use on mail.

2790 "Iseno-taifu" (Koyama Yasuko)

2791 "Goptokudaijino-sadaijin" (Mitsuoka Keiso)

2792 "Ooshikouchino-mitsune" (Miyazaki Shikou)

2793 "Yamabeno-akahito" (Matsumoto Eiko)

2794 "Suouno-naishi" (Miyake Soushu)

2795 "Double Cherry Blossoms" (Koyama Yasuko)

2796 "Iseno-taifu" (Koyama Yasuko)

2797 "A Wan Morning Moon" (Mitsuoka Keiso)

2798 "Goptokudaijino-sadaijin" (Mitsuoka Keiso)

2799 "White Chrysanthemums" (Miyazaki Shikou)

2800 "Ooshikouchino-mitsune" (Miyazaki Shikou)

2801 "Mt. Fuji" (Matsumoto Eiko)

2802 "Yamabeno-akahito" (Matsumoto Eiko)

2803 "Spring Night" (Miyake Soushu)

2804 "Suouno-naishi" (Miyake Soushu)

(Des M. Morita. Photo)

2006 (21 July). Letter Writing Day. Phosphorised paper. P 13½ (50y.) or 13 (80y.).

3446	2790	50y. multicoloured	1·10	90
	a. Vertical strip of 5. Nos. 3446/50		5·75	
3447	2791	50y. multicoloured	1·10	90
3448	2792	50y. multicoloured	1·10	90
3449	2793	50y. multicoloured	1·10	90
3450	2794	50y. multicoloured	1·10	90
3451	2795	80y. multicoloured	1·50	1·20
	a. Sheetlet of 10. Nos. 3451/60		16·00	
3452	2796	80y. multicoloured	1·50	1·20
3453	2797	80y. multicoloured	1·50	1·20
3454	2798	80y. multicoloured	1·50	1·20
3455	2799	80y. multicoloured	1·50	1·20
3456	2800	80y. multicoloured	1·50	1·20
3457	2801	80y. multicoloured	1·50	1·20
3458	2802	80y. multicoloured	1·50	1·20
3459	2803	80y. multicoloured	1·50	1·20
3460	2804	80y. multicoloured	1·50	1·20
3446/3460 Set of 15			18·00	15·00

Nos. 3446/50 were issued together in vertical *se-tenant* strips of five stamps within the sheet. Nos. 3451/60 were issued in sheetlets of ten stamps with enlarged inscribed left-hand margin.

2805 World and Flowers

2806 World, Mountain and Flowers

(Des A. Tamaki. Photo)

2006 (29 Sept). Letter Writing Week. 50th Anniv of Accession to United Nations Phosphorised paper. P 13.

3461	2805	90y. multicoloured	1·70	1·40
3462	2806	110y. multicoloured	1·90	1·60

2807 Vanda "Miss Joaquim"

2808 Mokara "Lion's Gold"

2809 Vanda "Mimi Palmer"

2810 Renanthera Singaporean

2811 Heron and Hollyhocks (detail) ("Flowers and Birds of Four Seasons") (Sakai Hoitsu)

2812 Iris and Moorhen (detail) ("Flowers and Birds of Four Seasons") (Sakai Hoitsu)

2006 (3 Oct). Greetings Stamps. 40th Anniv of Japan—Singapore Diplomatic Relations. Phosphorised paper. Self-adhesive. Litho. Die-cut perf 14×rouletting (50y. and 80y.) or 14 (others).

3463	2808	50y. multicoloured	1·10	90
	a. Horiz pair. Nos. 3463 and 3465		2·75	2·20
	b. Sheetlet of 6. Nos. 3463/8		9·00	
3464	2810	50y. multicoloured	1·10	90
	a. Horiz pair. Nos. 3464 and 3466		2·75	2·20
3465	2807	80y. multicoloured	1·50	1·20
3466	2809	80y. multicoloured	1·50	1·20
3467	2811	90y. multicoloured	1·70	1·40
3468	2812	110y. multicoloured	1·90	1·60
3463/3468 Set of 6			8·00	6·50

Nos. 3463 and 3465, 3464 and 3466, respectively were issued in horizontal *se-tenant* pairs within sheetlets of six stamps with an enlarged illustrated left margin and lower margin containing labels for use on mail. The stamps in each pair were separated from each other by a line of rouletting.

Stamps of a similar design were issued by Singapore.

2813 "Tange Sazen"

2814 "Carmen Comes Home"

2815 "Ugetsu Monogatari"

2816 "Tokyo Story"

2825 "Kamata Koshin-kyoku"

2826 "Yomigaeru Kinro"

2817 "Seven Samurai"

2818 "A Night in Hawaii"

2827 "MacArthur's Children"

2828 "HANA-BI"

2819 "Unknown"

2820 "Guitar o Motta Wataridori"

2829 "Paradise Lost"

2830 "Gamera"

2821 "Miyamoto Musashi"

2822 "Kyupora No. Aru Machi"

2831 "Twilight Samurai"

2832 "Godzilla"

2823 "Sailor-fuku to Kikanju"

2824 "Otoko wa Tsuraiyo"

(Des K. Fumiaki. Photo)

2006 (10 Oct). Japanese Cinema. Phosphorised paper. P 13.

3469	**2813**	80y. multicoloured	1·50	1·20
		a. Sheetlet of 10. Nos. 3469/78	16·00	
3470	**2814**	80y. multicoloured	1·50	1·20
3471	**2815**	80y. multicoloured	1·50	1·20
3472	**2816**	80y. multicoloured	1·50	1·20
3473	**2817**	80y. multicoloured	1·50	1·20
3474	**2818**	80y. multicoloured	1·50	1·20
3475	**2819**	80y. multicoloured	1·50	1·20
3476	**2820**	80y. multicoloured	1·50	1·20
3477	**2821**	80y. multicoloured	1·50	1·20
3478	**2822**	80y. multicoloured	1·50	1·20
3479	**2823**	80y. multicoloured	1·50	1·20
		a. Sheetlet of 10. Nos. 3479/88	16·00	
3480	**2824**	80y. multicoloured	1·50	1·20
3481	**2825**	80y. multicoloured	1·50	1·20
3482	**2826**	80y. multicoloured	1·50	1·20

3483	**2827** 80y. multicoloured	1·50	1·20
3484	**2828** 80y. multicoloured	1·50	1·20
3485	**2829** 80y. multicoloured	1·50	1·20
3486	**2830** 80y. multicoloured	1·50	1·20
3487	**2831** 80y. multicoloured	1·50	1·20
3488	**2832** 80y. multicoloured	1·50	1·20
3469/3488	*Set of* 20	27·00	22·00

Nos. 3469/78 and 3479/88 were issued in sheetlets of ten stamps with enlarged inscribed central margins.

2833 Autumn
Flowers and Ox
Cart

2834 Autumn
Flowers and Ox
Cart

(Des A. Hoshiyama. Photo)

2006 (23 Oct). 50th Anniv of International Ikebana Convention. Phosphorised paper. P 13.

3489	**2833** 80y. multicoloured	1·50	1·20
	a. Vertical pair. Nos. 3489/90	3·25	2·50
3490	**2834** 80y. multicoloured	1·50	1·20

2835 Treasured
Boar

2836 Zodiac
Boar

(Des E. Uchida and J. Kaifuchi. Photo)

2006 (1 Nov). New Year's Greetings.. Phosphorised paper. P 13×13½.

| 3491 | **2835** 50y. multicoloured | 1·10 | 90 |
| 3492 | **2836** 80y. multicoloured | 1·50 | 1·20 |

No. 3493 is vacant.

2837 Treasured
Boar

2838 Zodiac Boar

(Des E. Uchida and J. Kaifuchi. Photo)

2006 (1 Nov). New Year Lottery Stamps. Phosphorised paper. P 13×13½.

| 3494 | **2837** 50y. +3y | multicoloured | 1·20 | 95 |
| 3495 | **2838** 80y. +3y | multicoloured | 1·60 | 1·30 |

Each stamp carries a lottery number.

2839 Squirrel
(Sugita Yutaka)

2840 Bell (Arai
Sonoko)

2841 Clown
(Nagata Moe)

2842 Polar bear
(Watanabe Hiroshi)

2843 Bear Santa
Claus (Murakami
Tsutomu)

2844 Cat Santa Claus
(Murakami Tsutomu)

2845 Cyclamen

2846 Snowman

2847 Reindeer
(Watanabe Hiroshi)

2848 Wreath (Arai
Sonoko)

2006 (24 Nov). Greetings Stamps. Phosphor borders. Self-adhesive. Litho. Die-cut perf 14.

3496	**2839** 50y. multicoloured	1·10	90
	a. Sheetlet of 5. Nos. 3496/500	5·75	
3497	**2840** 50y. multicoloured	1·10	90
3498	**2841** 50y. multicoloured	1·10	90
3499	**2842** 50y. multicoloured	1·10	90
3500	**2843** 50y. multicoloured	1·10	90
3501	**2844** 80y. multicoloured	1·50	1·20
	a. Sheetlet of 5. Nos. 3501/5	7·75	
3502	**2845** 80y. multicoloured	1·50	1·20
3503	**2846** 80y. multicoloured	1·50	1·20
3504	**2847** 80y. multicoloured	1·50	1·20

3505   **2848** 80y. multicoloured ....   1·50   1·20
3496/3505   *Set of 10* .... 11·50   9·50
    Nos. 3496/500 and 3501/5, respectively were issued in *se-tenant* sheetlets of five stamps, with an illustrated lower margin containing labels for use on mail.

2849 Semi-cursive Style (Minagawa Gashu)

2850 Kinbun Style (Usuda Tousen)

2851 Reisho Style (Hayashi Shouen)

2852 Former Japanese Cursive (Yamazaki Kyouko)

2853 Kinbun Style (Sugano Seihou)

2854 Kinbun Style (Seki Masato)

2855 Inscribed on Kanae (Yoshida Seido)

2856 Kinbun Style (Nakano Hokumei)

2857 Tensho Style (Sadamasa Shoutou)

2858 Reisho Style (Kamigori Aichiku)

(Des M. Morita. Photo and embossed Cartor)

2006 (1 Dec). Greetings Stamps. Eto Calligraphy. Phosphorised paper. P 13.

3506	**2849**	80y. multicoloured	1·50	1·20
		a. Sheetlet of 10. Nos. 3506/15	16·00	
3507	**2850**	80y. multicoloured	1·50	1·20
3508	**2851**	80y. multicoloured	1·50	1·20
3509	**2852**	80y. multicoloured	1·50	1·20
3510	**2853**	80y. multicoloured	1·50	1·20
3511	**2854**	80y. multicoloured	1·50	1·20
3512	**2855**	80y. multicoloured	1·50	1·20
3513	**2856**	80y. multicoloured	1·50	1·20
3514	**2857**	80y. multicoloured	1·50	1·20
3515	**2858**	80y. multicoloured	1·50	1·20
3506/3515		*Set of 10*	13·50	11·00

    Nos. 3506/15 were issued in *se-tenant* sheetlets of ten stamps, with enlarged illustrated margins.

2859 Research Ship

2860 Research Airplane

2861 Penguins

2862 Penguins

2863 Research Ship and Penguins

2864 Penguins

2865 Sled Dog

2866 Sled Dog standing

2867 Ship and Scientist

2868 Tracked Vehicle

2869 Tracked Vehicle

2870 Research Airplane

2871 Research Ship and Sled Team

2872 Seal

2007 (23 Jan). 50th Anniversary of the Japanese Antarctic Research Expedition Phosphorised paper. P 13.

3516	**2859**	80y. multicoloured	1·50	1·20
		a. Horiz pair. Nos. 3516/17	3·25	2·50
		b. Sheetlet of 10. Nos. 3516/2	16·00	
3517	**2860**	80y. multicoloured	1·50	1·20
3518	**2861**	80y. multicoloured	1·50	1·20
		a. Horiz pair. Nos. 3518/19	3·25	2·50
3519	**2862**	80y. multicoloured	1·50	1·20
3520	**2863**	80y. multicoloured	1·50	1·20
		a. Horiz pair. Nos. 3520/1	3·25	2·50
3521	**2864**	80y. multicoloured	1·50	1·20
3522	**2865**	80y. multicoloured	1·50	1·20
		a. Horiz pair. Nos. 3522/3	3·25	2·50
3523	**2866**	80y. multicoloured	1·50	1·20
3524	**2867**	80y. multicoloured	1·50	1·20
		a. Horiz pair. Nos. 3524/5	3·25	2·50
3525	**2868**	80y. multioloured	1·50	1·20
		(b) Self-adhesive. Litho. Die-cut Perf 14.		
3526	**2869**	80y. multicoloured	1·60	1·30
		a. Sheetlet of 10. Nos. 3526/35	17·00	
3527	**2870**	80y. multicoloured	1·60	1·30
3528	**2871**	80y. multicoloured	1·60	1·30
3529	**2872**	80y. multicoloured	1·60	1·30
3530	**2873**	80y. multicoloured	1·60	1·30
3531	**2874**	80y. multicoloured	1·60	1·30
3532	**2875**	80y. multicoloured	1·60	1·30
3533	**2876**	80y. multicoloured	1·60	1·30
3534	**2877**	80y. multicoloured	1·60	1·30
3535	**2878**	80y. multicoloured	1·60	1·30
3516/3535		*Set of* 20	28·00	23·00

Nos. 3516/17, 3518/19, 3520/1, 3522/3 and 3524/5, respectively, were issued in horizontal se-tenant pairs within sheetlets of ten stamps, each pair forming a composite design. Nos. 3526/35 were issued in sheetlets of ten stamps, each sheet forming a composite design.

2873 Penguin

2874 Two Penguins

2879 Evangelion Unit 01   **2880** Ikari Shinji

2875 Sled Dog

2876 Penguin Chicks

2881 Ayanami Rei   **2882** Evangelion Unit 00

2877 Penguin and Chick

2878 Sled Dog

2883 Soryu Asuka Langley   **2884** Evangelion Unit 02

2885 Ayanami Rei and Soryu Asuka Langley

2886 Katsuragi Misato

2887 Nagisa Kaworu

2888 Sachiel, the Third Angle

2007 (23 Feb). Heroes and Heroines of Animation (5th issue). Neon Genesis Evangelion. Phosphorised paper. Litho. P 13.

3536	**2879**	80y. multicoloured	1·50	1·20
	a.	Horiz pair. Nos. 3536/7	3·25	2·50
	b.	Sheetlet of 10. Nos. 3536/45	16·00	
3537	**2880**	80y. multicoloured	1·50	1·20
3538	**2881**	80y. multicoloured	1·50	1·20
	a.	Horiz pair. Nos. 3538/9	3·25	2·50
3539	**2882**	80y. multicoloured	1·50	1·20
3540	**2883**	80y. multicoloured	1·50	1·20
	a.	Horiz pair. Nos. 3540/1	3·25	2·50
3541	**2884**	80y. multicoloured	1·50	1·20
3542	**2885**	80y. multicoloured	1·50	1·20
	a.	Horiz pair. Nos. 3542/3	3·25	2·50
3543	**2886**	80y. multicoloured	1·50	1·20
3544	**2887**	80y. multicoloured	1·50	1·20
	a.	Horiz pair. Nos. 3544/5	3·25	2·50
3545	**2888**	80y. multicoloured	1·50	1·20
3536/3545		Set of 10	13·50	11·00

Nos. 3536/7, 3538/9, 3540/1, 3542/3 and 3544/5, respectively, were issued in horizontal *se-tenant* pairs within sheetlets of ten stamps, each pair forming a composite design

2889 Honden, Yoshino Mikumari Shrine

2890 Romon Soshoku, Yoshino Mikumari Shrine

2891 Omine-Okugake-Michi

2892 Honden, Kumano Hayatama-taisha Shrine

2893 Honden, Kumano Hayatama-taisha Shrine

2894 Kumano-Fusumino-Okami-Zazo, Kumano Hayatama-taisha Shrine

2895 Kumano Sankei-Michi Nakahechi

2896 Statue, Kumano Sankei-Michi Nakahechi

2897 Tahoto, Kongo-Sanmaiin Temple

2898 Kyozo, Kongo-Sanmaiin Temple

(Des F. Kanematsu. Photo)

2007 (23 Mar). World Heritage. Phosphorised paper. P 13.

3546	**2889**	80y. multicoloured	1·50	1·20
	a.	Sheetlet of 10. Nos. 3546/55	16·00	
3547	**2890**	80y. multicoloured	1·50	1·20
3548	**2891**	80y. multicoloured	1·50	1·20
3549	**2892**	80y. multicoloured	1·50	1·20
3550	**2893**	80y. multicoloured	1·50	1·20
3551	**2894**	80y. multicoloured	1·50	1·20
3552	**2895**	80y. multicoloured	1·50	1·20
3553	**2896**	80y. multicoloured	1·50	1·20
3554	**2897**	80y. multicoloured	1·50	1·20
3555	**2898**	80y. multicoloured	1·50	1·20
3547/3555		Set of 10	13·50	11·00

Nos. 3546/55 were issued in sheetlets of ten stamps.

LOTTERY PRIZE MINIATURE SHEETS

The miniature sheets listed below, although valid for postage, were not sold at post offices but could only be obtained as prizes in the annual lotteries.

1950 (1 Feb). New Year. Imperf.
LMS1 91×28 mm. No. 580×5 .... £275 £225

1951 (1 Feb). New Year. P 13½.
LMS2 105×91 mm. No. 604×5 .... 60·00 60·00

1952 (20 Jan). New Year.
LMS3 103×92 mm. No. 647×4 .... £160 £130

1953 (20 Jan). New Year.
LMS4 102×89 mm. No. 699×4 .... £110 85·00

1954 (20 Jan). New Year.
LMS5 102×89 mm. No. 722×4 .... 60·00 47·00

1955 (20 Jan). New Year.
LMS6 103×89 mm. No. 735×4 .... 55·00 55·00

1956 (20 Jan). New Year.
LMS7 102×90 mm. No. 747×4 .... 41·00 36·00

1957 (20 Jan). New Year.
LMS8 103×90 mm. No. 763×4 .... 19·00 20·00

1958 (20 Jan) New Year.
LMS9 102×90 mm. No. 773×4 .... 8·25 8·25

1959 (20 Jan). New Year.
LMS10 103×90 mm. No. 792×4 .... 7·75 7·75

1960 (20 Jan). New Year.
LMS11 102×90mm. No. 816×4 .... 8·00 7·75

1961 (20 Jan). New Year.
LMS12 102×91 mm. No. 841×4 .... 8·50 8·00

1962 (20 Jan). New Year.
LMS13 102×90 mm. No. 883×4 .... 8·75 8·25

1963 (20 Jan). New Year.
LMS14 102×93 mm. No. 914×4 .... 5·50 5·25

1964 (20 Jan). New Year.
LMS15 102×93 mm. No. 914×4 .... 3·00 2·75

1965 (20 Jan). New Year.
LMS16 101×93 mm. No. 990×4 .... 2·30 2·30

1966 (20 Jan) New Year
LMS17 100×92 mm No. 1018×4 .... 1·90 2·00

1967 (20 Jan). New Year
LMS18 101×93 mm. No. 1084×4 .... 1·90 2·00

1968 (20 Jan). New Year.
LMS19 103×93 mm. No. 1108×4 .... 1·60 1·70

1969 (20 Jan). New Year.
LMS20 102×94 mm. No. 1147×4 .... 1·60 1·70

1970 (20 Jan). New Year.
LMS21 102×94 mm. No. 1190×4 .... 1·70 1·60

1971 (20 Jan). New Year.
LMS 22 103×93 mm. No. 1222×4 .... 1·60 1·60

1972 (20 Jan) New Year.
LMS23 94×73 mm. No. 1278×3 .... 1·30 1·30

1973 (20 Jan). New Year.
LMS 24 94×72 mm. Nos. 1310×3 .... 1·30 1·30

1974 (20 Jan). New Year.
LMS25 94×72 mm. No. 1337×3 .... 1·40 1·30

1975 (20 Jan). New Year.
LMS26 94×73 mm. No. 1375×3 .... 1·40 1·30

1976 (20 Jan). New Year.
LMS27 88×73 mm. No. 1417×3 .... 1·40 1·30

1977 (20 Jan). New Year.
LMS28 93×72 mm. No. 1443×2 .... 1·40 1·40

1978 (20 Jan). New Year.
LMS29 93×72 mm. No. 1482×2 .... 1·40 1·40

1979 (5 Feb). New Year.
LMS30 93×72 mm. No. 1516×2 .... 1·40 1·40

1980 (21 Jan). New Year.
LMS31 94×72 mm. No. 1554×2 .... 1·50 1·50

1981 (20 Jan). New Year.
LMS32 94×72 mm. No. 1614×2 .... 1·50 1·50

1982 (20 Jan). New Year.
LMS33 93×72 mm. No. 1652×2 .... 1·50 1·50

1983 (20 Jan). New Year.
LMS34 94×72 mm. No. 1691×2 .... 1·50 1·50

1984 (20 Jan). New Year.
LMS35 94×72 mm. No. 1726×2 .... 1·60 1·50

1985 (21 Jan). New Year.
LMS36 72×93mm No. 1766×2 .... 1·40 1·40

1986 (20 Jan). New Year.
LMS37 93×72 mm. No. 1824×2 .... 1·50 1·50

1986 (20 Sept) Summer.
LMS38 93×72 mm. Nos. 1843/4 .... 80·00 70·00

1987 (20 Jan). New Year.
LMS39 93×72 mm. Nos. 1678 and 1867 .... 1·90 1·70

1987 (21 Sept). Summer.
LMS40 93×72 mm. Nos. 1902/3 .... 14·00 12·50

1988 (20 Jan). New Year.
LMS41 93×72 mm. Nos. 1678 and 1923 .... 1·80 2·30

1988 (13 May). Spring.
LMS42 93×72mm Nos. 1940/1 .... 6·50 5·75

1988 (20 Sept). Summer.
LMS43 94×72 mm. Nos. 1952 and 1954 .... 5·25 4·75

1989 (20 Jan). New Year.
LMS44 93×72 mm Nos. 1678 and 1978 .... 1·80 2·30

1989 (19 May). Spring.
LMS45 93×72 mm. Nos. 1994/5 .... 5·75 5·00

1989 (20 Sept). Summer.
LMS46 93×72 mm. Nos. 2010/11 .... 7·00 6·25

1990 (16 Jan). New Year.
LMS47 93×72 mm. Nos. 2015 and 2029 .... 1·80 1·60

1991 (20 Jan). New Year.
LMS48 93×72 mm. No. 2127×2 .... 1·80 1·60

1992 (16 Jan). New Year.
LMS49 93×72 mm. No. 2175×2 .... 1·90 1·70

1993 (18 Jan). New Year.
LMS50 93×72 mm. Nos. 2211/12 .... 2·75 2·50

1994 (17 Jan). New Year.
LMS51 93×72 mm. Nos. 2280/1 .... 2·75 2·30

1995 (17 Jan). New Year.
LMS52 93×72 mm. Nos. 2335/6 .... 2·30 2·00

1996 (16 Jan). New Year.
LMS53 93×72 mm. Nos. 2396/7 .... 2·50 2·20

1997 (Jan). New Year.
LMS 54 93×72 mm. Nos. 2445/6 .... 2·50 2·20

1998 (16 Jan). New Year.
LMS55 93×72 mm. Nos. 2487/8 .... 2·30 2·00

1999 (Jan). New Year.
LMS56 93×72 mm. Nos. 2554/5 .... 2·75 2·30

2000 (17 Jan). New Year.
LMS57 94×73 mm. Nos. 2673/4 .... 4·50 4·00

2001 (10 Jan). New Year.
LMS58 94×72 mm. Nos. 2845/6 .... 3·75 3·50

2002 (8 Jan). New Year.
LMS59 94×72 mm. Nos. 2980/1 .... 3·00 2·75

2003 (20 Jan). New Year.
LMS60 94×72 mm. Nos. 3078/9 .... 3·00 2·75

2004 (19 Jan). New Year.
LMS61 94×72 mm. Nos. 3188/9 .... 3·00 2·75

2005 (17 Jan). New Year.
LMS62 94×72 mm. Nos. 3281/2 .... 3·00 2·75

2006 (16 Jan). New Year.
LMS63 94×72 mm. Nos. 3368/9 .... 3·00 2·75

2007 (Jan). New Year
LMS64 94×72mm. Nos. 3491/2 .... 3·00 2·75

STAMP BOOKLETS

The following checklist of booklets issued by Japan should be used in conjunction with the main listings; details of stamps and panes listed there are not repeated. Some early booklets were sold at over face value.

The booklets listed below are official issues. From 1986 there also exist private booklets, made up either from blocks of sheet stamps or from booklet panes which, from July 1987. could be obtained from the Post Office without cover These private issues are outside the scope of this catalogue

Prices are for complete booklets

Booklet No.	Date	Contents and Cover Price	Price
SB1	30.12.06	"Chrysanthemum" Series (T **28**) 5 panes, No. 136E×6; 3 panes. No. 139E×6 (1y.)	£9000
SB2	1.5.07	"Chrysanthemum" Series (T **28/9**) 2 panes, No. 137E×6; 6 panes. No. 140E×6; 3 panes. No. 144E×6 (3y. 50)	£2750
SB3	1.10.07	"Chrysanthemum" Series (T **28**) 3 panes, No. 136E×6; 4 panes. No. 139E×6 (1y.)	£8500
SB4	1.10.07	"Chrysanthemum" Series (T **26/9**) 2 panes, No. 137E×6; 3 panes. No. 140E×6; 2 panes, No. 142E×6; 3 panes, No. 144E×6(3y. 50)	£4000
SB5	25.12.11	"Chrysanthemum" Series (T **28**) 10 panes, No. 136E×6 (90s.)	15000
SB6	26.12.11	"Chrysanthemum" Series (T **28**) 5 panes, No. 139E×6 (90s.)	£4500
SB7	31.8.13	"Taisho" Series (T **38**). No. wmk 10 panes, No. 158C×6 (90s.)	£15000
SB8	31.8.13	"Taisho" Series (T **36**). No. wmk 5 panes, No. 160C×6 (90s)	£17000
SB9	31.8.13	"Taisho" Series (T **36**). No. wmk 5 panes, No. 158C 6; 3 panes. No.160C×6 (1y.)	£14000
		a. Do. but containing Nos. 158A and 160A	—
SB10	31.10.13	"Taisho" Series (T **36/7**). No. wmk 2 panes, No. 159B×6; 6 panes, No. 161B×6; 3 panes, No. 163B×6 (3y.)	£14000
SB11	20.5.14	"Taisho" Series (T **36**). Wmkd. 10 panes, No. 169aE (all sides perf) (90s.)	£13000
		a. Do. but containing No. 169aD	—
SB12	20.6.14	"Taisho" Series (T **36**). Wmkd. 5 panes, No. 171aE (all sides perf) (90s.)	£2000
		a. Do. but containing No. 171 aD	—
SB13	20.5.14	"Taisho" Series (T **36/7**). Wmkd. 2 panes, No. 170E×6; 6 panes, No. 172E-6; 3 panes No. 176E×6 (3y. 50)	£3250
SB14	8.23	"Taisho" (T **36**). Wmkd. 10 panes, No. 169a(A–C) (outer edges imperf) (90s.)	£700
SB15	8.23	"Taisho" Series (T**36**). Wmkd. 5 panes, No. 171a(A–C) (outer edges imperf) (90s.)	£400
SB16	4.25	"Taisho" Series (T **36**). Wmkd. 10 panes, No. 169aE (outer edges imperf) (90s.)	£1300
SB17	4.25	"Taisho" Series (T **36**). Wmkd. 5 panes. No. 171aE (outer edges imperil (90s.)	£650
SB18	13.5.28	"Taisho" Series (T **36**) Smaller die 10 panes, No. 232a. (90s.)	£550
SB19	13.5.28	"Taisho" Series (T **36**). Smaller die 5 panes, No. 233a. (90s.)	£275
SB20	16.10.37 –41	Gen. Nogi (T **83**) 2 panes, No. 315a. Cover: Leaf pattern in ochre and green (80s.)	£350
		a. Cover: Flowers and geometric shapes in greyish green (2.41)	£190
SB21	16.10.37 –41	Admiral Togo 1 pane, No. 317a. Cover: Checks in blue and red (80s.)	£375
		a. Cover. Flowers within diamonds in greyish blue (2 41)	45·00
SB22	15.2.49	Miner (T **184**) 1 pane, No. 490a (100y.)	£400
SB23	3.11.49	Miner (T **184**) 1 pane, No. 493a (160y.)	£400
SB24	20.11.54	Kannon Bosatsu (T **237**) 1 pane, No. 659a (100y.)	£225
SB25	20.4.59	Ducks (T **275**) and Kannon Bosatsu (T **237**) 1 pane, No. 657a (100y.)	38·00
SB26	1.4.63	Ducks (T **275**) and Cherry Blossom (T **405**) 1 pane, No. 657b (100y.)	38·00
SB27	1.8.64 –65	Ducks (T **275**) 5 panes, No. 657d. 1 line of inscr at foot of cover (100y.)	40·00
		a. Two lines of inscr (2.65)	60·00
SB28	1.8.64 –65	Cherry Blossom (T **405**) 5 panes, No. 860e. 1 line of inscr at foot of cover (200y.)	40·00
		a. Two lines of inscr (2.65)	35·00
SB29	1.6.67	Chrysanthemums (T **526**) 1 pane, No. 1049c. (60y.)	5·00
SB30	1.6.67	Chrysanthemums (T **526**) 1 pane, No. 1049b (90y.)	10·00
SB31	16 67	Ducks (T **275**) and Chrysanthemums (T **526**) 1 pane, No. 657e (100y.)	13·00
SB32	1.3.68	Chrysanthemums (T **526**) pane. No. 1050b (90y.)	40·00
SB33	1.3.68	Ducks (T275) *and* Chrysanthemums (T **526**) 1 pane, No. 657f (100y.)	16·00
SB34	1 7 68	Ducks (T **275**) and Postal Codes (T **585**) 1 pane, No. 657g (100y.)	42·00
SB35	15.3.70 –1 4.70	"EXPO 70" World Fair (T **648/50**) 1 pane, No. 1193a Gold inscr on cover (100y.)	4·00
		a. Silver inscr on cover (1.4)	4·00
SB36	22.6.70	"EXPO 70" World Fair (T **654/6**) 1 pane, No. 1200a Gold inscr on cover (100y.)	4·25
		a. Silver inscr on cover.	4·25
SB37	31.1.72	Cuckoo (T **273**) 1 pane, No. 1226a (60y.)	13·50
SB38	1.2.72	Deer (T **678**) and "Pine Tree" (T **680**) 1 pane, No. 1228a 1100y.)	4·00
SB39	10.3.76	Buddhisattva (T **240**) 1 pane, No. 1232a. (300y.)	7·50
SB40	20.2.81	Hanging Bell (T **1011**) 1 pane, No. 1590b (300y.)	4·50
SB41	23.8.86	Letter Writing Day (T **1255/6**) 1 pane, No. 1843a (500y.)	6·50
SB42	23.7.87	Letter Writing Day (T **1313/14**) 1 pane, No. 1902a (500y.)	8·00
SB43	30.9.87	Insects (T **1258, 1292**) 1 pane, No. 1911a (500 y.)	11·00
SB44	30 9 87	Insects (T **1280, 1293**) 1 pane, No. 1912a (500y.)	11·00
SB45	1.4.88	Shells (T **1011, 1015**) 1 pane, No. 1687a (500y.)	6·50
SB46	23.7.88	Letter Writing Day (T **1358, 1360**). Perf 1 pane, No. 1952a (500y.)	6·00
SB47	1.3.89	Letter Writing Day (T **1358, 1360**). Self-adhesive Nos. 1986×3 and 1987×3 (300y.)	8·00
SB48	1.4.89	Shells (T **1012, 1016**). Perf 1 pane, No 1588a. (330y.)	4·00
SB49	1.4 89	Shells (T **1012, 1016**) Self-adhesive Nos. 1991×2 and 1992×4 (330y.)	8·50
SB50	21.7.89	Letter Writing Day (T **1409/10**) 1 pane., No. 2010a (616y.)	6·00
SB51	23.7.90	Letter Writing Day (T **1496/7**) 1 pane, No. 2103a (615y.)	9·00
SB52	23.7.91	Letter Writing Day (T **1646/6**) 1 pane, No. 2156a (615y.)	9·00
SB53	23.7.92	Letter Writing Day (T **1581/2**) 1 pane, No. 2194a (615y.)	9·50
SB54	30.11.92	Birds (T **1604,1606**). Self-adhesive Nos. 2235×2 and 2237×4 (330y.)	10·00
SB55	26.2.93	Birds (T **1604, 1606**) 1 pane, No. 2218a (515y.)	45.00
SB56	23.7.93	Letter Writing Day (T **1641/2**) 1 pane, No. 2261a (515y.)	12.00
SB57	24.1.94	Birds (T **1605, 1608**) Self-adhesive Nos. 2236×4 and 2238×4 (520y.)	18.00

SB58	22.7.94	Letter Writing Day (T **1681/2**)	
		1 pane, No. 2306a (650y.)	28.00
SB59	21.7.95	Letter Writing Day (T **1738/9**)	
		1 pane, No. 2370a (650 y.)	12.00
SB60	23.7.96	Letter Writing Day (T **1791/2**)	
		1 pane, No. 2426a (650y.)	12.00
SB61	23.7.97	Letter Writing Day (T **1831/4**)	
		1 pane, No. 2467a (650y.)	25.00
SB62	23.7.98	Letter Writing Day (T **1896/1900**)	
		1 pane, No. 2533b (680y.)	14.00
SB63	23.7.99	Letter Writing Day (T **1957/60**, **1963**, **1967**, **1969**)	
		1 pane, No. 2598b (680y.)	15.00
SB64	21.7.00	Letter Writing Day (T **2140/3**, **2148**, **2150/1**, **2153**)	
		1 pane, No. 2783b (680y.)	21.00
SB65	23.07.01	Letter Writing Day.	
		Nos. 2922/25, 2928/9×2 and 2932×2 (680y.)	17.00

SB66	23.07.02	Letter Writing Day.	
		No. 3030b...	16.00
SB67	3.07.03	Letter Writing Day.	
		No. 3165b...	15.00
SB68	6.02.04	Greetings Stamps. Hello Kitty. Self-adhesive	
		No. 3209/18	14.00
SB69	6.02.04	Greetings Stamps. Hello Kitty. Self-adhesive	
		No. 3219/23...	10.00
SB70	23.07.04	Letter Writing Day.	
		No. 3247b...	14.00
SB71	22.7.05	Letter Writing Day.	
		No. 3326b...	13.00

DESIGN INDEX FOR JAPAN

PREFECTURE STAMPS

Prefecture stamps were often issued both as perforated stamps within sheets with an outer margin, and as panes of ten with three margins imperforate and a selvage at one end. Single stamps from these panes will have one side or two adjacent sides imperforate, depending on position.

In several cases stamps were issued by more than one Prefecture on the same day, for the convenience of collectors, these are listed under each Prefecture for which they were issued.

Aichi

1 Fish and Nagoya Castle

1989 (1 Aug). Photo. P 13.
1   **1**   62y. multicoloured .... 1·50   80

1990 (27 Apr). Flowers. Litho. P 13½.
2   62y. As Japan Type **1456** .... 1·20   80

2 Owl and Mount Horaiji

1992 (15 Oct). Photo. P 13½.
3   **2**   62y. multicoloured .... 1·50   90
     a. Pane. No. 3×10, with outer edges imperf .... 14·50

3 Horse-shaped Float

1996 (1 Oct). Nagoya Festival. T **3** and similar vert design. Multicoloured. Litho. P 13½.
4   80y. Type **3**.. 2·10   1·40
     a. Pair. Nos. 4/5 .... 4·50   4·50
5   80y. Two floats.. 2·10   1·40
Nos. 4/5 were issued in horizontal *se-tenant* pairs within the sheet.

4 "Satou Ichiei" (painting by Fujii Tokio)

1999 (13 Oct). Birth Centenary of Satou Ichiei (poet). T **4** and similar vert design. Multicoloured. Photo. P 13½.
6   80y. Type **4**.. 2·10   1·40
     a. Pair. Nos. 7/8 .... 4·50   4·50
     b. Pane. Nos. 7/8, each×5, with outer edges imperf .... 20·00
7   80y. *Beautiful Yamato* (painting by Munakata Shikou)............................... 2·10   1·40
Nos. 6/7 were issued in horizontal *se-tenant* pairs within the sheet.

5 Willow and Frog

(Des Hattori Yoshi'e. Photo)

2000 (20 Oct). P 13½.
8   **5**   80y. multicoloured .... 2·75   1·90
     a. Pane. No. 8×10, with outer edges imperf .... 27·00

6 Roadway, Oohashi Bridge

(Des Hasegawa Yuji. Photo)

2001 (2 July). Automobile City. T **6** and similar vert design. Multicoloured. Litho. P 13½.
9   50y. Type **6**.. 1·60   1·10
     a. Pair. Nos. 9/10.. 3·50   3·50
     b. Pane. Nos. 9/10, each×5, with outer edges imperf .... 15·00
10   50y. Tokyo stadium.................................... 1·60   1·10
Nos. 9/10 were issued in horizontal *se-tenant* pairs within the sheet.

Akita

1990 (27 Apr). Flowers. Litho. P 13½.
1   62y. As Japan Type **1438**........................... 1·20   80

1 Fireworks

1990 (2 July). Omagari Firework festival. Litho. P 13.
2 1 62y. multicoloured... 1·30   80

2 Coastline, Nyudo-zaki

1993 (12 Feb). Photo. P 13½.
3   **2**   41y. multicoloured .... 1·20   70
        a. Pane. No. 3×10, with outer edges
          imperf .... 14·00

3 Kanto Festival

1997 (7 July). Photo. P 13½.
4   **3**   80y. multicoloured .... 2·10   1·40
        a. Pane. No. 4×10, with outer edges
          imperf .... 20·00

4 Snow-covered Samurai Houses, Kakunodate

1999 (17 Dec). Litho. P 13½.
5   **4**   80y. multicoloured .... 2·20   1·50
        a. Pane. No. 5×10, with outer edges
          imperf .... 21·00

5 Trees and River

(Des Kosugou Fusae and Satou Mitusrou. Litho)

2000 (3 Apr). Cherry Trees. T **5** and similar horiz design. Multicoloured P 13½.
6   80y. Type **5**.. 2·50   1·70
        a. Vert strip of 4. Nos. 6/7, 9 and 11.... 10·50
        b. Sheet of 20. No. 6a×3, No. 8×4,
           No. 10×4.. 45·00
7   80y. Tree, central, Iwate............................. 2·50   1·70
8   80y. Group of trees, Fukishima................. 2·50   1·70
9   80y. Tree, left, Miyagi .... 2·50   1·70
10   80y. Cherry blossom, Aomori .... 2·50   1·70
11   80y. Group of trees with spreading
          branches, Yamagata......................... 2·50   1·70
6/11 Set of 6 .... 15·00   10·00
    Nos. 6/11 were also issued by Yamagata, Iwate, Miyagi, Aomori and Fukishima on 3 April 2000.

6 Kujuku Island

(Des Goshima Masawo. Photo)

2000 (7 July). P 13½.
12   **6**   80y. multicoloured .... 2·75   1·80
        a. Pane. No.12×10, with outer edges
          imperf .... 27·00

7 Igloo with Dog and Children

(Des Yaguchi Takao. Litho)

2001 (1 Oct). Kamakura Igloo. P 13½.
13   **7**   80y. multicoloured .... 2·50   1·70

8 Butterbur Flower (Akita)

(Des Sakuraba Toshihiro (Aomori), Sawaguchi Ken (Iwate), Izawa Kiyoshi (Miyagi), Konno Goro (Akita), Sato Kousen (Yamagata) or Kobayashi Goro (Fukushima). Photo).

2004 (19 Mar). Prefectural Flowers. T **8** and similar horiz design. Multicoloured P 13½.
14   50y. Type **8**... 1·60   1·10
15   50y. Paulownia (Iwate) .... 1·60   1·10
16   50y. Japanese Bush Clover (Miyagi) .... 1·60   1·10
17   50y. Apple Blossom (Aomori) .... 1·60   1·10
18   50y. Safflower (Yamagata) .... 1·60   1·10
19   50y. Alpine Rose (*Rhododendron*
          ferrugineum) (Fukushima)................. 1·60   1·10
14/19 Set of 6... 9·50   6·50
    Nos. 14/19 were also issued by Yamagata, Iwate, Miyagi, Aomori and Fukushima on 19 March 2004.

9 Kanto Festival

(Des Taguchi Takahiro. Litho)

2004 (1 June). 400th Anniv of Akita City. T **9** and similar vert design. Multicoloured. Litho. P 13½.

20		50y. Type **9**	1·60	1·10
		a. Pair. Nos. 20/1	3·50	3·50
21		50y. Namahage (new year's eve demon costume)	1·60	1·10

Nos. 20/1 were issued in horizontal *se-tenant* pairs within the sheet, each pair forming a composite design.

Aomori

1 Apples

1989 (2 Oct). Litho. P 13.

1	**1**	62y. multicoloured	1·30	60

1990 (27 Apr). Litho. P 13½.

2		62y. As Japan Type **1435**	1·20	80

2 Rapids, Oirase

1993 (22 Sept). Photo. P 13½.

3	**2**	62y. multicoloured	1·50	1·00
		a. Pane. No. 3×10, with outer edges imperf	14·00	

3 Nebuta Festival

1996 (23 July). Litho. P 13½.

4	**3**	80y. multicoloured	2·10	1·40

1998 (13 Nov). Litho. P 13.

5	**1**	80y. multicoloured	2·10	1·40
		a. Pane. No. 5×10, with outer edges imperf	20·00	

4 Shirakami Mountains

1999 (6 Sept). Litho. P 13½.

6	**4**	80y. multicoloured	2·10	1·40
		a. Pane. No. 6×10, with outer edges imperf	20·00	

5 Cherry Blossom

(Des Kosugou Fusae and Satou Mitusrou. Litho)

2000 (3 Apr). Cherry Trees. T **5** and similar horiz design. Multicoloured P 13½.

7		80y. Type **5**	2·50	1·70
		a. Sheet of 20. Nos. 8a×3, 7×4, 9×4....	45·00	—
8		80y. Tree, central, Iwate	2·50	1·70
		a. Strip of 4. Nos. 8, 10/12	10·50	
9		80y. Group of trees, Fukishima	2·50	1·70
10		80y. Tree, left, Miyagi	2·50	1·70
11		80y. Trees and river, Akita	2·50	1·70
12		80y. Group of trees with spreading branches, Yamagata	2·50	1·70
7/12 *Set of* 4			15·00	10·00

Nos. 7/12 were also issued by Yamagata, Iwate, Miyagi, Akita and Fukushima on 3 April 2000.

6 Mount Iwaki and Apples

(Des Satou Katsunori. Photo)

2002 (23 Oct). P 13½.

13	**6**	80y. multicoloured	2·20	1·50

7 Speed Skater and Ski Jumper

(Des Kaifuchi Junko. Photo)

2003 (24 Jan). Winter Asian Games, Aomori. P 13½.

14	**7**	50y. multicoloured	1·60	1·10

8 Apple Blossom (Aomori)

(Des Sakuraba Toshihiro (Aomori), Sawaguchi Ken (Iwate), Izawa Kiyoshi (Miyagi), Konno Goro (Akita), Sato Kousen (Yamagata) or Kobayashi Goro (Fukushima). Photo)

2004 (19 Mar). Prefecture Flowers. T **8** and similar horiz design. Multicoloured. P 13½.

15		50y. Type **8**	1·60	1·10
16		50y. Paulownia (Iwate)	1·60	1·10
17		50y. Japanese Bush Clover (Miyagi)	1·60	1·10
18		50y. Butterbur Flower (Akita)	1·60	1·10
19		50y. Safflower (Yamagata)	1·60	1·10
20		50y. Alpine Rose (*Rhododendron ferrugineum*) (Fukushima)	1·60	1·10
15/20	*Set of 6*		9·50	6·50

Nos. 15/20 were also issued by Yamagata, Iwate, Miyagi, Akita and Fukushima on 19 March 2004.

9 Apples (Aomori)

(Des Matsuda Hiromi. Photo)

2005 (28 June). Fruits of Tohoku. T **9** and similar horiz design. Multicoloured. P 13½.

21		50y. Type **9**	1·60	1·10
		a. Horiz strip of 4. Nos. 21/4	6·75	
22		50y. Apple (Iwate)	1·60	1·10
23		50y. Cherry (Yamagata)	1·60	1·10
24		50y. Peach (Fukushima)	1·60	1·10
21/24	*Set of 4*		6·50	4·50

Nos. 21/4 were issued in horizontal *se-tenant* strips of four stamps within the sheet.

Nos. 21/4 were also issued by Yamagata, Iwate and Fukushima on 28 June 2005.

Chiba

1 Raccoons

1989 (27 Oct). Litho. P 13.

1	1	62y. multicoloured	1·30	60

1990 (27 Apr). Litho. P 13½.

2	62y. As Japan Type **1445**	1·20	80

2 Woods in Autumn

1993 (1 Oct). Photo. P 13½.

3	2	41y. multicoloured	1·30	90
		a. Pane. No. 3×10, with outer edges imperf	13·50	

3 Cows

1995 (21 Nov). Holstein Show. Litho. P 13½.

4	**3**	80y. multicoloured	1·80	1·20
		a. Pane. No. 4×10, with outer edges imperf	17·00	

4 Tunnel Entrance

1997 (18 Dec). Tokyo-Wan Aqualine. T **4** and similar vert design. Multicoloured. Litho. P 13½.

5		80y. Type **4**	1·80	1·20
		a. Pair. Nos. 5/6	3·75	3·75
		b. Pane. Nos. 5/6, each×5, with outer edges imperf	17·00	
6		80y. Tunnel entrance (different)	1·80	1·20

Nos. 5/6 were issued in horizontal *se-tenant* pairs within the sheet.

Nos. 5/6 were also issued by Kanagawa on 18 December 1997.

5 Ooga Lotus Blossom

1999 (16 July). Litho. P 13½.

7	**5**	80y. multicoloured	2·10	1·40
		a. Pane. No. 7×10, with outer edges imperf	20·00	

6 Flowers, Trees and Children floating on Bubbles

(Des Koide Masaki. Photo)

2003 (16 May). National Afforestation Campaign. P 13½.

8	**6**	50y. multicoloured	1·60	1·10

7 Rose and Mount
Tsukubasan

(Des Ohya Takayumi. Photo)

2004 (23 June). Flowers of Kanto (1st issue). T **7** and similar vert designs. Multicoloured. P 13½.

9		50y. Type **7**	1·60	1·10
		a. Vert strip of 5. Nos. 9/13	8·25	
10		50y. Yoshi azalea and Lake Chuzenjiko	1·60	1·10
11		50y. Japanese azalea and Mt. Akagisan	1·60	1·10
12		50y. Primrose and Tajimagahara native primrose field	1·60	1·10
13		50y. Rape blossom and Nojimazaki lighthouse	1·60	1·10
9/13 *Set of 5*			8·00	5·50

Nos. 9/13 were issued in vertical strips of five stamps within the sheet.

Nos. 9/13 were also issued by Tochigi, Saitama, Gunma and Ibaraki on 23 June 2004.

See also Nos. 14/18.

8 Sunflowers at
Hana-hotaru
(Chiba)

(Des Ozaki Shingo. Photo)

2005 (23 June). Flowers of Kanto (2nd issue). T **8** and similar vert designs. Multicoloured. P 13½.

14		50y. Type **8**	1·60	1·10
		a. Vert strip of 5. Nos. 14/18	8·25	
15		50y. Nikko-kisuge (Nikko day lily) and Kirifuri Heights (Tochigi)	1·60	1·10
16		50y. Azaleas, Tsutsujigaoka Park (Gunma)	1·60	1·10
17		50y. Bush clover, Kairakuen garden (Ibaraki)	1·60	1·10
18		50y. Allspice flowers and Mt. Bukousan (Saitama)	1·60	1·10
14/18 *Set of 5*			8·00	5·50

Nos. 14/18 were issued in vertical strips of five stamps within the sheet.

Nos. 14/18 were also issued by Gunma, Saitama, Tochigi and Ibaraki on 23 June 2005.

Ehime

1 Building Façade

1989 (1 June). Dogo Spa. Photo. P 13.

1	**1**	62y. multicoloured	1·30	90

1990 (27 Apr). Litho. P 13½.

2		62y. As Japan Type **1471**	2·40	1·60

2 Kurushima Strait

1992 (23 June). Photo. P 13½.

3	**2**	62y. multicoloured	1·50	90
		a. Pane. No. 3×10, with outer edges imperf	14·50	

3 Nishiumi Marine Park

1996 (1 July). Photo. P 13½.

4	**3**	80y. multicoloured	2·10	1·40
		a. Pane. No. 4×10, with outer edges imperf	20·00	

1999 (1 Feb). Dogo Spa. Photo. P 13.

5	**1**	80y. multicoloured	2·10	1·40

4 Pagoda and
Bridge

1999 (26 Apr). Shimanami Highway and Bridges. T **4** and similar vert design. Multicoloured. Photo. P 13½.

6		80y. Type **4**	1·80	1·20
		a. Pair. Nos. 6/7	3·75	3·75
		b. Block of 10. Nos. 6/15	17·00	
7		80y. Islands	1·80	1·20
8		80y. Single span bridge	1·80	1·20
		a. Pair. Nos. 8/9	3·75	3·75
9		80y. Bridge pier at right	1·80	1·20
10		80y. Roadway and pier	1·80	1·20
		a. Pair. Nos. 10/11	3·75	3·75
11		80y. Ships	1·80	1·20
12		80y. Suspension wires and bridge	1·80	1·20
		a. Pair. Nos. 12/13	3·75	3·75
13		80y. Aerial view of bridge	1·80	1·20
14		80y. Suspension bridge from below	1·80	1·20
		a. Pair. Nos. 14/15	3·75	3·75
15		80y. Semi-circular bridge	1·80	1·20
6/15 *Set of* 10			18·00	12·00

Nos. 6/7, 8/9, 10/11, 12/13 and 14/15 were issued in horizontal *se-tenant* pairs within blocks of ten stamps within the sheet.

Nos. 6/15 were also issued by Hiroshima on 26 April 1999.

5 Uwajima Castle

(Des Kikuchi Akira. Photo)

2000 (28 Apr). P 13½.

16　**5**　80y. multicoloured .... 2·50　1·70

6 Masaoka Shiki
and Matsuyama
Castle

(Des Kikuchi Akira. Photo)

2001 (21 Sept). Death Centenary (2002) of Masaoka Shiki (haiku
poet). T **6** and similar vert design. Multicoloured. P 13½.

17　　50y. Type **6**...................................... 1·60　1·10

　　　a. Pair. Nos. 17/18 .... 3·50　3·50

18　　50y. *Bocchasn* locomotive and Dogo
　　　Spa .... 1·60　1·10

Nos. 17/18 were issued in *se-tenant* pairs within sheetlets of ten
stamps with enlarged illustrated margin.

7 Mikan (mandarin
oranges) and Sata-
misaki Promontory
(Ehime)

(Des Kikuchi Akira. Photo)

2002 (20 Mar). T **7** and similar vert designs. Multicoloured. P 13½.

19　　50y. Type **7**...................................... 1·50　1·00

　　　a. Vert strip of 4. Nos. 19/22 .... 6·25

20　　50y. Sudachi (sour citrus fruit) and Mt.
　　　Tsurugisan (Tokushima)................... 1·50　1·00

21　　50y. Yamamomo (bayberry) and Tengu
　　　highland (Kochi)........................... 1·50　1·00

22　　50y. Olive and Shodoshima island
　　　(Kagawa) .... 1·50　1·00

19/22 *Set of 4*... 6·00　4·00

Nos. 19/22 were issued in vertical strips of four stamps within the
sheet.

Nos. 19/22 were also issued by Tokushima , Kochi and Kagawa on
20 March 2002.

8 Zizouji Temple

2005 (8 July). Cultural Heritage. Shizuoka Temples (2nd series). T **8**
and similar vert designs. Multicoloured. Litho. P 13½.

23　　80y. Type **8**...................................... 2·50　1·70

　　　a. Sheet of 20. Nos. 23/42 .... 45·00

24　　80y. Seated Buddha, Anrakuji Temple... 2·50　1·70

25　　80y. Inscribed belfry gateway, Jurakuji
　　　Temple....................................... 2·50　1·70

26　　80y. Double roofed gateway,
　　　Kumadaniji Temple........................... 2·50　1·70

27　　80y. Pagoda, Yakuoji Temple................ 2·50　1·70

28　　80y. Statues, ramp, lanterns and
　　　pagoda, Hotsumisakiji Temple....... 2·50　1·70

29　　80y. Gateway and long steep steps,
　　　Shinjouji Temple............................. 2·50　1·70

30　　80y. Path, gateway, steps and main
　　　temple, Kongochoji Temple............ 2·50　1·70

31　　80y. Buddha seated on peacock,
　　　Ryukoji Temple .... 2·50　1·70

32　　80y. Bell and autumn colour,
　　　Butsumokuji Temple........................ 2·50　1·70

33　　80y. Dragon, Meisekiji Temple................ 2·50　1·70

34　　80y. Steps and many roofed buildings,
　　　Daihouji Temple............................ 2·50　1·70

35　　80y. Carved decorative gable,
　　　Kokubunji Temple........................... 2·50　1·70

36　　80y. Leafless tree and snow-covered
　　　building, Yokomineji Temple .... 2·50　1·70

37　　80y. Buddha, Kouonji Temple................ 2·50　1·70

38　　80y. Courtyard and building, Houjuji
　　　Temple .... 2·50　1·70

39　　80y. Inscribed pillars and gateway,
　　　Douryuji Temple............................. 2·50　1·70

40　　80y. Wall mounted statues, Goushouji
　　　Temple .... 2·50　1·70

41　　80y. Eagle surmounting gateway,
　　　Tennouji Temple............................. 2·50　1·70

42　　80y. Courtyard with stone lined path
　　　and building, Kokubunji Temple .... 2·50　1·70

23/42 *Set of 20*....................................... 50·00　34·00

Nos. 23/42 were issued in *se-tenant* sheets of 20 stamps.

Nos. 23/42 were also issued by Tokushima, Kochi and Kagawa on
8 July 2005.

Fukui

1990 (27 Apr). Flowers. Litho. P 13½.

1　　62y. As Japan Type **1453**.......................... 1·20　80

1 Girl wearing
Glasses

1991 (1 Oct). Litho. P 13.

2　**1**　62y. multicoloured .... 1·50　90

2 Beach and Trees,
Kehi-no-matsubara

1994 (1 Sept). Litho. P 13½.

3　**2**　50y. multicoloured .... 1·50　1·00

　　　a. Pane. No. 3×10, with outer edges
　　　imperf .... 14·50

237

3 Murasaki Shikibu
(novelist and poet)

1996 (24 June). Litho. P 13½.
4	3	80y. multicoloured	2·10	1·40
		a. Pane. No. 4×10, with outer edges imperf	20·00	

4 Dinosaur

1999 (22 Feb). Dinosaurs. T **4** and similar vert design. Multicoloured. Photo. P 13½.
5	80y. Type **4**	1·50	1·00
	a. Pair. Nos. 5/6	4·50	4·50
	b. Pane. Nos. 5/6, each×5, with outer edges imperf	20·00	
6	80y. Raptors	2·10	1·40

Nos. 5/6 were issued in horizontal *se-tenant* pairs within the sheet, each pair forming a composite design.

5 Zuwai (snow)
Crab

1999 (4 Nov). T **5** and similar vert design. Multicoloured. Litho. P 13½.
7	80y. Type **5**	2·10	1·40
	a. Pair. Nos. 7/8	4·50	4·50
	b. Pane. Nos. 7/8, each×5, with outer edges imperf	20·00	
8	80y. Cliffs, Tojinbo	2·10	1·40

Nos. 7/8 were issued in horizontal *se-tenant* pairs within the sheet.

6 Narcissi Blooms

(Des Ogata Masanao. Litho)

2001 (6 Nov). Narcissi. T **6** and similar vert design. Multicoloured. P 13½.
9	50y. Type **6**	1·60	1·10
	a. Pair. Nos. 9/8	4·25	4·25

	b. Pane. Nos. 9/8, each×5, with outer edges imperf	20·00	
10	80y. Flowers and cliffs	2·50	1·70

Nos. 9/10 were issued in horizontal *se-tenant* pairs within the sheet.

7 Tulip

(Des Kawanishi Shigeharu. Litho)

2005 (1 Apr). Flowers of Hokuriku. T **7** and similar vert designs. Multicoloured. P 13½.
11	50y. Type **7**	1·60	1·10
	a. Horiz strip of 4. Nos. 11/14	6·75	
12	50y. Hydrangea	1·60	1·10
13	50y. Rhododendron	1·60	1·10
14	50y. Lily	1·60	1·10
11/14	*Set of 4*	6·50	4·50

Nos. 11/14 were issued in horizontal *se-tenant* strips of four stamps within the sheet.

Nos. 11/14 were also issued by Toyama and Ishikawa on 1 April 2005.

Fukuoka

1990 (27 Apr). Litho. P 13½.
1	62y. As Japan Type **1473**	1·20	80

1 Hurdler

1990 (3 Sept). 45th National Athletics Meet. Photo. P 13.
2	1	62y. multicoloured	1·20	80

2 Songbird and
Lake

1992 (8 May). Afforestation. Photo. P 13½.
3	2	41y. multicoloured	90	60

3 Kurodabushi

1992 (3 Aug). Litho. P 13½.
4	**3**	62y. multicoloured	1·20	80

4 Fort and Map

1997 (3 June). T **4** and similar vert designs. Multicoloured. Litho.
P 13½.
5	80y. Type **4**..	1·80	1·20
	a. Horiz strip of 4. Nos. 5/8	7·50	
6	80y. Early rail way and map.....................	1·80	1·20
7	80y. Interchange and map........................	1·80	1·20
8	80y. Building and map	1·80	1·20
5/8 *Set of* 4..		7·20	4·75

Nos. 5/8 were issued in horizontal *se-tenant* strips of four stamps within the sheet, each strip forming a composite design.

Nos. 5/8 were also issued by Nagasaki and Saga on 3 June 1997.

5 Hakata Gion
Festival

1999 (1 July). Litho. P 13½.
9	**5**	80y. multicoloured	2·10	1·40
		a. Pane. No. 9×10, with outer edges imperf	20·00	

6 Hakata Doll

(Des Ookubo Kouzo. Litho.)

2000 (2 Aug). P 13½.
10	**6**	80y. multicoloured	2·75	1·90
		a. Pane. No. 10×10, with outer edges imperf	27·00	

7 Ooe Kouwaka-
mai Dance

(Des Harada Kunsuke. Litho.)

2001 (19 Jan). P 13½.
11	**7**	80y. multicoloured	2·40	1·60
		a. Pane. No. 11×10, with outer edges imperf	23·00	

8 Kitakyushu Expo-
Festival

(Des Mkita Yoshiaki. Photo)

2001 (4 July). P 13½.
12	**8**	80y. multicoloured	2·40	1·60
		a. Pane. No. 12×10, with outer edges imperf	23·00	

9 Ume Blossom
and Dazaifu-
Tenmangu Shrine
(Fukuoka)

(Des Iwasaki Chizuru. Photo)

2005 (1 June). Flowers and Scenery of Kyushu (1st series). T **9** and similar vert designs. Multicoloured. Litho. P 13½.
13	50y. Type **9**..	1·60	1·10
	a. Pair. Nos. 13/14	3·50	3·50
	b. Block of 10. Nos. 13/22	15·00	
14	50y. Sakura (cherry blossoms) and Kanmon bridge (Fukuoka)..............	1·60	1·10
15	50y. Kusunohana (camphor blossoms) and Ariake Sea (Saga)......................	1·60	1·10
	a. Pair. Nos. 15/16	3·50	3·50
16	50y. Unzen-Tsutsuji (azaleas) and Mt. Fugendake (Nagasaki)......................	1·60	1·10
17	50y. Tulips and Huis Ten Bosch (Nagasaki)................................	1·60	1·10
	a. Pair. Nos. 17/18	3·50	3·50
18	50y. Rindou (gentians) and Mt. Aso (Kumamoto)..............................	1·60	1·10
19	50y. Ume blossoms and Mt. Takasaki (Ooita)....................................	1·60	1·10
	a. Pair. Nos. 19/20	3·50	3·50
20	50y. amayu (crinums) and Nichinan beach (Miyazaki)	1·60	1·10
21	50y. Miyama-Kirishima (azaleas) and Kirishima mountains (Kagoshima)	1·60	1·10
	a. Pair. Nos. 21/22	3·50	3·50
22	50y. Hibiscus and Adan (screw-pine) (Kagoshima)............................	1·60	1·10
13/22 *Set of* 10		16·00	11·00

Nos. 13/22 were issued in *se-tenant* blocks of ten stamps within the sheet.

Nos. 13/22 were also issued by Saga, Nagasaki, Kumamoto, Oita, Miyazaki and Kagoshima on 1 June 2005.

Fukushima

1990 (27 Apr). Flowers. Litho. P 13½.
1   62y. As Japan Type 1440............................ 1·20   80

1 Peaches

1990 (1 June). Litho. P 13.
2   **1**   62y. multicoloured .... 1·20   80

2 Peony

1996 (26 Apr). Peonies of Sukagawa. Litho. P 13½.
3   **2**   80y. multicoloured .... 1·80   1·20
          a. Pane. No. 3×10, with outer edges
          imperf .... 17·00

3 Streamers

1999 (14 May). Summer Festivals. T **3** and similar vert design. Multicoloured. Photo. P 13½.
4   80y. Type **3**...................... 2·10   1·40
          a. Pair. Nos. 4/5 .... 4·50   4·50
          b. Pane. Nos. 4/5, each×5, with outer
          edges imperf .... 20·00
5   80y. Festival goers and banners .... 2·10   1·40
    Nos. 4/5 were issued in horizontal *se-tenant* pairs within the sheet, each pair forming a composite design.
    Nos. 4/5 were also issued by Miyagi on 14 May 1999.

4 Kiku-ningyo
(chrysanthemum
petal doll)

1999 (1 Oct). Litho. P 13½.
6   **4**   80y. multicoloured .... 2·10   1·40

5 Group of Trees

(Des Kosugou Fusae and Satou Mitusrou. Litho)

2000 (3 Apr). Cherry Trees. T **5** and similar horiz design. Multicoloured P 13½.
7   80y. Type **5**........................ 2·50   1·70
          b. Sheet of 20. Nos. 8a×3, 7×4, 11×4. 5·00
8   80y. Tree, central, Iwate...................... 2·50   1·70
          a. Strip of 4. Nos. 8/10, 12 .... 10·50
9   80y. Group of trees, Yamagata (different) 2·50   1·70
10   80y. Tree, left, Miyagi .... 2·50   1·70
11   80y. Cherry blossom, Aomori .... 2·50   1·70
12   80y. Trees and river, Akita........................ 2·50   1·70
7/12 *Set of 6* .... 15·00   10·00
    Nos. 7/12 were also issued by Yamagata, Iwate, Miyagi, Akita and Aomori on 3 April 2000.

6 Festival Goers

(Des Oomura Tokiko. Photo)

2000 (1 Dec). Hata Festival, Kohata. P 13½.
13   **6**   80y. multicoloured .... 2·75   1·80
          a. Pane. No. 13×10, with outer edges
          imperf .... 27·00

7 Mount. Bandaisan
and Dream Flying
Machine

(Des Isono Hiroo. Photo)

2001 (10 Apr). Fukushima Expo. P 13½.
14   **7**   80y. multicoloured .... 2·40   1·60
          a. Pane. No. 14×10, with outer edges
          imperf .... 23·00

8 Boardwalk
through Marshland,
Ozegahara

2002 (28 June). Oze. T **8** and similar vert design. Multicoloured.
Photo. P 13½.
15   50y. Type **8**.......................................   1·50   1·00
            a. Pair. Nos. 15/16 ....   3·25   3·25
16   50y. Day lilies, Ohe-shitsugen...............   1·50   1·00
    Nos. 15/16 were issued in horizontal *se-tenant* pairs within the
sheet.

9 Tsurugajo Castle
and Persimmons

(Des Satou Katsunori. Photo)

2003 (1 July). P 13½.
17   **9**   80y. multicoloured ....   2·40   1·60

10 Alpine Rose
(*Rhododendron
ferrugineum*)
(Fukushima)

(Des Sakuraba Toshihiro (Aomori), Sawaguchi Ken (Iwate), Izawa
Kiyoshi (Miyagi), Konno Goro (Akita), Sato Kousen (Yamagata) or
Kobayashi Goro (Fukushima). Photo)

2004 (19 Mar). Prefectural Flowers. T **10** and similar horiz design.
Multicoloured P 13½.
18   50y. Type **10**.......................................   1·60   1·10
19   50y. Paulownia (Iwate) ....   1·60   1·10
20   50y. Japanese Bush Clover (Miyagi) ....   1·60   1·10
21   50y. Butterbur Flower (Akita)..................   1·60   1·10
22   50y. Safflower (Yamagata) ....   1·60   1·10
23   50y. Apple Blossom (Aomori) ....   1·60   1·10
18/23 *Set of* 6..   9·50   6·50
Nos. 18/23 were also issued by Yamagata, Iwate, Miyagi, Aomori
and Akita on 19 March 2004.

11 Peach
(Fukushima)

(Des Matsuda Hiromi. Photo)

2005 (28 June). Fruits of Tohoku. T **11** and similar horiz design.
Multicoloured. P 13½.
24   50y. Type **11**.......................................   1·60   1·10
            a. Horiz strip of 4. Nos. 24/7 ....   6·75
25   50y. Apple (Iwate) ....   1·60   1·10
26   50y. Cherry (Yamagata)...........................   1·60   1·10
27   50y. Apples (Aomori) ....   1·60   1·10
24/27 *Set of* 4...   6·50   4·50

Nos. 24/7 were issued in horizontal *se-tenant* strips of four stamps
within the sheet.
Nos. 24/7 were also issued by Aomori, Iwate and Fukushima on 28
June 2005.

Gifu

1990 (27 Apr). Flowers. Litho. P 13½.
1   62y. As Japan Type **1454**..........................   1·50   1·00

1 Bridge at Spring
Festival

1990 (9 Oct). Takayama. T **1** and similar vert designs. Multicoloured.
Litho. P 13.
2   62y. Type **1**..   1·50   60
            a. Horiz strip of 4. Nos. 2/5 ....   6·25
3   62y. Ptarmigans................................   1·50   60
4   62y. Lantern and procession....................   1·50   60
5   62y. Houses in snow...............................   1·50   60
2/5 *Set of* 4...   6·00   2·40
Nos. 2/5 were issued in horizontal *se-tenant* strips of four stamps
within the sheet.

2 Flowers

1995 (26 Apr). Litho. P 13½.
6   **2**   80y. multicoloured ....   1·90   1·30
            a. Pane. No. 6×10, with outer edges
            imperf ....   18·00

3 Bridge at Spring
Festival (As Type **1**)

1995 (2 Oct). Hida. T **3** and similar vert designs. Multicoloured. Litho.
P 13.
7   80y. Type **3**..   1·80   60
            a. Horiz strip of 4. Nos. 7/10 ....   7·50
8   80y. Ptarmigans (As No. 3) ....   1·80   60
9   80y. Lantern and procession (As No. 4).   1·80   60
10   80y. Houses in snow (As No. 5).................   1·80   60
7/10 *Set of* 4..   7·25   2·40
Nos. 7/10 were issued in horizontal *se-tenant* strips of four stamps
within the sheet.
Nos. 7/10 differ from Nos. 2/5 both in the face value and an
inscription 'Beautiful Hida' situated along the lower edge of the
stamps (7/10).

4 Okaisho-Daiko
(ritual drum)

1998 (19 Mar). Photo. P 13½.
11	**4**	80y. multicoloured	2·10	1·40
		a. Pane. No. 11×10, with outer edges		
		imperf	20·00	

5 Ancient Cherry Tree

1999 (16 Mar). Photo. P 13½.
12	**5**	80y. multicoloured	2·10	1·40
		a. Pane. No. 12×10, with outer edges		
		imperf	20·00	

6 Tanigumi-Odori Folk
Dance

(Des Hattori Tetsuo. Photo)

2001 (28 Sept). Tradition and Nature of Ibi. T **6** and similar vert design. Multicoloured. P 13½.
13		50y. Type **6**.....................................	1·60	1·10
		a. Pair. Nos. 13/14	3·50	3·50
		b. Pane. Nos. 13/14, each×5, with		
		outer edges imperf	15·00	
14		50y. Persimmons, Fuyugaki......................	1·60	1·10

Nos. 13/14 were issued in horizontal *se-tenant* pairs within the sheet.

7 Gujou-odori
Dance

(Des Mizuno Masao. Photo)

2002 (1 July). P 13½.
15	**7**	50y. multicoloured	1·80	1·20

8 Cormorant
Fishing

(Des Sagamiya Toube. Photo)

2003 (1 May). Cormorant Fishing on Nagaragawa River and Gifu Castle. T **8** and similar vert design. Multicoloured. P 13½.
16		50y. Type **8**.......................................	1·60	1·10
		a. Pair. Nos. 16/17	3·50	3·50
17		50y. Gifu Castle	1·60	1·10

Nos. 16/17 were issued in horizontal *se-tenant* pairs within the sheet, each pair forming a composite design.

Gunma

1990 (27 Apr). Flowers. Litho. P 13½.
1		62y. As Japan Type **1443**.........................	1·20	80

1 Tortoise and the
Hare

1991 (23 Oct). Litho. P 13.
2	**1**	62y. multicoloured	1·50	90

2 Waterfall

1994 (6 June). Photo. P 13½.
3	**2**	80y. multicoloured	1·90	1·10
		a. Pane. No. 3×10, with outer edges		
		imperf	18·00	

3 River, Tree and
Mountain, Oze

1998 (21 May). T **3** and similar vert design. Multicoloured. Photo. P 13½.

4	80y. Type **3**	2·10	1·40
	a. Pair. Nos. 4/5	4·50	4·50
	b. Pane. Nos. 4/5, each×5, with outer edges imperf	20·00	
5	80y. Trees in autumn	2·10	1·40

Nos. 4/5 were issued in horizontal *se-tenant* pairs within the sheet.

4 Flints

1999 (17 Sept). Litho. P 13½.

6	**4**	80y. multicoloured	2·10	1·40
		a. Pane. No. 6×10, with outer edges imperf	20·00	

5 Railway Bridge

2000 (15 Dec). Railways. T **5** and similar vert design. Multicoloured. Litho. P 13½.

7	50y. Type **5**	1·60	1·10
	a. Pair. Nos. 7/8	3·50	3·50
8	50y. Railway buildings	1·60	1·10

Nos. 7/8 were issued in horizontal *se-tenant* pairs within the sheet.

6 Azuma Rhododendron and Tanigawa Mountain

2002 (28 June). Mount Tanigawadake. T **6** and similar vert design. Multicoloured. P 13½.

9	80y. Type **6**	2·20	1·50
	a. Pair. Nos. 9/10	4·75	4·75
10	80y. Ichi-no kurasawa in autumn	2·20	1·50

Nos. 9/10 were issued in horizontal *se-tenant* pairs within the sheet.

7 Yoshi Azalea and Lake Chuzenjiko

(Des Ohya Takayumi. Photo)

2004 (23 June). Flowers of Kanto (1st issue). T **7** and similar vert designs. Multicoloured. P 13½.

11	50y. Type **7**	1·60	1·10
	a. Vert strip of 5. Nos. 11/15	8·25	
12	50y. Rose and Mount Tsukubasan	1·60	1·10
13	50y. Japanese azalea and Mt. Akagisan	1·60	1·10
14	50y. Primrose and Tajimagahara native primrose field	1·60	1·10
15	50y. Rape blossom and Nojimazaki lighthouse	1·60	1·10
11/15	*Set of 5*	8·00	5·50

Nos. 11/15 were issued in vertical strips of five stamps within the sheet.

Nos. 11/15 were also issued by Tochigi, Saitama, Gunma and Ibaraki on 23 June 2004.

See Also Nos. 16/20.

8 Azaleas, Tsutsujigaoka Park (Gunma)

(Des Ozaki Shingo. Photo)

2005 (23 June). Flowers of Kanto (2nd issue). T **8** and similar vert designs. Multicoloured. P 13½.

16	50y. Type **8**	1·60	1·10
	a. Vert strip of 5. Nos. 16/20	8·25	
17	50y. Nikko-kisuge (Nikko day lily) and Kirifuri Heights (Tochigi)	1·60	1·10
18	50y. Sunflowers at Hana-hotaru (Chiba)	1·60	1·10
19	50y. Bush clover, Kairakuen garden (Ibaraki)	1·60	1·10
20	50y. Allspice flowers and Mt. Bukousan (Saitama)	1·60	1·10
16/20	*Set of 5*	8·00	5·50

Nos. 16/20 were issued in vertical strips of five stamps within the sheet.

Nos. 16/20 were also issued by Tochigi, Saitama, Chiba and Ibaraki on 23 June 2005.

Hiroshima

1 Junk and Islands

1989 (7 July). Setonikai. Type **1** and similar vert design. Multicoloured. Litho. P 13.

1	62y. Type **1**	1·30	60
	a. Pair. Nos. 1/2	2·75	2·75
2	62y. Islands and building	1·30	60

Nos. 1/2 were issued in horizontal *se-tenant* pairs within the sheet, each pair forming a composite design.

1990 (27 Apr). Litho. P 13½.

3	62y. As Japan Type **1467**	1·20	80

2 Drummer

1993 (4 June). Hana-taue. Photo. P 13½.

4	**2**	62y. multicoloured	1·50	80

3 Gateway in Water

1998 (17 July). Inland Sea. T **3** and similar vert design. Multicoloured. Photo. P 13½.

5	80y. Type **3**	2·10	1·40
	a. Pair. Nos. 5/6	4·50	4·50
	b. Pane. Nos. 5/6, each×5, with outer edges imperf	20·00	
6	80y. Roadway and bridge	2·10	1·40

Nos. 5/6 were issued in horizontal *se-tenant* pairs within the sheet, each pair forming a composite design.

4 Ibara Railway

1999 (11 Jan). Photo. P 13½.

7	**4**	80y. multicoloured	2·10	1·40
	a. Pane. No. 7×10, with outer edges imperf	20·00	

No. 7 was also issued by Okayama on 11 January 1999.

5 Islands

1999 (26 Apr). Shimanami Highway and Bridges. T **5** and similar vert design. Multicoloured. Photo. P 13½.

8	80y. Type **5**	1·80	1·20
	a. Pair. Nos. 8/9	3·75	3·75
	b. Block of 10. Nos. 8/17	17·00	
9	80y. Pagoda and Bridge	1·80	1·20
10	80y. Single span bridge	1·80	1·20
	a. Pair. Nos. 10/11	3·75	3·75
11	80y. Bridge pier at right	1·80	1·20

12	80y. Roadway and pier	1·80	1·20
	a. Pair. Nos. 12/13	3·75	3·75
13	80y. Ships	1·80	1·20
14	80y. Suspension wires and bridge	1·80	1·20
	a. Pair. Nos. 14/15	3·75	3·75
15	80y. Aerial view of bridge	1·80	1·20
16	80y. Suspension bridge from below	1·80	1·20
	a. Pair. Nos. 16/17	3·75	3·75
17	80y. Semi-circular bridge	1·80	1·20
8/17 *Set of* 10		18·00	12·00

Nos. 8/9, 10/11, 12/13, 14/15 and 16/17 were issued in horizontal *se-tenant* pairs within blocks of ten stamps within the sheet. Nos. 8/17 were also issued by Ehime on 26 April 1999.

6 Momiji (maple leaves) and Itsukushima Shrine Gate

(Des Ozaki Shingo. Litho)

2000 (1 May). T **6** and similar vert designs. Multicoloured. P 13½.

18	50y. Type **6**	1·50	1·00
	a. Vert strip of 5. Nos. 18/22	7·75	
19	50y. Nijisseikinashi (Japanese pear tree) and Tottori dune	1·50	1·00
20	50y. Botan (peonies) and Izumo-taisha Shrine	1·50	1·00
21	50y. Momonohana (peach blossoms) and traditional houses in Kurashiki	1·50	1·00
22	50y. Natsumikan (summer-orange blossoms) and the sea	1·50	1·00
18/22 *Set of* 5		7·50	5·00

Nos. 18/22 were also issued by Tottori, Shimane, Okayama and Yamaguchi on 1 May 2000

7 Nukui Dam

(Des Ooe Kiyoharu. Litho)

2002 (22 Feb). Northern Hiroshima. T **7** and similar vert design. Multicoloured. P 13½.

23	80y. Type **7**	2·20	1·50
	a. Pair. Nos. 23/4	4·75	4·75
24	80y. On-bashi Bridge	2·20	1·50

Nos. 23/4 were issued in horizontal *se-tenant* pairs within the sheet.

8 Cenotaph for Atomic Bomb Victims (Memorial Monument for Hiroshima)

(Des Yuki Morihiko. Litho)

2005 (22 Apr). Peace Memorial Park. T **8** and similar vert design. Multicoloured. P 13½.

25	50y. Type **8**	1·60	1·10
	a. Pair. Nos. 25/6	3·50	3·50
26	50y. Peace Memorial Museum	1·60	1·10

Nos. 25/6 were issued in horizontal *se-tenant* pairs within the sheet.

Hokkaido

1 Building Façade

1989 (15 Aug). Prefectural Government. Photo. P 13.

1	**1**	62y. multicoloured	1·50	80

2 Runner

1989 (1 Sept). 44th National Athletic Meet. Photo. P 13.

2	**2**	62y. multicoloured	1·30	60

3 Ice Hockey Players

1990 (1 Mar). Second Asian Winter Games. Photo. P 13.

3	**3**	62y. multicoloured	1·20	85

1990 (27 Apr). Flowers. Litho. P 13½.

4	62y. As Japan Type **1434**	3·75	2·50

4 Cranes

1990 (30 Oct). Photo. P 13.

5	**4**	62y. multicoloured	1·50	80

5 Lily of the Valley

1991 (23 May). Flora. T **5** and similar vert designs. Multicoloured. Litho. P 13.

6	62y. Type **5**		1·20	80
	a. Horiz strip of 4. Nos. 6/9		5·00	
7	62y. Pink lilac		1·20	80
8	62y. Lilies		1·20	80
9	62y. Rowan berries in snow		1·20	80
6/9 *Set of* 4			4·75	3·25

Nos. 6/9 were issued in horizontal *se-tenant* strips of four stamps within the sheet.

6 Foxes

1992 (29 May). Photo. P 13½.

10	**6**	62y. multicoloured	1·50	70

7 Largha Seals

1993 (17 May). Litho. P 13½.

11	**7**	62y. multicoloured	1·30	90

8 Stag, Ezo-shika

1994 (7 June). Photo. P 13½.

12	**8**	50y. multicoloured	1·50	70
		a. Pane. No. 12×10, with outer edges imperf	14·50	

9 Chipmunks,
Ezoshimarisu

1995 (3 Mar). Photo. P 13½.
13   **9**   80y. multicoloured .... 1·90   1·30

10 Lady's Slipper
Orchid

1995 (7 July). Litho. P 13½.
14   **10**   80y. multicoloured .... 1·90   1·30
    a. Pane. No. 14×10, with outer edges
      imperf .... 18·00

11 Kurione (sea
angel)

1996 (6 Feb). Litho. P 13½.
15   **11**   80y. multicoloured .... 1·80   1·20
    a. Pane. No. 15×10, with outer edges
      imperf .... 17·00

12 Roses

1996 (5 July). Litho. P 13½.
16   **12**   80y. multicoloured .... 2·10   1·40

13 Flowers

1997 (25 Apr). Ezo-murasakitsutsuji. Photo. P 13½.
17   **13**   80y. multicoloured .... 2·10   1·40
    a. Pane. No. 17×10, with outer edges
      imperf .... 20·00

14 Stoat

1997 (30 May). Hokkaido Ermine. Photo. P 13½.
18   **14**   50y. multicoloured .... 1·30   90
    a. Pane. No. 18×10, with outer edges
      imperf .... 12·50

15 Snow-covered
Berries

1998 (5 Feb). Flora. T **15** and similar vert design. Multicoloured. Litho.
  P 13½.
19   80y. Type **15**.................................... 1·80   1·20
    a. Pair. Nos. 19/20 .... 3·75   3·75
    b. Pane. Nos. 19/20, each×5, with
      outer edges imperf .... 17·00
20   80y. Pink blossom .... 1·80   1·20
  Nos. 19/20 were issued in horizontal se-tenant pairs within the
sheet.

16 Ice-flows

1999 (5 Feb). Land of Snow (1st series). T **16** and similar vert designs.
  Multicoloured. Photo. P 13½.
21   50y. Type **16**.................................... 1·20   80
    a. Horiz strip of 4. Nos. 21/4.................. 6·75
22   50y. Cranes .... 1·20   80
23   80y. Snowflake .... 2·10   1·40
24   80y. Snowman .... 2·10   1·40
21/24 Set of 4... 6·50   4·75
  Nos. 21/4 were issued in horizontal se-tenant strips of four stamps
within the sheet.
  See also Nos. 42/5.

1999 (28 Apr). Flora. Vert designs as T **5**. Multicoloured. Litho. P 13.
25   80y. Lily (As Type **5**) .... 2·10   1·40
    a. Horiz strip of 4. Nos. 25/8.................. 8·75
26   80y. Pink lilac (As No. 7)..................... 2·10   1·40
27   80y. Lilies (As No. 8) .... 2·10   1·40
28   80y. Rowan berries in snow (As No. 9)... 2·10   1·40
25/28 Set of 4... 8·50   5·50
  Nos. 25/8 were issued in horizontal se-tenant strips of four stamps
within the sheet.

17 Lavender Field

1999 (25 May). Northern Paradise (1st series). T **17** and similar horiz design. Multicoloured. Litho. P 13½.
29 50y. Type **17** .... 1·60 1·10
30 80y. Cornfield .... 2·40 1·60
  See also Nos. 46/9.

1999 (25 June). Fauna. As T **6** and **7**. Multicoloured. Photo (No. 31) or Litho (No. 32). P 13½.
31 80y. Foxes (As Type **6**) .... 2·10 1·40
32 80y. Largha seals (As Type **7**) .... 2·10 1·40

18 Eagle

1999 (23 July). Birds. T **18** and similar vert designs. Multicoloured. Litho. P 13½.
33 50y. Type **18** .... 1·30 90
   a. Horiz strip of 4. Nos. 33/6 .... 5·75
34 50y. Puffin .... 1·30 90
35 50y. Owl .... 1·30 90
36 50y. Crane .... 1·30 90
33/36 Set of 4 .... 5·50 3·50
  Nos. 33/6 were issued in horizontal se-tenant strips of four stamps within the sheet.

19 Sweet Corn

1999 (17 Sept). Vegetables and Children. T **19** and similar vert designs. Multicoloured. Litho. P 13½.
37 50y. Type **19** .... 1·50 1·00
   a. Horiz strip of 4. Nos. 37/40 .... 6·25
38 50y. Potatoes .... 1·50 1·00
39 50y. Asparagus .... 1·50 1·00
40 50y. Squash .... 1·50 1·00
37/40 Set of 4 .... 6·00 4·00
  Nos. 37/40 were issued in horizontal se-tenant strips of four stamps within the sheet.

20 Sleigh

1999 (11 Nov). Santa Claus. Litho. P 13½.
41 **20** 80y. multicoloured .... 2·20 1·50
   a. Pane. No. 41×10, with outer edges imperf .... 21·00

21 Nusamai Bridge

(Des Fujikura Toyoaki. Photo)

2000 (7 Feb). Land of Snow (2nd series). T **21** and similar vert designs. Multicoloured. P 13½.
42 80y. Type **21** .... 2·40 1·60
   a. Horiz strip of 4. Nos. 42/5 .... 9·75
43 80y. Otaru canal .... 2·40 1·60
44 80y. Sapporo clock tower .... 2·40 1·60
45 80y. Orthodox Church, Hakodate .... 2·40 1·60
42/45 Set of 4 .... 9·50 6·50
  Nos. 42/5 were issued in horizontal se-tenant strips of four stamps within the sheet.

22 Potato Field and Barn

(Des Kanai Hideaki. Photo)

2000 (19 July). Northern Paradise (2nd series). T **22** and similar vert designs. Multicoloured. Litho. P 13½.
46 50y. Type **22** .... 1·60 1·10
   a. Pair. Nos. 46/7 .... 3·50 3·50
47 50y. Barn and potato field .... 1·60 1·10
48 80y.+20y. Houses and hay field .... 3·25 2·20
   a. Pair. Nos. 48/9 .... 6·75 6·75
49 80y.+20y. Hay field and barns .... 3·25 2·20
46/49 Set of 4 .... 9·75 6·50
  Nos. 46/7 and 48/9 were issued in se-tenant pairs within the sheet. Nos. 48/9, each carry a premium for the aid of victims of the eruption of Mt. Usu and were on sale at all Japanese Post Offices.

23 Sable

(Des Kanda Hiroshi. Litho)

2001 (6 Feb). Ezo Sable. P 13½.
50 **23** 80y. multicoloured .... 2·40 1·60
   a. Pane. No. 50×10, with outer edges imperf .... 23·00

24 Orchid

(Des Murano Michiko and Nishimura Masami. Litho)

2001 (22 June). Flowers of Hokkaido. T **24** and similar vert designs. Multicoloured. P 13½×imperf.

51	50y. Type **24**	1·50	1·00
	a. Pane. No. 51×10, with outer edges imperf	14·50	
52	50y. *Papaver fauriei*	1·50	1·00
	a. Pane, No. 52×10, with outer edges imperf	14·50	

25 Poplar Avenue

(Des Maehashi Yasuhiro. Litho)

2001 (3 Sept). Northern Landscape. T **25** and similar vert designs. Multicoloured. P 13½.

53	80y. Type **25**	2·40	1·60
	a. Pane. Nos. 53/4, each×5, with outer edges imperf	23·00	
54	80y. Statue of Dr. William Clark (founder of Sapporo Agricultural College), Hitsujigaoka Hill	2·40	1·60

26 Ezo Flying Squirrels

(Des Tobishima Yoshiaki. Litho)

2002 (5 Feb). P 13½.

55	**26**	80y. multicoloured	2·20	1·50

27 Tulip Field and Windmill

(Des Nishimura Masami. Photo)

2002 (25 Apr). Colouring the North. T **27** and similar vert designs. Multicoloured. P 13½.

56	80y. Type **27**	2·20	1·50
	a. Pair. Nos. 56/7	4·75	4·75
57	80y. Sunflowers and field showing name of 'Hokuryu' (town)	2·20	1·50

Nos. 56/7 were issued in *se-tenant* pairs within the sheet.

28 Ainu Design

(Des Nishimura Masami. Photo)

2003 (5 Feb). Cultural and Natural Heritage. T **28** and similar vert designs. Multicoloured. P 13½.

58	80y. Type **28**	2·40	1·60
	a. Pair. Nos. 58/9	5·00	5·00
59	80y. Lake Mashuko	2·40	1·60

Nos. 58/9 were issued in *se-tenant* pairs within the sheet.

29 Kiritappu Wetland

(Des Maehashi Yasuhiro. Litho)

2004 (5 Feb). Cultural and Natural Heritage. T **29** and similar vert designs. Multicoloured. P 13½.

60	80y. Type **29**	2·50	1·70
	a. Pair. Nos. 60/1	5·25	5·25
61	80y. Wakka Primeval Garden	2·50	1·70

Nos. 60/1 were issued in *se-tenant* pairs within the sheet.

30 Sea Ice, *Garinko-go 2* (ice-breaker) and Steller's Sea Eagle

(Des Usui Masato. Photo)

2004 (28 May). P 13½.
62   **30** 80y. multicoloured .... 2·50   1·70

31 Sweetbrier

(Des Maehashi Yasuhiro (63 and 66) or Tanaka Kouzou (64/5). Photo)

2005 (26 Apr). Flowers of Hokkaido (2nd series). T **31** and similar vert designs. Multicoloured. P 13½.
63   50y. Type **31** .... 1·60   1·10
          a. Horiz strip of 4. Nos. 63/6 .... 6·75
64   50y. Lavender .... 1·60   1·10
65   50y. Yellow flowers .... 1·60   1·10
66   50y. Lily of the valley .... 1·60   1·10
63/66 *Set of 4* .... 6·50   4·50
   Nos. 63/6 were issued in horizontal *se-tenant* strips of four stamps within the sheet.

32 Sweetbrier and former Shana Post Office

(Des Shimoda Kouichi. Photo)

2005 (22 Aug). Northern Hokkaido. T **32** and similar vert designs. Multicoloured. P 13½.
67   80y. Type **32** .... 2·50   1·70
          a. Horiz strip of 4. Nos. 67/70 .... 10·50
68   80y. Sea otter .... 2·50   1·70
69   80y. Cherry blossom .... 2·50   1·70
70   80y. Tufted puffin .... 2·50   1·70
67/70 *Set of 4* .... 10·00   6·75
   Nos. 67/70 were issued in horizontal *se-tenant* strips of four stamps within the sheet, each strip forming a composite background design.

Hyogo

1990 (27 Apr). Flowers. Litho. P 13½.
1   62y. As Japan Type **1461** .... 1·20   80

1 Weathervane, Kobe

1991 (25 Oct). Litho. P 13.
2   **1** 62y. multicoloured .... 1·50   90

2 Stork and Tower, Shinkoro

1994 (23 June). Photo. P 13½.
3   **2** 50y. multicoloured .... 1·50   1·00
          a. Pane. No. 3×10, with outer edges imperf .... 14·50

3 Bridge

1998 (20 Mar). Kobe-Awaji-Naruto Expressway. T **3** and similar vert design. Multicoloured. Photo. P 13½.
4   80y. Type **3** .... 2·10   1·40
          a. Pair. Nos. 4/5 .... 4·50   4·50
          b. Pane. Nos. 4/5, each×5, with outer edges imperf .... 20·00
5   80y. Bridge (different) .... 2·10   1·40
   Nos. 4/5 were issued in *se-tenant* pairs within the sheet.
   Nos. 4/5 were also issued by Tokushima on 20 March 1998.

4 Kobe Luminarie (light festival)

1998 (9 Nov). Photo. P 13½.
6   **4** 80y. multicoloured .... 2·10   1·40
          a. Pane. No. 6×10, with outer edges imperf .... 20·00

5 Child as Bee and Flower

(Des Nagata Moe. Litho)

2000 (1 Mar). T **5** and similar vert design. Multicoloured. P 13½.
7   50y. Type **5** .... 1·50   1·00
          a. Pane. Nos. 7/8, each×5, with outer edges imperf .... 19·00
8   80y. Child as fairy and flowers (26×36 mm) .... 2·40   1·60

6 Pandas

(Des Yonezu Keita and Yamaguchi Noriyuki. Photo)

2001 (17 Jan). T **6** and similar vert design. Multicoloured.
P 13½×imperf.
9   50y. Type **6**... 2·10   1·40
           a. Pair. Nos. 9/10 .... 5·00   5·00
           b. Pane. Nos. 9/10, each×5, with
              outer edges imperf .... 22·00
10   80y. Night scene, Kobe............................ 2·40   1·60

7 Takarazuka
Revue

(Des Sakakibara Tadayuki and Ieda Masakazu. Litho)

2001 (21 Mar). Takarazuka. T **7** and similar vert design. Multicoloured.
P 13½.
11   80y. Type **7**....................................... 2·40   1·60
           a. Pair. Nos. 11/12 .... 5·00   5·00
           b. Pane. Nos. 11/12, each×5, with
              outer edges imperf .... 23·00
12   80y. Violets .... 2·40   1·60
Nos. 11/12 were issued in *se-tenant* pairs within the sheet.

8 Fairy riding Stork

(Des Nagata Moe. Litho)

2005 (6 June). Re-introduction of the Oriental White Stork. P 13½.
13   **8**   80y. multicoloured .... 2·50   1·70

9 Frontone (arched
facade)

(Des Sakakibara Tadayuki and Ieda Masakazu. Litho)

2005 (9 Dec). Kobe Luminarie (2nd series). T **9** and similar vert design.
Multicoloured. P 13½.
14   50y. Type **9**....................................... 1·60   1·10
           a. Pair. Nos. 14/15 .... 3·50   3·50
15   50y. Spalliera (wide facade).................... 1·60   1·10
Nos. 14/15 were issued in *se-tenant* pairs within the sheet.

Ibaraki

1990 (27 Apr). Flowers. Litho. P 13½.
1   62y. As Japan Type **1441** .... 1·20   80

1 Young Crows

1990 (1 May). Photo. P 13.
2   **1**   62y. multicoloured .... 1·50   80

2 Fukuroda-no-taki
Waterfall

1993 (26 Mar). Photo. P 13½.
3   **2**   62y. multicoloured .... 1·50   1·00
           a. Pane. No. 3×10, with outer edges
              imperf .... 14·50

3 Yacht, Lake
Kasumigaura

1997 (1 Sept). Photo. P 13½.
4   **3**   80y. multicoloured .... 2·10   1·40
           a. Pane. No. 4×10, with outer edges
              imperf .... 20·00

4 Koubuntei
Pavilion and Ume
Blossoms (Spring)

2001 (1 Feb). Kairakuen Garden. T **4** and similar vert designs. Multicoloured. Photo. P 13½.

5	50y. Type **4**	1·50	1·00
	a. Horiz strip of 4. Nos. 5/8	6·25	
6	50y. Chumon Gate (summer)	1·50	1·00
7	50y. Togyokusen spring (autumn)	1·50	1·00
8	50y. Lake and Koubuntei pavilion		
	(winter)	1·50	1·00
5/8 Set of 4		6·00	4·00

Nos. 5/8 were issued in horizontal *se-tenant* strips of four stamps within the sheet.

5 Mount Tsukuba, Itako (blind shaman) and Iris Flowers

(Des Ooyama Takayumi. Litho)

2003 (20 May). P 13½.

9	**5**	80y. multicoloured	2·40	1·60

6 Japanese Azalea and Mount Akagisan

(Des Ohya Takayumi. Photo)

2004 (23 June). Flowers of Kanto (1st issue). T **6** and similar vert designs. Multicoloured. P 13½.

10	50y. Type **6**	1·60	1·10
	a. Vert strip of 5. Nos. 10/13	8·25	
11	50y. Yoshi azalea and Lake Chuzenjiko	1·60	1·10
12	50y. Rose and Mount Tsukubasan	1·60	1·10
13	50y. Primrose and Tajimagahara native		
	primrose field	1·60	1·10
14	50y. Rape blossom and Nojimazaki		
	lighthouse	1·60	1·10
10/14 Set of 5		8·00	5·50

Nos. 10/14 were issued in vertical strips of five stamps within the sheet.

Nos. 10/14 were also issued by Tochigi, Saitama, Chiba and Gunma on 23 June 2004.

See also Nos. 16/20.

7 Iris Flowers, Mount Tsukuba and Lake Kasumigaura

(Des Ooyama Takayumi. Litho)

2005 (27 May). National Afforestation Campaign. P 13½.

15	**7**	50y. multicoloured	1·60	1·10

8 Bush Clover, Kairakuen Garden (Ibaraki)

(Des Ozaki Shingo. Photo)

2005 (23 June). Flowers of Kanto (2nd issue). T **8** and similar vert designs. Multicoloured. P 13½.

16	50y. Type **8**	1·60	1·10
	a. Vert strip of 5. Nos. 16/20	8·25	
17	50y. Nikko-kisuge (Nikko day lily) and		
	Kirifuri Heights (Tochigi)	1·60	1·10
18	50y. Sunflowers at Hana-hotaru (Chiba)	1·60	1·10
19	50y. Azaleas, Tsutsujigaoka Park		
	(Gunma)	1·60	1·10
20	50y. Allspice flowers and Mt. Bukousan		
	(Saitama)	1·60	1·10
16/20 Set of 5		8·00	5·50

Nos. 16/20 were issued in vertical strips of five stamps within the sheet.

Nos. 16/20 were also issued by Tochigi, Saitama, Chiba and Gunma on 23 June 2004.

Ishikawa

1 Bell Tower

1989 (2 Oct). Kenroku-en. Photo. P 13

1	**1**	62y. multicoloured	1·30	60

1990 (27 Apr). Litho. P 13½.

2	62y. As Japan Type **1452**	1·20	80

2 Child in Pearl Shell

1991 (2 Sept). 46th National Athletic Meet. Litho. P 13½.

3	**2**	41y. multicoloured	1·50	70

3 Bridge, Nanao-wan

1993 (2 Apr). Photo. P 13½.

4	**3**	62y. multicoloured	1·50	1·00
		a. Pane. No. 4×10, with outer edges imperf	14·50	

4 Kanazawa-jo
Castle

1995 (1 June). Photo. P 13½.

5	**4**	80y. multicoloured	1·90	1·30
		a. Pane. No. 5×10, with outer edges imperf	18·00	

5 Mount Hakusan

1998 (1 July). Photo. P 13½.

6	**5**	50y. multicoloured	1·30	90
		a. Pane. No. 6×10, with outer edges imperf	12·50	

6 Cherry Tree and
Kaiseki Pagoda

1999 (26 Apr). Kenrokuen Garden. T **6** and similar vert designs. Multicoloured. Photo. P 13½.

7	80y. Type **6**	2·10	1·40
	a. Horiz strip of 4. Nos. 7/10	8·75	
8	80y. Fountain	2·10	1·40
9	80y. Kinjo Reitaku well	2·10	1·40
10	80y. Snow-covered Kotoji Stone Lantern	2·10	1·40
7/10 *Set of 4*		8·50	5·50

Nos. 7/10 were issued in horizontal *se-tenant* strips of four stamps within the sheet.

7 Festival Goers
and Banners

1999 (11 June). Noto Kiriko Festival. Litho. P 13½.

11	**7**	80y. multicoloured	2·10	1·40
		a. Pane. No. 11×10, with outer edges imperf	20·00	

8 Samurai Warrior
and Kaga Gold
Lacquer Designs

(Des Ichimura Jun'ichi. Litho)

2001 (4 June). P 13½.

12	**8**	80y. multicoloured	2·40	1·60
		a. Pane. No. 12×10, with outer edges imperf	23·00	

9 *Adenophora
triphylla*
var. *hakusanensis*
and Mount Betsusan

(Des Kanae Kensuke. Photo)

2002 (1 July). Alpine Flora of Mount Hakusan. T **9** and similar vert designs. Multicoloured. P 13½.

13	50y. Type **9**	1·60	1·10
	a. Horiz strip of 4. Nos. 13/16	6·75	
14	50y. *Fritillaria camtschatcensis* and Mt. Betsusan	1·60	1·10
15	50y. *Geranium yesoense* var. *nipponicum* and Mt. Gozengamine	1·60	1·10
16	50y. *Anemone narcissiflora* and Mt. Gozengamine	1·60	1·10
13/16 *Set of 4*		6·50	4·50

Nos. 13/16 were issued in horizontal *se-tenant* strips of four stamps within the sheet.

10 Fukada Kyuya
and Mount Hakusan

(Des Kunitomo Hiroshi and Ootani Kazuyoshi. Litho)

2003 (4 July). Birth Centenary of Fukada Kyuya (mountaineer and writer). P 13½.

17	**10**	80y. multicoloured	2·40	1·60

11 Morning Glory
Flowers and Script

(Des Sagamiya Toube. Photo)

2003 (3 Oct). 300th Birth Anniv of Chiyojo (haiku poet). T **11** and similar vert design. Multicoloured. P 13½.

18	80y. Type **11**	2·40	1·60
	a. Pair. Nos. 18/19	5·00	5·00
19	80y. Chiyojo	2·40	1·60

Nos. 18/19 were issued in horizontal *se-tenant* pairs within the sheet, each pair forming a composite design.

12 Hydrangea

(Des Kawanishi Shigeharu. Litho)

2005 (1 Apr). Flowers of Hokuriku. T **12** and similar vert designs. Multicoloured. P 13½.

20	50y. Type **12**	1·60	1·10
	a. Horiz strip of 4. Nos. 20/3	6·75	
21	50y. Tulip	1·60	1·10
22	50y. Rhododendron	1·60	1·10
23	50y. Lily	1·60	1·10
20/3 *Set of 4*		6·50	4·50

Nos. 20/3 were issued in horizontal *se-tenant* strips of four stamps within the sheet.
Nos. 20/3 were also issued by Toyama and Fukui on 1 April 2005.

Iwate

1990 (27 Apr). Litho. P 13½.

1		62y. As Japan Type **1436**	1·20	80

1 Iwate Mountain

1991 (10 June). Litho. P 13.

2	**1**	62y. multicoloured	1·30	90

2 Coastline,
Rikuchu

1992 (23 June). Litho. P 13½.

3	**2**	62y. multicoloured	1·50	90
		a. Pane. No. 2×10, with outer edges imperf	14·50	

3 Caravan and
Mount Iwate

1998 (24 Apr). Photo. P 13½.

4	**3**	80y. multicoloured	2·10	1·40
		a. Pane. No. 4×10, with outer edges imperf	20·00	

4 Gentian

1999 (30 July). Litho. P 13½.

5	**4**	50y. multicoloured	1·80	1·20
		a. Pane. No. 5×10, with outer edges imperf	17·00	

5 Cherry Tree

(Des Kosugou Fusae and Satou Mitusrou. Litho)

2000 (3 Apr). Cherry Trees. T **5** and similar horiz design. Multicoloured. P 13½.

6	80y. Type **5**	2·50	1·70
	a. Vert strip of 4. Nos. 6/7, 9, 11	10·50	
	b. Sheet of 20. Nos. 6a×3, 8×4, 10×4	45·00	
7	80y. Group of trees with spreading branches, Yamagata	2·50	1·70
8	80y. Group of trees, Fukishima	2·50	1·70

253

9	80y. Tree, left, Miyagi	2·50	1·70
10	80y. Cherry blossom, Aomori	2·50	1·70
11	80y. Trees and river, Akita	2·50	1·70
6/11	*Set of 6*	15·00	10·00

Nos. 6/11 were also by Yamagata, Aomori, Miyagi, Akita and Fukushima on 3 April 2000.

6 Chusonji Temple

(Des Murata Rinzo. Litho)

2000 (1 Aug). P 13½.

12	**6**	80y. multicoloured	2·75	1·90
		a. Pane. No. 12×10, with outer edges imperf	27·00	

7 Paulownia (Iwate)

(Des Sakuraba Toshihiro (Aomori), Sawaguchi Ken (Iwate), Izawa Kiyoshi (Miyagi), Konno Goro (Akita), Sato Kousen (Yamagata) or Kobayashi Goro (Fukushima). Photo)

2004 (19 Mar). Prefectural Flowers. T **7** and similar horiz design. Multicoloured. P 13½.

13	50y. Type **7**	1·60	1·10
14	50y. Apple Blossom (Aomori)	1·60	1·10
15	50y. Japanese Bush Clover (Miyagi)	1·60	1·10
16	50y. Butterbur Flower (Akita)	1·60	1·10
17	50y. Safflower (Yamagata)	1·60	1·10
18	50y. Alpine Rose (*Rhododendron ferrugineum*) (Fukushima)	1·60	1·10
13/18	*Set of 6*	9·50	6·50

Nos. 13/18 were also issued by Yamagata, Aomori, Miyagi, Akita and Fukushima on 19 March 2004.

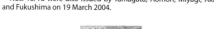

8 Apple (Iwate)

(Des Matsuda Hiromi. Photo)

2005 (28 June). Fruits of Tohoku. T **8** and similar horiz design. Multicoloured. P 13½.

19	50y. Type **8**	1·60	1·10
	a. Horiz strip of 4. Nos. 19/22	6·75	
20	50y. Apples (Aomori)	1·60	1·10
21	50y. Cherry (Yamagata)	1·60	1·10
22	50y. Peach (Fukushima)	1·60	1·10
19/22	*Set of 4*	6·50	4·50

Nos. 19/22 were issued in horizontal *se-tenant* strips of four stamps within the sheet.

Nos. 19/22 were also issued by Yamagata, Iwate and Fukushima on 28 June 2005.

Kagawa

1990 (27 Apr). Litho. P 13½.

1	62y. As Japan Type **1470**	4·75	3·25

1 Archer on Horseback

1991 (19 Feb). Yashima. Litho. P 13.

2	**1**	62y. multicoloured	1·20	80

2 Peace Statues

1993 (21 May). Photo. P 13½.

3	**2**	62y. multicoloured	1·50	1·00
		a. Pane. No. 3×10, with outer edges imperf	14·50	

3 Marugame Castle

1997 (15 May). Photo. P 13½.

4	**3**	80y. multicoloured	2·10	1·40
		a. Pane. No. 4×10, with outer edges imperf	20·00	

4 Seto-Ohashi Bridges

1998 (9 Nov). Photo. P 13½.

5	**4**	80y. multicoloured	2·10	1·40
		a. Pane. No. 5×10, with outer edges imperf	20·00	

5 Ritsurin Park

1999 (2 Aug). Litho. P 13½.
6   **5**   80y. multicoloured .... 2·10   1·40
      a. Pane. No. 6×10, with outer edges
      imperf .... 20·00

6 Olive and
Shodoshima Island
(Kagawa)

(Des Kikuchi Akira. Photo)

2002 (20 Mar). T **6** and similar vert designs. Multicoloured. P 13½.
7   50y. Type **6**.. 1·50   1·00
      a. Vert strip of 4. Nos. 7/10 .... 6·25
8   50y. Sudachi (sour citrus fruit) and Mt.
      Tsurugisan (Tokushima)................... 1·50   1·00
9   50y. Yamamomo (bayberry) and Tengu
      highland (Kochi)............................ 1·50   1·00
10   50y. Mikan (mandarin oranges) and
      Sata-misaki Promontory (Ehime) ... 1·50   1·00
7/10 *Set of 4* .... 6·00   4·00
    Nos. 7/10 were issued in vertical strips of four stamps within the sheet.
    Nos. 7/10 were also issued by Ehime, Kochi and Tokushima on 20 March 2002.

7 Kompira-Ohshibai
Theatre and Mount
Zouzusan

(Des Tsuji Kazuma. Litho)

2003 (24 Mar). Former Kompira-Ohshibai Theatre. P 13½.
11   **7**   80y. multicoloured .... 2·40   1·60

2005 (8 July). Cultural Heritage. Shizuoka Temples (2nd series). Ehime Type **8** and similar vert designs. Multicoloured. Litho. P 13½.
12   80y. As Ehime Type **8** .... 2·50   1·70
      a. Sheet of 20. Nos. 12/31 .... 45·00
13   80y. Seated Buddha, Anrakuji Temple... 2·50   1·70
14   80y. Inscribed belfry gateway, Jurakuji
      Temple .... 2·50   1·70
15   80y. Double roofed gateway,
      Kumadaniji Temple............................ 2·50   1·70
16   80y. Pagoda, Yakuoji Temple................... 2·50   1·70
17   80y. Statues, ramp, lanterns and
      pagoda, Hotsumisakiji Temple........ 2·50   1·70
18   80y. Gateway and long steep steps,
      Shinjouji Temple............................ 2·50   1·70
19   80y. Path, gateway, steps and main
      temple, Kongochoji Temple............ 2·50   1·70
20   80y. Buddha seated on peacock,
      Ryukoji Temple .... 2·50   1·70
21   80y. Bell and autumn colour,
      Butsumokuji Temple........................ 2·50   1·70
22   80y. Dragon, Meisekiji Temple................. 2·50   1·70
23   80y. Steps and many roofed buildings,
      Daihouji Temple .... 2·50   1·70
24   80y. Carved decorative gable,
      Kokubunji Temple............................ 2·50   1·70

25   80y. Leafless tree and snow-covered
      building, Yokomineji Temple .... 2·50   1·70
26   80y. Buddha, Kouonji Temple.................. 2·50   1·70
27   80y. Courtyard and building, Houjuji
      Temple .... 2·50   1·70
28   80y. Inscribed pillars and gateway,
      Douryuji Temple............................ 2·50   1·70
29   80y. Wall mounted statues, Goushouji
      Temple .... 2·50   1·70
30   80y. Eagle surmounting gateway,
      Tennouji Temple............................ 2·50   1·70
31   80y. Courtyard with stone lined path
      and building, Kokubunji Temple .... 2·50   1·70
12/31 *Set of 20* .... 50·00   34·00
    Nos. 12/31 were issued in *se-tenant* sheets of 20 stamps.
    Nos. 12/31 were also issued by Ehime, Kochi and Tokushima on 8 July 2005.

Kagoshima

1990 (27 Apr). Flowers. Litho. P 13½.
1   62y. As Japan Type **1479** .... 1·20   80

1 Mount Sakurajima

1990 (2 July). Litho. P 13.
2   **1**   62y. multicoloured .... 1·30   80

2 Festival Goers,
Ohara

1993 (1 Sept). Photo. P 13½.
3   **2**   41y. multicoloured .... 1·30   90
      a. Pane. No. 3×10, with outer edges
      imperf .... 12·50

3 Satsuma Ware
Bowl

1998 (1 Oct). 400th Satsuma-Yaki Festival. T **3** and similar vert design. Multicoloured. P 13½.
4   80y. Type **3**.. 2·10   1·40
      a. Pair. Nos. 4/5 .... 4·50   4·50
      b. Pane. Nos. 4/5, each×5, with outer
      edges imperf .... 20·00
5   80y. Vase.. 2·10   1·40
    Nos. 4/5 were issued in horizontal *se-tenant* pairs within the sheet.

4 Cycle Ball and
Sunset Bridge,
Kaseda (for bicycles
only)

(Des Hamamura Sumitaka. Litho)

2001 (1 Oct). P 13½.
6   **4**   80y. multicoloured .... 2·50   1·70

5 Tsubame (800 Series
Shinkansen) and Mount
Sakurajima

(Des Hamamura Sumitaka. Litho)

2004 (12 Mar). Inauguration of Kyushu-Shinkansen Line—Tsubame
(high-speed rail line). P 13½.
7   **5**   50y. multicoloured .... 1·60   1·10

6 Miyama-Kirishima
(azaleas) and
Kirishima mountains
(Kagoshima)

(Des Iwasaki Chizuru. Photo)

2005 (1 June). Flowers and Scenery of Kyushu (1st series). T **6** and
similar vert designs. Multicoloured. P 13½.
8   50y. Ume Blossom and Dazaifu-
        Tenmangu Shrine (Fukuoka)........... 1·60   1·10
        a. Pair. Nos. 8/9 .... 3·50   3·50
        b. Block of 10. Nos. 8/17 .... 15·00
9   50y. Sakura (cherry blossoms) and
        Kanmon bridge (Fukuoka)............ 1·60   1·10
10   50y. Kusunohana (camphor blossoms)
        and Ariake Sea (Saga)...................... 1·60   1·10
        a. Pair. Nos. 10/11 .... 3·50   3·50
11   50y. Unzen-Tsutsuji (azaleas) and Mt.
        Fugendake (Nagasaki).................... 1·60   1·10
12   50y. Tulips and Huis Ten Bosch
        (Nagasaki)..................................... 1·60   1·10
        a. Pair. Nos. 12/13 .... 3·50   3·50
13   50y. Rindou (gentians) and Mt. Aso
        (Kumamoto).................................. 1·60   1·10
14   50y. Ume blossoms and Mt. Takasaki
        (Ooita) .... 1·60   1·10
        a. Pair. Nos. 14/15 .... 3·50   3·50
15   50y. Hamayu (crinums) and Nichinan
        beach (Miyazaki) .... 1·60   1·10
16   50y. Type **6**..................................... 1·60   1·10
        a. Pair. Nos. 16/17 .... 3·50   3·50

17   50y. Hibiscus and Adan (screw-pine)
        (Kagoshima)........................... 1·60   1·10
8/17 *Set of* 10.. 16·00   11·00
        Nos. 8/17 were issued in *se-tenant* blocks of ten stamps within the
sheet.
        Nos. 8/17 were also issued by Fukuoka, Nagasaki, Saga, Miyazaki,
Kumamoto and Oita on 1 June 2005.

Kanagawa

1 Doll

1989 (2 June). Photo. P 13.
1   **1**   62y. multicoloured .... 1·30   90

1990 (27 Apr). Flowers. Litho. P 13½.
2   62y. As Japan Type **1447**............... 1·20   80

2 Shasui Waterfall
(Shasui-no-taki)

1992 (24 July). Photo. P 13½.
3   **2**   62y. multicoloured .... 1·50   90

3 Flowers,
Sengokubara Marsh

1996 (6 Sept). Photo. P 13½.
4   **3**   80y. multicoloured .... 2·10   1·40

4 Tunnel Entrance

1997 (18 Dec). Tokyo-Wan Aqualine. T **4** and similar vert design. Multicoloured. Litho. P 13½.

5	80y. Type **4**.....................................	1·80	1·20
	a. Pair. Nos. 5/6	3·75	3·75
	b. Pane. Nos. 5/6, eachx5, with outer edges imperf........................	17·00	
6	80y. Tunnel entrance (different)	1·80	1·20

Nos. 5/6 were issued in horizontal *se-tenant* pairs within the sheet. Nos. 5/6 were also issued by Chiba on 18 December 1997.

5 Minamoto no Yoritomo

1999 (2 Sept). Litho. P 13½.

7	**5**	80y. multicoloured	2·10	1·40
		a. Pane. No. 7×10, with outer edges imperf	20·00	

6 Decorated Bamboo Banners

(Des Wakabayashi Kaoru. Litho)

2000 (2 June). Hiratsuka Tanabata Festival. T **6** and similar vert design. Multicoloured. P 13½.

8	50y. Type **6**.....................................	1·50	1·00
	a. Pair. Nos. 8/9	3·25	3·25
	b. Pane. Nos. 8/9, eachx5, with outer edges imperf........................	14·50	
9	50y. Father and child........................	1·50	1·00

Nos. 8/9 were issued in horizontal *se-tenant* pairs within the sheet.

7 Castle and Chrysanthemums

(Des Shimoda Kouichi. Litho)

2000 (27 Oct). Odwara Castle. T **7** and similar vert design. Multicoloured. P 13½.

10	50y. Type **7**.....................................	1·80	1·20
	a. Pair. Nos. 10/11	3·75	3·75
	b. Pane. Nos 10/11, eachx5, with outer edges imperf	17·00	
11	50y. Blossom, gate and castle...................	1·80	1·20

Nos. 10/11 were issued in horizontal *se-tenant* pairs within the sheet.

8 Ship in Dock

(Des Hiroshige 3 and Ozaki Shingo. Photo)

2002 (1 May). Yokohama, Port Town. T **8** and similar vert design. Multicoloured. P 13½.

12	50y. Type **8**.....................................	1·50	1·00
	a. Pair. Nos. 12/13	3·25	3·25
	b. Pane. Nos. 12/13, each×5, with outer edges imperf	14·50	
13	50y. Port, ship and woman in Victorian dress	1·50	1·00

Nos. 12/13 were issued in horizontal *se-tenant* pairs within the sheet.

9 Rose and Buildings at Night, Minato-Mirai 21 Area

(Des Sato Akihiko. Photo)

2004 (1 June). Tourism. T **9** and similar vert designs. Multicoloured. P 13½.

14	50y. Type **9**.....................................	1·60	1·10
	a. Strip of 4. Nos. 14/17......................	6·75	
15	50y. Lily, Kanagawa Prefectural Government, Yokohama Customs, and Yokohama Memorial Museum buildings	1·60	1·10
16	50y. Wisterias and Enoshima Island	1·60	1·10
17	50y. Hydrangea and Lake Ashinoko, Hakone	1·60	1·10
14/17 *Set of 4*		6·50	4·50

Nos. 14/17 were issued in *se-tenant* strips of four stamps within the sheet.

Kochi

1990 (27 Apr). Litho. P 13½.

1	62y. As Japan Type **1472**..........................	1·90	1·30

1 Man and Child riding on Whale

1991 (26 June). Litho. P 13.

2	**1**	62y. multicoloured	1·80	80

2 Lighthouse

1995 (1 June). Photo. P 13½.

| 3 | **2** | 80y. multicoloured | 1·90 | 1·30 |
| | | a. Pane. No. 3×10, with outer edges imperf | 18·00 | |

3 Cliff-top Teahouse and Gateway, Katsura Beach

1999 (15 Nov). Sakamoto Ryoma (warrior and naval pioneer). T **3** and similar vert design. Multicoloured. Photo. P 13½.

4	80y. Type **3**	2·20	1·50
	a. Pair. Nos. 4/5	4·75	4·75
	b. Pane. Nos. 4/5, each×5, with outer edges imperf	21·00	
5	80y. Whale tail, telescope and Sakamoto Ryoma	2·20	1·50

Nos. 4/5 were issued in horizontal *se-tenant* pairs within the sheet.

4 Kochi Castle

2001 (1 Mar). Kochi Castle and Sunday Market. T **4** and similar vert design. Multicoloured. P 13½.

6	80y. Type **4**	2·40	1·60
	a. Pair. Nos. 4/5	5·00	5·00
7	80y. Sunday market	2·40	1·60

Nos. 6/7 were issued in horizontal *se-tenant* pairs within the sheet

5 Yamamomo (bayberry) and Tengu Highland (Kochi)

(Des Kikuchi Akira. Photo)

2002 (20 Mar). T **5** and similar vert designs. Multicoloured. P 13½.

8	50y. Type **5**	1·50	1·00
	a. Vert strip of 4. Nos. 8/11	6·25	
9	50y. Sudachi (sour citrus fruit) and Mt. Tsurugisan (Tokushima)	1·50	1·00
10	50y. Mikan (mandarin oranges) and Sata-misaki Promontory (Ehime)	1·50	1·00
11	50y. Olive and Shodoshima island (Kagawa)	1·50	1·00
8/11 *Set of 4*		6·00	4·00

Nos. 8/11 were issued in vertical strips of four stamps within the sheet.

Nos. 8/11 were also issued by Ehime, Tokushima and Kagawa on 20 March 2002.

6 Runners

(Des Kikuchi Akira. Photo)

2002 (6 Sept). 57th National Athletic Meet. P 13.

| 12 | **6** | 50y. multicoloured | 1·60 | 1·10 |

2005 (8 July). Cultural Heritage. Shizuoka Temples (2nd series). Ehime Type **8** and similar vert designs. Multicoloured. Litho. P 13½.

13	80y. As Ehime Type **8**	2·50	1·70
	a. Sheet of 20. Nos. 13/32	45·00	
14	80y. Seated Buddha, Anrakuji Temple	2·50	1·70
15	80y. Inscribed belfry gateway, Jurakuji Temple	2·50	1·70
16	80y. Double roofed gateway, Kumadaniji Temple	2·50	1·70
17	80y. Pagoda, Yakuoji Temple	2·50	1·70
18	80y. Statues, ramp, lanterns and pagoda, Hotsumisakiji Temple	2·50	1·70
19	80y. Gateway and long steep steps, Shinjouji Temple	2·50	1·70
20	80y. Path, gateway, steps and main temple, Kongochoji Temple	2·50	1·70
21	80y. Buddha seated on peacock, Ryukoji Temple	2·50	1·70
22	80y. Bell and autumn colour, Butsumokuji Temple	2·50	1·70
23	80y. Dragon, Meisekiji Temple	2·50	1·70
24	80y. Steps and many roofed buildings, Daihouji Temple	2·50	1·70
25	80y. Carved decorative gable, Kokubunji Temple	2·50	1·70
26	80y. Leafless tree and snow-covered building, Yokomineji Temple	2·50	1·70
27	80y. Buddha, Kouonji Temple	2·50	1·70
28	80y. Courtyard and building, Houjuji Temple	2·50	1·70
29	80y. Inscribed pillars and gateway, Douryuji Temple	2·50	1·70
30	80y. Wall mounted statues, Goushouji Temple	2·50	1·70
31	80y. Eagle surmounting gateway, Tennouji Temple	2·50	1·70
32	80y. Courtyard with stone lined path and building, Kokubunji Temple	2·50	1·70
13/32 *Set of 20*		50·00	34·00

Nos. 13/32 were issued in *se-tenant* sheets of 20 stamps.

Nos. 13/32 were also issued by Ehime, Tokushima and Kagawa on 8 July 2005.

Kumamoto

1 Kumamoto Castle

1989 (29 Sept). Photo. P 13.
1 **1** 62y. multicoloured .... 1·30 60

1990 (27 Apr). Flowers. Litho. P 13½.
2 62y. As Japan Type **1476** .... 1·20 80

2 Aqueduct discharging Water, Tsujun-kyo

1991 (1 Aug). Litho. P 13.
3 **2** 62y. multicoloured .... 1·50 90

3 Boy

1996 (1 Apr). Ushibuka-haiya Festival. Litho. P 13½.
4 **3** 80y. multicoloured .... 1·80 1·20
  a. Pane. No. 4×10, with outer edges
    imperf .... 17·00

4 Globe and Ball

1997 (17 Apr). World Men's Handball Championship. Photo. P 13½.
5 **4** 80y. multicoloured .... 2·10 1·40
  a. Pane. No. 5×10, with outer edges
    imperf .... 20·00

5 Traditional Fishing Boat

1999 (2 Aug). Litho. P 13½.
6 **5** 80y. multicoloured .... 2·10 1·40
  a. Pane. No. 6×10, with outer edges
    imperf .... 20·00

6 Yachiyoza Theatre

(Des Jinguji Tadashi and Kira Katsuhiko. Litho)

2002 (15 July). P 13½.
7 **6** 80y. multicoloured .... 2·20 1·50

7 Rindou (gentians) and Mt. Aso (Kumamoto)

(Des Iwasaki Chizuru. Photo)

2005 (1 June). Flowers and Scenery of Kyushu (1st series). T **7** and similar vert designs. Multicoloured. P 13½.
8 50y. Ume Blossom and Dazaifu-
    Tenmangu Shrine (Fukuoka)........... 1·60 1·10
  a. Pair. Nos. 8/9 .... 3·50 3·50
  b. Block of 10. Nos. 8/17 .... 15·00
9 50y. Sakura (cherry blossoms) and
    Kanmon bridge (Fukuoka)............... 1·60 1·10
10 50y. Kusunohana (camphor blossoms)
    and Ariake Sea (Saga)....................... 1·60 1·10
  a. Pair. Nos. 10/11 .... 3·50 3·50
11 50y. Unzen-Tsutsuji (azaleas) and Mt.
    Fugendake (Nagasaki)...................... 1·60 1·10
12 50y. Tulips and Huis Ten Bosch
    (Nagasaki) .... 1·60 1·10
  a. Pair. Nos. 12/13 .... 3·50 3·50
13 50y. Type **7** .... 1·60 1·10
14 50y. Ume blossoms and Mt. Takasaki
    (Ooita)... 1·60 1·10
  a. Pair. Nos. 14/15 .... 3·50 3·50
15 50y. Hamayu (crinums) and Nichinan
    beach (Miyazaki)............................... 1·60 1·10
16 50y. Miyama-Kirishima (azaleas) and
    Kirishima mountains (Kagoshima) ... 1·60 1·10
  a. Pair. Nos. 16/17 .... 3·50 3·50
17 50y. Hibiscus and Adan (screw-pine)
    (Kagoshima)....................................... 1·60 1·10

8/17 *Set of* 10.. 16·00 11·00
    Nos. 8/17 were issued in *se-tenant* blocks of ten stamps within the sheet.
    Nos. 8/17 were also issued by Fukuoka, Nagasaki, Saga, Miyazaki, Oita and Kagoshima on 1 June 2005.

Kyoto

1990 (27 Apr). Flowers. Litho. P 13½.
1   62y. As Japan Type **1459** .... 3·00 2·00

1 Maiko (apprentice geisha)

1990 (25 Sept). Photo. P 13.
2   **1**   62y. multicoloured .... 1·20 80

2 Ushiwaka-maru (Aikido master)

1995 (3 Apr). Photo. P 13½.
3   **2**   80y. multicoloured .... 1·90 1·30
    a. Pane. No. 3×10, with outer edges imperf .... 18·00

3 Kyoto University

1997 (18 June). Photo. P 13½.
4   **3**   80y. multicoloured .... 2·10 1·40
    a. Pane. No. 4×10, with outer edges imperf .... 20·00

4 Hiyoshi Dam

1998 (2 Mar). Photo. P 13½.
5   **4**   80y. multicoloured .... 2·10 1·40
    a. Pane. No. 5×10, with outer edges imperf .... 20·00

5 Amanohashidate Sand Bar

1999 (16 July). Litho. P 13½.
6   **5**   80y. multicoloured .... 2·10 1·40

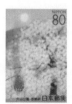

6 Cherry Blossoms, Maruyama Park (spring)

(Des Shimura Tadashi. Litho)

2000 (20 Oct). Four Seasons. T **6** and similar vert designs. Multicoloured. P 13
7   80y. Type **6** .... 2·75 1·90
    a. Strip of 4. Nos. 7/10 .... 11·50
    b. Pane. Nos. 7/8, each×5, with outer edges imperf .... 27·00
8   80y. Kamogawa river (summer) .... 2·75 1·90
9   80y. Togetsukyo bridge, Arashiyama (autumn) .... 2·75 1·90
    a. Pane. Nos. 9/10, each×5, with outer edges imperf .... 27·00
10   80y. Cedar forest, Kitayama (winter) ...... 2·75 1·90
7/10 *Set of* 4 .... 11·00 7·50
    Nos. 7/10 were issued in horizontal *se-tenant* strips of four stamps within the sheet.

7 Carriage decorated with Japanese Wisteria, Aoi-matsuri Festival

(Des Shimura Tadashi. Litho)

2003 (1 May). Traditional Events in Kyoto. T **7** and similar vert designs. Multicoloured. P 13.
11   50y. Type **7** .... 1·60 1·10
    a. Strip of 4. Nos. 11/14 .... 6·75
12   50y. Gion-masturi (festival float) .... 1·60 1·10
13   50y. Okuribi (fire to send off spirits at Mt. Nyoig) .... 1·60 1·10
14   50y. Jidai-matsuri (royal carriage) .... 1·60 1·10
11/14 *Set of* 4 .... 6·50 4·50
    Nos. 11/14 were issued in horizontal *se-tenant* strips of four stamps within the sheet.

Mie

1990 (27 Apr). Flowers. Litho. P 13½.
1   62y. As Japan Type **1457** .... 1·20   80

1 Ninja

1991 (10 Sept). Litho. P 13.
2   **1**   62y. multicoloured .... 1·50   90

2 Meoto-iwa
(wedded rocks) and
Plovers, Futami-
ga-ura

1994 (22 July). Photo. P 13½.
3   **2**   80y. multicoloured .... 1·90   1·30
      a. Pane. No. 3×10, with outer edges
        imperf .... 18·00

3 Hamayu (crinum)
Blossom

1996 (8 May). T **3** and similar vert design. Multicoloured. Litho.
    P 13½.
4   80y. Type **3**.. 1·80   1·20
      a. Pair. Nos. 4/5 .... 3·75   3·75
5   80y. Ama divers............................. 1·80   1·20
    Nos. 4/5 were issued in horizontal *se-tenant* pairs within the sheet.

4 Trees and
Mountains

1999 (16 Apr). Kumano Old Path. T **4** and similar vert designs.
    Multicoloured. Litho. P 13½.
6   80y. Type **4**..................................... 2·10   1·40
      a. Horiz strip. Nos. 6/9 .... 8·75
7   80y. Trees and shoreline .... 2·10   1·40
8   80y. Pathway.................................... 2·10   1·40
9   80y. Scree....................................... 2·10   1·40
6/9 *Set of 4*... 8·50   5·50
    Nos. 6/9 were issued in horizontal *se-tenant* strips of four stamps
within the sheet.

5 Free Fall

(Des Yoko'o Tadanori. Photo)

2000 (13 Sept). World Parachuting Championships. T **5** and similar
    vert design. Multicoloured. P 13½.
10   80y. Type **5**.................................... 2·75   1·90
      a. Pair. Nos. 10/11 .... 5·75   5·75
      b. Pane. Nos. 10/11, each×5, with
        outer edges imperf .... 27·00
11   80y. Parachutist.............................. 2·75   1·90
    Nos. 10/11 were issued in horizontal *se-tenant* pairs within the
sheet, each pair forming a composite design.

6 Matsuo Basho
(haiku poet) and
Iga-ueno Castle

(Des Harada Tsunao. Litho)

2002 (10 Sept). Iga-Ueno. T **6** and similar vert design. Multicoloured.
    P 13½.
12   80y. Type **6**..................................... 2·20   1·50
      a. Pair. Nos. 12/13 .... 4·75   4·75
13   80y. Iga-ueno castle and Haisei-den
        hall... 2·20   1·50
    Nos. 12/13 were issued in horizontal *se-tenant* pairs within the
sheet, each pair forming a composite design.

7 Ozu Yasujiro and
Mitchell Camera

2003 (23 Oct). Birth Centenary of Ozu Yasujiro (film director). P 13½.
14   **7** 80y. multicoloured .... 2·20   1·50
    No. 14 was issued in sheets of ten (5×2) stamps with enlarged
illustrated margin.

Miyagi

1990 (27 Apr). Flowers. Litho. P 13½.
1   62y. As Japan Type **1437** .... 1·20   80

1 Swans

1990 (1 Oct). Photo. P 13.
2   **1**   62y. multicoloured .... 1·50   80

2 Coastline,
Matsushima

1994 (20 Sept). Photo. P 13½.
3   **2**   80y. multicoloured .... 1·90   1·30
             a. Pane. No. 3×10, with outer edges
                imperf .... 18·00

3 *Zalkova* (Japanese
elm) Trees

1995 (1 Aug). Photo. P 13½.
4   **3**   50y. multicoloured .... 1·30   80
             a. Pane. No. 4×10, with outer edges
                imperf .... 12·50

4 Festival Goers and
Banners

1999 (14 May). Summer Festivals. T **4** and similar vert design.
Multicoloured. Photo. P 13½.
5   80y. Type **4**.. 2·10   1·40
        a. Pair. Nos. 5/6 .... 4·50   4·50
        b. Pane. Nos. 5/6, each×5, with outer
           edges imperf .... 20·00
6   80y. Streamers.. 2·10   1·40

Nos. 5/6 were issued in horizontal *se-tenant* pairs within the sheet,
each pair forming a composite design.
Nos. 5/6 were also issued by Fukishima on 14 May 1999.

5 Cherry Tree

(Des Kosugou Fusae and Satou Mitusrou. Litho)

2000 (3 Apr). Cherry Trees. T **5** and similar horiz design. Multicoloured.
P 13½.
7   80y. Type **5**.. 2·50   1·70
        a. Strip of 4. Nos. 7/8, 10,12................. 10·50
        b. Sheet of 20. Nos. 7a×3, 9×4, 11×4 . 45·00
8   80y. Group of trees with spreading
             branches, Yamagata............................ 2·50   1·70
9   80y. Group of trees, Fukishima................ 2·50   1·70
10   80y. Tree, central, Iwate.......................... 2·50   1·70
11   80y. Cherry blossom, Aomori .... 2·50   1·70
12   80y. Trees and river, Akita....................... 2·50   1·70
7/12 *Set of* 6 .... 15·00   10·00
Nos. 7/12 were also issued by Yamagata, Iwate, Aomori, Akita and
Fukushima on 3 April 2000.

6 Float and Festival
Dancers

(Des Hasegawa Shirou. Litho)

2001 (18 May). 400th Anniv of Sendai. P 13½.
13   **6**   80y. multicoloured .... 2·50   1·70
             a. Pane. No. 13×10, with outer edges
                imperf .... 24·00

7 Volleyball Players
and Bush Clover

(Des Honda Hideo. Photo)

2001 (7 Sept). 56th National Athletic Meet. P 13½.
14   **7**   50y. multicoloured .... 2·10   1·40
             a. Pane. No. 14×10, with outer edges
                imperf .... 20·00

8 Japanese Bush
Clover (Miyagi)

(Des Sakuraba Toshihiro (Aomori), Sawaguchi Ken (Iwate), Izawa Kiyoshi (Miyagi), Konno Goro (Akita), Sato Kousen (Yamagata) or Kobayashi Goro (Fukushima). Photo)

2004 (19 Mar). Prefectural Flowers. T **8** and similar horiz design. Multicoloured. P 13½.

15	50y. Type **8**	1·60	1·10
16	50y. Apple Blossom (Aomori)	1·60	1·10
17	50y. Paulownia (Iwate)	1·60	1·10
18	50y. Butterbur Flower (Akita)	1·60	1·10
19	50y. Safflower (Yamagata)	1·60	1·10
20	50y. Alpine Rose (*Rhododendron ferrugineum*) (Fukushima)	1·60	1·10
15/20	*Set of* 6	9·50	6·50

Nos. 15/20 were also issued by Yamagata, Aomori, Miyagi, Iwate and Fukushima on 19 March 2004.

Miyazaki

1990 (27 Apr). Flowers. Litho. P 13½.

1	62y. As Japan Type **1478**	1·20	80

1 Horses and Coastline, Toi-misaki

1991 (1 July). Photo. P 13.

2	**1**	62y. multicoloured	1·30	80

2 Drummer

1996 (1 Aug). Shimozuru Usudaiko Odori. Photo. P 13½.

3	2	80y. multicoloured	2·10	1·40

3 Nichinan Taihei Dance

1999 (1 Oct). Obi Town. T **3** and similar vert design. Multicoloured. Litho. P 13½.

4	80y. Type **3**	2·10	1·40
	a. Pair. Nos. 4/5	4·50	4·50
	b. Pane. Nos. 4/5, each×5, with outer edges imperf	20·00	
5	80y. Building and statue	2·10	1·40

Nos. 4/5 were issued in horizontal *se-tenant* pairs within the sheet.

4 Sekino'o-taki Waterfall

(Des Mataki Keiko. Photo)

2000 (12 Dec). Landscapes. T **4** and similar vert design. Multicoloured. P 13½.

6	80y. Type **4**	2·75	1·80
	a. Pair. Nos. 6/7	5·75	5·75
	b. Pane. Nos. 6/7, each×5, with outer edges imperf	27·00	
7	80y. Kirishima volcano	2·75	1·80

Nos. 6/7 were issued in horizontal *se-tenant* pairs within the sheet, each pair forming a composite design.

5 Noh Theatre

(Des Ootsuka Kouhei and Igata Jun. Photo)

2003 (3 Feb). Nobeoka—City of Noh. T **5** and similar vert design. Multicoloured. P 13½.

8	80y. Type **5**	2·40	1·60
	a. Pair. Nos. 8/9	5·00	5·00
9	80y. Tenkaichi Takigi-Noh (traditional dance)	2·40	1·60

Nos. 8/9 were issued in horizontal *se-tenant* pairs within the sheet.

6 Flowering Tree and Mountains

(Des Ninomiya Katsunori. Photo)

2004 (23 Apr). National Afforestation Campaign. P 13½.

10	**6**	50y. multicoloured	1·60	1·10

7 Hamayu (*crinums*) and Nichinan Beach (Miyazaki)

(Des Iwasaki Chizuru. Photo)

2005 (1 June). Flowers and Scenery of Kyushu. T **7** and similar vert designs. Multicoloured. P 13½.

11	50y. Type **7**		1·60	1·10
	a. Pair. Nos. 11/12		3·50	3·50
	b. Block of 10. Nos. 11/20		15·00	
12	50y. Sakura (cherry blossoms) and Kanmon bridge (Fukuoka)		1·60	1·10
13	50y. Kusunohana (camphor blossoms) and Ariake Sea (Saga)		1·60	1·10
	a. Pair. Nos. 13/14		3·50	3·50
14	50y. Unzen-Tsutsuji (azaleas) and Mt. Fugendake (Nagasaki)		1·60	1·10
15	50y. Tulips and Huis Ten Bosch (Nagasaki)		1·60	1·10
	a. Pair. Nos. 15/16		3·50	3·50
16	50y. Rindou (gentians) and Mt. Aso (Kumamoto)		1·60	1·10
17	50y. Ume blossoms and Mt. Takasaki (Ooita)		1·60	1·10
	a. Pair. Nos. 17/18		3·50	3·50
18	50y. Ume blossom and Dazaifu-Tenmangu Shrine (Fukuoka)		1·60	1·10
19	50y. Miyama-Kirishima (azaleas) and Kirishima mountains (Kagoshima)		1·60	1·10
	a. Pair. Nos. 19/20		3·50	3·50
20	50y. Hibiscus and Adan (screw-pine) (Kagoshima)		1·60	1·10
11/20 *Set of* 10			16·00	11·00

Nos. 11/20 were issued in *se-tenant* blocks of ten stamps within the sheet.

Nos. 11/20 were also issued by Fukuoka, Nagasaki, Saga, Oita, Kumamoto and Kagoshima on 1 June 2005.

Nagano

1 Monkeys

1989 (1 Apr). Photo. P 13.

1	**1**	62y. multicoloured	1·50	80

1990 (27 Apr). Flowers. Litho. P 13½.

2		62y. As Japan Type **1449**	3·75	2·50

2 Tsumago Inn

1990 (1 May). Inns. T **2** and similar vert design. Recess and photo. P 13.

3	62y. yellow-ochre and blackish brown		1·50	80
	a. Pair. Nos. 3/4		3·25	3·25
4	62y. olive-yellow and blackish brown		1·50	80

Designs: No. 3, Type **2**; No. 4 Magome.

Nos. 3/4 were issued in horizontal *se-tenant* pairs within the sheet.

3 Matsumoto-jo Castle

1993 (16 July). Photo. P 13½.

5	**3**	62y. multicoloured	1·50	1·00
		a. Pane. Nos. 5×10, with outer edges imperf	14·50	

4 Building, Kashiwabara

1994 (2 May). Photo. P 13½.

6	**4**	80y. multicoloured	1·90	1·10

5 Conductor and Orchestra

1996 (22 Aug). Saito Kinen Festival. Photo. P 13½×imperf.

7	**5**	80y. multicoloured	2·10	1·40

6 Campanula Flowers

1996 (22 Aug). Rindo. Litho. P 13½.

8	**6**	80y. multicoloured	2·10	1·40

7 Jomon's Venus

1998 (1 Apr). Photo. P 13½.
9   **7**   80y. multicoloured .... 2·10   1·40
    a. Pane. No. 9×10, with outer edges
    imperf .... 20·00

8 Horse Rider

1998 (17 July). Puppetry Festival. T **8** and similar vert design. Multicoloured. Litho. P 13½.
10   50y. Type **8**........................... 1·30   90
    a. Pair. Nos. 10/11 .... 2·75   2·75
    b. Pane. Nos. 10/11, each×5, with
    outer edges imperf .... 12·50
11   50y. Bird and man .... 1·30   90
Nos. 10/11 were issued in horizontal *se-tenant* pairs within the sheet, each pair forming a composite design.

9 Kiso Observatory, Tokyo University

1999 (9 Apr). Litho. P 13½.
12   **9**   80y. multicoloured .... 2·10   1·40
    a. Pane. No. 12×10, with outer edges
    imperf .... 20·00

10 Matsumoto Castle

1999 (26 Apr). Photo. P 13½.
13   **10**   80y. multicoloured .... 2·10   1·40
    a. Pane. No. 13×10, with outer edges
    imperf .... 20·00

1999 (16 July). Inns. Vert designs T **3**. Recess and photo. P 13.
14   62y. yellow-ochre and blackish brown . 2·10   1·40
    a. Pair. Nos. 14/15 .... 4·50   4·50
15   62y. olive-yellow and blackish brown ... 2·10   1·40
Designs: No. 14, Tsumago (As Type **3**); No. 15 Magome (As No. 4)
Nos. 14/15 were issued in horizontal *se-tenant* pairs within the sheet.

1999 (13 Oct). Photo. P 13.
16   **1**   80y. multicoloured .... 2·10   1·40

11 Cherry Blossom

(Des Isawa Kiyoshi. Photo)

2000 (3 Mar). P 13½.
17   **11**   80y. multicoloured .... 2·40   1·60
    a. Pane. No. 17×10, with outer edges
    imperf .... 23·00

12 Azumino

(Des Ooshima Kazuyoshi. Photo)

2000 (23 Mar). P 13½.
18   **12**   80y. multicoloured .... 2·40   1·60
    a. Pane. No. 18×10, with outer edges
    imperf .... 23·00

13 Fishing and Score

2000 (15 Dec). Shinano-no-kuni (prefecture song). T **13** and similar vert design. Multicoloured. Photo. P 13½.
19   50y. Type **13**........................... 1·60   1·10
    a. Pair. Nos. 10/11........................... 3·50   3·50
20   50y. Autumnal trees, bridge and score 1·60   1·10
Nos. 10/11 were issued in horizontal *se-tenant* pairs within the sheet.

14 Zenkoji Temple

265

2001 (23 May). Nagano Homeland. T **14** and similar vert design. Multicoloured. Litho. P 13½.

21	80y. Type **14**	2·50	1·70
	a. Pair. Nos. 10/11	5·25	5·25
	b. Pane. Nos. 21/22, each×5, with outer edges imperf	24·00	
22	80y. Mt. Iizunayama and apple blossoms	2·50	1·70

Nos. 21/2 were issued in horizontal *se-tenant* pairs within the sheet, each pair forming a composite design.

15 Dog's Tooth Violet Hakuba Mountains (Chushin area)

(Des Yamada Kyouko. Photo)

2003 (5 Mar). Flora. T **15** and similar vert designs. Multicoloured. P 13½.

23	50y. Type **15**	1·60	1·10
	a. Horiz strip of 4. Nos. 23/6	6·75	
24	50y. Skunk cabbage and Okususobana-shizen'en (Hokushin area)	1·60	1·10
25	50y. Lilies and Mt. Kirigamine (Nanshin area)	1·60	1·10
26	50y. Cosmos and Cosmos highway (Toshin area)	1·60	1·10
23/26 Set of 4		6·50	4·50

Nos. 23/6 were issued in horizontal *se-tenant* strips of four stamps within the sheet.

16 Apple Blossom

(Des Tanowaki Atsushi. Litho)

2005 (1 Apr). Flora. T **16** and similar vert designs. Multicoloured. P 13½.

27	50y. Type **16**	1·60	1·10
	a. Horiz strip of 4. Nos. 27/30	6·75	
28	50y. Renge-tsutsuji (renge azalea)	1·60	1·10
29	50y. Suzuran (lily of the valley)	1·60	1·10
30	50y. Rindou (gentian)	1·60	1·10
27/30 Set of 4		6·50	4·50

Nos. 27/30 were issued in horizontal *se-tenant* strips of four stamps within the sheet.

Nagasaki

1990 (27 Apr). Flowers. Litho. P 13½.

1	62y. As Japan Type **1475**	1·20	80

1 Ship and Gateway

1990 (1 Aug). Journey Expo. Litho. P 13.

2	1	62y. multicoloured	1·20	80

2 Dragon Dance, Kunci Festival

1994 (3 Oct). Photo. P 13½.

3	**2**	80y. multicoloured	1·90	1·30
		a. Pane. No. 3×10, with outer edges imperf	18·00	

1997 (3 June). Fukuoka. T **4** of Fukuoka and similar vert designs. Multicoloured. Litho. P 13.

4	80y. Fukuoka Type **4**	1·80	1·20
	a. Horiz strip of 4. Nos. 4/7	7·50	
5	80y. Early railway and map	1·80	1·20
6	80y. Interchange and map	1·80	1·20
7	80y. Building and map	1·80	1·20
4/7 Set of 4		7·25	4·75

Nos. 4/7 were issued in horizontal *se-tenant* strips of four stamps within the sheet each strip forming a composite design.

Nos. 4/7 were also issued by Saga and Fukuoka on 3 June 1997.

3 Mount Heisei Shinzan

1998 (20 May). Photo. P 13½.

8	**3**	80y. multicoloured	2·10	1·40
		a. Pane. No. 8×10, with outer edges imperf	20·00	

4 Dejima (artificial island)

1999 (1 Sept). Photo. P 13½.

9	**4**	80y. multicoloured	2·10	1·40
		a. Pane. No. 9×10, with outer edges imperf	20·00	

5 Former Alt House and Part of Former Ringer House

(Des Makita Yoshiaki. Litho)

2002 (1 Mar). Glover Garden (home of Thomas Blake Glover (industrialist)). T **5** and similar vert design. Multicoloured. P 13½.

10	50y. Type **5**..................................	1·50	1·00
	a. Pair. Nos. 10/11	3·25	3·25
11	50y. Part of former Ringer House and former Glover House	1·50	1·00

Nos. 10/11 were issued in horizontal se-tenant pairs within the sheet, each pair forming a composite design.

6 Tulips and Huis
Ten Bosch
(Nagasaki)

(Des Iwasaki Chizuru. Photo)

2005 (1 June). Flowers and Scenery of Kyushu. T **6** and similar vert designs. Multicoloured. P 13½.

12	50y. Type **6**..................................	1·60	1·10
	a. Pair. Nos. 12/13	3·50	3·50
	b. Block of 10. Nos. 12/21	15·00	
13	50y. Sakura (cherry blossoms) and Kanmon bridge (Fukuoka)...............	1·60	1·10
14	50y. Kusunohana (camphor blossoms) and Ariake Sea (Saga)........................	1·60	1·10
	a. Pair. Nos. 14/15	3·50	3·50
15	50y. Unzen-Tsutsuji (azaleas) and Mt. Fugendake (Nagasaki).....................	1·60	1·10
16	50y. Ume Blossom and Dazaifu-Tenmangu Shrine (Fukuoka)............	1·60	1·10
	a. Pair. Nos. 16/17	3·50	3·50
17	5y. Rindou (gentians) and Mt. Aso (Kumamoto)..........................	1·60	1·10
18	50y. Ume blossoms and Mt. Takasaki (Ooita)	1·60	1·10
	a. Pair. Nos. 18/19	3·50	3·50
19	50y. Hamayu (crinums) and Nichinan beach (Miyazaki)	1·60	1·10
20	50y. Miyama-Kirishima (azaleas) and Kirishima mountains (Kagoshima)	1·60	1·10
	a. Pair. Nos. 20/21	3·50	3·50
21	50y. Hibiscus and Adan (screw-pine) (Kagoshima)..........................	1·60	1·10
12/21	Set of 10	16·00	11·00

Nos. 12/21 were issued in se-tenant blocks of ten stamps within the sheet.

Nos. 12/21 were also issued by Fukuoka, Saga, Kumamoto, Oita, Miyazaki and Kagoshima on 1 June 2005.

Nara

1990 (27 Apr). Flowers. Litho. P 13½.

1	62y. As Japan Type **1462**	3·00	2·00

1 Mountain, Temple
and Building

1991 (25 Oct). Yoshino. T **1** and similar vert design. Multicoloured. Photo. P 13.

2	62y. Type **1**..................................	1·50	1·00
	a. Pair. Nos. 2/3	3·25	3·25
3	62y. Blossom..................................	1·50	1·00

Nos. 2/3 were issued in se-tenant pairs within the sheet.

1995 (6 Nov). Yoshino. Vert designs as T **1**. Multicoloured. Photo. P 13.

4	80y. Mountain, temple and building (As Type 1)................................	1·80	80
	a. Pair. Nos. 4/5	3·25	3·25
5	80y. Blossom (As No. 3)	1·80	80

Nos. 4/5 were issued in se-tenant pairs within the sheet.

2 Grass burning,
Mount Wakakusa

1996 (15 Nov). Photo. P 13½.

6	**2**	50y. multicoloured	1·30	90

3 Birds and
Landscape

1999 (28 Oct). Asuka. T **3** and similar vert design. Multicoloured. Litho. P 13½.

7	80y. Type **3**..................................	2·10	1·40
	a. Pair. Nos. 7/8	4·50	4·50
	b. Pane. Nos. 7/8, each×5, with outer edges imperf	20·00	
8	80y. Kofun (megalithic tomb)...................	2·10	1·40

Nos. 7/8 were issued in horizontal se-tenant pairs within the sheet.

4 Murouji's Five-
Storied Pagoda and
Rhododendrons

(Des Ogawa Hitomi. Photo)

2004 (26 Apr). National Heritage. P 13½.

9	**4**	80y. multicoloured	2·50	1·70

Niigata

1 Prefecture Hall

1989 (14 July). Photo. P 13
1   **1**   62y. multicoloured .... 1·30   70

1990 (27 Apr). Flowers. Litho. P 13½.
2   62y. As Japan Type **1450** .... 1·20   80

2 Koi Carp

1991 (1 May). Photo. P 13.
3   **2**   62y. multicoloured .... 1·80   70

3 Gogo-an
(Ryokon's hermit
hut)

1992 (1 May). Litho. P 13½.
4   **3**   41y. multicoloured .... 1·20   80

4 Soma Gyofu (poet)

1995 (1 May). Photo. P 13½.
5   **4**   80y. multicoloured .... 1·90   1·30
           a. Pane. No. 5×10, with outer edges
           imperf .... 18·00

5 Hanayome

1997 (18 June). *Seto no Hanayome (The Inland Sea Bride)*. Photo.
    P 13½.
6   **5**   50y. multicoloured .... 1·30   90
           a. Pane. No. 6×10, with outer edges
           imperf .... 12·50

6 Snow-covered
Buildings

1999 (12 Feb). Snow Festival. Litho. P 13½.
7   **6**   80y. multicoloured .... 2·10   1·40
           a. Pane. No. 7×10, with outer edges
           imperf .... 20·00

7 Kites

1999 (1 June). Kite Battle, Shirone. T **7** and similar vert design.
    Multicoloured. Litho. P 13½.
8   80y. Type **7**....................................... 2·10   1·40
           a. Pair. Nos. 8/9 .... 4·50   4·50
           b. Pane. Nos. 8/9, each×5, with outer
           edges imperf .... 20·00
9   80y. Kites (different) .... 2·10   1·40
    Nos. 8/9 were issued in horizontal *se-tenant* pairs within the sheet,
each pair forming a composite design.

8 Two Ibis

1999 (16 July). Toki (ibis (prefecture official bird)). T **8** and similar
    horiz design. Multicoloured. Litho. P 13½.
10   80y. Type **8**....................................... 2·10   1·40
           a. Pair. Nos. 10/11 .... 4·50   4·50
           b. Pane. Nos. 10/11, each×5, with
           outer edges imperf .... 20·00
11   80y. Ibis in flight .... 2·10   1·40
    Nos. 10/11 were issued in vertical *se-tenant* pairs within the sheet.

9 Cherry Blossoms,
Takada Castle at
Night

(Des Tsukuba Susumu. Litho)

2001 (10 Apr). P 13½.
12	**9**	80y. multicoloured	2·40	1·60
		a. Pane. No. 12×10, with outer edges imperf	23·00	

10 Fireworks

2001 (23 July). Grand Firework Festival, Nagaoka. T **10** and similar horiz design. Multicoloured. Litho. P 13½.
13		50y. Type **10**	1·50	1·00
		a. Pair. Nos. 13/14	3·25	3·25
		b. Pane. Nos. 13/14, each×5, with outer edges imperf	14·50	
14		50y. Fireworks (different)	1·50	1·00

Nos. 13/14 were issued in *se-tenant* pairs within the sheet, each pair forming a composite design.

11 Camellias and Kamoyama Kouen Park (Chu'etsu area)

(Des Yamada Kyouko. Litho)

2002 (1 May). Flowers of Echigo. T **11** and similar vert designs. Multicoloured. P 13½.
15		50y. Type **11**	1·50	1·00
		a. Strip of 4. Nos. 15/18	6·25	
16		50y. Daylily and Oonogame (Sado area)	1·50	1·00
17		50y. Iris and Ijimino Kouen Park (Ka'etsu area)	1·50	1·00
18		50y. *Shortia soldanelloides* and Mt. Myoukousan (Joetsu area)	1·50	1·00
15/18 Set of 4			6·00	4·00

Nos. 15/18 were issued in horizontal *se-tenant* strip of four stamps within the sheet.

Oita

1 Monkey

1989 (15 Aug). Litho. P 13.
1	**1**	62y. multicoloured	1·50	80

1990 (27 Apr). Litho. P 13½.
2		62y. As Japan Type **1477**	1·20	80

2 Tsurusaki Dancers

1992 (1 July). Photo. P 13½.
3	**2**	62y. multicoloured	1·20	80

3 Gion Festival, Hita

1998 (1 July). Photo. P 13½.
4	**3**	50y. multicoloured	1·30	90
		a. Pane. No. 4×10, with outer edges imperf	12·50	

4 Cliffs

1999 (1 Feb). Blue Tunnels. T **4** and similar horiz design. Multicoloured. Litho. P 13½.
5		80y. Type **4**	2·10	1·40
		a. Pair. Nos. 5/6	4·50	4·50
		b. Pane. Nos. 5/6, each×5, with outer edges imperf	20·00	
6		80y. Tunnel	2·10	1·40

Nos. 5/6 were issued in vertical *se-tenant* pairs within the sheet.

5 International Wheelchair Marathon

(Des Sasaki Goro. Litho)

2000 (11 Oct). P 13½.
7	**5**	80y. multicoloured	2·75	1·90
		a. Pane. No. 7×10, with outer edges imperf	27·00	

269

6 Ume Blossoms
and Mount Takasaki
(Ooita)

(Des Iwasaki Chizuru. Photo)

2005 (1 June). Flowers and Scenery of Kyushu. T **6** and similar vert
designs. Multicoloured. P 13½.

8		50y. Type **6**...............	1·60	1·10
		a. Pair. Nos. 8/9	3·50	3·50
		b. Block of 10. Nos. 8/17	15·00	
9		50y. Sakura (cherry blossoms) and Kanmon bridge (Fukuoka)...............	1·60	1·10
10		50y. Kusunohana (camphor blossoms) and Ariake Sea (Saga)............	1·60	1·10
		a. Pair. Nos. 10/11	3·50	3·50
11		50y. Unzen-Tsutsuji (azaleas) and Mt. Fugendake (Nagasaki)...............	1·60	1·10
12		50y. Tulips and Huis Ten Bosch (Nagasaki)...............	1·60	1·10
		a. Pair. Nos. 12/13	3·50	3·50
13		50y. Rindou (gentians) and Mt. Aso (Kumamoto)...............	1·60	1·10
14		50y. Ume blossom and Dazaifu-Tenmangu Shrine (Fukuoka)............	1·60	1·10
		a. Pair. Nos. 14/15	3·50	3·50
15		50y. Hamayu (crinums) and Nichinan beach (Miyazaki)	1·60	1·10
16		50y. Miyama-Kirishima (azaleas) and Kirishima mountains (Kagoshima)	1·60	1·10
		a. Pair. Nos. 16/17	3·50	3·50
17		50y. Hibiscus and Adan (screw-pine) (Kagoshima)...............	1·60	1·10
8/17 *Set of* 10...............			16·00	11·00

Nos. 8/17 were issued in *se-tenant* blocks of ten stamps within the
sheet.

Nos. 8/17 were also issued by Fukuoka, Nagasaki, Saga, Miyazaki,
Kumamoto and Kagoshima on 1 June 2005.

Okayama

1990 (27 Apr). Flowers. Litho. P 13½.

1		62y. As Japan Type 1466............	1·20	80

1 Pot with Lid

1991 (5 Apr). Bizen Ware. T **1** and similar vert design. Multicoloured.
Litho. P 13.

2		62y. Type **1**...............	1·20	80
		a. Pair. Nos. 2/3............	2·40	2·40
3		62y. Red glazed pot...............	1·20	80

Nos. 2/3 were issued in horizontal *se-tenant* pairs within the sheet.

2 Calligrapher

1995 (13 Oct). Niimi-no-sho Festival. Litho. P 13½.

3a	**2**	80y. multicoloured	2·10	1·40

3 Castle

1997 (30 May). 400th Anniv of Okayama Castle. Photo. P 13½.

4	**3**	80y. multicoloured	2·10	1·40
		a. Pane. No. 4×10, with outer edges imperf	20·00	

1999 (11 Jan). Photo. P 13½.

5		80y. As Hiroshima Type **4**	2·10	1·40
		a. Pane. No. 5×10, with outer edges imperf	20·00	

No. 5 was also issued by Hiroshima on 11 January 1999 .

4 Kurashiki District

1999 (25 May). Photo. P 13½.

6	**4**	80y. multicoloured	2·10	1·40
		a. Pane. No. 6×10, with outer edges imperf	20·00	

5 Cranes and Ume
Blossom

(Des Fujimoto Reiko. Photo)

2000 (2 Mar). 300th Anniv of Korkuen Garden. T **5** and similar vert
designs. Multicoloured. Photo. P13½.

7		80y. Type **5**...............	2·40	1·60
		a. Horiz strip of 4. Nos. 7/10................	9·75	
8		80y. Kayou-no-ike pond	2·40	1·60

9	80y. Yuishinzan mound		2·40	1·60
10	80y. Cranes flying over frozen stream ...		2·40	1·60
7/10 Set of 4			9·50	6·50

Nos. 7/10 were issued in horizontal *se-tenant* strips of four stamps within the sheet.

6 Momonohana
(peach blossoms)
and Traditional
Houses, Kurashiki

(Des Ozaki Shingo. Litho)

2000 (1 May). T **6** and similar vert designs. Multicoloured. P 13½.

11	50y. Type **6**	1·50	1·00
	a. Vert strip of 5. Nos. 11/15	7·75	
	b. Pane. Nos. 11/15, each×2, with outer edges imperf	14·50	
12	50y. Natsumikan (summer-orange blossoms) and Sea	1·50	1·00
13	50y. Nijisseikinashi (Japanese pear tree) and Tottori dune	1·50	1·00
14	50y. Botan (peonies) and Izumo-taisha Shrine	1·50	1·00
15	50y. Momiji (maple leaves) and Itsukushima Shrine Gate	1·50	1·00
11/15 Set of 5		7·50	5·00

Nos. 11/15 were issued in vertical strips of five stamps within the sheet.
Nos. 11/15 were also issued by Yamaguchi, Shimane, Tottori and Hiroshima on 1 May 2000.

7 Cherry Blossom,
Hiikawa River

(Des Moriyama Tomoki. Litho)

2002 (18 Mar). T **7** and similar vert design. Multicoloured. P 13½.

16	50y. Type **7**	1·50	1·00
	a. Pair. Nos. 16/17	3·25	3·25
	b. Pane. Nos. 16/17, each×5, with outer edges imperf	14·50	
17	50y. Pagoda, Bicchu-Kokubunji Temple	1·50	1·00

Nos. 16/17 were issued in horizontal *se-tenant* pairs within the sheet.
Nos. 16/17 were also issued by Shimane on 18 March 2002.

8 Main Hall, Kibitsu-
jinja Shrine and
Southern Zuijin
Gate

(Des Asaga Susumu. Photo)

2003 (5 Mar). Kibitsu Shrine. P 13½.

18	**8**	80y. multicoloured	2·40	1·60

9 Runner and
Momotaro Stadium

(Des Kashihara Marie. Photo)

2005 (1 Sept). 60th National Athletic Meet. P 13½.

19	**9**	50y. multicoloured	1·60	1·10

Okinawa

1 Temple, Shurei-no-
mon

1989 (15 May). Litho. P 13

1	**1**	62y. multicoloured	1·30	80

1990 (27 Apr). Flowers. Litho. P 13½.

2	62y. As Japan Type **1480**	1·20	80

2 Ryukyu Dancer

1990 (1 Aug). Photo. P 13.

3	**2**	62y. multicoloured	1·20	80

3 Black Pearls

1991 (1 Aug). Litho. P 13.

4	**3**	41y. multicoloured	1·50	70

4 Boat Race

1992 (17 Aug). Naha Ha-ree. Litho. P 13½.
5   **4**   62y. multicoloured .... 1·20   80

5 Tug of War

1994 (1 Aug). Photo. P 13½.
6   **5**   50y. multicoloured .... 1·20   80

6 Eisa Drummers

1995 (1 Aug). Photo. P 13½.
7   **6**   80y. multicoloured .... 1·90   1·30

7 Temple and Dragon

1996 (1 Aug). Shurijo. Photo. P 13½.
8   **7**   80y. multicoloured .... 2·10   1·40

8 Pineapples

1997 (2 June). Fruit. T **8** and similar vert design. Multicoloured. Photo. P 13½.
9   50y. Type **8**......................... 1·30   90
          a. Pair. Nos. 9/10......................... 2·75   2·75
10   50y. Mangoes .... 1·30   90
    Nos. 9/10 were issued in horizontal *se-tenant* pairs within the sheet.

9 Shanshin (three stringed instrument)

1998 (4 Mar). Photo. P 13½.
11   **9**   80y. multicoloured .... 2·10   1·40
              a. Pane. No. 11×10, with outer edges imperf......................... 20·00

10 Ryukyu Island 5 sen Stamp (Type **1**)

1998 (23 July). 50th Anniv of Okinawa Stamps. T **10** and similar vert design. Multicoloured. Photo. P 13½.
12   80y. Type **10**......................... 2·10   1·40
           a. Pair. Nos. 12/13 .... 4·50   4·50
13   80y. Ryukyu Island 5c. stamp (Type **218**)   2·10   1·40
    Nos. 12/13 were issued in horizontal *se-tenant* pairs within the sheet.

11 Woman

1999 (23 Mar). 125th Anniv of Post. T **11** and similar vert design. Multicoloured. Litho. P 13½.
14   80y. Type **11**......................... 2·10   1·40
           a. Pair. Nos. 4/5 .... 4·50   4·50
           b. Pane. Nos. 4/5, each×5, with outer edges imperf......................... 20·00
15   80y. Masks......................... 2·10   1·40
    Nos. 14/15 were issued in horizontal *se-tenant* pairs within the sheet.

12 Ryukyu Dancers

1999 (14 May). Photo. P 13½.
16   12   80y. multicoloured .... 2·10   1·40
            a. Pane. No. 16×10, with outer edges
            imperf .... 20·00

13 Boat, Fishers and
Iejima Tatchu Rock

1999 (23 July). Litho. P 13½.
17   13   80y. multicoloured .... 2·10   1·40
            a. Pane. No. 17×10, with outer edges
            imperf .... 20·00

14 Royal Family
Country Villa and
Bridge

1999 (28 Oct). Shikina-en Gardens. T **14** and similar vert design.
Multicoloured. Litho. P 13½.
18   50y. Type **14** .... 1·50   1·00
            a. Pair. Nos. 18/19 .... 3·25   3·25
            b. Pane. Nos. 18/19, each×5, with
            outer edges imperf .... 14·50
19   50y. Tea house and bridge .... 1·50   1·00
    Nos. 18/19 were issued in horizontal *se-tenant* pairs within the
sheet, each pair forming a composite design.

15 Abaca Cloth
(Tamanaha Yukou)

(Des Asato Moriaki. Litho)

2000 (17 Mar). P 13½.
20   15   50y. multicoloured .... 1·80   1·20
            a. Pane. No. 20×10, with outer edges
            imperf .... 17·00

16 Bankoku
Shinryokan
Conference Centre

(Des Chinen Hideyuki. Photo)

2000 (21 June). P 13½.
21   16   80y. multicoloured .... 2·75   1·80
            a. Pane. No. 21×10, with outer edges
            imperf .... 27·00

17 Memorial and
Flowers

(Des Chinen Hideyuki. Litho)

2001 (22 June). P 13½.
22   17   80y. multicoloured .... 2·40   1·60

18 Taiwan Cherry
and Iejima Island

(Des Amuro Fumio. Photo)

2002 (23 Aug). Flowers. T **18** and similar vert designs. Multicoloured.
P 13½.
23   50y. Type **18** .... 1·50   1·00
            a. Strip of 5. Nos. 23/27 .... 7·75
24   50y. Hibiscus and Kaichu-douro
            highway .... 1·50   1·00
25   50y. Bougainvillea and traditional
            house, Tsuboya .... 1·50   1·00
26   50y. Lilies and Higashi-hennazaki .... 1·50   1·00
27   50y. Seishika flowers and Seishika
            bridge .... 1·50   1·00
23/27 *Set of 5* .... 7·50   5·00
    Nos. 23/27, each×2, were issued in vertical *se-tenant* strips of
five stamps within sheets of ten stamps with enlarged illustrated
margin.

19 Monorail, Shurijo
Castle, and Coral
Tree Flowers

(Des Itou Miki. Litho)

2003 (8 Aug). Okinawa Urban Monorail. T **19** and similar vert design.
Multicoloured. P 13½.
28   50y. Type **19** .... 1·60   1·10
            a. Pair. Nos. 28/29 .... 3·50   3·50
29   50y. Monorail, Naha Airport, and
            hibiscus .... 1·60   1·10
    Nos. 28/29 were issued in horizontal *se-tenant* pairs within the
sheet.

20 Dancer and Theatre
Building

(Des Amuro Fumio. Litho)

2005 (21 Jan). Ryukyuan Dance and National Theatre Okinawa.
P 13½.

30	**20**	50y. multicoloured	....	1·60	1·10

21 Goya (bitter
melon)

(Des Oogimi Tsutomu. Litho)

2005 (6 May). P 13½.

31	**21**	50y. multicoloured	....	1·60	1·10

Osaka

1 Faces

1989 (2 Oct). Bunraku. Photo. P 13.

1	**1**	62y. multicoloured	....	1·30	70

1990 (27 Apr). Litho. P 13½.

2		62y. As Japan Type **1460**	....	1·20	80

2 Symbols of
Business

1992 (18 Sept). Business Park. Photo. P 13½.

3	**2**	41y. multicoloured	....	1·00	50

3 Danjiri Festival

1995 (4 Sept). Litho. P 13½.

4	**3**	80y. multicoloured	....	1·90	1·30

4 Gymnast

1999 (27 Sept). Litho. P 13½.

5	**4**	80y. multicoloured	....	2·10	1·40

5 Performers and
Puppets

(Des Kagitani Setsuko. Litho)

2000 (28 June). World Performing Arts Festival. P 13½.

6	**5**	80y. multicoloured	....	2·75	1·80

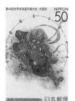

6 Thunder God
playing Table Tennis

(Des Terada Takashi. Photo)

2001 (3 Apr). Sports. T **6** and similar vert designs. Multicoloured.
P 13½.

7	50y. Type **6**	....	1·50	1·00
	a. Horiz strip. Nos. 7/10	....	6·25	
8	50y. Wind God playing table tennis	....	1·50	1·00
9	50y. Bowling	....	1·50	1·00
10	50y. Taekwondo	....	1·50	1·00
7/10	Set of 4	....	6·00	4·00

Nos. 7/10 were issued in horizontal *se-tenant* strips of four stamps
within the sheet.

7 Namdaemun,
Seoul and Doton-
bori, Osaka

(Des Kikuchi Akira. Litho)

2001 (6 July). 14th General Assembly of World Trade Organization.
  T **7** and similar vert designs. Multicoloured. P 13½.
11   80y. Type **7**.. 2·40   1·60
             a. Pair. Nos. 11/12 .... 5·00   5·00
12   80y. Bunraku actors, Japan and
             Nong-ak drummers, Korea .... 2·40   1·60
   Nos. 11/12 were issued in horizontal *se-tenant* pairs within the
sheet.

8 Osaka Dome and
Lion (part of railing,
Naniwabashi bridge)

(Des Morita Motoharu. Photo)

2002 (1 July). 85th Lions Clubs International Convention. P 13½.
13   **8**   80y. multicoloured .... 2·20   1·50

9 Scouts and Osaka
Castle

(Des Ootsuka Etuko. Photo)

2002 (15 July). 23rd Asia-Pacific Scout Jamboree. P 13½.
14   **9**   50y. multicoloured .... 1·80   1·20

10 Rotary Emblem
and Irises

(Des Morita Motoharu. Photo)

2004 (21 May). Rotary International Convention, Osaka. P 13½.
15   **10**   80y. multicoloured .... 2·50   1·70
   No. 15 was issued in sheetlets of ten (5×2) stamps with enlarged
illustrated margin.

Saga

1990 (27 Apr). Litho. P 13½.
1   62y. As Japan Type 1474............................. 1·20   80

1 Yoshinogari
Historical Park

1991 (12 Apr). Photo. P 13.
2   **1**   62y. multicoloured .... 1·20   80

2 Karatsu-Kunchi

1995 (2 Oct). Photo. P 13½.
3   **2**   80y. multicoloured .... 1·90   1·30
             a. Pane. No. 3×10, with outer edges
                imperf .... 18·00

3 Vase

1996 (17 May). World Ceramic Exhibition. Photo. P 13½.
4   **3**   80y. multicoloured .... 1·80   1·20

1997 (3 June). As Fukuoka T **4** and similar vert designs. Multicoloured.
  Litho. P 13½.
5   80y. As Fukuoka Type **4**.............................. 1·80   1·20
             a. Horiz strip of 4. Nos. 5/8 .... 7·50
6   80y. Early railway and map...................... 1·80   1·20
7   80y. Interchange and map.................... 1·80   1·20
8   80y. Building and map .... 1·80   1·20
5/8 *Set of 4*... 7·25   4·75
   Nos. 5/8 were issued in horizontal *se-tenant* strips of four stamps
within the sheet each strip forming a composite design.
   Nos. 5/8 were also issued by Nagasaki and Fukuoka on 3 June
1997.

4 Yoshinogari
Historical Park

1999 (11 Nov). Photo. P 13½.
9   **4**   80y. multicoloured .... 2·20   1·50
    a. Pane. No. 9×10, with outer edges
    imperf .... 21·00

5 Child in Air
Balloon

(Des Nakajima Kiyoshi. Litho)

2000 (1 Nov). International Balloon Festival. P 13½.
10   **5**   80y. multicoloured .... 2·75   1·90
    a. Pane. No. 10×10, with outer edges
    imperf .... 27·00

6 Iroe Komainu (lion
dog) and
"Sometsuke Arita
Sarayama-shokunin-
zukushi-ezu oozara
(blue and white
ceramic ware
depicting ceramic
workers)

(Des Arita Touji Bijutsukan. Litho)

2003 (10 Apr). Imari-Arita Ceramics. P 13½.
11   **6**   80y. multicoloured .... 2·40   1·60

7 Kusunohana
(camphor blossoms)
and Ariake Sea
(Saga)

(Des Iwasaki Chizuru. Photo)

2005 (1 June). T **7** and similar vert designs. Multicoloured. Litho.
  P 13½.
12   50y. Type **7** .... 1·60   1·10
    a. Pair. Nos. 12/13 .... 3·50   3·50
    b. Block of 10. Nos. 12/21 .... 15·00
13   50y. Sakura (cherry blossoms) and
    Kanmon bridge (Fukuoka) .... 1·60   1·10
14   50y. Ume Blossom and Dazaifu-
    Tenmangu Shrine (Fukuoka) .... 1·60   1·10
    a. Pair. Nos. 14/15 .... 3·50   3·50
15   50y. Unzen-Tsutsuji (azaleas) and Mt.
    Fugendake (Nagasaki) .... 1·60   1·10
16   50y. Tulips and Huis Ten Bosch
    (Nagasaki) .... 1·60   1·10
    a. Pair. Nos. 16/17 .... 3·50   3·50
17   50y. Rindou (gentians) and Mt. Aso
    (Kumamoto) .... 1·60   1·10
18   50y. Ume blossoms and Mt. Takasaki
    (Ooita) .... 1·60   1·10
    a. Pair. Nos. 18/19 .... 3·50   3·50
19   50y. Hamayu (crinums) and Nichinan
    beach (Miyazaki) .... 1·60   1·10
20   50y. Miyama-Kirishima (azaleas) and
    Kirishima mountains (Kagoshima) ... 1·60   1·10
    a. Pair. Nos. 20/21 .... 3·50   3·50
21   50y. Hibiscus and Adan (screw-pine)
    (Kagoshima) .... 1·60   1·10
12/21 *Set of* 10 .... 16·00   11·00
    Nos. 12/21 were issued in *se-tenant* blocks of ten stamps within
the sheet.
    Nos. 12/21 were also issued by Fukuoka, Nagasaki, Kumamoto,
Oita, Miyazaki and Kagoshima on 1 June 2005.

Saitama

1990 (27 Apr). Litho. P 13½.
1   62y. As Japan Type **1444** .... 1·20   80

1 Stylized Children

1990 (12 Oct). *Tōryanse* (children's song). Litho. P 13.
2   **1**   62y. multicoloured .... 1·20   80

2 Kuroyama-san-
taki Waterfalls

1995 (7 July). Photo. P 13½.
3   **2**   80y. multicoloured .... 1·90   1·30
    a. Pane. No. 3×10, with outer edges
    imperf .... 18·00

3 Hozoji Pond

1997 (1 Aug). Photo. P 13½.

4	**3**	50y. multicoloured	1·80	1·20
		a. Pane. No. 4×10, with outer edges imperf	17·00	

4 Collared Doves and Walkers

1997 (28 Oct). Walking Festival. Litho. P 13½.

5	**4**	80y. multicoloured	2·10	1·40
		a. Pane. No. 5×10, with outer edges imperf	20·00	

5 Dove and Buildings

(Des Shimoda Koichi. Photo)

2000 (1 May). New Urban Centre. T **5** and similar vert design. Multicoloured. P 13½.

6		50y. Type **5**	1·50	1·00
		a. Pair. Nos. 6/7	3·25	3·25
		b. Pane. Nos. 6/7, each×5, with outer edges imperf	14·50	
7		50y. Buildings and flowers	1·50	1·00

Nos. 6/7 were issued in horizontal *se-tenant* pairs within the sheet, each pair forming a composite design.

6 Yatai and Fireworks

(Des Itou Takumi. Photo)

2000 (1 Nov). Night Festival, Chichibu. T **6** and similar vert design. Multicoloured. P 13½.

8		80y. Type **6**	2·75	1·90
		a. Pair. Nos. 8/9	5·75	5·75

		b. Pane. Nos. 8/9, each×5, with outer edges imperf	27·00	
9		80y. Kasahoko	2·75	1·90

Nos. 8/9 were issued in horizontal *se-tenant* pairs within the sheet.

7 Bonsai Tree

(Des Sekine Masao. Photo)

2002 (26 Apr). P 13½.

10	**7**	80y. multicoloured	2·20	1·50

8 Primrose and Tajimagahara Primrose Field

(Des Ohya Takayumi. Photo)

2004 (23 June). Flowers of Kanto. T **8** and similar vert designs. Multicoloured. P 13½.

11		50y. Type **8**	1·60	1·10
		a. Vert strip of 5. Nos. 11/15	8·25	
12		50y. Yoshi azalea and Lake Chuzenjiko	1·60	1·10
13		50y. Japanese azalea and Mt. Akagisan	1·60	1·10
14		50y. Rose and Mount Tsukubasan	1·60	1·10
15		50y. Rape blossom and Nojimazaki lighthouse	1·60	1·10
11/15	*Set of 5*		8·00	5·50

Nos. 11/15 were issued in vertical strips of five stamps within the sheet.

Nos. 11/15 were also issued by Tochigi, Chiba, Gunma and Ibaraki on 23 June 2004.

9 Gymnast

(Des Kanayama Satoshi. Photo)

2004 (10 Sept). National Athletic Meet. P 13½.

16	**9**	50y. multicoloured	1·60	1·10

10 Allspice Flowers and Mount Bukousan (Saitama)

(Des Ozaki Shingo. Photo)

2005 (23 June). Flowers of Kanto (2nd issue). T **10** and similar vert designs. Multicoloured. P 13½.

17	50y. Type **10**		1·60	1·10
	a. Vert strip of 5. Nos. 17/21		8·25	
18	50y. Nikko-kisuge (Nikko day lily) and Kirifuri Heights (Tochigi)		1·60	1·10
19	50y. Sunflowers at Hana-hotaru (Chiba)		1·60	1·10
20	50y. Bush clover, Kairakuen garden (Ibaraki)		1·60	1·10
21	50y. Azaleas, Tsutsujigaoka Park (Gunma)		1·60	1·10
17/21 Set of 5			8·00	5·50

Nos. 17/21 were issued in vertical strips of five stamps within the sheet.

Nos. 17/21 were also issued by Gunma, Tochigi, Chiba and Ibaraki on 23 June 2005.

Shiga

1 Figurine

1989 (2 Oct). Shigaraki Ware. Litho. P 13.

1	**1**	62y. multicoloured	1·30	60

1990 (27 Apr). Flowers. Litho. P 13½.

2		62y. As Japan Type **1458**	3·00	2·00

2 Yachts, Lake Biwa

1993 (1 July). Photo. P 13½.

3	**2**	62y. multicoloured	1·50	1·00
		a. Pane. No. 3×10, with outer edges imperf	14·50	

3 Temple

1996 (1 July). Mount Hiei. Photo. P 13½.

4	**3**	80y. multicoloured	2·10	1·40
		a. Pane. No. 4×10, with outer edges imperf	20·00	

4 Trout and Rhododendron

(Des Kikuchi Akira. Litho)

2001 (1 Oct). Ninth International Conference on the Conservation and Management of Lakes. P 13½.

5	**4**	50y. multicoloured	1·60	1·10
		a. Pane. No. 5×10, with outer edges imperf	15·00	

Shimane

1990 (27 Apr). Flowers. Litho. P 13½.

1		62y. As Japan Type **1465**	1·20	80

1 Yasukibushi Dancer

1990 (15 Aug). Photo. P 13.

2	**1**	62y. multicoloured	1·20	80

2 Izumo-no-Okuni (dancer and founder Kubuki theatre)

1994 (2 May). Litho. P 13½.

3	**2**	80y. multicoloured	1·90	1·10
		a. Pane. No. 3×10, with outer edges imperf	18·00	

3 Railway bridge, Tsuwano

1999 (13 Oct). T **3** and similar horiz design. Multicoloured. Photo.
P 13½.
4	80y. Type **3**	2·10	1·40
	a. Pair. Nos. 4/5	4·50	4·50
	b. Pane. Nos. 4/5, each×5, with outer		
	edges imperf	20·00	
5	80y. Street, Hagi	2·10	1·40

Nos. 4/5 were issued in vertical *se-tenant* pairs within the sheet.
Nos. 4/5 were also issued by Yamaguchi on 13 October 1999.

4 Botan (peonies)
and Izumo-taisha
Shrine

(Des Ozaki Shingo. Litho)

2000 (1 May). T **4** and similar vert designs. Multicoloured. P 13½.
6	50y. Type **4**	1·50	1·00
	a. Vert strip of 5. Nos. 6/10	7·75	
	b. Pane. Nos. 6/10, each×2, with		
	outer edges imperf	14·00	
7	50y. Natsumikan (summer-orange		
	blossoms) and Sea	1·50	1·00
8	50y. Nijisseikinashi (Japanese pear		
	tree) and Tottori dune	1·50	1·00
9	50y. Momonohana (peach blossoms)		
	and traditional houses in Kurashiki	1·50	1·00
10	50y. Momiji (maple leaves) and		
	Itsukushima Shrine Gate	1·50	1·00
6/10 *Set of 5*		7·50	5·00

Nos. 6/10 were issued in vertical strips of five stamps within the
sheet.
Nos. 6/10 were also issued by Yamaguchi, Shimane, Okayama and
Hiroshima on 1 May 2000.

5 Matsue Castle and
Cherry Blossoms

(Des Hibi Sadao. Litho)

2001 (21 Mar). Matsue Castle and Tea Ceremony Culture. T **5** and
similar vert design. Multicoloured. P 13½.
11	80y. Type **5**	2·40	1·60
	a. Pair. Nos. 11/12	5·00	5·00
	b. Pane. Nos. 11/12, each×5, with		
	outer edges imperf	23·00	
12	80y. Meimei-an teahouse and camellias	2·40	1·60

Nos. 11/12 were issued in vertical *se-tenant* pairs within the sheet.

6 Pagoda, Bicchu-
Kokubunji Temple

(Des Moriyama Tomoki. Litho)

2002 (18 Mar). T **6** and similar vert design. Multicoloured. P 13½.
13	50y. Type **6**	1·50	1·00
	a. Pair. Nos. 13/14	3·25	3·25
	b. Pane. Nos. 13/14, each×5, with		
	outer edges imperf	14·00	
14	50y. Cherry Blossom, Hiikawa River	1·50	1·00

Nos. 13/14 were issued in horizontal *se-tenant* pairs within the
sheet.
Nos. 13/14 were also issued Okayama on 18 March 2002.

Shizuoka

1990 (27 Apr). Flowers. Litho. P 13½.
1	62y. As Japan Type **1455**	3·00	2·00

1 Tea Gatherer

1990 (2 May). Photo. P 13.
2	**1**	62y. multicoloured	1·20	50

2 Magpie and
Mount Fuji

1993 (23 June). Photo. P 13½.
3	**2**	41y. multicoloured	1·30	90
		a. Pane. No.3×10, with outer edges		
		imperf	12·50	

3 Tea Pickers

1997 (25 Apr). Photo. P 13½.
4	**3**	50y. multicoloured	1·30	90

4 Cattle and Mount
Fuji

1997 (25 Apr). Mount Fuji. T **4** and similar vert design. Multicoloured. Photo. P 13½.

5		80y. Type **4**	2·10	1·40
		a. Pair. Nos. 5/6	4·50	4·50
		b. Pane. Nos. 5/6, each×5, with outer edges imperf	20·00	
6		80y. Mount Fuji at dusk	2·10	1·40

Nos. 5/6 were issued in horizontal *se-tenant* pairs within the sheet.

5 Softball Players

1998 (22 June). Photo. P 13½.

7	**5**	80y. multicoloured	2·10	1·40
		a. Pane. No. 7×10, with outer edges imperf	20·00	

6 Shimizu Port

1999 (2 Aug). Litho. P 13½.

8	**6**	80y. multicoloured	2·10	1·40
		a. Pane. No. 8×10, with outer edges imperf	20·00	

7 Atami-baien Ume Orchard

(Des Kayama Yuzo. Litho)

2000 (29 Nov). Izu. T **7** and similar vert design. Multicoloured. P 13½.

9		50y. Type **7**	1·80	1·20
		a. Pair. Nos. 9/10	3·75	3·75
		b. Pane. Nos. 9/10, each×5, with outer edges imperf	17·00	
10		50y. Kawazu-nanadaru waterfalls and statues	1·80	1·20

Nos. 9/10 were issued in horizontal *se-tenant* pairs within the sheet.

8 Palace Festival Float

(Des Kayama Yuzo. Litho)

2001 (1 May). Hamamatsu Festival. T **8** and similar vert design. Multicoloured. P 13½.

11		80y. Type **8**	2·50	1·70
		a. Pair. Nos. 11/12	5·25	5·25
		b. Pane. Nos. 11/12, each×5, with outer edges imperf	24·00	
12		80y. Kite match	2·50	1·70

Nos. 11/12 were issued in horizontal *se-tenant* pairs within the sheet.

9 Football Players, Mount Fuji and Azaleas

(Des Yamazaki Masao. Photo)

2003 (29 Aug). National Athletic Meet. P 13½.

13	**9**	50y. multicoloured	1·60	1·10

10 Gerbera

(Des Takahashi Sana. Litho)

2004 (8 Apr). Flora. T **10** and similar vert designs. Multicoloured. Litho. P 13½.

14		80y. Type **10**	2·50	1·70
		a. Horiz strip of 4. Nos. 14/17	10·50	
15		80y. Carnations	2·50	1·70
16		80y. Roses	2·50	1·70
17		80y. Prairie gentian	2·50	1·70
14/17	Set of 4		10·00	6·75

Nos. 14/17 were issued in horizontal *se-tenant* strips of four stamps within the sheet.

11 Ryozenji Temple

2004 (5 Nov). Cultural Heritage. Temples (1st series). T **11** and similar vert designs. Multicoloured. Litho. P 13½.

18		80y. Type **11**	2·50	1·70
		a. Sheet of 20. Nos. 18/37	45·00	
19		80y. Bells encircling tree, Gokurakuji Temple	2·50	1·70
20		80y. Courtyard, Konsenji Temple	2·50	1·70
21		80y. Row of statues, Dainichiji Temple	2·50	1·70
22		80y. Roofs, statue and pagoda, Tatsueji Temple	2·50	1·70
23		80y. Veranda and pagoda, Kakurinji Temple	2·50	1·70
24		80y. Trees at night, Tairyuji Temple	2·50	1·70

25	80y. Shrine and steps, Byoudouji		
	Temple	2·50	1·70
26	80y. Decorated panels, Iwamotoji		
	Temple	2·50	1·70
27	80y. Stone turtle, Kongoufukuji Temple	2·50	1·70
28	80y. Plants, stone lantern and monks,		
	Enkouji Temple	2·50	1·70
29	80y. Steps and gateway, Kanjizaiji		
	Temple	2·50	1·70
30	80y. Interior, Nankoubou Temple	2·50	1·70
31	80y. Pebbles and roofs, Taizanji Temple	2·50	1·70
32	80y. Autumn leaves and statue, Eifukuji		
	Temple	2·50	1·70
33	80y. God (Bishamon)(statue), Sennyuji		
	Temple	2·50	1·70
34	80y. Trees, bell and pathway,		
	Shusshakaji Temple	2·50	1·70
35	80y. Wide path, tree, steps and		
	gateway, Kouyamaji Temple	2·50	1·70
36	80y. Metal staff, Zentsuji Temple	2·50	1·70
37	80y. Courtyard, Kouzouji Temple	2·50	1·70
18/37 *Set of 20*		50·00	34·00

Nos. 18/37 were issued in *se-tenant* sheets of 20 stamps.

Tochigi

1990 (27 Apr). Flowers. Litho. P 13½.

1	62y. As Japan Type **1442**	1·20	80

1 Walkers in
Countryside

1991 (29 May). Photo. P 13.

2	**1**	62y. multicoloured	1·20	80

2 Kirifuri-no-taki
Waterfall

1995 (27 Oct). Photo. P 13½.

3	**2**	50y. multicoloured	1·30	80
		a. Pane. No. 3×10, with outer edges		
		imperf	12·50	

3 Mountain and
Lake

1999 (1 Mar). Lake Chuzenji. T **3** and similar vert design. Multicoloured. Photo. P 13½.

4	80y. Type **3**	2·10	1·40
	a. Pair. Nos. 4/5	4·50	4·50
	b. Pane. Nos. 4/5, each×5, with		
	outer edges imperf	20·00	
5	80y. Autumn leaves and lake	2·10	1·40

Nos. 4/5 were issued in horizontal *se-tenant* pairs within the sheet.

4 Ashikaga School

(Des Aoki Shohei. Photo)

2001 (11 May). Ashikaga School. T **4** and similar vert design. Multicoloured. P 13½.

6	50y. Type **4**	2·10	1·40
	a. Pair. Nos. 6/7	4·50	4·50
	b. Pane. Nos. 6/7, each×5, with outer		
	edges imperf	20·00	
7	80y. Gate, Ashikaga School	2·10	1·40

Nos. 6/7 were issued in horizontal *se-tenant* pairs within the sheet.

5 Rape Blossom
and Nojimazaki
Lighthouse

(Des Ohya Takayumi. Photo)

2004 (23 June). Flowers of Kanto. T **5** and similar vert designs. Multicoloured. P 13½.

8	50y. Type **5**	1·60	1·10
	a. Vert strip of 5. Nos. 8/12	8·25	
9	50y. Yoshi azalea and Lake Chuzenjiko	1·60	1·10
10	50y. Japanese azalea and Mt. Akagisan	1·60	1·10
11	50y. Primrose and Tajimagahara native		
	primrose field	1·60	1·10
12	50y. Rose and Mount Tsukubasan	1·60	1·10
8/12 *Set of 5*		8·00	5·50

Nos. 8/12 were issued in vertical strips of five stamps within the sheet.

Nos. 8/12 were also issued by Tochigi, Saitama, Gunma and Ibaraki on 23 June 2004.

6 Nikko-kisuge
(Nikko day lily) and
Kirifuri Heights
(Tochigi)

(Des Ozaki Shingo. Photo)

2005 (23 June). Flowers of Kanto (2nd issue). T **8** and similar vert designs. Multicoloured. P 13½.

13		50y. Type **8**..................................	1·60	1·10
		a. Vert strip of 5. Nos. 13/17.................	8·25	
14		50y. Azaleas, Tsutsujigaoka Park (Gunma)............................	1·60	1·10
15		50y. Sunflowers at Hana-hotaru (Chiba)	1·60	1·10
16		50y. Bush clover, Kairakuen garden (Ibaraki)...........................	1·60	1·10
17		50y. Allspice flowers and Mt. Bukousan (Saitama)...........................	1·60	1·10
13/17 *Set of 5*...			8·00	5·50

Nos. 13/17 were issued in vertical strips of five stamps within the sheet.

Nos. 13/17 were also issued by Gunma, Saitama, Chiba and Ibaraki on 23 June 2005.

Tokushima

1990 (27 Apr). Litho. P 13½.

1	62y. As Japan Type **1469**...........................	1·50	1·00

1 Puppet (head and shoulders)

1991 (26 June). Litho. P 13.

2	**1**	62y. multicoloured	1·30	70

2 Awa-odori Dancers

1994 (1 Aug). Photo. P 13½.

3	**2**	50y. multicoloured	1·50	1·00

3 Bridge

1998 (20 Mar). Kobe-Awaji-Naruto Expressway. T **3** and similar vert design. Multicoloured. Photo. P 13½.

4	80y. Type **3**...................................	2·10	1·40
	a. Pair. Nos. 4/5	4·50	4·50
	b. Pane. Nos. 4/5, each×5, with outer edges imperf	20·00	
5	80y. Bridge (different)..........................	2·10	1·40

Nos. 4/5 were issued in *se-tenant* pairs within the sheet. Nos. 4/5 were also issued by Hyogo on 20 March 1998.

4 Awa-odori Dancers

(Des Iihara Kazuo. Litho)

2000 (31 July). P 13½.

6	**4**	80y. multicoloured	2·75	1·90
		a. Pane. No. 6×10, with outer edges imperf	27·00	

5 Sudachi (sour citrus fruit) and Mt. Tsurugisan (Tokushima)

(Des Kikuchi Akira. Photo)

2002 (20 Mar). T **5** and similar vert designs. Multicoloured. P 13½.

7		50y. Type **5**...................................	1·50	1·00
		a. Vert strip of 4. Nos. 7/10	6·25	
8		50y. Mikan (mandarin oranges) and Sata-misaki Promontory (Ehime) ...	1·50	1·00
9		50y. Yamamomo (bayberry) and Tengu highland (Kochi)...............................	1·50	1·00
10		50y. Olive and Shodoshima island (Kagawa)	1·50	1·00
7/10 *Set of 4*...			6·00	4·00

Nos. 7/10 were issued in vertical strips of four stamps within the sheet.

Nos. 7/10 were also issued by Ehime, Kochi and Kagawa on 20 March 2002.

2005 (8 July). Cultural Heritage. Shizuoka Temples (2nd series). Ehime Type **8** and similar vert designs. Multicoloured. Litho. P 13½.

11	80y. As Ehime Type **8**	2·50	1·70
	a. Sheet of 20. Nos. 11/30	45·00	
12	80y. Seated Buddha, Anrakuji Temple...	2·50	1·70
13	80y. Inscribed belfry gateway, Jurakuji Temple	2·50	1·70
14	80y. Double roofed gateway, Kumadaniji Temple............................	2·50	1·70
15	80y. Pagoda, Yakuoji Temple.................	2·50	1·70
16	80y. Statues, ramp, lanterns and pagoda, Hotsumisakiji Temple.......	2·50	1·70
17	80y. Gateway and long steep steps, Shinjouji Temple............................	2·50	1·70
18	80y. Path, gateway, steps and main temple, Kongochoji Temple............	2·50	1·70
19	80y. Buddha seated on peacock, Ryukoji Temple	2·50	1·70
20	80y. Bell and autumn colour, Butsumokuji Temple.......................	2·50	1·70
21	80y. Dragon, Meisekiji Temple...............	2·50	1·70
22	80y. Steps and many roofed buildings, Daihouji Temple	2·50	1·70
23	80y. Carved decorative gable, Kokubunji Temple............................	2·50	1·70
24	80y. Leafless tree and snow-covered building, Yokomineji Temple	2·50	1·70
25	80y. Buddha, Kouonji Temple...............	2·50	1·70
26	80y. Courtyard and building, Houjuji Temple	2·50	1·70

27 80y. Inscribed pillars and gateway,
    Douryuji Temple........................ 2·50 1·70
28 80y. Wall mounted statues, Goushouji
    Temple..................................... 2·50 1·70
29 80y. Eagle surmounting gateway,
    Tennouji Temple........................ 2·50 1·70
30 80y. Courtyard with stone lined path
    and building, Kokubunji Temple.... 2·50 1·70
11/30 Set of 20 .... 50·00 34·00
Nos. 11/30 were issued in *se-tenant* sheets of 20 stamps.
Nos. 11/30 were also issued by Ehime, Kochi and Kagawa on 8 July
2005.

5 Rainbow Bridge

1994 (23 Mar). Litho. P 13½.
6   **5**   50y. multicoloured .... 1·90 1·30
            a. Pane. No. 6×10, with outer edges
               imperf .... 18·00

Tokyo

1 Station Building

1989 (1 Nov). Tokyo Station. Litho. P 13.
1   **1**   62y. multicoloured .... 1·30 70

1990 (27 Apr). Litho. P 13½.
2   62y. As Japan Type **1448** .... 1·20 80

2 Shin-Tokyo Post Office

1990 (6 Aug). Litho. P 13.
3   **2**   62y. multicoloured .... 1·50 80

3 Fringed Orchids

1991 (1 July). Litho. P 13.
4   **3**   41y. multicoloured .... 1·30 80

4 Blossom and Forest, Mount
Takao-san

1993 (23 Apr). Photo. P 13½.
5   **4**   62y. multicoloured .... 1·50 1·00
            a. Pane. No. 5×10, with outer edges
               imperf .... 14·50

6 Akamon

7 Kaminarimon Gate

1995 (7 July). Photo. P 13½.
7   **6**   50y. multicoloured .... 1·20 70

1996 (8 Aug). Photo. P 13½×imperf.
8   **7**   80y. multicoloured .... 2·10 1·40

8

9

10

11

12

1997 (1 Oct). Places of Interest. Litho. P 13½.
9   **8**   80y. multicoloured .... 1·80 1·20
            a. Vert strip of 5. Nos. 9/13 .... 9·25
            b. Pane. Nos. 9/13, each×2, with
               outer edges imperf .... 17·00

10	**9**	80y. multicoloured		1·80	1·20
11	**10**	80y. multicoloured		1·80	1·20
12	**11**	80y. multicoloured		1·80	1·20
13	**12**	80y. multicoloured		1·80	1·20

9/13 *Set of 5* .... 9·00 6·00

Nos. 9/13 were issued in vertical strips of five stamps within the sheet.

13 Gateway

1998 (19 May). Business Show. Litho. P 13½.

14   **13**   80y. multicoloured .... 1·80 1·20

14 Tama Monorail

1998 (26 Nov). Photo. P 13½.

15   **14**   80y. multicoloured .... 2·10 1·40
      a. Pane. No. 15×10, with outer edges
       imperf .... 20·00

15 Orchid

1999 (12 Feb). T **15** and similar vert design. Multicoloured. Photo. P 13½.

16   80y. Type **15** .... 2·10 1·40
      a. Pair. Nos. 16/17 .... 4·50 4·50
      b. Pane. Nos. 16/17, each×5 .... 20·00
17   80y. Pink orchid .... 2·10 1·40

Nos. 16/17 were issued in horizontal *se-tenant* pairs within the sheet.

16 Fireworks and Bridge

1999 (1 July). Sumidagawa River Firework Display. T **16** and similar vert designs. Multicoloured. Photo. P 13½.

18   80y. Type **16** .... 2·10 1·40
      a. Pair. Nos. 18/19 .... 4·50

19   80y. Fireworks and bridge (different)..... 2·10 1·40
20   80y. Pink morning glory blossom .... 2·10 1·40
18/20 *Set of 3* .... 6·25 4·25

Nos. 18/19 were issued in horizontal *se-tenant* pairs within the sheet, each pair forming a composite design.

17 Whales

(Des Hasegawa Makoto and Shimoda Kouichi. Litho)

2000 (12 Jan). Tourism. T **17** and similar horiz designs. Multicoloured. P 13½.

21   50y. Type **17** .... 1·50 1·00
      a. Strip of 5. Nos. 21/5 .... 7·75
      b. Pane. Nos. 21/22, each×5, with
       outer edges imperf .... 14·00
22   50y. Mother and child .... 1·50 1·00
23   50y. Sanja-matsuri festival .... 1·50 1·00
24   50y. Family and gingko trees .... 1·50 1·00
25   50y. Odaiba-kaihin park at night........... 1·50 1·00
21/5 *Set of 5* .... 7·50 5·00

Nos. 21/5 were issued in horizontal strips of five stamps within the sheet.

18 Cosmos Flowers

(Des Kagawa Gentaro. Photo)

2000 (1 June). Seasonal Splendours (1st series). T **18** and similar vert designs. Multicoloured. P 13½.

26   50y. Type **18** .... 1·50 1·00
      a. Vert strip of 5. Nos. 26/30 .... 7·75
      b. Pane. Nos. 26/30, each×2, with
       outer edges imperf .... 14·00
27   50y. Roses .... 1·50 1·00
28   50y. Bird of Paradise flowers .... 1·50 1·00
29   50y. Camellias .... 1·50 1·00
30   50y. Freesias .... 1·50 1·00
26/30 *Set of 5* .... 7·50 5·00

Nos. 26/30 were issued in vertical strips of five stamps within the sheet.

See also Nos. 34/8, 43/6, 47/50, 51/4 and 55/8.

19 Children and Ducks

(Des Ikeda Gen'ei. Litho)

2000 (29 Sept). P 13½.

31   **19**   80y. multicoloured .... 2·75 1·90
      a. Pane. No. 31×10, with outer edges
       imperf .... 27·00

20 Shinjuku, New
Centre of Tokyo

(Des Kanayama Satoshi. Photo)

2000 (15 Nov). Greetings from Tokyo. T **20** and similar vert designs.
Multicoloured. P 13½.

32	80y.+20y. Type **20**	3·50	2·40
	a. Pair. Nos. 33/4	7·25	7·25
33	80y.+20y. Tokyo at night	3·50	2·40

Nos. 32/3 were issued in horizontal *se-tenant* pairs within the
sheet

The premium was for the victims of eruptions and earthquakes.

21 Cherry Blossom

(Des Kagawa Gentaro and Kanayama Satoshi. Photo)

2001 (1 June). Seasonal Splendours (2nd series). T **21** and similar vert
designs. Multicoloured. P 13½.

34	50y. Type **21**	1·60	1·10
	a. Vert strip of 5. Nos. 34/8	8·25	
	b. Pane. Nos. 34/8, each×2, with		
	outer edges imperf	15·00	
35	50y. Hydrangea	1·60	1·10
36	50y. Salvia	1·60	1·10
37	50y. Chrysanthemums	1·60	1·10
38	50y. Camellias	1·60	1·10
34/38 *Set of 5*		8·00	5·50

Nos. 34/8 were issued in vertical strips of five stamps within the
sheet.

22 Okuma
Auditorium and
Clock Tower

(Des Yabuno Ken. Litho)

2001 (19 Oct). P 13½.

39	**22**	80y. multicoloured	2·50	1·70
		a. Pane. No. 39×10, with outer edges		
		imperf	24·00	

23 Tokyo Millenario
(festival of lights)

(Des Shimoda Kouichi. Litho)

2001 (3 Dec). P 13½.

40	**23**	80y. multicoloured	2·40	1·60
		a. Pane. No. 40×10, with outer edges		
		imperf	23·00	

24 Morning Glory
Fair

2002 (28 June). Fairs and Markets. T **24** and similar vert design.
Multicoloured. P 13½.

41	80y. Type **24**	2·20	1·50
	a. Pair. Nos. 41/2	4·75	4·75
42	80y. Hozuki (ground cherry) fair	2·20	1·50

Nos. 41/2 were issued in horizontal *se-tenant* pairs within the
sheet.

25 Azaleas

(Des Kagawa Gentaro and Kanayama Satoshi. Photo)

2002 (2 Sept). Seasonal Splendours (3rd series). T **25** and similar vert
designs. Multicoloured. P 13½.

43	50y. Type **25**	1·50	1·00
	a. Strip of 4. Nos. 43/6	6·25	
44	50y. Lily	1·50	1·00
45	50y. Crape myrtle	1·50	1·00
46	50y. *Gingko biloba* (maidenhair tree)	1·50	1·00
43/46 *Set of 4*		6·00	4·00

Nos. 43/6 were issued in horizontal strips of four stamps within
the sheet.

26 Ume Blossom

(Des Kagawa Gentaro and Kanayama Satoshi. Photo)

2003 (1 Sept). Seasonal Splendours (4th series). T **26** and similar vert designs. Multicoloured. P 13½.

47		50y. Type **26**	1·60	1·10
		a. Strip of 4. Nos. 47/50	6·75	
48		50y. Wisteria	1·60	1·10
49		50y. Irises	1·60	1·10
50		50y. Tea blossom	1·60	1·10
47/50 Set of 4			6·50	4·50

Nos. 47/50 were issued in horizontal strips of four stamps within the sheet.

27 Magnolia Blossom

(Des Kagawa Gentaro. Photo)

2004 (1 June). Seasonal Splendours (5th series). T **27** and similar vert designs. Multicoloured. P 13½.

51		50y. Type **27**	1·60	1·10
		a. Strip of 4. Nos. 51/4	6·75	
52		50y. Azalea	1·60	1·10
53		50y. Anemone flaccida	1·60	1·10
54		50y. Bush clover	1·60	1·10
51/4 Set of 4			6·50	4·50

Nos. 51/4 were issued in horizontal strips of four stamps within the sheet.

28 Ebine Orchid

(Des Kagawa Gentaro. Photo)

2005 (1 June). Seasonal Splendours (6th series). T **28** and similar vert designs. Multicoloured. P 13½.

55		50y. Type **28**	1·60	1·10
		a. Strip of 4. Nos. 55/8	6·75	
56		50y. Crinum	1·60	1·10
57		50y. Kerria blossom	1·60	1·10
58		50y. Azalea	1·60	1·10
55/8 Set of 4			6·50	4·50

Nos. 55/8 were issued in horizontal strips of four stamps within the sheet.

Tottori

1990 (27 Apr). Litho. P 13½.

1		62y. As Japan Type **1464**	1·20	80

1 Fruit

1991 (26 Aug). Litho. P 13.

2	**1**	62y. multicoloured	1·20	80

2 Shanshan Festival

1996 (16 Aug). Photo. P 13½.

3	**2**	80y. multicoloured	2·10	1·40

3 Ship

1997 (11 July). Tottori Expo. Photo. P 13½.

4	**3**	80y. multicoloured	2·10	1·40
		a. Pane. No. 4×10, with outer edges imperf	20·00	

4 Nijisseikinashi (Japanese pear tree) and Dune

(Des Ozaki Shingo. Litho)

2000 (1 May). T **4** and similar vert designs. Multicoloured. P 13½.

5		50y. Type **4**	1·50	1·00
		a. Vertical strip. Nos. 5/9	7·75	
		b. Pane. Nos. 5/9, each×2, with outer edges imperf	14·00	
6		50y. Natsumikan (summer-orange blossoms) and Sea	1·50	1·00
7		50y. Botan (peonies) and Izumo-taisha Shrine	1·50	1·00
8		50y. Momonohana (peach blossoms) and traditional houses in Kurashiki	1·50	1·00
9		50y. Momiji (maple leaves) and Itsukushima Shrine Gate	1·50	1·00
5/9 Set of 5			7·50	5·00

Nos. 5/9 were issued in vertical strips of five stamps within the sheet.

Nos. 5/9 were also issued by Yamaguchi, Shimane, Okayama and Hiroshima on 1 May 2000.

5 Uradome Coast and Snow Crab

(Des Hitsuta Haruki and Ishiyama Masaki (50y.) or Hibi Sadao and Tanaka Masaki (80y.). Litho)

2001 (1 June). Homeland Tottori. T **5** and similar vert designs. Multicoloured. P 13½.

10		50y. Type **5**	1·60	1·10
	a.	Strip. Nos. 10/13	6·75	
11		50y. Dunes	1·60	1·10
12		50y. Paper Hina dolls in river	1·60	1·10
13		50y. Mt. Daisen	1·60	1·10
14		80y. Nageiredo Hall	2·75	1·80
	a.	Pair. Nos. 14/15	5·75	5·75
15		80y. Mukibanda Palaeolithic site	2·75	1·80
10/15 *Set of 6*			12·00	8·00

Nos. 10/13 were issued in horizontal *se-tenant* strips of four stamps within the sheet.

Nos. 14/15 were issued in horizontal *se-tenant* pairs within sheets of ten stamps with enlarged illustrated margin.

6 Flower Dome, Flowers and Mount Daisen

(Des Hitsuda Haruki. Litho)

2004 (23 Mar). Hana-Kairou Flower Park. P 13½.

16	**6**	80y. multicoloured	2·50	1·70

Toyama

1 Waterfall

1990 (18 Apr). Shomyo-no-taki. Litho. P 13.

1	**1**	62y. multicoloured	1·20	80

1990 (27 Apr). Flowers. Litho. P 13½.

2		62y. As Japan Type **1451**	1·20	80

2 Mount Tateyama

1992 (10 June). Photo. P 13½×imperf

3	**2**	62y. multicoloured	1·50	90

3 Bridge and Waterfall, Kurobe-kyokoku

1994 (25 Apr). Photo. P 13½.

4	**3**	80y. multicoloured	1·90	1·10
	a.	Pane. No. 4×10, with outer edges imperf	18·00	

4 Woman Dancer

1997 (20 Aug). Owara Kaze no Bon. T **4** and similar vert design. Multicoloured. Litho. P 13½.

5		80y. Type 4	1·80	1·20
	a.	Pair. Nos. 5/6	3·75	3·75
	b.	Pane. Nos. 5/6, each×5, with outer edges imperf	17·00	
6		80y. Male dancer	1·80	1·20

Nos. 5/6 were issued in horizontal *se-tenant* pairs within the sheet, each pair forming a composite design.

5 Firefly Squids

1999 (26 Apr). Photo. P 13½.

7	**5**	80y. multicoloured	2·10	1·40
	a.	Pane. No. 7×10, with outer edges imperf	20·00	

6 Dancer

1999 (14 Sept). Photo. P 13½.

8	**6**	80y. multicoloured	2·10	1·40
	a.	Pane. No. 8×10, with outer edges imperf	20·00	

7 Tateyama
Mountain Range
and Tulip Field

(Des Ichimura Jun'ichi and Shido Ko. Photo)

2000 (28 Apr). T **7** and similar vert design. Multicoloured. P 13½.
9　　　　50y. Type **7**...　1·50　　1·00
　　　　a. Pane. Nos. 9/10, each×5, with
　　　　　outer edges imperf ....　19·00
10　　　80y. Tulips...　2·50　　1·70

8 Badminton Player

(Des Sunahara Akira. Photo)

2000 (1 Sept). 55th National Athletic Meet. P 13½.
11　**8**　50y. multicoloured ....　1·80　　1·20
　　　　a. Pane. No. 11×10, with outer edges
　　　　　imperf ....　17·00

9 Sanmon Gate,
Zuiryuji Temple

(Des Ikadai Hideki. Litho)

2004 (19 Mar). Zuiryuji Temple. P 13½.
12　**9**　80y. multicoloured ....　2·50　　1·70

10 Child Dancers

(Des Iwata Chouhou. Litho)

2004 (20 Aug). Owara Dance, Bon Festival of Wind II. T **10** and similar
　vert designs. Multicoloured. P 13½.
13　　　　50y. Type **10**.............................　1·60　　1·10
　　　　a. Horiz strip of 4. Nos. 13/16 ....　6·75
14　　　50y. Women dancers ....　1·60　　1·10
15　　　50y. Men dancers ....　1·60　　1·10
16　　　50y. Musicians ....　1·60　　1·10
13/16 Set of 4..　6·50　　4·50

Nos. 13/16 were issued in horizontal *se-tenant* strips of four stamps
within the sheet, each strip forming a composite design.
Nos. 13 has a white left vertical edge and No. 16 has a white right
vertical edge, whereas No. 14/15 have the design to the edge of the
stamp.

11 Rhododendron

(Des Kawanishi Shigeharu. Litho)

2005 (1 Apr). Flowers of Hokuriku. T **11** and similar vert designs.
　Multicoloured. P 13½.
17　　　　50y. Type **11**......................................　1·60　　1·10
　　　　a. Horiz strip of 4. Nos. 17/20 ....　6·75
18　　　50y. Hydrangea................................　1·60　　1·10
19　　　50y. Tulip.......................................　1·60　　1·10
20　　　50y. Lily..　1·60　　1·10
17/20 Set of 4..　6·50　　4·50

Nos. 17/20 were issued in horizontal *se-tenant* strips of four stamps
within the sheet.
Nos. 17/20 were also issued by Ishikawa and Fukui on 1 April
2005.

Wakayama

1990 (27 Apr). Flowers. Litho. P 13½
1　　　62y. As Japan Type **1463**.......................　1·50　　1·00

1 Kumano Path

1990 (25 Sept). Photo. P 13.
2　**1**　62y. multicoloured ....　1·20　　80

2 Yachts,
Waka-no-ura

1994 (15 July). Litho. P 13½.
3　**2**　80y. multicoloured ....　1·90　　1·30
　　　　a. Pane. No. 3×10, with outer edges
　　　　　imperf ....　18·00

1998 (13 Nov). Litho. P 13.
4　**2**　80y. multicoloured ....　2·10　　1·40

3 Waterfall

1989 (1 Apr). Photo. P 13.
1   **1**   62y. multicoloured .... 1·50   80

1990 (27 Apr). Flowers. Litho. P 13½.
2   62y. As Japan Type **1439** .... 1·20   80

1999 (28 Apr). Southern Kii Penisula. T **3** and similar vert design. Multicoloured. Litho.
5   80y. Type **3** .... 2·10   1·40
     a. Pair. Nos. 5/6 .... 4·50   4·50
     b. Pane. Nos. 5/6, with outer edges
        imperf .... 20·00
6   80y. Island at sunset................... 2·10   1·40
   Nos. 5/6 were issued in horizontal *se-tenant* pairs within the sheet, each pair forming a composite design.

4 Mount Koya

1999 (26 July). Koyasan Temples. T **4** and similar vert design. Multicoloured. Litho. P 13½.
7   80y. Type **4**..................... 2·10   1·40
     a. Pair. Nos. 7/8 .... 4·50   4·50
     b. Pane. Nos. 7/8, each×5 with outer
        edges imperf .... 20·00
8   80y. Statue................. 2·10   1·40
   Nos. 7/8 were issued in horizontal *se-tenant* pairs within the sheet.

5 Azaleas, Wakayama Marina City, and Wakaura Bay

(Des Terada Kei. Photo)
2002 (1 Mar). P 13½.
9   **5**   80y. multicoloured .... 2·20   1·50

Yamagata

日本郵便

2 Trees in Autumn, Yama-dera

1995 (19 Sept). Photo. P 13½.
3   **2**   80y. multicoloured .... 1·90   1·30
     a. Pane. No. 3×10, with outer edges
        imperf .... 18·00

3 Dancers, Hanagasa Festival

1998 (5 June). Photo. P 13½.
4   **3**   50y. multicoloured .... 1·30   90
     a. Pane. No. 4×10, with outer edges
        imperf .... 12·50

1999 (26 Apr). Photo. P 13.
5   **1**   80y. multicoloured .... 2·10   1·40

4 Group of Trees

(Des Kosugou Fusae and Satou Mitusrou. Litho)
2000 (3 Apr). Cherry Trees. T **4** and similar horiz design. Multicoloured P 13½.
6   80y. Type **4**... 2·50   1·70
     a. Strip of 4. .... 10·50
     b. Sheet of 20. .... 45·00
7   80y. Tree, central, Iwate............................ 2·50   1·70
8   80y. Group of trees, Fukishima............... 2·50   1·70
9   80y. Tree, left, Miyagi.............................. 2·50   1·70
10   80y. Cherry blossom, Aomori .... 2·50   1·70
11   80y. Trees and river, Akita....................... 2·50   1·70
6/11 *Set of* 6 .... 15·00   10·00
   Nos. 6/11 were also issued by Aomori, Iwate, Miyagi, Akita and Fukushi on 3 April 2000.

1 Cherries

5 Safflowers,
Mogamigawa River,
and Mount Gassan

(Des Hongou Keiko. Photo)

2002 (31 May). National Afforestation Campaign. P 13½.

12	**5**	50y. multicoloured	1·60	1·10
		a. Pane. No. 12×10, with outer edges imperf	15·00	

6 Safflower
(Yamagata)

(Des Sakuraba Toshihiro (Aomori), Sawaguchi Ken (Iwate), Izawa Kiyoshi (Miyagi), Konno Goro (Akita), Sato Kousen (Yamagata) or Kobayashi Goro (Fukushima). Photo)

2004 (19 Mar). Prefectural Flowers. T **6** and similar horiz design. Multicoloured. P 13½.

13	50y. Type **6**	1·60	1·10
14	50y. Apple Blossom (Aomori)	1·60	1·10
15	50y. Paulownia (Iwate)	1·60	1·10
16	50y. Butterbur Flower (Akita)	1·60	1·10
17	50y. Japanese Bush Clover (Miyagi)	1·60	1·10
18	50y. Alpine Rose (*Rhododendron ferrugineum*) (Fukushima)	1·60	1·10
13/18	Set of 6	9·50	6·50

Nos. 13/18 were also issued by Yamagata, Aomori, Miyagi, Iwate and Fukushima on 19 March 2004.

7 Cherry (Yamagata)

(Des Matsuda Hiromi. Photo)

2005 (28 June). Fruits of Tohoku. T **7** and similar horiz design. Multicoloured. P 13½.

19	50y. Type **7**	1·60	1·10
	a. Horiz strip of 4. Nos. 19/22	6·75	
20	50y. Apple (Iwate)	1·60	1·10
21	50y. Apples (Aomori)	1·60	1·10
22	50y. Peach (Fukushima)	1·60	1·10
19/22	Set of 4	6·50	4·50

Nos. 19/22 were issued in horizontal *se-tenant* strips of four stamps within the sheet.

Nos. 19/22 were also issued by Aomori, Iwate and Fukushima on 28 June 2005.

Yamaguchi

1 Bird-shaped
Lanterns

1989 (1 Nov). Photo. P 13.

1	**1**	62y. multicoloured	1·30	70

1990 (27 Apr). Litho. P 13½.

2		62y. As Japan Type **1468**	1·20	80

2 Lanterns

1992 (7 July). Lantern Festival. Photo. P 13½.

3	**2**	62y. multicoloured	1·20	80

3 Street, Hagi

1999 (13 Oct). T **3** and similar horiz design. Multicoloured. P 13½.

4	80y. Type **3**	2·10	1·40
	a. Pair. Nos. 4/5	4·50	4·50
	b. Pane. Nos. 4/5, each×5 with outer edges imperf	20·00	
5	80y. Railway bridge, Tsuwano	2·10	1·40

Nos. 4/5 were issued in vertical *se-tenant* pairs within the sheet. Nos. 4/5 were also issued by Shimane on 13 October 1999.

4 Natsumikan
(summer-orange
blossoms) and Sea

(Des Ozaki Shingo. Litho)

2000 (1 May). T **4** and similar vert designs. Multicoloured. P 13½.

6	50y. Type **4**..........................	1·50	1·00
	a. Vert strip of 5. Nos. 6/10	7·75	
	b. Pane. Nos. 6/10, each×2 with outer edges imperf	14·00	
7	50y. Nijisseikinashi (Japanese pear tree) and Tottori dune......................	1·50	1·00
8	50y. Botan (peonies) and Izumo-taisha Shrine......................	1·50	1·00
9	50y. Momonohana (peach blossoms) and traditional houses in Kurashiki	1·50	1·00
10	50y. Momiji (maple leaves) and Itsukushima Shrine Gate..................	1·50	1·00
6/10 *Set of 5*		7·50	5·00

Nos. 6/10 were issued in vertical strips of five stamps within the sheet.

Nos. 6/10 were also issued by Tottori, Shimane, Okayama and Hiroshima on 1 May 2000.

5 Kintaikyo Bridge

(Des Ueda Eiko. Litho)

2000 (10 Oct). P 13½.

11	**5** 80y. multicoloured	2·75	1·90

6 Aji Wild Ducks

(Des Ozaki Shingo. Litho)

2001 (25 May). Japan EXPO, Yamaguchi. T **6** and similar vert designs. Multicoloured. P 13½.

12	50y. Type **6**	1·60	1·10
	a. Pane. Nos. 12/13, each×5 with outer edges imperf	20·00	
13	80y. Yamaguchi Kirara band and EXPO site..........................	2·50	1·70

7 Kaikyo-Messe Tower, Shimonoseki and Blue Whale

(Des Fujimoto Hideshi. Litho)

2002 (25 Apr). International Whaling Commission. P 13½.

14	**7** 80y. multicoloured	2·20	1·50

8 Kaneko Misuzu

(Des Ozaki Shingo. Photo)

2003 (11 Apr). Birth Centenary of Kaneko Misuzu (poet). T **8** and similar vert design. Multicoloured. P 13½.

15	80y. Type **8**......................	2·40	1·60
	a. Pair. Nos. 15/16	5·00	5·00
16	80y. 'Tairyo' (poem)......................	2·40	1·60

Nos. 15/16 were issued in horizontal *se-tenant* pairs within the sheet, each pair forming a composite design.

9 Lord Mouri Takachika's Procession

(Des Ozaki Shingo. Photo)

2003 (11 Apr). 400th Anniv of Hagi City. T **9** and similar vert design. Multicoloured. P 13½.

17	80y. Type **9**......................	2·50	1·70
	a. Pair. Nos. 17/18	5·25	5·25
18	80y. Lord Mouri Takachika's procession (different)......................	2·50	1·70

Nos. 17/18 were issued in horizontal *se-tenant* pairs within the sheet, each pair forming a composite design.

Yamanashi

1990 (27 Apr). Litho. P 13½.

1	62y. As Japan Type **1446**..........................	1·20	80

1 Bride

1991 (18 Apr). Photo. P 13.

2	**1** 62y. multicoloured	1·20	80

2 Waterfall

1996 (3 June). Shosenkyo Gorge. Litho. P 13½.
3   **2**   50y. multicoloured ....   1·30   90

3 Leaves, Lake and
Mountain

1999 (1 July). Five Lakes, Fuji. T **3** and similar vert designs.
Multicoloured. Litho. P 13½.
4   80y. Type **3**..   2·10   1·40
           a. Vert strip of 5. Nos. 4/8......................   11·00
           b. Pane. Nos. 4/8, each×2 with outer
              edges imperf ....   20·00
5   80y. Cherry blossom, lake and
              mountain ....   2·10   1·40
6   80y. Flower, lake, forest and mountain   2·10   1·40
7   80y. Shoreline, lake, jetty forest and
              mountain ....   2·10   1·40
8   80y. Trees, lake, hills and mountain........   2·10   1·40
4/8 *Set of 5*...   10·50   7·00
     Nos. 4/8 were issued in vertical *se-tenant* strips of five stamps
within the sheet.

4 Symbols of
Yamanashi, Mount
Fuji and Jewellry

(Des Ichinose Chizuko. Photo)

2001 (30 Mar). P 13½×imperf.
9   **4**   80y. multicoloured ....   2·40   1·60
           a. Pane. No. 9×10, with outer edges
              imperf ....   23·00

5 Butterfly and Mount
Mizugakisan, Azuma-
Shakunage

(Des Sakamoto Takao. Photo)

2001 (18 May). National Reforestation Campaign. P 13½.
10   **5**   50y. multicoloured ....   1·60   1·10
           a. Pane. No. 10×10, with outer edges
              imperf ....   15·00

6 Peach Blossom
and Shirane-sanzan
Mountains (Kyoto
area)

(Des Kasamatsu Kyosuke. Photo)

2001 (2 July). Yamanashi Scenery. T **6** and similar vert designs.
Multicoloured. Litho. P 13½.
11   50y. Type **6**..   1·50   1·00
           a. Vert strip of 5. Nos. 11/15..............   7·50
           b. Pane. Nos. 11/15, each×2 with
              outer edges imperf ....   14·00
12   50y. Iris and Mt. Kitadake (Kyochu area)   1·50   1·00
13   50y. Horses and Mt. Yatsugatake
              (Kyohoku area)...................................   1·50   1·00
14   50y. Snow-covered houses and Oshino-
              hakkai ponds (Gunnnai area) ....   1·50   1·00
15   50y. Cherry blossom, Minobu (Kyonan
              area) ....   1·50   1·00
11/15 *Set of 5*...   7·50   5·00
     Nos. 11/15 were issued in vertical *se-tenant* strips of five stamps
within the sheet.

7 Sunflower and
Mount Yatsugatake

(Des Sato Akihiko. Litho)

2005 (16 May). Flowers of Yamanashi. T **7** and similar vert designs.
Multicoloured. Litho. P 13½.
16   80y. Type **7**..   2·50   1·70
           a. Strip of 4. Nos. 16/19......................   10·50
17   80y. Gentian and Mt. Kitadake,
              Southern Japanese Alps....................   2·50   1·70
18   80y. Evening primrose and Mt. Fuji ....   2·50   1·70
19   80y. Lady's slipper and Mt. Fuji..............   2·50   1·70
16/19. *Set of 4*...   10·00   6·75
     Nos. 16/19 were issued in horizontal *se-tenant* strips of four stamps
within the sheet.

FOREIGN POST OFFICES IN JAPAN

In June 1859 Japan opened to foreign trade various ports and Great Britain and France followed the United States in opening consulates. Japan did not become a member of the Universal Postal Union until 1 June 1877 so the three powers established post offices to handle overseas mail.

A. BRITISH POST OFFICES

Under the terms of the Anglo-Japanese Treaty of Yedo, signed 26 August 1858, five Japanese ports were opened to British trade. British consulates were established at Decima (Nagasaki), Kanagawa (later transferred to Yokohama), Hiogo (Kobe) and Hakodadi (Hakodate). The postage stamps of Hong Kong became available at the Yokohama and Nagasaki consulates during October 1864 and at Hiogo in 1869, although cancellation of mail did not commence until 1866 at Yokohama and Nagasaki or 1876 at Hiogo.

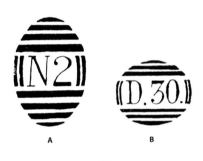

A   B

C

HAKODATE

A British consular office existed at Hakodate but it was never issued with a circular datestamp, oblilerator or Hong Kong stamps. No British covers are recorded from this consulate prior to opening of the Japanese Post Office.

HIOGO

The port of Hiogo (Kobe) was first opened to foreigners on 1 January 1868. The British Consular mail service at Hiogo commenced during 1869 for the foreigners at Hiogo, Kobe and Osaka. The cities of Hiogo and Kobe later merged to become the single city of Kobe. The consular office at Hiogo closed on 30 November 1879.
Type B (*supplied 1876*) *used* 1876-79
Type C (*supplied 1876*) *used* 1876-79

Queen Victoria stamps of HONG KONG *cancelled at Hiogo between 1876 and 1879 with postmarks detailed above.*

1863-71. Wmk Crown CC (Nos. 8/19).
Z1	2c. brown		£5000
Z2	4c. grey		£3750
Z3	6c. lilac		£4500
Z4	8c. orange		£4250
Z5	12c. blue		£5000
Z6	18c. lilac		
Z7	24c. green		£3750
Z8	30c. vermilion		
Z9	30c. mauve		£5000

Z10	48c. rose		£7000
Z12	96c. brownish grey		£7000

1876. Surcharged (Nos. 20/1).
Z13	16c. on 18c. lilac		

1877. Wmk Crown CC (No. 22).
Z15	16c. yellow		£6000

NAGASAKI

The British Consulate opened in Nagasaki on 14 June 1859, but, with few British residents at the port, the consular staff found it inconvenient to carry out postal duties so that few Nagasaki circular datestamps or "N2" cancellations exist. The postal service was terminated on 30 September 1879.

Type A ("N2") (*supplied* 1866) *used* 1876-79
Type C (*supplied* 1866) *used* 1876-79

Queen Victoria stamps of HONG KONG *cancelled at Nagasaki between 1876 and 1879 with postmarks detailed above.*

1863-71. Wmk Crown CC (Nos. 8/19).
Z16	2c. brown		£2000
Z17	4c. grey		£1800
Z18	6c. lilac		£1700
Z19	8c. orange		£1800
Z20	12c. blue		£1900
Z21	18c. lilac		£3500
Z22	24c. green		£3000
Z24	30c. mauve		£2500
Z25	48c. rose		£3250
Z27	96c. brownish grey		

1876. Surcharged (Nos. 20/1).
Z28	16c. on 18c. lilac		£2750
Z29	28c. on 30c. mauve		£1900

1877. Wmk Crown CC (No. 22).
Z30	16c. yellow		£2750

YOKOHAMA

The British Consulate opened in Kanagawa on 21 July 1859, but was relocated to Yokohama where it provided postal services from 1 July 1860 until a separate Post Office was established in July 1867. The British Post Office in Yokohama closed on 31 December 1879.

Type A ("Y1") (*supplied* 1866) *used* 1867-79
Type C (*supplied* 1866) *used* 1866-79

Queen Victoria stamps of HONG KONG *cancelled at Yokohama between 1866 and 1879 with postmarks detailed above.*

1862. No wmk (Nos. 1/8).
Z31	18c. lilac		£100

1863-71. Wmk Crown CC (Nos. 8/19).
Z32	2c. brown		19·00
Z33	4c. grey		20·00
	a. Perf 12½		£550
Z34	6c. lilac		25·00
Z35	8c. orange		25·00
Z36	12c. blue		19·00
Z37	18c. lilac		£650
Z38	24c. green		21·00
Z39	30c. vermilion		55·00
Z40	30c. mauve		19·00
Z41	48c. rose		50·00
Z43	96c. brownish grey		65·00

1876. Surcharged (Nos. 20/1).
Z44	16c. on 18c. lilac		£300
Z45	28c. on 30c. mauve		80·00

1877. Wmk Crown CC (No. 22).
Z46	16c. yellow		£120

POSTAL FISCAL STAMPS

1874. Inscr "STAMP DUTY". Wmk Crown CC. P 15½×15 (Nos. F1/3).
ZF47 $2 olive-green £120
ZF48 $3 dull violet £110
ZF49 $10 rose-carmine £1400

B. FRENCH POST OFFICES

The French acquired residential and trading rights under a treaty of 9 October 1858. The first French mail ship was sent to Japan in 1863 and the earliest known cover from Japan handled by a French Post Office was sent from Yokohama in May 1863. This, and subsequent mail from Yokohama up to September 1865. was forwarded via the French Post Office in Shanghai and was cancelled with the latter's 5104 dotted lozenge obliterator.

NAGASAKI AND HIOGO

It is believed there were consulate postal agencies operating in these ports from 1863 to 30 November 1879. They were not however issued with cancellers. Mail from Nagasaki seems to have been forwarded via the Shanghai office.

C. UNITED STATES OFFICES

The United States were the first Western power to agree a trade treaty with Japan, on 19 July 1858. The first post office was not officially established however until 1867, possibly because of the cessation of the Pacific mail boat service during the American civil war. A few items are known prior to this date carried by U.S. ships and it seems likely there was an unofficial service run by the consulates.

In January 1867 a Pacific mail boat service commenced and in July of that year Yokohama was supplied with unoverprinted United States stamps, the first ship departure from Yokohama after this date being 24 August 1867. Cancellers were subsequently issued to three other consulates.

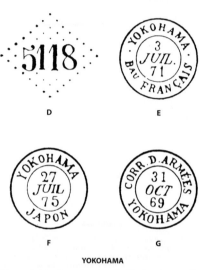

D E

F G

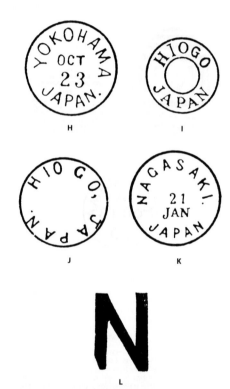

H I

J K

L

YOKOHAMA

The usual date of opening given for the French post office at Yokohama, 7 September 1865, seems to be that on which the office's own canceller came into use. There was almost certainly some form of unofficial service operating before this date, probably from the consulate. The post office was established in a separate building and was supplied with unoverprinted stamps of France.

Type D *used* 1865-76
Types E and F *used* 1865-80
Type G *used on military mail*
Anchor in lozenge (as Type D). A ship cancellation which was temporarily used at the land office from January to April 1867 following a fire which destroyed the post office. New figure cancellers were received in May 1867.

Recorded stamps:
Napoleon Empire (France Type **3**). perforated. 1 to 20, 40, 80c.
Napoleon Laureated (T **4/6**). 2 to 80c., 5f.
Ceres Paris Siege (T **1**). 10, 40c.
Ceres Bordeaux issue (T **7/8**) 4 to 80c.
Ceres perforated (T **1** and **9**). 4 to 80c. (thick and thin figures)
Peace and Commerce (T **10**). 4c. green, 10c. black, 15c. grey-lilac and blue, 20c. grey-lilac, 25c. ultramarine, 35c deep brown, 40, 75c., 1f.

The Yokohama office was closed on 31 March 1880.

HAKODADI (Hakodate). Type H *used* 1873-74.
HIOGO (Kobe). Types I and J *used* 1868-74.
NAGASAKI. Type K *used* November 1867.
YOKOHAMA. Type H *used* July 1867-74.

Various obliterators such as Type L were also used.

On 1 January 1875 the Japanese foreign postal service began. The two countries signed a postal treaty which resulted in the closure of all United States Post Offices on 31 December 1874.

BRITISH COMMONWEALTH OCCUPATION FORCE (JAPAN)

Nos. J1/7 were used by the Australian forces occupying Japan after the Second World War. Initially their military post offices supplied unoverprinted Australian stamps, but it was decided to introduce the overprinted issues to prevent currency speculation.

B.C.O.F.
JAPAN
1946

(1)

B.C.O.F.
JAPAN
1946

(2)

ɔ.F. ɔ.F.
1946 AN AN

Wrong fount "6" Normal Narrow "N"
(left pane R. 9/4) (right pane R.1/8)

1946 (11 Oct)–**48**. Stamps of Australia optd as T **1** (1d., 3d.) or T 2 (others) at British Commonwealth Command Headquarters, Kure. Japan.

J1	27	½d. orange (Wallaroo) (No. 179)............	4·25	7·50
		a. Wrong fount "6".................................	£110	£130
		b. Narrow "N"......................................	£120	£140
J2	46	1d. brn-pur (Queen Elizabeth) (No. 203)...	3·50	4·00
		a. Error. Blue overprint..........................	55·00	95·00
J3	31	3d. pur-brn (King George VI) (No. 187)	2·75	3·25
J4	34	6d. purple-brown (Laughing Kookaburra) (No. 189a) (8.6.47)......	18·00	14·00
		a. Wrong fount "6"..............................	£200	£190
		b. Stop after "JAPAN" (right pane R. 5/5)..	£225	£200
		c. Narrow "N"......................................	£225	£200
J5	36	1s. grey-green (Superb Lyrebird) (No. 191) (8.5.47)....................................	14·00	16·00
		a. Wrong fount "6"..............................	£250	£225
		b. Stop after "JAPAN" (right pane R. 5/5)..	£275	£250
		c. Narrow "N"......................................	£250	£225
J6	1	5s. maroon (Kangaroo on map of Australia) (No. 212) (8.5.47)	42·00	50·00
J7	38	5s. claret (Queen Elizabeth in coronationrobes) (No. 176) (8.5.47)	£100	£130
		a. Thin rough paper (No. 176a) (1948)	80·00	£130
J1/7		Set of 7...	£160	£200

The ½d., 1d. and 3d. values were first issued on 11 October 1946. and withdrawn two days later, but were re-issued together with the other values on 8 May 1947.

The following values with T **2** in the colours given were from proof sheets, which, however, were used for postage: ½d. (red), 1d. (red or black) and 3d. (gold, red or black). (*Prices for black opts* £100 *each, and for red or gold from* £300 *each, all un.*)

The use of B.C.O.F. stamps ceased on 12 February 1949.

Japanese Post Offices in China

10 Rin = 1 Sen
100 Sen = 1 Yen

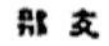

邮 文
(1)
Stamps of Japan overprinted with T 1

1900 (1 Jan)-**08**. Stamps of 1899-1908. Opt characters are 6mm apart in 5y. and 10y. P 11½–12.

1	**28**	5r. slate (R.)	7·00	5·75
		b. Perf 12½ (line)	30·00	30·00
2		½s. slate (R.) (27.3.01)	5·75	2·30
		b. Perf 12½ (line)	21·00	6·50
		d. Perf 13×13½ (comb)	55·00	17·00
3		1s. pale brown (R.)	7·50	2·10
		b. Perf 12½ (line)	17·00	5·00
		d. Perf 13×13½ (comb)	32·00	6·75
4		1½s. pale ultramarine (1.10.00)	17·00	5·25
		b. Perf 12½ (line)	25·00	10·50
5		1½s. violet (15.5.06)	8·50	1·70
		b. Perf 12½ (line)	18·00	8·00
		c. Perf 12×12½ (comb)	—	£200
		d. Perf 13×13½ (comb)	25·00	10·50
6		2s. yellow-green (R.)	8·50	1·70
		b. Perf 12½ (line)	10·00	5·50
		d. Perf 13×13½ (comb)	17·00	5·75
7		3s. dull maroon	10·50	2·10
		b. Perf 12½ (line)	11·50	4·25
		c. Perf 12×12½ (comb)	—	£150
8		3s. rosine (15.5.06)	7·00	1·50
		b. Perf 12½ (line)	9·50	2·25
		c. Perf 12×12½ (comb)	—	£200
		d. Perf 13×13½ (comb)	16·00	4·50
9		4s. rosine	10·50	2·75
		c. Perf 12×12½ (comb)	—	£200
		d. Perf 13×13½ (comb)	55·00	22·00
10		5s. orange-yellow (R.)	21·00	2·75
		b. Perf 12½ (line)	40·00	5·00
11	**29**	6s. maroon (20.8.07)	23·00	22·00
		b. Perf 12½ (line)	35·00	30·00
		c. Perf 12×12½ (comb)	—	£200
		d. Perf 13×13½ (comb)	—	£200
12		8s. olive (R.)	15·00	15·00
		b. Perf 12½ (line)	25·00	25·00
		d. Perf 13×13½ (comb)	—	—
13		10s. deep blue	15·00	1·50
		b. Perf 12½ (line)	19·00	3·00
		d. Perf 13×13½ (comb)	£160	75·00
14		15s. purple	33·00	2·30
		b. Perf 12½ (line)	30·00	5·00
		c. Perf 12×12½ (comb)	—	£200
		d. Perf 13×13½ (comb)	—	—
15		20s. orange	28·00	1·60
		b. Perf 12½ (line)	28·00	3·00
		c. Perf 12×12½ (comb)	—	£200
16	**30**	25s. pale blue-green (R.)	55·00	8·50
		b. Perf 12½ (line)	60·00	20·00
17		50s. brown	55·00	3·00
		b. Perf 12½ (line)	60·00	5·00
		d. Perf 13×13½ (comb)	—	£180
18	**31**	1y. carmine	£110	3·50
		b. Perf 12½ (line)	£120	3·50
19	**32**	5y. green (20.2.08)	£650	8000
20		10y. violet (20.2.08)	£1100	£150

As in Japan there a number of shades in this issue.
No. 6 overprinted in black is a fake.

1900 (28 Apr). Wedding of Prince Imperial.

21	**33**	3s. carmine (perf 11½–12)	55·00	34·00
		a. Perf 12½	85·00	41·00

1913. Stamps of 1913. White paper. No. wmk. P 12×12½.

22	**36**	½s. brown (31.10)	20·00	21·00
		a. Perf 13×13½	21·00	26·00
23		s. orange (31.10)	22·00	22·00
24		1½s. pale blue (31.80)	65·00	27·00
		a. Perf 13×13½	65·00	28·00
25		2s. green (31.10)	70·00	34·00
26		3s. carmine (31.8)	38·00	14·00
		a. Perf 13×13½	41·00	14·50
27	**37**	4s. scarlet (31.10)	90·00	80·00
28		5s. violet (31.10)	95·00	85·00
29		10s. deep blue (31.10)	95·00	23·00
30		20s. claret (31.10)	£325	£225
31		25s. olive (31.10)	£150	34·00
32	**38**	1y. pale green & choc (p11½–12) (31.10)	£1100	£800

1914 (20 May)–**19**. Stamps of 1914-25. Granite paper. W **39**.

(a) Perf 13×13½ .

33	**36**	½s. brown	5·25	2·75
		a. Perf 12×12½	7·75	5·25
34		1s. orange	5·75	2·75
		a. Perf 12×12½	8·75	4·25
35		1½s. pale blue	6·50	2·30
		a. Perf 12×12½	9·25	4·25
		b. Perf 11½–12	—	£225
36		2s. green	7·50	2·10
		a. Perf 12×12½	18·00	5·25
		b. Perf 11½×12	—	£350
37		3s. carmine	5·75	1·50
		a. Perf 12×12½	21·00	4·25
		b. Perf 11½×12	£200	—
38	**37**	4s. scarlet	17·00	8·50
39		5s. violet	30·00	20·00
		a. Perf 12×12½	26·00	7·75
40	6	s. brown (16.8.19)	38·00	34·00
		a. Perf 12×12½		
41	8	s. grey (16.8.19)	42·00	42·00
42		10s. deep blue	21·00	2·75
		a. Perf 12×12½	26·00	4·25
		b. Perf 11½–12	—	80·00
43		20s. claret	55·00	8·50
		a. Perf 12×12½	80·00	10·50
		b. Perf 11½–12	£1000	—
44		25s. olive	70·00	10·50
		a. Perf 12×12½	90·00	13·00
45	**38**	30s. chestnut (16.8.19)	£110	55·00
		a. Perf 11½×12	—	£300
46		50s. chocolate (1.6.8.19)	£130	55·00

(b) Perf 11½ –12

47	**38**	1y. pale green and chocolate	£170	13·00
48	**32**	5y. green	£2250	£750
49		10y. violet	£4500	£2500

The use of overprinted Japanese stamps was discontinued by Japanese military post offices on 21 February 1905, in post offices of the Kwangtung leased territory on 20 March 1908, and in Japanese post offices in the Chinese Eastern Railway Zone on 1 June 1918; the remaining offices were closed down on 31 December 1922.

STAMP BOOKLETS

Prices are for complete booklets

Booklet No.	Date	Contents and Cover Price	Price
SB1	1.5.07	3 panes, No. 5D×6; 4 panes. No. 8D×6 (1y.)	£10500
SB2	1.5.07	2 panes, No. 6D×6; 6 panes. No. 9D×6; 3 panes No. 13D×6 (3Y. 50)	£8000
SB3	25.11.11	10 panes, No. 5D×6 (90s.)	£10500
SB4	25.11.11	5 panes, No. 8D×6 (90s.)	£8000
SB5	31.8.13	10 panes, No. 24a×6 (90s.)	£13000
SB6	31.8.13	5 panes, No. 26a×6 (90s.)	£20000
SB7	31.10.13	2 panes, No. 25×6: 6 panes. No. 27×6; 3 panes, No. 29×6 (3y. 50)	£16000

POST OFFICES IN KOREA. See after No. 62 of Korea.

Japanese Occupation of Brunei

Japanese Occupation of Burma

Japanese forces landed in Northern Borneo on 15 December 1941 and the whole of Brunei had been occupied by 6 January 1942.

Brunei, North Borneo, Sarawak and, after a short period, Labuan, were administered as a single territory by the Japanese. Until September-October 1942, previous stamp issues, without overprint, continued to be used in conjunction with existing postmarks. From the Autumn of 1942 onwards unoverprinted stamps of Japan were made available and examples can be found used from the area for much of the remainder of the War. Japanese Occupation issues for Brunei, North Borneo and Sarawak were equally valid throughout the combined territory but not, in practice, equally available.

PRICES FOR STAMPS ON COVER

Nos. J1/16	from × 8
Nos. J17/20	—

(1) ("Imperial Japanese Government")

(2) ("Imperial Japanese Postal Service $3")

1942 (Oct)–**44**. Stamps of Brunei handstamped with T **1** in violet to blue. Wmk Mult Script CA (except Nos. J18/19, Mult Crown CA). P 14.

J1	**5**	1c. black	7·50	23·00
		a. Red opt	90·00	£110
J2		2c. green	50·00	£110
J3		2c. orange (1943)	4·25	9·00
J4		3c. blue-green	28·00	75·00
		a. Opt omitted (in pair with normal)	£2500	
J5		4c. orange	3·00	13·00
J6		5c. chocolate	3·00	13·00
		a. "5c." retouch	£150	£37
J7	**7**	6c. greenish grey (P 14×11½) (1944)	40·00	£225
J8		6c. scarlet	£550	£550
J9	**5**	8c. grey-black	£700	£850
J10	**7**	8c. red	5·50	12·00
		a. Opt omitted (in pair with normal)	£2000	
J11	**5**	6c. purple/*yellow*	9·00	26·00
J12	**7**	12c. blue	26·00	26·00
		a. Red opt	£275	£375
J13		15c. ultramarine (1944)	18·00	26·00
J14		25c. slate-purple	25·00	50·00
		a. Red opt	£400	£475
J15		30c. purple and orange-yellow	95·00	£180
J16		50c. black/*emerald*	38·00	60·00
		a. Red opt	£425	
J17		$1 black and red/*blue* (1944)	55·00	70·00
		a. Red opt	—	£900
J18		$5 carmine/*green* (1944)	£900	£2250
J19		$25 black/*red* (1944)	£900	£2250

The overprint varies in shade from violet to blue, and being handstamped, exists inverted, double, double one inverted and treble.

Nos. J3, J4, J7, J10 and J13 were not issued without the overprint (See footnote below Brunei No. 78).

1944 (11 May). *No. J1 surch with T* **2** *in orange-red.*

J20	**5**	3 on 1c. black	£6000	£6000
		a. Surch on No. 60 of Brunei	£7500	

Three separate handstamps were used to apply Type **2**, one for the top line, one for the bottom and the third for the two central characters.

PRICES FOR STAMPS ON COVER

Nos. J1/44	—
Nos. J45/6	from × 6
Nos. J47/56	from × 8
No. J56g	—
Nos. J57/72	from × 6
Nos. J73/5	from × 25
No. J76	from × 8
No. J77	from × 20
Nos. J78/81	from × 25
Nos. J82/4	from × 10
Nos. J85/7	from × 40
No. J88	from × 12
Nos. J89/97	from × 30
Nos. J98/104	from × 50
Nos. J105/111	from × 30

BURMA INDEPENDENCE ARMY ADMINISTRATION

The Burma Independence Army, formed by Aung San in 1941, took control of the Delta area of the Irrawaddy in May 1942. They reopened a postal service in the area and were authorised by the Japanese to overprint local stocks of stamps with the Burmese emblem of a peacock.

Postage and Official stamps with the peacock overprints or handstamps were used for ordinary postal purposes with the probable exception of No. J44.

DISTINGUISHING FEATURES. Type **1**. Body and head of Peacock always clearly outlined by broad uncoloured band. There are four slightly different sub-types of overprint Type **1**.

Type **2**. Peacock with slender neck and more delicately detailed tail. Clear spur on leg at right. Heavy fist-shaped blob of ink below and parallel to beak and neck.

Type **4**. No basic curve. Each feather separately outlined. Straight, short legs.

Type **5**. Much fine detail in wings and tail in clearly printed overprints. Thin, long legs ending in claws which, with the basic arc, enclose clear white spaces in well printed copies. Blob of colour below beak shows shaded detail and never has the heavy fist-like appearance of this portion in Type **2**.

Two sub-types may be distinguished in Type **5**, the basic arc of one having a chord of 14–15 mm and the other 12½–13 mm.

Type **6**. Similar to Type **5**, but with arc deeply curved and reaching nearly to the top of the wings. Single diagonal line parallel to neck below beak.

Collectors are warned against forgeries of these overprints, often in the wrong colours or on the wrong values.

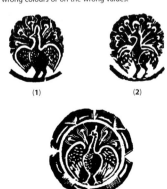

(1)   **(2)**

(3)

1942 (May). Stamps of Burma overprinted with the national device of a Peacock.

I. Overprinted at Myaungmya.

A. With Type **1** in black.

On Postage Stamps of King George V.

J1		9p. deep green (No. 3)	£110	
J2		3½a. deep blue (No. 8)	65·00	

On Official Stamp of King George V.

J3	6a. bistre (No. O8)	80·00	

On Postage Stamps of King George VI.

J4	**2**	9p. yellow-green	£150
J5	**3**	1a. purple-brown	£550
J6		4a. greenish blue (opt black on red)	£160
		a. Triple opt, black on double red	£450

On Official Stamps of King George VI.

J7	**2**	3p. bright violet	29·00	90·00
J8		6p. bright blue	20·00	65·00
J9	**3**	1a. purple-brown	21·00	55·00
J9a		1½a. turquoise-green	£650	
J10		2a. carmine	27·00	£100
J11		4a. greenish blue	27·00	80·00

The overprint on No. J6 was apparently first done in red in error, and then corrected in black. Some stamps have the black overprint so accurately superimposed that the red hardly shows. These are rare.

Nos. J5 and J9 exist with the Peacock overprint on both the typographed and the litho printings of the original stamps.

B. With Types **2** or **3** (rupee values), in black.

On Postage Stamps of King George VI.

J12	**2**	3p. bright violet	18·00	75·00
J13		6p. bright blue	50·00	£110
J14		9p. yellow-green	21·00	70·00
J15	**3**	1a. purple-brown	14·00	65·00
J16		2a. carmine	24·00	85·00
J17		4a. greenish blue	48·00	£110
		a. Opt double		
		b. Opt inverted	£700	
		c. Opt double, one inverted	£450	
		d. Opt double, both inverted	£700	
J18		1r. purple and blue	£300	
J19	**8**	2r. brown and purple	£170	

The Myaungmya overprints (including No. J44) are usually clearly printed.

(4)	(5)	(6)

Type **5** generally shows the details of the peacock much less clearly and, due to heavy inking, or careless impression, sometimes appears as almost solid colour.

Type **6** was officially applied only to postal stationery. However, the handstamp remained in the possession of a postal official who used it on postage stamps after the war. These stamps are no longer listed.

II. Handstamped (at Pyapon?) with T **4**, in black (so-called experimental type).

On Postage Stamps of King George VI.

J19a	**2**	6p. bright blue	85·00	
J19b	**3**	1a. purple-brown	£100	£250
J20		2a. carmine	£130	£300
J21		4a. greenish blue	£700	£700

Unused specimens of Nos. J20/1 are usually in poor condition.

III. Overprinted at Henzada with T **5** in blue, or blue-black.

On Postage Stamps of King George V.

J22		3p. slate (No. 1)	3·50	21·00
		a. Opt double	10·00	50·00

J23		9p. deep green (No. 3)	25·00	65·00
		a. Opt double	80·00	
J24		2a. vermilion (No. 5)	£100	£180

On Postage Stamps of King George VI.

J25	**2**	1p. red-orange	£225	£325
J26		3p. bright violet	38·00	80·00
J27		6p. bright blue	25·00	55·00
		a. Opt double	£100	£150
		b. Clear opt, on back and front	£325	
J28		9p. yellow-green	£900	
J29	**3**	1a. purple-brown	9·00	42·00
		a. Opt inverted	£1600	£850
J30		1½a. turquoise-green	21·00	70·00
		a. Opt omitted (in pair with normal)	£3000	
J31		2a. carmine	21·00	70·00
		a. Opt double	£1700	
J32		4a. greenish blue	42·00	£100
		a. Opt double	£250	
		b. Opt inverted	£2500	

On Official Stamps of King George VI.

J33	**2**	3p. bright violet	£130	£250
J34		6p. bright blue	£140	£250
J35	**3**	1½a. turquoise-green	£170	£300
J35a		2a. carmine	£350	£450
J36		4a. greenish blue	£1000	

(**6a**) ("Yon Thon" = "Office use")

V. Official Stamp of King George VI optd at Myaungmya with Type **6a** in black.

J44	**7**	8a. myrtle-green	95·00

No. J44 was probably for official use.

There are two types of T **6a**, one with base of peacock 8 mm long and the other with base about 5 mm long. The neck and other details also vary. The two types are found se-tenant in the sheet. Stocks of the peacock types were withdrawn when the Japanese Directorate-General took control of the postal services in the Delta in August 1942.

JAPANESE ARMY ADMINISTRATION

7	8 Farmer

1942 (1 June). Impressed by hand. Thick yellowish paper. No gum. P 12×11.

J45	**7**	(1a.) red	42·00	70·0

This device was the personal seal of Yano Sitza, the Japanese official in charge of the Posts and Telegraphs department of the Japanese Army Administration. It was impressed on paper already perforated by a line machine. Some stamps show part of the papermaker's watermark, either "ABSORBO DUPLICATOR" or "ELEPHANT BRAND", each with an elephant.

Other impressions of this seal on different papers, and showing signs of wear, were not valid for postal purposes.

(Des T. Kato. Typo *Rangoon Gazette* Press)

1942 (15 June). Value in annas. P 11 or 11×11½. Laid bâtonné paper. No gum.

J46 **8** 1a. scarlet........ 19·00 19·00

Some stamps show part of the papermaker's watermark, either "ELEPHANT BRAND" or "TITAGHUR SUPERFINE", each with an elephant.

(**9**)

(**10**)

1942 (22 Sept). (a) Nos. 314/17, 320/2, 325, 327 and 396 of Japan surch as T **9/10**.

J47 **9** ¼a. on 1s. chestnut (Rice harvesting)...... 35·00 42·00
a. Surch inverted........ £120 £120
b. Surch double, one inverted.... £170

J48 ½a. on 2s. bright scarlet (General Nogi)........ 42·00 45·00
a. Surch inverted........ £110 £120
b. Surch double, one inverted.... £170

J49 ¾a. on 3s. green (Power station)........ 70·00 75·00
a. Surch inverted........ £140 £140
b. Surch double, one inverted.... — £180

J50 1a. on 5s. claret (Admiral Togo)........ 65·00 60·00
a. Surch inverted........ £190 £190
b. Surch double, one inverted.... £225 £200
c. Surch omitted (in pair with normal)........ £350 £300

J51 3a. on 7s. green (Diamond Mts)........ £100 £120
a. Surch inverted........ £200

J52 4a. on 4s. emerald (Togo)........ 55·00 60·00
a. Surch inverted........ £190

J53 8a. on 8s. violet (Meiji Shrine)........ £150 £150
a. Surch inverted........ £250 £250
b. Surch double, one inverted.... £375
c. Surch in red........ £250 £275
d. Red surch inverted........ £375
e. Surch double (black and red). £850

J54 **10** 1r. on 10s. deep carmine (Yomei Gate).... 22·00 25·00
a. Surch inverted........ 85·00 95·00
b. Surch double........ 80·00 £100
c. Surch double (black and red). £450 £450
d. Surch omitted (in pair with normal)........ £300 £300
e. Surch omitted (in pair with inverted surch)........ £425

J55 2r. on 20s. ultramarine (Mt Fuji)........ 50·00 50·00
a. Surch inverted........ £120 £120
b. Surch double, one inverted.... £150
c. Surch omitted (in pair with normal black surch)........ £190 £190
d. Surch in red........ 50·00 50·00
e. Red surch inverted........ £120 £120
f. Red surch double........ £120 £120
g. Surch omitted (in pair with normal red surch)........ £250 £250
ga. Surch omitted (in pair with double red surch)........
h. Surch double (black and red) £400

J56 **9** 5r. on 30s. turquoise (Torii Shrine)........ 12·00 27·00
a. Surch inverted........ 85·00
b. Surch double........ £110
c. Surch double, one inverted.... £150
d. Surch omitted (in pair with normal surch)........ £225 £225
e. Surch omitted (in pair with inverted black surch)........ £325
f. Surch in red........ 26·00 32·00
fa. Red surch inverted........ 90·00 90·00
fb. J56a and J56fa *se-tenant*........ £475 £475
fc. Surch omitted (in pair with normal red surch)........ £225 £225

(b) No. 386 of Japan commemorating the fall of Singapore similarly surch.

J56*g* **9** 4a. on 4+2s. green and red........ £160 £170
h. Surch omitted (in pair with normal)........ £550
ha. Surch omitted (in pair with inverted surch)........ £600
i. Surch inverted........ £375

(New Currency. 100 cents = 1 rupee)

(**11**)

(**12**)

(**13**)

1942 (15 Oct). Previous issues, with "anna" surcharges obliterated, handstamped with new value in cents, as T **11** and **12** (No. J57 handstamped with new value only).

(a) On No. J46.

J57 5c. on 1a. scarlet........ 17·00 21·00
a. Surch omitted (in pair with normal)........ £1500

(b) On Nos. J47/53.

J58 1c. on ¼a. on 1s. chestnut........ 50·00 50·00
a. "1 c." omitted (in pair with normal)........ £800
b. "¼ a." inverted........ £275

J59 2c. on ½a. on 2s. bright scarlet........ 50·00 50·00

J60 3c. on ¾a. on 3s. green........ 55·00 55·00
a. Surch in blue........ £190

J61 5c. on 1a. on 5s. claret........ 75·00 65·00

J62 10c. on 3a. on 7s. green........ £130 £120

J63 15c. on 4a. on 4s. emerald........ 45·00 48·00

J64 20c. on 8a. on 8s. violet........ £650 £550
a. Surch on No. J53c (surch in red)........ £300 £160

The "anna" surcharges were obliterated by any means available, in some cases by a bar or bars, and in others by the butt of a pencil dipped in ink. In the case of the fractional surcharges, the letter "A" and one figure of the fraction, were sometimes barred out, leaving the remainder of the fraction to represent the new value, e.g. the "1" of "½" deleted to create the 2c. surcharge or the "4" of "¾" to create the 3c. surcharge.

1942. Nos. 314/17, 320/1 and 396 of Japan surcharged in cents only as T **13**.

J65 1c. on 1s. chestnut (Rice harvesting)........ 27·00 20·00
a. Surch inverted........ £120 £120

J66 2c. on 2s. brt scarlet (General Nogi)........ 50·00 32·00

J67 3c. on 3s. green (Power station)........ 75·00 55·00
a. Pair, with and without surch........ £275
b. Surch inverted........ £140
c. Surch in blue........ 95·00 £100
d. Surch in blue inverted........ £250 £275

J68 5c. on 5s. claret (Admiral Togo)........ 80·00 50·00
a. Pair, with and without surch£350
b. Surch in violet........ £150 £170
ba. Surch inverted........ £275

J69 10c. on 7s. green (Diamond Mts)........ 95·00 65·00

J70 15c. on 4s. emerald (Togo)........ 21·00 22·00
a. Surch inverted........ £130 £140
b. Pair, with and without surch........ — £250

J71 20c. on 8s. violet (Meiji Shrine)........ £170 85·00
a. Surch double........ £350

Nos. J67c and J68b were issued for use in the Shan States.

BURMESE GOVERNMENT

On 1 November 1942 the Japanese Army Administration handed over the control of the postal department to the Burmese Government. On 1 August 1943 Burma was declared by the Japanese to be independent.

14 Burma State Crest

15 Farmer

(Des U Tun Tin and Maung Tin from drawing by U Ba Than. Typo Rangoon)

1943 (15 Feb). No gum. P 11.

J72	**14**	5c. scarlet	21·00	25·00
		a. Imperf	22·00	25·00
		ab. Printed on both sides	90·00	

No. J72 was usually sold affixed to envelopes, particularly those with the embossed 1a. King George VI stamp, which it covered. Unused specimens off cover are not often seen and blocks are scarce.

1943. Typo. No gum. P 11½.

J73	**15**	1c. orange (22 March)	3·50	5·50
		a. Brown-orange	2·75	6·00
J74		2c. yellow-green (24 March)	60	1·00
		a. "3" for "2" in face value (R. 2/10)	£325	
		b. Blue-green	11·00	
J75		3c. light blue (25 March)	3·25	1·00
		a. On laid paper	20·00	29·00
		b. Imperf between (horiz pair)		£300
J76		5c. carmine (small "c") (17 March)	23·00	14·00
J77		5c. carmine (large "C")	3·25	4·75
		a. Imperf (pair)	£110	
		b. "G" for "C" (R. 2/6)	£180	
J78		10c. grey-brown (25 March)	6·50	5·50
		a. Imperf (pair)	£110	
		b. Imperf between (horiz pair)		£300
J79		15c. magenta (26 March)	30	2·75
		b. On laid paper	6·00	19·00
		ba. Inverted "C" in value (R. 2/3)	£180	
J80		20c. grey-lilac (29 March)	30	1·00
J81		30c. deep blue-green (29 March)	30	1·2

The 1c., 2c. and 3c. have large "C" in value as illustrated. The 10c. and higher values have small "c". Nos. J73/81 had the face values inserted individually into the plate used for No. J46 with the original face value removed. There were a number of printings for each value, often showing differences such as missing stops, various founts of figures or "c", etc., in the value tablets.

The face value error, No. J74a, was later corrected.

Some sheets of No. J75a show a sheet watermark of Britannia seated within a crowned oval spread across fifteen stamps in each sheet. This paper was manufactured by T. Edmonds and the other half of the sheet carried the watermark inscription "FOOLSCAP LEDGER". No stamps have been reported showing letters from this inscription, but a block of 25 is known on laid paper showing a different sheet watermark "HERTFORDSHIRE LEDGER MADE IN ENGLAND". Examples showing parts of these sheet watermarks are rare.

There are marked varieties of shade in this issue.

16 Soldier carving word "Independence"

17 Rejoicing Peasant

18 Boy with National Flag

Normal

Skyline flaw (R. 5/6)

(Des Maung Ba Thit (**16**), Naung Ohn Maung (**17**), and Maung Soi Yi (**18**). Typo State Press, Rangoon)

1943 (1 Aug). Independence Day.

(a) P 11.

J82	**16**	1c. orange	9·50	16·00
J83	**17**	3c. light blue	10·00	17·00
J84	**18**	5c. carmine	18·00	8·50
		a. Skyline flaw	95·00	
J82/4		Set of 3	35·00	38·00

(b) Rouletted.

J85	**16**	1c. orange	1·25	1·75
		b. Perf × roul	£110	£110
		c. Imperf (pair)	45·00	55·00
J86	**17**	3c. light blue	2·50	2·75
		b. Perf × roul	90·00	90·00
		c. Imperf (pair)	45·00	55·00
J87	**18**	5c. carmine	2·25	2·75
		b. Perf × roul	60·00	60·00
		c. Imperf (pair)	45·00	55·00
		d. Skyline flaw	22·00	24·00
J85/7		Set of 3	5·50	6·50

The stamps perf × rouletted may have one, two or three sides perforated.

The rouletted stamps often appear to be roughly perforated owing to failure to make clean cuts. These apparent perforations are very small and quite unlike the large, clean holes of the stamps perforated 11.

A few imperforate sets, mounted on a special card folder and cancelled with the commemorative postmark were presented to officials. These are rare.

19 Burmese Woman

20 Elephant carrying Log

21 Watch Tower, Mandalay

(Litho G. Kolff & Co, Batavia)

1943 (1 Oct). P 12½.

J88	**19**	1c. red-orange	20·00	15·00
J89		2c. yellow-green	50	2·00
J90		3c. deep violet	50	2·25
		a. Bright violet	1·75	4·00
J91	**20**	5c. carmine	65	60
J92		10c. blue	1·75	1·10
J93		15c. red-orange	1·00	1·00
J94		20c. yellow-green	1·00	1·75

J95		30c. olive-brown	1·00	2·00
J96	21	1r. red-orange	30	2·00
J97		2r. bright violet	30	2·25
J88/97 Set of 10			25·00	29·00

22 Bullock Cart

23 Shan Woman

ဗမာနိုင်ငံတော်

၂၀ ဆင်။

(**24** "Burma State" and value)

(Litho G. Kolff & Co, Batavia)

1943 (1 Oct). Issue for Shan States. P 12½.

J98	22	1c. olive-brown	29·00	35·00
J99		2c. yellow-green	32·00	35·00
J100		3c. bright violet	4·75	10·00
J101		5c. ultramarine	2·25	6·50
J102	23	10c. blue	14·00	17·00
J103		20c. carmine	30·00	17·00
J104		30c. olive-brown	20·00	48·00
J98/104 Set of 7			£120	£150

The Shan States, except for the frontier area around Keng Tung which was ceded to Thailand on 20 August 1943, were placed under the administration of the Burmese Government on 24 December 1943, and these stamps were later overprinted as T **24** for use throughout Burma.

1944 (1 Nov). Optd as T **24** (the lower characters differ for each value).

J105	22	1c. olive-brown	3·50	6·00
J106		2c. yellow-green	50	3·00
		a. Opt inverted	£425	£700
J107		3c. bright violet	2·25	7·00
J108		5c. ultramarine	1·00	2·00
J109	23	10c. blue	3·25	2·00
J110		20c. carmine	50	1·50
J111		30c. olive-brown	50	1·75
J105/11 Set of 7			10·00	21·00

Japanese Occupation of China

100 Cents = 1 Dollar

A. KWANGTUNG

Japanese troops occupied Canton on 21 October 1938 and by August 1945 had occupied most of Kwangtung Province. Unoverprinted stamps of China were used in the occupied area until smuggling of stamps from unoccupied China, to take advantage of discrepancies in currency values, caused the Japanese to overprint stamps for Kwangtung in 1942.

貼　粤

用　省

(**1**) (= "Special for Kwangtung")　(**2**)

1942 (13 June). Stamps of China optd with T **1**.

1	–	1c. yellow-orange (508)	1·90	2·40
2	**77**	1c. orange	2·40	3·75
3	**58**	2c. olive-green (396)	7·00	7·00
4	**72**	3c. brown-lake (464)	2·75	2·75
5	**77**	5c. green	2·40	3·75
6	**72**	8c. sage-green (F) (492A)	2·75	2·75
7	**77**	8c. turquoise-green	2·75	3·75
8	**72**	10c. green (469) (R.)	2·75	3·00
9		10c. green (493A) (R.)	3·75	5·00
10	**77**	10c. emerald-green	3·25	3·25
11	**72**	16c. olive-brown (471)	4·75	5·25
12	**77**	17c. olive-brown	3·25	3·00
13	–	20c. light blue (519)	3·25	3·75
14	**72**	30c. scarlet (494A)	3·75	2·75
15	**77**	30c. scarlet	3·25	3·75
16	**72**	50c. blue (495A) (R.)	3·75	7·75
17	**77**	50c. deep blue	3·25	3·75
18	**72**	$1 sepia and red-brown (H) (496A)	7·25	9·25
19		$2 red-brown and blue (H) (497A)	7·75	9·25
20		$5 deep green & scarlet (H) (498A)	7·00	8·50
21		$10 violet and green (H) (499A)	15·00	20·00
22		$20 ultramarine & purple (H) (500A)	7·00	9·25
23				
1/23 Set of 22			90·00	£110

1942 (20 Nov). Stamps of China optd with T **2**.

(a) Third Sun Yat-sen issue, 1938–41

24	**72**	2c. olive-green (B) (463)	65	70
25		3c. brown-lake (464)	65	70
26		5c. olive-green (466)	65	1·00
27		8c. sage-green (C) (467)	£275	£250
28		8c. sage-green (D) (468)	75	1·00
29		10c. green (469)	1·00	1·20
30		16c. olive-brown (471)	1·20	1·00
31		25c. violet-blue (472)	1·20	2·75
32		30c. scarlet (494A)	1·10	2·40
33		50c. blue (495A)	2·20	2·75
34		$1 sepia and red-brown (H) (496A)	6·25	7·75
35		$1 sepia and red-brown (H) (496B)	8·25	8·50
36		$2 red-brown and blue (H) (497A)	7·25	9·25
37		$2 red-brown and blue (H) (497B)	7·50	8·00
38		$5 deep green & scarlet (H) (498A)	10·00	12·00
39		$5 deep green & scarlet (H) (498B)	10·00	12·00
40		$10 violet and green (H) (499A)	15·00	20·00
41		$10 violet and green (H) (499B)	16·00	20·00
42		$20 ultramarine and purple (H) (500A)	14·00	20·00
43		$20 ultramarine and purple (H) (500B).	21·00	24·00
24/43 Set of 20			£350	£375

(b) Fourth Sun Yat-sen issue, 1941

44	**77**	2c. ultramarine	50	50
45		5c. green	50	50
46		8c. red-orange	55	50

301

47	8c. turquoise-green	55	90
48	10c. emerald-green	65	65
49	17c. olive-green	1·00	1·00
50	25c. purple	1·00	1·00
51	30c. scarlet	1·00	1·10
52	50c. deep blue	1·00	1·10
53	$1 black and brown	4·75	7·75
54	$2 black and blue	6·00	8·50
55	$5 black and scarlet	4·75	4·75
56	$10 black and green	8·50	12·50
57	$20 black and purple	10·50	13·00
44/57 *Set of* 14		37·00	48·00

(D **3**)　　(**3**)　　(**4**)

1945. POSTAGE DUE. No. D575 of China surch with Type D **3**.

D58	D **62** $100 on $2 orange	£700	£650

1945 (July). Canton provisionals. Nos. 29 and 28 surch as T **3**.

58	**72**	$200 on 10c. green	£120	75·00
59		$400 on 8c. sage-green	£120	75·00

1945 (22 Aug). Swatow provisional No. 508 of China surch with T **4**.

60	$400 on 1c. yellow-orange	£700	£600

Japanese forces in China capitulated on 9 September 1945.

B. MENGKIANG

(Inner Mongolia)

Japanese troops captured Kalgan on 27 August 1937 and Kweisui (renamed Huhehot) on 13 October. The Inner Mongolian leaders, Prince Yun and Prince Teh, were encouraged to federate the autonomous governments of South Chahar, North Shansi and the Mongol League which the Japanese had established. A Federated Committee for Mengkiang ("The Mongolian Borderlands") was set up at Kalgan on 22 November 1937, and on 1 September 1939 a Federated Autonomous Government of Mengkiang was formed at Huhehot, with Prince Teh as Chief Executive.

(**1**) Small　　(**2**) Large

See notes under "Six Districts" overprints in Japanese Occupation of North China.

(Optd by Chinese Bureau of Engraving and Printing, Peking)

1941. Stamps of Chino overprinted "Mengkiang".

(a) On T **58**, 1931–37 De La Rue Single circle issue A.
With T **1** (1 July)

1A	2c. olive-green (396)	1·20	2·00
2A	4c. green (397)	55·00	70·00
3A	15c. scarlet (400)	4·75	5·50
4A	20c. ultramarine (401)	10·50	8·50
5A	25c. ultramarine (402)	60·00	60·00

B. With T **2** (15 July)

1B	2c. olive-green (396)	1·60	2·00
2B	4c. green (397)	45·00	40·00
3B	15c. scarlet (400)	4·50	5·25
4B	20c. ultramarine (401)	10·00	11·50
5B	25c. ultramarine (402)	11·50	14·00

(b) On T **72**,1938–41, Chung Hwa. P 12½. No wmk.
A. With T **1** (July)

7A	3c. brown-lake (464)	1·10	1·10
8A	5c. olive-green (466)	2·50	5·50

9A	8c. sage-green (C) (467)	1·70	1·60
13A	$1 sepia and red-brown Die II (460)	85·00	80·00
14A	$1 sepia and red-brown Die III (473)...	£325	£325

B. With T **2** (15 July)

6B	2c. olive-green (B) (463)	2·30	3·00
7B	3c. brown-lake (464)	1·10	1·10
8B	5c. olive-green (466)	1·90	2·20
9B	8c. sage-green (C) (467)	2·00	2·00
10B	8c. sage-green (D) (468)	8·00	8·00
11B	10c. green (469)	2·20	2·20
12B	16c. olive-brown (471)	4·00	4·00
14B	$1 sepia and red-brown Die III (473)...	11·00	12·00
15B	$5 deep green and scarlet (475)	65·00	65·00

(c) On T **72**,1939–41, Dah Tung. P 14. No wmk
A. With T **1** (1 July)

17A	8c. sage-green (E) (491A)	70·00	—
18A	8c. sage-green (F) (492A)	3·25	3·25
19A	10c. green (493A)	4·00	4·00
20A	30c. scarlet (494A)	4·75	5·00
21A	50c. blue (495A)	7·25	7·25
22A	$1 sepia and red-brown (H) (496A)	11·00	11·50
23A	$2 red-brown and blue (H) (497A)	11·50	14·00
24A	$5 deep green and scarlet (H) (498A).	29·00	29·00
25A	$10 violet and green (H) (499A)	70·00	70·00
26A	$20 ultramarine and purple (H) (500A)	£100	£110

B. With T **2** (15 July)

16B	5c. olive (F) (490A)	1·60	1·70
17B	8c. sage-green (E) (491A)	3·25	3·25
19B	10c. green (493A)	2·20	2·00
20B	30c. scarlet (494A)	2·75	2·75
21B	50c. blue (495A)	7·25	7·25
22B	$1 sepia and red-brown (H) (496A)	20·00	20·00
23B	$2 red-brown and blue (H) (497A)	27·00	27·00
24B	$5 deep green and scarlet (H) (498A).	55·00	55·00
25B	$10 violet and green (H) (499A)	60·00	60·00
26B	$20 ultramarine and purple (H) (500A)	£100	£110

(d) As last but W **73**
A. With T **1** (1 July)

27A	5c. green (F) (489B)	£275	—
30A	30c. scarlet (494B)	65·00	65·00
31A	50c. blue (495B)	£275	—

B. With T **2** (15 July)

28B	5c. olive (F) (490B)	90·00	—
29B	10c. green (493B)	4·50	4·50
30B	30c. scarlet (494B)	4·75	5·75
31B	50c. blue (495B)	4·00	4·50

(e) On Martyrs (as T **60**),1932–34, Peking. P 14
A. With T **1** (1 July)

32A	½c. sepia (410)	10·50	13·00
33A	2½c. claret (412)	7·25	8·75
34A	13c. deep green (416)	£110	£110

B. With T **2** (15 July)

32B	½c. sepia (410)	16·00	22·00
33B	2½c. claret (412)	3·75	3·75
34B	13c. deep green (416)	1·60	1·10
35B	30c. maroon (419)	70·00	70·00

(f) On Martyrs (as T **60**), Hong Kong print. P 12,12½,13 or compound
No wmk

A. With T **1** (1 July)

36A	½c. sepia (507)	3·75	4·00
37A	1c. yellow-orange (508)	1·60	1·40
38A	1c. yellow-orange without secret sign (508b)	£110	—
39A	2c. blue (509)	4·75	4·75
40A	3c. brown (511)	2·75	2·50
42A	8c. brown-orange (514)	75·00	75·00
43A	10c. dull purple (515)	23·00	23·00
44A	13c. blue-green (516)	6·50	7·25
46A	17c. bronze-green (518)	4·25	4·25
47A	20c. light blue (519)	4·25	4·00
49A	25c. purple (521)	3·75	4·00
51A	50c. green (525)	4·25	3·50

B. With T **2** (15 July)

36B	½c. sepia (507)	1·60	1·70
37B	1c. yellow-orange (508)	4·00	3·50
38B	1c. yellow-orange without secret sign (508b)	65·00	—

40B	3c. brown (511)	3·50	3·50
41B	4c. lilac (512)	2·00	1·70
42B	8c. brown-orange (514)	16·00	20·00
43B	10c. dull purple (515)	70·00	70·00
44B	13c. blue-green (516)	23·00	3·00
45B	15c. maroon (517)	4·00	4·00
46B	17c. bronze-green (518)	3·75	3·75
47B	20c. light blue (519)	2·20	3·00
48B	21c. sepia (521)	4·00	4·00
50B	28c. olive (522)	4·00	4·00
51B	50c. green (525)	7·50	7·50

(g) As last but W 73
A. With T 1 (1 July)

52A	½c. sepia (526)	45·00	—
53A	1c. yellow-orange (527)	3·50	3·50
55A	2c. claret (529)	55·00	55·00
58A	10c. dull purple (534)	12·50	12·50
60A	17c. bronze-green (537)	80·00	—
63A	30c. maroon (542)	70·00	70·00
64A	40c. orange (543)	8·00	8·00
65A	50c. green (544)	11·50	11·50

B. With T 2 (15 July)

52B	½c. sepia (526)	11·50	14·00
53B	1c. yellow-orange (527)	1·00	1·00
54B	2c. blue (528)	7·00	—
55B	2c. claret (529)	55·00	55·00
56B	3c. brown (530)	3·50	3·50
57B	8c. brown-orange (533)	42·00	42·00
58B	10c. dull purple (534)	13·50	—
59B	13c. blue-green (535)	10·00	—
60B	17c. bronze-green (537)	47·00	—
61B	20c. light blue (538)	£140	—
62B	25c. purple (540)	3·25	3·50
63B	30c. maroon (542)	60·00	60·00
64B	40c. orange (543)	5·75	5·75
65B	50c. green (544)	60·00	65·00

(3)

(Surch by Chinese Bureau of Engraving and Printing, Peking)

1942 (1 June). Stamps of China and unissued "New Peking" printings, optd "Mengkiang" (top two characters) and surch half original value as T **3** (four characters at foot in 15c. and 25c.).

(a) On 1931–37 De La Rue single circle issue

66	**58**	1c. on 2c. olive-green (396)	20·00	20·00
67		2c. on 4c. green (397)	11·50	11·50
68		10c. on 20c. ultramarine (401)	32·00	32·00

(b) On Third Sun Yat-sen issue, 1938–41

69	**72**	1c. on 2c. olive-green (B) (463)	2·00	1·20
70		4c. on 8c. sage-green (C) (467)	9·50	11·50
71		4c. on 8c. sage-green (D) (468)	3·00	2·75
72		4c. on 8c. sage-green (F) (492A)	65	65
73		5c. on 10c. green (469)	1·00	65
74		8c. on 16c. olive-brown (471)	4·00	3·00
75		15c. on 30c. scarlet (494A)	4·75	6·50
76		15c. on 30c. scarlet (494B)	80·00	80·00
77		25c. on 50c. blue (495A)	7·00	8·00
78		50c. on $1 sepia & red-brown (460)	47·00	47·00
79		50c. on $1 sepia & red-brown (473)	9·50	9·50
80		50c. on $1 sepia & red-brn (496A)	5·75	7·25
81		$1 on $2 red-brown & blue (474)	60·00	60·00
82		$1 on $2 red-brown & bl (497A)	11·50	11·50
83		$5 on $10 violet & green (499A)	44·00	44·00
84		$10 on $20 ultram & pur (500A)	70·00	80·00

(c) On Martyrs types (as T **60**)

85		½c. on 1c. yellow-orange (411)	20·00	20·00
86		½c. on 1c. yellow-orange (508)	25	45
87		2c. on 4c. lilac (512)	3·75	3·75
88		10c. on 20c. light blue (519)	5·75	5·75
89		15c. on 30c. maroon (542)	60·00	60·00
90		20c. on 40c. orange (524)	11·50	12·00

91		20c. on 40c. orange (543)	18·00	18·00
92		25c. on 50c. green (525)	23·00	23·00

(d) On Sun Yat-sen "New Peking" printings

93	**58**	1c. on 2c. olive-green	7·00	12·00
94		2c. on 4c. yellow-green	50	65
95	**72**	8c. on 16c. olive-brown	1·60	2·30
96		50c. on $1 sepia and orange-brown	11·50	11·50
97		$1 on $2 brown and blue	29·00	35·00
98		$5 on $10 violet and green	65·00	65·00

(e) On Martyrs "New Peking" printings (as T **60**)

99		5c. on 10c. purple	4·00	7·25
100		10c. on 20c. brown-lake	4·75	7·25
101		15c. on 30c. maroon	1·80	2·75
102		20c. on 40c. orange	7·25	8·00
103		25c. on 50c. green	2·00	4·00

See note below No. 138 of Japanese Occupation of North China.

4 Dragon Pillar, Peking   **5** Miners

(Recess Imperial Printing Bureau, Tokyo)

1943 (16 Apr). Fifth Anniv of Establishment of Mengkiang Post and Telegraph Service. Granite paper. Wmk Characters in circle in sheet (none on some stamps). P 11½×11 or 12×11.

104	**4**	4c. red-orange	1·20	1·80
105		8c. deep blue	1·30	1·80

(Photo Imperial Printing Bureau, Tokyo)

1943 (8 Dec). Second Anniv of War in East Asia. P 12.

106	**5**	4c. blue-green	1·20	1·80
107		8c. lake	1·30	1·80

6 Stylized Horse   **7** Prince Yun   **8** Blast Furnace

(Photo Imperial Printing Bureau, Tokyo)

1944 (1 Sept). Fifth Anniv of Federation of Autonomous Governments of Mongolian Provinces. P 12½×12 (4c.) or 12×12½ (8c.).

108	**6**	4c. rose	1·00	1·80
109	**7**	8c. deep blue	1·00	1·80

(Photo Imperial Printing Bureau, Tokyo)

1944 (8 Dec). Productivity Campaign. P 12×12½.

110	**8**	8c. brown	1·20	2·75

1945. (June). Unissued "New Peking" printings optd as top characters of T **3**. No gum.

(a) On Sun Yat-sen types

111	**58**	2c. olive-green	9·50	8·00
112		4c. yellow-green	16·00	12·00
113		5c. green	10·00	10·00
114	**72**	$1 sepia and orange-brown	2·75	3·50
115		$2 brown and blue	11·50	11·50
116		$5 green and rose-red	40·00	40·00

(b) On Martyrs types (as T **60**)

117		1c. yellow-orange	80	80
118		8c. brown-orange	75	75
119		10c. purple	25	35
120		20c. brown-lake	1·70	2·30
121		30c. maroon	35	1·20
122		40c. orange	40	40

123	50c. green	7·25	8·00
111/123 *Set of* 13		90·00	90·00

角　壹　角　伍　圓　壹
(9)　　　　(10)　　　　(11)

1945 (July). Surch with new values in Chinese characters as T **9** (10c.), 10 (50c.) or 11 ($1).

(a) On Chinese stamps previously optd "Mengkiang"
A. With T **1** (small)

124A	60	10c. on ½c. (36) (R.)	4·50	5·50
126A	–	10c. on 1c. (37) (R.)	1·90	2·20
128A	–	10c. on 1c. (53) (R.)	75	90
129A	58	50c. on 2c. (1)	16·00	19·00
132A	72	50c. on 5c. (8) (R.)	6·75	7·00

B. With T **2** (large)

124B	60	10c. on ½c. (36) (R.)	3·50	4·00
125B		10c. on ½c. (52) (R.)	20·00	23·00
126B	–	10c. on 1c. (37) (R.)	95	1·10
127B	–	10c. on 1c. (38) (R.)	40·00	50·00
128B	–	10c. on 1c. (53) (R.)	1·20	1·40
129B	58	50c. on 2c. (1)	16·00	19·00
130B	72	50c. on 2c. (6)	1·00	1·50
131B	60	50c. on 4c. (41) (R.)	80	1·00
132B	72	50c. on 5c. (8) (R.)	70	1·40
133B		50c. on 5c. (16) (R.)	40	40

(b) On "New Peking" printings optd as top characters of T **3**

134	–	10c. on 1c. yellow-orange (R.) (Martyrs)		
135	58	50c. on 2c. olive-green (R.)	2·75	2·75
136		50c. on 4c. yellow-green (R.)	4·00	4·00
137		50c. on 5c. green (R.)	40	40
138	–	$1 on 8c. brown-orange (R.) (Martyrs)	30	1·70

After the Japanese surrender in 1945, Inner Mongolia was occupied by the Chinese Communists, who later created an Inner Mongolian Autonomous Region within the People's Republic.

C. NORTH CHINA

After the "Marco Polo Bridge incident" at Lukouchiao, near Peking, on 7 July 1937, the Japanese army began to try to conquer China. On 8 August it entered Peking, and on 14 December founded there a puppet Provisional Government of China. On 30 March 1940, this was combined with the Reformed Government of the Republic of China, established by the Japanese at Nanking on 27 March 1938, to form the Reorganised National Government of the Republic of China, with Wang Ching-wei as Chairman and Nanking as capital. Civil affairs in North China were conducted by the North China Political Council at Peking. The areas occupied by the Japanese army consisted mostly of large towns and lines of communication between them.

"NEW PEKING PRINTINGS". In 1941 the Chinese Bureau of Engraving and Printing was ordered to print stamps for the Japanese-controlled areas of North China in the designs current in areas under the Government of Chiang Kai-shek. The 8c. Martyrs type (No. 1) was the only value officially issued without some sort of overprint.

Stamps of this issue overprinted in 1942.45 comprise the 2c., 4c. and 5c. in the 1931–37 Sun Yat-sen type (second issue); the 9c., 16c. and 18c. and $1, $2, $5, $10 and $20 in the 1939–41 Dah Tung Book Co type; and the 1c., 4c., 10c., 20c., 30c., 40c. and 50c. in the 1932–34 Martyrs type. There are minute differences of design between the "New Peking" and earlier printings, but the "New Peking" printings may be distinguished easily by the fact that the execution is less finished, and the paper used is of poor quality, resembling newsprint.

The stamps were first issued with a dull yellowish gum and later without gum. The "New Peking" Martyr stamps are also usually ½ mm to ¾ mm wider than the Martyr issue of 1932–34.

"SIX DISTRICTS" OVERPRINTS. The characters below respectively represent the names of the Provinces of Honan, Hopeh, Shansi and Shantung and the District of Supeh, (Northern Kiangsu); the corresponding overprint for the sixth district, i. e. the autonomous District of Mengkiang (Inner Mongolia), will be found listed under

Mengkiang, Nos. 1 to 65, together with the other issues for that district.

Each overprint exists in two types, known as "small" and "large;" differing slightly in size but more particularly in shape. Overprinting was carried out to combat speculation. The currency in the south having depreciated, stamps could be smuggled to the Japanese-occupied north for re-sale at a profit. The overprints acted as controls, use being restricted to the province or district named on the stamp. Their sale was discontinued on 31 May 1942.

Some values were philatelically manipulated by postal officials but contradictory information and the absence of authoritative records makes it difficult to be sure which. Our list is of values known to exist.

1941 (5 June). "New Peking" printing. As No. 414 of China but re-engraved by the Chinese Bureau of Engraving and Printing, Peking. Recess. P 14.

1		8c. red-orange	8·25	55·00

南　河　　南　河
(A) Small Honan　　(B) Large Honan

北　河　　北　河
(C) Small Hopeh　　(D) Large Hopeh

西　山　　西　山
(E) Small Shansi　　(F) Large Shansi

東　山　　東　山
(G) Small Shantung　　(H) Large Shantung

北　蘇　　北　蘇
(I) Small Supeh　　(J) Large Supeh

1941. Stamps of China overprinted with Types A to J. Small types (1 July). Large types (15 July).

(a) On T **58**, 1931–37. De La Rue single circle issue
Honan
A. Small setting

2A	2c. olive-green (396)	60·00	75·00
3A	4c. green (397)	5·25	6·00
4A	15c. scarlet (400)	11·50	9·25
5A	20c. ultramarine (401)	65·00	65·00
6A	25c. ultramarine (402)	£150	—

B. Large setting

2B	2c. olive-green (396)	50·00	44·00
3B	4c. green (397)	5·00	5·75
4B	15c. scarlet (400)	11·00	12·50
6B	25c. ultramarine (402)	2·50	3·25

Hopeh
A. Small setting

2C	2c. olive-green (396)	3·50	2·75
3C	4c. green (397)	3·75	3·75
4C	15c. scarlet (400)	3·50	3·25
5C	20c. ultramarine (401)	80·00	75·00
6C	25c. ultramarine (402)	80·00	75·00

B. Large setting

2D	2c. olive-green (396)	1·10	65
3D	4c. green (397)	50·00	50·00
4D	15c. scarlet (400)	2·30	2·30
5D	20c. ultramarine (401)	1·50	1·20
6D	25c. ultramarine (402)	8·75	7·25

Shansi
A. Small setting

2E	2c. olive-green (396)	5·75	5·75
3E	4c. green (397)	35·00	35·00
4E	15c. scarlet (400)	8·00	9·50
6E	25c. ultramarine (402)	55·00	60·00

	B. Large setting		
2F	2c. olive-green (396)	5·75	5·75
3F	4c. green (397)	£110	£140
4F	15c. scarlet (400)	4·75	5·75
6F	25c. ultramarine (402)	8·00	11·50

	Shantung		
	A. Small setting		
2G	2c. olive-green (396)	3·25	3·25
3G	4c. green (397)	7·00	5·75
4G	15c. scarlet (400)	2·75	2·75
6G	25c. ultramarine (402)	£170	—

	B. Large setting		
2H	2c. olive-green (396)	1·20	1·20
3H	4c. green (397)	5·75	5·50
4H	15c. scarlet (400)	1·90	1·90
5H	20c. ultramarine (401)	3·75	3·75
6H	25c. ultramarine (402)	5·50	5·50

	Supeh		
	A.Small setting		
2I	2c. olive-green (396)	9·50	9·50
3I	4c. green (397)	47·00	47·00
4I	15c. scarlet (400)	2·75	2·75
5I	20c. ultramarine (401)	£200	—
6I	25c. ultramarine (402)	40·00	—

	B. Large setting		
2J	2c. olive-green (396)	12·50	12·50
3J	4c. green (397)	65·00	—
4J	15c. scarlet (400)	2·75	2·75
5J	20c. ultramarine (401)	3·25	3·25

(b) On T **72**, 1938–41, Ching Hwa. P 12½. No wmk

	Honan		
	A. Small setting		
9A	3c. brown-lake (464)	1·90	1·80
11A	5c. olive-green (466)	1·90	1·90
12A	8c. sage-green (C) (467)	1·20	1·20
17A	$1 sepia and red-brown (II) (460)	75·00	47·00
18A	$1 sepia and red-brown (III) (473)	3·50	3·50

	B. Large setting		
8B	2c. olive-green (B) (463)	2·10	2·40
9B	3c. brown-lake (464)	2·20	2·20
11B	5c. olive-green (466)	2·40	2·40
12B	8c. sage-green (C) (467)	4·50	4·50
13B	8c. sage-green (D) (468)	2·20	1·30
14B	10c. green (469)	12·00	13·00
16B	16c. olive-brown (471)	1·80	1·90
18B	$1 sepia and red-brown (III) (473)	11·50	11·50
20B	$5 deep green and scarlet (475)	3·00	3·00
22B	$20 ultramarine and purple (477)	22·00	22·00

	Hopeh		
	C. Small setting		
9C	3c. brown-lake (464)	1·60	1·60
11C	5c. olive-green (466)	1·70	1·60
12C	8c. sage-green (C) (467)	1·40	1·30
17C	$1 sepia and red-brown (II) (460)	£150	£170
19C	$2 red-brown and blue (474)	40·00	40·00
20C	$5 deep green and scarlet (475)	47·00	47·00

	D. Small setting		
7D	2c. olive-green (A) (462)	1·00	50
8D	2c. olive-green (B) (463)	50	60
9D	3c. brown-lake (464)	35	35
10D	5c. green (465)	80	65
11D	5c. olive-green (466)	50	35
12D	8c. sage-green (C) (467)	2·20	2·20
13D	8c. sage-green (D) (468)	2·20	2·20
14D	10c. green (469)	1·50	75
15D	15c. scarlet (470)	50·00	—
16D	16c. olive-brown (471)	1·90	80
18D	$1 sepia and red-brown (III) (473)	8·00	8·00
19D	$2 red-brown and blue (474)	10·00	10·00
20D	$5 deep green and scarlet (475)	50·00	50·00
21D	$10 violet and green (476)	£160	£160
22D	$20 ultramarine and purple (477)	£350	£350

	Shansi		
	E. Small setting		
9E	3c. brown-lake (464)	11·50	11·50
11E	5c. olive-green (466)	4·00	4·00

12E	8c. sage-green (C) (467)	2·75	2·75
17E	$1 sepia and red-brown (II) (460)	£275	†

	F. Large setting		
8F	2c. olive-green (B) (463)	65	65
9F	3c. brown-lake (464)	1·00	1·00
11F	5c. olive-green (466)	2·75	2·75
12F	8c. sage-green (C) (467)	1·30	1·00
13F	8c. sage-green (D) (468)	26·00	15·00
14F	10c. green (469)	3·50	4·00
16F	16c. olive-brown (471)	4·00	4·00
18F	$1 sepia and red-brown (III) (473)	10·00	10·00
19F	$2 red-brown and blue (474)	40·00	40·00
20F	$5 deep green and scarlet (475)	47·00	47·00

	Shantung		
	G. Small setting		
9G	3c. brown-lake (464)	85	1·20
11G	5c. olive-green (466)	1·20	1·20
12G	8c. sage-green (C) (467)	1·00	1·00
17G	$1 sepia and red-brown (II) (460)	47·00	47·00
18G	$1 sepia and red-brown (111) (473)	£350	£350

	H. Large setting		
7H	2c. olive-green (A) (462)	1·10	85
8H	2c. olive-green (B) (463)	75	50
9H	3c. brown-lake (464)	75	60
11H	5c. olive-green (466)	1·10	85
12H	8c. sage-green (C) (467)	85	45
13H	8c. sage-green (D) (468)	1·00	70
14H	10c. green (469)	1·40	95
16H	16c. olive-brown (471)	6·50	6·50
18H	$1 sepia and red-brown (III) (473)	22·00	12·50
19H	$2 red-brown and blue (474)	70·00	†
20H	$5 deep green and scarlet (475)	50·00	50·00

	Supeh		
	I. Small setting		
9I	3c. brown-lake (464)	19·00	19·00
11I	5c. olive-green (466)	3·25	3·00
12I	8c. sage-green (C) (467)	2·10	2·10
17I	$1 sepia and red-brown (II) (460)	£160	£160

	J. Large setting		
8J	2c. olive-green (B) (463)	1·20	1·60
9J	3c. brown-lake (464)	1·40	1·40
11J	5c. olive-green (466)	1·20	1·70
12J	8c. sage-green (C) (467)	2·75	2·75
13J	8c. sage-green (D) (468)	35·00	28·00
14J	10c. green (469)	3·00	4·00
16J	16c. olive-brown (471)	1·20	1·90
18J	$1 sepia and red-brown (III) (473)	13·00	13·00
20J	$5 deep green and scarlet (475)	£100	£100

(c) On T **72**, 1938–41 Dah Tung. Perf 14. No wmk

	Honan		
	A. Small setting		
27A	30c. scarlet (494A)	£300	7·25
28A	50c. blue (495A)	3·25	3·00
29A	$1 sepia and red-brown (496A)	6·50	6·50
30A	$2 red-brown and blue (497A)	70·00	70·00
31A	$5 deep green and scarlet (498A)	£300	23·00
32A	$10 violet and green (499A)	11·50	14·50
33A	$20 ultramarine and purple (500A)	8·00	9·75

	B. Large setting		
24B	5c. olive (490A)	60·00	60·00
25B	8c. sage-green (F) (492A)	65·00	65·00
26B	10c. green (493A)	£110	£120
27B	30c. scarlet (494A)	8·75	8·75
28B	50c. blue (495A)	£100	14·00
29B	$1 sepia and red-brown (496A)	5·00	5·00
30B	$2 red-brown and blue (497A)	5·25	6·25
31B	$5 deep green and scarlet (498A)	4·50	5·00
32B	$10 violet and green (499A)	18·00	24·00
33B	$20 ultramarine and purple (500A)	4·25	4·25

	Hopeh		
	C. Small setting		
24C	5c. olive (490A)	1·10	1·10
25C	8c. sage-green (F) (492A)	50·00	50·00
26C	10c. green (493A)	1·30	60
28C	50c. blue (495A)	1·90	1·90

29C	$1 sepia and red-brown (496A)	5·75	4·00
30C	$2 red-brown and blue (497A)	23·00	23·00
31C	$5 deep-green and scarlet (498A)	40·00	40·00
32C	£10 violet and green (499A)	55·00	47·00
33C	$20 ultramarine and purple (500A)	80·00	80·00

D. Large setting

23D	5c. green (489A)	£110	†
24D	5c. olive (490A)	60	50
25D	8c. sage-green (F) (492A)	1·20	1·20
26D	10c. green (493A)	1·00	30
27D	30c. scarlet (494A)	1·00	1·00
28D	50c. blue (495A)	1·90	1·90
29D	$1 sepia and red-brown (496A)	4·00	3·50
30D	$2 red-brown and blue (497A)	14·00	9·50
31D	$5 deep-green and scarlet (498A)	35·00	35·00
32D	$10 violet and green (499A)	40·00	40·00
33D	$20 ultramarine and purple (500A)	60·00	70·00

Shansi

E. Small setting

26E	10c. green (493A)	1·00	1·40
27E	30c. scarlet (494A)	2·30	2·30
28E	50c. blue (495A)	3·50	3·50
29E	$1 sepia and red-brown (496A)	8·75	8·75
30E	$2 red-brown and blue (497A)	11·50	13·00
31E	$5 deep-green and scarlet (498A)	70·00	70·00
32E	$10 violet and green (499A)	60·00	60·00
33E	$20 ultramarine and purple (500A)	£100	£110

F. Large setting

24F	5c. olive (490A)	65	60
25F	8c. sage-green (F) (492A)	1·00	1·00
26F	10c. green (493A)	4·00	4·00
27F	30c. scarlet (494A)	1·70	1·70
28F	50c. blue (495A)	4·75	4·75
29F	$1 sepia and red-brown (496A)	29·00	29·00
30F	$2 red-brown and blue (497A)	14·00	19·00
31F	$5 deep-green and scarlet (498A)	26·00	26·00
32F	$10 violet and green (499A)	55·00	55·00
33F	$20 ultramarine and purple (500A)	55·00	55·00

Shantung

G. Small setting

25G	8c. sage-green (F) (492A)	1·50	1·50
27G	30c. scarlet (494A)	6·75	7·25
28G	50c. blue (495A)	7·25	7·25
29G	$1 sepia and red-brown (496A)	17·00	17·00
30G	$2 red-brown and blue (497A)	24·00	24·00
31G	$5 deep-green and scarlet (498A)	40·00	40·00
32G	$10 violet and green (499A)	75·00	75·00
33G	$20 ultramarine and purple (500A)	£100	£110

H. Large setting

24H	5c. olive (490A)	1·20	1·00
25H	8c. sage-green (F) (492A)	90	75
26H	10c. green (493A)	1·20	1·00
27H	30c. scarlet (494A)	1·60	1·20
28H	50c. blue (495A)	7·25	6·50
29H	$1 sepia and red-brown (496A)	5·75	4·00
30H	$2 red-brown and blue (497A)	11·50	11·50
31H	$5 deep-green and scarlet (498A)	23·00	23·00
32H	$10 violet and green (499A)	55·00	55·00
33H	£20 ultramarine and purple (500A)	80·00	80·00

Supeh

I. Small setting

26I	10c. green (493A)	2·10	2·10
27I	30c. scarlet (494A)	3·25	3·50
28I	50c. blue (495A)	3·00	3·50
29I	$1 sepia and red-brown (496A)	19·00	23·00
30I	$2 red-brown and blue (497A)	27·00	32·00
31I	$5 deep-green and scarlet (498A)	23·00	23·00
32I	$10 violet and green (499A)	65·00	65·00
33I	$20 ultramarine & purple (500A)	80·00	90·00

J. Large setting

23J	5c. green (489A)	1·20	1·20
24J	5c. olive (490A)	1·50	1·30
25J	8c. sage-green (F) (492A)	1·30	1·30
26J	10c. green (493A)	3·50	3·50
27J	30c. scarlet (494A)	6·50	7·25
28J	50c. blue (495A)	3·75	4·50
29J	$1 sepia and red-brown (496A)	32·00	32·00
30J	$2 red-brown and blue (497A)	22·00	24·00

31J	$5 deep-green and scarlet (498A)	65·00	65·00
32J	$10 violet and green (499A)	70·00	70·00
33J	$20 ultramarine & purple (500A)	80·00	80·00

(d) As (c) but W 73

Honan

A. Small setting

37A	30c. scarlet (494A)	1·80	1·50

B. Large setting

34B	5c. green (489B)	1·80	1·20
35B	5c. olive (490B)	75·00	75·00
36B	10c. green (493B)	1·80	1·90
37B	30c. scarlet (494B)	4·50	3·75
38B	50c. blue (495B)	70·00	41·00

Hopeh

A. Small setting

37C	30c. scarlet (494B)	4·00	4·00

B. Large setting

34D	5c. green (489B)	90	90
35D	5c. olive (490B)	70	70
36D	10c. green (493B)	1·00	50
37D	30c. scarlet (494B)	1·20	1·20
38D	50c. blue (495B)	4·75	4·75

Shansi

A. Small setting

37E	30c. scarlet (494B)	65·00	65·00
38E	50c. blue (495B)	5·75	6·50

B. Large setting

34F	5c. green (489B)	1·20	1·20
35F	5c. olive (490B)	1·00	1·00
36F	10c. green (493B)	2·30	2·30
37F	30c. scarlet (494B)	38·00	38·00

Shantung

A. Small setting

37G	30c. scarlet (494B)	19·00	19·00
38G	50c. blue (495B)	8·00	9·50

B. Large setting

34H	5c. green (489B)	1·00	1·00
35H	5c. olive (490B)	1·00	1·00
36H	10c. green (493B)	6·50	6·50
37H	30c. scarlet (494B)	4·00	3·25
38H	50c. blue (495B)	2·50	3·50

Supeh

A. Small setting

37I	30c. scarlet (494B)	13·00	14·00
38I	50c. blue (495B)	14·00	14·50

B. Large setting

36J	10c. green (493B)	4·00	4·00

(e) On Martyrs (as T 60), 1932–34, Peking. P 14

Honan

A. Small setting

39A	½c. sepia (410)	5·25	5·25
40A	2½c. claret (412)	3·00	2·75
41A	13c. deep green (416)	80·00	80·00

B. Large setting

39B	½c. sepia (410)	32·00	40·00
40B	2½c. claret (412)	3·75	3·75
41B	13c. deep green (416)	2·20	1·90
42B	30c. maroon (419)	18·00	22·00
43B	40c. orange (420)	75·00	75·00

Hopeh

A. Small setting

39C	½c. sepia (410)	90	90
40C	2c. claret (412)	50	60
41C	13c. deep green (416)	2·20	2·20

B. Large setting

39D	½c. sepia (410)	35	60
40D	2½c. claret (412)	50	35
41D	13c. deep green (416)	1·20	1·10
42D	30c. maroon (419)	4·75	5·75
43D	40c. orange (420)	55·00	†

Shansi
A. Small setting

39E	½c. sepia (410)	1·70	3·00
40E	2½c. claret (412)	1·70	1·60
41E	13c. deep green (416)	£190	£190

B. Large setting

39F	½c. sepia (410)	1·00	1·20
40F	2½c. claret (412)	1·20	1·40
41F	13c. deep green (416)	1·90	1·90
42F	30c. maroon (419)	8·00	9·50

Shantung
A. Small setting

39G	½c. sepia (410)	1·90	1·20
40G	2½c. claret (412)	1·20	1·60
41G	13c. deep green (416)	19·00	19·00

B. Large setting

39H	½c. sepia (410)	1·00	1·00
40H	2½c. claret (412)	1·20	1·70
41H	13c. deep green (416)	1·20	1·10
42H	30c. maroon (419)	65·00	†

Supeh
A. Small setting

39I	½c. sepia (410)	3·50	3·50
40I	2½c. claret (412)	1·20	1·20
41I	13c. deep green (416)	95·00	95·00

B. Large setting

39J	½c. sepia (410)	17·00	—
40J	2½c. claret (412)	1·20	1·20
41J	13c. deep green (416)	1·80	1·80

(f) On Martyrs (as T **60**),1989–41 Hong Kong print. P 12, 12½,13 or compound. No wmk

Honan
A. Small setting

44A	½c. sepia (507)	7·25	8·00
45A	1c. yellow-orange (508)	1·90	1·90
47A	2c. blue (509)	4·75	4·50
48A	3c. brown (511)	1·20	1·90
50A	8c. brown-orange (514)	17·00	—
51A	10c. dull purple (515)	4·75	3·75
52A	13c. blue-green (516)	50·00	16·00
54A	17c. bronze-green (518)	14·00	14·00
55A	20c. light blue (519)	60·00	60·00
57A	25c. purple (521)	4·00	4·00

B. Large setting

44B	½c. sepia (507)	25·00	3·25
45B	1c. yellow-orange (508)	4·50	4·50
46B	1c. yellow-orange (508b)	4·25	4·25
48B	3c. brown (511)	4·50	4·50
49B	4c. lilac (512)	1·50	1·50
50B	8c. brown-orange (514)	4·50	4·50
52B	13c. blue-green (516)	12·50	15·00
53B	15c. maroon (517)	1·10	1·10
54B	17c. bronze-green (518)	7·75	3·50
55B	20c. light blue (519)	60·00	60·00
56B	21c. sepia (520)	3·75	3·75
58B	28c. olive (522)	15·00	3·50
60B	50c. green (525)	50·00	50·00

Hopeh
A. Small setting

44C	½c. sepia (507)	1·70	1·70
45C	1c. yellow-orange (508)	2·20	1·60
47C	2c. blue (509)	40	40
48C	3c. brown (511)	1·20	1·20
50C	8c. brown-orange (514)	2·75	2·75
51C	10c. dull purple (515)	65·00	—
52C	13c. blue-green (516)	2·75	2·75
54C	17c. bronze-green (518)	4·00	4·25
55C	20c. light blue (519)	3·25	3·25
57C	25c. purple (521)	4·00	4·00

B. Large setting

44D	½c. sepia (507)	1·40	1·40
45D	1c. yellow-orange (508)	1·70	1·20
47D	2c. blue (509)	30	30
48D	3c. brown (511)	2·75	3·50
49D	4c. lilac(512)	1·00	1·00
50D	8c. brown-orange (514)	1·20	1·50
51D	10c. dull purple (515)	2·75	2·30
52D	13c. blue-green (516)	3·75	3·75
53D	15c. maroon (517)	4·75	4·75
54D	17c. bronze-green (518)	2·75	2·75
55D	20c. light blue (519)	2·50	2·50
56D	21c. sepia (520)	4·00	4·00
57D	25c. purple (521)	4·00	4·00
58D	28c. olive (522)	3·50	3·25
60D	50c. green (525)	45·00	—

Shansi
A. Small setting

44E	½c. sepia (507)	4·00	4·75
45E	1c. yellow-orange (508)	2·30	2·30
48E	3c. brown (511)	7·25	7·25
50E	8c. brown-orange (514)	11·50	11·50
51E	10c. dull purple (515)	43·00	43·00
52E	13c. blue-green (516)	16·00	16·00
54E	17c. bronze-green (518)	4·50	4·50
55E	20c. light blue (519)	4·00	4·00
57E	25c. purple (521)	2·50	3·75

B. Large setting

44F	½c. sepia (507)	2·30	3·00
45F	1c. yellow-orange (508)	3·00	3·25
46F	1c. yellow-orange (508b)	80·00	—
47F	2c. blue (509)	60	60
48F	3c. brown (511)	15·00	—
49F	4c. lilac (512)	1·00	1·00
50F	8c. brown-orange (514)	14·00	14·00
51F	10c. dull purple (515)	47·00	47·00
52F	13c. blue-green (516)	16·00	16·00
53F	15c. maroon (517)	5·50	6·75
54F	17c. bronze-green (518)	3·50	3·50
55F	20c. light blue (519)	2·50	2·50
56F	21c. sepia (520)	3·25	3·25
57F	25c. purple (521)	55·00	—
58F	28c. olive (522)	4·75	4·75
60F	50c. green (525)	11·50	11·50

Shantung
A. Small setting

44G	½c. sepia (507)	3·50	3·50
45G	1c. yellow-orange (508)	2·50	2·50
48G	3c. brown (511)	3·50	4·00
50G	8c. brown-orange (514)	32·00	32·00
51G	10c. dull purple (515)	11·50	11·50
52G	13c. blue-green (516)	4·00	4·00
54G	17c. bronze-green (518)	4·00	4·00
55G	20c. light blue (519)	5·50	5·50
57G	25c. purple (521)	4·75	4·75

B. Large setting

44H	½c. sepia (507)	1·60	1·60
45H	1c. yellow-orange (508)	1·60	1·20
46H	1c. yellow-orange (508b)	60·00	60·00
47H	2c. blue (509)	1·60	1·60
48H	3c. brown (511)	4·00	5·50
49H	4c. lilac (512)	1·00	50
50H	8c. brown-orange (514)	2·75	2·75
52H	13c. blue-green (516)	3·75	3·75
53H	15c. maroon (517)	4·00	4·00
54H	17c. bronze-green (518)	2·75	2·75
55H	20c. light blue (519)	3·75	3·75
56H	21c. sepia (520)	4·00	4·00
58H	28c. olive (522)	4·00	3·25
59H	30c. maroon (523)	£140	†
60H	50c. green (525)	9·50	8·00

Supeh
A. Small setting

44I	½c. sepia (507)	4·75	4·75
45I	1c. yellow-orange (508)	65·00	—
46I	1c. yellow-orange (508b)	£200	—
47I	2c. blue (509)	11·50	11·50
48I	3c. brown (511)	1·90	1·90
50I	8c. brown-orange (514)	45·00	—
51I	10c. dull purple (515)	40·00	40·00
52I	13c. blue-green (516)	5·50	5·75
54I	17c. bronze-green (518)	5·50	5·50
55I	20c. light blue (519)	4·00	4·00
57I	25c. purple (521)	5·00	5·00

B. Large setting

44J	½c. sepia (507)	4·00	4·00
45J	1c. yellow-orange (508)	1·60	1·60
48J	3c. brown (511)	8·00	—
49J	4c. lilac (512)	1·00	1·00
50J	8c. brown-orange (514)	10·50	—
52J	13c. blue-green (516)	10·50	—
53J	15c. maroon (517)	5·75	5·75
54J	17c. bronze-green (518)	3·75	3·75
55J	20c. light-blue (519)	3·75	3·75
56J	21c. sepia (520)	4·00	4·00
57J	25c. purple (521)	14·00	14·00
58J	28c. olive (522)	5·00	5·00
60J	50c. purple (525)	60·00	—

(g) As last but W 73

Honan
A. Small setting

62A	1c. yellow-orange (527)	1·60	1·60
67A	10c. dull-purple (534)	27·00	27·00
69A	17c. bronze-green (537)	8·00	8·00
73A	40c. orange (543)	14·50	14·50

B. Large setting

61B	½c. sepia (526)	£150	3·00
62B	1c. yellow-orange (527)	3·50	3·75
63B	2c. blue (528)	65·00	65·00
64B	2½c. claret (529)	6·25	6·25
67B	10c. dull-purple (534)	22·00	23·00
68B	13c. blue-green (535)	3·50	3·50
69B	17c. bronze-green (537)	3·50	3·50
71B	25c. purple (540)	2·50	2·50
73B	40c. orange (543)	4·00	4·00

Hopeh
A. Small setting

62C	1c. yellow-orange (527)	1·00	1·00
67C	10c. dull-purple (534)	1·50	4·00
69C	17c. bronze-green (537)	3·50	3·50
72C	30c. maroon (542)	27·00	27·00
73C	40c. orange (543)	4·75	4·75

B. Large setting

61D	½c. sepia (526)	1·20	1·20
62D	1c. yellow-orange (527)	1·20	1·20
63D	2c. blue (528)	80	80
64D	2½c. claret (529)	1·00	1·40
65D	3c. brown (530)	1·70	2·30
66D	8c. brown-orange (533)	55·00	—
67D	10c. dull-purple (534)	2·30	2·30
68D	13c. blue-green (535)	1·90	1·90
69D	17c. bronze-green (537)	2·75	2·75
70D	20c. light blue (538)	45·00	—
71D	25c. purple (540)	2·50	2·50
72D	30c. maroon (542)	10·00	10·00
73D	40c. orange (543)	2·75	1·20
74D	50c. green (544)	45·00	—

Shansi
A. Small setting

62E	1c. yellow-orange (527)	1·20	80
64E	2½c. claret (529)	7·25	8·25
67E	10c. dull-purple (534)	8·00	8·00
69E	17c. bronze-green (537)	27·00	27·00
72E	30c. maroon (542)	£120	£120
73E	40c. orange (543)	29·00	29·00
74E	50c. green (544)	35·00	35·00

B. Large setting

61F	½c. sepia (526)	1·20	1·20
62F	1c. yellow-orange (527)	80	80
63F	2c. blue (528)	2·50	2·50
66F	8c. brown-orange (533)	70·00	—
67F	10c. dull-purple (534)	20·00	—
68F	13c. blue-green (535)	3·75	3·75
71F	25c. purple (540)	3·25	3·25
72F	30c. maroon (542)	£120	£120
73F	40c. orange (543)	4·50	4·50
74F	50c. green (544)	5·75	5·75

Shantung
A. Small setting

62G	1c. yellow-orange (527)	2·20	1·60
64G	2½c. claret (529)	2·40	2·40
67G	10c. dull-purple (534)	4·00	4·00
69G	17c. bronze-green (537)	8·00	8·75
72G	30c. maroon (542)	27·00	27·00
73G	40c. orange (543)	27·00	27·00
74G	50c. green (544)	£110	—

B. Large setting

61H	½c. sepia (526)	2·30	2·30
62H	1c. yellow-orange (527)	1·70	1·60
62Ha	1c. yellow-orange Perf 14 (no secret mark)	—	
63H	2c. blue (528)	13·00	—
64H	2c. claret (529)	7·25	5·00
67H	10c. dull purple (534)	16·00	—
68H	13c. blue-green (535)	3·25	3·50
69H	17c. bronze-green (537)	3·50	3·50
71H	25c. purple (540)	3·50	3·50
73H	40c. orange (543)	3·50	3·50
74H	50c. green (544)	7·25	7·25

Supeh
A. Small setting

61I	½c. sepia (526)	55·00	—
62I	1c. yellow-orange (527)	1·70	1·70
64I	2½c. claret (529)	23·00	23·00
67I	10c. dull-purple (534)	16·00	16·00
69I	17c. bronze-green (537)	80·00	80·00
72I	30c. maroon (542)	11·50	11·50
73I	40c. orange (543)	7·25	7·25
74I	50c. green (544)	80·00	80·00

B. Large setting

61J	½c. sepia (526)	2·75	2·75
62J	1c. yellow-orange (527)	2·30	2·30
63J	2c. blue (528)	1·60	1·60
65J	3c. brown (530)	45·00	—
66J	8c. brown-orange (533)	65·00	—
67J	10c. dull purple (534)	24·00	—
68J	13c. blue-green (535)	5·50	5·50
69J	17c. bronze-green (537)	4·75	4·75
71J	25c. purple (540)	4·75	4·75
72J	30c. maroon (542)	60·00	—
73J	40c. orange (543)	4·50	4·75

(1) 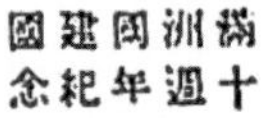   (2)

1942 (19 Feb). Fall of Singapore. Stamps of preceding issues with Large character overprints, further optd with T **1**, in red.

Honan

76B	**60**	4c. lilac	2·75	3·75
77B	**72**	8c. sage-green (C)	19·00	27·00
78B		8c. sage-green (D)	8·00	10·00

Hopeh

76D	**60**	4c. lilac	1·20	2·75
77D	**72**	8c. sage-green (C)	2·75	3·75
78D		8c. sage-green (D)	6·00	8·75
79D		8c. sage-green (F)	5·00	6·50

Shansi

76F	**60**	4c. lilac	2·75	3·00
77F	**72**	8c. sage-green (C)	7·00	9·25
78F		8c. sage-green (D)	18·00	21·00
79F		8c. sage-green (F)	6·00	6·75

Shantung

76H	**60**	4c. lilac	2·20	2·75
77H	**72**	8c. sage-green (C)	5·75	7·00
78H		8c. sage-green (D)	20·00	23·00
79H		8c. sage-green (F)	14·00	14·00

Supeh

75J	**58**	4c. lilac	40·00	47·00
76J	**60**	4c. lilac	4·75	5·50
77J	**72**	8c. sage-green (C)	12·00	16·00
78J		8c. sage-green (D)	12·50	17·00

Dates of issue: 1 June, Nos. 78B, 78D, 78F, 78J and 79F; 1 Aug. Nos. 75J, 77H; 19 Feb remainder.

1942 (1 Mar). 10th Anniv of Manchukuo. Stamps of preceeding issues with large character overprints, further optd with T **2**, in red.

Honan

80B	**72**	2c. olive-green (B) (8)	8·25	10·50
81B	**60**	4c. lilac (49)	12·50	16·00
82B	**72**	8c. sage-green (C) (12)	34·00	38·00
83B		8c. sage-green (D) (13)	31·00	32·00

Hopeh

80D	**72**	2c. olive-green (B) (8)	5·50	8·00
81D	**60**	4c. lilac (49)	5·50	6·50
82D	**72**	8c. sage-green (C) (12)	70·00	70·00
84D		8c. sage-green (F) (25)	8·00	9·00

Shansi

80F	**72**	2c. olive-green (8)	9·50	14·00
81F	**60**	4c. lilac (49)	11·00	14·00
82F	**72**	8c. sage-green (C) (12)	40·00	47·00
83F		8c. sage-green (D) (13)	60·00	65·00
84F		8c. sage-green (F) (25)	32·00	32·00

Shantung

80H	**72**	2c. olive-green (8)	2·75	4·00
81H	**60**	4c. lilac (49)	4·00	4·25
82H	**72**	8c. sage-green (C) (12)	16·00	19·00
83H		8c. sage-green (D) (13)	40·00	47·00
84H		8c. sage-green (F) (25)	3·25	4·00

Supeh

80J	**72**	2c. olive-green (8)	14·00	19·00
81J	**60**	4c. lilac (49)	11·50	14·00
82J	**72**	8c. sage-green (C) (12)	70·00	70·00
83J		8c. sage-green (D) (13)	65·00	70·00

The 2c. Type **58**, De La Rue (No. 2) was similarly overprinted for Honan, Shansi, Shantung and Supeh but the stamps were not officially issued (Price £35 each un.).

(3)

(Surch by Chinese Bureau of Engraving and Printing, Peking)

1942 (1 June). Stamps of China and unissued "New Peking" printings, optd "Hwa Pei" (two top characters, meaning "North China") and surch half original value as T **3**.

(a) On 1931–37 De La Rue single circle issue

85	**58**	1c. on 2c. olive-green (396)	22·00	22·00
86		2c. on 4c. green (397)	30	50

(b) On Third Sun Yat-sen issue, 1938–41

87	**72**	1c. on 2c. olive-green (A) (462)	4·25	4·25
88		1c. on 2c. olive-green (B) (463)	6·25	6·25
89		4c. on 8c. sage-green (C) (467)	65·00	65·00
90		4c. on 8c. sage-green (D) (468)	12·50	13·00
91		4c. on 8c. sage-green (F) (492A)	20·00	20·00
92		5c. on 10c. green (469)	25·00	25·00
93		5c. on 10c. green (493A)	7·75	13·00
94		5c. on 10c. green (493 B)	55	70
95		8c. on 16c. olive-brown (471)	1·80	2·50
96		15c. on 30c. scarlet (494A)	12·50	12·50
97		15c. on 30c. scarlet (494B)	32·00	39·00
98		25c. on 50c. blue (495A)	70·00	70·00
99		25c. on 50c. blue (4958)	4·50	8·00
100		50c. on $1 sepia & red-brown (457)	5·25	8·00
101		50c. on $1 sepia & red-brown (460)	2·00	3·00
102		50c. on $1 sepia & red-brown (473)	8·00	8·75
103		50c. on $1 sepia & red-brown (496A)	2·20	4·50
104		$1 on $2 red-brown and blue (458)	1·30	2·00
105		$1 on $2 red-brown and blue (461)	1·40	2·00
106		$1 on $2 red-brown and blue (474)	1·30	2·00
107		$1 on $2 red-brown & blue (497A)	1·40	2·00
108		$5 on $10 violet and green (499A)	1·10	2·00
109		$10 on $20 ultram & pur (500A)	1·10	2·00

(c) On Martyrs types (as T **60**)

110		½c. on 1c. yellow-orange (411)	1·30	3·00
111		½c. on 1c. yellow-orange (508)	10·50	8·75
112		½c. on 1c. yellow-orange (508b)	18·00	13·00

113		½c. on 1c. yellow-orange (527)	11·00	11·00
114		1c. on 2c. blue (509)	3·00	3·75
115		1c. on 2c. blue (528)	12·50	12·50
116		2c. on 4c. lilac (512)	44·00	44·00
117		4c. on 8c. orange-red (414)	90	90
118		4c. on 8c. brown-orange (514)	85	85
119		4c. on 8c. brown-orange (533)	30	40
120		5c.. on 10c dull purple (515)	1·90	2·50
121		5c. on 10c. dull purple (534)	40	1·30
122		10c. on 20c. light blue (519)	45	45
123		15c. on 30c. maroon (542)	8·00	8·75
124		20c. on 40c. orange (524)	3·25	80
125		20c. on 40c. orange (543)	3·75	95
126		25c. on 50c. green (525)	3·25	3·25
127		25c. on 50c. green (544)	3·50	3·50

(d) On Sun Yat-sen "New Peking" printings

128	**58**	1c. on 2c. olive-green	30	20
129		2c. on 4c. yellow-green	75	20
130	**72**	8c. on 16c. olive-brown	30	25
131		50c. on $1 sepia and orange-brown	2·75	2·75
132		$1 on $2 brown and blue	4·75	2·75
133		$5 on $10 violet and green	19·00	19·00

(e) On Martyrs "New Peking" printings (as T **60**)

134		4c. on 8c. brown-orange	50	70
135		10c. on 20c. brown-lake	3·00	3·00
136		15c. on 30c. maroon	4·50	4·50
137		20c. on 40c. orange	45	45
138		25c. on 50c. green	35	1·90

Postal rates in the occupied areas to the south were doubled in April 1942 because of currency depreciation, but those in the north were unchanged. These half-value surcharges thus indicated the actual purchase price in North China (and Mengkiang).

(4) (5)

1943 (30 Mar). Return to China of Foreign Concessions. Stamps of preceding issues further optd with T **4**, in red.

139	**58**	2c. on 4c. yellow-green (129)	25	80
140	**72**	4c. on 8c. sage-green (91)	1·20	1·40
141		8c. on 16c. olive-brown (130)	1·20	1·60

1943 (15 Aug). Fifth Anniv of Directorate General of Posts for North China. Stamps of preceding issues further optd with T **5**, in red.

142	**58**	2c. on 4c. yellow-green . (129)	35	65
143	**72**	4c. on 8c. sage-green (90)	35	85
144		8c. on 16c. olive-brown (130)	40	65

1943 (1 Nov). Stamps of China and unissued "New Peking" printings, optd "Hwa Pei" (= North China) as top characters of T **3**.

(a) On Third Sun Yat-sen issue 1938–41

145	**72**	10c. green (466)	40	35
146		$2 red-brown and blue (497A)	23·00	23·00
147		$5 deep green and scarlet (475)	16·00	16·00
148		$5 deep green and scarlet (498A)	8·00	8·00
149		$10 violet and green. (499A)	11·50	11·50
150		$20 ultramarine and purple (500A)	70·00	85·00

(b) On Martyrs issue

151	–	1c. yellow-orange (411)	65	65
152	–	1c. yellow-orange (508)	65	65

(c) On Sun Yat-sen "New Peking" printings

153	**58**	2c. olive-green	25	45
154		4c. yellow-green	25	1·20
155		5c. green	50	60
156	**72**	9c. sage-green	35	50
157		16c. olive-brown	25	45
158		18c. olive-brown	25	35
159		$1 sepia and orange-brown	3·50	1·00
160		$2 brown and blue	1·90	80
161		$5 green and rose-red	4·00	5·75

162	$10 violet and green	7·25	7·25
163	$20 ultramarine and purple	8·25	10·00

(d) On Martyrs "New Peking" printings (as T 60)

164	1c. yellow-orange......................................	25	20
165	10c. purple..	30	60
166	20c. brown-lake	40	50
167	30c. maroon..	35	35
168	40c. orange...	35	60
169	50c. green...	1·00	1·00

The 1c. was issued only with gum; the other values were issued both with and without gum. The 16c. was issued only with gum and the $20 only without gum; the remaining values were issued both with and without gum.

(6)

(7)

(8)

1944 (9 Jan). First Anniv of Declaration of War on Allies by Japanese controlled Nanking Govt. Optd with T **6**.

170	**58**	4c. yellow-green (154)	1·60	1·50
171	**72**	10c. green (145)......................................	1·60	1·50

1944 (30 Mar). Fourth Anniv of Establishment of North China Political Council. Optd with T **7**, in red.

172	**72**	9c. sage-green (156)...............................	80	1·20
173		18c. olive-brown (158)	80	2·30
174	–	50c. green (169).......................................	4·75	5·75
175	**72**	$1 sepia and orange-brown (159)	1·70	2·30
172/175 Set of 4..			7·25	10·00

1944 (July). Nos. 114/17 of Japanese Occupation of Nanking and Shanghai surch "Hwa Pei" and new values in Chinese characters variously as T **8**.

176	**5**	9c. on 50c. orange	1·10	1·40
177		18c. on $1 green (R.)..............................	1·20	1·70
178	**6**	36c. on $2 violet-blue (R.)....................	1·40	1·70
179		90c. on $5 carmine	1·70	1·90
176/179 Set of 4..			4·75	6·00

No. 176 is overprinted with Type **8**; No. 177 with six characters vertically; No. 178 with six characters in two columns; No. 179 with a group of four characters.

(9)

(10)

(11)

1944 (15 Aug). Sixth Anniv of Directorate General of Posts for North China. Optd with T **9**.

180	**72**	9c. sage-green (156) (R.)	75	1·20
181		18c. olive-green (158) (R.)	75	2·30
182	–	50c. green (169) (R.)...............................	1·20	1·70
183	**72**	$1 sepia and orange-brown (159)	2·75	3·25
180/183 Set of 4..			5·00	7·50

1944 (5 Dec). Death of Wang Ching-wei. Optd with T **10**.

184	–	20c. brown-lake (166) (B.)....................	2·30	2·75
185	–	50c. green (169) (B.)...............................	2·30	2·75
186	**72**	$1 sepia & orange-brown (159) (B.).....	4·75	5·50
187		$2 brown and blue (160)......................	1·40	1·40
184/187 Set of 4..			9·75	11·00

1944 (9 Jan). Second Anniv of Declaration of War on Allies by Nanking Govt. Oprd with T **11**.

188	–	20c. brown-lake (166)	2·30	3·25
189	–	50c. green (169) (R.)...............................	7·25	7·25
190	**72**	$1 sepia and orange-brown (159)	2·50	2·75
191		$2 brown and blue (160)......................	1·70	1·60
188/191 Set of 4..			12·50	13·00

(12)

13 Dragon Pillar

14 Long Bridge

15 Imperial City Tower

16 Marble Boat, Summer Palace

17

1945 (7 Feb). Nos. 118/19 of Japanese Occupation of Nanking and Shanghai, surch with new values as T **12**, in red, for use in North China.

192	**7**	50c. on $3 yellow-orange.........................	50	65
193		$1 on $6 blue..	50	65

(Litho Hsin Min Press, Peking)

1945 (30 Mar). Fifth Anniv of Establishment of North China Political Council. Views of Peking. No gum. P 14.

194	**13**	$1 yellow..	1·20	1·20
195	**14**	$2 blue..	25	1·20
196	**15**	$5 scarlet...	80	60
197	**16**	$10 green..	40	90
194/197 Set of 4..			2·40	3·50

(Litho Hsin Min Press, Peking)

1945 (5 May). Optd "Hwa Pei" as top characters in T **3**. No gum. P 14.

198	**17**	$1 red-brown...	25	20
199		$2 blue...	90	20
200		$5 red...	1·90	1·90
201		$10 green...	1·90	60
202		$20 purple...	1·90	1·40
203		$50 brown...	40·00	47·00
198/203 Set of 6..			42·00	46·00

These stamps exist in many shades and several varieties of paper. They were not issued without overprint.

Imperforate copies of the $50 in unissued colours and without overprint are proofs.

18 Wutai Mountain, Shansi

19 Kaifeng Iron Pagoda, Honan

20 International Bridge, Tientsin

21 Taishan Mountain, Shantung

22 G.P.O., Peking

(Litho Hsin Min Press, Peking)

1945 (15 Aug). Seventh Anniv of Directorate General of Posts for North China. No gum. P 14.

204	**18**	$5 green...	25	80
205	**19**	$10 grey-brown	60	80
206	**20**	$20 purple...	45	1·20
207	**21**	$30 slate-grey	70	1·20
208	**22**	$50 carmine...	1·90	2·30
204/208 Set of 5..			3·50	2·75

D. NANKING AND SHANGHAI

The Japanese army captured Shanghai on 9 November 1937, Nanking on 13 December 1937 and Hankow on 25 October 1938. On 27 March 1938 Nanking was made the seat of government of a Japanese-controlled Chinese government for areas in the Yangtse basin, and on 30 March 1940 it was made the capital of Wang Chingwei's government for all Japanese-occupied China. The stamps listed below were used in parts of Anhwei, Southern Kiangsu, Chekiang, Hupeh, Kiangsi, Hunan and Fukien.

(1)

(2)

1941 (23 Dec)–**42**. AIR. Air stamps of China, 1940–41, surch in Japanese currency as T **1**.

1	**61**	10s. on 50c. chocolate (559)	45	1·70
2		18s. on 90c. olive (561)	40	2·20
3		20s. on $1 apple-green (552)	17·00	17·00
4		20s. on $1 apple-green (562)	60	2·50
5		25s. on 90c. olive (561) (1.5.42)	35	1·80
6		35s. on $2 brown (563)	35	1·70

No. 6 further surch, in red (1.5.42)

7	**61**	60s. on 35s. on $2 brown	20	2·75
1/7 Set of 7			17·00	27·00

A second printing of No. 1 has the "10" directly above the first Chinese character instead of to the left of it.

1943 (1 Aug). Return of Shanghai Foreign Concessions. Stamps of China surch as T **2**.

8	**72**	25c. on 5c. green (465) (R.)	1·30	1·30
9	**77**	50c. on 8c. red-orange (B.)	1·30	1·30
10	**72**	$1 on 16c. olive-brown (471) (R.)	1·30	1·30
11	**77**	$2 on 50c. deep blue (R.)	1·30	1·30
8/11 Set of 4			4·75	4·75

The Post Office put these on sale at above face value, i. e. at $4 per set.

(Recess Chung Hwa Book Co, Hong Kong)

1943 (22 Nov). T **72** of China without overprint. P 12½.

12	**72**	15c. brown	15·00	28·00

A small quantity of this stamp was issued at Shanghai; the bulk of the printing was surcharged as below.

(3) Type **72**

(4)

$6 on 5c. Perf 14:

No. 34a

$6 on 8c. Perf 12½:

Nos. 36/37

$10 on 10c. Perf 12½:

No. 39

No. 63a

1943 (22 Nov)–**45**. Stamps of China and No. 12 above, surch in Chinese currency as T **3** (cent values) or **4** (dollar values).

(a) One Type 58, 1931–37 issue

13	$6 on 5c. yellow-grn (398) (30.3.45)	85	1·90
14	$20 on 15c. scarlet (400) (30.3.45)	95	1·40
15	$500 on 15c. blue-green (399) (3.9.45)	1·00	1·50
16	$1,000 on 20c. ultramarine (392) (7.7.45)		
17	$1,000 on 20c. ultramarine (401) (7.7.45)	3·00	3·00
18	$1,000 on 25c. ultramarine (402) (7.7.45)	3·00	3·00

(b) On Type 72

(i) Chung Hwa printings, 1938–41. No wmk. P 12½

19	25c. on 5c. olive-green (466)	2·10	3·50
20	30c. on 2c. olive-green (B) (443) (1.5.44)	65	1·70
21	50c. on 3c. brown-lake (464) (1.9.44)	30	35
22	50c. on 5c. olive-green (466) (1.3.44)	30	30
23	50c. on 8c. sage green (C) (467)	65	1·20
24	$1 on 8c. sage green (C) (467)	30	20
25	$1 on 8c. sage green (D) (468)	12·50	12·50
26	$1 on 15c. brown	55	65
27	$1.30 on 16c. olive-brown (471)	30	75
28	$1.50 on 3c. brown-lake (464) (1.9.44)	30	45
29	$2 on 5c. olive-green (466) (1.9.44)	1·20	1·20
30	$2 on 10c. green (469) (1.3.44)	30	35
31	$3 on 15c. brown (1.3.44)	30	35
32	$4 on 16c. olive-brown (471) (1.3.44)	45	30
33	$5 on 15c. brown (1.3.44)	30	30
34	$6 on 5c. green (465) (30.3.45)	65	1·50
	a. Perf 14 (484)	37·00	37·00
35	$6 on 5c. olive-green (466) (27.11.44)	75	40
36	$6 on 8c. sage green (C) (467) (30.3.45)	45	1·10
37	$6 on 8c. sage green (D) (468) (30.3.45) f750	£850	£850
	f750		
38	$6 on 10c. green (469) (1.9.44)	30	55
39	$10 on 10c. green (469) (27.11.44)	30	35
40	$10 on 16c. olive-brown (471) (1.3.44)	55	30
41	$20 on 3c. brown-lake (464) (30.3.45)	30	45
42	$20 on 15c. scarlet (470) (30.3.45)	1·20	2·50
43	$20 on 15c. brown (27.11.44)	45	45
44	$20 on $2 red-brown & blue (474) (1.9.44)	4·50	5·50
45	$100 on 3c. brown-lake (464) (7.7.45)	55	45
46	$500 on 8c. sage-green (C) (467) (3.9.45)	2·50	5·00
47	$500 on 10c. green (469) (3.9.45)	2·50	3·75
48	$500 on 15c. scarlet (470) (3.9.45)	2·75	2·50
49	$500 on 15c. brown (3.9.45)	2·50	2·75
50	$500 on 16c. olive-brown (471) (3.9.45)	2·00	4·50
51	$1,000 on 25c. violet-blue (472) (3.9.45)	2·30	4·50
52	$2,000 on 15 dp green & scar (475) (3.9.45)	6·50	6·00

(ii) Dah Tung printings, 1939–41. No wmk. P 14.

53	$1 on 8c. sage green (F) (492A) (1.3.44)	30	35
54	$1.70 on 30c. scarlet (494A)	75	1·50
	a. Perf 12½*	1·80	2·75
55	$2 on 5c. olive-grn (F) (490A) (30.3.45)	45	1·30
56	$2 on $1 sepia and red-brown (496A)	2·75	2·50
57	$3. on 8c sage green (F) (492A) (1.9.44) (flat top 3)	50	50
	a. Perf 12½*	17·00	13·00
58	$3 on 8c. sage green (E) (491A) (1.9.44) (round top 3)	39·00	39·00
59	$3 on 8c. sage green (F) (492A) (1.9.44) (round top 3)	55	55

60	$6 on 5c. olive-grn (F) (490A)		
	(27.11.44)	1·30	90
61	$6 on 5c. green (F) (489A) (30.3.45).....	45	55
62	$6 on 8c. sage green (F) (492A) (30.3.45)	40	70
	a. Perf 12½*	15·00	12·00
63	$10 on 10c. green (493A) (30.3.45)	1·20	2·10
	a. Perf 12½*	5·00	6·50
64	$20 on $2 red-brown & bl (497A)		
	(1.5.44)	1·30	1·30
65	$50 on 30c. scarlet (494A)	85	90
66	$50 on 50c. blue (495A) (30.3.45)	70	70
67	$50 on $5 dp green & scar (498A)		
	1.9.44)	1·00	1·00
68	$50 on $20 ultramarine & purple		
	(500A)	2·10	2·50
69	$100 on $10 violet & grn (499A)		
	(30.3.45)	1·80	1·80
70	$200 on $20 ultram & pur (500A)		
	(30.3.45)	65	1·10
71	$500 on 8c. sage green (E) (491A)		
	(3.9.45)	12·00	14·50
72	$500 on 8c. sage green (F) (492A)		
	(3.9.45)	28·00	25·00
73	$500 on 10c. green (493A) (3.9.45)	2·50	3·75
74	$1,000 on 30c. scarlet (494A) (3.9.45)..........	2·10	3·75
75	$1,000 on 50c. blue (495A) (3.9.45)............	2·00	2·75
76	$1,000 on $2 red-brown & bl (497A)		
	(7.7.45)	2·50	8·75
77	$2,000 on $5 dp green & scar (498A)		
	(3.9.45)	2·00	3·00

	(iii) Dah Tung printings, 1940–41. W **73**.		
78	$2 on $1 sepia & red-brown (P 12½)*	90	1·50
79	$6. on 5c green (F) (489B) (30.3.45).....	45	90
80	$6 on 5c. ol-grn (F) (490B) (30.3.45) ...	1·20	1·80
81	$50 on 30c. scarlet (494B) (1.3.44)........	£190	—
82	$50 on $5 deep green and scarlet		
	(498B) (27.11.44)	70	1·10
	a. Violet and black surch	3·00	10·00
83	$100 on $10 vio & grn (499B) (1.5.44)......	45	65
84	$200 on $20 ultramarine and purple		
	(500B) (1.5.44)	55	65
85	$500 on 10c. green (493B) (3.9.45)	2·10	2·50
86	$1,000 on 30c. scarlet (494B) (3.9.45)..........	3·00	3·50
87	$5,000 on $10 vio & grn (499B) (3.9.45)......	£110	£110
	a. Perf 12½*	11·00	13·00

*Not officially issued without surcharge.

No. 82a has the value tablet in violet and the Chinese characters in black.

	(c) On Martyrs issue as T **60**,1939–41 (3.9.45)		
88	$7.50 on ½c. sepia (507)	1·30	2·50
89	$15 on 1c. yellow-orange (508)..............	35	1·30
90	$15 on 1c. yellow-orange (508b).........	41·00	41·00
91	$30 on 2c. blue (509)	1·20	1·80
92	$30 on 2c. blue (528)	£130	£130
93	$200. on 1c. yellow-orange (508)..............	30	70
94	$200. on 8c brown-orange (514).............	70	1·20

	(d) On Type **77**,1941 New York issue		
95	5c. on ½c. sepia (1.5.44)	35	1·10
96	10c. on 1c. orange (1.3.44)	35	90
97	20c. on 1c. orange (1.5.44)	35	75
98	40c. on 5c. green (1.5.44)	35	85
99	$5 on 5c. green (30.3.45)	35	40
100	$10 on 10c. emerald-green (30.3.45)	35	40
101	$50 on ½c. sepia (7.7.45)	35	40
102	$50 on 1c. green (7.7.45)	40	45
103	$50 on 17c. olive-green (30.3.45)	40	45
104	$200 on 5c. green (7.7.45)	65	65
105	$200 on 8c. emerald-green (3.9.45).......	60	60
106	$200 on 8c. red-orange (3.9.45).............	65	75
107	$500 on $5 black and scarlet (30.3.45).......	1·30	2·00
108	$1,000 on 1c. green (7.7.45)	1·10	2·10
109	$1,000 on 25c. purple (30.3.45)	1·20	1·80
110	$1,000 on 30c. scarlet (3.9.45)	1·40	2·20
111	$1,000 on $2 black and green (7.7.45).......	1·90	1·90
112	$ 1,000 on $10 black and green (30.3.45)......	1·20	1·80
113	$2,000 on $5 black and scarlet (7.7.45)	1·40	1·90

5 Wheat and Cotton Flower   **6** Purple Mountain, Nanking

1944 (30 Mar). Fourth Anniv of Establishment of Chinese Puppet Government at Nanking. Recess. P 12½×12 (T **5**) or 12×12½ (T **6**).

114	**5**	50c. orange..............................	60	70
115		$1 green	60	70
116	**6**	$2 violet-blue	60	75
117		$5 carmine	60	75
114/117	Set of 4..		2·20	2·50

7 Map of Shanghai and Foreign Concessions

(D **8**)

1944 (1 Aug). First Anniv of Return to China of Shanghai Foreign Concessions. Recess. P 12×12½.

118	**7**	$3 yellow-orange	95	70
119		$6 blue	40	70

1944 (27 Nov). POSTAGE DUE. Postage Due stamps of China, 1932, surch as Type D **8**.

D120	D **62**	$1 on 2c. orange........................	65	1·80
D121		$2 on 5c. orange........................	65	1·70
D122		$5 on 10c. orange......................	65	1·70
D123		$10 on 20c. orange....................	65	1·50
D120/123	Set of 4		2·30	6·00

1945 (30 Mar). Fifth Anniv of Establishment of Chinese Puppet Government at Nanking. Surch with new values as T **4**.

124	**5**	$15 on 50c. orange..................	60	1·30
125		$30 on $1 green	60	1·30
126	**6**	$60 on $2 violet-blue	60	1·30
127		$200 on $5 carmine	60	1·30
124/127	Set of 4		2·20	4·75

(9)

(Surch by Union Printing Co, Shanghai)

1945 (9 Aug). Air Raid Precaution Propaganda Issue. Air stamps of China, 1940–41, no wmk, surch as T **9**.

128	**61**	$150 on 15c. blue-green (Vm.)	60	1·00
129		$250 on 25c. orange (G.)	60	1·00
130		$600 on 60c. blue (Vm.)	60	1·00
131		$1,000 on $1 apple-green (C.)	60	1·00
128/131	Set of 4		2·20	3·50

These stamps were for use on all kinds of mail.

Japanese Occupation of Hong Kong

Japanese Occupation of Malaya

Hong Kong surrendered to the Japanese on 25 December 1941. The postal service was not resumed until 22 January 1942 when the G.P.O. and Kowloon Central Office re-opened.

Japanese postmarks used in Hong Kong can be identified by the unique combination of horizontal lines in the central circle and three stars in the lower segment of the outer circle. Dates shown on such postmarks are in the sequence Year/Month/Day with the first shown as a Japanese regnal year number so that shows 17 = 1942 and so on.

Initially six current Japanese definitives, 1, 2, 3, 4, 10 and 30s. (Nos. 297, 315/17, 322 and 327) were on sale, but the range gradually expanded to cover all values between ½s. and 10y. with Nos. 313/14, 318, 325, 328/31, 391, 395/6, 398/9 and 405 of Japan also available from Hong Kong post offices during the occupation. Philatelic covers exist showing other Japanese stamps, but these were not available from the local post offices.

Supply of these Japanese stamps was often interrupted and, during the period between 28 July 1942 and 21 April 1943, circular "Postage Paid" handstamps were sometimes used. A substantial increase in postage rates on 16 April 1945 led to the issue of the local surcharges, Nos. J1/3.

PRICES FOR STAMPS ON COVER	
Nos. J1/55	*from × 10*
Nos. J56/76	*from × 12*
Nos. J77/89	*from × 20*
Nos. J90/1	*from × 15*
Nos. J92/115	*from × 6*
Nos. J116/18	—
Nos. J119/32	*from × 12*
Nos. J133/45	*from × 10*
Nos. J146/223	*from × 6*
Nos. J224/58	*from × 12*
No. J259	*from × 15*
Nos. J260/96	*from × 12*
Nos. J297/310	*from × 20*
Nos. J311/17	—
Nos. JD1/10	*from × 30*
Nos. JD11/16	*from × 12*
Nos. JD17/20	*from × 30*
Nos. JD21/7	*from × 20*
Nos. JD28/33	*from × 30*
Nos. JD34/41	*from × 60*

(1) (2)

1945 (16 Apr). Stamps of Japan surch with T **1** (No. J1) or as T **2**.
J1	1.50 yen on 1s. brown	32·00	29·00
J2	3 yen on 2s. scarlet	12·00	22·00
J3	5 yen on 5s. claret	£900	£150

Designs (18½×22 mm):—1s. Girl Worker; 2s. Gen. Nogi; 5s. Admiral Togo.

No. J3 has four characters of value similarly arranged but differing from T **2**.

Japanese forces invaded Malaya on 8 December 1941 with the initial landings taking place at Kota Bharu on the east coast. Penang fell, to a force which crossed the border from Thailand, on 19 December, Kuala Lumpur on 11 January 1942 and the conquest of the Malay peninsula was completed by the capture of Singapore on 15 February.

During the Japanese Occupation various small Dutch East Indies islands near Singapore were administered as part of Malaya. Stamps of the Japanese Occupation of Malaya were issued to the post offices of Dabo Singkep, Puloe Samboe, Tanjong Balei, Tanjong Batu, Tanjong Pinang and Terempa between 1942 and 1945. The overprinted issues were also used by a number of districts in Atjeh (Northern Sumatra) whose postal services were administered from Singapore until the end of March 1943.

Malayan post offices were also opened in October 1943 to serve camps of civilians working on railway construction and maintenance in Thailand. Overprinted stamps of the Japanese Occupation of Malaya were used at these offices between October 1943 and the end of the year after which mail from the camps was carried free. Their postmarks were inscribed in Japanese Katakana characters, and, uniquely, showed the Japanese postal symbol.

JOHORE

The postal service in Johore was reconstituted in mid-April 1942 using Nos. J146/60 and subsequently other general issues. Stamps of Johore overprinted "DAI NIPPON 2602" were, however, only used for fiscal purposes. Overprinted Johore postage due stamps were not issued for use elsewhere in Malaya.

POSTAGE DUE STAMPS

(1) (Upright) (2) Second character sideways (R. 6/3)

1942 (1 Apr). Nos. D1/5 of Johore optd as T **1** in brown.
JD1	D **1**	1c. carmine	50·00	85·00
		a. Black opt	20·00	70·00

313

JD2	4c. green	80·00	95·00
	a. Black opt	65·00	80·00
JD3	8c. orange	£140	£150
	a. Black opt	80·00	95·00
JD4	10c. brown	50·00	70·00
	a. Black opt	16·00	50·00
JD5	12c. purple	90·00	£100
	a. Black opt	42·00	50·00

1943. Nos. D1/5 of Johore optd with T **2**.

JD6	D **1**	1c. carmine	8·50	29·00
		a. Second character sideways	£325	£600
JD7		4c. green	8·00	32·00
		a. Second character sideways	£350	£600
JD8		8c. orange	9·50	32·00
		a. Second character sideways	£425	£700
JD9		10c. brown	9·00	42·00
		a. Second character sideways	£400	£750
JD10		12c. purple	11·00	60·00
		a. Second character sideways	£450	£850
JD6/10 *Set of 5*			42·00	£180

KEDAH

Postal services resumed by 31 January 1942 using unoverprinted Kedah values from 1c. to 8c. which were accepted for postage until 13 May 1942.

During the Japanese occupation Perlis was administered as part of Kedah.

DAI NIPPON   **DAI NIPPON**

2602   **2602**

(3)   (4)

1942 (13 May)–**43**. Stamps of Kedah (Script wmk) optd with T **3** (1c. to 8c.) or **4** (10c. to $5), both in red.

J1	**1**	1c. black (No. 68*a*)	5·50	8·50
J2		2c. bright green (No. 69)	27·00	30·00
J3		4c. violet	6·50	4·00
		a. Short sheaf	£180	£150
J4		5c. yellow	5·50	4·50
		a. Black opt (1943)	£200	£225
J5		6c. carmine (No. 56) (Blk.)	4·25	15·00
		a. *Carmine-red* (No. 56a)	50·00	75·00
J6		8c. grey-black	4·25	2·75
J7	**6**	10c. ultramarine and sepia	15·00	15·00
J8		12c. black and violet	30·00	42·00
J9		25c. ultramarine and purple	9·50	16·00
		a. Black opt (1943)	£300	£275
J10		30c. green and scarlet	70·00	80·00
J11		40c. black and purple	35·00	50·00
J12		50c. brown and blue	35·00	50·00
J13		$1 black and green	£140	£150
		a. Opt inverted	£700	£800
J14		$2 green and brown	£170	£170
J15		$5 black and scarlet	65·00	95·00
		a. Black opt (1943)	£1100	£1000
J1/15 *Set of 15*			£550	£650

Nos. J1/15 were gradually replaced by issues intended for use throughout Malaya. Kedah and Perlis were ceded to Thailand by the Japanese on 19 October 1943.

KELANTAN

Postal services resumed on 1 June 1942. Stamps used in Kelantan were overprinted with the personal seals of Sunagawa, the Japanese Governor, and of Handa, the Assistant Governor.

(5)
Sunagawa
Seal

(6) Handa
Seal

$1·00

40 CENTS   ■   ■

(7)   (8)

1 Cents

(9)

1942 (June). Stamps of Kelantan surch.

(a) As T **7** or **8** (dollar values). Optd with T **5** in red.

J16	**4**	1c. on 50c. grey-olive and orange	£250	£180
J17		2c. on 40c. orange and blue-green	£750	£300
J18		4c. on 30c. violet and scarlet	£1900	£1200
J19		5c. on 12c. blue (R.)	£275	£190
J20		6c. on 25c. vermilion and violet	£325	£190
J21		8c. on 5c. red-brown (R.)	£400	£140
J22		10c. on 6c. lake	80·00	£120
		a. "CENST" for "CENTS"	£7500	
J23		12c. on 8c. grey-olive (R.)	55·00	£110
J24		25c. on 10c. purple (R.)	£1400	£1300
J25		30c. on 4c. scarlet	£2000	£2000
J26		40c. on 2c. green (R.)	65·00	85·00
		a. Surch double (B.+R.)	£3750	
J27		50c. on 1c. grey-olive and yellow	£1600	£1300
J28	**1**	$1 on 4c. black and red (R., bars Blk.)	50·00	80·00
J29		$2 on 5c. green and red/*yellow*	50·00	80·00
J30		$5 on 6c. scarlet	50·00	80·00
		a. Surch double	£450	

(b) As T **7**. Optd with T **6** in red.

J31	**4**	12c. on 8c. grey-olive	£200	£325
		a. Type **6** omitted (in horiz pair with normal)	£3750	

(c) As T **9**. Optd with T **5** in red.

J32	**4**	1c. on 50c. grey-olive and orange	£180	95·00
		a. "Cente" for "Cents" (R. 5/1)	£2250	£1100
J33		2c. on 40c. orange and blue-green	£180	£110
		a. "Cente" for "Cents" (R. 5/1)	£2250	£1200
J34		5c. on 12c. blue (R.)	£160	£140
		a. "Cente" for "Cents" (R. 5/1)	£1900	
J35		8c. on 5c. red-brown (R.)	£130	75·00
		a. "Cente" for "Cents" (R. 5/1)	£1600	£950
J36		10c. on 6c. lake	£400	£425
		a. "Cente" for "Cents" (R. 5/1)	£3500	

(d) As T **9**. Optd with T **6** in red.

J41	**4**	1c. on 50c. grey-olive and orange	£120	£160
		a. "Cente" for "Cents" (R. 5/1)	£1500	
J42		2c. on 40c. orange and blue-green	£130	£170
		a. "Cente" for "Cents" (R. 5/1)	£1600	
J43		8c. on 5c. red-brown (R.)	70·00	£130
		a. "Cente" for "Cents" (R. 5/1)	£1300	
J44		10c. on 6c. lake	95·00	£160
		a. "Cente" for "Cents" (R. 5/1)	£1400	

As stamps of the above series became exhausted the equivalent values from the series intended for use throughout Malaya were introduced. Stamps as Nos. J28/30, J32/3 and J35/6, but without Type **5** or **6**, are from remainders sent to Singapore or Kuala Lumpur after the state had been ceded to Thailand (*Price from* £16 *each unused*). Nos. J19, J21, J23 and J25/6 have also been seen without Type **5** (*Price from* £80 *each unused*).

The 12c. on 8c., 30c. on 4c., 40c. on 2c. and 50c. on 1c. surcharged with Type **9**, formerly listed as Nos. J37/40, are now believed to exist only as remainders without the Type **5** red handstamp (*Price from* £20 *each, unused*).

Kelantan was ceded to Thailand by the Japanese on 19 October 1943.

MALACCA

Postal services from Malacca resumed on 21 April 1942, but there were no stamps available for two days.

PRICES. Those quoted are for single stamps. Blocks of four showing complete handstamp are worth from five times the price of a single stamp.

(**10**) "Military Administration Malacca State Government Seal"

1942 (23 Apr). Stamps of Straits Settlements handstamped as T **10**, in red, each impression covering four stamps.

J45	**58**	1c. black	£100	80·00
J46		2c. orange	60·00	65·00
J47		3c. green	65·00	75·00
J48		5c. brown	£150	£150
J49		8c. grey	£225	£120
J50		10c. dull purple	95·00	£100
J51		12c. ultramarine	£110	£120
J52		15c. ultramarine	80·00	95·00
J53		40c. scarlet and dull purple	£600	£650
J54		50c. black/*emerald*	£900	£900
J55		$1 black and red/*blue*	£1100	£1000

The 30c., $2 and $5 also exist with this overprint, but these values were not available to the public. (*Price for set of* 3 £11000 *unused*).

POSTAGE DUE STAMPS

1942 (23 Apr). Postage Due stamps of Malayan Postal Union handstamped as T **10**, in red, each impression covering four stamps.

JD11	D **1**	1c. slate-purple	£200	£180
JD12		4c. green	£225	£225
JD13		8c. scarlet	£2750	£1800
JD14		10c. yellow-orange	£450	£425
JD15		12c. ultramarine	£650	£600
JD16		50c. black	£2500	£1600

Nos. J45/55 and JD11/16 were replaced during May 1942 by the overprinted issues intended for use throughout Malaya.

PENANG

Postal services on Penang Island resumed on 30 March 1942 using Straits Settlements stamps overprinted by Japanese seals of the Government Accountant, Mr. A. Okugawa, and his assistant, Mr. Itchiburi.

DAI NIPPON

2602

PENANG

(**11**)	(**12**)	(**13**)	
Okugawa Seal	Itchiburi Seal		

1942 (30 Mar). Straits Settlements stamps optd.

(a) As T **11** (three forms of the seal).

J56	**58**	1c. black	9·50	11·00
J57		2c. orange	24·00	22·00
		a. Pair, one without handstamp	£1300	
J58		3c. green	20·00	22·00
J59		5c. brown	24·00	26·00
J60		8c. grey	26·00	35·00
J61		10c. dull purple	50·00	50·00
J62		12c. ultramarine	38·00	50·00
J63		15c. ultramarine	50·00	50·00
J64		40c. scarlet and dull purple	95·00	£110
J65		50c. black/*emerald*	£225	£225
J66		$1 black and red/*blue*	£250	£275
J67		$2 green and scarlet	£850	£700
J68		$5 green and red/*emerald*	£2250	£1500

(b) With T **12**.

J69	**58**	1c. black	£160	£130
J70		2c. orange	£160	£110
J71		3c. green	£100	£100
J72		5c. brown	£2250	£2250
J73		8c. grey	90·00	95·00
J74		10c. dull purple	£160	£170
J75		12c. ultramarine	£100	£120
J76		15c. ultramarine	£120	£130

Straits Settlements 1, 2, 3, 4 and 5c. values exist with a similar but circular seal containing four characters, but these were not available to the public.

1942 (15 Apr). Straits Settlements stamps optd with T **13** by Penang Premier Press.

J77	**58**	1c. black (R.)	5·50	3·00
		a. Opt inverted	£475	£475
		b. Opt double	£300	£300
J78		2c. orange	4·75	4·00
		a. "PE" for "PENANG"	£100	85·00
		b. Opt inverted	£160	
		c. Opt double	£475	
J79		3c. green (R.)	4·75	4·50
		a. Opt double, one inverted	£400	
J80		5c. brown (R.)	2·75	8·00
		a. "N PPON"	£190	
		b. Opt double	£475	£425
J81		8c. grey (R.)	2·25	1·40
		a. "N PPON"	55·00	60·00
		b. Opt double, one inverted	£450	
J82		10c. dull purple (R.)	1·50	2·25
		a. Opt double	£425	£425
		b. Opt double, one inverted	£400	£400
J83		12c. ultramarine (R.)	3·75	17·00
		a. "N PPON"	£500	
		b. Opt double	£400	
		c. Opt double, one inverted	£550	£550
J84		15c. ultramarine (R.)	1·75	3·75
		a. "N PPON"	£100	£110
		b. Opt inverted	£400	£400
		c. Opt double	£500	£500
J85		40c. scarlet and dull purple	4·75	17·00
J86		50c. black/*emerald* (R.)	3·75	29·00
J87		$1 black and red/*blue*	6·00	40·00
		a. Opt inverted	£1000	
J88		$2 green and scarlet	55·00	85·00
J89		$5 green and red/*emerald*	£550	£650
J77/89		Set of 13	£600	£750

Nos. J77/89 were replaced by the overprinted issues intended for use throughout Malaya.

SELANGOR

Postal services resumed in the Kuala Lumpur area on 3 April 1942 and gradually extended to the remainder of the state. Stamps of the general overprinted issue were used, but the following commemorative set was only available in Selangor.

SELANGOR
EXHIBITION
DAI NIPPON
2602
MALAYA

(**14**)

1942 (3 Nov). Selangor Agri-horticultural Exhibition. Nos. 294 and 283 of Straits Settlements optd with T **14**.

J90	**58**	2c. orange	12·00	24·00
		a. "C" for "G" in "SELANGOR" (R. 1/9)	£400	£450
		b. Opt inverted	£300	£400
J91		8c. grey	13·00	24·00
		a. "C" for "G" in "SELANGOR" (R. 1/9)	£400	£450
		b. Opt inverted	£300	£400

SINGAPORE

The first post offices re-opened in Singapore on 16 March 1942.

(**15**) "Malaya
Military
Government
Division Postal
Services Bureau
Seal"

(Handstamped at Singapore)

1942 (16 Mar). Stamps of Straits Settlements optd with T **15** in red.

J92	**58**	1c. black	14·00	17·00
J93		2c. orange	13·00	13·00
		a. Pair, one without handstamp	£2000	
J94		3c. green	50·00	70·00
J95		8c. grey	22·00	18·00
J96		15c. ultramarine	16·00	15·00
J92/6 Set of 5			£100	£120

The overprint Type **15** has a double-lined frame, although the two lines are not always apparent, as in the illustration. Three chops were used, differing slightly in the shape of the characters, but forgeries also exist. It is distinguishable from Type **1**, used for the general issues, by its extra width, measuring approximately 14 mm against 12½ mm.

The 6, 10, 30, 40, 50c., $2 and $5 also exist with this overprint, but were not sold to the public.

Nos. J92/6 were replaced on the 3 May 1942 by the stamps overprinted with Type **1** which were intended for use throughout Malaya.

TRENGGANU

Postal services resumed in Trengganu on 5 March 1942 using unoverprinted stamps up to the 35c. value. These remained in use until September 1942.

1942 (Sept). Stamps of Trengganu (Script wmk) optd as T **1** at Kuala Lumpur.

J97	**4**	1c. black (No. 26a)	90·00	90·00
		a. Chalk-surfaced paper (No. 26)	—	£160
		b. Red opt	£225	£225
		c. Brown opt (chalk-surfaced paper).	£450	£275
J98		2c. green (No. 27a)	£140	£140
		a. Chalk-surfaced paper (No. 27)	—	£250
		b. Red opt	£275	£300
		c. Brown opt	£500	£325
J99		2c. on 5c. deep reddish purple/*bright yellow* (No. 59)	40·00	40·00
		a. Red opt	55·00	75·00
J100		3c. chestnut (No. 29a)	90·00	80·00
		a. Brown opt	£700	£450
J101		4c. scarlet-vermilion (No. 30a)	£170	£140
J102		5c. dp reddish purple/*bright yellow* (No. 32a)	10·00	19·00
		a. Purple/*yellow* (No. 32)	£130	£140
		b. Red opt	27·00	
J103		6c. orange (No. 33a)	9·00	25·00
		a. Red opt	£200	
		b. Brown opt	£700	£700
J104		8c. grey (No. 34a)	9·00	13·00
		a. Chalk-surfaced paper (No. 34)	£160	
		b. Brown to red opt	55·00	70·00
J105		8c. on 10c. bright blue (No. 60)	13·00	50·00
		a. Red opt	21·00	
J106		10c. bright blue	24·00	45·00
		a. Red opt	£225	
		b. Brown opt	£750	£750
J107		12c. bright ultramarine (No. 36)	8·00	45·00
		a. Red opt	27·00	60·00
		b. Ordinary paper	30·00	

J108		20c. dull purple and orange	8·50	40·00
		a. Red opt	21·00	
J109		25c. green and deep purple	7·50	48·00
		a. Red opt	22·00	
		b. Brown opt	£800	£800
J110		30c. dull purple and black	9·50	40·00
		a. Red opt	32·00	55·00
J111		35c. carmine/*yellow*	27·00	50·00
		a. Red opt	30·00	
J112		50c. green and bright carmine	80·00	95·00
J113		$1 purple and blue/*blue*	£4000	£4000
J114		$3 green and brown-red/*green* (No. 43a)	65·00	£110
		a. Green and lake/*green* (No. 43)	£225	
		b. Red opt	65·00	
J115	**5**	$5 green and red/*yellow*	£180	£250
J116		$25 purple and blue	£1400	
		a. Red opt	£5000	
J117		$50 green and yellow	£12000	
J118		$100 green and scarlet	£1500	

DAI NIPPON

2602

MALAYA

(16)

1942 (Sept). Stamps of Trengganu (Script wmk) optd with T **16**.

J119	**4**	1c. black (No. 26a)	14·00	12·00
J120		2c. green (No. 27a)	£225	£225
J121		2c. on 5c. deep reddish purple/*bright yellow* (No. 59)	6·00	8·00
J122		3c. chestnut (No. 29a)	13·00	26·00
J123		4c. scarlet-vermilion (No. 30a)	13·00	11·00
J124		5c. dp reddish purple/*bright yellow* (No. 32a)	5·50	13·00
J125		6c. orange (No. 33a)	5·50	13·00
J126		8c. grey (No. 34a)	80·00	27·00
J127		8c. on 10c. bright blue (No. 60)	5·50	10·00
J128		12c. bright ultramarine (No. 36)	5·00	28·00
J129		20c. dull purple and orange	16·00	17·00
J130		25c. green and deep purple	7·00	40·00
J131		30c. dull purple and black	7·50	35·00
J132		$3 green and brown-red/*green* (No. 43a)	80·00	£150
J119/32 Set of 14			£425	£550

1943. Stamps of Trengganu (Script wmk) optd with T **2**.

J133	**4**	1c. black (No. 26a)	16·00	18·00
		a. chalk-surfaced paper	42·00	
J134		2c. green (No. 27a)	14·00	32·00
J135		2c. on 5c. bright reddish purple/*bright yellow* (No. 59)	9·50	23·00
J136		5c. brt reddish purple/*bright yellow* (No. 32a)	12·00	32·00
J137		6c. orange (No. 33a)	13·00	38·00
J138		8c. grey (No. 34a)	65·00	£110
J139		8c. on 10c. bright blue (No. 60)	26·00	55·00
J140		10c. bright blue	95·00	£250
J141		12c. bright ultramarine (No. 36)	16·00	50·00
J142		20c. dull purple and orange	21·00	50·00
J143		25c. green and deep purple	18·00	50·00
J144		30c. dull purple and black	22·00	55·00
J145		35c. carmine/*yellow*	22·00	70·00
J133/45 Set of 13			£300	£750

POSTAGE DUE STAMPS

1942 (Sept). Nos. D1/4 of Trengganu optd with T **1** sideways.

JD17	D **1**	1c. scarlet	50·00	85·00
JD18		4c. green	90·00	£130
		a. Brown opt	50·00	90·00
JD19		8c. yellow	14·00	50·00
JD20		10c. brown	14·00	50·00

The Trengganu 8c. postage due also exists overprinted with Type **16**, but this was not issued (*Price* £600 unused).

Trengganu was ceded to Thailand by the Japanese on 19 October 1943.

GENERAL ISSUES

The following stamps were produced for use throughout Malaya, except for Trengganu.

1942 (3 Apr). Stamps optd as T **1**.

(a) On Straits Settlements.

J146	**58**	1c. black (R.)	3·25	3·25
		a. Black opt	£400	£400
		b. Violet opt	£1000	£650
J147		2c. green (V.)	£3000	£2000
J148		2c. orange (R.)	3·00	2·25
		a. Black opt	£130	£140
		b. Violet opt	£250	£225
		c. Brown opt	£900	£650
J149		3c. green (R.)	2·75	2·25
		a. Black opt	£400	£400
		b. Violet opt	£1000	£750
J150		5c. brown (R.)	22·00	28·00
		a. Black opt	£550	£550
J151		8c. grey (R.)	4·50	2·25
		a. Pair, one without handstamp	†	£2000
		b. Black opt	£275	£275
J152		10c. dull purple (R.)	50·00	45·00
		a. Brown opt	£1000	£750
J153		12c. ultramarine (R.)	80·00	£130
J154		15c. ultramarine (R.)	3·50	3·75
		a. Violet opt	£700	£550
J155		30c. dull purple and orange (R.)	£2750	£2750
J156		40c. scarlet and dull purple (R.)	£100	95·00
		a. Brown opt	£750	£400
J157		50c. black/*emerald* (R.)	55·00	48·00
J158		$1 black and red/*blue* (R.)	80·00	75·00
J159		$2 green and scarlet (R.)	£140	£170
J160		$5 green and red/*emerald* (R.)	£180	£200

The 2c. green is known with the overprint in red, but this was not available to the public (*Price*, £350 *unused*).

(b) On Negri Sembilan.

J161	**6**	1c. black (R.)	19·00	13·00
		a. Violet opt	22·00	20·00
		b. Brown opt	13·00	17·00
		c. Black opt	55·00	38·00
		d. Pair. Nos. J161/a	£275	
		e. Pair. Nos. J161 and J161b	£350	
J162		2c. orange (R.)	27·00	19·00
		a. Violet opt	50·00	27·00
		b. Black opt	35·00	28·00
		c. Brown opt	65·00	55·00
J163		3c. green (R.)	38·00	20·00
		a. Violet opt	23·00	29·00
		b. Brown opt	£160	60·00
		c. Black opt	60·00	45·00
J164		5c. brown	38·00	21·00
		a. Pair, one without opt	£1800	
		b. Brown opt	17·00	15·00
		c. Red opt	15·00	11·00
		d. Violet opt	50·00	38·00
		e. Pair. Nos. J164c/d	£375	
J165		6c. grey (R.)	£150	£120
		a. Brown opt	£325	£325
J166		8c. scarlet	£140	£120
J167		10c. dull purple	£225	£200
		a. Red opt	£400	£300
		b. Brown opt	£550	£400
J168		12c. bright ultramarine (Br.)	£1800	£1800
J169		15c. ultramarine (R.)	22·00	8·00
		a. Violet opt	95·00	30·00
		b. Brown opt	27·00	12·00
J170		25c. dull purple and scarlet	28·00	38·00
		a. Red opt	60·00	75·00
		b. Brown opt	£500	£400
J171		30c. dull purple and orange	£250	£200
		a. Brown opt	£1400	£1100
J172		40c. scarlet and dull purple	£1400	£1100
		a. Brown opt	£1200	£1000
J173		50c. black/*emerald*	£1200	£1200
J174		$1 black and red/*blue*	£225	£250
		a. Red opt	£180	£200
		b. Brown opt	£425	£425
J175		$5 green and red/*emerald*	£600	£700
		a. Red opt	£1200	£1200

Nos. J161a and J163a exist with the handstamped overprint sideways.

(c) On Pahang.

J176	**15**	1c. black	50·00	45·00
		a. Red opt	55·00	50·00
		b. Violet opt	£375	£275
		c. Brown opt	£300	£225
J177		3c. green	£425	£325
		a. Red opt	£225	£275
		b. Violet opt	£650	£475
J178		5c. brown	14·00	12·00
		a. Red opt	£225	£110
		b. Brown opt	£300	£110
		c. Violet opt	£500	£275
		d. Pair. Nos. J178/b	£850	
J179		8c. grey	£1000	£800
J180		8c. scarlet	20·00	8·00
		a. Red opt	£110	50·00
		b. Violet opt	£100	55·00
		c. Brown opt	£110	65·00
		d. Pair. Nos. J180a/c	£450	
J181		10c. dull purple	£350	£150
		a. Red opt	£300	£225
		b. Brown opt	£400	£250
J182		12c. bright ultramarine	£2000	£2000
		a. Red opt	£1200	£1200
J183		15c. ultramarine	£150	£110
		a. Red opt	£425	£250
		b. Violet opt	£750	£500
		c. Brown opt	£550	£325
J184		25c. dull purple and scarlet	21·00	29·00
J185		30c. dull purple and orange	12·00	28·00
		a. Red opt	£140	£170
J186		40c. scarlet and dull purple	20·00	32·00
		a. Red opt	£475	£325
		b. Red opt	85·00	90·00
J187		50c. black/*emerald*	£1200	£1200
		a. Red opt	£1300	£1300
J188		$1 black and red/*blue* (R.)	£150	£160
		a. Black opt	£300	£300
		b. Brown opt	£700	£700
J189		$5 green and red/*emerald*	£700	£850
		a. Red opt	£1000	£1100

(d) On Perak.

J190	**51**	1c. black	60·00	35·00
		a. Violet opt	£275	£110
		b. Brown opt	80·00	80·00
J191		2c. orange	30·00	20·00
		a. Violet opt	70·00	70·00
		b. Red opt	60·00	40·00
		c. Brown opt	55·00	50·00
J192		3c. green	26·00	28·00
		a. Violet opt	£500	£325
		b. Brown opt	£180	£150
		c. Red opt	£350	£250
J193		5c. brown	7·00	6·00
		a. Pair, one without opt	£1100	
		b. Brown opt	40·00	28·00
		c. Violet opt	£300	£200
		d. Red opt	£225	£200
J194		8c. grey	80·00	48·00
		a. Red opt	£425	£225
		b. Brown opt	£400	£250
J195		8c. scarlet	40·00	42·00
		a. Violet opt	£550	£300
J196		10c. dull purple	26·00	24·00
		a. Red opt	£375	£225
J197		12c. bright ultramarine	£250	£225
J198		15c. ultramarine	24·00	32·00
		a. Red opt	£250	£200
		b. Violet opt	£475	£325
		c. Brown opt	£400	£275
J199		25c. dull purple and scarlet	14·00	25·00
		a. Red opt	£300	
J200		30c. dull purple and orange	17·00	32·00
		a. Pair, one without opt	£1800	
		b. Brown opt	£700	£450
		c. Red opt	35·00	55·00
		ca. Pair, one without opt	£2250	
J201		40c. scarlet and dull purple	£500	£375
		a. Brown opt	£550	£450

J202	50c. black/*emerald*		40·00	50·00
	a. Red opt		50·00	60·00
	b. Brown opt		£450	£350
J203	$1 black and red/*blue*		£450	£400
	a. Brown opt		£450	£375
J204	$2 green and scarlet		£3750	£3750
J205	$5 green and red/*emerald*		£500	
	a. Brown opt		£1800	

(e) On Selangor.

J206	**46**	1c. black, S	12·00	25·00
		a. Red opt, SU	42·00	38·00
		b. Violet opt, SU	45·00	42·00
J207		2c. green, SU	£1700	£1300
		a. Violet opt, SU	£2000	£1300
J208		2c. orange (P 14×14½), S	95·00	60·00
		a. Red opt, U	£200	£170
		b. Violet opt, U	£225	£160
		c. Brown opt, S	85·00	80·00
J209		2c. orange (P 14), S	£120	80·00
		a. Red opt, U	£225	£170
		b. Violet opt, U	£400	£170
		c. Brown opt, S	—	£170
J210		3c. green, SU	23·00	15·00
		a. Red opt, SU	18·00	15·00
		b. Violet opt, SU	65·00	50·00
		c. Brown opt, SU	18·00	15·00
J211		5c. brown, SU	6·00	5·50
		a. Red opt, SU	13·00	16·00
		b. Violet opt, SU	21·00	22·00
		c. Brown opt, SU	60·00	50·00
J212		6c. scarlet, SU	£400	£400
		a. Red opt, S	£200	£250
		b. Brown opt, S	£950	£950
J213		8c. grey, S	17·00	17·00
		a. Red opt, SU	60·00	40·00
		b. Violet opt, U	35·00	35·00
		c. Brown opt, S	£180	75·00
J214		10c. dull purple, S	13·00	21·00
		a. Red opt, S	75·00	60·00
		b. Brown opt, S	£160	90·00
J215		12c. bright ultramarine, S	60·00	70·00
		a. Red opt, S	£120	£130
		b. Brown opt, S	£130	£120
J216		15c. ultramarine, S	16·00	22·00
		a. Red opt, SU	55·00	55·00
		b. Violet opt, U	£150	95·00
		c. Brown opt, S	£100	65·00
J217		25c. dull purple and scarlet, S	80·00	£100
		a. Red opt, S	60·00	80·00
J218		30c. dull purple and orange, S	11·00	24·00
		a. Brown opt, S	£450	£275
J219		40c. scarlet and dull purple, S	£150	£150
		a. Brown opt, S	£400	£200
		b. Red opt, S	£325	
J220		50c. black/*emerald*, S	£150	£160
		a. Red opt, S	£160	£170
		b. Brown opt, S	£550	£400
J221	**48**	$1 black and red/*blue*	30·00	45·00
		a. Red opt	£120	£150
J222		$2 green and scarlet	35·00	60·00
		a. Pair, one without opt	£1800	
J223		$5 green and red/*emerald*	70·00	90·00
		b. Red opt	£750	£800

On T **46** the overprint is normally sideways (with "top" to either right or left), but on T **48** it is always upright.

S = Sideways.
U = Upright.
SU = Sideways or upright (our prices being for the cheaper).

Specialists recognise nine slightly different chops as Type **1**. Initial supplies with the overprint in red were produced at Singapore. Later overprintings took place at Kuala Lumpur in violet, red or brown and finally, black. No. J155 was from the Kuala Lumpur printing only. Except where noted, these overprints were used widely in Malaya and, in some instances, Sumatra.

The following stamps also exist with this overprint, but were not available to the public:

Straits Settlements (in red) 6, 25c.
Kelantan (in black) 10c.
Negri Sembilan 2c. green (Blk. or Brn.), 4c. (Blk.), 6c. scarlet (Blk.), 8c. grey (Blk.), 12c. (Blk.), $2 (Blk. or Brn.).
Pahang (in black, 2c. also in brown) 2, 4, 6c., $2.
Perak 2c. green (R.), 6c. (Blk.).
Selangor 4c. (Blk.).

1942 (May). Optd with T **16**.

(a) On Straits Settlements.

J224	**58**	2c. orange	2·50	60
		a. Opt inverted	14·00	23·00
		b. Opt double, one inverted	55·00	65·00
J225		3c. green	50·00	65·00
J226		8c. grey	6·50	3·25
		a. Opt inverted	19·00	35·00
J227		15c. blue	16·00	10·00
J224/7	Set of 4		70·00	70·00

(b) On Negri Sembilan.

J228	**6**	1c. black	2·50	60
		a. Opt inverted	9·00	25·00
		b. Opt double, one inverted	35·00	50·00
J229		2c. orange	8·50	50
J230		3c. green	6·00	50
J231		5c. brown	1·75	3·25
J232		6c. grey	3·75	2·50
		a. Opt inverted	†	£1500
		b. Stop omitted at right (R. 10/4)	£110	£120
J233		8c. scarlet	7·50	1·25
J234		10c. dull purple	3·25	2·50
J235		15c. ultramarine	17·00	2·50
J236		25c. dull purple and scarlet	5·50	17·00
J237		30c. dull purple and orange	8·00	3·00
J238		$1 black and red/*blue*	80·00	95·00
J228/38	Set of 11		£130	£110

(c) On Pahang.

J239	**15**	1c. black	3·25	3·50
		a. Opt omitted (in pair with normal)	£550	
J240		5c. brown	1·25	70
J241		8c. scarlet	26·00	2·75
		a. Opt omitted (in pair with normal)	£1400	
J242		10c. dull purple	11·00	7·50
J243		12c. bright ultramarine	3·00	16·00
J244		25c. dull purple and scarlet	5·50	23·00
J245		30c. dull purple and orange	3·25	11·00
J239/45	Set of 7		48·00	60·00

(d) On Perak.

J246	**51**	2c. orange	3·50	2·75
		a. Opt inverted	48·00	50·00
J247		3c. green	1·25	1·50
		a. Opt inverted	16·00	27·00
		b. Opt omitted (in pair with normal)	£550	
J248		8c. scarlet	70	50
		a. Opt inverted	4·50	7·00
		b. Opt double, one inverted	£225	£250
		c. Opt omitted (in horiz pair with normal)	£400	
J249		10c. dull purple	16·00	7·00
J250		15c. ultramarine	8·00	2·00
J251		50c. black/*emerald*	3·50	5·00
J252		$1 black and red/*blue*	£475	£500
J253		$5 green and red/*emerald*	45·00	70·00
		a. Opt inverted	£275	£350
J246/53	Set of 8		£500	£550

(e) On Selangor.

J254	**46**	3c. green	2·00	3·75
J255		12c. bright ultramarine	1·10	15·00
J256		15c. ultramarine	7·50	1·50
J257		40c. scarlet and dull purple	2·00	5·00
J258	**48**	$2 green and scarlet	10·00	45·00
J254/8	Set of 5		20·00	65·00

On T **46** the overprint is sideways, with "top" to left or right. The following stamps also exist with this overprint, but were not available to the public:

Perak 1, 5, 30c. (*Price for set of 3* £400 *unused*).
Selangor 1, 5, 10, 30c., $1, $5 (*Price for set of 6* £750 *unused*).

DAI NIPPON
2602
MALAYA

2 Cents

(17)

DAI NIPPON
YUBIN

2 Cents

(18) "Japanese Postal Service"

1942 (Nov). No. 108 of Perak surch with T **17**.
J259 **51** 2c. on 5c. brown.................................. 1·25 3·50
    a. Inverted "s" in "Cents" (R. 3/5)........... 55·00 80·00

1942 (Nov). Perak stamps surch or opt only, as in T **18**.
J260 **51** 1c. black.. 6·00 10·00
    a. Opt inverted............................... 19·00 40·00
J261 2c. on 5c. brown........................... 2·00 6·50
    a. "DAI NIPPON YUBIN" inverted.......... 17·00 38·00
    b. Ditto and "2 Cents" omitted.............. 45·00 65·00
    c. Inverted "s" in "Cents" (R. 3/5)......... 60·00 £110
J262 8c. scarlet..................................... 6·00 2·25
    a. Opt inverted............................... 11·00 24·00
J260/2 Set of 3.................................... 12·50 17·00

A similar overprint exists on the Selangor 3c. but this was not available to the public (*Price £350 unused*).

On 8 December 1942 contemporary Japanese 3, 5, 8 and 25s. stamps were issued without overprint in Malaya and the 1, 2, 4, 6, 7, 10, 30 and 50s. and 1y. values followed on 15 February 1943.

大日本郵便
(**19**)

6 cts.   6 cts.   2 Cents
(**20**)   (**21**)   (**22**)

6 cts. $1·00
(**23**)   (**24**)

1942 (4 Dec)–**44**. Stamps of various Malayan territories optd "Japanese Postal Service" in Kanji characters as T **2** or **19**, some additionally surch as T **20** to **24**.

(a) Stamps of Straits Settlements optd with T **2**.
J263 **58** 8c. grey (Blk.) (1943)................... 1·40 50
    a. Opt inverted............................... 55·00 70·00
    b. Opt omitted (in pair with normal)...... £850
    c. Red opt..................................... 2·50 3·50
J264 12c. ultramarine (1943).................... 1·25 12·00
J265 40c. scarlet and dull purple (1943)...... 2·50 5·00
J263/5 Set of 3.................................... 4·75 16·00

(b) Stamps of Negri Sembilan optd with T **2** or surch also.
J266 **6** 1c. black.. 30 2·75
    a. Opt inverted............................... 11·00 27·00
    b. Sideways second character.............. 32·00 35·00
    ba. Opt inverted with sideways
        second character...................... £750
J267 2c. on 5c. brown (surch as T **20**)...... 80 1·50
J268 6c. on 5c. brown (surch T **21**) (1943)... 40 1·75
    a. Opt Type **2** and surch as Type **21**
        both inverted......................... £225 £225
J269 25c. dull purple and scarlet (1943)...... 1·10 17·00
J266/9 Set of 4.................................... 2·25 21·00

(c) Stamp of Pahang optd with T **2** and surch also.
J270 **15** 6c. on 5c. brown (surch T **20**) (1943)... 50 75
J271 6c. on 5c. brown (surch T **21**) (1943).... 1·00 1·75

(d) Stamps of Perak optd with T **2** or surch also.
J272 **51** 1c. black.. 1·00 70
    a. Sideways second character.............. £225 £250
J273 2c. on 5c. brown (surch as T **20**)........ 60 50
    a. Opt Type **2** and surch Type **20**
        both inverted......................... 18·00 32·00
    b. Opt Type **2** inverted.................... 18·00 32·00
    c. Sideways second character.............. 50·00 50·00
J274 2c. on 5c. brown (surch T **22**)........... 60 50
    a. Surch Type **22** inverted................ 18·00 32·00
    b. Opt Type **2** and surch Type **22**
        both inverted......................... 24·00 35·00
    c. Sideways second character.............. 25·00 32·00
    ca. Surch Type **22** inverted............... £1400
    cb. Opt Type **2** with sideways second
        character and surch Type **22** both
        inverted.............................. £1400

J275 5c. brown..................................... 55 65
    a. Opt inverted............................... 38·00 42·00
    b. Sideways second character.............. £550 £400
J276 8c. scarlet..................................... 55 2·25
    a. Opt inverted............................... 15·00 28·00
    b. Sideways second character.............. 50·00 70·00
    ba. Opt inverted with sideways
        second character...................... £750
    c. Opt omitted (in pair with normal)...... £1100
J277 10c. dull purple (1943).................... 60 50
J278 30c. dull purple and orange (1943)....... 4·75 7·00
J279 50c. black/*emerald* (1943)............... 3·75 21·00
J280 $5 green and red/*emerald* (1943)....... 65·00 £110
J272/80 Set of 9................................. 70·00 £130

(e) Stamps of Selangor optd with T **2** (sideways on T **46**).
J281 **46** 1c. black (1943)............................ 1·00 3·00
J282 3c. green..................................... 40 45
    a. Sideways second character.............. 17·00 26·00
J283 12c. bright ultramarine.................... 45 1·60
    a. Sideways second character.............. 65·00 80·00
J284 15c. ultramarine............................ 3·75 3·25
    a. Sideways second character.............. 50·00 55·00
J285 **48** $1 black and red/*blue* (1943)........ 3·00 23·00
    a. Opt inverted............................... £225 £225
    b. Sideways second character.............. £375 £400
J286 $2 green and scarlet (1943)................ 10·00 48·00
J287 $5 green and red/*emerald* (1943)....... 22·00 80·00
    a. Opt inverted............................... £250 £300
J281/7 Set of 7.................................. 35·00 £140

(f) Stamps of Selangor optd with T **19** or surch also.
J288 **46** 1c. black (R.) (1943)...................... 35 50
J289 2c. on 5c. brown (surch as T **21**) (R.)
    (1943)..................................... 1·25 50
J290 3c. on 5c. brown (surch as T **21**)
    (1943)..................................... 30 4·75
    a. "s" in "cts." inverted (R. 4/3)............ 30·00 70·00
    b. Comma after "cts" (R. 9/3).............. 30·00 70·00
J291 5c. brown (R.) (1944)...................... 1·75 4·75
J292 6c. on 5c. brown (surch T **21**) (1944).... 1·00 1·75
J293 6c. on 5c. brown (surch T **23**) (1944).... 40 70
    a. "6" inverted (R. 7/8)..................... £900
    b. Full stop between "6" and "cts"
        (R. 8/6)................................ £475
    c. Surch and opt double.................... £475
J294 15c. ultramarine............................ 4·00 4·00
J295 $1 on 10c. dull purple (surch T **24**)
    (18.12.1944)............................ 40 1·25
J296 $1.50 on 30c. dull purple and orange
    (surch T **24**) (18.12.1944)............. 40 1·25
J288/96 Set of 9................................ 9·00 18·00

The error showing the second character in Type **2** sideways occurred on R. 6/3 in the first of four settings only.

The 2c. orange, 3c. and 8c. grey of Perak also exist overprinted with Type **2**, but these stamps were not available to the public (*Price for set of* 3 £100 *unused*).

Examples of No. J275 are known postally used from the Shan States (part of pre-war Burma).

25 Tapping Rubber

26 Fruit

27 Tin dredger

28 War Memorial, Bukit Bartok, Singapore

29 Fishing village

30 Japanese shrine, Singapore

31 SagoPalms   **32** Straits of Johore   **33** Malay Mosque, Kuala

(Litho Kolff & Co, Batavia)

1943 (29 Apr–1 Oct). P 12½.
J297	**25**	1c. grey-green (1 Oct)	1·75	55
J298	**26**	2c. pale emerald (1 June)	1·00	20
J299	**25**	3c. drab (1 Oct)	50	20
J300	**27**	4c. carmine-rose	2·75	20
J301	**28**	8c. dull blue	50	20
J302	**29**	10c. brown-purple (1 Oct)	70	20
J303	**30**	15c. violet (1 Oct)	1·00	4·25
J304	**31**	30c. olive-green (1 Oct)	1·50	35
J305	**32**	50c. blue (1 Oct)	4·50	4·25
J306	**33**	70c. blue (1 Oct)	18·00	12·00
J297/306 *Set of 10*			29·00	20·00

The 2c. and 4c. values exist, printed by typography, in paler shades either imperforate or rouletted. It is suggested that these may have been available in Singapore at the very end of the Japanese Occupation.

34 Ploughman   **35** Rice-Planting

1943 (1 Sept). Savings Campaign. Litho. P 12½.
J307	**34**	8c. violet	9·50	2·75
J308		15c. scarlet	6·50	2·75

(Des Hon Chin. Litho)

1944 (15 Feb). "Re-birth" of Malaya. P 12½.
J309	**35**	8c. rose-red	15·00	3·25
J310		15c. magenta	4·00	3·25

(36)   (37)   (38)

1944 (16 Dec). Stamps intended for use on Red Cross letters. Surch with T **36/8** in red.

(a) On Straits Settlements.
J311	**58**	50c. on 50c. black/*emerald*	10·00	24·00
J312		$1 on $1 black and red/*blue*	21·00	35·00
J313		$1.50 on $2 green and scarlet	32·00	70·00

(b) On Johore.
J314	**29**	50c. on 50c. dull purple and red	7·00	20·00
J315		$1.50 on $2 green and carmine	4·00	12·00

(c) On Selangor.
J316	**48**	$1 on $1 black and red/*blue*	3·50	14·00
J317		$1.50 on $2 green and scarlet	5·00	20·00
J311/17 *Set of 7*			75·00	£180

Nos. J311/17 were issued in Singapore but were withdrawn after one day, probably because supplies of Nos. J295/6 were received and issued on the 18 December.

A similar 6c. surcharge exists on the Straits Settlements 5c. but this was not available to the public (*Price* £500 *unused*).

STAMP BOOKLETS

1942. Nos. SB3/4 of Perak and SB2 of Selangor with covers optd with T **1**.
SB1	$1 booklet containing twenty 5c. (No. J193) in blocks of 10	£2750
SB2	$1.30 booklet containing 5c. and 8c. (Nos. J193/4), each in block of 10	£2750
SB3	$1.30 booklet containing 5c. and 8c. (Nos. J211 and J213), each in block of 10	£2750

POSTAGE DUE STAMPS

Postage Due stamps of the Malayan Postal Union overprinted.

1942 (3 Apr). *Handstamped as T* **1** *in black.*
JD21	D **1**	1c. slate-purple	12·00	27·00
		a. Red opt	£150	£150
		b. Brown opt	£140	£150
JD22		3c. green	70·00	75·00
		a. Red opt	£250	£275
JD23		4c. green	60·00	40·00
		a. Red opt	55·00	55·00
		b. Brown opt	£160	£160
JD24		8c. scarlet	£110	90·00
		a. Red opt	£160	£130
		b. Brown opt	£200	£200
JD25		10c. yellow-orange	28·00	50·00
		a. Red opt	£275	£275
		b. Brown opt	80·00	85·00
JD26		12c. ultramarine	25·00	50·00
		a. Red opt	£275	£275
JD27		50c. black	65·00	85·00
		a. Red opt	£450	£475

1942. Optd with T **16**.
JD28	D **1**	1c. slate-purple	3·00	10·00
JD29		3c. green	17·00	23·00
JD30		4c. green	15·00	11·00
JD31		8c. scarlet	24·00	20·00
JD32		10c. yellow-orange	2·00	17·00
JD33		12c. ultramarine	1·75	32·00
JD28/33 *Set of 6*			55·00	£100

The 9c. and 15c. also exist with this overprint, but these were not issued (*Price* £650 *each unused*).

1943–45. Optd with T **2**.
JD34	D **1**	1c. slate-purple	2·25	4·75
JD35		3c. green	2·25	4·50
		a. Opt omitted (in pair with normal)	£750	
JD36		4c. green	60·00	45·00
JD37		5c. scarlet	1·50	5·00
JD38		9c. yellow-orange	80	8·50
		a. Opt inverted	22·00	28·00
JD39		10c. yellow-orange	2·25	9·00
		a. Opt inverted	75·00	75·00
JD40		12c. ultramarine	2·25	17·00
JD41		15c. ultramarine	2·25	9·00
JD34/41 *Set of 8*			65·00	90·00

Japanese Occupation of Netherlands Indies

In the Second World War, the Japanese landed in Borneo and Celebes on 11 January 1942. After winning the naval battle of the Java Sea, they landed on 1 March in Java, which surrendered on 8 March. The defenceless remainder of the Netherlands Indies was soon occupied. Three Japanese administrative areas were established: (i) Java; (ii) Malaya and Sumatra; (iii) the Japanese Naval Control Area, covering the other islands of the Netherlands Indies.

I. JAVA

100 Sen or Cents = 1 Rupee

PRINTERS. Nos. 1 to 26 were lithographed by G. Kolff & Co, Batavia.

1 Eastern Asia

(Litho Kolff & Co, Batavia)

1943 (9 Mar). First Anniv of Japanese Occupation of Java. Designs with vert panel of characters as in T **1**. P 12½.

1	2s. red-brown		5·25	4·00
2	3½s. carmine		5·25	4·00
3	5s. green		7·25	4·00
4	10s. light blue		20·00	4·75
1/4	Set of 4		34·00	15·00

Designs:—3½s. Farmer ploughing ricefield; 5s. Mt. Soemer; 10s. Bantam Bay.

2 Native Soldier

(Litho Kolff & Co, Batavia)

1943 (20 Mar). Savings Campaign. P 12½.

5	**2**	3½c. rose	42·00	11·50
6		10c. blue	60·00	6·75

3 Wajang Doll   **4** Map of Java

5 Bird of Vishu
and Mt. Soemer

(Des D. Ruhl (Nos. 8/10), Basoeki-Abdoellah (others). Litho Kolff & Co, Batavia)

1943 (29 Apr)–**45**. Designs with horiz panel of characters as at foot of T **3**/**5**. P 12½.

7		3½c. carmine (29.4.43)	3·75	2·10
8		5s. green (20.1.45)	3·75	2·10
9		10c. blue (29.4.43)	3·75	2·10
		a. Perf 12	6·25	5·75
10		20c. grey-olive (3.6.43)	3·75	2·10
11		40c. purple (3.6.43)	4·25	2·10
12		60c. red-orange (3.6.43)	5·25	4·00
13		80s. lake-brown (20.1.45)	10·00	4·75
14		1r. violet (20.1.45)	26·00	5·75
7/14		Set of 8	55·00	23·00

Designs: As T **3** (18×22½ mm)—3½c. Native head; 10c. Borobudur Temple; 40c. Seated dancer and Borobudur Temple. As T **5** (20×28 mm)—80s. Ploughing with oxen; 1r. Terraced rice-fields.

II. SUMATRA

100 Cents = 1 Rupee

During 1942 and 1943 various local overprints were applied to stamps of the Netherlands Indies in the following residencies of Sumatra and the adjacent islands:—Atjeh, Bangka, Benkoelen, Billiton, Djambi, Lampong, Palembang, Sumatra's E. Coast, Sumatra's W. Coast and Tapanoeli. These overprints are of great interest to specialists, but as they are of a local character, we do not list them.

During the Japanese Occupation various small islands near Singapore were administered as part of Malaya. Stamps of the Japanese Occupation of Malaya (listed in Part 1 (*British Commonwealth*) under Malaysia) were issued to the post offices of Dabo Singkep, Puloe Samboe, Tanjong Balei, Tanjong Batu, Tanjong Pinang and Terempa between 1942 and 1945. The overprinted issues were also used by a number of districts in Northern Sumatra whose postal services were administered from Singapore until the end of March 1943.

6 Lake Toba   (**7**)

(**8**)

(Litho Kolff & Co, Batavia)

1943 (29 Apr)–**44**. Various designs with horizontal panel of characters as at foot of T **6**. P 12½.

15		1c. olive-green (1.8.44)	2·50	1·80
16		2c. yellow-green (1.8.44)	2·50	1·80
17		3c. greenish blue (1.8.44)	2·50	1·80
18		3½c. rose-red (29.4.43)	4·75	1·80
19		4c. ultramarine (1.8.44)	3·25	1·80
20		5c. red-orange (1.8.44)	2·50	1·30
21		10c. grey-blue (29.4.43)	6·25	1·30
22		20c. lake-brown (1.8.44)	3·25	1·30
23		30c. bright purple (1.8.44)	3·75	2·30
24		40c. chocolate (1.8.44)	4·25	2·50
25		50c. bistre-brown (1.8.44)	10·50	4·00
26		1r. violet-blue (1.8.44)	50·00	6·25
15/26		Set of 12	85·00	25·00

Designs: (18×22½ mm)—1, 2, 3c. Batak house; 3½, 4, 5c. Minangkabau house; 10, 20c. Ploughing with oxen; 40c. As Type **6**. (20×28 mm)—50c., 1r. Carabao Canyon.

1944 (1 Jan). Various stamps optd for use in the whole of Sumatra as T **7** (handstamps, five types) orb (machine-printed).

(a) 1933–37 unwatermarked stamps of Netherlands Indies (T **46/7**)

A. Handstamped as T **7**

27A	**46**	3½c. slate	1·00	2·40
28A	**47**	10c. scarlet	12·50	17·00
29A		12½c. vermilion	16·00	28·00
30A		15c. ultramarine	8·75	16·00
31A		25c. blue-green	5·00	8·25
32A		30c. indigo	26·00	35·00
33A		35c. violet	75·00	£100
34A		42½c. yellow	55·00	65·00
35A		50c. indigo	25·00	34·00
36A		2g.50 purple	£250	£325

B. Optd with T **8**

31B	**47**	25c. blue-green	£325	£400

(b) 1938–40 stamps of Netherlands Indies (T **46/7**). W **61**

A. Handstamped as T **7**

37A	**46**	1c. slate-violet	75	2·00
38A		2c. purple	75	2·00
39A		2½c. olive-bistre	75	2·00
40A		3c. yellow-green	34·00	48·00
41A	**47**	10c. scarlet	£120	£160
42A		15c. ultramarine	5·00	8·25
43A		20c. purple	19·00	34·00
44A		25c. blue-green	4·75	8·25
45A		30c. indigo	25·00	34·00
46A		35c. violet	5·75	8·25
47A		40c. yellow-green	5·75	8·25
48A		2g. blue-green	£500	£700
49A		5g. olive-bistre	55·00	80·00

B. Optd with T **8**

42B	**47**	15c. ultramarine	2·20	6·50
43B		20c. purple	1·10	2·00
44B		25c. blue-green	2·20	3·50
46B		35c. violet	2·20	3·50
47B		40c. yellow-green	3·50	3·50
49B		5g. olive-bistre	23·00	34·00

(c) 1941 stamps of Netherlands Indies (T **67/8**)

A. Handstamped as T **7**

50A	**67**	10c. vermilion (I)	8·75	10·00
51A		10c. vermilion (II)	9·00	10·00
52A		15c. bright blue	3·75	6·25
53A		17½c. orange	3·50	6·25
54A		20c. magenta	31·00	40·00
55A		25c. green	31·00	40·00
56A		30c. yellow-brown	8·25	13·00
57A		35c. purple	23·00	11·50
58A		40c. yellow-green	65·00	£100
59A	**67**	50c. brown-lake	16·00	25·00
60A		60c. bright blue	14·50	21·00
61A		80c. vermilion	18·00	30·00
62A		1g. violet	6·00	8·25
63A		2g. blue-green	25·00	35·00
64A		5g. yellow-brown	£225	£275
65A		10g. green	44·00	70·00
66A	**68**	25g. orange	£400	£550

B. Optd with T **8**

50B	**67**	10c. vermilion (I)	1·30	2·00
		a. Perf 13	36·00	55·00
		b. Opt inverted		
51B		10c. vermilion (II)	6·00	8·25
52B		15c. bright blue	2·40	3·50
53B		17½c. orange	2·20	3·50
54B		20c. magenta	44·00	50·00
55B		25c. green	3·25	4·00
56B		30c. yellow-brown	1·60	3·50
58B		40c. yellow-green	2·40	5·00
59B		50c. brown-lake	3·50	4·00
60B		60c. bright blue	3·25	4·00
61B		80c. vermilion	4·00	5·25
62B		1g. violet	5·00	6·25
		a. Opt inverted		
63B		2g. blue-green	4·50	7·00
64B		5g. yellow-brown	£250	£350
65B		10g. green	48·00	65·00

(d) 1941 stamps (dancers) of Netherlands Indies. Handstamped as T **7**

66	–	3c. green	1·00	2·50
67	**71**	4c. brown-olive	1·00	2·50
68	–	5c. blue	1·00	2·50
69	–	7½c. violet	1·00	2·50

(e) 1940 stamps of Netherlands (T **94**). Handstamped as T **7**

70	**94**	5c. blue-green	12·00	15·00
71		12½c. ultramarine	6·00	13·00

III. JAPANESE NAVAL CONTROL AREA

(BORNEO, CELEBES, MOLUCCAS AND LESSER SUNDA IS.)

100 Cents = 1 Gulden

On 15 July 1942, the Japanese naval authorities ordered all Netherlands Indies stamps in the area under their control to be overprinted with an anchor and the Japanese characters "Dai Nippon". This was done at the capital of each district: The following different types exist:-

1.   BORNEO: Bandjermasin, Pontianak (4 types), Samarinda (5 types).

2.   CELEBES: Macassar, Menado.

3.   MOLUCCAS: Amboina. (A circular opt containing 8 Japanese characters was also applied here.)

4.   LESSER SUNDA IS: Bali and Lombok, Lombok, Timor.

We confine ourselves to listing the Macassar overprint, which is the one most commonly found.

(9)

1942. Various stamps handstamped with T **9**, in black, violet, blue or red.

(a) Stamps of Nether/ands Indies, 1933–37, no wmk

80	**46**	1c. slate-violet	1·10	5·25
81		3c. yellow-green	1·40	5·25
82		3½c. slate	7·00	13·00
83		4c. bronze-green	31·00	50·00
84		5c. ultramarine	12·50	19·00
85	**47**	25c. blue-green	7·00	9·50
86		30c. indigo	50·00	50·00
87		35c. violet	8·25	14·50
88		50c. indigo	70·00	95·00

(b) Stamps of Netherlands Indies, 1938–40. W **61**

89	**46**	1c. slate-violet	5·00	20·00
90		2c. purple	1·10	4·50
91		2½c. olive-bistre	95	4·50
92		3c. yellow-green	90	4·50
93		4c. bronze-green	15·00	23·00
94		5c. ultramarine	38·00	50·00
95	**47**	10c. scarlet	65·00	80·00
96		15c. ultramarine	11·50	18·00
97		20c. purple	1·20	4·50
98		25c. blue-green	5·25	10·00
99		30c. indigo	28·00	38·00
100		35c. violet	1·20	4·50
101		40c. yellow-green	1·20	4·50
102		80c. scarlet	£250	£375
103		1g. violet		
104		2g. blue-green		
105		5g. olive-bistre		

(c) Netherlands Indies, 1933, Special Flights Air Stamp

106	**48**	30c. blue	£275	£400

(d) Netherlands Indies, 1940, numeral type

107	**19**	5c. blue (427)	1·30	4·00

(e) Stamps of Netherlands Indies, 1941 (Queen)

108	**67**	10c. vermilion (I)	3·75	5·00
109		10c. vermilion (II)	3·75	5·00
110		15c. bright blue	4·75	19·00
111		17½c. orange	1·40	5·00
112		20c. magenta	28·00	40·00
113		25c. green	34·00	55·00

114		30c. yellow-brown	5·00	12·50
115		35c. purple	55·00	70·00
116		40c. yellow-green	23·00	33·00
117		50c. brown-lake	12·00	14·00
118		60c. bright blue	5·75	10·50
119		80c. vermilion	10·00	18·00
120		1g. violet	7·50	14·00
121		2g. blue-green	50·00	80·00
122		5g. yellow-brown		
123	**68**	25g. orange		

(f) Stamps of Netherlands Indies, 1941 (dancers)

124	–	2½c. claret	5·75	9·50
125	–	3c. green	2·50	4·75
126	**71**	4c. brown-olive	3·50	4·50
127	–	5c. blue	7·50	18·00
128	–	7½c. violet	1·10	5·00

(g) Stamps of Netherlands, 1940 (Queen)

129	**94**	5c. blue-green		
130		12½c. ultramarine		

1942. POSTAGE DUE. Postage Due stamps of Netherlands Indies, 1913–41, handstamped with T **9**, in various colours.

(a) Enschedé print, 1913–40 (Nos. D226, etc)

D131	D **7**	1c. salmon	14·00	23·00
D132		2½c. salmon	1·90	4·50
D133		3½c. salmon	4·00	8·50
D134		5c. salmon	2·20	4·50
D135		7½c. salmon	2·20	4·50
D136		10c. salmon	1·60	4·50
D137		20c. salmon	2·20	4·50
D138		20c. on 37½c. salmon (D384)	65·00	£100
D139		25c. salmon	1·90	4·50
D140		30c. salmon	4·75	10·50
D141		40c. salmon	2·50	5·00

(b) Kolff print, 1941 (Nos. D445, etc)

D142	D **7**	1c. pale salmon	8·50	17·00
D143		5c. pale salmon	2·50	5·00
D144		15c. pale salmon	2·20	4·50
D145		20c. pale salmon	2·20	5·00
D146		40c. pale salmon	2·50	5·00
D147		1g. light blue	7·25	12·50

1943. Air. Stamps of Netherlands Indies handstamped with T **9** and further surch, in red.

(a) Stamp of 1933–37, no wmk

148	**46**	f.2" on 1c. slate-violet	16·00	25·00

(b) Stamp of 1938–40, W **61**

151	**46**	"f. 8.50" on 2½c. olive-bistre	50·00	80·00

Examples of the 2f. on 1c. (no wmk), 2f. on 5c. (Numeral), 7f. on 22c. (wmk), 8f.50 on 2½c. (wmk) and 8f.50 on 3c. (with or without wmk) overprinted in red with an additional line of text were for use on telegraph money orders.

10 Japanese
Flag and Palms

11 Mt. Fuji, Flag
and Bird

(Typo, 2c. to 20c.; recess, others. Govt Ptg Wks, Japan)

1943 (2 July–8 Aug). Wmk vert wavy lines. P 13.

152	**10**	2c. brown (8.8)	1·00	47·00
153		3c. yellow-green (8.8)	1·00	47·00
154		3½c. brown-orange (8.8)	1·90	47·00
155		5c. blue (8.8)	1·00	23·00
156		10c. carmine	1·00	23·00
157		15c. ultramarine (8.8)	1·10	23·00
158		20c. dull violet (8.8)	1·10	23·00
159	**11**	25c. orange (8.8)	4·25	23·00
160		30c. blue (8.8)	5·00	27·00
161		50c. slate-green (8.8)	10·50	29·00
162		1g. brown-purple (8.8)	50·00	39·00
152/162 *Set of* 11			70·00	£325

Japanese Occupation of North Borneo

Japanese forces landed in Northern Borneo on 15 December 1941 and the whole of North Borneo had been occupied by 19 January 1942.

Brunei, North Borneo, Sarawak and, after a short period, Labuan, were administered as a single territory by the Japanese. Until 12 December 1942, previous stamp issues, without overprint, continued to be used in conjunction with existing postmarks. From November 1942 onwards unoverprinted stamps of Japan were made available and examples can be found used from the area for much of the remainder of the War. Japanese Occupation issues for Brunei, North Borneo and Sarawak were equally valid throughout the combined territory but not, in practice, equally available.

PRICES FOR STAMPS ON COVER		
Nos.	J1/17	from × 5
Nos.	J18/19	from × 6
Nos.	J20/32	from × 25
Nos.	J33/4	from × 2
Nos.	J35/48	from × 12

(1)   **2** Mt. Kinabalu   **3** Borneo Scene

1942 (30 Sept). Stamps of North Borneo handstamped with T **1**.

(a) In violet on Nos. 303/17.

J1	1c. green and red-brown	£160	£225
	a. Black opt	£275	£200
	ab. Pair, one without opt	£3250	
J2	2c. purple and greenish blue	£160	£225
	a. Black opt	£375	£225
J3	3c. slate-blue and green	£130	£225
	a. Black opt	£400	£325
J4	4c. bronze-green and violet	£190	£275
	a. Black opt	50·00	£130
J5	6c. deep blue and claret	£140	£275
	a. Black opt	£400	£325
J6	8c. scarlet	£180	£190
	a. Pair, one without opt	£3250	
	b. Black opt	£250	£190
J7	10c. violet and bronze-green	£170	£275
	a. Black opt	£375	£275
J8	12c. green and bright blue	£180	£425
	a. Black opt	£600	£425
J9	15c. blue-green and brown	£170	£425
	a. Pair, one without opt	£3250	
	b. Black opt	£650	£425
J10	20c. violet and slate-blue	£200	£500
	a. Black opt	£750	£500
J11	25c. green and chocolate	£200	£500
	a. Black opt	£750	£500
J12	50c. chocolate and violet	£275	£600
	a. Black opt	£850	£600
J13	$1 brown and carmine	£275	£750
	a. Black opt	£950	£750
J14	$2 violet and olive-green	£475	£950
	a. Pair, one without opt	£4500	
	b. Black opt	£1300	£900
J15	$5 indigo and pale blue	£550	£1000
		£1600	£1200

(b) In black on Nos. 318/19 ("WAR TAX").

J16	1c. green and red-brown	£600	£300

	a. Pair, one without opt		†	£3250
	b. Violet opt		—	£750
J17	2c. purple and greenish blue	£1400	£500
	a. Pair, one without opt		†	£4750
	b. Violet opt		—	£900

(Litho Kolff & Co., Batavia)

1943 (29 Apr). P 12½.

J18	**2**	4c. red	21·00	45·00
J19	**3**	8c. blue	17·00	45·00

(4)

(5)

("Imperial Japanese Postal Service North Borneo")

1944 (30 Sept). Nos. 303/15 of North Borneo optd with T **4** at Chinese Press, Kuching.

J20	1c. green and red-brown	5·00	12·00
J21	2c. purple and greenish blue	7·50	9·00
	a. Optd on No. J2	£425	
J22	3c. slate-blue and green	5·00	10·00
	a. Optd on No. J3	£425	
J23	4c. bronze-green and violet	9·50	18·00
J24	6c. deep blue and claret	6·50	6·50
J25	8c. scarlet	9·00	17·00
	a. Optd on No. J6	£425	
J26	10c. violet and bronze-green	8·50	13·00
	a. Optd on No. J7	£425	
	b. Optd on No. J7a	£200	£375
J27	12c. green and bright blue	13·00	13·00
	a. Optd on No. J8	£425	
J28	15c. blue-green and brown	12·00	16·00
	a. Optd on No. J9	£425	
J29	20c. violet and slate-blue	25·00	45·00
	a. Optd on No. J10	£1800	
J30	25c. green and chocolate	25·00	45·00
	a. Optd on No. J11	£1800	
J31	50c. chocolate and violet	70·00	£120
	a. Optd on No. J12	£2500	
J32	$1 brown and carmine	90·00	£150
J20/32 *Set* of 13		£250	£425

The spacing between the second and third lines of the overprint is 12 mm on the horizontal stamps, and 15 mm on the upright.

1944 (11 May). No. J1 surch with T **5**.

J33	**81**	$2 on 1c green and red-brown	£4500	£3750

(6)

7 Girl War-worker

(8) ("North Borneo")

1944 (11 May). North Borneo No. 315 surch with T **6**.

J34	$5 on $1 brown and carmine	£4000	£3000
	a. Surch on No. J13	£6500	£4500

1944 (2 Oct)–45. Contemporary stamps of Japan as T **7** (various subjects) optd with T **8** at Chinese Press, Kuching.

J35	1s. red-brown (No. 391) (1.45)	8·00	25·00
J36	2s. scarlet (No. 392b) (10.44)	7·50	21·00
J37	3s. emerald-green (No. 316) (8.45)	7·50	25·00
J38	4s. yellow-green (No. 395) (10.44)	13·00	21·00
J39	5s. claret (No. 396) (1.45)	9·00	24·00
J40	6s. orange (No. 319) (8.45)	14·00	25·00
	a. Opt double, one inverted	£450	£450
J41	8s. violet (No. 321) (11.44)	6·50	25·00
	a. Opt double	£350	
J42	10s. carmine and pink (No. 399) (1.45)	8·00	25·00
J43	15s. blue (No. 401) (11.44)	10·00	25·00
J44	20s. blue-slate (No. 325) (11.44)	80·00	90·00
J45	25s. brown and chocolate (No. 326) (2.45)	55·00	75·00
J46	30s. turquoise-blue (No. 327)	£170	95·00
J47	50s. olive and bistre (No. 328) (8.45)	70·00	70·00
J48	1y. red-brown and chocolate (No. 329) (5.45)	70·00	£100
J35/48 *Set* of 14		£475	£600

Designs:—2s. General Nogi; 3s. Hydro-electric Works; 4s. Hyuga Monument and Mt Fuji; 5s. Admiral Togo; 6s. Garambi Lighthouse, Formosa; 8s. Meiji Shrine; 10s. Palms and map of S.E. Asia; 15s. Airman; 20s. Mt Fuji and cherry blossoms; 25s. Horyu Temple; 30s. Torii, Itsukushima Shrine at Miyajima; 50s. Kinkaku Temple; 1y. Great Buddha, Kamakura.

Examples of some values have been found with hand-painted forged overprints.

POSTAGE DUE STAMPS

1942 (30 Sept). Nos. D85/6 and D88 of North Borneo handstamped with T **1** in black.

JD1	D **2**	2c. brown	—	£3500
JD2		4c. scarlet	—	£3500
JD3		8c. green	—	£3500

Japanese Occupation of Sarawak

Japanese forces landed in North Borneo on 16 December 1941 and Sarawak was attacked on 23 December 1941.

Brunei, North Borneo, Sarawak and after a short period, Labuan, were administered as a single territory by the Japanese. Until September–October 1942, previous stamp issues, without overprint, continued to be used in conjunction with existing postmarks. From 1 October 1942 onwards unoverprinted stamps of Japan were made available and examples can be found used from the area for much of the remainder of the War. Japanese Occupation issues for Brunei, North Borneo and Sarawak were equally valid throughout the combined territory but not, in practice, equally available.

PRICES FOR STAMPS ON COVER		
Nos. J1/21	from × 8	
Nos. J22/6	—	

布政國本本日大

(1) ("Imperial Japanese Government")

1942 (Oct). Stamps of Sarawak handstamped with T **1** in violet.

J1	**21**	1c. purple	32·00	80·00
		a. Pair, one without opt	£2500	
J2		2c. green	£120	£180
		a. Black opt	£110	
J3		2c. black	£110	£130
		a. Black opt	£170	£190
J4		3c. black	£400	£400
J5		3c. green	65·00	£100
		a. Black opt	£150	
J6		4c. bright purple	80·00	£100
		a. Black opt	£150	
J7		5c. violet	95·00	£110
		a. Black opt	£150	
J8		6c. carmine	£150	£150
J9		6c. lake-brown	95·00	£110
		a. Black opt	£140	£150
J10		8c. red-brown	£375	£375
		a. Black opt	£600	
J11		8c. carmine	75·00	£120
		a. Black opt	£275	£350
J12		10c. scarlet	90·00	£120
		a. Black opt	£150	
J13		12c. blue	£170	£190
		a. Black opt	£275	
J14		12c. orange	£170	£200
J15		15c. orange	£425	£425
		a. Black opt	£500	
J16		15c. blue	£120	£140
J17		20c. olive-green and carmine	70·00	£110
		a. Black opt	£150	
J18		25c. violet and orange	£110	£120
		a. Black opt	£160	
J19		30c. red-brown and violet	70·00	£110
		a. Black opt	£150	
J20		50c. violet and scarlet	70·00	£110
		a. Black opt	£275	
		b. Blue opt	£500	
J21		$1 scarlet and sepia	£110	£150
		a. Black opt	£350	
J22		$2 bright purple and violet	£225	£325
		a. Blue opt	£400	
J23		$3 carmine and green	£1800	£1800
		a. Black opt	£2500	
J24		$4 blue and scarlet	£250	£400
J25		$5 scarlet and red-brown	£250	£400
J26		$10 black and yellow	£250	£400

The overprint, being handstamped, exists inverted or double on some values. Those on Nos. J20b, J21a and J22a are diagonal. The remainder are horizontal.

Stamps of T **21** optd with Japanese symbols within an oval frame are revenue stamps, while the same stamps overprinted with three Japanese characters between two vertical double rules, were used as seals.

"Nos. J1/26 have been extensively forged. Recent research indicates that complete or part sets on cover cancelled by Japanese circular postmarks in violet dated "17 11 21" (21 Nov 1942) or "18 3 1" (1 Mar 1943) have forged overprints.".

Ryukyu Islands

1948. 100 Sen = 1 Yen
1858. 100 Cents = 1 Dollar (U.S.)

U.S. MILITARY GOVERNMENT

After the hard-fought campaign from 1 April to 21 June 1945, U.S. forces occupied Okinawa, the largest of the Ryukyu Islands. A U.S. Military Postal Service was established in August 1945 and later, a free local service for civilians. In 1947 Kume island issued a mimeographed handstamped adhesive and surviving stocks of Japanese stamps were issued handstamped with the personal chops of local postmasters. These are outside the scope of this catalogue.

PRINTERS. All stamps of the Ryukyu Islands were printed by the Japanese Government Printing Works *except where otherwise stated.*

1 Cycad Palm

2 Easter Lily

3 Tribute Junk

4 Farmer with Hoe

5

(Des Shutaro Higa. Typo)

1948-49. W **5**. P 13.

A. 1st printing. Dull colours, grey paper, yellow gum, rough perf (1.7.48)
B. 2nd printing. Bright colours, white paper, white gum, clean cut perf (18.7.49)

			A		B	
1	**1**	5s. bright purple	6·00	4·75	2·30	2·75
2	**2**	10s. green	2·75	3·75	6·75	5·25
3	**1**	20s. green	2·75	3·75	5·50	4·50
4	**3**	30s. red	4·50	4·75	2·30	2·30
5	**2**	40s. bright purple	50·00	48·00	2·30	2·30
6	**3**	50s. dull ultramarine	3·50	4·50	6·00	5·00
7	**4**	1y. dull ultramarine	£550	£225	6·00	5·50
1/7	*Set of 7*		£550	£275	28·00	25·00

The designs of the 20s. and 40s. differ in some details from those of the 5s. and 10s. respectively.

6 Shi-Shi Roof Tiles

7 Shuri Woman

8 Former Okinawa Palace, Shuri

9 Dragon's Head

10 Okinawa Women

11 Common Spider and Strawberry Conches and Radula Scallop

(Des T. Omura, A. Natoyama, K. Yamamoto, M. Shimoji, K. Kazu, K. Oshiro, respectively. Photo)

1950 (21 Jan)–**58**. No. wmk. P 13×13½.

8	**6**	50s. carmine/*toned*	45	45
9	**9**	50s. carmine/*white* (6.9.58)	45	45
10	**7**	1y. blue	3·50	2·75
11	**8**	2y. purple	15·00	7·25
12	**9**	3y. carmine-rose	38·00	11·00
13	**10**	4y. slate	18·00	11·00
14	**11**	5y. myrtle-green	11·00	6·00
8/14	*Set of 7*		80·00	35·00

The above were put into general use on 1 February 1950.

12 Dove over Map of Ryukyus

E **13** Sea-horse

(Des K. Ganeko. Photo)

1950 (15 Feb). AIR. P 13×13½.

15	**12**	8y. blue	£120	39·00
16		12y. green	75·00	29·00
17		16y. carmine	23·00	23·00
15/17	*Set of 3*		£200	80·00

(Des K. Sakumoto. Photo)

1950 (15 Feb). SPECIAL DELIVERY. P 13×13½.

E18	E **13**	5y. blue	38·00	23·00

14 University and Shuri Castle

15 Pine Tree

(Des K. Oshiro. Photo)

1951 (12 Feb). Inauguration of Ryukyu University. P 13½.

19	**14**	3y. red-brown	75·00	23·00

(Des M. Adaniya. Photo)

1951 (19 Feb). Afforestation Week. P 13½.

20	**15**	3y. deep green	70·00	23·00

RYUKYU PROVISIONAL CENTRAL GOVERNMENT
1 April 1951

16 Flying Goddess

(Des S. Yamada. Photo)

1951 (10 Oct)—**54**. AIR. P 13×13½.

21	**16**	13y. deep blue	3·25	1·40
22		18y. green	4·50	3·50
23		30y. magenta	6·00	2·30
24		40y. purple (16.8.54)	7·75	4·25
25		50y. yellow-orange (16.8.54)	9·00	7·25
21/25	*Set of 5*		27·00	17·00

(17)

18 Dove and Bean Seedling

(Des S. Ashitomi. Photo)

1952 (1 Apr). Establishment of Ryukyuan Government. P 13½.

30	**18**	3y. carmine-lake	£170	36·00

19 Madanbashi Bridge

20 Presence Chamber, Shuri Palace

21 Shuri Gate

Type I | Type II | Type III

Three types of 10 yen

Type I. Narrow-spaced rules; "10 yen" 7 mm.
Type II. Wide-spaced rules; "10 yen" 7 mm.
Type III. Wide-spaced rules; "10 yen" approx 78 mm.

The above types represent three different printings. In addition to the above printing characteristics, two different sizes of type were used for the two characters at the top. Both large and small size characters occur in the sheet on the first printing, whilst large, small and mixed characters occur on the 2nd and 3rd printings. Large, small and mixed characters also occur on the 100y.

1952. Nos. 8 and 11 surch as T **17**, by Shun Printing Co. Asato, Okinawa.

26	10y. on 50s. carmine/*toned*, Type I (1 Jan)	28·00	21·00
27	10y. on 50s. carmine/*toned*, Type II (5 June)	12·00	7·00
28	10y. on 50s. carmine/toned,Type III (8 Dec)	34·00	28·00
29	100y. on 2y. purple	£2250	£1300

A number of varieties exist but are generally not constant throughout the printing. Forgeries are known.

22 Sogenji Temple Wall

23 Bensaitendo Temple

24 Sonohyamutake Gate

25 Tamaudum Mausoleum, Shuri

26 Hosho-chai Bridge

(Des K. Oshiro. Photo)

1952 (10 Nov)–**53**. P 13½×13.

31	**19**	1y. rose-carmine	35	25
32	**20**	2y. green	45	25
33	**21**	3y. turquoise	70	35
34	**22**	6y. blue (20.1.53)	4·50	3·00
35	**23**	10y. rose-red (20.1.53)	5·50	3·50
36	**24**	30y. olive-green (20.1.53)	13·50	7·25
37	**25**	50y. purple (20.1.53)	17·00	11·00
38	**26**	100y. brown-purple (20.1.53)	23·00	7·25
31/38	*Set of 8*		60·00	30·00

GOVERNMENT OF THE RYUKYU ISLANDS

(U.S. Civil Administration)

1 April 1952

By the Treaty of San Francisco, 8 September 1951, which ended the war with Japan, the Ryukyu Islands were to remain under Japanese sovereignty, but were to be administered by the U.S.A.

27 Reception at Shuri Castle

28 Perry and American Fleet at Naha Harbour

(Des M. Adaniya (3y.), M. Yamada (6y.). Photo)

1953 (26 May). Centenary of Commodore Perry's Visit to Okinawa. P 13½×13 (3y.) or 13×13½ (6y.).

39	**27**	3y. reddish purple	16·00	7·25
40	**28**	6y. chalky blue	2·30	3·50

29 Chofu Ota and Matrix

(Des K. Oshiro. Photo)

1953 (1 Oct). Third Press Week. P 13½×13.

41	**29**	4y. yellow-brown	18·00	6·00

30 Wine Flask to fit around Waist   **31** Tung Dar Bon (lacquer bowl)   **32** Kasun (textile pattern)

(Des R. Nakamura (4y.), M. Aaya (others). Photo)

1954 (25 June)–**55**. P 13×13½.

42	**30**	4y. brown	1·40	70
43	**31**	15y. red (20.6.55)	3·50	3·00
44	**32**	20y. yellow-orange (20.6.55)	3·25	3·25
42/44	*Set of 3*		7·25	6·25

33 Shigo Toma   **34** Noguni Shrine and Pen-nib   **35** Stylized Trees and Sweet Potatoes

(Des M. Adaniya. Photo)

1954 (1 Oct). Fourth Press Week. P 13½×13.

45	**33**	4y. blue	20·00	7·25

(Des M. Adaniya and K. Kakinohana. Photo)

1955 (26 Nov). 350th Anniv of Introduction of Sweet Potato Plant. P 13½×13.

46	**34**	4y. blue	16·00	7·25

(Des M Adaniya. Photo)

1956 (18 Feb). Afforestation Week. P 13½.

47	**35**	4y. blue-green	12·00	6·00

36 Willow Dance   **37** Straw-hat Dance   **38** Nidotekito Dance

(Des M. Adaniya and K. Kakinohana. Photo)

1956 (1 May). National Dances. P 13.

48	**36**	5y. reddish purple	1·20	90
49	**37**	8y. bluish violet	2·30	2·00
50	**38**	14y. red brown	3·50	3·25
48/50	*Set of 3*		6·25	5·50

39 Telephone and Dial   **40** Floral Garland

(Des K. Oshiro and K. Kakinohana. Photo)

1956 (8 June). Inauguration of Telephone Dialling System. P 13×13½.

51	**39**	4y. bluish violet	22·00	12·00

(Des M. Adaniya. Photo)

1956 (1 Dec). New Year. P 13½.

52	**40**	2y. red, yellow, green & dp violet-blue	3·25	1·80

41 Flying Goddess   **42** "Rocket" Pencils

(Des S. Yamada. Eng S. Kurihara. Recess)

1957 (1 Aug). AIR. P 13½.

53	**41**	15y. bluish green	8·25	3·50
54		20y. carmine-lake	13·50	7·25
55		35y. green	16·00	9·00
56		45y. brown	20·00	11·00
57		60y. grey	23·00	14·50
53/57	*Set of 5*		75·00	40·00

(Des S. Isagawa. Photo)

1957 (1 Oct). Seventh Press Week. P 13½×13.

58	**42**	4y. ultramarine	1·20	90

43 Phoenix   **44** Various Ryukyuan Postage Stamps

(Des S. Isagawa. Photo)

1957 (20 Dec). New Year. P 13½.
59   **43**   2y. multicoloured 45   25

(Des S. Tamanaha. Photo)

1958 (1 July). Tenth Anniv of First Ryukyuan Postage Stamps. P 13½.
60   **44**   4y. multicoloured .... 1·20   90

New Currency

45 Stylized Dollar
Sign over Yen
Symbol

(Des M. Adaniya and S. Isagawa. Typo Asahido Ptg Co, Naha)

1958 (16 Sept)–**61.** No gum. P 10½ –11 and compound.
61	**45**	½c. orange-yellow..........................	80	70
62		1c. green..	1·30	1·10
63		2c. grey blue...................................	2·00	1·80
64		3c. carmine-red..............................	1·80	1·60
65		4c. emerald.....................................	2·00	1·80
66		5c. yellow-brown............................	4·50	3·50
67		10c. turquoise-blue........................	6·75	4·25
68		25c. light violet-blue......................	9·00	7·25
		a. With gum (20.4.61).............	14·50	14·50
69		50c. grey...	18·00	11·00
		a. With gum (20.4.61).............	14·50	14·50
70		$1 purple..	14·50	7·25
61/70	*Set of 10*	....	55·00	36·00

There are numerous varieties of shade and paper in this issue.

46 Gateway of Courtesy   **47** Lion Dance

(Des S. Isagawa. Photo)

1958 (15 Oct). Restoration of Shun Gateway. P 13½.
71   **46**   3c. multicoloured .... 1·50   1·10
Nos. 71 was issued in sheets of 10.

Lithographed stamps in this design, perforated 13½ and with a lengthy Japanese inscription (headed "Shureimon Specimen Stamp") printed on the back in blue, are facsimiles. They were given away free in 1972 to help defeat speculation in this stamp; they were issued in sheets of 10 bearing the imprint of the "Union of Stamp Speculation Opponents".

A further facsimile, by the All-Japan Stamp Trading Association, has simulated perforations; each stamp is marked on the reverse with three characters meaning "replica".

(Des S. Yamada. Photo)

1958 (10 Dec). New Year. P 13½.
72   **47**   1½ multicoloured 55   25

48 Trees   **49** Atlas Moth

(Des S. Tamanaha Photo)

1959 (30 Apr). Afforestation Week. P 13½.
73   **48**   3c. multicoloured 70   65

(Des M. Adaniya. Photo)

1959 (23 July). Japanese Biological Teachers' Conference, Okinawa. P 13½.
74   **49**   3c. multicoloured .... 2·75   1·20

50 Hibiscus   **51** Tropical Fish   **52** Zebra Moon, Banded Bonnet and Textile Cone

53 Leaf Butterfly   **54** Jellyfish   **55** Yakazi (Ryukyuan Toy)

(Des S. Tamanaha (½ c.), S. Isagawa (3c., 8c.), M. Adaniya (13c., 17c.) Photo)

1959 (10 Aug). Large inscriptions. P 13×13½.
75	**50**	½c. multicoloured	35	25
76	**51**	3c. multicoloured	1·40	45
77	**52**	8c. multicoloured	13·50	6·00
78	**53**	13c. multicoloured	3·25	2·30
79	**54**	17c. multicoloured	23·00	11·00
75/79	*Set of 5*	....	37·00	18·00

See also Nos. 87/91.

(Des S. Isagawa. Photo)

1959 (1 Dec). New Year. P 13×13½.
80   **55**   1½c. multicoloured 70   55

(56)   **57** University Badge

1959 (20 Dec). AIR. Nos. 53/7 such as T **56,** by Nakamaru Press, Naha.

81	**41**	9c. on 15y. bluish green (R.)		2·75	1·80
		a. Surch inverted		£650	
82		14c. on 20y. carmine-lake (B.)		3·50	3·50
83		19c. on 35y. green (R.)		8·25	6·00
84		27c. on 45y. brown (B.)		17·00	7·75
85		35c. on 60y. grey (R.)		18·00	11·00
81/85	*Set of 5*			45·00	27·00

(Des K. Shiroma. Photo)

1960 (22 May). Tenth Anniv of University of the Ryukyus. P 13×13½.

86	**57**	3c. yellow, black, red and blue		1·40	70

58 Leaf Butterfly   **(59)**

1960 (1 July)–**61**. As Nos. 75/9 but with smaller inscriptions as in T **58**. 13c. has design reversed as T **58**.

87		½c. multicoloured (9.10.61)		55	35
88		3c. multicoloured (23.8.61)		2·30	45
89		8c. multicoloured		5·75	2·30
90		13c. multicoloured		2·00	1·20
91		17c. multicoloured		15·00	6·00
87/91	*Set of 5*			23·00	9·25

1960 (3 Aug). AIR. Various stamps surch as T **59**, by Kyodo Press.

92	**30**	9c. on 4y. brown		4·50	1·50
		a. Surch inverted		£8500	
93	**36**	14c. on 5y. reddish purple (Br.)		5·00	2·30
94	**31**	19c. on 15y. red (R.)		4·50	2·75
95	**38**	27c. on 14y. red-brown (B)		8·75	4·50
96	**32**	35c. on 20y. yellow-orange (G.)		10·00	7·25
92/96	*Set of 5*			29·00	16·00

60 "Munjuru"   **61** "Inohabushi"

62 "Hatomabushi"   **63** "Hanafu"

(Des S. Tamanaha, M. Adaniya and S. Isagawa. Photo)

1960 (1 Nov). Ryukyuan Dances (1st issue). P 13.

97	**60**	1c. multicoloured		1·80	1·10
98	**61**	2½c. multicoloured		3·25	1·50
99	**62**	5c. multicoloured		1·10	1·00
100	**63**	10c. multicoloured		1·60	1·00
97/100	*Set of 4*			7·00	4·25

For designs as Types **60/3** but additionally inscribed "RYUKYUS" see Nos. 107/11.

64 Torch and Coastal Scene

65 Start of Race

(Des M. Adaniya and S. Tamanaha. Photo)

1960 (6 Nov). Eighth Kyushu Athletic Meeting. P 13.

101	**64**	3c. orange-red, dp bluish grn & lt bl		6·75	2·75
102	**65**	8c. grey-green and orange		1·80	1·20

66 Little Egret and Rising Sun   **67** Bull Fight

(Des S. Isagawa. Photo)

1960 (1 Dec). National Census. P 13½.

103	**66**	3c. brown		6·75	3·25

(Des S. Tamanaha. Photo)

1960 (10 Dec). New Year. P 13½.

104	**67**	1½. chocolate, yellow-buff & dp blue		3·00	1·40

68 Native Pine Tree   **69** Naha, Junk, Liner and City Seal

(Des S. Tamanaha. Photo)

1961 (1 May). Afforestation Week. P 13½.

105	**68**	3c. deep green, red and yellow-green		2·00	1·60

(Des S. Isagawa. Photo)

1961 (20 May). 40th Anniv of Naha City. P 13.

106	**69**	3c. turquoise		2·75	1·80

70 "Shudun"   **71** "Haodori"

72 "Nobori Kuduchi"   **73** "Koteibushi"

(1c. to 10c. des as Nos. 97/100; 20c. des S. Omine; 25c., 50c., $1 des S. Isagawa. Photo)

1961–71. Ryukyuan Dances (2nd issue). 1c. to 10c. as T **60/3** but additionally inscr "RYUKYUS" as in T **70/3**. P 13.

107	**60**	1c. multicoloured (5.12.61)	20	20
108	**61**	2½c. multicoloured (20.6.62)	20	20
109		4c. multicoloured (1.11.71)	25	35
110	**62**	5c. multicoloured (20.6.62)	25	25
111	**63**	10c. multicoloured (20.6.62)	55	45
112	**70**	20c. multicoloured (20.1 64)	3·25	1·30
113	**71**	25c. multicoloured (1.2.62)	1·10	90
114	**72**	50c. multicoloured (1.9.61)	3·25	1·30
115	**73**	$1 multicoloured (1.9.61)	6·25	45
107/115	*Set of 9*		14·00	5·00

74 Flying Goddess   **75** Flying Goddess playing Flute

76 Wind God   **77** Wind God

78 Flying Goddess over Trees   **79** White Silver Temple

(Des S. Yamada. Photo)

1961 (21 Sept). AIR. P 13½.

116	**74**	9c. multicoloured	45	20
117	**75**	14c. multicoloured	70	65
118	**76**	19c. multicoloured	1·10	80
119	**77**	27c. multicoloured	3·50	90
120	**78**	35c. multicoloured	2·30	1·60
116/120	*Set of 5*		7·25	3·75

(Des S. Tamanaha. Litho Nakamaru Press, Naha)

1961 (1 Oct). Unification of Itoman District and Takamine, Miwa and Kanegushiku Villages. P 11.

121	**79**	3c. red-brown	2·30	1·80

80 Books and Bird   **81** Sunrise and Eagles

(Des S. Isagawa. Litho)

1961 (12 Nov). Tenth Anniv of Ryukyu Book Week. P 13½.

122	**80**	3c. multicoloured	1·40	1·10

(Des S. Yamada. Photo)

1961 (10 Dec). New Year. P 13½.

123	**81**	1½c. red, black and gold	3·50	1·80

82 Government Building, Steps and Trees   **83** Government Building

(Des M. Adaniya (1½c.), S. Tamanaha (3c.). Photo)

1962 (1 Apr). Tenth Anniv of the Government of the Ryukyu Islands. P 13½.

124	**82**	1½c. multicoloured	80	70
125	**83**	3c. multicoloured	1·10	90

84 *Anopheles Hyrcanus sinensis* (Mosquito)   **85** Shuri Gate and Campaign Emblem

(Des S. Isagawa (3c.), S. Tamanaha (8c.). Photo)

1962 (7 Apr). Malaria Eradication. P 13½.

126	**84**	3c. multicoloured	80	70
127	**85**	8c. multicoloured	1·40	1·40

86 Windmill, Dolls and Horse

(Des M. Adaniya. Photo)

1962 (5 May). Children's Day. P 13½.

128	**86**	3c. multicoloured	1·50	1·10

87 *Hibiscus lilaceus*   **88** *Ixora chinensis*   **89** *Erythrina indica*

90 *Caesalpinia pulcherrima*   **91** *Schima mertensiana*   **92** *Impatiens balsamina*

93 *Hamaomoto* (herb)   **94** *Alpinia speciosa*

(Des S. Isagawa (½c., 17c.), T. Kinjo and Y. Arakaki (2c., 3c. (No. 132)), M. Adaniya (3c. (No. 131), 13c.). S. Tamanaha (8c., 15c.). Photo)

1962 (1 June)–**71**. Ryukyuan Flowers. P 13½.

129	**87**	½c. multicoloured	25	20
130	**88**	2c. multicoloured (30.9.71)	25	25
131	**89**	3c. multicoloured	55	20
132	**90**	3c. multicoloured (10.5.71)	25	25
133	**91**	8c. multicoloured	80	45
134	**92**	13c. multicoloured	1·10	65
135	**93**	15c. multicoloured (15.10.63)	1·80	1·00
136	**94**	17c. multicoloured	1·40	90
129/136		*Set of 8*	5·75	3·50

95 Akaeware Bowl

(Des E. Yamazato. Photo)

1962 (5 July). Philatelic Week. P 13½.
137   **95**   3c. multicoloured .... 5·00   3·00

96 Kendo (Japanese Fencing)   **97** "Hare and Water" (textile design)

(Des S. Isagawa. Photo)

1962 (25 July). All-Japan Kendo Meeting. P 13×13½.
138   **96**   3c. multicoloured .... 6·00   3·25

(Des M Adaniya. Photo)

1962 (10 Dec). New Year. P 13½.
139   **97**   1½ c. multicoloured .... 2·30   1·40

98 Reaching Maturity (clay relief)   **99** Trees and Wooded Hills

(Des S. Tamanaha. Photo)

1963 (15 Jan). Adults' Day. P 13½.
140   **98**   3c. gold, black and blue .... 1·10   70

(Des K. Oshiro. Photo)

1963 (25 Mar). Afforestation Week. P 13½.
141   **99**   3c. multicoloured .... 1·10   90

100 *Etithyllum strictum*   **101** Okinawa Highway

(T **100/101** des S. Isagawa. Photo)

1963 (5 Apr). P 13×13½.
142   **100**   1½c. multicoloured 35   25

1963 (30 Apr). Opening of Okinawa Highway. P 13½.
143   **101**   3c. multicoloured .... 1·50   1·20

102 Black Kites over Islands   **103** Shioya Bridge

(Des M. Adaniya. Photo)

1963 (10 May). Bird Week. P 13½.
144   **102**   3c. multicoloured .... 2·30   1·40

(Des S. Omine. Photo)

1963 (5 June). Opening of Shioya Bridge, Okinawa. P 13½.
145   **103**   3c. multicoloured .... 1·40   1·20

104 Lacquerware Bowl   **105** Convair 880 Jetliner and Shuri Gate   **106** Convair 880 Jetliner over Sea

(Des E. Yamazato and S. Isagawa. Photo)

1963 (1 July). Philatelic Week. P 13½.
146   **104**   3c. multicoloured .... 3·50   2·75

(Des S. Tamanaha (5½c.), M. Adaniya (7c.). Photo)

1963 (28 Aug). AIR. P 13×13½.
147   **105**   5½c. multicoloured 35   25
148   **106**   7c. black, red and blue............................... 45   35

107 Map and Emblem   108 Nakagusuku Castle Ruins

(Des K. Oshiro. Photo)

1963 (16 Sept). Meeting of Junior International Chamber, Naha. P 13½.
149   **107**   3c. multicoloured .... 1·00   90

(Des M. Adaniya. Photo)

1963 (1 Nov). Ancient Buildings Protection Week. P 13½.
150   **108**   3c. multicoloured .... 1·40   90

109 Flame   **110** Bingata "dragon"   **111** Carnation
(textile design)

(Des S. Omine. Photo)

1963 (10 Dec). 15th Anniv of Declaration of Human Rights. P 13½.
151   **109**   3c. multicoloured 90   65

(Des S. Isagawa. Photo)

1963 (10 Dec). New Year. P 13½.
152   **110**   1½c. multicoloured 90   45

(Des S. Isagawa. Photo)

1964 (10 May). Mothers' Day. P 13½.
153   **111**   3c. multicoloured 90   55

112 Pineapples and Sugar-cane

113 Hand-woven Sash

(Des S. Omine. Photo)

1964 (1 June). Agricultural Census. P 13½.
154   **112**   3c. multicoloured 55   40

(Des K. Oshiro. Photo)

1964 (1 July). Philatelic Week. P 13½.
155   **113**   3c. ochre, deep blue and rose-pink 70   65
         a. Ochre, deep blue & deep carmine   90   80

114 Girl Scout and Emblem

(Des S. Tamanaha. Photo)

1964 (31 Aug). Tenth Anniv of Ryukyuan Girl Scouts. P 13½.
156   **114**   3c. multicoloured 55   35

115 Transmitting Tower   **116** "Bowl" Receiving Aerial   **117** Shuri Gate and Olympic Torch

(Des S. Omine (3c.), S. Isagawa (8c.). Photo)

1964 (1 Sept). Inauguration of Ryukyu Japan Microwave Link. Optd in black with "1964" and bars cancelling "1963". P 13.
157   **115**   3c. green and black................................... 1·10   90
         a. Inverted "1" in "1964"....................... 23·00   23·00
158   **116**   8c. blue and black.................................... 1·50   1·40
No. 157a. occurs on position 8.

(Des M. Adaniya. Photo)

1964 (6 Sept). Passage of Olympic Torch through Okinawa. P 13½×13.
159   **117**   3c. multicoloured 45   35

118 "Naihanchi" (Karate stance)   **119** "Makiwara" (Karate training)

120 "Kumite" Exercise   **121** "Miyara Dunchi" (old Ryukyuan Residence)

(Des K. Oshiro (160), S. Isagawa (161), M. Adamya (162). Photo)

1964 (5 Oct)–**65**. Karate ("self-defence"). Designs multicoloured, background colours given. P 13½.

160	**118**	3c. brown-purple	70	55
161	**119**	3c. yellow (5.2.65)	65	55
162	**120**	3c. grey (5.6.65)	55	55
160/162		*Set of* 3	1·70	1·50

(Des S. Omine. Photo)

1964 (1 Nov). Ancient Buildings Protection Week. P 13½.

163	**121**	3c. multicoloured	45	35

122 Bingata "snake" (textile design)

123 Boy Scouts, Badge and Shuri Gate

(Des S. Tamanaha. Photo)

1964 (10 Dec). New Year. P 13½.

164	**122**	1½c. multicoloured	55	40

(Des S. Isagawa. Photo)

1965 (6 Feb). Tenth Anniv of Hyukyuan Boy Scouts. P 13½.

165	**123**	3c. multicoloured	60	45

124 "Samisen" (musical instrument)

125 Stadium

(Des M. Adaniya. Photo)

1965 (1 July). Philatelic Week. P 13½.

166	**124**	3c. multicoloured	60	45

(Des S. Tamanaha. Photo)

1965 (1 July). Completion of Onoyama Sports Ground. P 13½.

167	**125**	3c. multicoloured	35	25

126 Kin Power Station

127 ICY Emblem and "Globe"

(Des S. Isagawa. Photo)

1965 (1 July). Completion of Kin Power Plant. P 13½.

168	**126**	3c. multicoloured	45	35

(Des S. Isagawa. Photo)

1965 (24 Aug). International Co-operation Year and 20th Anniv of United Nations. P 13½.

169	**127**	3c. multicoloured	35	25

128 City Hall, Naha

129 Semaruhakogame Turtle

130 Taimai or Hawksbill Turtle

131 Yamagame or Hill Tortoise

(Des S. Isagawa. Photo)

1965 (18 Sept). Completion of Naha City Hall. P 13½.

170	**128**	3c. multicoloured	35	25

(Des K. Oshiro (171), S. Omine (172), S. Tamanaha (173). Photo)

1965 (20 Oct)–**66**. Ryukyuan Turtles. P 13½.

171	**129**	3c. multicoloured	80	45
172	**130**	3c. multicoloured (20.1.66)	80	45
173	**131**	3c. multicoloured (20.4.66)	80	45
171/173		*Set of* 3	2·20	1·20

132 Bingata "horse" (textile design)

133 Pryer's Woodpecker

134 Sika Deer

135 Dugong

(Des S. Omine. Photo)

1965 (10 Dec). New Year. P 13½.
174   **132**   1½c. multicoloured 35   25
No. 174 also exists with the gold colour (value and Japanese inscription) omitted. It is believed that this can be faked by bleaching out the gold without affecting the grey background underneath.

(Des S. Tamanaha (175), S. Omine (176), S. Isagawa (177). Photo)

1966. "Natural Monument" (Wildlife). P 13½.
175   **133**   3c. multicoloured (15 Feb) 65   35
176   **134**   3c. multicoloured (15 Mar) 65   35
177   **135**   3c. multicoloured (20 Apr) 65   35
175/177 *Set of 3* .... 1·80   95

136 Pacific Swallow   **137** Lilies and Ruins

(Des S. Omine. Photo)

1966 (10 May). Bird Week. P 13½.
178   **136**   3c. multicoloured 55   40

(Des M. Adamya. Photo)

1966 (23 June). Memorial Day (Battle of Okinawa). P 13×13½.
179   **137**   3c. multicoloured 35   30

138 University of the Ryukyus   **139** Lacquer Box

(Des M. Adaniya. Photo)

1966 (1 July). Transfer of University of the Ryukyus to Government Administration. P 13×13½.
180   **138**   3c. multicoloured 35   30

(Des K. Oshiro. Photo)

1966 (1 Aug). Philatelic Week. P 13½.
181   **139**   3c. multicoloured 35   30

140 Ryukyuan Tiled House   **141** "GRI" Museum, Shuri

(Des S. Omine. Photo)

1966 (20 Sept). 20th Anniv of United Nations Educational, Scientific and Cultural Organization. P 13½.
182   **140**   3c. multicoloured 35   30

(Des M. Adaniya. Photo)

1966 (6 Oct). Completion of Government Museum, Shuri. P 13½.
183   **141**   3c. multicoloured 35   30

142 Nakasone-Tuimya Tomb   **143** Bingata "ram" (textile design)

(Des S. Tamanaha. Photo)

1966 (1 Nov). Ancient Buildings Protection Week. P 13½.
184   **142**   3c. multicoloured 35   30

(Des S. Isagawa. Photo)

1966 (10 Dec). New Year. P 13½.
185   **143**   1½c. multicoloured 55   35

144 Clown Fish   **145** Box Fish

146 Forceps Fish   **147** Spotted Triggerfish

148 Saddleback Butterfly   **149** Tsuboya Urn

(Des S. Omine (186), K. Oshiro (187), S. Tamanaha (188), M. Adaniya
(189), S. Isagawa (190). Photo)

1966 (20 Dec)–**67**. Tropical fishes. P 13½.
186	**144**	3c. multicoloured	75	45
187	**145**	3c. multicoloured (10.1.67)	75	45
188	**146**	3c. multicoloured (10.4.67)	75	45
189	**147**	3c. multicoloured (10.5.67)	75	45
190	**148**	3c. multicoloured (10.6.67)	75	45
186/190	*Set of 5*		3·50	2·00

(Des M. Adaniya. Photo)

1967 (20 Apr). Philatelic Week. P 13½.
191	**149**	3c. multicoloured	45	30

150 Episcopal Mitre

151 Venus Comb Murex

152 Chiragra Spider Conch

153 Great Green Turban

154 Bubble Conch

155 Roof Tiles and Emblem

(Des K. Oshiro. Photo)

1967–68. Sea Shells. P 13½.
192	**150**	3c. multicoloured (20.7.67)	65	35
193	**151**	3c. multicoloured (30.8.67)	65	35
194	**152**	3c. multicoloured (18.1.68)	70	45
195	**153**	3c. multicoloured (10.2.68)	70	45
196	**154**	3c. multicoloured (5.6.68)	70	45
192/196	*Set of 5*		3·00	1·80

(Des M. Adaniya. Photo)

1967 (11 Sept). International Tourist Year. P 13½.
197	**155**	3c. multicoloured	35	30

156 Mobile Clinic   **157** Hojo Bridge, Enkaku

(Des M. Adaniya. Photo)

1967(13 Oct). 15th Anniv of Anti-TB Association. P 13½.
198	**156**	3c. multicoloured	35	30

(Des S. Tamanaha. Photo)

1967 (1 Nov). Ancient Buildings Protection Week. P 13½.
199	**157**	3c. multicoloured	35	30

158 Bingata "monkey" (textile design)   **159** TV Tower and Map   **160** Dr. Nakachi and Assistant

1967 (11 Dec). New Year. Photo. P 13½.
200	**158**	1c. multicoloured	35	30

(Des S. Tamanaha. Photo)

1967 (22 Dec). Opening of TV Broadcasting Stations in Miyako and Yaeyama. P 13½.
201	**159**	3c. multicoloured	35	30

(Des S. Tamanaha. Photo)

1968 (15 Mar). 120th Anniv of First Ryukyu Vaccination (by Dr. Kijin Nakachi). P 13½.
202	**160**	3c. multicoloured	35	30

161 Medicine Case (after Sokei Dana)   **162** Young Man, Book, Map and Library

(Des S. Isagawa Photo)

1968 (18 Apr). Philatelic Week. P 13½.
203	**161**	3c. multicoloured	55	35

(Des S. Isagawa. Photo)

1968 (13 May). Library Week. P 13½.

| 204 | **162** | 3c. multicoloured | 50 | 35 |

163 Postmen with Ryukyu Stamp of 1948

(Des K. Oshiro. Photo)

1968 (1 July). 20th Anniv of First Ryukyu Islands' Stamps. P 13½.

| 205 | **163** | 3c. multicoloured | 45 | 35 |

164 Temple Gate

165 Old Man Dancing

(Des S. Tamanaha. Recess and photo)

1968 (15 July). Restoration of Enkaku Temple Gate. P 13½.

| 206 | **164** | 3c. multicoloured | 45 | 35 |

(Des S. Tamanaha. Photo)

1968 (15 Sept). Old People's Day. P 13½.

| 207 | **165** | 3c. multicoloured | 45 | 35 |

166 *Mictyris longicarpus*

167 *Uca dubia*

168 *Baptozius vinosus*

169 *Cardisoma carnifex*

170 *Ocypode ceratophthalma*

(Des S. Isagawa. Photo)

1968–69. Crabs. P 13½.

208	**166**	3c. multicoloured (10.10.68)	90	65
209	**167**	3c. multicoloured (5.2.69)	90	65
210	**168**	3c. multicoloured (5.3.69)	90	65
211	**169**	3c. multicoloured (15.5.69)	90	65
212	**170**	3c. multicoloured (2.6.69)	90	65
208/212		*Set of 5*	4·00	3·00

171 Saraswati Pavilion

172 Player

(Des K. Oshiro. Photo)

1968 (1 Nov). Ancient Buildings Protection Week. P 13½.

| 213 | **171** | 3c. multicoloured | 40 | 30 |

(Des S. Isagawa Photo)

1968 (23 Nov). 35th All-Japan East v. West Men's Softball Tennis Tournament, Onoyama. P 13½.

| 214 | **172** | 3c. multicoloured | 45 | 35 |

173 Bingata "cock" (textile design)

174 Boxer

175 Inkwell Screen

(Des Y. Arakaki. Photo)

1968 (10 Dec). New Year. P 13½.

| 215 | **173** | 1½c. multicoloured | 80 | 35 |

(Des K. Oshio. Photo)

1969 (3 Jan). 20th All-Japan Boxing Championships. P 13½.

| 216 | **174** | 3c. multicoloured | 45 | 35 |

(Des Y. Arakaki. Photo)

1969 (17 Apr). Philatelic Week. P 13½.

| 217 | **175** | 3c. multicoloured | 45 | 25 |

176 UHF Antennae and Map

177 Gate of Courtesy

(Des S. Isagawa. Photo)

1969 (1 July). Inauguration of Okinawa-Sakishima UHF Radio Service. P 13½.

218	**176**	3c. multicoloured	35	25

1969 (1 Aug). 22nd All-Japan Formative Education Study Conference, Naha. Photo. P 13½.

219	**177**	3c. multicoloured	35	25

178 "Tug of War" Festival

179 "Hari" Canoe Race

180 "Izaiho" Religious Ceremony

181 "Ushideiku" Dance

182 "Sea God" Dance   **(183)**

1969-70. Traditional Religious Ceremonies. Photo. P 13½.

220	**178**	3c. multicoloured (1.8.69)......................	65	45
221	**179**	3c. multicoloured (5.9.69)......................	65	45
222	**180**	3c. multicoloured (3.10.69)	65	45
223	**181**	3c. multicoloured (20.1.70)	65	45
224	**182**	3c. multicoloured (27.2.70)	65	45
220/224		*Set of 5*..	3·00	2·00

1969 (15 Oct). Nos. 131 surch with T **183**.

225	**89**	½c. on 3c. multicoloured.........................	70	65

184 Nakamura-Ke   **185** Kyuzo Toyama and Map

(Des K. Miyage. Photo)

1969 (1 Nov). Ancient Buildings Protection Week. P 13½.

226	**184**	3c. multicoloured	35	25

(Des J. Onaga. Photo)

1969 (5 Dec). 70th Anniv of Toyama's Ryukyu-Hawaii Emigration Project. "1970" cancelled by bars and "1969" inserted in black. P 13½.

227	**185**	3c. multicoloured	45	35
		a. Opt omitted	£1700	

186 Bingata "dog and flowers" (textile design)

187 Sake Flask

(Des Y. Arakaki. Photo)

1969 (10 Dec). New Year. P 13½.

228	**186**	1½c. multicoloured	55	35

(Des T. Kinjo. Photo)

1970 (15 Apr). Philatelic Week. P 13½.

229	**187**	3c. multicoloured	40	25

188 "Shushin-Kaneiri"

189 "Chu-nusudu"

(Des K. Oshiro. Recess)

1970 (25 Sept)–**71**. Famous Ryukyuans. P 13½.
241	**194**	3c. claret	65	65
242	**195**	3c. deep bluish green (22.12.70)	80	65
243	**196**	3c. black (22.1.71)	65	65
241/243		Set of 3	1·90	1·80

190 "Mekarushi"

191 "Nidotichiuchi"

197 "Population"

198 "Great Cycad of Une"

(Des C. Ashitomi. Photo)

1970 (1 Oct). Population Census. P 13½.
244	**197**	3c. multicoloured	35	30

192 "Kokonomaki"

(Des S. Isagawa. Photo)

1970 (28 Apr–25 Aug). "Kumi-Odori" Ryukyu Theatre. P 13½.
230	**188**	3c. multicoloured	75	60
231	**189**	3c. multicoloured (29.5)	75	60
232	**190**	3c. multicoloured (30.6)	75	60
233	**191**	3c. multicoloured (30.7)	75	60
234	**192**	3c. multicoloured (25.8)	75	60
230/234		Set of 5	3·50	2·75
MS235	94×102 mm. Nos. 230×4		6·00	6·00
MS236	94×102 mm. Nos. 231×4 (29.5)		6·00	6·00
MS237	94×102 mm. Nos. 232×4 (30.6)		6·00	6·00
MS238	94×102 mm. Nos. 233×4 (30.7)		6·00	6·00
MS239	94×102 mm. Nos. 234×4 (25.8)		6·00	6·00

(Des K. Miyagi. Photo)

1970 (2 Nov). Ancient Buildings Protection Week. P 13½.
245	**198**	3c. multicoloured	45	30

199 Ryukyu Islands, Flag and Japanese Diet

200 "Wild Boar" (Bingata textile design)

(Des S. Isagawa. Photo)

1970 (15 Nov). Election of Ryukyu Representatives to the Japanese Diet. P 13½.
246	**199**	3c. multicoloured	90	65

(Des T. Kinjo. Photo)

1970 (10 Dec). New Year. P 13½.
247	**200**	1½c. multicoloured	55	35

193 Observatory

(Des C. Ashitomi. Photo)

1970 (22 May). Completion of Underwater Observatory, Busena-Misaki, Nago. P 13½.
240	**193**	3c. multicoloured	80	35

194 Noboru Jahana (politician)

195 Saion Gushichan Bunjaku (statesman)

196 Choho Giwan (Regent)

201 "Jibata" (hand-loom)

202 "Filature" (spinning-wheel)

203 Farm-worker wearing "Shurunnu" Coat and "Kubagasa" Hat

204 Woman using "Shiri-Ushi" (rice huller)

210 Yabuchi Island

(Des S. Isagawa (No. 255), K. Oshiro (256), J. Onaga (257). Photo)

1971 (30 July)–**72**. Government Parks. P 13½.

255	**208**	3c. multicoloured	35	35
256	**209**	3c. multicoloured (30.8.71)	35	35
257	**210**	4c. multicoloured (20.1.72)	35	35
255/257	*Set of 3*		95	95

205 Fisherman's "Umi-Fujo" (box) and "Yutui" (bailer)

(Des S. Isagawa (Nos. 248/9), C. Ashitomi (others). Photo)

1971 (16 Feb-15 June). Ryukyu Handicrafts. P 13½.

248	**201**	3c. multicoloured	45	35
249	**202**	3c. multicoloured (16.3)	45	35
250	**203**	3c. multicoloured (30.4)	45	35
251	**204**	3c. multicoloured (20.5)	45	35
252	**205**	3c. multicoloured (15.6)	45	35
248/252	*Set of 5*		2·00	1·60

211 Deva King, Torinji Temple

212 "Rat" (Bingata textile pattern)

213 Student-nurse and Candle

(Des S. Tamanaha. Photo)

1971 (1 Dec). Ancient Buildings Protection Week. P 13½.

258	**211**	4c. multicoloured	55	45

(Des T. Kinjo. Photo)

1971 (10 Dec). New Year. P 13½.

259	**212**	2c. multicoloured	70	55

(Des K. Miyagi. Photo)

1971 (24 Dec). 25th Anniv of Nurses' Training Scheme. P 13½.

260	**213**	4c. multicoloured	55	45

206 "Taku" (container)

207 Civic Emblem with Old and New City Views

(Des Y. Arakaki. Photo)

1971 (15 Apr). Philatelic Week. P 13½.

253	**206**	3c. multicoloured	45	30

(Des C. Ashitomi. Photo)

1971 (20 May). 50th Anniv of Naha's City Status. P 13×13½.

254	**207**	3c. multicoloured	55	45

208 Restored Battlefield, Okinawa

209 Haneji Inland Sea

214 Islands and Sunset

215 Coral Reef

Ryukyu Islands

216 Island and
Short-tailed
Albatrosses

217 Dove and Flags of Japan
and U.S.A.

218 "Yushibin"
(ceremonial sake
container)

(Des T. Kinjo and Y. Arakaki (No. 261), S. Isagawa (262), O. Ashitomi
(263). Photo)

1972 (21 Mar–14 Apr). Maritime Scenery. P 13½.

261	**214**	5c. multicoloured	35	70
262	**215**	5c. multicoloured (30.3)	35	70
263	**216**	5c. multicoloured (14.4)	90	90
261/263	*Set of 3*		1·40	2·10

(Des S. Tamanaha. Photo)

1972 (17 Apr). Ratification of Treaty for Return of Ryukyu Islands to
Japan. P 13½.

264	**217**	5c. multicoloured	70	1·10

(Des Y. Arakaki. Photo)

1972 (20 Apr). Philatelic Week. P 13½.

265	**218**	5c. multicoloured	55	1·10

The Ryukyu Islands were restored to Japanese Administration at
midnight 14/15 May 1972. Since then stamps of Japan have been
used in the islands.

Korea

1st printing   1st printing

5, 10 and 25p.   10p.   10p.

1st printing   1st printing   Later printings

25p   50p.

KOREAN EMPIRE

According to legend, the first Korean kingdom was founded in 2333 B.C., and Korean chronology still uses this starting point. Recorded history begins with the three kingdoms into which the country was divided from 57 B.C. to 668 A.D., when the Kingdom of Silla conquered the second of its rivals. Koryu, a minor state founded in 918, took control from Silla in 935 and in 1392 was in its turn overthrown by the founder of the Yi dynasty, which lasted until 1910. Japanese designs on Korea began with an invasion by Hideyoshi in 1592-98, during which Japanese sea-lines were cut by the ironclad "turtle ship" of Admiral Li Sun Sin. From 1637, when Korea was defeated by the Manchus, until 1895, it owed suzerainty to China. During this period it was a "hermit kingdom," till in 1876 it was forced to open diplomatic relations with Japan.

1884.	100 Mon = 1 Tempo
1895.	5 Poon = 1 Cheun
1900.	10 Re (or Rin) = 1 Cheun
	100 Cheun = 1 Weun

SURNAMES. We follow the usual Korean style of putting the surname first in proper names.

FORGERIES. Most stamps of the 1884-1903 period have been forged; the forgeries range from the very crude to the very deceptive.

I. KINGDOM OF CHO-SUN

King Kojong
15 January 1864–12 October 1897

1   2

(Des Saito Chuzo. Typo Stamp Bureau, Ministry of Finance. Tokyo)

1884 (18 Nov). P 8½ to 10 and compound.

1	1	5m. rose	£110	£6000
		a. Perf 11 or 11×11½	£180	
2	2	10m. blue	29·00	£4250
		a. Perf 11	£120	

On 4 to 7 December 1884 there was an attempted revolt, during which the P.O. at Seoul was burnt down and the Minister of Posts was killed. Genuinely used stamps are therefore very rare. The use of postage stamps was not resumed until 1895.

A 25m. orange, 50m. green and 100m. blue and pink, in similar types, were prepared for use but never issued as they were not delivered until after the postal service had ceased. They were subsequently sold in 1886 to a firm in Inchon (*price £18 each, un*).

New Currency

3 Korean Flag

GUM. Stamps in Type **3** are nearly always without gum and copies with gum are worth a very considerable premium over the unused prices quoted

Printing Differences

5p. The first printing is always distinguished by the distinct dot in the frame line above the centre of the scroll work above the value panel. The shade is different in later printings.

10p. The dot described above also applies to the first printing and is absent from later printings but sometimes thickening of the frame line may appear like a dot. Most copies of the first printing also show a small dot in the "E" or else a break in the bottom Korean character in the right- hand panel and these are not present in later printings. The shade differences are not very helpful.

25p. Again the dot in the frame line also distinguishes the first printing and in addition most copies also have a distinct coloured line in the right-hand frame lines by the upper corner ornament. The shades are also distinctive.

50p. The first printing is always distinguished by the absence of a stop after "50". This was added in later printings and varies in size from stamp to stamp. The shade is unchanged except that an additional deeper shade occurred in later printings.

(Litho A. B. Graham Bank Note Co, Washington)

1895–98. P 12 in Tokyo.

		(a) First printing (22.7.95)		
3	3	5p pale apple-green	90·00	30·00
		a. Imperf between (vert pair)	£475	
4		10p. deep bright blue	£170	45·00
5		25p. lake	£180	48·00
		a. Imperf between (vert pair)	£600	
		b. Imperf between (horiz pair)		£475
6		50p. slate-lilac	85·00	45·00
		(b) Later printings (1896-98)		
7	3	5p. green (shades)	32·00	19·00
		a. Imperf between (horiz pair)	£475	
		b. Imperf between (vert pair)	£475	
		c. Perf 13 (1898)	30·00	24·00
8		10p. blue (shades)	70·00	22·00
9		25p. rose-lake (shades)	75·00	30·00
		a. Imperf between (vert pair)	£425	£425
		b. Imperf between (horiz pair)	£425	£425
10		50p. slate-lilac (p 13)	27·00	16·00
		a. Deep slate-lilac	18·00	11·00
		b. Perf 12×13 and compound	90·00	90·00

II. EMPIRE OF TAI-HAN

Emperor Kwangmu
12 October 1897–17 July 1907

King Kojong declared Korea to be an empire, under the name of Tai-Han, on 12 October 1897, and was crowned Emperor on 17 October.

(4) Sub-type A (5)

As in the last issue, numerous varieties of the handstamp, Type **4**, exist.

Various forms of Type **5** may be found, with the Arabic "1" either sloping or vertical. Stamps of this issue also exist with Type **5** handstamped by local postmasters.

1897 (14 Oct). Typographed or handstamped as T **4** ("Tai-Han"), in Chinese at top and Korean at bottom. The two characters were sometimes applied separately. P 12.

A. In red

11A	**3**	5p. pale apple green (3)	£150	£100
12A		5p. green (7)	95·00	35·00
		a. Sub-type A	£250	£180
		b. Perf 13	95·00	35·00
13A		10p. blue (8)	£100	47·00
		a. Sub-type A		£180
14A		25p. rose-lake (9)	£110	48·00
		a Sub-type A	£375	£180
		b. Do. on No. 5		£325
15A		50p. slate-lilac (6)	£300	£190
		a. Sub-type A		£300
16A		50p. slate-lilac (p 10) (10)	95·00	45·00
		a. Sub-type A	£300	£180
		b. P 12×13 and comp		£190
		c. Vert pr P 7½ between	—	—

B. In black

11B	**3**	5p. pale apple green (3)	£11000	£300
12B		5p. green (7)	£325	£140
		b. Perf 13	£325	150
13B		10p. blue (8)	£300	£160
14B		25p. rose-lake (9)	£375	£225
15B		50p. slate-lilac (6)	£450	£325
16B		50p. slate-lilac (p 10) (10)	£350	£190
		b. P 12×13 and comp		£250
		c. Vert pr P 7½ between	—	—

When the supply of stamps overprinted by typography was exhausted, post offices were allowed to produce their own overprints. In the larger offices handstamps were used, of which four main types are known. In the handstamping process the bottom character was sometimes omitted, characters are found inverted or double and characters of different colours may be found on the same stamp; handstamps in brown were caused by change from a black to a red inkpad. In smaller offices the characters were written by brush; stamps with these handwritten characters are rare.

1899–1900. Previous issues surch as T **5**, by Ministry of Agriculture, Commerce and Industry. P 12.

(a) On stamps of 1895-98

17	**3**	1(p.) on 5p. pale apple green (3) (R.)		
		(4.00)	£2250	£900
18		1(p.) on 25p. rose-lake (9)	£500	£160

(b) On stamps of 1897 (handstamped T **4**, in red)

19	**3**	1(p.) on 5p. pale apple green (11) (R.)		
		(3.00)	£5500	3250
20		1(p.) on 5p. green (12) (R.) (3.00)	£950	£250
		a. Arabic "1" omitted	£1800	
		b. Roman "I" for "1"	£1100	£300
		c. Perf 13	£950	£250
21		1(p.) on 25p. rose-lake (14)	90·00	55·00
		a. Imperf between (horiz pair)		
		b. Roman "I" for "1"	£110	65·00
		c. Arabic "1" omitted	£1100	£375
		d. Korean numeral (right) omitted	£1100	£375
		e. Chinese numeral (left) omitted		
		f. Handstamped T **4** in black	£1500	£450

Varieties a/e are known to exist on No. 21f.

New Currency

6 7 8
National Emblems

(Des Chi Chang Han. Typo Printing Bureau, Ministry of Agriculture, Commerce and Industry, Seoul)

1900 (15 Jan)–**03**. T **6/8** and similar designs.

A. Perf 10

22A	2re. grey (7.7.00)	16·00	3·75
	a. Pale grey	6·00	2·20
23A	1ch. green (7.7.00)	16·00	5·25
24A	2ch. blue (T **7**) (15.1.00)	55·00	37·00
	a. Imp between (pr)	£550	
25A	2ch. blue (T **8**) (15.3.01)	50·00	48·00
26A	3ch. orange (15.1.00)	13·50	11·00
	a. Imp between (horiz pr)		£500
	b. Brownish orange	13·50	11·00
	ba. Imp between (vert pr)		£500
27A	4ch. carmine (5.7.00)	48·00	18·00
28A	5ch. pink (5.7.00)	21·00	9·50
29A	6ch. deep blue (5.7.00)	24·00	13 50
	a. Blue	26·00	15·00
30A	10ch. bright purple (15.3.01)	33·00	10·50
31A	15ch. grey-purple (1.10.00)	£160	£130
32A	20ch. Venetian red (15.11.00)	£300	£180

B. Perf 11–11½

22B	2re. grey (7.7.00)	9·50	3·00
	a. Pale grey	9·50	3·00
	b. Imp between (pr), ptd both sides		
23B	1ch. green (7.7.00)	11·00	5·25
24B	2ch. blue (T **8**) (15.3.01)	8·75	7·50
26B	3ch. orange (15.1.00)	13·50	8·00
	b. Brownish orange	13·50	8·00
27B	4ch. carmine (5.7.00)	34·00	15·00
28B	5ch. pink (5.7.00)	18·00	11·00
29B	6ch. deep blue (5.7.00)	19·00	12·50
30B	10ch. bright purple (15.3.01)	24·00	18·00
31B	15ch. grey-purple (1.10.00)	37·00	28·00
	a. Deep grey purple	37·00	28·00
32B	20ch. Venetian red (15.11.00)	55·00	41·00

C. Perf 11 (1.6.01)

33C	50ch. olive-green and pink	£275	£150
	d. Perf 12½ (thin paper) (6.03)	£225	
34C	1wn. blue, black, olive and red	£800	£225
	d. Perf 12½ (thin paper) (6.03)	£425	
35C	2wn. green and purple	£1300	£300
	d. Perf 12½ (thin paper) (6.03)	£650	

A number of other gauges of perforation have been reported such as 9½×10, 10×10½ , 10½ , 10½×10, 11×11½ , 11½ and 11½×11 but these may be due to irregularity of the pins in the main 10 and 11 perforators.

The 50ch. and 1 and 2wn. perf 12½ were intended for use pending the arrival of the 1903 definitive issue ordered from France but in the event the latter was placed on sale first. Some were used postally and the balance was withdrawn and later included in souvenir books prepared in 1905 and 1906 for presentation to diplomats, etc.

In 1906 the 6ch. was reprinted in chalky blue, perf. 12×13, for use in these books (Price £200 un).

9 Imperial Crown

(Eng by a Japanese engraver. Litho Printing Bureau, Ministry of Agriculture, Commerce and Industry, Seoul)

1902 (18 Oct). 40th Anniv of Emperor's Accession as King. P 11-11½.
36	**9**	3ch. orange		65·00	33·00

The Emperor succeeded to the throne in January 1864, so that the stamp was issued fifteen months prematurely

Imperforate examples come from presentation books (price £325 un).

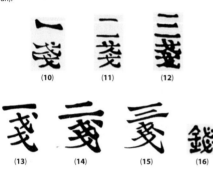

(10)   (11)   (12)

(13)   (14)   (15)   (16)

Types **10** to **15** are in two parts, the horizontal strokes (one, two or three) representing the value figures and the bottom part being the character for "cheun".

These were made from woodblocks, arranged in settings of 100, each block being slightly different. However, the value strokes can easily be divided into two main groups, one with short strokes set wide apart and the other with longer strokes set close together

1902 (Dec)–**03**. Stamps of previous issues surch by Printing Bureau, Ministry of Agriculture, Commerce and Industry. Seoul. P 12.

A. Wide surch as Types **10** to **12**
37A	1ch. on 25p. (9)	70·00	55·00
	a. Surch inverted	£180	—
	b. Imp between (vert pr)	£300	—
38A	1ch. on 25p. (14A)	£150	80·00
39A	2ch. on 25p. (9)	60·00	27·00
40A	2ch. on 25p. (14A)	95·00	75·00
41A	2ch. on 25p. (14B)	—	—
42A	2ch. on 50p. (10)	—	£475
	a. Surch inverted	£600	£600
44A	3ch. on 25p. (14A)	—	—
46A	3ch. on 50p. (10)	40·00	25·00
47A	3ch. on 50p. (16A)	75·00	55·00
	a. Sub-type A	—	—
48A	3ch. on 50p. (16B)	—	—

B. Narrow surch as Types **13** to **15**
37B	1ch. on 25p. (9)	22·00	7·50
38B	1ch. on 25p. (14A)	—	—
39B	2ch. on 25p. (9)	26·00	8·75
40B	2ch. on 25p. (14A)		65·00
41B	2ch. on 25p. (14B)	£375	£180
42B	2ch. on 50p. (10)		£475
43B	3ch. on 25p. (9)	65·00	£110
44B	3ch. on 25p. (14A)	—	—
45B	3ch. on 50p. (6)		£250
46B	3ch. on 50p. (10)	27·00	15·00
	a. P 12×13 and comp.	£190	£160
	b. Imp between (pr)	—	£225
47B	3ch. on 50p. (16A)	—	—
	a. Sub-type A		£300
48B	3ch. on 50p. (16B)	£225	£180

Surch with T **16** (Japanese "sen" character) and strokes
49	3ch. on 50p. slate-lilac (p 13) (10)	£1300	£650
	a. Surch inverted	£1700	£650

Manuscript surcharges were also made by brush in provincial post offices and these are very scarce.

17 Falcon, Sceptre and Orb

(Des E Clemencet. Typo French Govt Ptg Wks, Paris)

1903 (1 June). P 13½×14.
50	**17**	2 rin grey	12·50	5·00
51		1ch. brown-purple	13·00	6·50
52		2ch. green	13·50	6·50
53		3ch. orange	15·00	6·50
54		4ch. rose	22·00	7·25
55		5ch. cinnamon	23·00	8·50
56		6ch. lilac	27·00	10·00
57		10ch. blue	31·00	13·50
58		15ch. red/*yellow*	50·00	24·00
59		20ch. brown-purple/*yellow*	65·00	29·00
60		50ch. red/*green*	£190	£100
61		1wn. lilac/*pale lilac*	£350	£225
62		2wn. purple/*orange*	£450	£300
50/62		*Set of 13*	£1100	£650

By a treaty of 1 April 1905, the Korean postal service was taken over by Japan, and Japanese stamps came into use. The Emperor Sunjon, who succeeded his father on 20 July 1907, was forced to give up his throne and Korea was annexed by Japan on 29 August 1910, and became a Japanese colony, with the name of Chosen. In November 1942, Korea was made an integral part of the Japanese Empire.

After the defeat of Japan in August 1945, Russian and United States military administrations were set up in Korea to the North and south of the 38th Parallel respectively; in 1948 South Korea and North Korea became independent republics.

CHINESE POST OFFICES

In 1883 a German, P. G. von Möllendorf, was hired to organize a customs system and customs houses were established at Inchon, Pusan and Wonsan, with headquarters at Seoul. It is not certain when the Chinese Customs Post began operating a mail service from these houses but it was in existence by 1889 The service used unoverprinted Chinese Customs and Imperial stamps, using the following cancellations, although stampless mail is also known.

A

B
With or without lines above
and below date

C

D

FUSAN (Pusan). *Type* D
JENCHUAN (Inchon). *Types* A *and* C
SEOUL. *Type* A *and* B
YUENSAN (Wonsan). *As Type* A *but inscr* "CUSTOM HOUSE YUENSAN".

The postal service was discontinued about 1901.

JAPANESE POST OFFICES

Japanese post offices were opened at Pusan ("Fusan") on 10 November 1876, at Wonsan ("Gensan") in April 1880, at Chemulpo (now Inchon) ("Ninsen" or "Jinsen") in December 1883, at Seoul in July 1888 and in Mokpo in October 1897, and the stamps of Japan were on sale in them. Korean and Chinese money was accepted at par, but, as these currencies were over-valued, speculation ensued. To stop this, Japanese stamps were overprinted.

10 Rin = 1 Sen. 100 Sen = 1 Yen

社 明
(1)

1900 (1 Jan–1 Oct) Stamps of Japan of 1899-1900 optd with T **1**. P 11½–12.

1	28	5r. slate (R.)	18·00	15·00
		a. Perf 12½	£375	£110
2		1s. pale brown (R.)	22·00	10·50
		a. Perf 12½	55·00	22·00
3		1½s. pale ultramarine (1.10)	£350	£225
		a. Perf 12½	£300	£180
		b. Perf 13×13½		
4		2s. yellow-green (R.)	32·00	21·00
5		3s. dull maroon	21·00	8·00
		a. Perf 12½	60·00	18·00
6		4s. rosine	£100	50·00
		a. Perf 12½		
7		5s. orange-yellow (R.)	90·00	33·00
8	29	8s. olive (R.)	£350	£225
9		10s. deep blue	44·00	7·50
		a. Perf 12½	75·00	21·00
10		15s. purple	£110	10·50
11		20s. orange	£110	8·00
		a. Perf 12½	£150	26·00
12	30	25s. pale blue-green (R.)	£325	80·00
13		50s. brown	£200	27·00
14	31	1y. deep carmine	£550	16·00
		a. Perf 1 2½	£600	43·00

1900 (28 Apr). Wedding of Prince Imperial. No. 152 of Japan optd with T **1**. P 11½–12.

15	33	3s. carmine	£130	41·00
		a. Perf 12½	£140	80·00
		b. Perf 12×12½	£140	80·00

As Japanese money had by then become widely circulated in Korea, the overprinted stamps were withdrawn on 1 April 1901. The stamps of Japan were then used in Japanese post offices, and, from 1905 to 1946, at all post offices in Korea.

SOUTH KOREA

1946. 100 Cheun = 1 Weun
1953. 100 Weun = 1 Hwan
1962. 100 Chon = 1 Won

A. UNITED STATES MILITARY GOVERNMENT

United States troops landed in Korea on 8 September 1945 and
set up a Military Government of Korea south of the 38th Parallel. The
occupation force was withdrawn by 29 June 1949.
The stamps of Japan were in use until 30 June 1946.

36 Kyongju
Observatory   **37** Hibiscus   **38** Map of Korea

(31)   **33** National
Emblem   Wmk **81**
of Japan

39 Golden Crown
of Silla   **40** Admiral Li Sun
Sin   **41** Korean Alphabet

1946 (1 Feb). Stamps of Japan surch as T **31**.
69		5ch. on 5s. claret (396)	13·50	12·00
70		5ch. on 14s. lake and purple-brown (324)	2·50	3·00
		a. Error. 5ch. on 40s. purple (407)	£160	
71		10ch. on 40s. purple (407)	2·50	3·00
72		20ch. on 6s. ultramarine (397)	2·50	3·00
		a. Error. 20ch. on 27s. dull lake (404)	£160	
73		30ch. on 27s. dull lake (404)	2·50	3·00
		a. Error. 30ch. on 6s. (397)	90·00	
74		5w. on 17s. dull slate-violet (402)	13·50	12·00
69/74	Set of 6		33·00	32·00

IMPERFORATE STAMPS. In the following issues up to early 1955
most stamps exist imperforate and many also imperforate between
but there are so many that we have not attempted to list them.

(Des Kim Choong Hyeun. Litho Govt Printing Bureau. Japan)

1946 (1 May). Liberation from Japanese Rule. T **33** and similar vert
design. W **81** of Japan. P 10½.
75	–	3ch. dull orange	1·50	1·00
76	–	5ch. green	1·50	1·00
77	–	10ch. bright scarlet	1·50	1·00
78	–	20ch. royal blue	1·50	1·00
79	**33**	30ch. maroon	3·00	1·20
80		1w. yellow-brown	5·25	1·60
75/80	Set of 6		13·00	6·00
Design:—3ch. to 20ch., Family and flag.

34 Dove of Peace and
Map of Korea   **35** U.S. and Korean Flags

(Des Ryang Chae Hyeun. Typo Chung Kyo Sa Ptg Office)

1946 (15 Aug). First Anniv of Liberation. P 10½.
81	**34**	50ch. violet	10·00	4·00

(Des Oh Choong Whan. Typo Kyung Hwa Ptg Office)

1946 (9 Sept). Resumption of Postal Service between Korea and
U.S.A. P 11.
82	**35**	10w. scarlet	8·50	3·25

(Des Oh Choong Whan. Typo Kyung Hwa Ptg Office)

1946 (10 Sept–10 Nov). Roul 12.
83	**36**	50ch. blue (5.10)	1·80	1·50
84	**37**	1w. light brown (10.11)	2·20	1·90
		a. Perf 11	3·75	2·20
85	**38**	2w. indigo (5.10)	2·40	1·90
		a. Perf 11	£130	65·00
86	**39**	5w. magenta (5.10)	22·00	11·00
		a. Perf 11	£130	£110
		b. Bright carmine	22·00	11·00
87	**40**	10w. green	24·00	17·00
		a. Perf 11	£120	90·00
83/87	Set of 5		47·00	30·00
No gum, except for Nos. 84a and 86a, and No. 86b which exists
both with and without gum.

(Des Oh Choong Whan. Typo Kyung Hwa Ptg Office)

1946 (9 Oct). 500th Anniv of Creation of Korean Alphabet. P 10½.
88	**41**	50ch. blue	8·75	4·50

PRINTERS. Nos. 89 to 136 were lithographed by the Korea Books
Printing Co, *unless otherwise stated.*

42 Li Jun,
patriot   **43** Independence
Arch, Seoul   **44** 16th-century
"Turtle" Ship

(Des Oh Choong Whan)

1947 (1 Aug)–**48**. T **42** and similar portrait type and T **43/4**. W **81** of
Japan. P 11½×11.
89	**42**	5w. yellow-green	11·00	7·00
90	–	10w. light blue (Admiral Li Sun Sin)	11·00	7·00
		a. Perf 11½	11·00	7·00
91	**43**	20w. carmine (10.4.48)	7·50	3·75
92	**44**	50w. purple-brown (10.4.48)	£130	37·00
89/92	Set of 4		£140	49·00

45 Letters Surrounding Globe   **46** Douglas DC-4 Airliner

(Des Oh Choong Whan)

1947 (1 Aug). Resumption of International Postal Service. W **81** of Japan. P 11½×11.
93   **45**   10w. light blue...   17·00   7·25

(Des Kim Sun Yoo)

1947 (1 Oct). AIR. Inauguration of an Air Mail Service. W **81** of Japan. P 11½×11.
94   **46**   50w. carmine...   13·50   3·75
For 150w. values, see Nos. 126/7.

47 Hand and Ballot Slip   **48** Casting Votes

(Des Oh Choong Whan)

1948 (10 May). South Korea Election. W **81** of Japan. P 11×11½.
95   **47**   2w. orange...   20·00   6·50
96   5w. magenta...   33·00   10·00
97   10w. violet...   47·00   16·00
98   **48**   20w. carmine...   65·00   24·00
99   50w. blue...   47·00   21·00
95/99 Set of 5...   £190   70·00

49 Korean Flag and Laurel   **50** Capitol and Ears of Rice
Wreath

(Des Kim Yung Choo)

1948 (1 June). Olympic Games. T **49** and similar type. W **81** of Japan. P 11×11½ (vert) or 11½×11 (horiz).
100   **49**   5w. deep green...   £150   55·00
101   10w. violet...   65·00   20·00
Design: Vert—10w. Runner with torch.

MINIATURE SHEETS. Many of the stamps from 1948 to 1956 exist in miniature sheets from limited printings which were presented to postal and government officials.

(Des Song Chung Hoon)

1948 (1 July). Meeting of First National Assembly. W **81** of Japan. P 11½×11 or 11½.
102   **50**   4w. red-brown...   27·00   10·50

51 Korean Family   **52** Dr. Syngman Rhee
                (First President)

(Des Kim Yung Choo)

1948 (1 Aug). Promulgation of Constitution. T **51** and similar type. W **81** of Japan. P 11½ .
103   4w. green...   £120   30·00
104   10w. brown...   50·00   19·00
Design: Horiz—10w. Flag of Korea.

(Des Kim Yung Choo)

1948 (5 Aug). Election of First President. W **81** of Japan. P 11½.
105   **52**   5w. deep blue...   £400   £130

B. REPUBLIC OF KOREA

A Republic was proclaimed in South Korea on 15 August 1948.

53 Hibiscus   **54** Li Jun   **55** Kyongju
                    Observatory

Two Types of 5w.
I.   Blurred impression. Top inscr 9mm wide; "1948" 3 mm wide; stops in "8.15." hardly visible.
II.   Clear impression with inscriptions redrawn: top inscr 9½ mm, "1948" 4 mm and stops bold and clear.

(Des Kim Yung Choo (4w.) or Eom Do Man (5w.))

1948 (15 Aug). Proclamation of Republic. T **53** and similar design. W **81** of Japan (sideways). P 11×11½.
106   4w. light blue...   50·00   24·00
107   5w. magenta (I)...   90·00   30·00
        a. Type (II)...   £300   £100
Design: Vert.— 4w. Dove and olive branch.

(Des Kim Yung Choo)

1948 (1 Oct)-**49**. W **81** of Japan. P 11.
108   **54**   4w. carmine...   1·50   1·10
109   **55**   14w. deep blue...   1·50   1·10
        a. Pale blue (1949)...   £200   42·00

347

56 Doves and UN Emblem   **57** Citizen and Date

(Des Li Ki Wan)

1949 (12 Feb). Arrival of United Nations Commission. W **81** of Japan. P 11.

110	**56**	10w. blue	60·00	18·00

(Des Li Ki Wan. Litho Koryu Moonhwa Ptg Co)

1949 (25 Apr). National Census. W **81** of Japan P 11.

111	**57**	15w. violet	75·00	21·00

58 Children and Plant

(Des Li Ki Wan. Litho Koryu Moonhwa Ptg Co)

1949 (5 May). 20th Anniv of Children's Day. W **81** of Japan. P 11.

112	**58**	15w. violet	44·00	11·00

59 Hibiscus   **60** Map of Korea and Magpies

61 Dove and Globe   **62** Admiral Li Sun Sin

(Des Eom Do Man (15w.), Kim Chul Woo (65, 200w.), Pak Yung Ki (400w.), Pak Choon Kyo (500w.), Kim Yung Choo (others). Litho Koryu Moonhwa Ptg Co (2, 5, 20, 50, 100w.), Korea Books Ptg Co (15, 65, 200, 400, 500w.) or both (1, 10, 30w.))

1949 (7 June-1 Dec). As T **59/62** (various designs). W **81** of Japan. P 10½ x 11½.

113		1w. rose-red	7·75	3·25
114		2w. slate-grey (1.7)	6·75	2·75
115		5w. yellow-green (1.7)	27·00	7·50

116		10w. turquoise-green (1.7)	3·00	1·10
117		15w. scarlet (1.12)	1·10	1·00
118		20w. brown (1.7)	1·50	1·00
119		30w. turquoise-green (1.7)	1·50	1·00
120		50w. violet-blue (1.7)	1·50	1·00
121		65w. blue (1.12)	2·50	1·90
122		100w. olive-green	1·50	1·00
123		200w. emerald-green (1.10)	1·10	1·00
124		400w. brown (1.10)	1·10	1·00
125		500w. deep blue (1.10)	1·10	1·00
113/125 *Set of 13*			50·00	22·00

Designs: Vert. (as T **59**)—1w. Postman; 2w. Worker and factory; 5w. Harvesting rice; 10w. Manchurian cranes; 20w. Diamond Mts.; 30w. Ginseng plant; 50w. South Gate, Seoul; 100w. Tabo Pagoda, Kyongju Horiz (31½×19½mm)—400w. Diamond Mts.

1949 (7 June). AIR. Redrawn. Lines of shading wider apart. W **81** of Japan. P 11.

126	**46**	150w. blue	3·75	1·50
		a. Error "KORFA"	30·00	30·00
127		150w. green	22·00	13·00

No. 126a. occurs on stamp No. 34 in the sheet of 50.

The printing in green was the result of an official error; it was decided to issue stamps of both colours at the same time.

This issue of regular air stamps was released on the occasion of the first air mail service to the United States.

63 Symbol and Phoenix   **64** Steam Train

(Des Kim Wook. Litho Koryu Moonhwa Ptg Co)

1949 (25 Aug). First Anniv of Independence. W **81** of Japan. P 11.

128	**63**	15w. deep blue	60·00	13·50

(Des Kim Wook)

1949 (18 Sept). Fiftieth Anniv of Korean Railways. W **81** of Japan. P 11 or 11½×11.

129	**64**	15w. ultramarine	£160	37·00

65 Korean Flag   **66** Post-horse Warrant

(Des Kim Wook)

1949 (15 Oct). 75th Anniv of Universal Postal Union. Flag in national colours. W **81** of Japan (sideways). P 11½.

130	**65**	15w. deep blue, red & greenish yellow	33·00	15·00

Unwatermarked stamps are forgeries.

1950 (1 Jan). 50th Anniv of Korea's Membership of Universal Postal Union. W **81** of Japan P 11×11½ (15w.) or 11½×11 (65w.).

131	**66**	15w. yellow-green	50·00	15·00
132		65w. red-brown	22·00	7·50

67 Douglas DC-2 Airplane and Globe   **68** Demonstrators   **69** Capitol, Seoul

(Des Kim Sun Yoo)

1950 (1 Jan). AIR. Opening of Internal Air Mail Service. W **81** of Japan. P 11 or 11×11½.

133	**67**	60w. pale blue	37·00	7·50

1950 (10 Mar). 31st Anniv of Abortive Proclamation of Independence. W **81** of Japan. P 11½×11.

134	**68**	15w. olive green	48·00	15·00
135		65w. pale violet	22·00	6·00

1950 (30 May). Second South Korean Election. W **81** of Japan. P 11.

136	**69**	30w. black, green, scarlet and blue	30·00	6·75

70 Dr. Syngman Rhee   **71** Flag and Mountains

(Litho Tongyang Chungpan Ptg Co)

1950 (20 Nov). Unification of Korea. Various designs. W **81** of Japan P 11.

137	**70**	100w. light blue	7·50	3·00
138	**71**	100w. yellow-green	9·50	3·00
139	–	200w. deep green	6·75	2·20
137/139	*Set of* 3		21·00	7·50

Design: Horiz (35×24 mm)—200w. Map of Korea and flags of United Nations and Korea.

This issue was made when U.N. troops were in occupation of most of North Korea, before Chinese intervention forced them to retreat.

73 Manchurian Crane   **74** Astrological Tiger (ancient painting)

75 Dove and Korean Flag   **76** Post-horse Warrant   **77** "Fairy" (8th century painting)

(Des Pak Mun Cho (1000w.), Choe Chung Han (others). Litho. Tongyang Chungpan Ptg Co)

1951 (1 Apr–1 July). No wmk. P 11.

140	**73**	5w. brown	3·25	2·20
		a. Roul 12½	1·80	1·80
141	**74**	20w. violet	4·00	3·00
		a. Roul 12½	1·80	1·80
142	**75**	50w. green	30·00	16·00
		a. Roul 12½	6·00	4·50
143	**76**	100w. blue	50·00	16·00
		a. Roul 12½	8·75	4·50
144	**77**	1000w. green (1.7)	60·00	15·00
140/144	*Set of* 5 (cheapest)		70·00	25·00

The 5 and 20w. were issued with and without gum, the 50 to 1000w. with gum and the rouletted stamps without gum.

See also Nos. 181/94.

(78)   (79)

1951 (5 June-3 Dec). Various stamps surcharged.

(a) With T **78**

145	100w. on 4w. carmine (108) (B.)	6·25	3·75
	a. Surch inverted	50·00	

(b) As T **79** (slanting figures)

146	200w. on 15w. scarlet (117) (B.)	12·00	5·75
	a. Surch inverted	50·00	
147	300w. on 4w. carmine (108) (B.) (3.12)	4·75	3·75
	a. Surch inverted	42·00	
148	300w. on 10w. turquoise-green (116) (Br.) (3.12)	13·50	4·00
	a. Surch inverted	50·00	
149	300w. on 14w. deep blue (109) (Br.) (3.12)	9·50	3·75
	a. Surch inverted	50·00	
	b. Pale blue (110a)	£3500	£900
150	300w. on 15w. scarlet (117) (B.) (3.12)	4·75	3·75
	a. Surch inverted	50·00	
151	300w. on 20w. brown (118) (B.)	6·00	4·50
	a. Surch inverted	70·00	
152	300w. on 30w. turquoise-green (119) (Br.) (3.12)	4·75	3·75
	a. Surch inverted	50·00	
153	300w. on 50w. violet-blue (120) (Br.) (3.12)	4·50	3·25
154	300w. on 65w. blue (121) (Br.) (3.12)	5·00	3·75
155	300w. on 100w. olive-green (122) (B.) (3.12)	4·75	3·00
	a. Surch inverted	70·00	

(c) As T **79** but upright figures

156	300w. on 10w. turquoise-green (116) (Br.)	14·00	5·25
	a. Surch inverted	90·00	—
157	300w. on 50w. violet-blue (120) (Br.)	£130	15·00

The surcharges on Nos. 145 and 156/7 were both lithographed and typographed; those on Nos. 146 and 151 were lithographed only; other surcharges were typographed only. Varieties of surcharge occur.

80 Statue of Liberty and Flags

(No. 169 des Nam Ki Hi. Others des Pak Mun Cho. Litho Tongyang Chungpan Ptg Co)

1951 15 Sept)–**52**. Participation in Korean War. T **80** and similar design. Flags in national colours. W **81** of Japan. P 11x10.

A. Type **80** in bright emerald
B. Similar design but showing U.N. Emblem and doves, in blue
(Same prices for unused or used)

	Inscriptions	A	B
158	500w. Australia	12·00	10·50
159	500w. Belgium	12·00	10·50
160	500w. Britain	12·00	10·50
161	500w. Canada	12·00	10·50
162	500w. Colombia	12·00	10·50
163	500w. Denmark (25.10.51)	60·00	37·00
164	500w. Ethiopia	12·00	10·50
165	500w. France	12·00	10·50
166	500w. Greece	12·00	10·50
167	500w. India (25.10.51)	50·00	37·00
168	500w. Italy (with crown) (25.10.51)	60·00	44·00
169	500w. Italy (without crown) (10.2.52)	13·50	22·00
170	500W. Luxembourg (25.10.51)	50·00	37·00
171	500w. Netherlands	12·00	10·50
172	500w. New Zealand	12·00	10·50
173	500w. Norway (25.10.51)	50·00	37·00
174	500w. Philippines	12·00	10·50
175	500w. Sweden	12·00	10·50
176	500w. Thailand	12·00	10·50
177	500w. Turkey	12·00	10·50
178	500w. Union of South Africa (inscr 14 mm)	12·00	10·50
	a. Inscription 15 8 mm.		
179	500w. U.S.A.	10·50	8·75
158/179A/B	Set of 44	£425	£350

(81)

82 Buddha of Sokkuram

83 Pulguksa Temple. Kyongju

84 Monument to King Muryol. Kyongju

85 Shrine of Admiral Li Sun Sin, Tongyong

1951 (15 Nov). AIR. No. 126 surch with T **81**.

180	**46**	500w. on 150w. blue	10·50	3·75
		a. Surch inverted	£110	
		b. Error. "KORFA"	60·00	50·00
		ba. Surch inverted		

(T **82/5** des Pak Mun Cho. Litho)

1952–53. W **81** of Japan.

(a) Ptd by Tongyang Chungpan Ptg Co. 200w. size 20×24 mm, others 19½×23½ or 23½×19½ mm. Rough perf 10 to11 and compound

181	**74**	20w. violet	3·75	3·00
182	**75**	50w. green	50·00	22·00
183	**76**	100w. blue	4·50	1·50
184	**82**	200w. brown-red (22.2.52)	3·75	1·50
185	**83**	300w. emerald (22.2.52)	3·00	75
186	**77**	1000w. green	£300	27·00

(b) Ptd by Korean Govt Pig Agency Size 20×24½ mm. P 12½.

187	**75**	50w. green (9.52)	5·50	2·50
188	**78**	100w. blue (9.52)	3·25	1·80
189	**82**	200w. brown-red (9.52)	2·50	1·10
190	**83**	300w. emerald (9.52)	4·50	1·10
191	**84**	500w. carmine-red (22.10.52)	5·25	1·50

192		500w. deep blue (1953)	44·00	£150
193	**77**	1000w. green (7.52)	11·00	75
194	**85**	2000w. deep blue (22.10.52)	3·75	75
181/194		Set of 14	£400	£190

Nos. 187/90 and 193 are slightly re-drawn versions of Nos. 142, 143 (or 183), 184, 185 and 144 (or 186).

No. 192 was only sold affixed to postcards, so is not found with gum intact.

See also Nos. 200/1, 205, 245 and 271.

PRINTERS. The following issues were printed by the Korean Government Printing Agency, *unless otherwise stated*. Issues to Nos. **MS**784 were all produced by lithography.

86 President Syngman Rhee

87 Douglas DC-3 Airplane over Freighter

(Des Kang Bak)

1952 (10 Sept). President's Election to Second Term of Office. W **81** of Japan. P 12½.

195	**86**	1000w. deep bluish green	13·50	7·50

(Des Pak Mun Cho)

1952 (15 Oct). AIR. W **81** of Japan. P 12½.

196	**87**	1200w. purple-brown	2·50	75
197		1800w. bright turquoise-blue	2·50	75
198		4200w. bright violet	6·50	1·00
196/198		Set of 3	10·50	2·30

See also Nos. 210/2.

New Currency

88 Tree-planting

89 Monument to King Muryol. Kyongju

90 *Metopta rectifasciata* (moth) and Korean Flag

91 Pagoda Park, Seoul

92 Sika Deer

93 Sika Deer

(Des Hwang Tong Han (**88**). Pak Mun Cho (**89**). Kang Ho Suk (**90**, **92**). Kang Bak (**91**, **93**))

1953 (5 Apr)–**55**. W **81** of Japan (sideways on vert designs). P 12½.

199	**88**	1h. turquoise-blue	1·50	60
200	**84**	2h. turquoise-blue	1·90	40
201		5h. emerald	2·30	40
202	**89**	5h. myrtle green (19.10.55)	2·75	1·20
203	**88**	10h. emerald	7·00	1·40
204	**80**	10h. bistre-brown (16.4.54)	11·00	1·90
205	**86**	20h. dull orange-brown	8·00	1·50
206	**91**	30h. deep blue (16.4.54)	2·30	1·40

207	**92**	100h. lake-brown (1.4.54)	17·00	2·75
208	**93**	500h. orange (1.4.54)	85·00	5·50
209		1000h. yellow-brown (1.4.54)	£200	6·25
199/209 *Set of* 11			£300	21·00

See also Nos. 242/51, 270/88 and 308/20.

1953 (5 Apr) AIR. Colours changed and new currency. W **81** of Japan P 12½.

210	**87**	12h. deep blue	3·00	65
211		18h. deep reddish violet	3·75	75
212		42h. deep bluish green	4·50	1·20
210/212 *Set of* 3			10·00	2·30

94 Field Hospital   **95** YMCA Badge and Map

(Des Hwang Tong Han)

1953 (1 Aug). Red Cross Fund. T **94** and vert design. Crosses in red. W **81** of Japan (sideways on No. 213). P 13½.

213	**94**	10h. +5h. blue-green	17·00	4·75
214	–	10h. +5h. blue	17·00	4·75

Design . — No. 214, Nurse supporting wounded soldier.

(Des Kang Bak)

1953 (25 Oct). 50th Anniv of Korean Young Men's Christian Association. W **81** of Japan. P 13½.

215	**95**	10h. orange-red and blue-black	11·00	3·75

96 Douglas DC-6   **97** Rocks off Airliner over East Gate, Seoul   **98** Tokto Island Tokto Island

(Des Kang Bak)

1954 (1 July). AIR. W **81** of Japan. P 12½.

216	**96**	25h. brown	6·25	1·40
217		35h. bright reddish purple	6·25	1·60
218		38h. green	6·25	1·80
219		58h. chalky blue	6·25	2·00
220		71h. deep blue	15·00	2·40
216/220 *Set of* 5			36·00	8·25

See also Nos. 258/60 and 296/8.

(Des Kang Ho Suk)

1954 (15 Sept). W **81** of Japan. P 12½ .

221	**97**	2h. reddish purple	3·75	2·30
222		8h. blue	8·25	2·30
223	**98**	10h. bright blue-green	12·00	2·30
221/223 *Set of* 3			22·00	6·25

99 Erosion Control   **100** Presidents Syngman Rhee and Eisenhower

(Des Li Keun Hong)

1954 (12 Dec). Fourth World Forestry Congress, Dehra Dun, India. W **81** of Japan. P 12½.

224	**99**	10h. pale green and green	7·00	1·20
225		19h. pale green and green	7·00	1·90

(Des Kang Bak)

1954 (25 Dec). Korea— United States Mutual Defence Treaty. W **81** of Japan (sideways). P 13½.

226	**100**	10h. violet-blue	5·00	1·50
227		19h. brown	5·50	1·50
228		71h. grey-green	9·25	2·30
226/228 *Set of* 3			18·00	4·75

101 "Rebirth of Industry"   I Original   II Redrawn

(Des Chung Sung Cha)

1955 (10 Feb)–**56**. Reconstruction. P 12½.

I. Top right-hand character as I

A. W **81** of Japan (10.2.55)

229A	**101**	10h. brown	5·50	2·75
230A		15h. violet	5·50	2·75
231A		20h. pale blue	£1100	19·00
232A		50h. magenta	15·00	1·50

B. No wmk. Yellowish laid paper (19.10.55)

230B	**101**	15h. violet	5·00	90
231B		20h. pale blue	5·00	95
232B		50h. magenta	9·50	1·30

Nos. 230/2B are on vertically laid paper; No. 231B also exists on horizontally laid paper.

II. Top right-hand character as II

No wmk. Vert or horiz laid white paper (5.6.56)

233	**101**	10h. brown	6·25	2·30
234		15h. violet	6·25	2·30
235		20h. pale Blue	6·25	75
		a. Booklet pane of six	£160	
233/235 *Set of* 3			17·00	4·75

The booklet pane has a margin around the block of stamps. See also Nos. 268/9a.nd 328/9.

102 Rotary Emblem   **103** President Syngman Rhee   **104** Independence Arch, Seoul

(T **102/4** des Kang Bak)

1955 (23 Feb). 50th Anniv of Rotary International. W **81** of Japan.
P 13½.

236	**102**	20h. violet......................................	9·25	2·75
237	**102**	25h. deep bluish green...........................	4·75	1·50
238		71h. bright purple	4·75	1·50
236/238	Set of 3		17·00	5·25

1955 (26 Mar). 80th Birthday of President. W **81** of Japan. P 13½.

239	**103**	20h. blue..	27·00	7·75

1955 (15 Aug). Tenth Anniv of Liberation. W **81** of Japan. P 13½.

240	**104**	40h. turquoise-green	11·50	1·90
241		100h. red-brown...............................	11·50	2·75

105 Hibiscus   **106** King Sejong   **107** Kyongju
                                                        Observatory

(T **105/7** des Kang Bak)

1955 (19 Oct)–**56**. No wmk. Laid paper P 12½.

(a) Top right-hand character as I. Yellowish paper

242	**92**	100h. brown-purple	75·00	6·25
243	**91**	200h. violet (1.11.55)	15·00	2·30

(b) Top right-hand character as II. White paper

244	**88**	1h. light blue (1.6.56)	70	45
245	**84**	2h. light blue (1.6.56)	80	45
246	**89**	5h. emerald (10.6.56)	80	35

(c) Character as II. No character "hwan" after figure of value. White
paper (4.12.56)

247	**105**	10h. deep magenta...........................	1·80	70
248	**106**	20h. purple.......................................	3·50	70
249	**107**	50h. slate-violet...............................	4·00	70
250	**92**	100h. brown-purple	28·00	4·00
251	**93**	500h. yellow-brown	70·00	4·75
242/251	Set of 10		£180	19·00

The Type I and Type II characters are illustrated after No. 228.
Nos. 242/3 and 249/51 exist on vertically laid paper only; No. 245
on horizontally laid only; and Nos. 244 and 246/8 on both kinds. Nos.
247/8a.re very scarce on the horizontally laid paper.
See also Nos. 270/88 and 308/20.

108 Runners and   **109** UN Emblem
Torch

(T **108/9** des Kang Bak)

1955 (23 Oct). 36th National Athletic Meeting. W **81** of Japan. P 13½.

252	**108**	20h. brown-purple	7·00	1·90
253		55h. deep grey-green	7·00	1·90

1955 (24 Oct). Tenth Anniv of United Nations. W **81** ofJapan. P 13½.

254	**109**	20h. deep turquoise-green	5·50	1·50
255		55h. light blue....................................	5·50	1·50

110 Admiral Li Sun Sin and   **111** Admiration
16th-century "Turtle" Ship   Pagoda

(T **110/1** des Kang Bak)

1955 (11 Nov). Tenth Anniv of Korean Navy. No wmk. Vert. laid paper.
P 13½.

256	**110**	20h. violet blue...............................	10·50	2·50

1956 (26 Mar). 81st Birthday of President. No wmk. Vert. laid paper.
P 13½.

257	**111**	20h. deep bluish green...............................	7·75	2·20

1956 (20July). AIR. Right-hand character in bottom inscr as II. No
wmk. Vert or horiz laid paper. P 12½.

258	**96**	70h. deep turquoise-green......................	11·50	3·75
259		110h. brown.......................................	11·50	3·75
260		205h. deep magenta...........................	19·00	3·75
258/260	Set of 3		38·00	10·00

The Type I and Type II characters are illustrated after No. 228.

112 President   **113** Torch and
Syngman Rhee   Olympic Rings

(Des Kang Bak)

1956 (15 Aug). President's Election to Third Term of Office. No wmk.
P 13½.

261	**112**	20h. deep brown	£120	27·00
262		55h. deep violet-blue......................................	55·00	11·50

(Des Min Chul Hong)

1956 (1 Nov). Olympic Games. No wmk. Vert laid paper. P 12½.

263	**113**	20h. red-brown....................................	6·25	2·30
264		55h. blue-green....................................	6·25	2·30

114 Central P.O., Seoul   **115**

(Des Kang Bak)

1956 (4 Dec). Stamp Day. T **114** and vert designs inscr "4289.12.4". No wmk. Laid paper, vert on 50h., horiz on others. P 12½.

265		20h. turquoise green	15·00	2·75
266		50h. rose	23·00	4·75
267		55h. grey-green	11·50	1·90
265/267	*Set of 3*		45·00	8·50

Designs: Vert.— 50h. Stamp of 1884. Horiz—55h. Man leading post-pony.

1957. Reconstruction. Top right hand character as II. W **115**. P 12½.

268	**101**	15h. violet (21.1)	7·25	75
269		50h. carmine-red (25.6)	9·25	1·90

MINIATURE SHEETS. Beginning in 1957 miniature sheets were put on sale at post offices. Miniature sheets of earlier issues were intended only for presentation purposes.

116 South Gate, Seoul

117 Tiger

118 Haegumgang

(T **116/8** des Min Chul Hong)

1957. W **115** (sideways on horiz designs). P 12½.

(a) With character for "hwan" after figure of value

270	**88**	1h. light blue (22.2)	95	40
271	**84**	2h. light blue (22.2)	1·20	40
272	**89**	5h. emerald (27.2)	1·20	40

(b) No. character after figure of value

273	**88**	2h. light blue (15.6)	75	40
274	**89**	4h. light blue (25.6)	1·20	40
275		5h. emerald (25.6)	1·20	40
276	**105**	10h. deep magenta (22.2)	2·75	60
277	**116**	10h. green (25.6)	1·30	10
278	**106**	20h. purple (21.1)	6·50	1·20
279	**105**	20h. deep magenta (25.6)	1·50	40
280	**117**	30h. reddish violet (5.7)	1·50	40
281	**106**	40h. purple (15.6)	1·70	30
		a. Booklet pane of 6·00	£225	
282	**107**	50h. slate-violet (21.1)	9·25	60
283	**118**	65h. brown-purple (5.7)	3·75	1·50
284	**107**	100h. slate-violet (15.6)	4·25	45
285	**92**	200h. brown-purple (15.6)	5·00	45
286	**91**	400h. bright violet (5.7)	75·00	4·75
287	**93**	500h. yellow-brown (5.7)	75·00	6·50
288		1000h. bistre-brown (5.7)	£150	11·50
270/288	*Set of 19*		£300	28·00

MS289 Set of 10 sheets (110×83 mm) each, with one of Nos. 273/4, 277, 279/81, 283/6. Imperf. No gum £1100
No. 281a. has an imperforate frame around the block of stamps.
See also Nos. 308/20.

119 ITU Emblem and Radio Mast

120 Korean Scout and Badge

(T **119/20** des Kang Bak)

1957 (31 Jan). Fifth Anniv of Korea's Admission to the International Telecommunications Union. W **115**. P 13½.

290	**119**	40h. blue	3·00	1·30
291		55h. emerald	3·00	1·30
MS292 110×83 mm. Nos. 290/1. Imperf. No gum			£950	

1957 (27 Feb). 50th Anniv of Boy Scout Movement. W **115**. P 13½.

293	**120**	40h. purple	2·75	1·30
294		55h. reddish purple	2·75	1·30
MS295 110×83mm. Nos. 293/4. Imperf.			£3250	

1957 (22 Mar). AIR Right hand character in bottom inscr as II. W **115**. P 12½.

296	**96**	70h. deep turquoise-green	14·00	3·75
297		110h. brown	14·00	3·75
298		205h. deep magenta	19·00	3·75
296/298	*Set of 3*		42·00	10·25

The Type I and Type II characters are illustrated after No. 228.

121 King Sejong

122 Ministry of Communications Symbol

1957 (1 Sept). Pusan Flood Relief Fund. W **115**. P 12½.

299	**121**	40h. +10h. blue-green	11·50	2·30
		b. Wmk **122**	11·50	2·30
MS300 110×84 mm. Nos. 299. Imperf. No gum			£250	

The design is as Type **106** with premium and inscription added.

123 Mercury, Flags and Freighters

124 Star of Bethlehem and Pine Cone

(Des Kang Bak)

1957 (7 Nov). Korean-American Treaty of Friendship. W **115**. P 13½.

301	**123**	40h. orange	2·30	85
302		205h. emerald	4·75	1·70
MS303 110×84 mm. Nos. 301/2. Imperf. No gum			£1700	

(Des Mim Chul Hong)

1957 (11 Dec). Christmas and New Year. T **124** and similar designs. W **115**. P 12½.

304		15h. brown, green and orange	11·00	1·90
305		25h. green, red and yellow	11·00	1·90
306		30h. blue, green and yellow	22·00	2·75
304/306	*Set of 3*		40·00	6·00
MS307 Three sheets each 90×60 mm. Nos. 304/6. Imperf.			£3750	

Designs: Christmas tree and —25h. Tassels; 30h. Dog by window.

1957 (18 Dec)–**59**. W **122** (sideways on veil designs). No character after figure of value. P 12½.

308	**88**	1h. light blue	75	40
309	**89**	4h. light blue	1·20	40
310		5h. emerald (20.11.58)	1·20	40
311	**116**	10h. green	1·50	40
312	**105**	20h. deep magenta	2·10	30

313	**117**	30h. reddish violet (15.8.58)	2·30	30
314	**106**	40h. purple	2·30	30
315	**118**	55h. brown-purple (20.9.59)	3·25	75
316	**107**	100h. slate-violet	4·00	40
317	**92**	200h. brown-purple (20.11.59)	4·75	40
318	**91**	400h. bright violet (20.11.59)	£110	3·00
319	**93**	500h. yellow-brown (15.12.58)	95·00	3·00
320		1000h. bistre-brown (15.12.58)	£170	7·75
308/320	*Set of 13*		£350	16·00

For Nos. 311/4 in miniature sheet, see No. **MS**338.

125 Winged Letter

126 Korean Children regarding Future

129 Rejoicing Crowds in Pagoda Park, Flag and Torch

130 Marines going Ashore from Landing craft

(T **129**/30 des Kang Bak)

1959 (1 Mar). 40th Anniv of Abortive Proclamation of Independence. W **122**. P 13½.

334	**129**	40h. reddish purple and chocolate	1·50	60
MS335		90×60 mm. No. 334. Imperf.	£140	£130

(Des Min Chul Hong)

1958 (20 May). Postal Week. W **122**. P 12½.

321	**125**	40h. deep blue and red	2·30	75
MS322		90×60 mm. No. 321. Imperf.	£2250	

1959 (15 Apr). 10th Anniv of Korean Marine Corps. W **122**. P 13½.

336	**130**	40h. bronze-green	1·50	60
MS337		90×60 mm. Nos. 336 Imperf.	15·00	12·50

1959 (20 May). Third Postal Week. Sheet containing Nos. 311/4. Imperf.

MS338	70×105 mm.	11·50	10·50

(Des Kang Bak)

1958 (15 Aug). Tenth Anniv of Republic. T **126** and similar vert design inscr "4291-8-15". W **122**. P 13½.

323		20h. grey	1·90	60
324		40h. carmine-red	2·75	85
MS325	110×84 mm. Nos. 323/4. Imperf.		£550	£500

Design:—40h. Hibiscus flowers forming figure "10".

131

132 Diesel Train

(T **131**/2 des Kang Bak)

1959 (17 Aug). 10th Anniv of Korea's Admission to World Health Organization. W **122**. P 13½.

339	**131**	40h. purple and pink	1·50	60
MS340		90×60 mm. No. 339. Imperf.	13·00	10·50

1959 (18 Sept). 60th Anniv of Korean Railways. W **122**. P 13½.

341	**132**	40h. sepia and yellow-brown	2·50	1·00
MS342		90×60 mm. No. 341. Imperf.	31·00	25·00

127 UNESCO Headquarters, Paris

128 Children flying Kites

(Des Kang Bak)

1958 (3 Nov). Inauguration of United Nations Educational, Scientific and Cultural Organization Headquarters, Paris. W 22. P 13½.

326	**127**	40h. brown-orange and deep green	1·50	55
MS327		90×60 mm. No. 326 Imperf.	225·00	200·00

1958 (20 Nov–15 Dec). Reconstruction. Top right hand character as I.I. W **122**. P 12½.

328	**101**	15h. violet	6·25	2·30
329		50h. carmine-red (15.12)	11·50	75

133 Runners in Relay Race

134 Red Cross and Korea

(Des Kang Choon Whan)

1959 (3 Oct). 40th Korean National Games. W **122**. P 13½.

343	**133**	40h. brown and pale blue	1·70	70
MS344		90×60 mm. No. 343. Imperf.	19·00	17·00

(Des Kang Bak)

1958 (11 Dec). Christmas and New Year. T **128** and similar designs. W **122**. P 12½.

330		15h. emerald green	2·30	75
331		25h. red. yellow and blue	2·30	75
332		30h. red, ultramarine and yellow	3·75	1·20
330/332	*Set of 3*		7·50	2·40
MS333	Three sheets each 90×60 mm. Nos. 330/2. Imperf.		£250	£250

Designs: — 25h. Christmas tree, tassels and wicker basket (cooking sieve); 30h. Children in traditional festive costume.

(Des Kang Bak)

1959 (27 Oct). Red Cross. T **134** and similar horiz design inscr "1959 4292". W **122**. P 13½.

345		40h. red and blue-green	1·50	45
346		55h. carmine red and mauve	1·50	45
MS347	110×60 mm. Nos. 345/6. Imperf.		42·00	38·00

Design:— 55h. Red Cross on Globe.

135 Korean Postal Flags Old and New

136 Mice in Korean Costume and New Year Emblem

(Des Kang Choon Whan)

1959 (4 Dec). 75th Anniv of Korean Postal Service. W **122**. P 13½.
348   **135**   40h. red and blue.................................... 1·50   55
MS349 90×60 mm. Nos. 348. Imperf............................ 23·00 21·00

(Des Kang Choon Whan)

1959 (15 Dec). Christmas and New Year. T **136** and similar vert designs. W **122**. P 12½.
350   15h. pink, deep blue and grey.................. 1·50   35
351   25h. red, yellow-green and blue.............. 1·50   40
352   30h. red, black and mauve...................... 3·00   50
350/352 *Set of 3*.. 5·50   1·10
MS353 Three sheets each 90×60 mm. Nos. 350/2.
   Imperf.. 95·00 85·00
Designs:— 25h. Carol singers; 30h. Crane.

137 UPU Monument

138 Honey Bee and Clover

(Des Kang Choon Whan)

1960 (1 Jan). 60th Anniv of Admission of Korea to Universal Postal Union. W **122**. P 13½.
354   **137**   40h. chocolate and turquoise-blue......... 1·90   75
MS355 90×60 mm. No. 354. Imperf............................ 39·00 35·00

(Des Kang Bak (10h.). La Boo Yung (20h.))

1960 1 Apr). Children's Savings Campaign. T **138** and similar vert designs. W **122**. P 12½.
356   10h. yellow, sepia and emerald................ 1·50   75
357   20h. brown, ultramarine and pink........... 1·90   75
Design:— 20h. Snail and Korean money-bag.
For Nos. 356/7 in miniature sheet, see No. MS375.
See also Nos. 452/3, 515/6 and 569/70.

139 Uprooted Tree

140 Pres. Eisenhower

(T **139/40** des Kang Choon Whan)

1960 (7 Apr). World Refugee Year. W **115**. P 13½.
358   **139**   40h. red, blue and green......................... 1·50   55
MS359 90×60 mm. No. 358. Imperf............................ 60·00 55·00

1960 (19 June). Visit of President Eisenhower of United States. W **122**. P 13½.
360   **140**   40h. dull ultramarine, verm & turq-grn   4·75   1·90
MS361 90×60 mm. No. 360. Imperf............................ 39·00 38·00

141 Schoolchildren

(Des Kang Choon Whan)

1960 (3 Aug). 75th Anniv of Educational System. W **122**. P 13½.
362   **141**   40h. reddish pur, chestnut & yell-ol....... 1·50   45
MS363 90×60 mm. No. 362. Imperf............................ 9·25   8·50

142 Assembly

143 "Liberation"

(T **142/3** des Kang Choon Whan)

1960 (8 Aug). Inauguration of House of Councillors. W **122**. P 13½.
364   **142**   40h. grey-blue....................................... 1·50   45
MS365 90×60 mm. No. 364. Imperf............................ 9·25   8·50

1960 (15 Aug). 15th Anniv of Liberation. W **122**. P 13½.
366   **143**   40h. lake, light blue and ochre.............. 1·90   55
MS367 90×60 mm. No. 366. Imperf............................ 9·25   8·50

144 Weightlifting

145 Barn Swallow and Insulators

(Des La Boo Yung)

1960 (25 Aug). Olympic Games. T **144** and similar horiz design. W **122**. P 13½.
368   20h. brown, flesh and turquoise.............. 1·70   75
369   40h. brown, ultramarine and turquoise   1·70   75
MS370 90×60 mm. Nos. 368/9. Imperf....................... 29·00 26·00
Design:—40h. South Gate, Seoul.

(Des La Boo Yung)

1960 (28 Sept). 75th Anniv of Korean Telegraph Service. W **122**. P 13½.
371   **145**   40h. reddish violet, grey and light blue   1·70   75
MS372 90×60 mm. No. 371. Imperf............................ 8·50   7·50

146 "Rebirth of Republic"

147 "Torch of Culture"

(T **146/7** des Kang Choon Whan)

1960 (1 Oct). Establishment of New Government. W **122**. P 13½.
373　**146**　40h. emerald, blue and red-orange........　1·50　45
MS374　90×60 mm. No. 373. Imperf................................　7·75　7·00

1960 (7 Oct). Postal Week and International Correspondence Week. Sheet containing Nos. 356/7. Imperf.
MS375　90×60 mm..　5·50　5·00

1960 (15 Oct). Cultural Month. W **122**. P 13½.
376　**147**　40h. yellow, pale blue & bright blue.......　1·50　45
MS377　90×60 mm. No. 376. Imperf................................　7·75　6·75

148 UN Flag

149 UN Emblem and Gravestones

(Des Cho Kyung Heng)

1960 (24 Oct). 15th Anniv of United Nations. W **122**. P 13½.
378　**148**　40h. blue, green and mauve......................　1·50　45
MS379　90×60 mm. No. 378. Imperf................................　7·75　6·75

(Des Choi Moon Yung)

1960 (1 Nov). Establishment of U.N. Memorial Cemetery. W **122**. P 13½.
380　**149**　40h. brown and orange.............................　1·50　45
MS381　90×60 mm. No. 380. Imperf................................　7·75　6·75

150 "National Stocktaking"

151 Festival Stocking

(Des Kang Choon Whan)

1960 (15 Nov). Census of Population and Resources. W **122**. P 13½.
382　**150**　40h. carmine, drab and grey-blue...........　1·50　45
MS383　90×60 mm. No. 382. Imperf................................　7·75　6·75

(Des Cho Kyung Heng (15h.), Kang Choon Whan (25h.), Li Sung Ja (30h.))

1960 (15 Dec). Christmas and New Year Issue. T **151** and similar vert designs. W **122**. P 12½.
384　　15h. brown, orange-yellow and grey.....　2·30　40
385　　25h. red, green and ultramarine.............　3·00　40
386　　30h. red, yellow and ultramarine............　3·75　75
384/386　Set of 3...　8·25　1·40
MS387 Three sheets each 90×60 mm. Nos. 384/6. Imperf.　32·00　27·00
Designs:—15h. Ox's head; 20h. Girl bowing in New Year's greeting.

152 Wind-sock and Ancient Rain-gauge

153 Family, Sun and Globe

(T **152/3** des Kang Choon Whan)

1961 (23 Mar). World Meteorological Day. W **122**. P 13½.
388　**152**　40h. ultramarine and pale blue...............　1·50　45
MS389　90×60 mm. No. 388. Imperf................................　4·75　4·25

1961 (7 Apr). World Health Day. W **122**. P 13½.
390　**153**　40h. red-brown and orange.....................　1·50　45
MS391　90×60 mm. No. 390. Imperf................................　4·75　4·25

154 Students' Demonstration

155 Workers and Conference Emblem

(T **154/5** des Kang Choon Whan)

1961 (19 Apr). First Anniv of the April Revolution (Overthrow of Pres Syngman Rhee). W **122**. P 13½.
392　**154**　40h. deep bluish green, red & brt bl.......　1·90　75
MS393　90×60 mm. No. 392. Imperf................................　11·50　10·50

1961 (6 May). International Community Development Conference, Seoul. W **122**. P 13½.
394　**155**　40h. blue-green...　1·50　55
MS395　90×60 mm. No. 394. Imperf................................　7·00　6·25

156 Girl Guide, Camp and Badge

157 Soldier's Grave

(T **156/7** des Kang Choon Whan)

1961 (10 May). 15th Anniv of Korean Girl Guide Movement. W **122**. P 13½.
396   **156**   40h. blue-green.................................. 1·90   55
MS397 90×60 mm. No. 396. Imperf................................. 15·00   14·00

1961 (6 June). Memorial Day. W **122**. P 13½.
398   **157**   40h. black and drab.................................. 3·00   1·30
MS399 90×60 mm. No. 398. Imperf................................. 11·50   10·50

158 Soldier with Torch   **159** "Three Liberations"

(Des Kang Choon Whan after Kim Kyung Soo)

1961 (16 June). Revolution of 16 May (Seizure of Power by Gen. Pak Chung Hi). W **122**. P 13½.
400   **158**   40h. red-brown and yellow...................... 3·00   1·30
MS401 90×60 mm. No. 400. Imperf................................. 11·00   9·75

(Des Kang Choon Whan)

1961 (15Aug). Liberation Day. W **122**. P 13½.
402   **159**   40h. multicoloured .... 3·00   1·30
MS403 90×60 mm. No. 402. Imperf................................. 6·25   5·50

160 Korean Forces, Flag   **161** "Korean Art"
and Destroyer   (Kyongbok Palace
         Art Gallery)

(Des Kang Choon Whan)

1961 (1 Oct). Armed Forces Day. W **122**. P 13½.
404   **160**   40h. red, ultramarine, brn & flesh .... 3·00   1·20
MS405 90×60 mm. No. 404. Imperf................................. 5·50   4·75

(Des Han Hong Taik)

1961 (1 Nov). Tenth Korean Art Exhibition. W **122**. P 13½.
406   **161**   40h. chocolate and light brown .... 1·90   55
MS407 90×60 mm. No. 406. Imperf................................. 4·75   4·25

162 Birthday Candle   **163** Mobile X-Ray Unit

(T **162/3** des Kang Choon Whan)

1961 (4 Nov). 15th Anniv of United Nations Educational, Scientific and Cultural Organization. W **122**. P 13½.
408   **162**   40h. deep blue and dull green .... 1·90   55
MS409 90×60 mm. No. 408. Imperf................................. 4·75   4·25

1961 (16 Nov). Tuberculosis Vaccination Week. W **122**. P 13½.
410   **163**   40h. reddish brown, black & pale brn ... 1·50   55
MS411 90×60 mm. No. 140. Imperf................................. 4·75   4·25

164 Ginseng   **165** King Sejong   **166** White-bellied
                                       Black Woodpecker

167 Rice Harvester   **168** Korean Drum

(Des Kim Myung Sook (100h.), Kang Choon Whan (others))

1961 (1 Dec)-**62**. No wmk. P 12½.
412   **164**   20h. lake (10.3.62)................................. 2·30   60
413   **165**   30h. dull purple..................................... 6·25   60
414   **166**   40h. deep blue and red......................... 5·50   60
415   **167**   40h. deep green (27.5.62)...................... 9·25   75
416   **168**   100h. red-brown................................... 12·50   1·50
412/416 Set of 5 .... 32·00   3·75
See also Nos. 439/41, 443, 471/4, 543/5 548 and for stamps inscribed "REPUBLIC OF KOREA", see Nos. 643/4 and 789.

169 Douglas DC-8 Jetliner   **170** I.T.U. Emblem as Satellite
over Pagoda

(Des Kang Choon Whan)

1961 (1 Dec). AIR. T **169** and similar horiz designs. P 12½.
417   50h. violet and light blue....................... 23·00   6·25
418   100h. sepia and turquoise .... 31·00   10·00
419   200h. deep brown and turquoise .... 46·00   12·50
420   400h. deep bluish green and turquoise... 55·00   13·00
417/420 Set of 4 .... £140   38·00
Designs.—Plane over: 100h. West Gate, Suwon; 200h. Gateway and wall of Toksu Palace, Seoul; 400h. Pavilion, Kyongbok Palace, Seoul.
See also Nos. 454/7, 512/4 and 563/6.

(Des Kang Choon Whan)

1962 (31 Jan). Tenth Anniv of Admission to International Telecommunications Union. P 13½.
421   **170**   40h. red and deep blue .... 2·30   1·00
MS422 90×59 mm. No. 421. Imperf................................. 14·00   12·50

171 Triga Mark II Reactor   **172** Mosquito and Emblem

(T **171/2** des Kang Choon Whan)

1962 (30 Mar). First Korean Atomic Reactor. W **122**. P 13½.
423   **171**   40h. deep green, drab and light blue ....   2·30   55

1962 (7 Apr). Malaria Eradication. P 13½.
424   **172**   40h. vermillion and deep bluish green..   1·50   75
MS425   90×60 mm No.424.Imperf. ....   3·75   3·25

173 Girl and Y.W.C.A. Emblem   **174** Emblem of Asian Film
    Producers' Federation

(T **173/4** des Kang Choon Whan)

1962 (20 Apr). 40th Anniv of Young Women's Christian Association.
P 13½.
426   **173**   40h. deep blue and red-orange ....   2·30   55

1962(12 May). Ninth Asian Film Festival, Seoul. W **122**. P 13½.
427   **174**   40h. violet, red and turquoise ....   3·00   55

175 Soldiers crossing   **176** 20-oared "Turtle" Ship
Han River Bridge

(Des Im Bong Jea (30h.), Kang Choon Whan (40h.), Yem In Teak
(200h.))

1962 (16–27 May). First Anniv of 16 May Revolution. T **175** and similar
designs. W **122**. P 13½.
428   30h. sage green and red-brown..............   3·00   1·10
429   40h. red-brown, brt yellow-green & turq   3·00   1·10
430   200h. chrome yellow, verm & dull ultram   34·00   8·50
428/430 Set of 3   36·00   9·50
MS431 Three sheets each 90×140 mm. Nos...428/30
Imperf. Sheets inscr in Korean £120   £110
MS432 As last but sheets inscr in English. Wmkd.
"E" of POSTAGE" omitted...............................   £250   £225
a. No wmk. "POSTAGE" corrected (27.5)...................   £350   £325
Designs: Horiz—30h. "Industrial Progress" (men moving cogwheel
up slope); 200h. "Egg" containing Korean badge and industrial
skyline.
The sheets with erroneous inscription were withdrawn from sale
and replaced with No. **MS432a**.

New Currency

(Des Kang Choon Whan)

1962 (14 Aug). 370th Anniv of Hansan Naval Victory over Japanese.
T **176** and similar horiz design. P 13½.
433   2w. deep blue and light blue..............   19·00   1·50
434   4w. black, reddish-violet and turquoise   24·00   2·30
Design—4w. 16-oared "turtle' ship.

177 Chindo Dog   **178** *Hanabusaya   **179** Statue of
    asiatica*   Goddess Mikuk Besal

180 Farmers' Dance   **181** 12th-century   **182** Mison
    Wine-jug

183 13th-century   **184** Scout Badge
Printing-block and   and Korean Flag
Impression used for
Tripitaka Koreana

(Des Kang Choon Whan)

1962 (1 Sept)-**63**. New Currency. No wmk. Plain paper. P 12½.
435   **177**   20ch orange-brown (31.12.62) ....   1·50   40
436   **178**   40ch. blue (10.9.62)..............................   1·50   40
437   **179**   50ch. lake-brown (31.12 62) ....   1·50   40
438   **180**   1w. blue (5.2.63).................................   3·00   40
439   **164**   2w. brown-lake (7.11.62) ....   4·75   40
440   **165**   3w. dull purple...................................   5·00   40
441   **167**   4w. deep green...................................   5·50   40
442   **181**   5w. turquoise-blue (31.12.62) ....   6·25   85
443   **168**   10w. red-brown (7.11.62).....................   95·00   3·75
444   **182**   20w. magenta (10.9.63).......................   15·00   1·90
445   **183**   40w. purple-brown (5.2.63) ....   £140   4·75
435/445 Set of 11   £250   12·50
See also Nos. 467/76 and 537/50. For stamps inscribed "REPUBLIC
OF KOREA", see Nos. 641 etc. and 785 etc. For Types **182/3** redrawn,
see Nos. 709/10. For 40ch. as Type **178** but in vertical format, see No.
785.

(Des Kang Choon Whan)

1962 (5 Oct). 40th Anniv of Korean Scout Movement. W **115**
(sideways) (No. 446) or W **122** (No. 447). P 13½.
446   **184**   4w. chocolate, red and blue...................   1·90   75
447   4w. deep green, red and blue ....   1·90   75
MS448 Two sheets, each 90×60 mm. No wmk.
Imperf. (a) As Nos. 446; (b) As No. 447.................   15·00   14·00

185 Mackerel, Trawler and Nets   **186** ICAO Emblem

(T **185/6** des Kang Choon Whan)

1962 (10 Oct). Tenth Indo-Pacific Fishery Council Meeting, Seoul. P 13½.
449   **185**   4w. ultramarine and turquoise-blue.....   5·00   75

1962 (11 Dec). Tenth Anniv of Korea's Entry into International Civil Aviation Organization. P 13½.
450   **186**   4w. blue and brown..........   2·30   75
MS451 90×60 mm. No. 450. Imperf............   10·00   9·00

1962 (28 Dec)-**63**. Children's Savings Campaign. As Nos. 356/7 but new currency. No wmk. Plain paper. P 12½.
452   1w. yellow, sepia and emerald (5.2.63) .   7·00   1·20
453   2w. brown, ultramarine and pink..........   11·50   1·50
   See also Nos. 515/6 and 569/70.

1962 (28 Dec)-**63**. AIR. As Nos. 417/20 but new currency. No wmk. Plain paper. P 12½.
454   5w. turquoise-blue and violet (5.2.63) .   95·00   17·00
455   10w. bistre-brown and blue-green..........   85·00   17·00
456   20w. deep brown & blue-green (5.2.63)   £275   31·00
457   40w. myrtle green & turq-bl (5.2.63).......   95·00   31·00
454/457 Set of 4............   £500   85·00
   See also Nos. 512/14 and 563/6.

 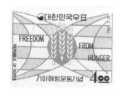

187 Electric Power Plant   **188** Campaign Emblem

(T **187/8** des Kang Choon Whan)

1962 (28 Dec). Inauguration of First Korean Economic Five Year Plan. T **187** and similar horiz design. P 12½.
458   **187**   4w. deep violet and yellow-orange.......   21·00   2·30
459   4w. ultramarine and light blue ....   21·00   2·30
Design: —Nos. **459**, Irrigation dam.
   See also Nos. 482/3, 528/9, 593/4 and 634/5.

1963 (21 Mar). Freedom from Hunger. W **122** (sideways). P 13½.
460   **188**   4w. green, buff and deep blue...............   1·50   55
MS461 90×60 mm. No. 460. Imperf................   4·75   4·00

189 Globe and Letters   **190** Centenary Emblem and Map

(T **189/90** des Kang Choon Whan)

1963 (1 Apr). First Anniv of Asian-Oceanic Postal Union. W **122** (sideways). P 13½.
462   **189**   4w. reddish purple, olive & deep blue..   2·30   55
MS463 90×60 mm No. 462 Imperf....................   4·75   4·25

1963 (8 May). Centenary of Red Cross. W **122** (sideways). P 13½.
464   **190**   4w. red, grey and light blue ....   1·50   55
465   4w. red, grey and salmon..................   1·50   55
MS466 140×90 mm. Nos. 464/5. Imperf. ....   14·00   12·50

191 Sika Deer   **192** Bell of King Kyongdok

(Des Kang Choon Whan)

1963 (20 May)-**64**. W **122**. Granite paper. P 12½.
467   **177**   20ch. orange-brown (10.5.64).....................   75   25
468   **178**   40ch. blue.............................   75   25
469   **179**   50ch. lake-brown (1.4.64)   75   25
470   **180**   1w. blue.............................   3·50   25
471   **164**   2w. brown-lake (1.6.63)................   5·00   40
472   **165**   3w. dull purple..................   14·50   30
473   **167**   4w. deep green................   6·50   30
474   **168**   10w. red-brown..............   5·50   40
475   **182**   20w. magenta (10.5.64)............   11·50   1·50
476   **183**   40w. maroon (10.7.63)............   55·00   2·30
477   **191**   50w. yellow-brown (10.9.63)............   70·00   1·50
478   **192**   100w. bottle green (10.9.63)............   £110   3·00
467/478 Set of 12............   £250   9·75
   See also Nos. 537/52.
   For stamps inscribed "REPUBLIC OF KOREA", see Nos. 641 etc. For Type **191** redrawn, see Nos. 711.

1963 (10 July). Flood Relief. As No. 473 but colour changed and inscr with premium.
479   **167**   4w. +1w. deep ultramarine ....   9·25   1·20

193 "15" and Hibiscus   **194** Nurse and Emblem

(T **193/4** des Kang Choon Whan)

1963 (15 Aug). 15th Anniv of Republic. W **122**. P 13½.
480   **193**   4w. vermilion, bluish violet & light blue   3·00   1·10

1963 (26 Aug). 15th Anniv of Korean Army Nursing Corps. W **122**. P 13½.
481   **194**   4w. black, dp bluish grn & lt yell-gm ....   2·30   95

1963 (1 Sept). Five Year Plan. Designs as T **187** dated"1963". W **122**. P 12½.
482   4w. deep violet and bluish grey ....   16·00   1·50
483   4w. chocolate and cinnamon............   16·00   1·50
   Designs:—No. 482, Cement factory, Mun'gyong, and bag of cement; Nos. 483, Miner and coal train, Samch'ok Region.

195   Rock Temples of   **196**
Abu Simbel

(Des Suh Hai Ok)

1963 (1 Oct). Nubian Monuments Preservation. W **122**. P 13½.
484   **195**   3w. bronze green and pale drab .... 5·50   2·20
         a. Horiz pair. Nos. 484/5 .... 11·50
485   **196**   4w. bronze green and pale drab .... 5·50   2·20
MS486 90×60 mm. Nos. 484/5. Imperf. .... 8·50   7·50
     Nos. 484/5 were issued together in horizontal *se-tenant* pairs
within the sheet, each pair forming a composite design.

197 Rugby Football and   **198** Nurse and Motor
Athlete   Clinic

(T **197/8** des Kang Choon Whan)

1963 (4 Oct). 44th National Games. W **122**. P 13½.
487   **197**   4w. deep green, brown and pale blue   3·75   1·30

1963 (6 Nov). Tenth Anniv of Korean Tuberculosis Prevention Society.
W **122**. P 13½.
488   **198**   4w. indigo and orange-red...................... 1·90   75

199 Eleanor Roosevelt   **200** UN Headquarters

(Des Suh Hai Ok)

1963 (10 Dec). 15th Anniv of Declaration of Human Rights. T **199** and
another design inscr "1963.12.10". W **122**. P 13½.
489   3w. orange-brown and deep blue....... 1·50   55
490   4w. deep blue, yellow-olive and buff ... 1·50   55
MS491 90×60 mm. Nos. 489/90. Imperf. .... 6·25   5·50
     Design: — 4w. Freedom torch and globe.

(Des Suh Hai Ok)

1963 (12 Dec). 15th Anniv of UN Recognition of Korea. W **122**.
P 13½.
492   **200**   4w. yellow-olive, pale blue and black... 1·50   45
MS493 90×60 mm. Nos. 492. Imperf............................ 5·00   4·50

360

201 Pres. Pak Chong Hi and   **202** "Tai-Keum"
Capitol   (Bamboo Flute)

(Des Kang Choon Whan)

1963 (17 Dec). Inauguration of President Pak Chong Hi. W **122**.
P 13½.
494   **201**   4w. dp bluish green, blue grn & blk ...... 60·00   15·00

(Des Kang Choon Whan)

1963 (17 Dec). Musical Instruments and Players. T **202** and similar
designs. W **122**. P 13½.
495   4w. deep olive, brown and drab .... 5·25   1·30
496   4w. black, blue and light blue................ 5·25   1·30
497   4w. deep olive, magenta and pink.......... 5·25   1·30
498   4w. sepia, violet and grey .... 5·25   1·30
499   4w. ultramarine, yellow-brown and pink 5·25   1·30
500   4w. turquoise blue, black and light blue 5·25   1·30
501   4w. bluish violet, bistre and greenish
               yellow .... 5·25   1·30
502   4w. ultramarine, brown and pale mauve 5·25   1·30
503   4w. black, blue and dull purple................ 5·25   1·30
504   4w. black, red-brown and pink................ 5·25   1·30
495/504 *Set of 10* .... 47·00   11·50
     Musical instruments (and players): Vert.— No. 495, T **202**; 496,
"Wul-keum" (banjo); 497, "Tang-piri" (flageolet); 498, "Na-bal"
(trumpet); 499, "Hyang-pipa" (lute); 500, "Pyen-kyeng" (jade chimes);
501, "Taipyeng-so" (clarinet), 502, "Chang-ko" (double-ended drum).
Horiz — 503. "Wa-kong-hu" (harp); 504, "Kaya-ko" (zither).

203 Symbols of Metric System   **204** "UNESCO"

(T **203/4** des Kang Choon Whan)

1964 (1 Jan). Introduction of Metric System in Korea. W **122**. P 13½.
505   **203**   4w. multicoloured .... 1·50   45
         a. Imperf (pair)... 75·00

1964 (30 Jan) Tenth Anniv of Korean United Nations Educational,
Scientific and Cultural Organization Committee. W **122**. P 13½.
506   **204**   4w. dull ultramarine, red and light blue 1·90   70

205 Symbols of   **206** Y M.C.A. Emblem and
Industry and Census   Profile of Young Man

(Des Suh Hai Ok)

1964 (23 Mar). National Industrial Census (1963). W **122**. P 13½.
507 **205** 4w. red-brown, black and grey .... 1·90   70

(Des Kang Bak)

1964 (12 Apr). 50th Anniv of Korean Young Men's Christian Association. W **122**. P 13½.
508 **206** 4w. vermilion, blue and apple green.... 1·50   45

207 Fair Emblem, Ginseng Root
and Freighter

(Des Kang Choon Whan)

1964 (22 Apr). New York Worlds Fair. T **207** and another design inscr "NEW YORK WORLD'S FAIR". W **122**. P 13½.
509   40w. brown, black-green & ochre-yell.... 3·75   1·30
510   100w. ultramarine, brown and light blue 35·00   7·75
MS511 90×60mm. Nos. 509/10. Imperf. .... 80·00   75·00
Design: —100w. Korean Pavilion at Fair.

1964 (10 May). AIR. As Nos. 455/7 but W **122**. Granite paper. P 12½.
512   10w. sepia and light turquoise-blue .... 15·00   4·75
513   20w. deep brown and light turquoise-
green .... 55·00   7·75
514   40w. deep bluish green and light blue... 29·00   6·25
512/514 Set of 3 .... 90·00   17·00

1964 (10 May). Children's Savings Campaign. As Nos. 452/3 but W **122**. Granite paper. P 12½.
515   1w. yellow, sepia and emerald .... 20·00   8·75
516   2w. brown, ultramarine and pink.......... 13·00   2·30
See also Nos. 569/70.

208 Secret Garden

209 Wheel and Globe

(Des Kang Bak (1, 4, 8, 9w.), Kang Choon Whan (others))

1964 (25 May). T **208** and similar horiz designs. Background in pale blue. W **122**. P 13½.
517   1w. green .... 1·50   45
518   2w. deep olive (Whahong Gate)............. 1·50   45
519   3w. dp bluish green (Uisang Pavilion).. 1·50   45
520   4w. yellow-green (Mt. Songni) .... 3·00   95
521   5w. deep violet (Paekma River)............. 5·50   1·50
522   6w. ultramarine (Anab Pond) .... 7·00   1·90
523   7w. chocolate (Choksok Pavilion) .... 10·00   2·75
524   8w. brown (Kwanghan Pavilion)........... 10·50   2·75
525   9w. bluish violet (Whaom Temple).... 10·50   2·75
526   10w. deep green (Chonjeyon Falls).......... 15·00   3·00
517/526 Set of 10 .... 60·00   15·00
MS527 Five sheets each 90×60 mm. 1w. and ... 10w.; 2w. and 9w.; 3w. and 8w. ; 4w.and 7w.; 5w. and 6w. Imperf. .... 95·00   85·00

1964 (15 June). Five Year Plan. Designs as T **187** dated "1964". W **122**. P 12½.
528   4w. black and light blue .... 5·50   1·20
529   4w. blue and yellow .... 5·50   1·20
Designs: — Nos. 528, Trawlers and fish; 529, Oil refinery and barrels.

(Des Kang Bak)

1964(15June). Colombo Plan Day. W **122**. P 13½.
530 **209** 4w. yellow-brown, bistre-brn & yell-ol. 1·50   55
MS531 90×60 mm. No. 530. Imperf..................... 5·50   4·75

210 "Helping Hand"   **211** Running

(Des Kang Bak)

1964 (17 Aug). 15th Anniv of Korea's Admission to World Health Organization. W **122**. P 13½.
532 **210** 4w. black, yellow-green & apple green 1·50   55
MS533 90×60 mm. No. 532. Imperf. .... 5·50   4·75

(Des Kang Choon Whan)

1964 (3 Sept). 45th National Games, Inchon. W **122**. P 13½.
534 **211** 4w. pink, black-green & brt purple........ 3·75   1·30
     a. Pink, green and bright purple .... 3·75   1·30

212 UPU Monument, Berne, and
Ribbons

(Des Kang Bak)

1964 (15 Sept). 90th Anniv of Universal Postal Union. W **122**. P 13½.
535 **212** 4w. red-brown, blue and rose .... 1·50   55
MS536 90×60 mm. No. 535. Imperf..................... 5·75   5·00

213 Longhorn
Beetle

214 Factory, Fishes
and Corn

215 Boddhisatva,
Sokkuram Shrine

216 Tile, Silla
Dynasty

217 "Azure Dragon",
Koguryo period

(Des Kang Choon Whan (**213**), Oh Choong Whan (**217**), Kim Soon Deuk (**214/6**))

1964 (20 Sept)–66. No wmk. Granite paper. P 12½.
537 **177** 20ch orange brown (12.10.64)................. 75   25
538 **178** 40ch. blue...................................... 75   25
539 **179** 50ch. brown-lake (15.2.65) 75   25
540 **213** 60ch. deep purple-brown (1.1.66)......... 95   30

541	**180**	1w. blue	2·30	25
542	**179**	1w. 50 greenish grey (20.2.66)	75	30
543	**164**	2w. brown-purple (12.10.64)	3·75	25
544	**165**	3w. brown-purple (12.10.64)	23·00	25
545	**167**	4w. deep green (12.10.64)	75	25
546	**181**	5w. turquoise-blue (12.10.64)	31·00	1·50
547	**214**	7w. magenta (1.1.66)	3·00	75
548	**168**	10w. red-brown (12.10.64)	4·75	25
549	**182**	20w. magenta (12.10.64)	4·75	40
550	**183**	40w. maroon (12.10.64)	7·75	1·50
551	**191**	50w. yellow-brown (12.10.64)	19·00	1·50
552	**192**	100w. deep green	70·00	2·30
553	**215**	200w. dp green & light green (1.9.65)	27·00	3·00
554	**216**	300w. dp green & ochre (1.9.65)	55·00	3·75
555	**217**	500w. steel-blue & lt blue (1.9.65)	27·00	3·75
537/555		Set of 19	£250	19·00

Clever postal forgeries exist of Nos. 549/51. They were withdrawn and replaced by Nos. 709/11.

For stamps as Type **167** with charity premium, see Nos. 607 and 609. For stamps inscribed "REPUBLIC OF KOREA", see Nos. 641, etc.

218 Federation Emblem

219 Olympic "V" Emblem

(Des Kang Choon Whan)

1964 (29 Sept). Fifth Meeting of international Federation of Asian and Western Pacific Contractors' Associations. W **122**. P 13½.

556	**218**	4w. dp green, lt green & red-brown	1·50	55

(Des Kang Choon Bak (Nos. 558, 561), Kang Choon Whan (others))

1964 (10 Oct). Olympic Games, Tokyo. T **219** and similar designs. W **122**. P 13½.

557		4w. indigo, turquoise and light brown	3·00	1·00
558		4w. magenta, blue and blue-green	3·00	1·00
559		4w. brown, ultramarine and light blue	3·00	1·00
560		4w. Venetian red, brown and deep blue	3·00	1·00
561		4w. orange-brown, brt purple & dp blue	3·00	1·00
557/561		Set of 5	13·50	4·50
MS562		Five sheets each 90×60 mm. As Nos. 557/61 but without wmk. Imperf.	23·00	21·00

Designs: Vert.— Nos. 557, T **219**. Horiz— Nos. 558, Running; 559, Rowing; 560, Horse-jumping; 561, Gymnastics.

1964 (16 Oct). AIR. As Nos. A54/7 but new values. No wmk. Granite paper. P 12½.

563		39w. deep olive-drab and light blue	11·50	2·30
564		64w. grey-green and light blue	10·00	2·75
565		78w. ultramarine and turquoise-green	27·00	4·75
566		112w. deep bluish green and light blue	13·00	2·75
563/566		Set of 4	55·00	11·50

220 Unissued 1884 100m. Stamp

221 Pine Cone

(Des Kang Choon Whan)

1964 (4 Dec). 80th Anniv of Korean Postal Services. T **220** and similar vert design. P 13½.

567		3w. grey-blue, bluish violet and mauve	3·75	95
568		4w. black, bluish violet and yellow-olive	5·50	1·20

Design:—4w. Hong Yong Sik, first Korean Postmaster-general.

1964 (20 Dec). Children's Savings Campaign. As Nos. 515/6 but no wmk. Granite paper. P 12½.

569		1w. yellow, sepia and emerald	95·00	9·25
570		2w. brown, ultramarine and pink	13·00	1·50

(Des Kang Choon Whan)

1966 (15 Jan--15 Dec). Korean Plants. T **221** and similar vert designs. Plants in natural colours; background colours given. P 13½.

571		4w. pale turquoise-green (15.1)	2·30	75
572		4w. pale sepia (15.2)	2·30	75
573		4w. blue (15.3)	2·30	75
574		4w. emerald (15.4)	2·30	75
575		4w. pale pink (15.5)	2·30	75
576		4w. blue-grey (15.6)	2·30	75
577		4w. light apple-green (15.7)	2·30	75
578		4w. grey (15.8)	2·30	75
579		4w. pale flesh (15.9)	2·30	75
580		4w. pale turquoise-blue (15.10)	2·30	75
581		4w. buff (15.11)	2·30	75
582		4w. ultramarine (15.12)	2·30	75
571/582		Set of 12	25·00	8·00
MS583		Twelve sheets each 90×60 mm. Nos. 571/82. Imperf. (Issued same dates)	37·00	30·00

Plants:—Nos. 571, Type **221**; 572, Plum blossom; 573, Forsythia; 574, Azalea; 575, Lilac; 576, Wild rose; 577 Balsam; 578, Hibiscus; 579, Crepe myrtle; 580, Ullung chrysanthemum; 581, Paulownia (tree); 582, Bamboo.

222 Folk Dancing

223 Flag and Doves

(Des Kang Choon Whan)

1965 (26 Mar). Pacific Area Travel Association Conference, Seoul. P 13½.

584	**222**	4w. bluish violet, brown & turq grn	1·40	45
MS585		90×60 mm. No. 584. Imperf.	3·75	3·25

(Des Kim Soon Deuk and Kang Choon Whan)

1965 (20 Apr). Military Aid for Vietnam. P 13½.

586	**223**	4w. sepia, turquoise-blue and pale greenish yellow	1·40	45
MS587		90×60 mm. No. 586. Imperf.	3·75	3·25

224 "Food Production"

225 "Family Scales"

(T **224/5** des Chun Hee Han and Kang Choon Whan)

1965 (1 May). Agricultural Seven Year Plan. P 13½.

588	**224**	4w. choc, yellowish grn & greenish blk	1·40	45

1965 (8 May). Family Planning Month. P 13½.
589   **225**   4w. dp bluish green, drab & pale grn.....   1·40   45
MS590 90×60 mm. No. 589. Imperf.................................   3·50   3·25

226 I.T.U. Emblem   **227** Flags of Australia.
and Symbols   Belgium, Great Britain, Canada
                            and Colombia

(Des Kang Choon Whan)

1965 (17 May). Centenary of International Telecommunications Union. P 13½.
591   **226**   4w. black, red and greenish blue ....   1·40   45
MS592 90×60 mm. No. 591. Imperf.................................   3·50   3·25

1965 (1 June). Five Year Plan. Designs as T **187** dated "1965". P 13½.
593   4w. ultramarine and light pink................   2·30   1·20
594   4w. sepia and light yellow-brown..........   2·30   1·20
    Designs—Nos. 593, Korea (freighter) at quayside and crates: 594, Fertiliser plant and wheat.

(Des Kim Soon Deuk)

1965 (25 June). 15th Anniv of Outbreak of Korean War. T **227** and similar horiz designs. P 13½.
595   4w. multicoloured ....   1·50   70
596   4w. multicoloured ....   1·50   70
597   4w. multicoloured ....   1·50   70
598   4w. multicoloured ....   1·50   70
599   4w. multicoloured ....   5·50   1·50
595/599 *Set of 5*.. 10·50   3·75
MS600 Five sheets each 9×60 mm. Nos. 595/9.
    Imperf. .... 11·50 10·50
    Designs: U.N. Emblem and flags of—Nos. 596, Denmark, Ethiopia, France, Greece and India; Nos. 597, Italy, Luxembourg, Netherlands, New Zealand and Norway; Nos. 598, Philippines, Sweden, Thailand, Turkey and South Africa; Nos. 599, General MacArthur and flags of Korea, U.N. and U.S.A.

228 Flag and Sky-   **229** Ants and Leaf
writing ("20")

(Des Chun Hee Han)

1965 (15 Aug). 20th Anniv of Liberation. T **228** and similar vert design inscr "1965.8.15". P 13½.
601   4w. red, deep violet-blue and light blue   3·00   55
602   10w. red, light blue & deep violet-blue ..   3·75   75
    Design: —10w. South Gate and fireworks.

(Des Oh Choong Whan)

1965 (20 Sept). Savings Campaign. P 13½.
603   **229**   4w. sepia, lt ochre & lt yellow-green.....   1·40   45
    The above stamp is dated "20.6.65".

230 Hoisting Flag   **231** Radio Aerial

(Des Chun Hee Han)

1965 (28 Sept). 15th Anniv of Recapture of Seoul. P 13½.
604   **230**   3w. blackish ol, turq bl & yell-orge ....   3·00   1·20

(Des Kang Choon Whan and Oh Choong Whan)

1965 (28 Sept). 80th Anniv of Korean Telecommunications. T **231** and similar horiz design inscr "1865-1965". P 13½.
605   3w. olive-green, black and light blue ...   2·30   45
606   10w. black, blue and olive-yellow............   4·75   75
    Design — 10w. Telegraphist of 1885.

1965 (1 Oct). Flood Relief. As No. 545, but colour changed and inscr with premium.
607   **167**   4w. +2w. Prussian blue.............................   4·75   1·20

232 Pole Vaulting   **233** I.C.Y. Emblem

(Des Kim Soon Deuk)

1965 (5 Oct). National Athletic Meeting, Kwangju. P 13½.
608   **232**   3w. multicoloured ....   2·30   95

1965 (11 Oct). Aid for Children. As No. 545, but colour changed and inscr with premium.
609   **167**   4w. +2w. reddish purple............................   4·75   1·20

(Des Kim Soon Deuk (3w.), Oh Choong Whan (10w.))

1965 (24 Oct). International Co-operation Year and 20th Anniv of United Nations. T **233** and similar design. P 13½.
610   3w. red, yellowish green and deep
               green ....   1·20   45
611   10w. dp ultramarine, green and
               turquoise-blue ....   2·30   75
MS612 Two sheets, each 90×60 mm. Imperf. (a) No.
    610; (b) No. 611 ....   7·75   7·00
    Design. Vert—10w. UN flag and headquarters. New York.

234 Child posting Letter   **235** Children
                                       with Toboggan

(Des Kim Soon Deuk (3w.), Oh Choong Whan (10w.))

1965 (4 Dec). 10th Communications Day. T **234** and similar design.
P 13½.

613	3w. multicoloured	3·00	95
614	10w. red, blue and sage-green	6·25	1·70

Design: —10w. Airmail envelope and telephone receiver.

(Des Kang Choon Whan (3w.), Kim Soon Deuk (4 w.))

1965 (11 Dec). Christmas and New Year. T **235** and similar vert design.
P 12½.

615	3w. ultramarine, orange-red and dull green	2·30	55
616	4w. ultramarine, orange-red & light turquoise-green	3·75	55
MS617	90×60 mm. Nos. 615/6. Imperf	4·75	4·00

Design: —4w. Boy and girl in traditional costume.

236 Freedom House   **237** Mandarins

(Des Kim Soon Deuk)

1966 (15 Feb). Opening of Freedom House, Panmunjom. P 12½.

618	**236**	7w. black, emerald & pale yell-grn	2·30	75
619		39w. black, lilac and pale green	13·00	3·00
MS620	90×60 mm. Nos. 618/9. Imperf		23·00	19·00

(Des Kang Choon Whan)

1966 (15 Mar). Korean Birds. T **237** and similar horiz designs.
Multicoloured. P 12½.

621		3w. Type **237**	2·30	1·30
622		5w. Manchurian crane	2·50	1·30
623		7w. Ring-necked pheasant	3·75	1·30
621/623 *Set of 3*			7·75	3·50
MS624	Three sheets each 90×60 mm. Nos. 621/3. Imperf		14·00	12·00

238 Pine Forest   **239** Printing Press   **240** Curfew Bell and
                      and Pen   Young Koreans

(Des Chun Hee Han)

1966 (5 Apr). Reafforestation Campaign. P 12½.

625	**238**	7w. brown, bottle grn & yellowish grn	1·50	55

(Des Kim Soon Deuk)

1966 (7 Apr). Tenth Newspaper Day. P 12½.

626	**239**	7w. maroon, yellow & turquoise-grn	1·30	55

(Des Kang Choon Whan)

1966 (1 May). Youth Guidance Month. P 12½.

627	**240**	7w. orange, light green & new blue	1·30	55

241 W.H.O. Building   **242** Pres. Pak, Handclasp
                                 and Flags

(Des Kim Soon Deuk)

1966 (3 May). Inauguration of World Health Organization Headquarters, Geneva. P 12½.

628	**241**	7w. black, pale slate-blue and lemon	1·50	60
629		39w. scarlet, violet-grey and lemon	11·50	3·50
MS630	90×60 mm. No. 628. Imperf		4·75	3·50

(Des Oh Choong Whan)

1966 (10 May) President Pak Chung Hi's State Tour of South-East Asia. P 12½.

631	**242**	7w. black, red, blue and yellow	7·75	2·50

243 Girl Scout and Flag   **244** Student and Ewha
                                 Women's University

(Des Kim Soon Deuk)

1966 (10 May). 20th Anniv of Korean Girl Scouts P 12½.

632	**243**	7w. black, emerald and yellow	2·30	85

(Des Oh Choong Whan)

1966 (31 May). 80th Anniv of Korean Women's Education. P 12½.

633	**244**	7w. multicoloured	1·30	55

1966 (1 June) Five Year Plan. Designs as 7187 dated "1966". P 12½.

634	7w. ultramarine and light blue	3·75	1·20
635	7w. black and bistre-yellow	3·75	1·20

Designs: —No. 634, Map and transport; No. 635, Radar aerials and telephone.

245 Carrier Pigeons   **246** Alaska Pollack

(Des Kang Bak)

1966 (13 June). International Correspondence Week. Unissued sheet (90×60 mm.), surch. as shown in T **245** and optd. "6", "1966.6.13–19" with bars obliterating old inscr. Imperf.

MS636	7(w.) on 40 (h.) dp grn, light green & red	3·75	3·50

(Des Kang Choon Whan)

1966 (15 June). Korean Fishes. T **246** and similar horiz designs. Multicoloured. P 12½.

637		3w. Type **246**	3·00	85
638		5w. Manchurian trout	3·75	85
639		7w. Yellow corvina	4·75	1·00
637/639 *Set of 3*			10·50	2·40
MS640	Three sheets, each 90×60 mm. Nos. 637/9. Imperf		11·50	10·00

247 Incense-burner   **248** 12th-century   **249** Buddha,
                Porcelain Vessel   Kwanchok Temple

(Des Kim Soon Deuk (**247**), Chun Hee Han (**248/9**))

1966 (1 July–20 Aug). Definitive types of previous issues but inscr
"REPUBLIC OF KOREA" and T **247/9**. Granite paper. P 12½.

641	**213**	60ch. deep yellow-green (20.8)	40	10
642	**180**	1wn. bluish green (20.8)	4·25	40
643	**164**	2wn. turquoise-green (20.8)	40	10
644	**165**	3wn. purple-brown (20.8)	40	10
645	**181**	5wn. slate-blue (20.8)	5·00	75
646	**214**	7wn. greenish blue (20.8)	5·50	30
647	**247**	13wn. violet-blue	5·50	75
648	**248**	60wn. deep yellow-green	31·00	1·50
649	**249**	80wn. slate-green	11·50	1·50
641/649		Set of 9	60·00	5·00

For stamp as Type **214** with charity premium, see No. 672.

250 Children and   **251** Factory within
Hemispheres   Pouch

(Des Kim Soon Deuk)

1966 (28 July) 15th Assembly of World Conference of Teaching
Profession (WCOTP), Seoul. P 12½.

650	**250**	7w. violet, lt yellow-brn & lt violet-bl	1·50	55
MS651		90×60 mm. No. 650. Imperf	3·75	3·50

(Des Chun Hee Han)

1966 (1 Sept). Savings Campaign. P 12½.

652	**251**	7w. multicoloured	1·30	55

252 People on Map of Korea   **253** *Luciola lateralis*

(Des Chun Hee Han)

1966 (1 Sept). National Census. P 12½.

653	**252**	7w. multicoloured	1·30	55

(Des Kang Choon Whan)

1966 (15 Sept). Insects. T **253** and similar horiz designs. Multicoloured.
P 12½.

654		3w. Type **233**	2·30	85
655		5w. *Hexacentrus japonicus* (grasshopper)	2·30	85
656		7w. *Sericinus monfela* (butterfly)	3·00	1·00
654/656		Set of 3	6·75	2·40
MS657		Three sheets, each 90×60 mm. Imperf.		
		(a) No. 654; (b) No. 655; (c) No. 656	11·00	10·00

254 C.I. S.M. Emblem and   **255** Soldiers and Flags
"Round Table" Meeting

(T **254/5** des Chun Hee Han)

1966 (29 Sept). 21st General Assembly of the International Military
Sports Council (C.I.S.M.), Seoul. P 12½.

658	**254**	7w. multicoloured	1·30	55
MS659		90×60 mm. No. 658. Imperf	3·75	3·50

1966 (1 Oct). First Anniv of Korean Troops in Vietnam. P 12½.

660	**255**	7w. multicoloured	9·25	2·30

256 Wrestling   **257** Lions Emblem and Map

(Des Kim Soon Deuk)

1966 (10 Oct). 47th Athletic Meeting, Seoul. P 12½.

661	**256**	7w. multicoloured	2·50	1·20

(Des Kang Choon Whan)

1966 (15 Oct). Fifth Orient and South-East Asian Lions Convention,
Seoul. P 12½.

662	**257**	7w. multicoloured	1·50	55
MS663		90×60 mm. No. 662. Imperf	3·75	3·50

258 University Emblem,   **259** A.P. A.C.L. Emblem
"20" and Shields

(T **258/9** des Kim Soon Deuk)

1966 (15 Oct). 20th Anniv of Seoul University. P 12½.

664	**258**	7w. multicoloured	1·50	55

1966 (31 Oct). 12th Conference of Asian People's Anti-Communist
League (A.P.A.C L.), Seoul. P 12½.

665	**259**	7w. multicoloured	1·50	55
MS666		90×60 mm. No. 665. Imperf	3·50	3·25

260 Presidents Pak   **261** UNESCO
and Johnson   Symbols and Emblem

(Des Kang Choon Whan)

1966 (31 Oct). President Johnson's Visit to Korea. P 12½.

667	**260**	7w. multicoloured	2·30	75

668	83w. multicoloured	13·00	3·75

MS669 90×60 mm. Nos. 667/8. Imperf................ 15·00 14·00

(Des Kim Soon Deuk)

1966 (4 Nov). 20th Anniv of United Nations Educational, Scientific and Cultural Organization. T 12½.

670	**261**	7w. multicoloured	1·50	45

MS671 90×60 mm. No. 670. Imperf.................... 3·75 3·50

1966 (10 Nov) Hurricane Relief. As No. 646 but colour changed and premium added.

672	**214**	7w. +2w. rose-carmine................	6·25	1·50

262 "Lucky Bag"   **263** Eurasian Badger

(Des Chun Hee Han (5w.), Kang Choon Whan (7w.))

1966 (10 Dec). Christmas and New Year T **262** and similar design, but vert. Multicoloured. P 12½×13 (5w.) or 13×12½ (7w.).

673	5w. Type **262**................	2·30	40
674	7w. Sheep................	3·75	40

MS675 Two sheets, each 90×60 mm. Nos. 673/4. Imperf................ 7·75 7·00

(Des Kang Choon Whan)

1966 (15 Dec). Korean Fauna. T **263** and similar horiz designs. Multicoloured. P 12½.

676	3w. Type **263**................	3·00	1·10
677	5w. Asiatic black bear................	3·00	1·10
678	7w. Tiger................	3·75	1·10
676/678	Set of 3................	8·75	3·00

MS679 Three sheets, each 90×60 mm. Nos. 676/8. Imperf................ 14·50 13·50

264 "Syncom" Satellite   **265** Presidents Pak and Lübke

(Des Chun Hee Han)

1967 (31 Jan). Anniv of Korea's Admission to International Telecommunications Union. P 12½.

680	**264**	7w. multicoloured	1·50	70

MS681 90×60 mm. No. 680. Imperf................ 4·25 3·75

(Des Kang Choon Whan)

1967 (2 Mar). Visit of President Lübke of West Germany. P 12½.

682	**265**	7w. multicoloured	2·50	1·20

MS683 90×60 mm. No. 682 Imperf................ 4·75 4·25

266 Coin Factories and Houses   **267** Okwangdae Mask

(Des Kim Soon Deuk)

1967 (3 Mar). First Anniv of Korean Revenue Office. P 12½.

684	**266**	7w. sepia and light yellow-green.........	1·50	55

(Des Kang Choon Whan)

1967 (15 Mar). Folklore. T **267** and similar designs showing masks. Multicoloured. P 12½.

685	4w. Type **267**................	2·30	70
686	5w. Sandi mask (horiz)................	2·30	75
687	7w. Mafoe mask................	3·00	1·00
685/687	Set of 3................	6·75	2·20

MS688 Three sheets, each 90×60 mm. Nos. 685/7. Imperf................ 11·00 9·75

268 J.C.I. Emblem and   **269** Map Emblem
Pavillion

(Des Chun Hee Han)

1967 (13 Apr). International Junior Chamber of Commerce Conference, Seoul. P 12½.

689	**268**	7w. multicoloured	1·40	45

MS690 90×60 mm. No. 689. Imperf................ 3·75 3·50

(Des Kang Choon Whan)

1967 (24 Apr). Fifth Asian Pacific Dental Congress, Seoul. P 12½.

691	**269**	7w. multicoloured	1·40	45

MS692 90×60 mm. No. 691. Imperf................ 3·75 3·50

270 Korean Pavilion   **271** Worker and
Soldier

(T **270/1** des Chun Hee Han)

1967 (28 Apr). World Fair, Montreal. P 12½.

693	**270**	7w. black, red and yellow................	3·75	75
694		83w. black, red and light blue................	23·00	5·50

MS695 90×60 mm. Nos. 693/4. Imperf................ 19·00 18·00

1967 (8 May). Veterans Day. P 12½.

696	**271**	7w. multicoloured................	1·50	45

272 Wheel and Rail   **273** Sword Dance

(Des Oh Choong Whan)

1967 (1 June). Second Five Year Plan. T **272** and similar horiz design, dated "1967". P 12½.

697		7w. black, yellow and orange-brown ...	7·00	1·20

698   7w. yellow-orange, red-brown & black   7·00   1·20
Designs: —No. 697, T **272;** No. 698, Nut and bolt.
See also Nos. 773/4, 833/4, 895/6 and 981/2.

(Des Kang Choon Whan)

1967 (15 June). Folklore. T **273** and similar multicoloured designs
showing dances. P 12½.
699   4w. Type **273** ....   2·30   70
700   5w. Peace dance (vert) ....   2·30   75
701   7w. Buddhist dance (vert) ....   3·00   1·00
699/701 *Set of* 3 ....   6·75   2·20
MS702 Three sheets, each 90×60 mm. Nos. 699/701.
   Imperf ....   11·00   10·00

274 Soldier and
Family

275 President Pak and
Phoenix

(Des Kim Soon Deuk)

1967 (20 June). Fund for Korean Troops Serving in Vietnam. P 12½.
703   **274**   7w. +3w. black and light purple ....   7·75   1·20

(Des Kang Choon Whan)

1967 (1 July). Inauguration of President Pak for Second Term. P 12½.
704   **275**   7w. multicoloured ....   23·00   3·75
MS705   90×60 mm. No. 704. Imperf..............................   65·00   60 00

276 Scout, Badge and Camp

(Des Chun Hee Han (7w.), Oh Choong Whan (20w.))

1967 (10 Aug). Third Korean Scout Jamboree. T **276** and similar horiz
design. Multicoloured. P 12½.
706   7w. Type **276** ....   1·50   70
707   20w. Scout badge, bridge and tent ....   5·50   2·20
MS708 Two sheets, each 90×60 mm. Nos. 706/7.
   Imperf ....   11·00   10·00

277 Mison (shrub)

278 13th-century
Printing-block
and Impression
used for *Tripitaka
Koreana*

279 Sika Deer

1967 (25 Aug). T **182/3** and **191** redrawn as T **277/9**. Position of
denominations altered, finely traced background added and
colours changed. Inscr "REPUBLIC OF KOREA". Granite paper.
P 12½.
709   **277**   20wn. green and light green ....   70·00   1·50
710   **278**   40wn. deep green and yellow-olive..........   42·00   1·50
711   **279**   50wn. deep brown and bistre ....   8·50   1·50
709/711 *Set of* 3 ....   £110   4·00
   The designs were redrawn because postal forgeries had been
made of the original designs.

280 Girls on Swing

281 Freedom Centre

(Des Kang Choon Whan)

1967 (15 Sept). Folklore. T **280** and similar multicoloured designs
showing children's games. P 12½.
712   4w. Type **280** ....   3·75   75
713   5w. Girls on seesaw (vert) ....   3·75   95
714   7w. Girls dancing (vert)..........................   6·25   1·10
712/714 *Set of* 3 ....   12·50   2·50
MS715 Three sheets, each 90×60 mm. Nos. 712/4.
   Imperf ....   20·00   19·00

(Des Chun Hee Han (5w.), Kang Choon Whan (7w.))

1967 (25 Sept). First World Anti-Communist League Conference,
Taipei. T **281** and another multicoloured design. P 12½.
716   5w. Type **281** ....   1·50   45
717   7w. Hand grasping chain (vert)..............   1·50   45
MS718 Two sheets, each 90×60 mm. Nos. 716/7.
   Imperf ....   11·00   10·00

282 Boxing

283 Students'
Memorial. Kwangjoo

284 Decade
Emblem

(Des Oh Choong Whan (5w.), Chun Hee Han (7w.))

1967 (5 Oct). National Athletic Meeting, *Seoul.* T **282** and similar vert
design. Multicoloured. P 12½.
719   5w. Type **282** ....   2·30   75
720   7w. Basketball ....   3·00   75

(Des Oh Choong Whan)

1967 (3 Nov). Students' Day. P 12½.
721   **283**   7w. multicoloured ....   1·50   45

(Des Sin Bong Hee)

1967 (20 Nov). International Hydrological Decade. P 12½.
722   **284**   7w. multicoloured ....   1·50   45

285 Children
spinning Top

286 Playing
Shuttlecock

287 Microwave
Transmitter

(Des Kang Choon Whan)

1967 (10 Dec). Christmas and New Year. T **285** and similar vert design.
P 12½.
723   5w. ultramarine, vermilion and light
          pink...   3·00   40

724	7w. red-brown, ultramarine and bistre	3·75	30

MS725 Two sheets, each 90×60 mm. Nos. 723/4.
Imperf .... 7·75 7·00
Design:—7w. Monkey and Signs of the Zodiac.

(Des Kang Choon Whan)

1967 (15 Dec). Folklore. T **286** and similar multicoloured designs.
P 12½.

726	4w. Type **286**	3·00	1·00
727	5w. "Dalmaji" (horiz)	3·00	1·00
728	7w. Archery (vert)	3·00	1·00
726/728 *Set of* 3		8·00	2·75

MS729 Three sheets, each 90×60 mm. Nos. 726/8.
Imperf .... 12·50 11·50

(Des Chun Hee Han)

1967 (21 Dec). Inauguration of Microwave Telecommunications
Service. P 12½.

730	287	7w. black, brt yellow-grn & greenish bl	1·50	70

MS731 90×60 mm. No. 730. Imperf .... 3·75 3·50

288 Carving, King
Songdok's Bell

289 5th-6th-
century Earrings

290 Korean Flag

(Des Chun Hee Han)

1968 (1 Feb). Granite paper. P 13×12½.

732	288	1w. sepia and lemon......................	40	10
733	289	5w. greenish yellow & dp bluish grn.....	3·00	55
734	290	7w. red and deep blue	1·50	25
732/734 *Set of* 3			4·50	80

See also Nos. 787/8 and 790.
For flag design, as T **290** but with premium added see Nos. 771,
780 and 827.

291 WHO Emblem

292 E.A.T.A. Emblem
and Korean Motif

(Des Oh Choong Whan)

1968 (7 Apr). 20th Anniv of World Health Organization. P 12½.

735	291	7w. multicoloured	1·50	45

MS736 90×60 mm. No. 735. Imperf .... 3·75 3·50

(Des Chun Hee Han)

1968 (9 Apr). 2nd Conference of East Asia Travel Association (E.A.T.A.),
Seoul. P 12½.

737	292	7w. multicoloured	1·50	45

MS738 90×60 mm. No. 737. Imperf .... 4·75 4·25

293 C.A.C.C.I. Emblem,
Korean Door-knocker
and Factories

294 President Pak and
Emperor Haile Selassie

(T **293/4** des Oh Choong Whan)

1968 (6 May). 2nd Conference of Confederation of Asian Chambers
of Commerce and Industry (C.A.C.C.I.), Seoul. P 12½.

739	293	7w. multicoloured	1·50	45

MS740 90×60 mm. No. 739. Imperf................... 4.25 3.75

1968 (18 May). Visit of Emperor of Ethiopia. P 12½.

741	294	7w. multicoloured	3·75	1·50

MS742 90×60 mm. No. 741. Imperf................... 7·75 7·00

295 Post-bag

296 Atomic andDevelopment
Symbols

(Des Chun Hee Han)

1968 (31 May). Postman's Day. T **295** and similar horiz design.
Multicoloured. P 12½.

743	5w. Type **295**	1·50	70
744	7w. Postman	1·50	70

(Des Maing Do Sun)

1968 (1 June). Promotion of Science and Technology. P 12½.

745	296	7w. Royal bl. lt sage-grn & orge-red......	1·50	45

297 Kyung Hi University
and Conference Emblem

298 "Liberation"

(T **297/8** des Maing Do Sun)

1968 (18 June). Second Conference of International Association of
University Presidents. P 12½.

746	297	7w. multicoloured	1·50	45

MS747 91×60 mm. No. 746. Imperf.................... 5·50 5·00

1968 (1 July). Liberation of Suppressed Peoples' Campaign. P 12½.

748	298	7w. multicoloured	1·50	45

299 Reservist

300 Stylised Peacock

(T **299/300** des Chun Hee Han)

1968 (1 Aug). Army Reservists' Fund. P 13×12½.

749	299	7w. +3w. black and green	13·00	1·50

1968 (15 Aug). 20th Anniv of Republic. P 12½.

750	300	7w. multicoloured	1·50	45

301 Fair Entrance **302** Assembly
Emblem

(Des Chun Hee Han)

1968 (9 Sept). First Korean Trade Fair, Seoul. P 12½.
751 **301** 7w. multicoloured .... 1·50 45

(Des Oh Choong Whan)

1968 (16 Sept). Third General Assembly of Asian Pharmaceutical
Association Federation. P 12½.
752 **302** 7w. multicoloured .... 1·50 45

303 Scout Badge **304** Soldier and **305** Colombo Plan
Battle Scene Emblem and Globe

(Des Chun Hee Han)

1968 (30 Sept). Sixth Far East Scout Conference, Seoul. P 12½.
753 **303** 7w. multicoloured .... 2·30 75

(Des Chun Hee Han)

1968 (1 Oct). 20th Anniv of Korean Armed Forces. T **304** and similar
vert designs. P 12½.
754 7w. yellow-orange and light green .... 7·75 2·30
a. Vert strip of 5 Nos. 754/8................. 40·00
755 7w. royal blue and light blue .... 7·75 2·30
756 7w. royal blue and yellow-orange 7.75 2.30
757 7w. light blue and royal blue .... 7·75 2·30
758 7w. light green and yellow-orange .... 7·75 2·30
754/758 *Set of 5* .... 35·00 10·50
Designs.—No. 755, Sailor and naval guns; 756. Servicemen and
flags; 757. Airman and fighter planes; 758. Marine and landings.
Nos. 754/8 were issued together in vertical *se-tenant* strips of five
within the sheet.

(Des Chun Hee Han)

1968 (8 Oct). 19th Meeting of Colombo Plan Consultative Committee,
Seoul. P 12½.
759 **305** 7w. multicoloured .... 1·50 40

306 (I) Olympic Emblems **307** (II)

(Des Chun Hee Han)

1968 (12 Oct). Olympic Games, Mexico. T **306/7** and similar vert
designs. Multicoloured. P 12½.
760 7w. Type **306** .... 14·50 4·75
a. Horiz pair. Nos. 760/1 .... 30·00 10·00
761 7w. Type **307** .... 14·50 4·75
762 7w. Cycling (I) .... 14·50 4·75
a. Horiz pair. Nos. 762/3 .... 30·00 10·00
763 7w. Cycling (II) .... 14·50 4·75
764 7w. Boxing (I) .... 14·50 4·75
a. Horiz pair. Nos. 764/5 .... 30·00 10·00
765 7w. Boxing (II) .... 14·50 4·75
766 7w. Wrestling (I) .... 14·50 4·75
a. Horiz pair. Nos. 766/7 .... 30·00 10·00
767 7w. Wrestling (II)............................. 14·50 4·75
760/767 *Set of 8*.. £100 34·00
MS768 Four sheets each 90×60 mm. Imperf.
(a) Nos. 760/1; (b) Nos. 762/3; (c) Nos. 764/5;
(d) Nos. 766/7 .... 46·00 42·00
The two types of each design may be identified by the position of
the country names at the foot of the design—ranged right in types
I. and left in types II. On three of the designs (excluding "Cycling")
the figures of value are on left and right respectively. Types I and II of
each design were issued together in horizontal *se-tenant* pairs within
their sheets.

308 Statue of Woman **309** Coin and Symbols

(T **308/9** des Oh Choong Whan)

1968 (15 Oct). 60th Anniv of Women's Secondary Education. P 12½.
769 **308** 7w. multicoloured .... 1·50 40

1968 (1 Nov). National Wealth Survey. P 12½.
770 **309** 7w. multicoloured .... 1·50 40

(Des Chun Hee Han)

1968 (1 Nov). Disaster Relief Fund. As No. 734, but with additional
inscr and premium added. P 13×12½.
771 **290** 7w. +3w. red and deep blue .... 42·00 7·75
See also Nos. 780 and 827.

310 Shin Eui Ju **311** Demonstrators
Memorial

(Des Chun Hee Han)

1968 (23 Nov). Anniv of Student Uprising, Shin Eui Ju (1945). P 12½.
772 **310** 7w. multicoloured .... 1·90 55

(Des Oh Choong Whan)

1968 (5 Dec). Second Five Year Plan. Horiz Designs as T **272,** but
dated "1968". Multicoloured. P 12½.
773 7w. Express motorway .... 13·00 1·20
774 7w. "Clover-leaf" motorway junction.... 7·75 1·20

(Des Chun Hee Han)

1968 (10 Dec). Human Rights Year. P 12½.
775   **311**   7w. multicoloured .... 1·50   40

312 Christmas   **313** Cockerel
Lanterns

(Des Oh Choong Whan)

1968 (11 Dec). Christmas and Lunar New Year ("Year of the Cock").
P 12½.
776   **312**   5w. multicoloured .... 11·50   55
777   **313**   7w. multicoloured .... 11·50   55
MS778 Two sheets each 90×60 mm. Nos. 776/7.
  Imperf.. 15·00   14·00

314 Korean House and   **315** Torch, and
UN Emblems   Monument, Pagoda
                              Park, Seoul

(Des Chun Hee Han)

1968 (12 Dec). 20th Anniv of South Korea's Admission to United
Nations. P 12½.
779   **314**   7w. multicoloured .... 1·50   40

1969 (15 Feb). Military Helicopter Fund. As No. 734, but colours
changed and inscr with premium added. P 13×12½.
780   **290**   7w. +3w. red, dp vio-bl & p turq-grn..... 11·50   1·30

(Des Chun Hee Han)

1969 (1 Mar). 50th Anniv of Samil (Independence) Movement
P 12½.
781   **315**   7w. multicoloured .... 1·50   45

316 Hyun Choong Sa   **317** Pres. Pak and Yang
and "Turtle" Ships   di-Pertuan Agong

(Des Chun Hee Han)

1969 (28 Apr). Dedication of Rebuilt Hyun Choong Sa (shrine of
Admiral Li Sun Sin). P 12½.
782   **316**   7w. multicoloured .... 1·50   45

(Des Kang Choon Whan)

1969 (29 Apr). Visit of Yang di-Pertuan Agong (Malaysian Head-of-
State). P 12½.
783   **317**   7w. multicoloured .... 3·75   1·20
MS784 90×60 mm. No. 783. Imperf................................ 65·00   60·00

318 Stone Temple   **319** Wine Jug   **320** "Duck" Vase
Lamp

321 Porcelain Jar,   **322** Seated
Yi Dynasty   Buddha (bronze)

(Des Kang Choon Whan (T **318/22**). Litho (Nos. 785, 789, 793) or
photo)

1969 (1 May)–**70**. Definitive types of previous issues re-drawn and
T **318/22** Granite paper (Nos. 785, 789, 793). P 12½ (Nos. 785,
789, 793), 12½×13½ (No. 792) or 13½×12½ (others).
785   **178** 40ch. emerald (1. 6.69).............................. 1·50   40
786   **318**   5w. purple (1.7.69) .... 1·10   25
787   **290**   7w. blue .... 3·75   40
788   7w. light new blue* (1.10.69)................ 1·50   30
789   **168** 10w. blue (1.6.69) .... 31·00   70
790   **290** 10w. deep ultramarine (25.2.70) .... 1·50   25
791   **319** 20w. myrtle green (1.6.69) .... 2·30   40
792   **320** 30w. bluish green (25.2.70)................. 3·75   75
793   **183** 40w. royal blue St light pink (1.6.69) .... 46·00   2·30
794   **321** 40w. mauve & ultramarine (1.9.69).......... 2·75   75
795   **322** 100w. lt yellow-brn & pur (1.10.69) .... 95·00   2·30
785/795 *Set of 11* .... £170   8·00
*No. 788 has the face value shown as "7" only, omitting the noughts
shown on No. 787 and earlier versions of the design.
  Of the re-drawn designs No. 785 is now vertical, but is still without
the "REPUBLIC OF KOREA" inscription. Nos. 785, 789 and 793, are
smaller, size 18×22 mm or 22×18 mm (No. 789). Nos. 789 and 793 are
inscribed "REPUBLIC OF KOREA" and are without the noughts which
appeared on previous versions.

323 "Red Cross" between   **324** "Building the Nation's
Faces   Economy"

(Des Chun Hee Han. Litho)

1969 (5 May). 50th Anniv of League of Red Cross Societies. P 12½.
796   **323**   7w. multicoloured .... 1·90   45
MS797 90×60 mm. No. 796. Imperf.............................. 5·50   5·00

(Des Kang Choon Whan. Litho)

1969 (20 May). "Second Economy Drive". P 12½.
798   **324**   7w. multicoloured .. .. 1·50   45

325 Presidents Pak and
Nguyen-van-Thieu

326 Reafforestation
and Flooded Fields

(Des Chun Hee Han. Litho)

1969 (27 May). Visit of President Nguyen-van-Thieu of South Vietnam.
P 12½.
799 **325** 7w. multicoloured .... 3·00 1·20
MS800 90×60 mm. No. 799. Imperf................................ 8·50 6·75

(Des Kim Sung Sil. Litho)

1969 (10 June). Flood and Drought Damage Prevention Campaign.
T **326** and similar vert design. Multicoloured. P 12½.
801 7w. Type **326** .... 1·50 40
802 7w. Withered and flourishing plants...... 1·50 40

327 Ignition of Second-stage
Rocket

(Des Kang Choon Whan. Litho)

1969 (15 Aug). First Man on the Moon. T **327** and similar horiz
designs. P 12½.
803 10w. light blue, blue-black and
vermilion .... 3·75 1·10
a Strip of 5. Nos. 803/7............... 20·00
804 10w. light blue, blue-black and
vermilion .... 3·75 1·10
805 20w. multicoloured .... 3·75 1·10
806 20w. multicoloured .... 3·75 1·10
807 40w. light blue, vermilion and blue-
black .... 3·75 1·10
803/807 Set of 5 .... 17·00 5·00
MS808 160×110 mm. Nos. 803/7. Imperf........... 35·00 31·00
Designs:—No. 803, Type **327**; 804, Separation of modules from
rocket; 805, Diagram of lunar orbit; 806, Astronauts on Moon; 807,
Splashdown of "Apollo 11".
Nos. 803/7 were issued together in se-tenant strips of five within
the sheet.

328 Stepmother admonishing
Kongji

329 Kongji and Sparrows

330 Kongji and Ox

331 Kongji in Sedan-chair

(Des Chun Hee Han. Litho)

1969 (1 Sep). Korean Fairy Tales (1st series). "Kongji and Patji". P 12½.
809 **328** 5w. multicoloured .... 3·75 95
810 **329** 7w. multicoloured .... 3·75 95
811 **330** 10w. multicoloured .... 6·25 1·30
812 **331** 20w. multicoloured .... 6·25 1·30
809/812 Set of 4.. 18·00 4·00
MS813 Four sheets each 90×60 mm. Imperf.
(a) No. 809; (b) No. 810; (c) No. 811; (d) No. 812...... 25·00 22·00
See also Nos. 828/**MS**832, 839/**MS**843, 844/**MS**848 and 853/
MS857.

332 Steam
Locomotive of 1899

333 Northrop F-5A Freedom
Jet Fighters

(Des Kim Sung Sil (No. 814), Kim Kyung Ho (815). Litho)

1969 (18 Sept). 70th Anniv of Korean Railways. T **332** and similar vert
design. Multicoloured. P 12½×13.
814 7w. Type **332** .... 1·90 70
815 7w. Early steam and modern diesel
locos .... 1·90 70

(Des Kang Choon Whan. Photo (No. 816) or litho (817))

1969 (1 Oct). 20th Anniv of Korean Air Force. T **333** and similar horiz
design. Multicoloured. P 13½×13 (No. 816) or 13×12½ (817).
816 10w. Type **333** .... 5·50 75
817 10w. McDonnell Douglas F-4D Phantom
II jet fighter................................ 7·00 75

334 Game of Cha-jun

335 Molecule and Institute
Building

(Des Chun Hee Han. Litho)

1969 (3 Oct). 10th Korean Traditional Arts Contest, Taegu. P 13×12½.
818 **334** 7w. multicoloured .... 1·20 40

(Des Hong Won Sook. Litho)

1969 (23 Oct). Completion of Korean Institute of Science and
Technology. P 13×12½.
819 **335** 7w. multicoloured .... 1·20 40

336 Presidents Pak and
Hamani

337 Football

(Des Kang Choon Whan. Litho)

1969 (27 Oct). Visit of President Hamani of Niger Republic. P 13×12½.

820	**336**	7w. multicoloured	2·30	1·00
MS821	90×60 mm. No. 820. Imperf		14·00	12·50

(Des Kim Kyung Ho (No. 822), Kim Sung Sil (823/4), Hong Won Sook (825), Chun Hee Han (826). Litho)

1969 (28 Oct). 50th Anniv of National Athletic Meeting. T **337** and similar multicoloured designs. P 12½×13 (822/3) or 13×12½ (others).

822		10w. Type **337**	3·00	75
823		10w. Volleyball	3·00	75
824		10w. Korean wrestling (horiz)	3·00	75
825		10w. Fencing (horiz)	3·00	75
826		10w. Taekwondo (karate) (horiz)	3·00	75
822/826	*Set of 5*		13·50	3·50

1969 (1 Nov). Searchlight Fund. As No. 734, but with additional inscription and face value redrawn to include premium. Litho. P 13×12½.

827	**290**	7w. +3w. red and blue	39·00	1·70

This stamp can be easily distinguished from the earlier charity stamp, No. 771, by the absence of noughts after the face value on No. 827.

338 Princess and the Doctors   **339** Hare arriving at Palace

340 Preparing to remove the Hare's Liver   **341** Escape of the Hare

(Des Chun Hee Han. Litho)

1969 (1 Nov). Korean Fairy Tales (2nd series). "The Hare's Liver". P 13×12½.

828	**338**	5w. multicoloured	2·30	70
829	**339**	7w. multicoloured	2·30	70
830	**340**	10w. multicoloured	2·30	95
831	**341**	20w. multicoloured	3·75	95
828/831	*Set of 4*		9·50	3·00
MS832	Four sheets each 90×60 mm. Imperf.			
	(a) No. 828; (b) No. 829; (c) No. 830; (d) No. 831		22·00	20·00

(Des Kim Kyung Ho. Litho)

1969 (5 Dec). Second Five Year Plan. Horiz designs as T **272**, but dated "1969" Multicoloured. P 13×12½.

833		7w. "Agriculture and Fisheries"	1·50	45
834		7w. Industrial emblems. .	1·50	45

342 Students ringing "Education"   **343** Toy Dogs

(Des Chun Hee Han. Litho)

1969 (5 Dec). 1st Anniv of National Education Charter. P 12½×13.

835	**342**	7w. multicoloured	1·20	3·75

(Des Hong Won Sook (5w.), Kim Sung Sil (7w.). Photo)

1969 (11 Dec). Lunar New Year ("Year of the Dog"). T **343** and similar horiz design. Multicoloured. P 13½×13.

836		5w. Type **343**	1·50	45
837		7w. Candle and lattice doorway	1·50	45

344 Korean Woman and UPU Monument, Berne

(Des Chun Hee Han. Photo)

1970 (1 Jan). 70th Anniv of Korea's Admission to Universal Postal Union. P 13×13½.

838	**344**	10w. multicoloured	11·50	3·75

345 Mother meets the Tiger   **346** Tiger in Disguise

347 Children chased up a Tree   **348** Children escape to Heaven

(Des Chun Hee Han. Litho)

1970 (5 Jan). Korean Fairy Tales (3rd series). "The Sun and the Moon". P 13×12½.

839	**345**	5w. multicoloured	2·30	70
840	**346**	7w. multicoloured	2·30	70
841	**347**	10w. multicoloured	2·30	95
842	**348**	20w. multicoloured	3·75	1·20
839/842	*Set of 4*		9·50	3·25
MS843	Four sheets each 90×60 mm. Imperf.			
	(a) No. 839; (b) No. 840; (c) No. 841; (d) No. 842		22·00	20·00

349 Woodcutter hiding Fairy's Dress   **350** Fairy as Woodcutter's Wife

351 Fairy and Children fly to Heaven **352** Happy Reunion

(Des Chun Hee Han. Litho)

1970 (5 Mar). Korean Fairy Tales (4th series). "The Woodcutter and the Fairy". P 13×12½.

844	**349**	10w. multicoloured	2·75	1·00
845	**350**	10w. multicoloured	2·75	1·00
846	**351**	10w. multicoloured	2·75	1·00
847	**352**	10w. multicoloured	2·75	1·00
844/847		Set of 4	10·00	3·50

MS848 Four sheets each 90×60 mm. Imperf.
(a) No. 844; (b) No. 845; (c) No. 846; (d) No. 847 ...... 22·00 20·00

353 IEY Emblem on Open Book **354** Seated Buddha and Korean Pavilion

(Des Kang Choon Whan. Litho)

1970 (10 Mar). International Education Year. P 12½ ×13.
849   **353**   10w. multicoloured .... 6·25   2·30

(Des Kang Choon Whan. Litho)

1970 (15 Mar). "EXPO 70" World Fair, *Osaka, Japan*. P 13×12½.
850   **354**   10w. multicoloured .... 6·25   1·60

355 "4-H" Club Emblem **356** Bank Emblem and Cash

(Des Chun Hee Han. Litho)

1970 (28 Mar). 15th "4-H" Club (young farmers' organization) Central Contest, Suwon. P 12½×13.
851   **355**   10w. multicoloured .... 1·90   75

(Des Kim Kyung Ho. Litho)

1970 (9 Apr). 3rd General Meeting of Asian Development Bank, Seoul. P 13×12½.
852   **356**   10w. multicoloured .... 1·90   75

357 Heungbu tending Swallow **358** Heungbu finds Treasure in Pumpkin

359 Nolbu with Pumpkin **360** Nolbu chased by Devil

(Des Chun Hee Han. Litho)

1970 (5 May). Korean Fairy Tales (5th series). "Heungbu and Nolbu". P 12½.

853	**357**	10w. multicoloured	6·25	1·20
854	**358**	10w. multicoloured	6·25	1·20
855	**359**	10w. multicoloured	6·25	1·20
856	**360**	10w. multicoloured	6·25	1·20
853/856		Set of 4	23·00	4·25

MS857 Four sheets each 90×60 mm. Imperf.
(a) No. 853; (b) No. 854; (c) No. 855; (d) No. 856 ...... 60·00 55·00

361 Royal Palanquin (Yi dynasty) **362** New Headquarters Building

(Des Kim Sung Sil (No. 858), Hong Won Sook (859, 861), Kim Kyung Ho (860). Photo)

1970 (20 May). Early Korean Transport. T **361** and similar designs. P 13×13½ (No. 858) or 13½×13 (others).

858		10w. multicoloured	2·75	95
859		10w. multicoloured	2·75	95
860		10w. multicoloured	2·75	95
861		10w. black, yellow-ochre & greenish blue	2·75	95
858/861		Set of 4	10·00	3·50

Designs: Horiz—No. 859, Tramcar, 1899; 860, Emperor Sunjong's Cadillac, 1903; 861, An Chang Nam's Nieuport 28 biplane, 1922.

(Des Kang Choon Whan. Photo)

1970 (30 May). Opening of New Universal Postal Union Headquarters Building, Berne. P 13½×13.
862   **362**   10w. multicoloured . ... 1·50   40

363 Dish Aerial and Hemispheres **364** "PEN" and Quill Pen

(Des Kang Choon Whan. Photo)

1970 (2 June). Inauguration of Satellite Communications Stations, Kum San. P 13×13½.

863   **363**   10w. multicoloured .... 1·90   75

(Des Kim Sung Sil. Photo)

1970 (28 June). 37th International PEN (literary organization) Congress, Seoul. P 13×13½.

864   **364**   10w. multicoloured .... 1·50   40

365 Section of Motorway   **366** Postal Code Symbol

(Des Kang Choon Whan. Photo)

1970 (30 June). Opening of Seoul–Pusan Motorway. P 13×13½.

865   **365**   10w. multicoloured... 1·90   75

(Des Kim Sung Sil. Photo)

1970 (1 July). Introduction of Postal Codes. P 13×13½.

866   **366**   10w. multicoloured .... 1·50   40

367 Parcel Sorting Area   **368** Children's Hall and Boy

(Des Chun Hee Han. Photo)

1970 (1 July). Inauguration of Postal Mechanization. P 13×13½.

867   **367**   10w. multicoloured .... 1·50   40
MS868 130×90 mm. Nos. 866/7×2 .... £100   90·00

(Des Chun Hee Han. Photo)

1970 (25 July). Opening of Children's Hall, Seoul. P 13×13½.

869   **368**   10w. multicoloured .... 1·50   40

GUM. From No. 870 onwards many issues have matt, almost invisible gum.

369 "Mountain and River" (Yi In Moon)

(Des Kang Choon Whan. Photo)

1970 (31 Aug). Korean Painting of the Yi Dynasty (1st series). T **369** and similar multicoloured designs. P 13½×13. (No. 872) or 13×13½ (others).

870   10w. Type **369**   2·75   75
871   10w. "Jongyangsa Temple" (Chong Son)   2·75   75
872   10w. "Mountain and River by Moon-
        light" (Kim Doo Ryang) (*vert*) .... 2·75   75
870/872 *Set of 3* .... 7·50   2·00
MS873 Three sheets each 130×90 mm. Nos.
     870/2×2 Imperf .... 14·00   12·50
     See also Nos. 887/MS890, 897/MS900, 947/MS953, 956/MS959 and 961/MS966.

370 PTTI Emblem   **371** WAC and Corps Badge

(Des Hong Won Sook. Litho)

1970 (6 Sept). Councillors' Meeting, Asian Chapter of Postal, Telegraph and Telephone International (Post Office Trade Union Federation). P 13×12½.

874   **370**   10w. multicoloured .... 1·50   45

(Des Chun Hee Han. Photo)

1970 (6 Sept). 20th Anniv of Korean Women's Army Corps. P 13×13½.

875   **371**   10w. multicoloured .... 1·50   45

372 President Pak and Flag

(Des Kang Choon Whan (876), Chun Hee Han (877))

1970. T **372** and similar design. Photo. P 13×13½ (No. 876) or 13½×13 (877).

876   **372**   10w. multicoloured (28.9) .... 9·25   3·75
877   –   10w. black, turq-grn & bl (30.11)............... 14·00   3·75
     Design: Vert — No. 877, Pres. Pak and industrial complex.

373 Presidents Pak and Sanchez Hernández   **374** "People and Houses"

(Des Kang Choon Whan)

1970 (28 Sept). Visit of President Sánchez Hernández of El Salvador. Litho. P 13×12½.

878   **373**   10w. multicoloured .... 3·00   1·50
MS879 90×60 mm. No. 878. Imperf (inscr
     "SALVADOL") .... 39·00   38·00
       a. Spelling corrected to "SALVADOR"............... £100   80·00

(Des Hong Won Sook. Litho)

1970 (1 Oct). National Census. P 13×12½.
880 **374** 10w. multicoloured .... 1·50 40

375 Diving

(Des Kim Sung Sil (No. 882), Chun Hee Han (others). Photo)

1970 (6 Oct). 51st National Athletic Games, Seoul. T **375** and similar horiz designs. Multicoloured. P 12½×13½.
881 10w. Type **375**. .... 4·75 1·20
882 10w. Hockey .... 4·75 1·20
883 10w. Baseball .... 4·75 1·20
881/883 *Set of 3* .... 13·00 3·25
MS884 Three sheets each 91×87 mm. Nos. 881/3×2.
Imperf .... 30·00 29·00

376 Police Badge and Activities   **377** Bell and Globe

(Des Lee Keun Moon)

1970 (21 Oct). National Police Day. Litho. P 12½.
885 **376** 10w. multicoloured .... 1·50 55

(Des Chun Hee Han)

1970 (24 Oct). 25th Anniv of United Nations. Photo. P 13×13½.
886 **377** 10w. multicoloured .... 1·50 45

(Des Kang Choon Whan)

1970 (30 Oct). Korean Paintings of the Yi Dynasty (2nd series). Vert designs, similar to T **369**, showing animals. Multicoloured. Photo. P 13½×13.
887 30w. "Fierce Tiger" (Shim Sa Yung) .... 12·50 1·90
888 30w. "Cats and Sparrows" (Pyun Sang Byuk) .... 12·50 1·90
889 30w. "Dog with Puppies" (Yi Am) .... 12·50 1·90
887/889 *Set of 3* .... 34·00 5·25
MS890 Three sheets each 130×90 mm. Nos. 887/9×2. £170 £160
Nos. 887/**MS**890 also exist imperforate.

378 Kite and Reel   **379** Quotation and Emblems on Globe

(Des Chun Hee Han (No. 891), Hong Won Sook (892). Photo)

1970 (1 Dec). Lunar New Year ('Year of the Pig"). T **378** and similar vert design. Multicoloured. P 13×13½.
891 10w. Type **378** .... 1·50 40
892 10w. Toy pig .... 1·50 40
MS893 Two sheets each 90×60 mm. Nos. 891/2×3 ... 15·00 14·00

(Des Chun Hee Han. Photo)

1970 (4 Dec). 15th Communications Day. P 13×13½.
894 **379** 10w. multicoloured. .... 1·50 55

(Des Hong Won Sook (No. 895), Kim Sung Sil (896). Photo)

1970 (5 Dec). Second Five Year Plan. Horiz designs as T **272**, but dated "1970". Multicoloured. P 13½×13.
895 10w. "Port Development" .... 1·50 40
896 10w. "House Construction" .... 1·50 40

(Des Kang Choon Whan. Photo)

1970 (30 Dec). Korean Paintings of the Yi Dynasty (3rd series). Vert designs, similar to T **369**. Multicoloured. P 13½×13.
897 10w. "Chokpyokdo" (river cliff) (Kim Hong Do) .... 2·75 75
898 10w. "Hen and Chicks" (Pyun Sang Byuk) 2·75 75
899 10w. "The Flute player" (Shin Yun Bok) ... 2·75 75
897/899 *Set of 3* .... 7·50 2·00
MS900 Three sheets each 130×90 mm. Nos. 897/9×2.
Perf or imperf .... 28·00 25·00

380 Fields ("Food Production")   **381** Coal-mining

(Des Hong Won Sook (No. 901), Chun Hee Han (902), Lee Keun Moon (903). Photo)

1971 (5 Jan). Economic Development (1st series). T **380** and similar multicoloured designs. P 13½×13 (No. 901) or 13×13½ (others).
901 10w. Type **380**. .... 1·90 55
902 10w. Dam ("Electric Power") (horiz) .... 1·90 55
903 10w. Map on crate ("Exports") (horiz) ..... 1·90 55
901/903 *Set of 3* .... 5·25 1·50
MS904 Three sheets each 90×60 mm. Nos. 901/3.
Imperf .... 21·00 19·00
See also Nos. 905/8 and 910/13.

(Des Lee Keun Moon. Photo)

1971 (5 Feb). Economic Development (2nd series). T **381** and similar multicoloured designs. P 13×13½ (No. 906) or 13½×13 (others).
905 10w. Type **381** .... 1·50 40
906 10w. Cement works (vert) .... 1·50 40
907 10w. Fertilizer plant .... 1·50 40
905/907 *Set of 3* .... 4·00 1·10
MS908 Three sheets each 90×60 mm. Nos. 905/7×2.
Imperf .... 21·00 19·00

382 Globe, Torch and Spider   **383** Motorway Junction

(Des Lee Keun Moon. Litho)

1971 (1 Mar). Anti-Espionage Month. P 12½×13.
909 **382** 10w. multicoloured .... 1·50 45

(Des Lee Keun Moon (No. 910), Chun Hee Han (911), Kim Sung Sil (912). Photo)

1971 (5 Mar). Economic Development (3rd series). T **383** and similar multicoloured designs. P 13×13½ (No. 910) or 13½×13. (others).

910	10w. Type **383**	1·50	40
911	10w. Scales ("Gross National Income") (horiz)	1·50	40
912	10w. Bee and coins ("Increased Savings" (horiz)	1·50	40
910/912 *Set of 3*		4·00	1·10

MS913 Three sheets each 90×60 mm................................
Nos. 910/12×2. Imperf .... 16·00 14·50

384 Reservist and Badge

385 WHO Emblem, Stethoscope and Microscope

(Des Chun Hee Han. Photo)

1971 (3 Apr). 3rd Home Reserve Forces Day. P 13½×13.
914   **384**   10w. multicoloured .... 1·50   45

(Des Hong Won Sook. Photo)

1971 (7 Apr). 20th World Health Day. P 13½×13.
915   **385**   10w. multicoloured .... 1·40   55

386 Underground Train

387 Footballer

(Des Kim Sung Sil. Litho)

1971 (12 Apr). Construction of Seoul Underground Railway System. P 12½×13.
916   **386**   10w. multicoloured .... 1·40   40

(Des Kim Sung Sil. Litho)

1971 (2 May). 1st Asian Soccer Games, Seoul. P 12½×13.
917   **387**   10w. multicoloured .... 1·90   75

PRINTERS. From No. 917 onwards all issues were printed in photogravure by the Korean Government Printing Agency, *unless otherwise stated.*

388 Veteran and Association Flag

389 Girl Scouts

(Des Chun Hee Han)

1971 (8 May). 20th Korean Veterans' Day. P 13×13½.
918   **388**   10w. multicoloured .... 1·40   45

(Des Chun Hee Han)

1971 (10 May). 25th Anniv of Korean Girl Scouts Federation. P 13×13½.
919   **389**   10w. multicoloured .... 1·40   30

390 Torch and Economic Symbols

391 "Telecommunications"

(Des Hong Won Sook)

1971 (16 May). 10th Anniv of Revolution of 16 May. P 13×13½.
920   **390**   10w. multicoloured .... 1·40   40

(Des Hong Won Sook)

1971 (17 May). 3rd World Telecommunications Day. P 13×13½.
921   **391**   10w. multicoloured .... 1·40   45

392 Food and Agriculture Organization

394 President Pak, Emblem and Motorway

393 "Boating" (Shin Yun Bok)

(Des Kang Choon Whan)

1971 (30 May). "The Work of the United Nations Organization". T **392** and similar horiz designs, each showing different emblem. P 13½×13.

922	10w. mauve, black & pale turquoise-grn	3·75	1·20
	a. Block of 25. Nos. 922/46	£100	
923	10w. light blue, black and mauve.............	3·75	1·20
924	10w. multicoloured	3·75	1·20
925	10w. light blue, black and mauve.............	3·75	1·20
926	10w. mauve, black & pale turquoise-grn	3·75	1·20
927	10w. light blue, black and mauve.............	3·75	1·20
928	10w. mauve, black and light blue.............	3·75	1·20
929	10w. black, pale turquoise-green & mve	3·75	1·20
930	10w. mauve, black and light blue.............	3·75	1·20
931	10w. light blue, black and mauve.............	3·75	1·20
932	10w. mauve, black and light blue.............	3·75	1·20
933	10w. black, mauve & pale turquoise-grn	3·75	1·20
934	10w. mauve, light blue and black.............	3·75	1·20
935	10w. black, mauve & pale turquoise-grn	3·75	1·20
936	10w. mauve, black and light blue.............	3·75	1·20
937	10w. light blue, black and mauve.............	3·75	1·20
938	10w. mauve, black and light blue.............	3·75	1·20
939	10w. black, mauve & pale turquoise-grn	3·75	1·20
940	10w. mauve, black and light blue.............	3·75	1·20
941	10w. light blue, black and mauve.............	3·75	1·20
942	10w. mauve, black & pale turquoise-grn	3·75	1·20

943	10w. black, light blue and mauve	3·75	1·20
944	10w. multicoloured	3·75	1·20
945	10w. black, new blue and mauve	3·75	1·20
946	10w. black, mauve & pale turquoise-grn	3·75	1·20
922/946	Set of 25	85·00	27·00

Emblems:—No. 922, International Labour Organization; 923, Type **392**; 924, General Assembly and New York Headquarters; 925, UNESCO; 926, World Health Organization; 927, World Bank; 928, International Development Association; 929, Security Council; 930, International Finance Corporation; 931, International Monetary Fund; 932, International Civil Aviation Organization; 933, Economic and Social Council; 934, South Korean flag; 935, Trusteeship Council; 936, UPU; 937, ITU; 938, World Meteorological Organization; 939, International Court of Justice; 940, International Maritime Consultative Organization; 941, UNICEF; 942, International Atomic Energy Agency; 943, United Nations Industrial Development Organization; 944, United Nations Commission for the Unification and Rehabilitation of Korea; 945, United Nations Development Programme; 946, United Nations Conference on Trade and Development.

Nos. 922/46 were issued together in *se-tenant* sheets of 50, each design appearing twice in the sheet.

(Des Kang Choon Whan)

1971 (20 June). Korean Paintings of the Yi Dynasty (4th series). T **393** and similar multicoloured designs. P 13½×13 (No. 952) or 13×13½ (others).

947	10w. Type **393**	6·25	1·90
	a. Vert strip of 5. Nos. 947/51.	32·00	
948	10w. "Greeting Travellers" (Shin Yun Bok)	6·25	1·90
949	10w. "Tea Ceremony" (Shin Yun Bok)	6·25	1·90
950	10w. "Lady and Servants on Country Road" (Shin Yun Bok)..........................	6·25	1·90
951	10w. "Couple Walking" (Shin Yun Bok)....	6·25	1·90
952	10w. "Fairy and Boy beneath Pine Tree" (Li Chae Kwan) (vert)........................	6·25	1·90
947/952	Set of 6	34·00	10·50
MS953	Six sheets each 130×90 mm. Nos. 947/52×2	75·00	65·00

Nos. 947/51 represent "Folk Customs" and were issued together vertically *se-tenant* within the sheet of 25.

(Des Chun Hee Han)

1971 (1 July). Re-election of Pres. Pak for Third Term. P 13½×13.

954	**394**	10w. multicoloured..............................	23·00	2·30
MS955		90×60 mm. No. 954×2	75·00	70·00

(Des Kang Choon Whan)

1971 (20 July). Korean Paintings of the Yi Dynasty (5th series). Multicoloured designs, similar to T **393**. P 13×13½ (No. 956) or 13½×13 (others).

956	10w. "Chasing the Cat" (Kim Deuk Shin)	3·00	1·30
957	10w. "Valley Family" (Li Chae Kwan) (vert)	3·00	1·30
958	10w. "Man Reading" (Li Chae Kwan) (vert)	3·00	1·30
956/958	Set of 3	8·00	3·50
MS959	Three sheets each 130×90 mm. Nos. 956/8×2	25·00	23·00

395 Campfire and Badge

396 Cogwheel and Asian Map

(Des Chun Hee Han)

1971 (2 Aug). 13th World Scout Jamboree, Asagiri, Japan. P 13×13½.

960	**395**	10w. multicoloured	1·40	40

(Des Kang Choon Whan)

1971 (20 Aug). Korean Paintings of the Yi Dynasty (6th series). Genre Paintings by Kim Hong Do. Designs similar to T **393**, but vert. Multicoloured. P 13½×13.

961	10w. "Classroom".	5·50	2·75
	a. Horiz strip of 5. Nos. 961/5.	29·00	
962	10w. "Wrestling Match".	5·50	2·75
963	10w. "Dancer with Musicians".	5·50	2·75
964	10w. "Weavers".	5·50	2·75
965	10w. "Drawing Water at the Well".	5·50	2·75
961/965	Set of 5	25·00	12·50
MS966	Five sheets each 130×90 mm. Nos. 961/5×2.	60·00	55·00

Nos. 961/5 were issued together horizontally *se-tenant* within the sheet of 25.

(Des Kang Choon Whan)

1971 (27 Sept). 3rd Asian Labour Ministers' Conference, Seoul. P 13½×13.

967	**396**	10w. multicoloured	1·40	45
MS968		90×60 mm. No. 967×2	50·00	45·00

397 Judo

(Des Chun Hee Han)

1971 (8 Oct). 52nd National Athletic Meeting, Seoul. T **397** and similar horiz design. Multicoloured. P 12½×13½.

969	10w. Type **397**	2·30	75
970	10w. Archery	2·30	75
MS971	Two sheets each 91×87 mm. Nos. 969/70×3. P 14½×13½	70·00	65·00

398 Korean Symbol on Palette

399 Doctor and Globe

(Des Chun Hee Han)

1971 (11 Oct). 20th National Fine Art Exhibition. P 13½×13.

972	**398**	10w. multicoloured	1·40	30

(Des Chun Hee Han)

1971 (13 Oct). 7th Congress of Medical Associations from Asia and Oceania. P 13½×13.

973	**399**	10w. multicoloured	1·40	30

400 Emblem and "Vocational Skills"

401 Calipers and "K" Emblem

(Des Lee Keun Moon)

1971 (20 Oct). 2nd National Vocational Skill Contest for High School Students. P 13×13½.
974   **400**   10w. multicoloured .... 1·40   30
MS975 90×60 mm. No. 974×2 .... 42·00 38·00

(Des Lee Keun Moon)

1971 (11 Nov). 10th Anniv of Industrial Standardisation. P 13½ ×13.
976   **401**   10w. multicoloured .... 1·40   30

402 Fairy-tale Rats   **403** Emblem and Hangul Alphabet

(Des Kim Sung Sil)

1971 (1 Dec). Lunar New Year ("Year of the Rat"). T **402** and similar vert design. Multicoloured. P 13×13½.
977   10w. Type **402** .... 1·90   40
978   10w. Flying crane................................. 1·90   40
MS979 Two sheets each 90×60 mm. Nos. 977/8×3 ... 55·00 49·00

(Des Kim Sung Sil)

1971 (3 Dec). 50th Anniv of Hangul Hakhoe (Korean Language Research Society). P 13×13½.
980   **403**   10w. multicoloured .... 1·40   30

(Des Kang Choon Whan (No. 981). Hong Won Sook (982))

1971 (5 Dec). Second Five Year Plan. Horiz designs as T **272.** but dated '1971'. Multicoloured. P 13½×13.
981   10w. Atomic power plant .... 1·50   40
982   10w. Hydro-electric power project .... 1·50   40

404 Korean Red Cross Building on Map   **405** Globe and Open Book

(Des Chun Hee Han)

1971 (31 Dec). South-North Korean Red Cross Conference, Panmunjom. P 13½×13.
983   **404**   10w. multicoloured .... 1·50   60
MS984 125×90 mm. No. 983×2 .... 12·50 11·00

(Des Chun Hee Han)

1972 (5 Jan). International Book Year. P 13×13½.
985   **405**   10w. multicoloured .... 1·20   30
MS986 90×60 mm. No. 985×2 .... 11·50 10·50

406 "Intelsat 4" and Korean Earth Station   **407** Speed Skating

(Des Kim Sung Sil)

1972 (31 Jan). 20th Anniv of Korea's Membership of International Telecommunications Union. P 13½×13.
987   **406**   10w. multicoloured .... 1·20   40

(Des Chun Hee Han (No. 988), Lee Keun Moon (989))

1972 (3 Feb). Winter Olympic Games, Sapporo, Japan. T **407** and similar vert design. Multicoloured. P 13×13½.
988   10w. Type **407** .... 1·50   60
989   10w. Figure-skating .... 1·50   60
MS990 90×60 mm. Nos. 988/9 .... 11·50 10·50

408 Forestry Map   **409** Scarab Beetles and Emblem

(Des Kim Sung Sil)

1972 (10 Mar). "Trees for Unity" Campaign. P 13×13½.
991   **408**   10w. multicoloured .... 1·20   40

(Des Lee Keun Moon]

1972 (19 Mar). 20th Anniv of Korean Junior Chamber of Commerce. P 13½ ×13.
992   **409**   10w. multicoloured .... 1·20   40

410 ECAFE Emblem and Industrial Symbols   **411** Flags of Member Countries

(Des Chun Hee Han)

1972 (28 Mar). 25th Anniv of United Nations Economic Commission for Asia and the Far East. P 13×13½.
993   **410**   10w. multicoloured .... 1·20   40

(Des Kim Yong Bae)

1972 (1 Apr). 10th Anniv of Asian and Oceanic Postal Union. P 13½×13.
994   **411**   10w. multicoloured .... 1·20   40

412 Reserve Forces'
Flag

413 Emblem and
Butterflies (*Terias
harina*)

(Des Chun Hee Han)

1972 (1 Apr). Home Reserve Forces Day. P 13×13½.
995 **412** 10w. multicoloured .... 1·50   45

(Des Lee Keun Moon)

1972 (20 Apr). 50th Anniv of Korean Young Women's Christian
Association. P 13×13½.
996 **413** 10w. multicoloured .... 1·70   45

414 Rural Activities

415 "Anti-Espionage"
and Korean Flag

(Des Kim Yong Bae)

1972 (1 May). "New Community" (rural development) Movement.
P 13×13½.
997 **414** 10w. multicoloured .... 1·20   40

(Des Kim Sung Sil)

1972 (1 May). Anti-Espionage Month. P 13×13½.
998 **415** 10w. multicoloured .... 1·20   40

416 Children with Balloons

417 Leaf Ornament
from Gold Crown

(Des Kim Sung Sil)

1972 (5 May). 50th Children's Day. P 13½×13.
999 **416** 10w. multicoloured .... 1·20   40

(Des Kang Choon Whan)

1972 (10 May). Treasures from Tomb of King Munyong. T **417** and
similar multicoloured design. P 13×13½ (No. 1000) or 13½×13
(1001).
1000   10w. Type **417** .... 1·20   40
1001   10w. Gold earrings (horiz) .... 1·20   40

418 Lake Paengnokdam,
Mt. Halla Park

419 Kalkot, Koje Island,
Hanryo Straits Park

(Des Kang Choon Whan)

1972 (30 May). National Parks (1st series). P 13½×13.
1002 **418** 10w. multicoloured .... 3·00   45
1003 **419** 10w. multicoloured .... 3·00   45
See also Nos. 1018/19 and 1026/7.

420 Marguerite and
Conference Emblem

421 Gwanghwa Gate
and National Flags

(Des Kim Sung Sil)

1972 (5 June). UN Environmental Conservation Conference,
Stockholm. P 13×13½.
1004 **420** 10w. multicoloured .... 1·20   40
MS1005 90×60 mm. No. 1004×2 .... 7·75   7·00

(Des Kim Yong Bae)

1972 (14 June). 7th Ministerial Meeting of Asian and Pacific Council
(ASPAC), Seoul. P 13×13½.
1006 **421** 10w. multicoloured .... 1·20   40

422 Pasture ("Development
of Rural Economy")

423 "Love Pin"

(Des Kim Sung Sil (No. 1007), Lee Keun Moon (others))

1972 (1 July). Third Five Year Plan. T **422** and similar horiz designs,
dated "1972". Multicoloured. P 13½×13.
1007   10w. Type **422** .... 1·90   55
1008   10w. Foundry ladle ("Heavy Industries")   1·90   55
1009   10w. Crate and Globe ("Increased
        Exports") .... 1·90   55
1007/1009 *Set of 3* .... 5·25   1·50

(Des Kim Sung Sil)

1972 (1 Aug). Disaster Relief Fund. P 13½×12½.
1010 **423** 10w. +5w. carmine-red & new blue .... 1·90   75

424 Judo

425 Family Reunion through Red Cross

(Des Chun Hee Han (No. 1011), Lee Keun Moon (1012), Kim Yong Bae (1013), Kim Sung Sil (1014))

1972 (26 Aug). Olympic Games, Munich. T **424** and similar vert designs. Multicoloured. P 13×13½.

1011	20w. Type **424**		1·20	55
	a. Pair. Nos. 1011/12		2·50	1·20
1012	20w. Weightlifting		1·20	55
1013	20w. Wrestling		1·20	55
	a. Pair. Nos. 1013/14		2·50	1·20
1014	20w. Boxing		1·20	55
1011/1014	Set of 4		4·25	2·00

MS1015 Two sheets each 90 × 60 mm. (a) Nos. 1011/12; (b) Nos. 1013/14 .... 12·50 11·00

Nos. 1011/12 and 1013/14 were respectively issued together in *se-tenant* pairs within their sheets.

(Des Kim Sung Sil)

1972 (30 Aug). 1st Plenary Meeting of South-North Korean Red Cross Conference, Pyongyang. P 13½×13.

1016	**425**	10w. multicoloured	1·90	75
MS1017	125×90 mm. No. 1016×2		27·00	26·00

426 Bulkuk Temple, Kyongju Park

427 Statue and Bobju Temple, Mt. Sokri Park

(Des Kang Choon Whan)

1972 (20 Sept). National Parks (2nd series). P 13½×13.

1018	**426**	10w. multicoloured	1·40	45
1019	**427**	10w. multicoloured	1·40	45

428 Conference Emblem within "5"

429 Lions Badge between Korean Emblems

(Des Kim Sung Sil)

1972 (25 Sept). 5th Asian Judicial Conference, Seoul. P 13½×13.

1020	**428**	10w. multicoloured	1·20	40

(Des Lee Keun Moon)

1972 (26 Sept). 11th Orient and South-East Asian Lions Convention, Seoul. P 13½×13.

1021	**429**	10w. multicoloured	1·20	40

The horizontal rows of No. 1021 form a continuous design within the sheet.

430 Scout taking Oath

431 Dolls and Ox's Head

(Des Chun Hee Han)

1972 (5 Oct). 50th Anniv of Korean Boy Scout Movement. P 13½×13.

1022	**430**	10w. multicoloured	1·50	45

(Des Kim Sung Sil (No. 1023), Lee Keun Moon (1024))

1972 (1 Dec). Lunar New Year ("Year of the Ox"). T **431** and similar vert design. Multicoloured. P 13×13½.

1023	10w. Type **431**		1·20	40
1024	10w. Revellers in balloon		1·20	40
MS1025	Two sheets each 90×60 mm. Nos. 1023/4×2		9·25	8·50

432 Temple, Mt. Naejang Park

433 Madeungryong Pass, Mt. Sorak Park

(Des Kang Choon Whan)

1972 (10 Dec). National Parks (3rd series). P 13×13½ (No. 1026) or 13½×13 (1027).

1026	**432**	10w. multicoloured	1·20	40
1027	**433**	10w. multicoloured	1·20	40

434 President Pak, Flag and "Development"

(Des Chun Hee Han)

1972 (27 Dec). Re-election of President Pak. P 13×13½.

1028	**434**	10w. multicoloured	7·75	1·50
MS1029	130×90 mm. Nos. 1028×2		65·00	60·00

435 National Central   **436** Temple, Mt. Sorak
Museum, Kyongbok Palace

(Des Kang Choon Whan)

1973 (20 Feb). Korean Tourist Attractions (1st series). P 13½×13.
1030   **435**   10w. multicoloured ....   1·20   40
1031   **436**   10w. multicoloured ....   1·20   40
  See also Nos. 1042/3, 1048/9, 1057/8 and 1075/6.

441 Kujangbok (king's   **442** Wonsam (woman's
ceremonial costume)   ceremonial costume)

(Des Kim Sung Sil)

1973 (30 Mar). Korean Court Costumes of the Yi Dynasty (1st series).
  P 13½ ×13.
1037   **441**   10w. multicoloured ....   3·75   70
1038   **442**   10w. multicoloured ....   3·75   70
MS1039 Two sheets each 125×90 mm. Nos.
  1037/8×2 ....   16·00   15·00
  See also Nos. 1045/**MS**1047, 1053/**MS**1055, 1060/**MS**1062 and
1078/**MS**1080.

437 Korean Family   **438** "V" Sign and Flags

(Des Lee Keun Moon)

1973 (1 Mar). Korean Unification Campaign. P 13×13½.
1032   **437**   10w. multicoloured ....   1·20   30

(Des Lee Keun Moon)

1973 (1 Mar). Return of Korean Forces from South Vietnam.
  P 13×13½.
1033   **438**   10w. multicoloured ....   1·20   30

443 Nurse with Lamp   **444** Reservists and
                              Flag

(Des Chun Hee Han)

1973 (1 Apr). 50th Anniv of Korean Nurses' Association. P 13½ ×13.
1040   **443**   10w. multicoloured   95   25

(Des Chun Hee Han)

1973 (7 Apr). Home Reserve Forces Day. P 13×13½.
1041   **444**   10w. multicoloured ....   1·20   40

439 Construction   **440** WMO Emblem
Workers and   and Satellite
Cogwheel

(Des Kim Yong Bae)

1973 (10 Mar). 10th Workers' Day. P 13×13½.
1034   **439**   10w. multicoloured   85   30

445 Palmi Island   **446** Sain-am Rock,
                           Mt. Dokjol

(Des Kim Myung Sook)

1973 (23 Mar). Centenary of World Meteorological Organization.
  P 13×13½.
1035   **440**   10w. multicoloured   85   30
MS1036 90×60 mm. No. 1035×2 ....   4·75   4·25

(Des Kang Choon Whan)

1973 (20 Apr). Korean Tourist Attractions (2nd series). P 13×13½.
1042   **445**   10w. multicoloured ....   1·20   30
1043   **446**   10w. multicoloured ....   1·20   30

447 Table Tennis Player

(Des Kang Choon Whan)

1973 (23 May). Victory of South Korean Women's Team in World Table Tennis Championships, Sarajevo. P 13×13½.
1044 **447** 10w. multicoloured .... 1·90 70

452 Children's Choir

(Des Kang Choon Whan)

1973 (25 June). 20th Anniv of World Vision International. P 13×13½.
1050 **452** 10w. multicoloured .... 1·20 30

448 Konryongpo (king's costume) **449** Jokui (queen's ceremonial costume)

(Des Kim Sung Sil)

1973 (30 May). Korean Court Costumes of the Yi Dynasty (2nd series). P 13½×13.
1045 **448** 10w. multicoloured .... 3·50 60
1046 **449** 10w. multicoloured .... 3·50 60
MS1047 Two sheets each 125×90 mm. Nos. 1045/6×2 .... 14·00 13·00

453 Love Pin and "Disasters" **454** Steel Convertor

(Des Lee Keun Moon)

1973 (1 July). Disaster Relief Fund. P 12½ ×13½.
1051 **453** 10w. +5w. multicoloured........................... 1·20 45
Horizontal rows of No. 1051 form a continuous design within the sheet.

(Des Lee Keun Moon)

1973 (3 July). Inauguration of Pohang Steel Works. P 13×13½.
1052 **454** 10w. multicoloured 95 30

455 Kangsapo (crown prince's) Costume **456** Tangui (princess's) Costume

(Des Kim Sung Sil)

1973 (30 July). Korean Court Costumes of the Yi Dynasty (3rd series). P 13½×13.
1053 **455** 10w. multicoloured .... 3·00 60
1054 **456** 10w. multicoloured .... 3·00 60
MS1055 Two sheets each 125×90 mm. Nos. 1053/4×2.. 10·50 8·50

450 Admiral Li Sun Sin's Shrine, Asan **451** Limestone Cavern, Kusan-ni

(Des Kang Choon Whan)

1973 (20 June). Korean Tourist Attractions (3rd series). P 13×13½.
1048 **450** 10w. multicoloured .... 1·50 40
1049 **451** 10w. multicoloured .... 1·50 40

457 Table Tennis
Bat and Ball

(Des Chun Hee Han)

1973 (1 Aug). Table Tennis Gymnasium Construction Fund.
P13½×12½.
1056 **457** 10w. +5w. cerise and blue-green .... 1·20   30

458 Namhae Suspension   **459** Hongdo Island
Bridge

(Des Kang Choon Whan)

1973 (20 Aug). Korean Tourist Attractions (4th series). P 13½×13.
1057   **458**   10w. multicoloured .... 1·20   30
1058   **459**   10w. multicoloured .... 1·20   30

460 Interpol and Korean
Police Emblems

(Des Lee Keun Moon)

1973 (3 Sept). 50th Anniv of International Criminal Police
Organization (Interpol). P 13½×13.
1059   **460**   10w. multicoloured 85   20

461 Kumkwanchobok (court   **462** Hwalot (queen's
official's) Costume   wedding) Costume

(Des Kim Sung Sil)

1973 (30 Sept). Korean Court Costumes of the Yi Dynasty (4th series).
P 13½×13.
1060   **461**   10w. multicoloured .... 1·50   55
1061   **462**   10w. multicoloured .... 1·50   55
MS1062 Two sheets each 125×90 mm.
Nos. 1060/1×2.................................... 8·50   8·00

463 Mask of Old   **463a** Magpie   **464** Siberian
Man   Chipmunk

464a Lily   **465** Manchurian   **466** Sommal Lily
                Cranes

467 Motorway   **468** Honey Bee   **468a** Pot with
and Farm   Lid

468b Jar   **468c** Ceramic   **469** Gold Crown,
                 Horseman   Silla Dynasty

469a Admiral   **469b** Muryangsu-   **469c** Pobjusa
Yi Soon Shin   jeon Hall, Busok   Temple
                Temple

469d Gold   **469e** Carved   **469f** Flying
Crown   Dragon (tile,   Deities (relief
             Baekje   from bronze bell,
             Dynasty)   Sangweon
                             Temple)

(Des Kim Sung Sil (No. 1063a), Chun Hee Han (1065, 1067, 1069c), Kim Yong Bae (1069a), Kang Choon Whan (1069b), Park Yeo Song (1069d), Lee Keun Moon (others))

1973 (10 Oct)–**78**. P 12½×13½ (Nos. 1063a, 1068c, 1069b, 13 (1069f) or 13½×12½ (others).

1063	**463**	1w. chocolate (20.1.74)	45	15
1063a	**463a**	3w. black and light blue (1.10.77)	75	25
1064	**464**	5w. lake-brown (10.3.74)	40	15
1064a	**464a**	6w. blue-green and yellow-green (10.10.75)	45	15
1065	**465**	10w. deep ultramarine and blue	1·20	25
1066	**466**	10w. vermilion, black and blue-green (10.11.73)	1·50	40
1067	**467**	10w. bluish green and rose-red (10.12.73)	75	15
1068	**468**	30w. chocolate and greenish yellow (20.1.74)	85	15
1068a	**468a**	50w. sage-green and blackish brown (15.3.75)	75	25
1068b	**468b**	60w. blackish brown and pale yellow (15.3.75)	75	25
1068c	**468c**	80w. blackish brown and light brown (15.9.77)	1·50	30
1069	**469**	100w. yell & dp choc (10.3.74)	39·00	2·30
1069a	**469a**	100w. claret (10.10.75)	1·90	25
1069b	**469b**	200w. purple-brown and pink (20.10.77)	1·90	30
1069c	**469c**	300w. chocolate and pale lilac (15.8.77)	2·75	70
1069d	**469d**	500w. multicoloured (15.8.77)	23·00	1·50
1069e	**469e**	500w. blackish purple and red-brown (10.11.78)	11·50	1·20
1069f	**469f**	1000w. greenish black (20.9.78)	10·00	1·50
1063/1069f		Set of 18	90·00	9·25

For design similar to Type **465** but with frame, see Type **703**.

470 Tennis

(Des Chun Hee Han)

1973 (12 Oct). 54th National Athletic Meeting, Pusan. T **470** and similar horiz design. Multicoloured. P 12½×13½.

1070		10w. Type **470**	95	30
1071		10w. Hurdling	95	30

471 Children with Stamp Albums

472 Soyang River Dam

(Des Kim Sung Sil)

1973 (12 Oct). Philatelic Week. P 13½×13.

1072	**471**	10w. multicoloured	75	30
MS1073		90×60 mm. No. 1072×2	15·00	14·00

(Des Chun Hee Han)

1973 (15 Oct). Inauguration of Soyang River Dam. P 13½×13.

1074	**472**	10w. multicoloured	55	15

473 Mt. Mai, Chinan

474 Tangerine Grove, Cheju Island

(Des Kang Choon Whan)

1973 (20 Oct). Korean Tourist Attractions (5th series). P 13½×13.

1075	**473**	10w. multicoloured	75	25
1076	**474**	10w. multicoloured	75	25

475 Match, Cigarette and Flames

(Des Kim Yong Bae)

1973 (1 Nov). 10th Fire Prevention Day. P 13×13½.

1077	**475**	10w. multicoloured	55	15

476 Pyongsangbok (official's wife) Costume

477 Kokunbok (military officer's) Costume

(Des Kim Sung Sil)

1973 (30 Nov). Korean Court Costumes of the Yi Dynasty (5th series). P 13½×13.

1078	**476**	10w. multicoloured	1·50	45
1079	**477**	10w. multicoloured	1·50	45
MS1080		Two sheets each 125×90 mm. Nos. 1078/9×2	8·50	8·00

478 Tiger and Candles

479 Korean Girl and Flame Emblem

(Des Lee Keun Moon and Pak Kang Chung)

1973 (1 Dec). Lunar New Year ("Year of the Tiger"). T **478** and similar vert design. Multicoloured. P 13×13½.
1081   10w. Type **478** 75   30
1082   10w. Decorated top 75   30
MS1083 Two sheets each 90×60 mm. Nos. 1081/2×2   9·25   7·75

(Des Chun Hee Han)

1973 (10 Dec). 25th Anniv of Declaration of Human Rights. P 13½×13.
1084   **479**   10w. multicoloured 60   15

480 Boeing 747-200 Jetliner and Polar Zone

(Des Kim Yong Bae)

1973 (20 Dec). AIR. T **480** and similar horiz designs. P 13½×13.
1085   110w. new blue and pink............................ 10·00   3·75
1086   135w. rosine and yellow-green .... 11·00   3·75
1087   145w. rose-red and new blue..................... 14·00   4·75
1088   180w. bright lilac and yellow..................... 35·00   7·00
1085/1088 Set of 4 .... 65·00   17·00
Designs: Boeing 747-200 jetliner and postal zones on map— 135w. South-East Asia; 145w. India, Australasia and North America; 180w. Europe, Africa and South America.

481 "Komunko" (zither)

482 "Nagak" (trumpet triton)

(Des Chun Hee Han)

1974 (20 Feb). Traditional Musical Instruments (1st series). P 13×13½.
1089   **481**   10w. multicoloured .... 1·20   30
1090   **482**   30w. multicoloured .... 3·00   60
MS1091 Two sheets each 125×90 mm. (a) No.
1089×2: (b) No. 1090×2......................... 13·00   12·00
See also Nos. 1098/**MS**1100, 1108/**MS**1110, 1117/**MS**1119 and 1132/**MS**1134.

483 Apricots   **484** Strawberries

(Des Lee Keun Moon)

1974 (30 Mar). Fruits (1st series). P 13×13½.
1092   **483**   10w. multicoloured 75   30
1093   **484**   30w. multicoloured .... 2·30   45
MS1094 Two sheets each 90×60 mm. (a) No.
1092×2, (b) No. 1093×2......................... 11·00   10·00
See also Nos. 1104/**MS**1106, 1111/**MS**1113, 1120/**MS**1122 and 1143/**MS**1145.

485 Reservist and Factory   **486** WPY Emblem

(Des Chun Hee Han)

1974 (6 Apr). Home Reserve Forces Day. P 13½×13.
1095   **485**   10w. multicoloured 55   15

(Des Pak Kang Chung)

1974 (10 Apr). World Population Year. P 13×13½.
1096   **486**   10w. multicoloured 45   15
MS1097 90×60 mm. No. 1096×2..................... 4·75   4 25

487 "Tchouk" (ceremonial instrument)

488 "Eu" (ceremonial instrument)

(Des Chun Hee Han)

1974 (20 Apr). Traditional Musical Instruments (2nd series). P 13×13½.
1098 **487** 10w. multicoloured .... 1·00   25
1099 **488** 30w. multicoloured .... 2·30   55
MS1100 Two sheets each 126×90 mm. (a) No.
   1098×2; (b) No. 1099×2 .... 9·25   8·50

494 UNESCO
Emblem and
Extended Fan

(Des Pak Kang Chung)

1974 (14 June). 20th Anniv of South Korean United Nations Educational, Scientific and Cultural Organization Commission. P 13×13½.
1107 **494** 10w. multicoloured 45   10

489 Mail Train and
Communications Emblem

490 CAFEA–ICC
Emblem on Globe

(Des Chun Hee Han)

1974 (22 Apr). Communications Day. P 13½×13.
1101 **489** 10w. multicoloured 95   25

(Des Pak Kang Chung)

1974 (6 May). 22nd Session of International Chamber of Commerce's Commission on Asian and Far Eastern Affairs, Seoul. P 13×13½.
1102 **490** 10w. multicoloured 45   10

495 "A-chaing" (stringed instrument)

491 Port Installations

(Des Lee Keun Moon)

1974 (10 May). Inauguration of New Port Facilities, Inchon. P 13½×13.
1103 **491** 10w. multicoloured 55   10

496 "Kyobang-ko" (drum)

(Des Chun Hee Han)

1974 (20 June). Traditional Musical Instruments (3rd series). P 13×13½.
1108 **495** 10w. multicoloured 95   15
1109 **496** 30w. multicoloured .... 1·90   40
MS1110 Two sheets each 125×90 mm. Nos.
   1108/9×2 .... 8·50   7 75

492 Peaches

493 Grapes

(Des Lee Keun Moon)

1974 (30 May). Fruits (2nd series). P 13×13½.
1104 **492** 10w. multicoloured 75   30
1105 **493** 30w. multicoloured .... 2·30   45
MS1106 Two sheets each 90×60 mm. Nos.
   1104/5×2 .... 10·50   9·50

497 Pears

498 Apples

(Des Lee Keun Moon)

1974 (30 July). Fruits (3rd series). P 13×13½.
1111 **497** 10w. multicoloured 60 15
1112 **498** 30w. multicoloured .... 2·30 45
MS1113 Two sheets each 91×61 mm. Nos. 1111/2×2 11·00 9·75

499 Cross and Emblems

500 Emblem and Korean Map on Globe

(Des Kim Yong Bae)

1974 (13 Aug). "Explo 74" Second International Training Congress on Evangelism. P 13×13½.
1114 **499** 10w. multicoloured 40 10
1115 **500** 10w. multicoloured 40 10

501 Underground Train

(Des Kang Choon Whan)

1974 (15 Aug). Opening of Seoul Underground Railway. P 13×13½.
1116 **501** 10w. multicoloured .... 1·00 25

502 "So" (pan pipes)

503 "Haikem" (two-stringed fiddle)

(Des Chun Hee Han)

1974 (20 Aug). Traditional Musical Instruments (4th series). P 13×13½.
1117 **502** 10w. multicoloured 95 30
1118 **503** 30w. multicoloured .... 1·90 45
MS1119 Two sheets each 125×90 mm. Nos. 1117/18×2 .... 7·75 7 00

504 Cherries

505 Persimmons

(Des Lee Keun Moon)

1974 (30 Sept). Fruits (4th series). P 13×13½.
1120 **504** 10w. multicoloured 70 25
1121 **505** 30w. multicoloured .... 1·50 45
MS1122 Two sheets each 91×61 mm. Nos. 1120/1×2 5 50 5 00

506 Rifle Shooting

507 Rowing

(Des Kim Sung Sil)

1974 (8 Oct). 55th National Athletic Meeting, Seoul. P 12½×13½.
1123 **506** 10w. multicoloured 45 15
1124 **507** 30w. multicoloured .... 1·30 40

508 UPU Emblem

509 Symbols of Member Countries

(Des Pak Kang Chung)

1974 (9 Oct). Centenary of Universal Postal Union. P 13½×13.
(a) POSTAGE
1125 **508** 10w. multicoloured 45 15
(b) AIR
1126 **508** 110w. multicoloured .... 2·30 1·00
MS1127 Two sheets each 90×60 mm. Nos. 1125/6×2. .... 20·00 18·00

(Des Kim Sung Sil)

1974 (11 Oct). First World Conference of People-to-People International. P 13×13½.
1128 **509** 10w. multicoloured 45 10

510 Korean Stamps of 1884

511 Taekwondo Contestants

(Des Chung Hi Jin)

1974 (17 Oct). Philatelic Week and 90th Anniv of First Korean Stamps. P 13½×13.
1129 **510** 10w. multicoloured 55 10
MS1130 91×61 mm. No. 1129×2. .... 8·50 7 75

(Des Pak Kang Chung)

1974 (18 Oct). First Asian Taekwondo Championships, Seoul. P 13½×13.
1131 **511** 10w. multicoloured 55 10

512 "Pak" (clappers)

513 "Pyenchong" (chimes)

514 Lungs

(Des Chun Hee Han)

1974 (20 Oct). Traditional Musical Instruments (5th series). P 13×13½.
1132 **512** 10w. multicoloured 95 25
1133 **513** 30w. multicoloured .... 1·90 45
MS1134 Two sheets each 126×90 mm. Nos.
1132/3×2 .... 7·75 7 00

(Des Kim Yong Bae)

1974 (1 Nov). Tuberculosis Control Fund. P 13½×12½.
1135 **514** 10w. +5w. carmine-red & emerald 95 25

515 Presidents Pak and Ford

516 Yook Young Soo (wife of President Pak)

(Des Chun Hee Han)

1974 (22 Nov). State Visit of President Ford of United States. P 13½×13.
1136 **515** 10w. multicoloured 85 30
MS1137 89×59 mm. No. 1136×2. .... 7·75 7·00

(Des Chun Hee Han)

1974 (29 Nov). Yook Young Soo Memorial Issue. P 13×13½.
1138 **516** 10w. emerald 85 30
     a. Block of 4. Nos. 1138/41 .... 3·75
1139   10w. yellow-orange 85 30
1140   10w. reddish violet. 85 30
1141   10w. new blue 85 30
1138/1141 Set of 4. .... 3·00 1·10
MS1142 91×125 mm. Nos. 1138/41 .... 35·00 31·00
   Nos. 1138/41 were issued together in *se-tenant* blocks of four within the sheet.

517 Tangerines

518 Chestnuts

(Des Lee Keun Moon)

1974 (30 Nov). Fruits (5th series). P 13×13½.
1143 **517** 10w. multicoloured 55 15
1144 **518** 30w. multicoloured .... 1·30 40
MS1145 Two sheets each 91×61 mm. Nos.
1143/4×2 .... 5·75 5·25

519 "Good Luck" Purse

520 Toy Rabbits

(Des Pak Kang Chung (T **519**), Kim Sung Sil (T **520**). Litho)

1974 (1 Dec). Lunar New Year ("Year of the Rabbit"). Granite paper. P 12½×13.
1146 **519** 10w. multicoloured 60 20
1147 **520** 10w. multicoloured 60 20
MS1148 Two sheets each 91×61 mm. Nos. 1146/7×2 7·75 7·00

521 UPU Emblem and "75"

522 UPU Emblem and Paper Dart

(Des Pak Kang Chung)

1975 (1 Jan). 75th Anniv of Korea's Membership of Universal Postal Union. P 13×13½.
1149	**521**	10w. multicoloured	45	10
1150	**522**	10w. multicoloured	45	10

523 Dove with "Good Luck" Card

524 Dr. Schweitzer, Map and Syringe

(Des Kim Sung Sil)

1975 (1 Jan). Inauguration of National Welfare Insurance System. P 13.
1151	**523**	10w. multicoloured	40	10

(Des Kim Yong Bae)

1975 (14 Jan). Birth Centenary of Dr. Albert Schweitzer (philosopher and missionary). P 13½×13.
1152	**524**	10w. bistre	95	40
		a. Block of 4. Nos. 1152/5	4·00	
1153		10w. magenta	95	40
1154		10w. orange	95	40
1155		10w. blue-green	95	40
1152/1155	*Set of 4*		3·50	1·40

Nos. 1152/5 were issued together in *se-tenant* blocks of four within the sheet.

525 Salpuli Dancer

526 Exorcism Dance

(Des Chun Hee Han)

1975 (20 Feb). Folk Dances (1st series). P 13.
1156	**525**	10w. multicoloured	70	25
1157	**526**	10w. multicoloured	70	25
MS1158		Two sheets each 90×60 mm. Nos. 1156/7×2	3·75	3·50

See also Nos. 1168/**MS**1170, 1175/**MS**1177, 1193/**MS**1195 and 1208/**MS**1210.

527 Globe and Rotary Emblem

528 Women and IWY Emblem

(Des Lee Keun Moon)

1975 (23 Feb). 70th Anniv of Rotary International. P 13½×13.
1159	**527**	10w. multicoloured	40	10

(Des Lee Keun Moon)

1975 (8 Mar). International Women s Year. P 13½×13.
1160	**528**	10w. multicoloured	40	10

529 Violets

530 Anemones

(Des Kim Sung Sil)

1975 (15 Mar). Flowers (1st series). P 13×13½.
1161	**529**	10w. multicoloured	75	25
1162	**530**	10w. multicoloured	75	25

See also Nos. 1171/2, 1184/5, 1199/1200 and 1213/14.

531/4 Saemaeul Forest Reserve
(*illus further reduced—actual size* 103×33 *mm*)

(Des Chun Hee Han)

1975 (20 Mar). National Afforestation Campaign. P 13×13½.
1163	**531**	10w. multicoloured	75	30
		a. Horiz strip of 4. Nos. 1163/6	3·25	
1164	**532**	10w. multicoloured	75	30
1165	**533**	10w. multicoloured	75	30
1166	**534**	10w. multicoloured	75	30
1163/1166	*Set of 4*		2·75	1·10

Nos. 1163/6 were issued together in *se-tenant* horizontal strips of four within the sheet, forming the composite design shown.

535 HRF Emblem on Map of Korea

(Des Chun Hee Han)

1975 (12 Apr). Homeland Reserve Forces Day. P 13.
1167   **535**   10w. multicoloured   60   10

536 Butterfly Dance   **537** Victory Dance

(Des Chun Hee Han)

1975 (20 Apr). Folk Dances (2nd series). P 13.
1168   **536**   10w. multicoloured   75   25
1169   **537**   10w. multicoloured   75   25
MS1170 Two sheets each 90×60 mm. Nos. 1168/9×2   3·50   3·00

538 Rhododendron   **539** Clematis

(Des Kim Sung Sil)

1975 (15 May). Flowers (2nd series). P 13×13½.
1171   **538**   10w. multicoloured   75   25
1172   **539**   10w. multicoloured   75   25

540 Metric Symbols   **541** Soldier and Incense Pot

(Des Lee Keun Moon)

1975 (20 May). Centenary of Metre Convention. P 13½×13.
1173   **540**   10w. multicoloured   40   10

(Des Kim Yong Bae)

1975 (6 June). 20th Memorial Day. P 13½×13.
1174   **541**   10w. multicoloured   40   10

542 Mokjoong Dance   **543** Malttugi Dance

(Des Chun Hee Han)

1975 (20 June). Folk Dances (3rd series). P 13×13½.
1175   **542**   10w. multicoloured   75   25
1176   **543**   10w. multicoloured   75   25
MS1177 Two sheets each 90×60 mm. Nos. 1175/6×2   3·50   3·00

544 Flags of South Korea, United Nations and United States of America   **545** Flags of Ethiopia, France, Greece, Canada and South Africa

546 Flags of Luxembourg, Australia, United Kingdom, Colombia and Turkey   **547** Flags of Netherlands, Belgium, Philippines, New Zealand and Thailand

(Des Lee Keun Moon)

1975 (25 June). 25th Anniv of Korean War. P 13½×13.
1178   **544**   10w. multicoloured   75   30
     a. Horiz strip of 4. Nos. 1178/81 ....   3·25
1179   **545**   10w. multicoloured   75   30
1180   **546**   10w. multicoloured   75   30
1181   **547**   10w. multicoloured   75   30
1178/1181   Set of 4 ....   2·75   1·10
     Nos. 1178/81 were issued together in *se-tenant* horizontal strips of four within the sheet.

548 Presidents Pak and Bongo

(Des Lee Keun Moon)

1975 (5 July). State Visit of President Bongo of Gabon. P 13½×13.
1182   **548**   10w. multicoloured 55   10
MS1183   90×60 mm. No. 1182×2 .... 2·75   2·40

552 Freedom Flame   **553** Balloon Emblems

(Des Ahn Sung Kyung)

1975 (15 Aug). 30th Anniv of Liberation. P 13½×13.
1191   **552**   20w. multicoloured 70   25
1192   **553**   20w. multicoloured 70   25

549 Iris   **550** Thistle

(Des Kim Sung Sil)

1975 (15 July). Flowers (3rd series). P 13×13½.
1184   **549**   10w. multicoloured 75   25
1185   **550**   10w. multicoloured 75   25

554 Drum Dance   **555** Bara Dance

(Des Chun Hee Han)

1975 (20 Aug). Folk Dances (4th series). P 13.
1193   **554**   20w. multicoloured .... 1·00   45
1194   **555**   20w. multicoloured .... 1·00   45
MS1195   Two sheets each 90×60 mm. Nos.
   1193/4×2 .... 5·50   5·00

551 Scout Scarf

(Des Lee Keun Moon)

1975 (29 July). "Nordjamb 75" World Scout Jamboree, Norway. T **551** and similar vert designs. Multicoloured. P 13×13½.
1186   10w. Type **551** 75   30
     a. Horiz strip of 5. Nos. 1186/90 .... 4·00
1187   10w. Scout oath 75   30
1188   10w. Scout camp 75   30
1189   10w. Axe and rope 75   30
1190   10w. Campfire 75   30
1186/1190   Set of 5 .... 3·50   1·40
   Nos. 1186/90 were issued together in se-tenant horizontal strips of five within the sheet.

556 Taekwondo Contestant   **557** Assembly Hall

(Des Chung Hi Jin)

1975 (25 Aug). Second World Taekwondo Championships, Seoul. P 13×13½.
1196   **556**   20w. multicoloured 45   10

(Des Chun Hee Han)

1975 (1 Sept). Completion of National Assembly Hall. P 13½×13.
1197   **557**   20w. multicoloured 45   10

558 Dumper Truck and
Emblem

(Des Chung Hi Jin)

1975 (7 Sept). Contractors Associations Convention, Seoul.
  P 13½×13.
1198 **558** 20w. multicoloured 45   10

559 Broad-bell   **560** Bush Clover
Flower

(Des Kim Sung Sil)

1975 (15 Sept). Flowers (4th series). P 13×13½.
1199 **559** 20w. multicoloured .... 1·20   30
1200 **560** 20w. multicoloured .... 1·20   30

561 Morse Key and Dish Aerial

(Des Chun Hee Han)

1975 (28 Sept). 90th Anniv of Korean Telecommunications.
  P 13½×13.
1201 **561** 20w. black, orange and purple 45   10

562 Yeongweol Caves   **563** Mount Sorak

(Des Chun Hee Han)

1975 (28 Sept). International Tourism Day. P 13½×13.
1202 **562** 20w. multicoloured 45   10
1203 **563** 20w. multicoloured 45   10

564 Flag and Missiles   **565** "Gymnastics"   **566** "Handball"

(Des Chun Hee Han)

1975 (1 Oct). Armed Forces Day. P 13×13½.
1204 **564** 20w. multicoloured 40   10

(Des Kim Yong Bae)

1975 (7 Oct). 56th National Athletic Meeting. P 13×13½.
1205 **565** 20w. multicoloured 40   10
1206 **566** 20w. multicoloured 40   10

567 "Kangaroo"   **568** Sogo Dance   **569** Bupo Nori
Collector   Dance

(Des Kim Sung Sil)

1975 (8 Oct). Philatelic Week. P 13×13½.
1207 **567** 20w. multicoloured 40   10

(Des Chun Hee Han)

1975 (20 Oct). Folk Dances (5th series). P 13×13½.
1208 **568** 20w. multicoloured .... 1·10   45
1209 **569** 20w. multicoloured .... 1·10   45
MS1210 Two sheets each 90×60 mm, Nos. 1208/9×2   4·75   4·25

570 UN Emblem and   **571** Red Cross and
Handclasps   Emblems

(Des Chung Hi Jin)

1975 (24 Oct). 30th Anniv of United Nations. P 13×13½.
1211 **570** 20w. multicoloured 40   10

(Des Chung Hi Jin)

1975 (30 Oct). 10th Anniv of Korean Red Cross. P 13×13½.
1212 **571** 20w. multicoloured 45   10

572 Camellia   **573** Gentian

(Des Kim Sung Sil)

1975 (15 Nov). Flowers (5th series). P 13×13½.

1213	**572** 20w. multicoloured	1·70	55
1214	**573** 20w. multicoloured	1·70	55

580 Institute Emblem and Science Emblems

(Des Ahn Seung Kyung)

1976 (10 Feb). 10th Anniv of Korean Institute of Science and Technology. P 13½ ×13.

1222	**580** 20w. multicoloured	40	10

574 Union Emblem   **575** Children Playing   **576** Dragon

(Des Kim Sung Sil. Photo)

1975 (30 Nov). 10th Anniv of Asian Parliamentary Union. P 13.

1215	**574** 20w. multicoloured	40	10

(Des Ahn Seung Kyung (T **575**), Kim Yong Bae (T **576**))

1975 (1 Dec). Lunar New Year ("Year of the Dragon"). P 13×13½.

1216	**575** 20w. multicoloured	55	15
1217	**576** 20w. multicoloured	55	15
MS1218 Two sheets each 90×60 mm. Nos. 1216/17×2		3·75	3·50

581 Japanese White-necked Crane   **582** Great Bustard

(Des Kim Sung Sil)

1976 (20 Feb). Birds (1st series). P 13×13½.

1223	**581** 20w. multicoloured	1·50	40
1224	**582** 20w. multicoloured	1·50	40
See also Nos. 1243/4, 1251/2, 1257/8 and 1266/7.			

577 Electric Train

(Des Chun Hee Han)

1975 (5 Dec). Opening of Cross-country Electric Railway. P 13½ ×13.

1219	**577** 20w. multicoloured	75	15

583 Globe and Telephones

(Des Chun Hee Han)

1976 (10 Mar). Telephone Centenary. P 13½×13.

1225	**583** 20w. multicoloured	40	10

578 *Dilipa fenestra*   **579** *Luehdorfia puziloi*

(Des Kim Jae Min)

1976 (20 Jan). Butterflies (1st series). P 13½×13.

1220	**578** 20w. multicoloured	1·50	30
1221	**579** 20w. multicoloured	1·50	30
See also Nos. 1226/7, 1246/7, 1254/5 and 1264/5.			

584 *Papilio xuthus*   **585** *Parnassius bremeri*

(Des Kim Jae Min)

1976 (20 Mar). Butterflies (2nd series). P 13½ ×13.

1226	**584** 20w. multicoloured	1·50	30
1227	**585** 20w. multicoloured	1·50	30

586 "National Development"

(Des Ahn Seung Kyung)

1976 (3 Apr). Homeland Reserve Forces Day. P 13½ ×13.
1228 **586** 20w. multicoloured 40 10

587 Eye and
People

588 President Pak
and Flag

(Des Chun Hee Han)

1976 (7 Apr). World Health Day. Prevention of Blindness. P 13×13½.
1229 **587** 20w. multicoloured 40 10

(Des Lee Keun Moon)

1976 (22 Apr). Sixth Anniv of Saemaul Movement (community self-
help programme). T **588** and similar vert designs. Multicoloured.
P 13×13½.
1230	20w. Type **588**	1·50	45
	a. Horiz strip of 5. Nos. 1230/4	7·75	
1231	20w. People ("Intellectual edification")..	1·50	45
1232	20w. Village ("Welfare")	1·50	45
1233	20w. Produce and fields ("Production") .	1·50	45
1234	20w. Produce and factory ("Increase of		
	Income")	1·50	45
1230/1234 *Set of 5*		6·75	2·00

Nos. 1230/4 were issued together in *se-tenant* horizontal strips of
five within the sheet.

589 Ruins of Moenjodaro

590 US Flags of 1776
and 1976

(Des Chung Hi Jin)

1976 (1 May). Campaign for Preservation of Moenjodaro (Pakistan).
P 13½×13.
1235 **589** 20w. multicoloured 45 10

(Des Kim Yong Bae)

1976 (8 May). Bicentenary of American Revolution. T **590** and similar
vert designs. Each black, ultramarine and carmine. P 13×13½.
1236	100w. Type **590**	3·00	1·20
1237	100w. Statue of Liberty	3·00	1·20
1238	100w. Map of United States	3·00	1·20
1239	100w. Liberty Bell	3·00	1·20
1240	100w. American astronaut	3·00	1·20
1236/1240 *Set of 5*		13·50	5·50
MS1241 91×61 mm. No. 1236		6·25	5·50

591 Camp Scene
on Emblem

592 Blue-winged
Pitta

593 White-bellied
Black Woodpecker

594 Buddha and
Temple

(Des Chung Hi Jin)

1976 (10 May). 30th Anniv of Korean Girl Scouts Federation.
P 13×13½.
1242 **591** 20w. multicoloured 95 15

(Des Kim Sung Sil)

1976 (20 May). Birds (2nd series). P 13×13½.
1243 **592** 20w. multicoloured .... 1·50 40
1244 **593** 20w. multicoloured .... 1·50 40

(Des Lee Keun Moon)

1976 (10 June). UNESCO Campaign for Preservation of Borobudur
Temple (in Indonesia). P 13×13½.
1245 **594** 20w. multicoloured 40 10

595 Eastern Pale Clouded
Yellow (*Colias erate*)

596 Chinese Windmill
(*Atrophaneura alcinous*)

(Des Chun Hee Han)

1976 (20 June). Butterflies (3rd series). P 13½×13.
1246 **595** 20w. multicoloured .... 1·50 30
1247 **596** 20w. multicoloured .... 1·50 30

597 Protected
Family

598 Volleyball

599 Boxing

(Des Chun Hee Han)

1976 (1 July). National Life Insurance. P 13×13½.
1248　**597**　20w. multicoloured .... 　40　　10

(Des Chung Hi Jin)

1976 (17 July). Olympic Games, Montreal. P 13×13½.
1249　**598**　20w. multicoloured .... 　45　　10
1250　**599**　20w. multicoloured .... 　45　　10

600 Black Wood
Pigeon

601 Oystercatcher

(Des Kim Sung Sil)

1976 (20 July). Birds (3rd series). P 13×13½.
1251　**600**　20w. multicoloured .... 　1·50　　40
1252　**601**　20w. multicoloured .... 　1·50　　40

602 Children and Books

(Des Lee Keun Moon. Photo)

1976 (10 Aug). Books for Children. P 13½×13.
1253　**602**　20w. multicoloured .... 　40　　10

603 *Hestina assimilis*

604 Blue Triangle
(*Graphium sarpedon*)

(Des Chun Hee Han. Photo)

1976 (20 Aug). Butterflies (4th *series*). P 13½×13.
1254　**603**　20w. multicoloured .... 　2·20　　85
1255　**604**　20w. multicoloured .... 　2·20　　85

604a Corps
Members and Flag

605 Black-faced
Spoonbill

606 Black Stork

(Des Chun Hee Han. Photo)

1976 (15 Sept). First Anniv of Korean Civil Defence Corps. P 13×13½.
1256　**604a** 20w. multicoloured .... 　40　　10

(Des Kim Sung Sil. Photo)

1976 (20 Sept). Birds (4th series). P 13×13½.
1257　**605**　20w. multicoloured .... 　1·50　　40
1258　**606**　20w. multicoloured .... 　1·50　　40

607 Chamsungdan,
Mani Mountain

608 Ilchumun Gate,
Tongdosa

(Des Chun Hee Han. Photo)

1976 (28 Sept). International Tourism Day. P 13½×13.
1259　**607**　20w. multicoloured .... 　75　　25
1260　**608**　20w. multicoloured .... 　75　　25

609 Cadet and Parade

610 "Musa Basjoo"
(flower arrangement,
Cheong Jo the Great)

(Des Chun Hee Han. Photo)

1976 (1 Oct). 30th Anniv of Korean Military Academy. P 13½×13.
1261　**609**　20w. multicoloured .... 　45　　15

1976 (5 Oct). Philatelic Week. Photo. P 13×13½.
1262　**610**　20w. black, red and pale drab.................. 　45　　10
MS1263　91×61 mm. No. 1262×2...................... 　3·75　　3·50

611 Yellow-legged
Tortoiseshell (*Nymphalis
xanthomelas*)

612 *Fabriciana nerippe*

(Des Chun Hee Han. Photo)

1976 (20 Oct). Butterflies (5th series). P 13½×13.
1264　**611**　20w. multicoloured .... 　2·30　　95
1265　**612**　20w. multicoloured .... 　2·30　　95

613 European
Black Vulture

614 Whistling
Swan

(Des Kim Sung Sil. Photo)

1976 (20 Nov). Birds (5th series). P 13.
1266	**613**	20w. multicoloured	3·75	1·40
1267	**614**	20w. multicoloured	3·75	1·40

615 Snake
(bas-relief, Kim
Yu Shin's tomb)

616 Door Knocker
with Manchurian
Cranes

(Des Lee Keun Moon (No. 1268), Chun Hee Han (No. 1269). Photo)

1976 (1 Dec). Lunar New Year ("Year of the Snake"). P 13.
1268	**615**	20w. multicoloured	55	25
1269	**616**	20w. multicoloured	55	25
MS1270		Two sheets, each 90×60 mm. Nos. 1268/9×2	3·75	3·50

617 "Training Technicians"

618 Oil Tanker ("Heavy
Industries")

(Des Chun Hee Han. Photo)

1977 (20 Jan). Fourth Five Year Economic Development Plan. P 13.
1271	**617**	20w. multicoloured	60	15
1272	**618**	20w. multicoloured	60	15

619 Dish Aerial

620 Korean Broadcasting
Centre

(Des Chun Hee Han. Photo)

1977 (31 Jan). 25th Anniv of Korean Membership of International
Telecommunications Union. P 13.
1273	**619**	20w. multicoloured	45	15

(Des Lee Keun Moon. Photo)

1977 (16 Feb). 50th Anniv of Broadcasting in Korea. P 13.
1274	**620**	20w. multicoloured	45	15

621 Jar with Grape
Design

622 Celadon Vase

(Des Lee Keun Moon. Photo)

1977 (15 Mar). Korean Ceramics (1st series). P 13.
1275	**621**	20w. multicoloured	1·90	30
1276	**622**	20w. multicoloured	1·90	30

See also Nos. 1285/6, 1287/8, 1290/1 and 1300/1.

623 "Two-
children" Family

624 Reserve Soldier

625 Diagram of
Brain

(Des Chun Hee Han. Photo)

1977 (1 Apr). Family Planning. P 13½×13.
1277	**623**	20w. emerald, pale turquoise-green and pale yellow-orange	1·90	25

(Des Lee Keun Moon. Photo)

1977 (2 Apr). Ninth Homeland Reserve Forces Day. P 13.
1278	**624**	20w. multicoloured	40	10

(Des Chun Hee Han. Photo)

1977 (21 Apr). 10th Anniv of Science Day. P 13.
1279	**625**	20w. multicoloured	40	10

626 Medical Books and
Equipment

627 Child with
Flowers

(Des Kang Choon Whan. Photo)

1977 (25 Apr). 35th International Military Medicine Meeting. P 13.
1280	**626**	20w. multicoloured	55	10

(Des Lee Keun Moon. Photo)

1977 (5 May). 20th Anniv of Children's Charter. P 13.
1281	**627**	20w. multicoloured	40	10

628 Veterans' Flag and Emblem

629 Statue of Buddha, Sokkulam Grotto

(Des Chun Hee Han. Photo)

1977 (8 May). 25th Anniv of Korean Veterans' Day. P 13.
1282   **628**   20w. multicoloured 55   10

(Des Chun Hee Han. Photo)

1977 (25 May). 2600th Anniv of Buddha's Birth. P 13.
1283   **629**   20w. brown-olive and blackish brown ... 55   10
MS1284   90×60 mm. No. 1283×2.. 4·75   4·25

630 Celadon Jar

631 Porcelain Vase

(Des Lee Keun Moon. Photo)

1977 (15 June). Korean Ceramics (2nd series). P 13.
1285   **630**   20 w. multicoloured 75   30
1286   **631**   20 w. multicoloured 75   30

632 "Buddha" Celadon Wine Jar

633 Celadon Vase

(634)

(Des Lee Keun Moon. Photo)

1977 (15 July). Korean Ceramics (3rd series). P 13.
1287   **632**   20w. multicoloured 75   25
1288   **633**   20w. multicoloured 75   25

1977 (25 July). Flood Relief. No. 791 surch with T **634.**
1289   **319**   20w. +10w. myrtle-green .... 7·75   6·75

635 Celadon Vase, Black Koryo Ware

636 White Porcelain Bowl

(Des Lee Keun Moon. Photo)

1977 (15 Aug). Korean Ceramics (4th series). P 13.
1290   **636**   20w. multicoloured 75   25
1291   **636**   20w. multicoloured 75   25

637 Ulleung-do Island

638 Haeundae Beach

(Des Chun Hee Han. Photo)

1977 (28 Sept). World Tourism Day. P 13.
1292   **637**   20w. multicoloured 45   10
1293   **638**   20 w. multicoloured 45   10

639 Servicemen

640/1 "Mount Inwang Clearing Up after the Rain" (detail from drawing by Chung Seon)

(Des Ahn Seung Kyung. Photo)

1977 (1 Oct). Armed Forces Day. P 13.
1294   **639**   20w. multicoloured 40   10

(Des Kim Sung Sil. Photo)

1977 (4 Oct). Philatelic Week. P 13.
1295   **640**   20w. multicoloured 95   25
                  a. Horiz pair. Nos. 1295/6...................... 2·00   55
1296   **641**   20w. multicoloured 95   25
MS1297   90×60 mm. Nos. 1295/6 .... 7·00   6·25
        Nos. 1295/6 were issued together in horizontal *se-tenant* pairs within the sheet, each pair forming the composite design illustrated.

642 Rotary Emblem and Koryo Dynasty Bronze Bell

643 South Korean Flag over Everest

(Des Park Yeo Song. Photo)

1977 (10 Nov). 50th Anniv of Korean Rotary Club. P 13.
1298   **642**   20w. multicoloured 70   15

(Des Park Yeo Song. Photo)

1977 (11 Nov). South Korean Conquest of Mount Everest. P 13.
1299   **643**   20w. multicoloured 70   15

644 Punch'ong
Bottle

645 Celadon
Cylindrical Bottle

(Des Lee Keun Moon. Photo)

1977 (15 Nov). Korean Ceramics (5th series). P 13.
1300 **644** 20w. multicoloured 75 25
1301 **645** 20w. multicoloured 75 25

646 Hands
preserving
Nature

647 Children with
Kites

648 Horse
(bas-relief, Kim
Yu Shin's tomb)

(Des Chun Hee Han. Photo)

1977 (30 Nov). Nature Conservation. P 13½×12½.
1302 **646** 20w. new blue, emerald & yell-brn 75 15

(Des Ahn Seung Kyung (1303), Park Yeo Song (1304). Photo)

1977 (1 Dec). Lunar New Year ("Year of the Horse"). P 13.
1303 **647** 20w. multicoloured 45 15
1304 **648** 20w. multicoloured 45 15
MS1305 Two sheets, each 90×60 mm. (a) No.
1303×2; (b) No. 1304×2 .... 4·25 4·00

649 Clay Pigeon Shooting

650 Air Pistol Shooting

651 Air Rifle Shooting

652 Korean Airlines
Boeing 747–200

(Des Kim Sung Sil (No. 1306), Ahn Seung Kyung (No. 1307),
Chun Hee Han (No. 1308). Photo)

1977 (3 Dec). 42nd World Shooting Championships, Seoul. P 13.
1306 **649** 20w. multicoloured 55 10
1307 **650** 20w. multicoloured 55 10
1308 **651** 20w. multicoloured 55 10
1306/1308 Set of 3 .... 1·50 25
MS1309 Three sheets, each 90×60 mm. (a) No.
1306×2; (b) No. 1307×2; (c) No. 1308×2 .... 11·50 10·50

(Des Park Yeo Song. Photo)

1977 (11 Dec). 25th Anniv of Korean Membership of ICAO
(International Civil Aviation Organization). P 13.
1310 **652** 20w. multicoloured 60 15

653 "Exports"

(Des Ahn Seung Kyung. Photo)

1977 (22 Dec). Korean Exports. P 13.
1311 **653** 20w. multicoloured 45 10

654 Ships and World Map

(Des Ahn Seung Kyung. Photo)

1978 (13 Mar). National Maritime Day. P 13.
1312 **654** 20w. multicoloured 40 10

655 Three-storey
Pagoda, Hwaom
Temple

656 Seven-storey
Pagoda,
T'app'yong-ri

(Des Kim Sung Sil. Photo)

1978 (20 Mar). Stone Pagodas (1st series). P 13.
1313 **655** 20w. multicoloured .... 1·20 30
1314 **656** 20w. multicoloured .... 1·20 30
See also Nos. 1319/20, 1322/5 and 1340/1.

657 Ants with Coins

658 Seoul Sejong Cultural Centre, Hahoe Mask and Violin

(Des Ahn Seung Kyung. Photo)

1978 (1 Apr). Savings Encouragement. P 13.
1315 **657** 20w. multicoloured 55 10

(Des Lee Keun Moon. Photo)

1978 (1 Apr). Opening of Seoul Sejong Cultural Centre. P 13.
1316 **658** 20w. multicoloured 70 15

659 Standard Bearer

660 Pigeon with Young

(Des Chun Hee Han. Photo)

1978 (1 Apr). 10th Homeland Reserve Forces Day. P 13.
1317 **659** 20w. multicoloured 40 10

(Des Lee Keun Moon. Photo)

1978 (1 May). Family Planning. P 12½×13½.
1318 **660** 20w. black and light green......................... 1·00 30

661 Pagoda, Punhwang Temple

662 Pagoda, Miruk Temple

(Des Kim Sung Sil. Photo)

1978 (20 May). Stone Pagodas (2nd series). P 13.
1319 **661** 20w. multicoloured .... 1·20 30
1320 **662** 20w. multicoloured .... 1·20 30

663 National Assembly

(Des Chun Hee Han. Photo)

1978 (31 May). 30th Anniv of National Assembly. P 13.
1321 **663** 20w. multicoloured 40 10

664 Tabo Pagoda, Pulguk Temple

665 Three-storey Pagoda, Pulguk Temple

(Des Kim Sung Sil. Photo)

1978 (20 June). Stone Pagodas (3rd series). P 13.
1322 **664** 20w. multicoloured 75 25
1323 **665** 20w. multicoloured 75 25

666 Ten-storey Pagoda, Kyongch'on Temple

667 Nine-storey Octagonal Pagoda, Wolchong Temple

668 Emblem and Hands with Tools

(Des Kim Sung Sil. Photo)

1978 (20 July). Stone Pagodas (4th series). P 13½×12½.
1324 **666** 20w. multicoloured .... 1·20 30
1325 **667** 20w. multicoloured .... 1·20 30

(Des Lee Keun Moon. Photo)

1978 (5 Aug). 24th International Youth Skill Olympics, Pusan. P 13.
1326 **668** 20w. multicoloured 40 10
MS1327 90×60 mm. No. 1326×2.................................... 3·00 2·75

669 Crater Lake on Mount Baeguda and Bell of Joy

670 Army Nursing Officer

671 Sobaeksan Observatory and Telescope

(Des Lee Keun Moon. Photo)

1978 (15 Aug). 30th Anniv of Republic of Korea. P 13.
1328 **669** 20w. multicoloured 40 10

(Des Kim Sung Sil. Photo)

1978 (26 Aug). 30th Anniv of Army Nursing Corps. P 13.
1329 **670** 20w. multicoloured 40 10

(Des Chun Hee Han. Photo)

1978 (13 Sept). Opening of Sobaeksan Observatory. P 13.
1330 **671** 20w. multicoloured 45 10

678 Young Men and YMCA Emblem

679 Hand smothering Fire

(Des Chun Hee Han. Photo).

1978 (28 Oct). 75th Anniv of Korean Young Men's Christian Association. P 13.
1338 **678** 20w. multicoloured 40 10

672 Kyonghoeru Pavilion, Kyongbok Palace

673 Baeg-do Island

(Des Lee Keun Moon. Photo)

1978 (28 Sept). World Tourism Day. P 13.
1331 **672** 20w. multicoloured 40 10
1332 **673** 20w. multicoloured 40 10

(Des Chun Hee Han. Photo)

1978 (1 Nov). Fire Prevention Campaign. P 13.
1339 **679** 20w. multicoloured 30 10

674 Customs Officers and Flag

675 Armed Forces

(Des Chun Hee Han. Photo)

1978 (28 Sept). Centenary of Customs House. P 13.
1333 **674** 20w. multicoloured 40 10

(Des Chun Hee Han. Photo)

1978 (1 Oct). 30th Anniv of Korean Armed Forces. P 13.
1334 **675** 20w. multicoloured 40 10

680 Thirteen-storey Pagoda, Jeonghye Temple

681 Three-storey Pagoda, Jinjeon Temple

(Des Kim Sung Sil. Photo)

1978 (20 Nov). Stone Pagodas (5th series). P 13.
1340 **680** 20w. multicoloured 55 10
1341 **681** 20w. multicoloured 55 10

676 Earthenware Figures, Silla Dynasty

677 Painting of a Lady (Shin Yoon-bok)

(Des Park Yeo Song. Photo)

1978 (1 Oct). Culture Month. P 13.
1335 **676** 20w. brownish black and pale sage green 40 10

(Des Chun Hee Han. Photo)

1978 (24 Oct). Philatelic Week. P 13.
1336 **677** 20w. multicoloured 45 10
MS1337 91×60 mm. No. 1336×2..................... 3·75 3·50

682 Snow Scene

683 Sheep (bas-relief, Kim Yu Shin's tomb)

(Des Kim Sung Sil (No. 1342), Park Yeo Song (No. 1343). Photo)

1978 (1 Dec). Lunar New Year ("Year of the Sheep"). P 13.
1342 **682** 20w. multicoloured 45 10
1343 **683** 20w. multicoloured 45 10
MS1344 Two sheets, each 90×60 mm. Nos.
1342/3×2 .... 3·50 3·00

684 People within Hibiscus **685** President Pak

(Des Chun Hee Han. Photo)

1978 (5 Dec). 10th Anniv of National Education Charter. P 13.
1345 **684** 20w. multicoloured 40 10

(Des Lee Keun Moon. Photo)

1978 (27 Dec). Presidential Inauguration. P 13.
1346 **685** 20w. multicoloured 85 30
MS1347 90×60 mm. No. 1346×2 .... 12·50 11·00

686 Golden Mandarinfish **687** Lace Bark Pine

(Des Ahn Seung Kyung. Photo)

1979 (20 Feb). Nature Conservation. P 13.
1348 **686** 20w. multicoloured .... 1·50 15
1349 **687** 20w. multicoloured .... 1·50 15

688 Samil Monument **689** Worker and Bulldozer

(Des Park Yeo Song. Photo)

1979 (1 Mar). 60th Anniv of Samil Independence Movement. P 13.
1350 **688** 20w. multicoloured 40 10

(Des Lee Keun Moon. Photo)

1979 (10 Mar). Labour Day. P 13.
1351 **689** 20w. multicoloured 40 10

690 Tabo Pagoda, Pulguk Temple **691** Gilt-bronze Maitreya **692** Gold Crown of Silla

693 Celadon Vase **694** "Tano Day Activities" (silk screen)

(Des Chun Hee Han. Photo)

1979 (1 Apr). Korean Art. P 13.
1352 **690** 20w. multicoloured 45 15
1353 **691** 20w. multicoloured 45 15
1354 **692** 20w. multicoloured 45 15
1355 **693** 20w. multicoloured 45 15
1356 **694** 60w. multicoloured 85 30
1352/1356 *Set of 5* .... 2·40 80
MS1357 90×126 mm. No. 1356×2 .... 3·25 3·00

695 Hand holding Symbols of Security **696** Pulguk Temple and PATA Emblem

(Des Kim Hyun. Photo)

1979 (1 Apr). Strengthening National Security. P 13.
1358 **695** 20w. multicoloured 40 10

(Des Chun Hee Han. Photo)

1979 (16 Apr). 28th Pacific Area Travel Association Conference, Seoul. P 13.
1359 **696** 20w. multicoloured 40 10

697 Presidents Pak and Senghor **698** Basketball

(Des Chun Hee Han. Photo)

1979 (22 Apr). Visit of President Senghor of Senegal. P 13.
1360 **697** 20w. multicoloured 40 10
MS1361 90×60 mm. No. 1360×2 .... 1·50 1·40

(Des Chun Hee Han. Photo)

1979 (29 Apr). Eighth World Women's Basketball Championships, Seoul. P 13.
1362 **698** 20 w. multicoloured 55 10

707 Porcelain Jar, Yi Dynasty

708 Kyongju Observatory

709 Mounted Warrior (pottery vessel)

699 Children playing

700 Children on Swing

710 Paikryung Island

711 Ryu Kwan Soon

712 Chung Yak Yong (writer)

(Des Kim Sung Sil. Photo)

1979 (5 May). International Year of the Child. P 13.
1363 **699** 20w. multicoloured 40 10
MS1363a 90×60mm. No. 1363 ×2 .... 1·50 1·40

(Des Chun Hee Han. Photo)

1979 (7 May). Family Planning. P 13½×12½.
1364 **700** 20w. multicoloured 75 30

713 Porcelain Jar, Chosun Dynasty

714 Ahn Joong Geun

715 Ahn Chang Ho

701 Mandarins

702 *Neofinettia falcata* (orchid)

(Des Ann Seung Kyung. Photo)

1979 (20 May). Nature Conservation. P 13.
1365 **701** 20w. multicoloured .... 1·50 25
1366 **702** 20w. multicoloured .... 1·50 25

716 Korvo Celadon Incense Burner

717 Kim Ku (organizer of Korean Independence Party)

718 Brick with Mountain Landscape

703 Manchurian Cranes

704 Mt. Sorak

704a Tolharubang (stone grandfather)

719 Hong Yung Sik (postal reformer)

720 Duck (lid of incense burner)

721 Dragon's Head Flagpole Finial

705 National Flag

706 *Hibiscus syriacus*

706a Earthenware Model of Wagon

722   Duck Earthenware Vessels   **723**

724 Tiger

(Des Chun Hee Han (10, 20, 200, 400w.), Jeon Hee Han (15, 30, 90w.), Lee Boo Yeol (60w.), Lee Keun Moon (100w. (both)), Kim Sung Sil (others). Eng Kim Kee Hwan (300w.), Shin Hyun Tae (450, 550, 1000w.). Recess (100 (1377a), 300, 450, 550w.), recess and litho (1000, 5000w.), photo (others))

1979 (31 May)–**93**. P 13 (100, 300, 450, 550, 1000, 5000w.), 13×13½ (15, 50, 80, 90w.) or 13½×13 (others).

1367	**703**	10w. black & brt yellowish green.........	70	25
1368	**704**	15w. slate-grn & bl-grn (10.4.801........	40	10
1369	**704a**	20w. bistre, black and turquoise-blue (30.12.86)..	40	10
		a. Coil. Imperf×p 13 (1.2.87)..............	1·00	45
1370	**705**	30w. multicoloured (10.9.80)...............	45	10
		a. Coil. P 13×imperf (1.2.87)...............	1·40	30
1371	**706**	40w. multicoloured (20.8.81)..............	55	10
		a. Coil. Imperf×p 13 (1.9.90)...............	1·20	30
1372	**706a**	50w. brown-lake, sepia and bright orange (28.9.90)..............................	40	10
		a. Coil. P 13×imperf (1993).................	1·00	30
1373	**707**	60w. pale grey, brown-purple and deep mauve (10.5.82)......................	45	10
		a. Coil. Imperf×p 13 (1993).................	75	25
1374	**708**	70w. multicoloured (15.3.83)...............	75	15
		a. Coil. P 13×imperf (22.10.84)..........	1·90	55
1375	**709**	80w. yell, blk & verm (15.6.83)............	85	25
		a. Coil. Imperf×p 13 (16.9.86)............	1·70	60
1376	**710**	90w. buff, deep green and bright orange (10.4.80)................................	1·10	25
1377	**711**	100 w. dp mag & brt mve (8.10.82)......	95	25
1377a	**712**	100w. greenish black (20.10.86)	2·75	25
1378	**713**	150w. black, bistre and greenish blue (2.7.90)...	1·00	25
1379	**714**	200w. olive-brn & yell-ol (8.10.82)	1·50	30
1380	**715**	300w. deep violet-blue (25.11.83)	2·30	30
1381	**716**	400w. sage green, agate & deep yellow-green (14.11.81).............................	5·00	40
1381a		400w. greenish blue, brown-ochre, reddish brown and greenish grey (20.7.83)	3·50	40
1382	**717**	450w. purple-brown (10.6.86).............	2·75	40
1383	**718**	500w. blackish green and apple green (20.7.83).....................................	2·75	40
1383a	**717**	550w. indigo (10.12.86)	3·00	40
1384	**719**	600w. multicoloured (25.6.90).............	3·00	75
1385	**720**	700w. multicoloured (15.6.83).............	4·25	75
1386	**721**	800w. multicoloured (10.7.90)	3·75	1·20
1387	**722**	1000w. cinnamon and agate (25.11.83).	25	45
		a. Pair. Nos. 1387/8...........................	9·00	95
1388	**723**	1000w. cinnamon and agate (25.11.83)..	4·25	45
1389	**724**	5000w. multicoloured (1.12.83)	27·00	5·50
1367/1389		Set of 26	70·00	12·50

Nos. 1387/8 were issued together in *se-tenant* pairs within the sheet. For similar 10w. but blue see No. 1065.

725 People   **726** Common Goral   **727** *Convallaria*
suffering   *leiskei* Miquel
from Traffic
Pollution

(Des Kim Sung Sil. Photo)

1979 (5 June). Environmental Protection. P 12½×13½.

1390	**725**	20w. deep brown and emerald	75	25

(Des Ahn Seung Kyung. Photo)

1979 (20 June). Nature Conservation. P 13.

1391	**726**	20w. multicoloured	1·50	15
1392	**727**	20w. multicoloured	1·50	15

728 Presidents Pak and   **729** Exhibition Building
Carter   and Emblem

(Des Lee Keun Moon. Photo)

1979 (29 June). Visit of President Carter of United States. P 13.

1393	**728**	20w. multicoloured	40	10
MS1394		90×60mm. No. 1393×2....................	1·50	1·40

(Des Park Yeo Song. Photo)

1979 (3 July). Opening of Korea Exhibition Centre. P 13.

1395	**729**	20w. multicoloured	30	10

730 Boeing 747-200
Jetliner and Globe

(Des Lee Boo Yeol)

1979(1 Aug). 10th Anniv of Korean Air Lines. P 13.

1396	**730**	20w. multicoloured	40	10

731 "The Courtesans' Sword Dance"
(Shin Yun-bok)

(Das Park Yeo Song. Photo)

1979 (1 Sept). United Slates Exhibition "5000 Years of Korean Art" (1st issue). P 13.
1397 **731** 60w. multicoloured 85 30
MS1398 89×125 mm. No.1397×2................................... 4·25 3·75
See also Nos. 1402/3, 1406/7, 1420/**MS**1422, 1426/7, 1433/4, 1441/2 and 1457/8.

732 Mount Mai, North Cholla Province

733 Dragon's Head Rock, Cheju Island

(Des Kim Jae Min and Lee Keun Moon. Photo)

1979 (28Sept). World Tourism Day. P 13.
1399 **732** 20w. multicoloured 40 10
1400 **733** 20w. multicoloured 40 10

734 Heart, Donors and Blood Drop

(Des Chun Hee Han. Photo)

1979 (1 Oct). Blood Donors. P 13½×13.
1401 **734** 20w. rose-red and emerald......................... 75 15

735 White Porcelain Jar with Grape Design

736 Mounted Warrior (pottery vessel)

(Des Park Yeo Song. Photo)

1979 (15 Oct). Exhibition "5000 Years of Korean Art" (2nd issue). P 13×13½ (1402) or 13½×13 (1403).
1402 **735** 20w. multicoloured 60 15
1403 **736** 20w. multicoloured 60 15

737 "Moon Travel" (Park Chung Jae)

(Des Kim Sung Sil. Photo)

1979 (30 Oct). Philatelic Week. P 13½×13.
1404 **737** 20w. multicoloured 30 10
MS1405 90×66 mm. No. 1404×2........................... 1 40 1·30

738 Hahoe Mask

739 Golden Amitabha with Halo

(Des Park Yeo Song. Photo)

1979 (15 Nov). Exhibition "5000 Years of Korean Art" (3rd issue). P 13×13½.
1406 **738** 20w. multicoloured 55 15
1407 **739** 20w. multicoloured 55 15

740 Rain Frog

741 Asian Polypody

(Des Ahn Seung Kyung. Photo)

1979 (25 Nov). Nature Conservation. P 13×13½.
1408 **740** 20w. multicoloured .... 1·60 15
1409 **741** 20w. multicoloured .... 1·60 15

742 Monkey (bas-relief, Kim Yu Shin's tomb)

743 Children playing Yut

(Des Lee Keun Moon and Jeon Hee Han. Photo)

1979 (1 Dec). Lunar New Year ("Year of the Monkey"). P 13×13½.

1410	**742**	20w. multicoloured	40	10
1411	**743**	20w. multicoloured	40	10

MS1412 Two sheets, each 90×60 mm. (a) No.
1410×2; (b) No. 1411×2...................................... 1·40   1·20

744 Pres. Choi Kyu Hah

(Des Jeon Hee Han. Photo)

1979 (21 Dec). Presidential Inauguration. P 13½×13.

1413	**744**	20w. multicoloured	50	10

MS1414 91×61 mm. No. 1413×2............................ 5·75   5·50

745 Firefly   **746** Meesun Tree   **747** Pres. Pak
(*Pyrocoelia rufa*)

(Des Ahn Seung Kyung. Photo)

1980 (20 Jan). Nature Conservation. P 13×13½.

1415	**745**	30w. multicoloured	1·60	15
1416	**746**	30w. multicoloured	1·60	15

(Des Lee Keun Moon. Photo)

1980 (2 Feb). President Pak Commemoration. P 13×13½.

1417	**747**	30w. Indian red	50	15
		a. Pair. Nos. 1417/18	1·10	35
1418		30w. blackish purple	50	15

MS1419 90×60 mm. Nos. 1417/18.......................... 4·50   4·25

Nos. 1417/18 were issued together in *se-tenant* pairs within the sheet.

748 Earthenware Kettle

749 "Landscape" (Kim Hong Do)

(Des Lee Keun Moon. Photo)

1980 (20 Feb). Exhibition "5000 Years of Korean Art" (4th issue). P 13½×13 (30w.) or 13×13½ (60w.).

1420	**748**	30w. multicoloured	65	15
1421	**749**	60w. multicoloured	1·00	30

MS1422 90×128 mm. No. 1421×2.............................. 3·50   3·50

750 "Lotus"   **751** "Magpie and Tiger"

(Des Kim Jae Min. Photo)

1980 (10 Mar). Folk Paintings (1st series). P 13×13½ (30w.) or 13½×13 (60w.).

1423	**750**	30w. multicoloured	65	15
1424	**751**	60w. multicoloured	1·60	55

See also Nos. 1429/**MS**1432, 1437/40 and 1453/6.

752 Merchant Ships

(Des Lee Boo Yeol. Photo)

1980 (13 Mar). Korean Merchant Navy. P 13×13½.

1425	**752**	30w. multicoloured	40	10

753 "Heavenly Horse"   **754** Banner Staff with
(tomb painting)   Dragon-head Finial

(Des Park Yeo Song. Photo)

1980 (20 Apr). Exhibition "5000 Years of Korean Art" (5th issue). P 13×13½ (1426) or 13½×13 (1427).

1426	**753**	30w. multicoloured	65	15
1427	**754**	30w. multicoloured	65	15

755 "Fruition"   756 "Red Phoenix"

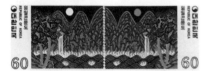

757   "Sun and Moon over   758
(half-size illustration)

(Des Kim Sung Sil. Photo)

1980 (22 Apr). Tenth Anniv of Saemaul Movement (community self-help programme). P 13×13½.
1428 **755** 30w. multicoloured 40   10

(Des Lee Keun Moon. Photo)

1980 (10May). Folk Paintings (2nd series). P 13×13½.
1429 **756** 30w. multicoloured 55   15
1430 **757** 60w. multicoloured .... 1·60   45
          a. Horiz pair. Nos. 1430/1 .... 3·50   95
1431 **758** 60w. multicoloured .... 1·60   45
1429/1431 *Set of 3* .... 3·50   95
MS1432 127×91 mm. Nos. 1430/1 .... 5·75   5·50
Nos. 1430/1 were issued together in *se-tenant* pairs within the sheet, each pair forming a composite design.

759 "Man on Horse"   760 "Tiger"
(mural)   (granite sculpture)

(Des Park Yeo Song. Photo)

1980 (20 May). Exhibition "5000 Years of Korean Art" (6th issue). P 13×13½ (1433) or 13½×13 (1434).
1433 **759** 30w. multicoloured 65   15
1434 **760** 30w. multicoloured 65   15

761 UN Flag and   762 "Venus de Milo"
Rifle   and Contestants

(Des Ann Seung Kyung. Photo)

1980 (25 June). 30th Anniv of Intervention of United Nations Forces in Korean War. P 13×13½.
1435 **761** 30w. multicoloured 40   10

(Des Jeon Hee Han. Photo!

1980 (8 July). Miss Universe Beauty Contest, Seoul. P 13×13½.
1436 **782** 30w. multicoloured 40   10

763 "Rabbits   764 "Dragon in
pounding Grain in   Cloud"
a Mortar"

(Des Lee Keun Moon. Photo)

1980 (10 July). Folk Paintings (3rd series). P 13×13½.
1437 **763** 30w. multicoloured 65   25
1438 **764** 30w. multicoloured 65   25

765 "Pine Tree"   766 "Flowers and
                   Birds" (detail, folding
                   screen)

(Des Lee Keun Moon. Photo)

1980 (9 Aug). Folk Paintings (4th series). P 13×13½ (1439) or 13½×13 (1440).
1439 **765** 30w. multicoloured 65   25
1440 **766** 30w. multicoloured .... 1·20   30

767 Human-faced   768 "White Tiger" (mural)
Roof Tile

(Des Park Yeo Song. Photo)

1980 (20 Aug). Exhibition "5000 Years of Korean Art" (7th issue). P 13×13½ (1441) or 13½×13 (1442).
1441 **767** 30w. multicoloured 55   15
1442 **768** 30w. multicoloured 55   15

769 Footballer

770 Pres. Chun Doo Hwan

(Des Jeon Hee Han. Photo)

1980 (23 Aug). Tenth President's Cup Football Tournament. P 13×13½.

1443	**769**	30w. multicoloured	40	10

(Des Jeon Hee Han. Photo)

1980 (1 Sept). Presidential Inauguration. P 13½×13.

1444	**770**	30w. multicoloured	50	15
MS1445	90×60 mm. No. 1444×2		3·25	2·75

771 Woman Soldier and Emblem

(Des Jeon Hee Han. Photo)

1980 (6 Sept). 30th Anniv of Women's Army Corps. P 13½×13.

1446	**771**	30w. multicoloured	40	10

772 River Baegma

773 Three Peaks of Dodam

(Des Jeon Hee Han. Photo)

1980 (28 Sept). World Tourism Day. P 13½×13.

1447	**772**	30w. brown-rose and deep purple	40	10
1448	**773**	30w. greenish yellow, bright blue-green and new blue	40	10

774 Corn-cob and Micrometer

775 Tree

(Des Kim Sung Sil. Photo)

1980 (20 Oct). Population and Housing Census. P 13×13½.

1449	**774**	30w. multicoloured	40	10

(Des Park Yeo Song. Photo)

1980 (27 Oct). 75th Anniv of Korean Red Cross. P 13×13½.

1450	**775**	30w. multicoloured	50	10

776 "Angels delivering Mail" (Kim Ki Chul)

(Des Ahn Seung Kyung. Photo)

1980 (6 Nov). Philatelic Week. P 13½×13.

1451	**776**	30w. multicoloured	40	10
MS1452	91×60 mm. No. 1461×2		1·50	1·30

777   "Ten Long-life Symbols"   **778**

779   "Ten Long-life Symbols"   **780**

(Des Lee Keun Moon. Photo)

1980 (10 Nov). Folk Paintings (5th series). P 13½×13.

1453	**777**	30w. multicoloured	1·50	25
		a. Horiz strip of 4. Nos. 1453/6	6·25	
1454	**778**	30w. multicoloured	1·50	25
1455	**779**	30w. multicoloured	1·50	25
1456	**780**	30w. multicoloured	1·50	25
1453/1456	Set of 4		5·50	90

Nos. 1453/6 were issued together in horizontal *se-tenant* strips of four within the sheet, each strip forming a composite design.

781 Deva King (sculpture)

782 Cable Ship and Cross-section of Cable

(Des Park Yeo Song. Recess)

1980 (20 Nov). Exhibition "5000 Years of Korean Art" (8th issue).
P 12½×13.
1457 **781** 30w. black 65 15
1458 30w. scarlet....................... 65 15

(Des Ann Seung Kyung. Photo)

1980 (28 Nov). Inauguration of Korea-Japan Submarine Cable.
P 13×13½.
1459 **782** 30w. multicoloured 50 10

783 Cock (bas-relief,   **784** Cranes
Kim Yu Shin's tomb)

(Des Jeon Hee Han (1460), Park Yeo Song (1461). Photo)

1980 (1 Dec). Lunar New Year ('Year of the Cock'). P 13×13½.
1460 **783** 30w. multicoloured 50 10
1461 **784** 30w. multicoloured 50 10
MS1462 Two sheets, each 90×60 mm. (a) No.
1460×2; (b) No. 1461×2....................... 3·00 2·75

785 Pres. Chun Doo Hwan
and Factory within *Hibiscus
syriacus*

(Des Jeon Hee Han. Photo)

1981 (3 Mar). Presidential Inauguration. P 13½×13.
1463 **785** 30w. multicoloured 40 10
MS1464 90×60 mm. No. 1463×2 .... 1·40 1·30

786 *Korea Sun* (tanker)   **787** *Asia Yukho*
(freighter)

(Des Jeon Hee Han. Photo)

1981 (13 Mar). Ships (1st series). P 13×13½ (1465) or 13½ ×13
(1466).
1465 **786** 30w. multicoloured 60 10
1466 **787** 90w. multicoloured 90 25
See also Nos. 1470/1, 1482/5 and 1501/2.

788 National Assembly
Building

(Des Kim Sung Sil. Photo)

1981 (17 Apr). Inaugural Session of 11th National Assembly.
P 13½×13.
1467 **788** 30w. blackish brown and gold 40 10

789 Symbols of   **790** Disabled Person
Disability and   in Wheelchair at
IYDP Emblem   Foot
of Steps

(Des Lee Keun Moon and Lee Boo Yeol. Photo)

1981 (20 Apr). International Year of Disabled Persons. P 13×13½.
1468 **789** 30w. multicoloured 40 10
1469 **790** 90w. multicoloured 85 40

791 *Saturn* (bulk carrier)   **792** *Hanjin Seoul* (container
ship)

(Des Jeon Hee Han. Photo)

1981 (10 May). Ships (2nd series). P 13½×13.
1470 **791** 30w. dp purple, brt purple & new blue .. 60 10
1471 **792** 90w. grey, deep blue and bright rose ..... 1·00 30

793 Council   **794** "Clean Rivers   **795** White Storks
Emblem on   and Air"   visiting Breeding
Ribbon   Grounds

(Des Lee Boo Yeol. Photo)

1981 (5 June). Advisory Council on Peaceful Unification Policy.
P 13×13½.
1472 **793** 40w. multicoloured 40   10

(Des Lee Keun Moon and Lee Boo Yeol. Photo)

1981 (5 June). World Environment Day. P 13×13½.
1473 **794** 30w. multicoloured 40   10
1474 **795** 90w. multicoloured 90   25

796 Presidents Chun and
Suharto of Indonesia

797 Pres. Chun and
Sultan of Malaysia

798 Handshake and Flags
of S. Korea and Singapore

799 Pres. Chun and King
of Thailand

800 Presidents Chun and
Marcos of Philippines

801 Pres. Chun and Flags of S. Korea,
Singapore, Thailand, Indonesia, Malaysia
and Philippines

(Des Lee Keun Moon (1480), Kim Sung Sil (others). Photo)

1981 (25 June). Presidential Visit to Association of South East Asian
Nations (A.S.E.A.N.) Countries. P 13×13½ (1480) or 13½×13
(others).
1475 **796** 40w. multicoloured 65   10
       a. Strip of 5. Nos. 1475/9 .... 4·25
1476 **797** 40w. multicoloured 65   10
1477 **798** 40w. multicoloured 65   10
1478 **799** 40w. multicoloured 65   10
1479 **800** 40w. multicoloured 65   10
1480 **801** 40w. multicoloured 65   10
1475/1480 *Set of 6* .... 3·50   55
MS1481 Two sheets, each 126×90 mm. Imperf.
  (a) Nos. 1475/9; (b) No. 1480×2 .... 5·50   5·00
  Nos. 1475/9 were issued together in *se-tenant* strips of five within
the sheet.

802 *Chung Ryong No. 3* (tug)   **803** *Soo Gung No. 71*
                           (trawler)

(Des Jeon Hee Han. Photo)

1981 (10 July). Ships (3rd series). P 13½ ×13.
1482 **802** 40w. multicoloured 75   15
1483 **803** 100w. multicoloured .... 1·30   40

804 *Al Debaran* (log carrier)   **805** *Hyundai No. 1* (car
                            carrier)

(Des Chun Hee Han. Photo)

1981 (10 Aug). Ships (4th series). P 13½ ×13.
1484 **804** 40w. multicoloured 75   15
1485 **805** 100w. multicoloured .... 1·30   30

806 Korean with   **807** Glider
Flag and Dates
on Graph

808 Elastic-powered   **809** Line-controlled
Plane   Plane

810 Radio-controlled   **811** Radio-controlled
Plane   Helicopter

(Des Chun Hee Han. Photo)

1981 (15 Aug). 36th Anniv of Liberation. P 13×13½.
1486　**806**　40w. multicoloured ....　40　10

(Des Kim Sung Sil. Photo)

1981 (20 Sept). Third Model Aeronautic Competition. P 13½×13.
1487　**807**　10w. multicoloured ....　60　10
　　　　　　　a. Strip of 5. Nos. 1487/91 ....　4·00
1488　**808**　20w. multicoloured ....　60　10
1489　**809**　40w. multicoloured ....　60　20
1490　**810**　50w. multicoloured ....　75　30
1491　**811**　80w. multicoloured ....　1·00　40
1487/1491 Set of 5...　3·25　1·00
Nos. 1487/91 were issued together in se-tenant strips of five within the sheet.

812 W.H.O. Emblem and Citizens

813 Seoul Communications Tower

814 Ulreung Island

(Des Lee Boo Yeol. Photo)

1981 (22 Sept). 32nd Session of World Health Organization Regional Committee for the Western Pacific, Seoul. P 13½.
1492　**812**　40w. multicoloured ....　40　10

(Des Lee Keun Moon. Photo)

1981 (28 Sept). World Tourism Day. P 13×13½.
1493　**813**　40w. multicoloured ....　40　10
1494　**814**　40w. multicoloured ....　40　10

815 Cycling

816 Swimming

(Des Lee Keun Moon. Photo)

1981 (10 Oct). 62nd National Sports Meeting, Seoul. P 13½×13.
1495　**815**　40w. multicoloured ....　50　10
1496　**816**　40w. multicoloured ....　50　10

817 Presidents Chun and Carazo Odio

818 Hand holding Plate with FAO Emblem

(Des Lee Keun Moon. Photo)

1981 (12 Oct). Visit of President Carazo Odio of Costa Rica. P 13½×13.
1497　**817**　40w. multicoloured ....　45　10

(Des Kim Sung Sil. Photo)

1981 (16 Oct). World Food Day. P 13×13½.
1498　**818**　40w. multicoloured ....　45　10

819 Airliner and Clouds

820 South Gate of Seoul and Olympic Rings

(Des Son Chung Sik. Photo)

1981 (30 Oct). National Aviation Day. P 13½×13.
1499　**819**　40w. brt orange, dp reddish brn & silver　50　10

(Des Chun Hee Han. Photo)

1981 (30 Oct). Choice of Seoul as 1988 Olympic Host City. P 13×13½.
1500　**820**　40w. multicoloured ....　65　15

821 Stolt Hawk (chemical carrier)

822 Passenger Ferry

823 "Hong-gliding" (Kim Kyung Jun)

(Des Chun Hee Han. Recess)

1981 (10 Nov). Ships (5th series). P 13×12½.
1501　**821**　40w. black ....　65　15
1502　**822**　100w. deep blue...................................　1·20　30

(Des Chun Hee Han. Photo)

1981 (18 Nov). Philatelic Week. P 13½×13.
1503　**823**　40w. multicoloured ....　40　10
MS1504　90×60 mm. No. 1503×2 ....　1·80　1·70

824 Camellia and Dog

825 Children flying Kites

(Des Kwon Myung Kwang. Photo)

1981 (1 Dec). Lunar New Year ("Year of the Dog"). P 13×13½.
1505 **824** 40w. multicoloured 40 10
1506 **825** 40w. multicoloured 40 10
MS1507 Two sheets, each 90×60 mm. (a) No.
1505×2; (b) No. 1506×2 .... 3·75 3·50

830 Dividers and World Map

831 Music and *Hibiscus syriacus*

(Des Kim Sung Sil. Photo)

1982 (21 Apr). Centenary of International Polar Year. P 13½×13.
1512 **830** 60w. multicoloured 65 15

(Des Chun Hee Han. Photo)

1982 (6 May). Children's *Day*. P 13½×13.
1513 **831** 60w. multicoloured 50 10

826 "Hangul Hakhoe"

827 Telephone and Dish Aerial

(Des Lee Hea Ok. Photo)

1981 (3 Dec). 60th Anniv of Hangul Hakhoe (Korean Language Society). P 13½×13.
1508 **826** 40w. multicoloured 50 10

(Des Kim Sung Sil. Photo)

1982 (4 Jan). Inauguration of Korean Telecommunication Authority. P 13×13½.
1509 **827** 60w. multicoloured 60 10

832 Pres. Chun and Samuel Doe

(Des Lee Keun Moon. Litho)

1982 (9 May). Visit of Samuel Doe (Liberian Head of State). P 13.
1514 **832** 60w. multicoloured 60 15
MS1515 100×60 mm. No. 1514×2. Imperf .... 1·80 1·70

833 Centenary Emblem

834 Statue of Liberty and Seoul South Gate

(Des Lee Hea Ok. Photo)

1982 (18 May). Centenary of Korea-United States Friendship Treaty. P 13½×13.
1516 **833** 60w. multicoloured 50 15
a. Pair. Nos. 1516/17 .... 1·10 35
1517 **834** 60w. multicoloured 50 15
MS1518 90×60 mm. Nos. 1516/17 .... 3·75 3·50
Nos. 1516/17 were issued together in *se-tenant* pairs within the sheet.

828 Scout Emblem and Logs forming "75"

829 Young Woman

(Des Son Chung Sik. Photo)

1982 (22 Feb). 75th Anniv of Boy Scout Movement. P 13×13½.
1510 **828** 60w. multicoloured 65 15

(Des Son Chung Sik. Photo)

1982 (20 Apr). 60th Anniv of Korean Young Women's Christian Association. P 13×13½.
1511 **829** 60w. multicoloured 50 10

835 Presidents Chun and Mobutu

(Des Lee Keun Moon. Litho)

1982 (7 June). Visit of President Mobutu of Zaire. P 13.
1519 **835** 60w. multicoloured 50 15
MS1520 100×60 mm. No. 1519×2. Imperf .... 1·80 1·70

836 "Territorial Expansion by Kwanggaeto the Great" (Lee Chong Sang)

837 "General Euljimunduck's Great Victory at Salsoo" (Park Kak Soon)

(Des Lee Keun Moon. Photo)

1982 (15 June). Documentary Paintings (1st series). P 13×13½.
1521 **836** 60w. multicoloured 85 40
1522 **837** 60w. multicoloured .... 1·30 45
    See also Nos. 1523/4, 1537/8 and 1548/9.

838 "Shilla's Repulse of Tang's Invading Army" (Oh Seung Woo)

839 "General Kang Kam Chan's Great Victory at Kyiju" (Lee Yong Hwan)

(Des Lee Keun Moon. Photo)

1982 (15 July). Documentary Paintings (2nd series). P 13×13½.
1523 **838** 60w. multicoloured 75 30
1524 **839** 60w. multicoloured 75 30

840 Convention Emblem and Globe

841 Presidents Chun and Moi of Kenya

842 Presidents Chun and Shagari of Nigeria

843 Presidents Chun and Bongo of Gabon

844 Presidents Chun and Diouf of Senegal

845 Flags of South Korea and Canada

(Des Chun Hee Han. Photo)

1982 (20 July). 55th International Y's Men's Club Convention, Seoul. P 13×13½.
1525 **840** 60w. multicoloured 40 10

(Des Son Chung Sik (1530), Kim Sung Sil (others). Photo)

1982 (17 Aug). Presidential Visits to Africa and Canada. P 13½×13.
1526 **841** 60w. multicoloured 50 10
1527 **842** 60w. multicoloured 50 10
1528 **843** 60w. multicoloured 50 10
1529 **844** 60w. multicoloured 50 10
1530 **845** 60w. multicoloured 50 10
1526/1530 *Set of 5*... 2·30 45
MS1531 Five sheets, each 90×60 mm. (a) No.
    1526×2; (b) No. 1527×2; (c) No. 1528×2; (d) No.
    1529×2; (e) No. 1530×2 .... 12·50 11·50

846 National Flag

847 Emblem and Player

(Des Lee Boo Yeol. Photo)

1982 (22 Aug). Centenary of National Flag. P 13½×13.
1532 **846** 60w. multicoloured 50 10
MS1533 90×60 mm. No. 1532×2 .... 2·50 2·30

(Des Chun Hee Han. Photo)

1982 (25 Aug). Second Seoul International Table Tennis Championships. P 13½×13.
1534 **847** 60w. multicoloured 60 10

848 Baseball Player

849 Exhibition Centre

(Des Lee Keun Moon. Recess)

1982 (4 Sept). 27th World Baseball Championship Series, Seoul. P 13×12½.

1535	**848**	60w. chocolate	60	15

(Des Lee Hea Ok. Photo)

1982 (17 Sept). Seoul International Trade Fair. P 13½×13.

1536	**849**	60w. multicoloured	40	10

850 "Admiral Yi Sun Sin's Great Victory at Hansan" (Kim Hyung Ku)

851 "General Kim Chwa Jin's Chungsanri Battle" (Sohn Soo Kwang)

(Des Lee Keun Moon. Photo)

1982 (15 Oct). Documentary Paintings (3rd series). P 13×13½.

1537	**850**	60w. multicoloured	1·10	40
1538	**851**	60w. multicoloured	1·10	40

852 "Miners reading Consolatory Letters" (Urn Soon Keun)

853 Presidents Chun and Suharto

(Des Chun Hee Han. Photo)

1982 (15 Oct). Philatelic Week. P 13½×13.

1539	**852**	60w. multicoloured	40	10
MS1540		90×60 mm. No. 1539×2.	1·70	1·50

(Des Kim Sung Sil. Litho)

1982 (16 Oct). Visit of President Suharto of Indonesia. P 13.

1541	**853**	60w. multicoloured	40	10
MS1542		100×60 mm. No. 1541×2. Imperf	1·50	1·40

854 JCI Emblem over World Map

855 "Intelsat 5" and "4-A" orbiting Globe

(Des Son Chung Sik. Photo)

1982 (3 Nov). 37th Junior Chamber International World Congress, Seoul. P 13½×13.

1543	**854**	60w. multicoloured	40	10

(Des Chun Hee Han. Photo)

1982 (20 Nov). Second United Nations Conference on the Exploration and Peaceful Uses of Outer Space, Vienna. P 13×13½.

1544	**855**	60w. multicoloured	50	10

856 Pig (bas-relief. Kim Yu Shin's tomb)

857 Magpies and Korean Moneybag

(Des Kim Sung Sil (1545), Chun Hee Han (1546). Photo)

1982 (1 Dec). Lunar New Year ("Year of the Pig"). P 13×13½.

1545	**856**	60w. multicoloured	50	10
1546	**857**	60w. multicoloured	50	10
MS1547		Two sheets, each 90×60 mm. (a) No.		
		1545×2; (b) No. 1546×2	4·25	3·75

858 "General Kwon Yul's Great Victory at Haengju" (Oh Seung Woo)

859 "Kim Chong Suh's Exploitation of Yukjin" (Kim Tae)

(Des Lee Keun Moon. Photo)

1982 (15 Dec). Documentary Paintings (4th series). P 13×13½.
1548 858 60w. multicoloured .... 1·30   40
1549 859 60w. multicoloured .... 1·30   40

860 Flags of South   861 Hand
Korea and Turkey   writing Letter

(Des Kim Sung Sil. Litho)

1982 (20 Dec). Visit of President Evran of Turkey. P 13.
1550 860 60w. multicoloured   50   10
MS1551 100×60 mm. Nos. 1550×2. Imperf.................. 1·70   1·50

(Des Lee Boo Yeol. Photo)

1982 (31 Dec). Letter Writing Campaign. P 13×13½.
1552 861 60w. multicoloured   40   10

862 Emblem, Airliner,
Container Ship and Cranes

(Des Lee Hea Ok. Photo)

1983 (26 Jan). International Customs Day. P 13½×13.
1553 862 60w. multicoloured   60   10

863 Hyundai "Pony 2"   864 Keohwa Jeep

(Des Chun Hee Han. Photo)

1983 (25 Feb). Korean-made Vehicles (1st series). P 13½×13.
1554 863 60w. multicoloured   85   25
        a. Pair. Nos. 1554/5................................... 1·80   55
1555 864 60w. multicoloured   85   25
    Nos. 1554/5 were issued together in se-tenant pairs within the sheet.
    See also Nos. 1558/9, 1564/5, 1572/3 and 1576/7.

865 Pres. Chun and Sultan of Malaysia

(Des Lee Boo Yeol. Photo)

1983 (22 Mar). Visit of Sultan of Malaysia. P 13½×13.
1556 865 60w. multicoloured   40   10
MS1557 90×60 mm. No. 1556×2............................... 1·40   1·30

866 Daewoo "Maepsy"   867 Kia "Bongo" Minibus

(Des Chun Hee Han. Photo)

1983 (25 Mar). Korean-made Vehicles (2nd series). P 13½×13.
1558 866 60w. multicoloured   85   25
        a. Pair. Nos. 1558/9................................... 1·80   55
1559 867 60w. multicoloured   85   25
    Nos. 1558/9 were issued together in se-tenant pairs within the sheet.

868 Former General Bureau   869 Central Post Office,
of Postal Administration   Seoul

(Des Lee Keun Moon. Photo)

1983 (22 Apr). "Philakorea 84" International Stamp Exhibition, Seoul, and Centenary of Korean Postal Service (1st series). P 13½×13.
1560 **868** 60w. multicoloured 65 15
1561 **869** 60w. multicoloured 65 15
See also Nos. 1566/7, 1574/5 and 1603/6.

870 Old Village Schoolroom

(Des Lee Boo Yeol. Photo)

1983 (15 May). Teacher's Day. P 13½×13.
1562 **870** 60w. multicoloured 50 10
MS1563 90×60 mm. Nos. 1562×2................................. 2·10 1·90

871 Asia Motors Co. Bus   **872** Kia "Super Titan" Truck

(Des Chun Hee Han. Photo)

1983 (25 May). Korean-made Vehicles (3rd series). P 13½×13.
1564 **871** 60w. multicoloured 85 25
1565 **872** 60w. multicoloured 85 25

873 Early Postman   **874** Modern Postman

(Des Lee Keun Moon. Photo)

1983 (10 June). Philakorea 84 International Stamp Exhibition, Seoul, and Centenary of Korean Postal Service (2nd series). P 13½×13.
1566 **873** 70w. multicoloured 85 25
1567 **874** 70w. multicoloured 85 25

875 "Communications in Outer Space" (Chun Ja Eun)   **876** Whooper Swans at Sunrise

(Des Lee Hea Ok. Photo)

1983 (20 June). World Communications Year. P 13½×13.
1568 **875** 70w. multicoloured 40 10
MS1569 90×60 mm. Nos. 1568×2................................. 1·50 1·40

(Des Lee Boo Yeol. Photo)

1983 (1 July). Inauguration of Communications Insurance. P 13½×13.
1570 **876** 70w. multicoloured 85 15

877 Emblems of Science and Engineering

(Des Hong Hye Yeon. Photo)

1983 (4 July). Korean Symposium on Science and Technology, Seoul. P 13½×13.
1571 **877** 70w. multicoloured 60 15

878 Daewoo Dump Truck   **879** Hyundai Cargo Truck

(Des Chun Hee Han. Photo)

1983 (25 July). Korean-made Vehicles (4th series). P 13½×13.
1572 **878** 70w. multicoloured 95 25
1573 **879** 70w. multicoloured 95 25

880 Mail carried by Horse   **881** Mail Truck and Douglas DC-8-60 Super Sixty Jetliner

(Des Lee Keun Moon. Photo)

1983 (10 Aug). Philakorea 84 International Stamp Exhibition, Seoul, and Centenary of Korean Postal Service (3rd series). P 13½×13.
1574	**880**	70w. multicoloured	1·00	25
1575	**881**	70w. multicoloured	1·00	25

882 Dong-A Concrete Mixer Truck   **883** Dong-A Tanker

(Des Chun Hee Han. Photo)

1983 (25 Aug). Korean-made Vehicles (5th series). P 13½×13.
1576	**882**	70w. multicoloured	95	25
1577	**883**	70w. multicoloured	95	25

884 Pres. Chun and King Hussein

(Des Chun Hee Han. Litho)

1983 (10 Sept). Visit of King Hussein of Jordan. P 13.
1578	**884**	70w. multicoloured	50	10
MS1579	100×60 mm. Nos. 1578×2. Imperf.		1·60	1·40

885 Woman with Fan   **886** IPU Emblem and Flags

(Des Lee Bong Sup and Chun Hee Han. Photo)

1983 (25 Sept). 53rd American Society of Travel Agents World Conference, Seoul. P 13½×13.
1580	**885**	70w. multicoloured	50	10

(Des Lee Hea Ok. Photo)

1983 (4 Oct). 70th Inter-Parliamentary Union Conference, Seoul. P 13½×13.
1581	**886**	70w. multicoloured	50	10
MS1582	90×60 mm. Nos. 1581×2		1·60	1·40

887 Gymnastics   **888** Football

(Des Kim Sung Sil. Photo)

1983 (6 Oct). 64th National Sports Meeting, Inchon. P 13×13½.
1583	**887**	70w. multicoloured	70	15
1584	**888**	70w. multicoloured	70	15

889 Presidents Chun and U San Yu of Burma   **890** Presidents Chun and Giani Zail Singh of India

891 Presidents Chun and Jayewardene of Sri Lanka   **892** Flags of S. Korea and Australia

893 Flags of S. Korea and New Zealand

(Des Chun Hee Han (1585), Kim Sung Sil (1586), Lee Keun Moon (1587), Lee Hea Ok (1588), Hong Hye Yeon (1589). Photo)

1983 (8 Oct). Presidential Visits to Burma, India, Sri Lanka, Australia and New Zealand. P 13½×13.
1585	**889**	70w. multicoloured	1·60	75
1586	**890**	70w. multicoloured	1·60	75
1587	**891**	70w. multicoloured	1·60	75
1588	**892**	70w. multicoloured	1·60	75
1589	**893**	70w. multicoloured	1·60	75
1585/1589	Set of 5		7·25	3·50
MS1590	Five Sheets, each 90×60 mm. (a) No. 1585×2; (b) Nos. 1586×2; (c) Nos. 1587×2; (d) Nos. 1588×2; (e) Nos. 1589×2		28·00	25·00

Following the assassination of several Korean cabinet ministers in Burma, the tour was cancelled; the stamps were withdrawn from sale on 10 October.

894 Rain Drops containing Symbols of Industry, Light and Food

895 Centenary Dates

(Des Hong Hye Yeon. Litho)

1983 (15 Oct). Development of Water Resources and Tenth Anniv of Soyang-gang Dam. P 13.

1591 **894** 70w. multicoloured 50   10

(Des Choi Hye Kyung. Photo)

1983 (31 Oct). Centenary of First Korean Newspaper *Hansong Sunbo*. P 13×13½.

1592 **895** 70w. multicoloured 50   10

899 Rat (bas-relief, Kim Yu Shin's tomb)

900 Manchunan Cranes and Pine

901 Bicentenary Emblem

(Des Kim Sung Sil. Photo)

1983 (1 Dec). Lunar New Year ("Year of the Rat"). P 13×13½.

1598 **899** 70w. multicoloured 50   10
1599 **900** 70w. multicoloured 50   10
MS1600 Two sheets, each 90×60 mm. (a) No.
    1598×2; (b) Nos. 1599×2 .... 5·25   4.75

(Des Kim Kyo Man. Photo)

1984 (14 Jan). Bicentenary of Catholic Church in Korea. P 13×13½.

1601 **901** 70w. carmine-red, dp violet & silver 50   10
MS1602 90×60 mm. Nos. 1601×2 .... 3·25   3·00

896 Tree with Lungs and Cross of Lorraine

897 Presidents Chun and Reagan

(Des Hong Hye Yeon. Photo)

1983 (6 Nov). 30th Anniv of Korean National Tuberculosis Association. P 13x13½.

1593 **896** 70w. multicoloured 50   10

(Des Lee Keun Moon. Photo)

1983 (12 Nov). Visit of President Reagan of United States of America. P 13½×13.

1594 **897** 70w. multicoloured 50   10
MS1595 90×60 mm. Nos. 1594×2 .... 2·50   2·30

902 5m. and 10m. Stamps, 1884

903 5000w. Stamp, 1983

(Des Lee Keun Moon. Photo)

1984 (10 Feb). Philakorea 84 International Stamp Exhibition, Seoul, and Centenary of Korean Postal Service (4th series). P 13½×13.

1603 **902** 70w. multicoloured 70   15
1604 **903** 70w. multicoloured 70   15

898 Child collecting Stamps

(Des Lee Hea Ok. Photo)

1983 (18 Nov). Philatelic Week. P 13×13½.

1596 **898** 70w. multicoloured 50   10
MS1597 90×60 mm. No. 1596×2 .... 2·50   2·30

904 Old Postal Emblem and Post Box

905 Modern Postal Emblem and Post Box

(Des Lee Keun Moon. Photo)

1984 (10 Mar). Philakorea 84 International Stamp Exhibition, Seoul, and Centenary of Korean Postal Service (5th series). P 13½×13.

1605	**904**	70w. multicoloured	70	15
1606	**905**	70w. multicoloured	70	15

906 Pres. Chun and Sultan

(Des Kim Sung Sil. Litho)

1984 (7 Apr). Visit of Sultan of Brunei. P 13.

1607	**906**	70w. multicoloured	50	10
MS1608		100×60 mm. Nos. 1607×2. Imperf.	1·70	1·50

907 Pres. Chun and Shaikh Khalifa

(Des Lee Keun Moon. Litho)

1984 (20 Apr). Visit of Shaikh Khalifa of Qatar. P 13.

1609	**907**	70w. multicoloured	50	10
MS1610		100×60 mm. Nos. 1609×2. Imperf.	1·70	1·50

908 Child posting Letter   **909** Postman in City

(Des Lee Hea Ok. Photo)

1984 (22 Apr). Centenary of Korean Postal Administration. P 13½×13.

1611	**908**	70w. multicoloured	50	10
1612	**909**	70w. multicoloured	50	10
MS1613		Two sheets, each 90×60 mm. (a) Nos. 1611×2; (b) Nos. 1612×2	3·25	2·75

910 Pope John Paul II   **911** Cogwheel, Workers' Tools and Flowers

(Des Chun Hee Han. Recess (1614), recess and litho (1615))

1984 (3 May). Visit of Pope John Paul II. P 13.

1614	**910**	70w. black	60	10
1615		70w. multicoloured	60	10
MS1616		100×60 mm. Nos. 1614/15.	2·50	2·30

(Des Kim Sung Sil. Photo)

1984 (11 May). Labour Festival. P 13½×13.

1617	**911**	70w. multicoloured	45	10

912 Globe, Jetliner, Container Ship and Emblem   **913** Map and Flags of South Korea and Sri Lanka

(Des Chun Hee Han. Photo)

1984 (21 May). 63rd/64th Sessions of Customs Co-operation Council, Seoul. P 13½×13.

1618	**912**	70w. multicoloured	70	10

(Des Chun Hee Han. Photo)

1984 (27 May). Visit of President Jayewardene of Sri Lanka. P 13½×13.

1619	**913**	70w. multicoloured	50	10
MS1620		90×60 mm. Nos. 1619×2	1·60	1·40

914 Symbols and Punctuation Marks   **915** Expressway   **916** Laurel, "Victory" and Olympic Rings

(Des Hong Hye Yeon. Photo)

1984 (18 June). 14th Asian Advertising Congress, Seoul. P 13×13½.

1621	**91**	70w. multicoloured	50	10

(Des Chun Hee Han. Photo)

1984 (22 June). Opening of 88 Olympic Expressway. P 13×13½.

1622	**915**	70w. multicoloured	70	15

(Des Kim Sung Sil. Photo)

1984 (23 June). 90th Anniv of International Olympic Committee. P 13×13½.

1623	**916**	70w. multicoloured	50	15

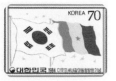

917 ABU Emblem and Microphone   918 Flags of S. Korea and Senegal

(Des Lee Keun Moon. Photo)

1984 (30 June). 20th Anniv of Asia-Pacific Broadcasting Union. P 13½×13.
1624 **917** 70w. multicoloured 50   10

(Des Kim Sung Sil. Litho)

1984 (9 July). Visit of President Abdou Diouf of Senegal. P 13.
1625 **918** 70w. multicoloured 50   15
MS1626 100×60 mm. Nos. 1625×2. Imperf................. 2·30   2·00

919 Archery

920 Fencing

(Des Lee Hea Ok. Recess and litho)

1984 (28 July). Olympic Games, Los Angeles. P 13.
1627 **919** 70w. multicoloured 80   30
1628 **920** 440w. multicoloured .... 3·00   75

921 Crucifixion   922 Cross, Vine and Dove

(Des Kim Sung Sil. Recess and litho)

1984 (16 Aug). Centenary of Korean Protestant Church. P 13.
1629 **921** 70w. multicoloured 80   30
     a. Pair. Nos. 1629/30 .... 1·70   65
1630 **922** 70w. multicoloured 80   30
MS1631 80×100 mm. Nos. 1629/30.......................... 6·00   5·50
     Nos. 1629/30 were issued together in *se-tenant* pairs within the sheet.

923/926 "Wedding" (Kim Kyo Man)
(illustration approx. ½-size)

(Des Lee Keun Moon. Photo)

1984 (1 Sept). Folk Customs (1st series). P 13×13½.
1632 **923** 70w. multicoloured 80   30
     a. Horiz. strip of 4. Nos. 1632/5 .... 3·50
1633 **924** 70w. multicoloured 80   30
1634 **925** 70w. multicoloured 80   30
1635 **926** 70w. multicoloured 80   30
1632/1635 *Set of 4* .... 3·00   1·10
MS1636 90×61 mm. Nos. 1635.............................. 2·50   2·30
     Nos. 1632/5 were issued together in *se-tenant* horizontal strips of four, each strip forming a composite design.
     See also Nos. 1667/8, 1683/4, 1734/8, 1808/11, 1840/3, 1858/61 and 1915/18.

927 Pres. Chun and Mt. Fuji

(Des Kim Sung Sil. Litho)

1984 (6 Sept). Presidential Visit to Japan. P 13.
1637 **927** 70w. multicoloured 60   15
MS1638 100×60mm. Nos. 1637×2. Imperf................. 2·20   1·90

928 Flags of S. Korea and Gambia   929 Symbols of International Trade

(Des Lee Hea Ok. Litho)

1984 (12 Sept). Visit of President Sir Dawada Kairaba Jawara of Gambia. P 13.
1639 **928** 70w. multicoloured 60   15
MS1640 100×60 mm. Nos. 1639×2. Imperf................. 2·20   1·90

(Des Park Young Shin. Photo)

1984 (18 Sept). Sitra '84 International Trade Fair, Seoul. P 13×13½.
1641 **929** 70w. multicoloured 50   10

930 Namsan Tower and National Flags

931 Badminton

(Des Hong Hye Yeon. Litho)

1984 (21 Sept). Visit of President El Hadj Omar Bongo of Gabon. P 13.

1642	**930**	70w. multicoloured	60	10
MS1643		100×60 mm. Nos. 1642×2. Imperf	1·90	1·70

(Des Chun Hee Han. Photo)

1984 (11 Oct). 65th National Sports Meeting, Taegu. T **931** and similar horiz design. Multicoloured. P 13½ ×13.

1644	70w. Type **931**	50	10
1645	70w. Wrestling	50	10

932 Magnifying Glass and Exhibition Emblem

933 South Gate, Seoul, and Stamps

(Des Lee Hea Ok (1646), Chun Hee Han (1647), Kim Sung Sil (**MS**1649). Recess and litho (**MS**1649). photo (others))

1984 (22 Oct). Philakorea 1984 International Stamp Exhibition. Seoul. P 13½×13½ (1646) or13½×13 (1647).

1646	**932**	70w. multicoloured	50	10
1647	**933**	70w. multicoloured	50	10
MS1648		Two sheets, each 124×90 mm. (a) Nos. 1646×4; (b) Nos. 1647×4	7·75	7·00
MS1649		124×90 mm. 5000w. Nos. 1389. P 13½×13	37·00	32·00

Imperforate examples of Nos. **MS**1649 were sold only through the League of Philately.

934 Presidents Chun and Gayoom

935 "100" and Industrial Symbols

(Des Chun Hee Han. Litho)

1984 (29 Oct). Visit of President Maumoon Abdul Gayoom of the Maldive Islands. P 13.

1650	**934**	70w. multicoloured	50	10
MS1651		100×60 mm. Nos. 1650 ×2. Imperf	2·20	1·90

(Des Chun Hee Han. Photo)

1984 (31 Oct). Centenary of Korea Chamber of Commerce and Industry. P 13×13½.

1652	**935**	70w. multicoloured	50	10

936 Children playing Jaegi-chagi

937 Ox (bas-Relief, Kim Yu Shin's tomb)

(Des Lee Lea Ok.Photo)

1984 (1 Dec). Lunar New Year ("Year of the Ox"). P 13×13½.

1653	**936**	70w. multicoloured	60	15
1654	**937**	70w. multicoloured	60	15
MS1665		Two sheets, each 90×60 mm. (a) Nos. 1653×2; (b) Nos. 1664×2	3·75	3·50

938 I.Y.Y. Emblem

(Des Hong Hye Yeon. Photo)

1985 (25 Jan). International Youth Year. P 13½×13.

1656	**938**	70w. multicoloured	50	10

939 Pounding Rice for New Year's First Full Year Cake

940 Welcoming Moon

(Des Lee Hea Ok. Photo)

1985 (19 Feb). Folk Customs (2nd series). P 13×13½.

1657	**939**	70w. multicoloured	80	25
1658	**940**	70w. multicoloured	80	25

941 Seoul Olympics Emblem

942 Hodori (mascot)

(Des Yang Seung Choon (1659), Kim Hyun (1660). Photo)

1985 (20 Mar). Olympic Games, Seoul (1988) (1st issue). P 13×13½.
1659	**941**	70w. +30w. multicoloured	80	30
1660	**942**	70w. +30w. multicoloured	80	30
MS1661		90×60 mm. Nos. 1659/60	2·20	1·90

See also Nos. 1673/5, 1687/9, 1694/6, 1703/10, 1747/50, 752/5, 1784/8, 1814/18, 1826/8, 1835/7, 1844/8 and **MS**1857.

943 "Still Life with Doll" (Lee Chong Woo)

944 "Rocky Mountain in Early Spring Morning" (Ahn Jung Shik)

(Des Chun Hee Han. Photo)

1985 (10 Apr). Modern Art (1st series). P 13½×13.
1662	**943**	70w. multicoloured	80	30
1663	**944**	70w. multicoloured	80	30

See also Nos. 1680/1, 1757/60, 1791/4 and 1875/8.

945 Flags, Statue of Liberty and Pres. Chun

946 Flags, Seoul South Gate and National Flower

(Des Hong Hye Yeon. Eng Hong Young Sun. Recess and litho)

1985 (24 Apr). Presidential Visit to United States. P 13.
1664	**945**	70w. multicoloured	50	10
MS1665		100×60 mm. Nos. 1664×2. P 13½	2·20	1·90

(Des Chun Hee Han. Photo)

1985 (6 May). Visit of President Mohammad Zia-ul-Haq of Pakistan. P 13×13½.
1666	**946**	70w. multicoloured	60	15
MS1667		90×60 mm. No. 1666×2	2·30	2·00

947 Underwood Hall

948 Flags and Map

(Des Kim Sung Sil. Eng Hong Young Sun. Recess and litho)

1985 (6 May). Centenary of Yonsei University. P 13.
1668	**947**	70w. black, buff and yellowish green	50	10

(Des Kim Sung Sil. Litho)

1985 (18 May). Visit of President Luis Alberto Monge of Costa Rica. P 13½×13.
1669	**948**	70w. multicoloured	60	15
MS1670		90×60 mm. Nos. 1669×2	2·10	1·90

949 Silver Carp   **950** Sailfish

(Des Kim Sung Sil. Photo)

1985 (30 May). Fishes (1st series). P 13½ x13.
1671	**949**	70w. multicoloured	80	25
1672	**950**	70w. multicoloured	80	25

See also Nos. 1730/3, 1797/1800, 1881/4, 1903/6 and 1951/4.

951 Rowing   **952** National Flags

(Des Kim Hyun. Photo)

1985 (10 June). Olympic Games, Seoul (1988) (2nd issue). T **951** and similar vert design. Multicoloured. P 13×13½.
1673		70w.+30w. Type **951**	80	30
1674		70w.+30w. Hurdling	80	30
MS1675		90×60 mm. Nos. 1673/4	2·20	1·90

For designs similar to Type **951** see Nos. 1687/**MS**1689 and 1694/**MS**1696.

(Des Lee Hea Ok Litho)

1985 (15 June). Visit of President Hussain Muhammad Ershad of Bangladesh. P 13½×13.
1676	**952**	70w. multicoloured	60	15
MS1677		90×60 mm. Nos. 1676×2. Imperf.	1·70	1·50

953 National Flags

954 "Spring Day on the Farm" (Huh Paik Ryun)

955 "The Exorcist" (Kim Chung Hyun)

(Des Hong Hye Yeon. Litho)

1985 (25 June). Visit of President João Bernardo Vieira of Guinea-Bissau. P 13½×13.
1678 **953** 70w. multicoloured 70   15
MS1679 90×60 mm. Nos. 1678×2. Imperf.................. 1·70   1·50

(Des Chun Hee Han. Photo)

1985 (5 July). Modem Art (2nd series). P 13½×13 (1680) or 13×13½ (1681).
1680 **954** 70w. multicoloured 80   30
1681 **955** 70w. multicoloured 80   30

956 Heavenly Lake, Mt. Paekdu and National Flower

(Des Lee Keun Moon. Litho)

1985 (14 Aug). 40th Anniv of Liberation. P 13.
1682 **956** 70w. multicoloured 60   15

957 Wrestling   **958** Janggi

(Des Lee Hea Ok. Photo)

1985 (20Aug). Folk Customs (3rd series). P 13×13½.
1683 **957** 70w. multicoloured 80   25
1684 **958** 70w. multicoloured 80   25

959 *The Spring of My Home* (Lee Won Su and Hong Nan Pa)   **960** *A Leaf Boat* (Park Hong Keun and Yun Yong Ha)

(Des Hong Hye Yeon. Photo)

1985 (10 Sept). Korean Music (1st series). P 13×13½.
1685 **959** 70w. multicoloured 80   25
1686 **960** 70w. multicoloured 80   25
   See also Nos. 1728/9, 1776/7, 1854/5, 1862/3, 1893/4, 1935/6, 1996/7 and 2064/5.

(Des Kim Hyun. Photo)

1985 (16 Sept). Olympic Game, Seoul (1988) (3rd issue). Vert designs as T 951. Multicoloured. P 13×13½.
1687 70w.+30w. Basketball 80   30
1688 70w.+30w. Boxing.. 80   30
MS1689 90×60 mm. Nos. 1687/8................................ 2·20   1·90

961 Satellite, "100" and Dish Aerial   **962** Meetings Emblem

(Des Chun Hee Han. Photo)

1958 (28 Sept). Centenary of First Korean Telegraph Service. P 13½×13.
1690 **961** 70w. multicoloured 60   15

(Des Kim Sung Sil. Photo)

1985 (8 Oct). World Bank and International Monetary Fund Meeting, Seoul. P 13×13½.
1691 **962** 70w. multicoloured 60   15

963 U.N. Emblem and Doves Michelangelo)   **964** Red Cross and Hands (detail, "Creation of Adam",

(Des Lee Hea Ok. Photo)

1985 (24 Oct). 40th Anniv of United Nations Organization. P 13½×13.
1692 **963** 70w. multicoloured 60   15

(Des Lee Keun Moon. Photo)

1985 (26 Oct). 80th Anniv of Korea Red Cross. P 13½×13.
1693 **964** 70w. black, bright scarlet and blue......... 70   25

(Des Kim Hyun. Photo)

1985 (1 Nov). Olympic Games, Seoul (1988) (4th issue). Vert designs as T 951. Multicoloured. P 13×13½.
1694 70w.+30w. Cycling.. 80   30
1695 70w.+30w. Canoeing 80   30
MS1696 90×60 mm. Nos. 1694/5................................ 2·20   1·90

965 Cancelled Stamp on Envelope

966 Tiger (bas-relief, Kim Yu Shin's tomb)

(Des Kim Sung Sil. Photo)

1985 (18 Nov). Philatelic Week. P 13½×13.
1697 **965** 70w. multicoloured 60   15

(Des Lee Keun Moon. Recess and litho)

1985 (2 Dec). Lunar New Year ("Year of the Tiger"). P 13×13½.
1698 **966** 70w. multicoloured 70   30

967 Mt. Fuji and Boeing 747 Jetliner

(Des Lee Keun Moon. Photo)

1985 (18 Dec). 20th Anniv of Korea-Japan Treaty on Basic Relations. P 13×13½.
(a) POSTAGE
1699 **967** 70w. multicoloured 80   30
(b) AIR
1700 **967** 370w. multicoloured .... 3·00 95

968 Doves and Globe

969 Show Jumping

(Des Kim Hyun. Photo)

1986 (15 Jan). International Peace Year. P 13×13½.
1701 **968** 70w. multicoloured 60   15
1702   400w. multicoloured .... 4·25 1·50
Nos. 1702 was issued in sheetlets of two blocks of four stamps.

(Des Cho Young Je. Photo)

1986 (25 Mar). Olympic Games. Seoul (1988) (5th issue). T **969** and similar vert designs. Multicoloured. P 13×13½.

(a) POSTAGE
1703 70w.+30w. Type **969** 85   40
1704 70w.+30w. As No. 1704 85   40
1705 70w.+30w. Football 85   40
1706 70w.+30w. Gymnastics 85   40

(b) AIR
1707 370w.+100w. Type **969** .... 2·50 1·20
1708 400w.+100w. As No. 1704 .... 3·00 1·40
1709 440w.+100w. As No. 1705 .... 3·50 1·50
1710 470w.+100w. As No. 1706 .... 4·00 1·70
1703/1710 Set of 8. .... 15·00 6·75
Nos. 1707/10 were each issued in sheetlets of four stamps.
For designs similar to Type **969** see Nos. 1747/50, 1752/5, 1784/ **MS**1788 and 1814/**MS**1818.

970 Pres. Chun, Big Ben, and Korean and British Flags

971 Pres Chun, Eiffel Tower, and Korean and French Flags

972 Pres. Chun. Belgian Parliament, and Korean and Belgian Flags

973 Pres. Chun, Cologne Cathedral, and Korean and West German Flags

(Des Chun Hee Han (1711), Lee Hea Ok (1712), Hong Hye Yeon (1713), Lee Keun Moon (1714). Litho)

1986 (4 Apr). Presidential Visit to Europe. P 13.
1711 **970** 70w. multicoloured 85   30
1712 **971** 70w. multicoloured 85   30
1713 **972** 70w. multicoloured 85   30
1714 **973** 70w. multicoloured 85   30
1711/1714 Set of 4. .... 3·00 1·10
MS1715 4 sheets, each 100×60 mm. Perf 13½.
(a) Nos. 1711×2; (b) No. 1712×2; (c) No. 1713×2;
(d) No. 1714×2 .... 14·00 12·50

974 Kyongju Observatory

975 Kwanchon Observatory

976 General Assembly Emblem

(Des Kim Young Ki and Hong Hye Yeon. Photo)

1986 (21 Apr). Science (1st series). Appearance of Halley's Comet.
P 13½×13.
1716　**974**　70w. multicoloured .... 2·50　85
　　　a. Horiz pair. Nos. 1716/17.................... 5·25　1·80
1717　**975**　70w. multicoloured .... 2·50　85
　　Nos. 1716/17 were issued together in *se-tenant* pairs within the
sheet.
　　See also Nos. 1781/2, 1833/4, 1864/5 and 1898/9.

(Des Kim Sung Sil. Photo)

1986 (21 Apr). Fifth Association of National Olympic Committees
General Assembly, Seoul. P 13×13½.
1718　**976**　70w. multicoloured .... 70　15

981　Swallowtail　　　　**982**　*Papilio bianor*

(Des Lee Keun Moon. Litho)

1986 (22 May). Ameripex 86 International Stamp Exhibition, Chicago.
P 13½.
1719　**977**　70w. multicoloured .... 3·50　1·50
　　　a. Sheetlet of 6. Nos. 1719/24 .... 22·00
1720　**978** 370w. multicoloured .... 3·50　1·50
1721　**979** 400w. multicoloured .... 3·50　1·50
1722　**980** 440w. multicoloured .... 3·50　1·50
1723　**981** 450w. multicoloured .... 3·50　1·50
1724　**982** 470w. multicoloured .... 3·50　1·50
1719/1724　Set of 6 .... 19·00　8·00
　　Nos. 1719/24 were issued together in *se-tenant* sheetlets of six
stamps, forming a composite design.

977　Swallowtail (*Papilio machaon*) and Flowers

978　*Papilio bianor*

979　Swallowtails

980　Swallowtail and Frog

983　Male and Female Symbols　**984**　National Flags
in Balance

(Des Kim Keel Hong. Litho)

1986 (31 May). Centenary of Korean Women's Education. P 13.
1725　**983**　70w. multicoloured .... 60　10

(Des Kim Sung Sil. Litho)

1986 (10 June). Visit of President André Kolingba of Central African
Republic. P 13.
1726　**984**　70w. multicoloured .... 60　10
MS1727　100×60mm. No. 1726×2. Imperf.................... 1·60　1·40

985　*Half Moon*　　　**986**　*Let's Go and*
(Yun Keuk Young)　　　*Pick the Moon*
　　　　　　　　　　　(Yun Seok Jung
　　　　　　　　　　　and Park Tae Hyun)

(Des Chang Wan Doo. Photo)

1986 (25 June). Korean Music (2nd series). P 13×13½.
1728　**985**　70w. multicoloured .... 1·00　30
1729　**986**　70w. multicoloured .... 1·60　55

987 Eoreumchi

988 Sweetfish

989 Sardine

990 Hammerhead Sharks

(Des Kwon Myung Kwang and Kim Sung Sil. Photo)

1986 (25 July). Fishes (2nd series). P 13½ × 13.
1730	**987**	70w. multicoloured	1·70	55
1731	**988**	70w. multicoloured	1·70	55
1732	**989**	70w. multicoloured	1·70	55
1733	**990**	70w. multicoloured	1·70	55
1730/1733		Set of 4	6·25	2·00

991 Flag Carrier and Gong
Player

992   Musicians   **993**

994   Ribbon Dancers and Couple with Child   **995**

(Des Kim Kyo Man. Photo)

1986 (26 Aug). Folk Customs (4th series). Farm Music. P 13½×13.
1734	**991**	70w. multicoloured	1·30	30
		a. Horiz strip of 5. Nos. 1734/8	7·00	
1735	**992**	70w. multicoloured	1·30	30
1736	**993**	70w. multicoloured	1·30	30
1737	**994**	70w. multicoloured	1·30	30
1738	**995**	70w. multicoloured	1·30	30
1734/1738		Set of 5	5·75	1·40

Nos. 1734/8 were issued together in se-tenant strips of five within the sheet, each strip forming a composite design.

996 Child

(Des Lee Hea Ok. Photo)

1986 (1 Sept). Family Planning. P 13×13½.
1739	**996**	80w. multicoloured	1·00	25

997/999 Han River, Seoul (½ -size illustration)

(Des Kim Hyun. Litho)

1986 (10 Sept). Completion of Han River Development. P 13.
1740	**997**	30w. multicoloured	1·30	30
		a. Horiz strip of 3 Nos. 1740/2	4·00	
1741	**998**	60w. multicoloured	1·30	30
1742	**999**	80w. multicoloured	1·30	30

Nos. 1740/2 were issued together in horizontal se-tenant strips of three within the sheet, each strip forming the composite design illustrated.

1000 Emblem
Display

1001 Firework

(Des An Jeong Un. Photo)

1986 (20 Sept). Tenth Asian Games. Seoul (1st issue). P 13×13½.
1743	**1000**	80w. multicoloured	80	30
1744	**1001**	80w. multicoloured	80	30
MS1745		Two sheets, each 90×60 mm. (a) Nos.		
		1743×2; (b) Nos. 1744×2	14·00	12·50

See also No. **MS**1751

1002 "5", Delegates and Juan
Antonio Samaranch (President of
International Olympic Committee)

(Des Kim Hyun. Photo)

1986 (30 Sept). Fifth Anniv of Choice of Seoul as 1988 Olympic
Games Host City. P 13×13½.
1746	**1002**	80w. multicoloured	1·00	40

(Des Cho Young Je. Photo)

1986 (10 Oct). Olympic Games, Seoul (1988) (6th issue). Vert. designs as T **969**. Multicoloured. P 13×13½.

(a) POSTAGE

1747	80w.+50w. Weightlifting	1·70	85
1748	80w.+50w. Handball	1·70	85

(b) AIR

1749	370w.+100w. As Nos. 1747	3·00	1·40
1750	400w.+100w. As Nos. 1748	3·00	1·40
1747/1750 *Set of 4*		8·50	4·00

Nos. 1749/50 were each issued in sheetlets of four stamps.

1003 Main Stadium   **1004** Boy fishing for Stamp

(Des Kim Hyun. Litho)

1986 (31 Oct). Tenth Asian Games, Seoul (2nd issue). Sheet 130×90 mm. P 13×13½.

MS1751	**1003** 550w. multicoloured	24·00	22·00

(Des Cho Young Je. Photo)

1986 (1 Nov). Olympic Game, Seoul (1988) (7th issue). Vert designs as T **969**. Multicoloured. P 13×13½.

(a) POSTAGE

1752	80w. +50w. Judo	1·70	85
1753	80w. +50w. Hockey	1·70	85

(b) AIR

1754	440w. +100w. As No. 1752	3·50	1·50
1755	470w. +100w. As No. 1753	4·00	1·70
1752/1755 *Set of 4*		9·75	4·50

Nos. 1754/5 were each issued in sheetlets of four stamps.

(Des Chang Wan Doo. Photo)

1986 (18 Nov). Philatelic Week. P 13½×13.

1756	**1004** 80w. multicoloured	70	25

1005 "Chunhyang-do" (Kim Un Ho)   **1006** "Flowers"(Lee Sang Bum)

1007 "Portrait of a Friend" (Ku Bon Wung)   **1008** "Woman in a Ski Suit" (Son Ung Seng)

(Des Chun Hee Han. Photo)

1986 (1 Dec). Modern Art (3rd series). P 13½×13.

1757	**1005** 80w. multicoloured	1·30	40
1758	**1006** 80w. multicoloured	1·30	40
1759	**1007** 80w. multicoloured	1·30	40
1760	**1008** 80w. multicoloured	1·30	40
1757/1760 *Set of 4*		4·75	1·40

1009 Rabbit   **1010** Eastern Broad-billed Roller

(Des Hong Hye Yeon. Photo)

1986 (1 Dec). Lunar New Year ("Year of the Rabbit"). P 13×13½.

1761	**1009** 80w. multicoloured	85	30

(Des Kim Sung Sil. Photo)

1986 (20 Dec). Birds. T **1010** and similar horiz designs Multicoloured.

A. Sheet stamps. P 13×13½

1762A	80w. Type **1010**	1·30	40
	a. Strip of 5. Nos. 1762A/6A	7·00	
1763A	80w. Japanese waxwing	1·30	40
1764A	80w. Black-naped oriole	1·30	40
1765A	80w. Black-capped kingfisher	1·30	40
1766A	80w. Hoopoe	1·30	40
1762A/1766A *Set of 5*		5·75	1·80

Nos. 1762A/6A were issued together in horizontal *se-tenant* strips of five stamps.

B. Coil stamps. P 13× imperf

1762B	80w. Type **1010**	3·00	75
	a. Strip of 5. Nos. 1762B/6B	16·00	
1763B	80w. Japanese waxwing	3·00	75
1764B	80w. Black-naped oriole	3·00	75
1765B	80w. Black-capped kingfisher	3·00	75
1766B	80w. Hoopoe	3·00	75
1762B/1766B *Set of 5*		13·50	3·50

Nos. 1762B/6B were issued together in vertical coils of five stamps.

1011 Siberian Tiger
(*Panthers tigris altaica*)

1012 Bleeding
Heart (*Dicentra
spectabilis*)

(Des Kim Ok Nam. Photo)

1987 (25 Feb). Endangered Animals. T **1011** and similar horiz designs.
Multicoloured. P 13½×13.

1767	80w. Type **1011**	2·20	70
	a. Vert strip of 4. Nos. 1767/70	9·25	
1768	80w. Leopard cat (*Felis bengalensis*)	2·20	70
1769	80w. Red fox (*Vulpes vulpes*)	2·20	70
1770	80w. Wild boar (*Sus scrofa*)	2·20	70
1767/1770	Set of 4	8·00	2·50

Nos. 1767/70 were issued together in vertical *se-tenant* strips of
four within the sheet.

(Des Lee Hea Ok. Photo)

1987 (20 Mar).Flowers. T **1012** and similar vert designs.
Multicoloured.

A. Sheet stamps. P 13½×13

1771A	550w. Type **1012**	2·50	60
	a. Horiz strip of 5. Nos. 1771A/5A	13·00	
1772A	550w. Diamond bluebell (*Hanabusaya asiatica*)	2·50	60
1773A	550w. *Erythronium japonicum*	2·50	60
1774A	550w. Pinks (*Dianthus chinensis*)	2·50	60
1775A	550w. Chrysanthemum zawadskii	2·50	60
1771A/1775A	Set of 5	11·00	2·75

B. Coil stamps. Imperf×p 13

1771B	550w. Type **1012**	4·00	1·00
	a. Horiz strip of 5. Nos. 1771B/5B	21·00	
1772B	550w. Diamond bluebell (*Hanabusaya asiatica*)	4·00	1·00
1773B	550w. *Erythronium japonicum*	4·00	1·00
1774B	550w. Pinks (*Dianthus chinensis*)	4·00	1·00
1775B	550w. Chrysanthemum zawadskii	4·00	1·00
1771B/1775B	Set of 5	18·00	4·50

Nos. 1771A/5A were issued together in horizontal *se-tenant* strips
of five stamps.

1013 Barley Field
(Park Wha Mok and
Yun Yong Ha)

1014 *Magnolia*
(Cho Young Shik
and Kim Dong Jin)

(Des Hong Hye Yeon. Photo)

1987 (25 Mar). Korean Music (3rd series). P 13×13½.

1776	**1013** 80w. multicoloured	3·00	1·00
1777	**1014** 80w. multicoloured	3·00	1·00

1015 National Flags and
Korean National Flower

1016 "100", Light Bulb
and Hyang Woen Jeong

(Des Chun Hee Han. Litho)

1987 (6 Apr). Visit of President Ahmed Abdallah Abderemane of
Comoros. P 13½×13.

1778	**1015** 80w. multicoloured	60	10
MS1779	90×60 mm. Nos. 1778×2	2·20	1·90

(Des Na Je O. Photo)

1987 (10 Apr). Centenary of Electric Light in Korea. P 13½×13.

1780	**1016** 80w. multicoloured	60	10

1017 Punggi
Wind Observatory

1018 Rain
Gauge

(Des Kim Young Ki. Photo)

1987 (21 Apr). Science (2nd series). P 13½×13.

1781	**1017** 80w. agate and grey-brown	3·00	1·00
	a. Horiz pair. Nos. 1781/2	6·25	2·10
1782	**1018** 80w. grey-brown and agate	3·00	1·00

Nos. 1781/2 were issued together in horizontal *se-tenant* pairs
within the sheet, each pair forming the composite design illustrated.

1019 Globes. Crane and
Ship

1020 Flags and Doves

(Des Kim Kang Yong. Photo)

1987 (25 Apr). 15th International Association of Ports and Harbours
General Sessio, Seoul. P 13½×13.

1783	**1019** 80w. multicoloured	60	10

(Des Kim Hyun. Photo)

1987 (25May). Olympic Games, Seoul (1988) (8th issue). Vert designs
as T **969**. Multicoloured. P 13×13½.

1784	80w. +50w. Wrestling	1·20	40
1785	80w. +50w. Tennis	1·20	40
1786	80w. +50w. Diving	1·20	40
1787	80w. +50w. Show jumping	1·20	40
1784/1787	Set of 4	4·25	1·40
MS1788	Four sheets, each 90×60 mm.		

(a) No. 1784×2; (b) No. 1786×2; (c) No. 1786×2;
(d) No. 1787×2   11·00   10·00

(Des Chun Hee Han. Litho)

1987 (8 June). Visit of President U San Yu of Burma. P 13½×13.
1789 **1020** 80w. multicoloured 60 10
MS1790 90×60 mm. No. 1789×2................................. 1·90 1·70

(Des Hwang Bu Yong. Litho)

1987 (30 June). Completion of Automatic Telephone Network (1795) and Communications for Information Year (1796). P 13×13½.
1795 **1025** 80w. multicoloured 70 25
1796 **1026** 80w. multicoloured 70 25

1021 "Valley of Peach Blossoms" (Pyen Kwan Sik)
1022 "Rural Landscape" (Lee Yong Wu)

1027 Pilchards
1028 Eel

1029 Barbel
1030 Ray

(Des Kwon Myung Kwang and Kim Sung Sil. Photo)

1987 (25 July). Fishes (3rd series). P 13½×13.
1797 **1027** 80w. multicoloured .... 2·50 95
1798 **1028** 80w. multicoloured .... 2·50 95
1799 **1029** 80w. multicoloured .... 2·50 95
1800 **1030** 80w. multicoloured .... 2·50 95
1797/1800 Set of 4... 9·00 3·50

1023 "Man" (Lee Ma Dong)
1024 "Woman with Water Jar on Head" (sculpture, Yun Hyo Chung)

1987 (22 June). Modern Art (4th series). Photo (1791/2), recess and litho (1793/4). P 13½×13.
1791 **1021** 80w. multicoloured .... 2·50 95
1792 **1022** 80w. multicoloured .... 2·50 95
1793 **1023** 80w. multicoloured .... 2·50 95
1794 **1024** 80w. multicoloured .... 2·50 95
1791/1794 Set of 4... 9·00 3·50

1031 Statue of Indomitable Koreans (detail) and Flags
1032 Monument to the Nation and Aerial View of Hall

(Des Cho Young Je. Photo)

1987 (14 Aug). Opening of Independence Hall. P 13½×13.
1801 **1031** 80w. multicoloured .... 1·10 30
1802 **1032** 80w. multicoloured .... 1·10 30
MS1803 Two sheets each 126×90 mm. (a) No. 1801×2; (b) No. 1802×2................................. 24·00 22·00

1025 Map and Digital Key Pad
1026 Emblem

1033 Map and Pen within Profile

1034 Flags and Seoul South Gate

(Des Chang Wan Young. Photo)

1987 (20 Aug). 16th Pacific Science Congress, Seoul. P 13×13½.
1804 **1033** 80w. multicoloured 70 15
MS1805 90×60 mm. Nos. 1804×2................................... 3·00 2·75

(Des Chun Hee Han. Litho)

1987 (8 Sept). Visit of President Virgilio Barco of Colombia. P 13½×13.
1806 **1034** 80w. multicoloured 70 15
MS1807 90×60 mm. Nos. 1806×2................................... 2·20 1·90

1035/1038 Festivities (½-size illustration)

(Des Kim Hyun. Photo)

1987 (10 Sept). Folk Customs (5th series). Harvest Moon Day. P 13×13½.
1808 **1035** 80w. multicoloured .... 3·50 1·00
    a. Horiz strip of 4. Nos. 1808/11 .... 14·50
1809 **1036** 80w. multicoloured .... 3·50 1·00
1810 **1037** 80w. multicoloured .... 3·50 1·00
1811 **1038** 80w. multicoloured .... 3·50 1·00
1808/1811 *Set of 4* .... 12·50 3·50
Nos. 1808/11 were issued together in horizontal *se-tenant* strips of four within the sheet, each strip forming a composite design.

1039 Telephone Dials forming Number

1040 Service Flags and Servicemen

(Des Cho Young Je. Photo)

1987 (28 Sept). Installation of over 10,000,000 Telephone Lines. P 13½×13.
1812 **1039** 80w. multicoloured 70 25

(Des Kim Sung Sil. Litho)

1987 (30 Sept). Armed Forces Day. P 13.
1813 **1040** 80w. multicoloured 70 25

(Des Kim Hyun. Photo)

1987 (10 Oct). Olympic Games. Seoul (1988) (9th issue). Vert designs as T **969**. Multicoloured. P 13×13½.
1814   80w. + 50w. Table tennis........................... 1·20 40
1815   80w. + 50w. Shooting .... 1·20 40
1816   80w. + 50w. Archery .... 1·20 40
1817   80w. + 50w. Volleyball .... 1·20 40
1814/1817 *Set of 4* .... 4·25 1·40
MS1818 4 sheets, each 90×60 mm. (a) No. 1814×2;
    (b) No. 1815×2; (c) No. 1816×2; (d) No. 1817×2...... 11·00 10·00

1041 Stamps around Child playing Trumpet

1042 Korean Scientist and Map

1043 Dragon

(Des Bang Jae Ki. Photo)

1987 (18 Nov). Philatelic Week. P 13×13½.
1819 **1041** 80w. multicoloured 70 25

(Des Chun Hee Han. Litho)

1987 (28 Nov). First Anniv of South Korea's Signing of Antarctic Treaty. P 13×13½.
1820 **1042** 80w. multicoloured .... 1·30 40

(Des Kim Kyo Man. Photo)

1987 (1 Dec). Lunar New Year ("Year of the Dragon"). P 13×13½.
1821 **1043** 80w. multicoloured .... 1·00 30

1044 Scattered Sections of Apple

1045 Base and Gentoo Penguins

(Des Lee Hea Ok.Litho)

1988 (4 Jan). Compulsory Pension Programme. P 13½×13.
1822 **1044** 80w. multicoloured 70 25

(Des Chun Hee Han. Photo)

1988 (16 Feb). Completion of Antarctic Base. P 13×13½.
1823 **1045** 80w multicoloured .... 1·00 30

1046 Flag, Olympic Stadium and Pres. Roh Tae Woo

(Des Lee Keun Moon. Photo)

1988 (24 Feb). Presidential Inauguration. P 13½×13.
1824 **1046** 80w. multicoloured .... 1·30   40
MS1825 90×60 mm. Nos. 1824×2................................. 19·00   17·00

      1047 Yachting   **1048** Taekwondo

(Des Chun Hee Han. Photo)

1988 (5 Mar). Olympic Games, Seoul (10th issue). P 13×13½.
1826 **1047** 80w. +20w. multicoloured 85   40
1827 **1048** 80w. +20w. multicoloured 85   40
MS1828 Two sheets, each 90×60 mm. (a) No.
    1826×2; (b) Nos. 1827×2.. 8·75   7·75

      1049 Crane   **1050** Crane
                                     taking-off

   1051 Crane with   **1052** Two Cranes
   Wings spread

(Des Bang Jae Ki. Photo)

1988 (1 Apr). Japanese White-necked Crane (*Grus vipio*). P 13×13½.
1829 **1049** 80w. multicoloured .... 1·60   70
       a. Horiz strip of 4. Nos. 1829/32 .... 6·75
1830 **1050** 80w. multicoloured .... 1·60   70
1831 **1051** 80w. multicoloured .... 1·60   70
1832 **1052** 80w. multicoloured .... 1·60   70
1829/1832 *Set of 4*... 5·75   2·50
    Nos. 1829/32 were issued together in horizontal *se-tenant* strips of
four within the sheet.

   1053 Water   **1054** Sundial
   Clock

(Des Kim Young Ki. Photo)

1988 (21 Apr). Science (3rd series). P 13½×13.
1833 **1053** 80w. multicoloured 85   30
       a Horiz pair. Nos. 1833/4 .... 1·80   65
1834 **1054** 80w. multicoloured 85   30
    Nos. 1833/4 were issued together in horizontal *se-tenant* pairs
within the sheet, each pair forming a composite design.

   1055 Torch Carrier   **1056** Stadium

(Des Lee Hea Ok. Photo (1835), recess and litho (1836))

1988 (6 May). Olympic Games. Seoul (11th issue). P 13½×13.
1835 **1055** 80w. +20w. multicoloured 85   40
1836 **1066** 80w. +20w. multicoloured 85   40
MS1837 Two sheets, each 90×60 mm. (a) Nos.
    1835×2; (b) Nos. 1836×2....................................... 6·00   5·50

   1057 Globe and   **1058** Computer
   Red Cross as Candle   Terminal

(Des Na Je O. Photo)

1988 (7 May). 125th Anniv of International Red Cross. P 13½×13.
1838 **1057** 80w. multicoloured 70   25

(Des Hwang Bu Yong. Litho)

1988 (1 June). First Anniv of National Use of Telepress. P 13×13½.
1839 **1058** 80w. multicoloured 70   25

1059/1062 Festivities (½ -*size illustration*)

(Des Lee Hee Ok. Photo)

1988 (25 Aug). Folk Customs (6th series). Tano Day. P 13×13½.
1840 **1059** 80w. multicoloured .... 1·30 40
    a. Horiz strip of 4. Nos. 1840/3 .... 5·50
1841 **1060** 80w. multicoloured .... 1·30 40
1842 **1081** 80w. multicoloured .... 1·30 40
1843 **1062** 80w. multicoloured .... 1·30 40
1840/1843 *Set of 4*... 4·75 1·40
    Nos. 1840/3 were issued together in horizontal *se-tenant* strips of four within the sheet, each strip forming a composite design.

1069 Gomdoori   **1070** Archery
(mascot)

(Des Chun Hee Han. Photo)

1988 (15 Oct). Paralympic Game, Seoul. P 13×13½.
1852 **1069** 80w. multicoloured .... 1·10 60
1853 **1070** 80w. multicoloured 80 30

1063 Olympic Flag and   **1064** Olympic Monument
Pierre de Coubertin
(founder of modern
Games)

1065 View of   **1066** Women in
Seoul   Korean Costume

(Des Yang Seung Choon (1844/5), Hwang Bu Yong (others). Recess and photo (1844), recess and litho (1845), photo (others))

1988 (16Sept). Olympic Games, Seoul. (12th issue). P 13½×13 (horiz) or 13×13½ (vert).
1844 **1063** 80w. multicoloured 85 30
1845 **1064** 80w. multicoloured 85 30
1846 **1065** 80w. multicoloured 85 30
1847 **1066** 80w. multicoloured 85 30
1844/1847 *Set of 4*... 3·00 1·10
MS1848 Four sheets, each 90×60 mm. (a) No.
    1844×2; (b) No. 1845×2; (c) No. 1846×2; (d) No.
    1847×2 .... 8·75 7·75

1071 *Homesick*   **1072** *The Pioneer*   **1073** Girls on
(Lee Eun Sang and   (Yoon Hae Young   See-saw
Kim Dong Jin)   and Cho Doo Nam)

(Des Hong Hye Yeon. Photo)

1988 (15 Nov). Korean Music (4th series). P 13×13½.
1854 **1071** 80w. multicoloured 80 30
1855 **1072** 80w. multicoloured 80 30

(Des Kim Kyo Man. Photo)

1988 (1 Dec). Lunar New Year. ("Year of the Snake"). P 13×13½.
1856 **1073** 80w. multicoloured 70 25

1074 Flags at Opening
Ceremony

(Des Lee Keun Moon. Litho)

1988 (20 Dec). Olympic Games, Seoul (13th issue). Sheet 130×90 mm. P 13×12½.
MS1857 **1074**550w. multicoloured................................ 16·00 14·00

1067 Stamps   **1068** Pouring Molten
forming Torch Flame   Metal from Crucible

(Des Kim Hyun. Photo)

1988 (19 Sept). Olymphilex "88 Olympic Stamps Exhibition, Seoul. P 13×13½.
1849 **1067** 80w. multicoloured 70 25
MS1850 90×60 mm. No. 1849×2...................................... 2·20 1·90

(Des Chang Wan Young. Photo)

1988 (8 Oct). 22nd International Iron and Steel Institute Conference, Seoul. P 13×13½.
1851 **1068** 80w. multicoloured 70 25

1075/1078 Mask Dance (⅓-size illustration)

(Des Lee Hea Ok. Photo)

1989 (25 Feb). Folk Customs (7th series). P 13×13½.
1858 **1075** 80w. multicoloured .... 1·30   40
    a. Horiz strip of 4. Nos. 1858/61 .... 5·50
1859 **1076** 80w. multicoloured .... 1·30   40
1860 **1077** 80w. multicoloured .... 1·30   40
1861 **1078** 80w. multicoloured .... 1·30   40
1858/1861 *Set of 4*... 4·75   1·40
  Nos. 1858/61 were issued together in horizontal *se-tenant* strips of four within the sheet, each strip forming a composite design.

1079 *Arirang*   **1080** *Doraji-taryong*

(Des Won In Jae. Photo)

1989 (27 Mar). Korean Music (5th series). P 13×13½.
1862 **1079** 80w. multicoloured 70   25
1863 **1080** 80w. multicoloured 70   25

1081 Wooden   **1082** Metal   **1083** Teeth, Globe,
Type Printing   Printing   Pencil and Book

(Des Kim Young Ki. Photo)

1989 (21 Apr). Science (4th series). P 13½×13.
1864 **1081** 80w. deep brown, bistre and stone .... 1·70   40
    a. Horiz pair. Nos. 1864/5 .... 3·75   85
1865 **1082** 80w. deep brown, bistre and stone .... 1·70   40
  Nos. 1864/5 were issued together in horizontal *se-tenant* pairs within the sheet, each pair forming a composite design.

(Des Chun Hee Han. Photo)

1989 (26 Apr). 14th Asian-Pacific Dental Congress. P 13×13½.
1866 **1083** 80w. multicoloured 60   15

1084 Hand   **1085** Emblem   **1086** Profiles
with Stick in   within Heart
Heart

(Des Kim Sang Rak. Photo)

1989 (8 May). Respect for the Elderly. P 13½×13.
1867 **1084** 80w. multicoloured...................................... 2·40   30

(Des Bang Jae Ki,.Photo)

1989 (20 May). Rotary International Convention, Seoul. P 13×13½.
1868 **1085** 80w. multicoloured 60   15

(Des Kim Im Yong. Photo)

1989 (27 May). 19th International Council of Nurses Congress, Seoul. P 13×13½.
1869 **1086** 80w. multicoloured 60   15

1087   **1088** "Longevity"   **1089** Satellite
"Communication"   Aerial   Globe and Dish

(Des Kim Hyun. Photo)

1989 (1 June). National Information Technology Month. P 13×13½
1870 **1087** 80w. multicoloured 60   15

(Des Lee Keun Moon. Photo)

1989 (5June). World Environment Day. P 13×13½.
1871 **1088** 80w. multicoloured 60   15

(Des Ku Dong Jo. Photo)

1989 (1 July). Tenth Anniv of Asia-Pacific Telecommunity. P 13×13½.
1872 **1089** 80w. multi-coloured..................................... 60   15

1090 "Liberty guiding the   **1091** Apple and Flask
People" (detail, Eugene
Delacroix)

(Des Lee Hea Ok. Litho)

1989 (14 July). Bicentenary of French Revolution. P 13½×13.
1873 **1090** 80w. multicoloured 60   15

(Des Chang Wan Young. Photo)

1989 (12 Aug). Fifth Asian and Oceanic Biochemists Federation Congress, Seoul. P 13½×13.
1874 **1091** 80w. multicoloured 60   15

1092 "White Ox" (Lee Joong Sub)

1093 "Street Stall" (Park Lae Hyun)

1094 "Little Girl" (Lee Bong Sang)

1095 "Autumn Scene" (Oh Ji Ho)

(Des Chun Hee Han. Recess and litho (1875, 1877), photo (1876, 1878))

1989 (4 Sept). Modern Art (5th series). P 13×13½ (horiz) or 13½×13 (vert).
1875	**1092**	80w. multicoloured	80	30
1876	**1093**	80w. multicoloured	80	30
1877	**1094**	80w. multicoloured	80	30
1878	**1095**	80w. multicoloured	80	30
1875/1878		Set of 4	3·00	1·10

1096 Hunting Scene and Ancient Law Code

1097 Goddess of Law

(Des Lee Hea Ok. Litho)

1989 (12 Sept). Seoul Olympics Commemorative Festival and World Sports Festival for Ethnic Koreans. P 13½×13.
1879	**1096**	80w. multicoloured	60	15

(Des Won In Jae. Litho)

1989 (18 Sept). First Anniv of Constitutional Court. P 13½×13.
1880	**1097**	80w. multicoloured	60	15

1098 Japanese Parrot Fish

1099 Spined Loach

1100 Torrent Catfish

1101 Pinecone Fish

(Des Kim Sung Sil. Photo)

1989 (30 Sept). Fishes (4th series). P 13½×13.
1881	**1098**	80w. multicoloured	85	30
1882	**1099**	80w. multicoloured	85	30
1883	**1100**	80w. multicoloured	85	30
1884	**1101**	80w. multicoloured	85	30
1881/1884		Set of 4	3·00	1·10

1102 Emblem

1103 Control Tower and Boeing 747 Jetliner

(Des Kim Im Yong. Photo)

1989 (4 Oct). 44th international Eucharistic Congress, Seoul. P 13½×13.
1885	**1102**	80w. multicoloured	60	15

(Des Lee Keun Moon. Photo)

1989 (17 Oct). 29th International Civil Airports Association World Congress, Seoul. P 13½×13.
1886	**1103**	80w. multicoloured	60	15

1104 Scissors cutting burning Banner

1105 Lantern

(Des Chun Hee Han. Photo)

1989 (1 Nov). Fire Precautions Month. P 13½×13.
1887	**1104**	80w. multicoloured	2·40	30

(Des Chun Hee Han. Photo)

1989 (18 Nov). Philatelic Week. P 13×13½.
1888	**1105**	80w. multicoloured	70	25
MS1889		90×60 mm. Nos. 1888×2	2·20	1·90

1106 Cranes   **1107** New Year Custom

(Des Na Je 0. Photo)

1989 (1 Dec). Lunar New Year ("Year of the Horse"). P 13×13½ (1890)
or 13½×13 (1891).
1890 **1106** 80w. multicoloured 60   15
1891 **1107** 80w. multicoloured 60   15
MS1892 Two sheets, each 90×60 mm. (a) No.
1890×2; (b) No. 1891×2.. 3·50   3·00

1108 *Pakyon Fall*   **1109** *Chonan Samgori*

(Des Kim Im Yong. Photo)

1990 (26 Feb). Korean Music (6th series). P 13×13½.
1893 **1108** 80w. multicoloured 70   25
1894 **1109** 80w. multicoloured 70   25

1110 Clouds, Umbrella   **1111** Child with
and Satellite   Rose

(Des Chang Wan Young. Photo)

1990 (23 Mar). World Meteorological Day. P 13½×13.
1895 **1110** 80w. multicoloured 60   15

(Des Lee Hea Ok. Photo)

1990 (24 Mar). 40th Anniv of United Nations Children's Fund Work in
Korea. P 13×13½.
1896 **1111** 80w. multicoloured 60   15

1112 Cable, Fish and   **1113** Gilt-   **1114** Spear and
Route Map   bronze   Dagger Moulds
     Maitreya

(Des Lee Keun Moon. Photo)

1990 (21 Apr). Completion of Cheju Island–Kohung Optical
Submarine Cable. P 13½×13.
1897 **1112** 80w. multicoloured 60   15

(Des Chun Hee Han. Photo)

1990 (21 Apr). Science (5th series). Metallurgy. P 13½×13.
1898 **1113** 100w. multicoloured 70   25
   a Horiz pair. Nos. 1898/9 .... 1·50   55
1899 **1114** 100w. multicoloured 70   25
Nos. 1189/9 were issued together in horizontal *se-tenant* pairs
within the sheet, each pair forming a composite design.

1115 Housing and "20"   **1116** Youths

(Des Kim Sang Rak. Photo)

1990 (21 Apr). 20th Anniv of Saemaul Movement (community self-
help programme). P 13½×13.
1900 **1115** 100w. multicoloured 60   15

(Des Bang Jae Ki. Photo)

1990 (1 May). Youth Month. P 13½×13.
1901 **1116** 100w. multicoloured 60   15

1117 Butterfly
Net catching
Pollution

(Des Kim Hyun. Photo)

1990 (5 June). World Environment Day. P 13½×13.
1902 **1117** 100w. multicoloured .... 4·75   30
   a. Coil. Imperf×p13 .... 1·70   75

1118 Belted Beard Grunt   **1119** Puffer

1120 Salmon Trout　　　**1121** Bitterling

(Des Won In Jae. Photo)

1990 (2 July). Fishes (5th series). P 13½×13.
1903	**1118**	100w. multicoloured	85	30
1904	**1119**	100w. multicoloured	85	30
1905	**1120**	100w. multicoloured	85	30
1906	**1121**	100w. multicoloured	85	30
1903/1906		Set of 4	3·00	1·10

1122 Automatic Sorting Machines

(Des Won In Jae. Litho)

1990 (4 July). Opening of Seoul Mail Centre. P 13½×13.
1907 **1122** 100w. multicoloured.................................. 60　15
MS1908 90×60 mm. No. 1907×2................................ 2·20　1·90

1123 Bandaged Teddy Bear in Hospital Bed　　**1124** Campfire

(Des Lee Hea Ok. Photo)

1990 (25 July). Road Safety Campaign. P 13½×13.
1909 **1123** 100w. multicoloured.................................. 1·60　30

(Des Ahn Seung Kyung. Litho)

1990 (8 Aug). Eighth Korean Boy Scouts Jamboree, Kosong. P 13×13½.
1910 **1124** 100w. multicoloured .... 60　15

1125 Lily　　　**1126** Asters

1127 Pheasant's Eye　　**1128** Scabious

(Des Lee Yun Hee. Photo)

1990 (25 Aug). Wild Flowers (1st series). P 13×13½.
1911	**1125**	370w. multicoloured	2·10	85
1912	**1126**	400w. multicoloured	2·40	95
1913	**1127**	440w. multicoloured	2·50	1·00
1914	**1128**	470w. multicoloured	2·75	1·10
1911/1914		Set of 4	8·75	3·50

See also Nos. 1956/9, 1992/5, 2082/5, 2133/6, 2162/5, 2191/4 and 2244/7.

1129 Washing Wool　　**1130** Spinning

1131 Dyeing Spun Yam　　**1132** Weaving

(Des Lee Hea Ok. Recess and litho)

1990 (25 Sept). Folk Customs (8th series). Hand Weaving. P 13½×13.
1915 **1129** 100w. rose-red, bistre-yellow & blk.......... 85　30
　　　a. Strip of 4. Nos. 1915/18 .... 3·75
1916 **1130** 100w. multicoloured.................................. 85　30
1917 **1131** 100w. multicoloured.................................. 85　30
1918 **1132** 100w. multicoloured.................................. 85　30
1915/1918 Set of 4... 3·00　1·10
Nos. 1915/18 were issued together in *se-tenant* strips of four stamps within the sheet.

1133 Church　　**1134** Top of Tower　　**1135** Peas in Pod

(Des Chun Hee Han. Litho)

1990 (29 Sept). Centenary of Anglican Church in Korea. P 13×13½.
1919 **1133** 100w. multicoloured.................................. 60　15

(Des Lee Keun Moon. Litho)

1990 (15 Oct). Tenth Anniv of Seoul Communications Tower. P 13×13½.
1920 **1134** 100w. brownish black, brt bl & rosine 60 15

(Des Chun Hee Han. Photo)

1990 (20 Oct). Census. P 13×13½.
1921 **1135** 100w. multicoloured...................... 60 15

1136 "40" and U.N. Emblem

(Des Lee Keun Moon. Litho)

1990 (24 Oct). 40th Anniv of United Nations Development Programme. P 13½×13.
1922 **1136** 100w. multicoloured...................... 60 15

1137 Inlaid Case with Mirror   **1138** Children feeding Ram   **1139** Cranes

(Des Chun Hee Han. Recess and photo)

1990 (16 Nov). Philatelic Week. P 13×13½.
1923 **1137** 100w. multicoloured...................... 70 15
MS1924 90×60 mm. No. 1923×2.................. 4·00 3·50

1990 (1 Dec). Lunar New Year ("Year of the Sheep"). Photo. P 13×13½.
1925 **1138** 100w. multicoloured...................... 60 15
1926 **1139** 100w. multicoloured...................... 60 15
MS1927 90×60 mm. Nos. 1925/6.................. 4·75 4·25

1140 Mascot   **1141** Ying and Yang (exhibition emblem)

(Des Cho Young Je. Litho)

1990 (12 Dec). Expo '93 World's Fair, Taejon (1st issue). P 13×13½.
1928 **1140** 100w. multicoloured...................... 85 30
1929 **1141** 440w. multicoloured...................... 2·20 95
MS1930 Two sheets, each 90×60 mm. (a) No. 1928×2; (b) No. 1929×2...................... 7·00 6·00
See also Nos. 1932/**MS**1934.

1142 Books and Emblem

(Des Ahn Seung Kyung. Photo)

1991 (1 Feb). 30th Anniv of Saemaul Minilibrary. P 13½×13.
1931 **1142** 100w. multicoloured...................... 60 15

1143 Earth   **1144** Expo Tower

(Des Cho Young Je. Litho)

1991 (23 Mar). Expo '93 World's Fair, Taejon (2nd issue). P 13×13½.
1932 **1143** 100w. multicoloured...................... 85 30
1933 **1144** 100w. multicoloured...................... 85 30
MS1934 Two sheets, each 90×60 mm. (a) No. 1932×2; (b) No. 1933×2...................... 4·25 3·75

1145 In a Flower Garden (Ilh Hyo Sun and Kwon Kil Sang)   **1146** Way to the Orchard (Park Hwa Mok and Kim Kong Sun)

(Des Kim Im Yong. Photo)

1991 (27 Mar). Korean Music (7th series). P 13×13½.
1935 **1145** 100w. multicoloured...................... 80 30
1936 **1146** 100w. multicoloured...................... 80 30

1147 Moth   **1148** Beetle

1149 Butterfly   **1150** Beetle   **1151** Cicada

1152 Water Beetle   **1153** Hornet   **1154** Ladybirds

1155 Dragonfly   **1156** Grasshopper

(Des Kim Sung Sil. Photo)

1991 (8 Apr). Insects. Photo. P 13½×13.
1937	**1147** 100w. multicoloured................................	1·00	25
	a. Strip of 10. Nos. 1937/4.................	10·50	
1938	**1148** 100w. multicoloured................................	1·00	25
1939	**1149** 100w. multicoloured................................	1·00	25
1940	**1150** 100w. multicoloured................................	1·00	25
1941	**1151** 100w. multicoloured................................	1·00	25
1942	**1152** 100w multicoloured	1·00	25
1943	**1153** 100w. multicoloured................................	1·00	25
1944	**1154** 100w. multicoloured................................	1·00	25
1945	**1155** 100w. multicoloured................................	1·00	25
1946	**1156** 100w. multicoloured................................	1·00	25
1937/1946	*Set of 10*	9·00	2·30

Nos. 1937/46 were issued together in *se-tenant* strips of ten stamps within the sheet

1157 Flautist and Centre   **1158** Flag and Provisional Government Building

(Des Kim Hyun. Photo)

1991 (10 Apr). 40th Anniv of Korean Traditional Performing Arts Centre. P 13×13½.
1947	**1157** 100w. multicoloured................................	60	20

(Des Byun Choo Suk. Photo)

1991 (13 Apr). 72nd Anniv of Establishment of Korean Provisional Government in Shanghai. P 13½×13.
1948	**1158** 100w. multicoloured................................	60	20

1159 Urban Landscape and Emblem   **1160** Bouquet

(Des Chun Hee Han. Photo)

1991 (20 Apr). Employment for Disabled People. P 13½×13.
1949	**1159** 100w. multicoloured................................	60	20

(Des Chang Wan Young. Photo)

1991 (15 May). Teachers' Day. P 13½×13.
1950	**1160** 100w. multicoloured................................	60	20

1161 *Microphysogobio longidorsalis*   **1162** *Gnathopogon majimae*

1163 *Therapon oxyrhynchus*   **1164** *Psettina ijimae*

(Des Bang Jae Ki. Photo)

1991 (8 June). Fishes (6th series). P 13½×13.
1951	**1161** 100w. multicoloured................................	80	25
1952	**1162** 100w. multicoloured................................	80	25
1953	**1163** 100w. multicoloured................................	80	25
1954	**1164** 100w. multicoloured................................	80	25
1951/1954	*Set of 4*................................	2·75	90

1165 Animals waiting to board Bus   **1166** *Aerides japonicum*

(Des Kim Im Yong. Photo)

1991 (26 June). Waiting One's Turn Campaign. P 13×13½.
1955	**1165**100w. multicoloured................................	1·60	30

(Des Lee Hea Ok. Photo)

1991 (26 July). Wild Flowers (2nd series). T **1166** and similar vert designs. Multicoloured. P 13×13½.
1956	100w. Type **1166**................................	70	25
1957	100w. *Heloniopsis orientalis*................	70	25
1958	370w. *Aquilegia buergeriana*................	1·80	70
1959	440w. *Gentiana zollingeri*................	2·20	80
1956/1959	*Set of 4*................................	4·75	1·80

1167 Scout with
Semaphore Flags

1168 "YMCA"

(Des Won In Jae. Photo)

1991 (8 Aug). 17th World Scout Jamboree. P 13×13½.
1960 **1167** 100w. multicoloured.................................. 65 15
MS1961 90×60 mm. No. 1960×2.................................... 1·40 1·20

(Des Chun Hee Han. Photo)

1991 (22 Aug). Young Men's Christian Association World Assembly,
Seoul. Photo. P 13×13½.
1962 **1168** 100w. multicoloured..................................... 65 15

1169 Rusted Train
and Family
Members Reunited

1170 Globe, Rainbow,
Dove and UN Emblem

1991 (11 Sept). North-South Reunification. Litho. P 13×13½.
1963 **1169** 100w. multicoloured.......................... 80 20

(Des Chun Hee Han. Photo)

1991 (18 Sept). Admission of South Korea to United Nations
Organization. P 13½×13.
1964 **1170** 100w. multicoloured...................................... 65 15

1171 Unra

1172 Jing

1173 Galgo

1174 Saeng-hwang

(Des Kim Sang Rak. Photo)

1991 (26 Sept). Traditional Musical Instruments (1st series).
P 13×13½.
1965 **1171** 100w. multicoloured................................. 70 30
1966 **1172** 100w. multicoloured................................. 70 30
1967 **1173** 100w. multicoloured................................. 70 30
1968 **1174** 100w. multicoloured................................. 70 30
1965/1968 *Set of 4* .... 2·50 1·10
See also Nos. 1981/4.

1175 Film and
Theatrical Masks

1176 Globe and
Satellite

(Des Chun Hee Han. Lithol

1991 (1 Oct). Culture Month. P 13×13½.
1969 **1175** 100w. multicoloured.................................... 65 15

(Des Kwon Myung Kwang. Photo)

1991 (7 Oct). Telecom 91 International Telecommunications
Exhibition, Geneva. P 13×13½.
1970 **1176** 100w. multicoloured 65 15

1177 Hexagonals

1178 Bamboo

1179 Geometric

1180 Tree

1181 Light
Bulb turning off
Switch

1991 (26 Oct). Korean Beauty (1st series). Kottams (patterns on walls)
from Jakyung Hall, Kyungbok Palace. Photo. P 13×13½.
1971 **1177** 100w. multicoloured .... 1·00 30
a. Strip of 4. Nos. 1971/4. .... 4·25
1972 **1178** 100w. multicoloured .... 1·00 30
1973 **1179** 100w. multicoloured .... 1·00 30
1974 **1180** 100w. multicoloured .... 1·00 30
1971/1974 *Set of 4*.. 3·50 1·10
Nos. 1971/4 were issued together in *se-tenant* strips of four stamps
within the sheet.
See also Nos. 2006/9, 2068/71, 2103/6, 2157/60, 2219/22, 2257/60,
2308/15, 2349/56 and 2437/40.

(Des Choi Mi. Photo)

1991 (1 Nov). Energy Saving Campaign. P 13½×13.
1975 **1181** 100w. multicoloured................................. 1·60 30

1182 "Longevity" **1183** Flying Kites **1184** Stamps

1991 (2 Dec). Lunar New Year ("Year of the Monkey"). Recess and photo. P 13×13½.
1976 **1182** 100w. multicoloured................................. 65 15
1977 **1183** 100w. multicoloured................................. 65 15
MS1978 Two sheets, each 90×60 mm. (a) No. 1976×2; (b) No. 1977×2................................. 3·50 3·25

(Des Chun Hee Han. Photo)

1991 (5 Dec). Philatelic Week. P 13×13½.
1979 **1184** 100w. multicoloured................................. 65 15
MS1980 90×60 mm. No. 1979×2................................. 1·60 1·50

1185 Yonggo **1186** Chwago

1187 Kkwaenggwari **1188** T'ukchong

(Des Kim Sang Rak. Photo)

1992 (24 Feb). Traditional Musical Instruments (2nd series). P 13×13½.
1981 **1185** 100w. multicoloured 70 30
1982 **1186** 100w. multicoloured 70 30
1983 **1187** 100w. multicoloured 70 30
1984 **1188** 100w. multicoloured 70 30
1981/1984 Set of 4 .... 2·50 1·10

1189 White Hibiscus **1190** Pink Hibiscus

(Des Choi Mi. Photo)

1992 (9 Mar). *Hibiscus syriacus* (national flower). P 13×13½.
1985 **1189** 100w. multicoloured................................. 1·10 40
1986 **1190** 100w. multicoloured................................. 1·10 40

1191 Satellite **1192** Yoon Pong Gil

(Des Chang Wan Young. Photo)

1992 (21 Apr). Science Day. P 13½×13.
1987 **1191** 100w. multicoloured 55 15

(Des Chun Hee Han. Recess and litho)

1992 (29 Apr). 60th Death Anniv of Yoon Pong Gil (independence fighter). P 13×13½.
1988 **1192** 100w. multicoloured 55 15

1193 Children and Heart **1194** Japanese Warship attacking Korean Settlement

(Des Ahn Seung Kyung. Photo)

1992 (4 May). Child Protection. P 13½×13.
1989 **1193** 100w. multicoloured................................. 1·60 25

(Des Chun Hee Han. Litho)

1992 (23 May). 400th Anniv of Start of Im-Jin War. P 13½×13.
1990 **1194** 100w. multicoloured................................. 55 15

1195 Farmer

(Des Chun Hee Han. Recess and litho)

1992 (25 May). 60th International Fertilizer Industry Association Conference, Seoul. P 13×13½.
1991 **1195** 100w. multicoloured.................................... 55   15

(Des Chang Chung Hack. Photo)

1992 (22 June). Wild Flowers (3rd series). Vert designs as T **1186.** Multicoloured. P 13×13½.
1992	100w. *Lychnis wilfordii*	65	30
1993	100w. *Lycoris radiata*	65	30
1994	370w. *Commelina communis*	1·70	65
1995	440w. *Calanthe striata*	2·00	70
1992/1995	*Set of 4*	4·50	1·80

1196 *Longing for Mt. Keumkang* (Han Sang Ok and Choi Young Shurp)

1197 The Swing (Kim Mal Bong and Geum Su Hyeon)

1198 Gymnastics

(Des Kim Im Yong. Photo)

1992 (13 July). Korean Music (8th series). P 13×13½.
1996 **1196** 100w. multicoloured.................................... 70   25
1997 **1197** 100w. multicoloured.................................... 70   25

(Des Lee Hea Ok. Photo)

1992 (25 July). Olympic Games, Barcelona. T **1198** and similar vert design. Multicoloured. P 13×13½.
1998   100w. Type **1198**.. 65   15
1999   100w. Pole vaulting.. 65   15

1199 Stylized View of Exhibition

1200 Expo 93

(Des Cho Young Je. Litho)

1992 (7 Aug). Expo '93 World's Fair, Taejon (3rd issue). P 13½×13.
2000 **1199** 100w. multicoloured.................................... 55   15
2001 **1200** 100w. multicoloured.................................... 55   15
MS2002 Two sheets, each 90×60 mm. (a) No. 2000×2; (b) No. 2001×2.................................... 3·50   3·00

1201 Korea Exhibition Centre and South Gate, Seoul

1202 Tolharubang (stone grandfather), Cheju

(Des Lee Hea Ok. Photo)

1992 (22 Aug). 21st Universal Postal Union Congress, Seoul (1994) (1st issue). P 13½×13.
2003 **1201** 100w. multicoloured.................................... 55   15
2004 **1202** 100w. multicoloured.................................... 55   15
MS2005 Two sheets, each 90×60 mm. (a) No. 2003×2; (b) No. 2004×2.................................... 3·25   3·00
See also Nos. 2075/**MS**2077, 2088/**MS**2089 and 2112/**MS**2117.

1203 Woven Pattern

1204 Fruit and Flower Decorations

1205 Carved Decorations

1206 Coral, Butterfly and Pine Resin Decorations

(Des Won In Jae. Recess and photo)

1992 (21 Sept). Korean Beauty (2nd series). Madeups (tassels). P 13×13½ .
2006 **1203**	100w. multicoloured...................................	80	30
	a. Strip of 4. Nos. 2006/9....................	3·50	
2007 **1204**	100w. multicoloured...................................	80	30
2008 **1205**	100w. multicoloured...................................	80	30
2009 **1206**	100w. multicoloured...................................	80	30
2006/2009	*Set of 4*	3·00	1·10

Nos. 2006/9 were issued together in *se-tenant* strips of four stamps within the sheet.

1207 Lee Pong Chang

1208 Hwang Young Jo (Barcelona, 1992)

1209 Sails on Map of Americas

(Des Choi Mi. Recess and litho)

1992 (10 Oct). 60th Death Anniv of Lee Pong Chang (independence fighter). P 13×13½ .
2010 **1207** 100w. purple-brown and salmon 55   15

(Des Lee Hea Ok. Litho)

1992 (10 Oct). Korean Winners of Olympic Marathon. T **1208** and similar vert design. Multicoloured. P 13×13½ .
2011	100w. Type **1208**................	70	30
	a. Pair. Nos. 2011/12	1·50	65
2012	100w. Shon Kee Chung (Berlin, 1936)	70	30
MS2013	90×60 mm. Nos. 2011/12.	4·50	4·00

Nos. 2011/12 were issued together in *se-tenant* pairs within the sheet.

(Des Cho Jong Hyun. Photo)

1992 (12 Oct). 500th Anniv of Discovery of America by Columbus. P 13×13½.
2014	**1209** 100w. multicoloured.....................	55	15

 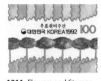

1210 Heads and Speech Balloon   **1211** Flowers and Stamps

(Des Kim Hyun. Photo)

1992 (2 Nov). Campaign for Purification of Language. P 13×13½.
2015	**1210** 100w. multicoloured	1·60	30

(Des Lee Keun Moon. Photo)

1992 (14 Nov). Philatelic Week. P 13½ ×13.
2016	**1211** 100w. multicoloured....................	55	15
MS2017	60×90 mm. No. 2016×2.........................	1·80	1·60

1212 Cockerels in Snow-covered Yard   **1213** Flying Kites

(Des Chun Hee Han. Photo)

1992 (1 Dec). Lunar New Year ("Year of the Cock"). P 13×13½.
2018	**1212** 100w. multicoloured.....................	60	15
2019	**1213** 100w. multicoloured.....................	60	15
MS2020	Two sheets, each 90×60 mm. (a) No.		
	2018×2; (b) No. 2019×2.........................	3·00	2·50

1214 Emblem, Globe and Woman holding Bowl

(Des Cho Sung Jin. Litho)

1992 (5 Dec). International Nutrition Conference, Rome. P 13½×13.
2021	**1214** 100w. multicoloured	55	15

1215 View of Centre and Logo   **1216** Pres. Kim Young Sam, Flag and Mt. Paekdu Lake

(Des Choi Mi. Litho)

1993 (15 Feb). Inauguration of Seoul Arts Centre's Opera House. P 13½×13.
2022	**1215** 110w. multicoloured.....................	65	25

(Des Chun Hee Han. Litho)

1993 (25 Feb). Inauguration of 14th President. P 13½×13.
2023	**1216** 110w. multicoloured	90	30
MS2024	90×60 mm. No. 2023×2........................	7·25	6·50

1217 National Flag   **1218** White Stork   **1218a** Black-Night Heron (*Nycticorax nyticorax*)

1219 White Magnolia   **1219a** *Vitis amurensis*   **1220** Korean White Pine

1220a Purpuricenus literatus (beetle)   **1220b** Water Cock (Gallicrex cinerea)   **1221** Squirrel

1222 Chinese Lanterns   **1222a** Japanese White Eye (Zosterops japonica)   **1223** Scops Owl

1223a Dishcloth Gourd (Luffa cyclindrica)   **1224** *Hibiscus syriacus*   **1225** Narcissi

1226 Painted Porcelain Jar

1227 Pine Tree

1227a Crayfish (*Cambaroides similes*)

1236a Cheju Ponies

1237 Gilt-bronze Buddha Triad

1227b Far Eastern Curlew (*Numenius madagascariensis*)

1228 Little Tern

1228a Hibiscus (*Hibiscus syriacus*)

1238 Celadon Pitcher

1239 Stone Guardian Animal (from Tomb of King Muryong)

1229 Turtle

1229a Snow Crab (*Chionoecetes opilio*)

1230 Sky Lark

1231 Drum and Drum Dance

1232 Celadon Cockerel Water Dropper

1233 Haho'l Mask and Ssirurm Wrestlers

1240 Bronze Incense Burner

1241a Crown from Tomb of Sinch'on-ni

(Des Chun Hee Han (10, 160, 200, 370, 420, 440, 480w.), Lee Hea Ok (20, 80, 300, 930, 1050, 1170, 1190w.), Kim Im Yong (30, 50, 60, 70, 90, 100, 130, 140, 170, 180, 210, 260, 400w.), Youn Seon Young (400w.), Choi Mi (110, 120, 500, 700w.), Won In Jae (710, 900, 910w.), Lee Gi Song (800, 1000w.), Park Eun Kyung (700w (2064a)), Kim Sung Am (40w. (2028a)). Recess and litho (900, 930w. (2049)), litho (170w.) or photo (others))

1234 Celadon Pomegranate Water Dropper

1234a Hong Yong-sik (First Postmaster General

1993 (22 Mar)–**01**. P 13½×13 (10, 20, 40 to 150, 190, 500, 600, 710, 800, 910w.) or 13×13½ (others).

2025	**1217**	10w. multicoloured (8.4.93)	35	15
2026	**1218**	20w. multicoloured (24.5.93)	25	15
2026a	**1218a**	20w. multicoloured (17.1.00)	25	10
2027	**1219**	30w. multicoloured (24.5.93)	35	15
2027a	**1219a**	30w. multicoloured (9.10.01)	65	40
2028	**1220**	40w. multicoloured (24.5.93)	45	15
2028a	**1229a**	40w. multicoloured (p 13×13½) (10.6.00)	35	30
2028b	**1220b**	50w. multicoloured (19.2.98)	35	15
2029	**1221**	60w. multicoloured (19.12.94)	55	15
2030	**1222**	70w. multicoloured (15.3.95)	55	15
2030a	**1222a**	80w. multicoloured (1.7.97)	35	15
2031	**1223**	90w. multicoloured (22.4.94)	70	25
2031a	**1223a**	100w. multicoloured (5.3.97)	55	15
2032	**1224**	110w. multicoloured (30.3.93)	1·00	15
		a. Coil. Imperf×p 13	1·30	25
2033		120w. multicoloured (11.11.95)	90	15
2034	**1225**	130w. multicoloured (20.8.94)	90	25
		a. Coil. Imperf×p 13 (1.9.94)	1·30	25
		b. Booklet pane. No. 2034×20 (28.2.95)	19·00	
2034c	**1225**	140w. multicoloured (1.11.97)	1·00	15

1235 Gilt-bronze Bongnae-san Incense Burner

1236 King Sejong and Alphabet

2035 **1226** 150w. multicoloured. Booklets
(20.3.96).. 1·40   80
  a. Booklet pane. No. 2035×20..... 29·00
  b. Coil. Imperf×p 13 .... 1·40   80
2036 **1227** 160w. multicoloured (29.4.93) .... 1·50   25
2036*a* **1227a** 170w. yellow-orange, black and bright
rose (1.9.97)................................ 1·30   30
  b. Coil. P 13 x imperf (18.11.97)... 90   30
2036*c* **1227b** 170w. multicoloured (15.12.97)......... 55   25
  ca. With additional Braille
embossing (15.10.98) .... 1·80   50
2037 **1228** 180w. multicoloured (12.9.94) .... 1·40   25
2037*a* **1228a** 190w. multicoloured (1.9.97) .... 1·20   30
  b. Coil. Imperf x p 13 (18.11.97) .. 1·00   30
2038 **1229** 200w. multicoloured (19.12.94) .... 1·40   30
2038*a* **1229a** 200w. multicoloured (p 13 x 13½)
(5.3.01) 90   40
2038*b* **1228** 210w. multicoloured (1.11.95) .... 1·40   25
2038*c* **1228** 260w. multicoloured (1.11.97) .... 1·80   40
2039 **1230** 300w. multicoloured (22.1.96) .... 1·30   40
2040 **1231** 370w. multicoloured........................... 2·75   50
2041 **1232** 400w. multicoloured (28.9.95) .... 1·50   40
2042 **1231** 420w. multicoloured (20.3.96) .... 3·00   50
2043 **1233** 440w. multicoloured .... 3·50   55
2044   480w. multicoloured (20.3.96) .... 3·00   55
2045 **1234** 500w. multicoloured (6.11.95) .... 2·00   65
2045*a* **1234a** 600w. multicoloured (15.11.99)......... 2·30   80
2046 **1235** 700w. multicoloured (15.6.95) .... 4·00   80
2046*a* **1235a** 700w. multicoloured (17.1.00) .... 2·20   80
2046*b* **1236** 710w. multicoloured (29.4.93) .... 5·00   70
2046*c* **1236a** 800w. multicoloured (4.4.98)............. 2·75   65
2047 **1237** 900w. multicoloured (20.9.93) .... 6·00   95
2048 **1236** 910w. multicoloured (15.2.94) .... 6·00   90
2049 **1238** 930w. multicoloured (*turquoise-blue
background*) (1.10.94) .... 2·75   50
2049*a* **1238** 930w. multicoloured (*light brown
background*) (11.3.95) .... 3·25   2·40
  ab. Booklet pane. No. 2049a×10
(20.3.95)................................. 36·00
2049*b* **1239** 1000w. multicoloured (16.12.96) .... 4·50   1·30
2050 **1238** 1050w. multicoloured (25.10.95) .... 5·50   95
2050*a* **1240** 1170w. multicoloured (1.11.97) .... 5·00   2·10
2050*b* **1238** 1190w. multicoloured (1.11.97) .... 5·00   2·30
2050*c* **1241a** 2000w. multicoloured (15.11.99) .... 6·00   1·60
2025/2050*c* *Set of 44* .... 90·00   24·00
  The booklet panes have two edges imperforate, giving stamps
with one side imperf.
  The Braille embossing on No. 2036ca reads "10.15" the date of
White Crane Day.

1243 Student
and Computer

1244 Emblem
and Map

(Des Lee Keun Moon. Photo)

1993 (27May). Korean Student Inventions Exhibition. P 13×13½.
2051 **1243** 110w. deep bright mauve and silver... 60   15

(Des Kim Im Yong. Photo)

1993 (14 June). International Human Rights Conference, Vienna,
Austria. P 13×13½.
2052 **1244** 110w. multicoloured 60   15

1245 Hand
scooping Globe
from Water

1246 Matsu-take
Mushroom
(*Tricholoma
matsutake*)

1993 (1 July). "Water is Life". Photo. P 13½×13.
2053 **1245** 110w. multicoloured..................... 1·20   25

(Des Kim Sang Rak. Photo)

1993 (26 July). Fungi (1st series). T **1246** and similar vert designs.
Multicoloured. P 13×13½.
2054   110w. Type **1246**............................. 70   25
2055   110w. *Ganoderma lucidu*........................ 70   25
2056   110w. *Lentinula edodes*.......................... 70   25
2057   110w. Oyster fungus (*Pleuntus
ostreatus*) 70   25
2054/2057 *Set of 4* .... 2·50   90
  See also Nos. 2095/**MS**2099, 2146/**MS**2150, 2207/**MS**2211, 2249/
MS2252 and 2293/**MS**2297.

1247 Government Pavilion

1248 International Pavilion
and Mascot

1249 Recycling Art Pavilion

1250 Telecom Pavilion

(Des Kim Im Yong (2058, 2060), Youn Seon Young (2059, 2061). Litho)

1993 (7 Aug). Expo '93 World's Fair, Taejon (4th issue). P 13½×13.
2058 **1247** 110w. multicoloured................... 60   25
2059 **1248** 110w. multicoloured................... 60   25
2060 **1249** 110w. multicoloured................... 60   25
2061 **1250** 110w. multicoloured................... 60   25
2058/2061 *Set of 4* .... 2·20   90
MS2062 Four sheets, each 90×60 mm. (a) No.
2058×2; (b) No. 2059×2; (c) No. 2060×2; (d) No.
2061×2 .... 6·50   6·00

1251 Emblems

1252 *O Dol Ddo
Gi* (Cheju Island
folk song)

1253 *Ong He Ya*
(barley threshing
song)

(Des Youn Seon Young. Photo)

1993 (28 Aug). 19th Congress of International Society of Orthopaedic and Trauma Surgery. P 13×13½.
2063 **1251** 110w. multicoloured 60 15

(Des Byun Choo Suk. Photo)

1993 (13 Sept). Korean Music (9th series). P 13×13½.
2064 **1252** 110w. multicoloured 70 25
2065 **1253** 110w. multicoloured 70 25

1254 Janggu Drum Dance   **1255** Emblem

(Des Lee Keun Moon. Photo)

1993 (27 Sept). Visit Korea Year (1994). P 13×13½.
2066 **1254** 110w. multicoloured 60 15
2067 **1255** 110w. multicoloured 60 15
See also Nos. 2086/7.

1256 "Twin Tigers" (military officials, 1st to 3rd rank)   **1257** "Single Crane" (civil officials. 4th to 9th rank)

1258 "Twin Cranes" (civil officials, 1st to 3rd rank)   **1259** "Dragon" (King)

(Des Lee Hea Ok. Photo)

1993 (11 Oct). Korean Beauty (3rd series). Hyoongbae (embroidered insignia of the Chosun dynasty). P 13×13½.
2068 **1256** 110w. multicoloured 70 25
    a. Strip or block of 4. Nos. 2068/71 3·00
2069 **1257** 110w. multicoloured 70 25
2070 **1258** 110w. multicoloured 70 25
2071 **1259** 110w. multicoloured 70 25
2068/2071 *Set of 4* .... 2·50 90
Nos. 2068/71 were issued together in *se-tenant* strips and blocks of four stamps within the sheet.

1260 Campaign Emblem   **1261** "Eggplant and Oriental Long-nosed Locust" (Shin Saim Dang)

1993 (1 Nov). Anti-litter Campaign. Photo. P 13½×13.
2072 **1260** 110w. multicoloured .... 1·30 25

(Des Lee Hea Ok. Photo)

1993 (13 Nov). Philatelic Week. P 13×13½.
2073 **1261** 110w. multicoloured 60 25
MS2074 90×60 mm. No. 2073×2 .... 1·60 1·40

1262 "Weaving"   **1263** Ribbon and Globe as "30", Freighter and Ilyushin Il-86 Jetliner

(Des Won In Jae. Photo)

1993 (18 Nov). 21st Universal Postal Union Congress, Seoul (1994) (2nd issue). T **1262** and similar multicoloured design showing paintings by Kim Hong Do. P 13½×13 (2075) or 13×13½ (2076).
2075   110w. Type **1262** 60 25
2076   110w. "Musicians and a Dancer" (*vert*) 60 25
MS2077 Two sheets, each 90×60 mm. (a) No. 2075×2; (b) No. 2076×2 .... 3·00 2·25

(Des Choi Mi. Litho)

1993 (30 Nov). 30th Trade Day. P 13½×13.
2078 **1263** 110w. multicoloured 60 25

1264 Sapsaree and Kite   **1265** Puppy with New Year's Greetings Bow

(Des Yoo Ae Ro. Photo)

1993 (1 Dec). Lunar New Year ("Year of the Dog"). P 13½×13 (2079) or 13×13½ (2080).
2079 **1264** 110w. multicoloured 60 25
2080 **1265** 110w. multicoloured 60 25
MS2081 Two sheets, each 90×60 mm. (a) No. 2079×2; (b) No. 2080×2 .... 3·00 2·75

(Des Chang Chung Hack. Photo)

1993 (20 Dec). Wild Flowers (4th series). Vert designs as T **1166**. P 13×13½ .

2082	110w. Weigela hortensis	70	25
2083	110w. Iris ruthenica	70	25
2084	110w. Aceriphyllum rosii	70	25
2085	110w. Marsh marigold (Caltha palustris)	70	25
2082/2085 Set of 4		2·50	90

1266 Flautist on Cloud

1267 T'alch'um Mask Dance

(Des Kim Kyo Man. Photo)

1994 (11 Jan). Visit Korea Year (2nd issue). P 13×13½.

2086	**1266**	110w. multicoloured	60	15
2087	**1267**	110w. multicoloured	60	25

1268 Map'ae, Horse, Envelope and Emblem

1269 Monument

(Des Won In Jae. Photol

1994 (24 Jan). 21st Universal Postal Union Congress, Seoul (3rd issue). P 13½×13.

2088	**1268**	300w. multicoloured	1·40	55
		a. Booklet pane. No. 2088×10	15·00	
MS2089	90×60 mm. No. 2088×2		3·50	3·00

The booklet pane has its top and bottom edges imperforate, giving stamps with one side imperf.

The Map'ae was a token which gave authority to impress post horses.

(Des Youn Seon Young. Photo)

1994 (28 Feb). 75th Anniv of Samil (Independence) Movement. P 13×13½ .

2090	**1269**	110w. multicoloured	60	15

1270 Great Purple (Sasakia charonda)

1271 Family of Mandarins

(Des Chang Wan Young. Photo)

1994 (7 Mar). Protection of Wildlife and Plants (1st series). T **1270** and similar horiz design. Multicoloured. P 13½×13.

2091		110w. Type **1270**	70	30
2092		110w. Allomyrina dichotoma (beetle)..	70	30
MS2093	Two sheets, each 90×60 mm. (a) No. 2091×2; (b) No. 2092×2		3·50	3·00

See also Nos. 2143/MS2145, 2186/MS2188, 2241/MS2243, 2275/MS2279, 2326/MS2330, 2383/MS2387 and 2481/MS2485.

1994 (14 May). International Year of the Family. Photo. P 13½×13.

2094	**1271**	110w. multicoloured	60	15

(Des Kim Sang Rak. Photo)

1994 (30 May). Fungi (2nd series). Vert designs as T **1246**. Multicoloured. P 13×13½ .

2095	110w. Common morel (Morchella esculenta)	70	25
2096	110w. Gomphus floccosus	70	25
2097	110w. Cortinarius purpurascens	70	25
2098	110w. Oudemansiella platyphylla	70	25
2095/2098 Set of 4		2·50	90
MS2099	Four sheets, each 90×60 mm. (a) No. 2095×2; (b) No. 2096×2; (c) No. 2097×2; (d) No. 2098×2	6·50	6·00

1272 Museum

1273 Text and Dove

(Des Choi Mi. Litho)

1994 (10 June). Inauguration of War Memorial Museum, Yongsan (Seoul). P 13½×13.

2100	**1272**	110w. multicoloured	60	15

(Des Hwang Bu Yong. Photo)

1994 (13 June). Philakorea 1994 International Stamp Exhibition, Seoul (1st issue). P 13½×13.

2101	**1273**	910w. multicoloured	4·00	1·60
		a. Booklet pane. No. 2101×10	41·00	
MS2102	90×60 mm. No. 2101		4·75	4·25

The booklet pane has its top and bottom edges imperforate, giving stamps with one side imperf.

See also Nos. 2107/MS2111.

1274 Taeguk (Yin-Yang) Fan

1275 Crane Fan

1276 Pearl Fan

1277 Wheel Fan

(Des Lee Hea Ok. Photo)

1994 (18 July). Korean Beauty (4th series). Fans. P 13×13½.

2103	**1274**	110w. multicoloured	70	25
		a. Strip or block of 4. Nos. 2103/6	3·00	
2104	**1275**	110w. multicoloured	70	25
2105	**1276**	110w. multicoloured	70	25
2106	**1277**	110w. multicoloured	70	25
2103/2106 Set of 4			2·50	90

Nos. 2103/6 were issued together in *se-tenant* strips and blocks of four stamps within the sheet.

1278 "Wintry Days" (Kim Chong Hui)   **1279** "Grape" (Choe Sok Hwan)

1280 "Riverside Scene" (Kim Duk Sin)   **1281** Manchurian Crane and Mountains

(Des Hwang Bu Yong)

1994 (16 Aug). Philakorea 1994 International Stamp Exhibition, Seoul (2nd issue).

(a) Photo. P 13½×13.

2107	**1278**	130w. multicoloured	60	15
		a. Booklet pane. No. 2107×10	6·25	
2108	**1279**	130w. multicoloured	60	15
		a. Booklet pane. No. 2108×10	6·25	
2109	**1280**	130w. multicoloured	60	15
		a. Booklet pane. No. 2109×10	6·25	
2107/2109 Set of 3			1·60	40

MS2110 Three sheets, each 90×60 mm. (a) No. 2107×2; (b) No. 2108×2; (c) No. 2109×2 .... 4·00   3·50

The booklet panes have their top and bottom edges imperforate, giving stamps with one side imperf.

(b) Sheet 138×90 mm containing T **1281** and similar multicoloured designs showing Ten Symbols of Long Life. Recess and litho. P 13½×13 (horiz) or 13½ (vert).

MS2111 130w. Type **1281**; 300w. Manchurian cranes and sun; 370w. Manchurian cranes in treetops; 400w. Deer (vert); 440w. Turtle in stream (vert); 470w. Tree and stream (vert); 930w. Trees (vert)................ 10·50   9·75

1282 "Sword Dance" (Sin Yun Bok)   **1283** Old Map

(Des Kwon Myung Kwang (2112/13), Won In Jae (others). Photo)

1994 (22 Aug). 21st Universal Postal Union Congress, Seoul (4th issue). T **1282** and similar multicoloured designs. Photo. P 13½×13 (370w.) or 13×13½ (others).

2112		130w. Type **1282**	60	15
		a. Booklet pane. No. 2112×10	6·25	
2113		130w. "Book Shelves" (detail of folk painting showing stamps)	60	15
		a. Booklet pane. No. 2113×10.	6·25	
2114		130w. Congress emblem	60	15
		a. Booklet pane. No. 2114×10	6·25	
2115		370w. Hong Yung Sik (postal reformer) and Heinrich von Stephan (founder of U.P.U.) (horiz)	60	15
		a. Booklet pane. No. 2115×10.	6·25	
2112/2115 Set of 4			2·20	55

MS2116 Four sheets, each 90×60 mm. (a) No. 2112×2; (b) No. 2113×2; (c) No. 2114×2; (d) No. 2115×2 .... 7·25   6·75

MS2117 125×86 mm. Nos. 2112/15................. 4·00   3·50

The booklet panes have their outer edges imperforate, giving stamps with one side imperf.

(Des Kim Hye Won. Photo)

1994 (27 Sept). 600th Anniv of Adoption of Seoul as Capital of Korea (1st issue). P 13×13½.

2118	**1283**	130w. multicoloured	60	15

See also No. 2139.

1284 Mail Van   **1285** Airplane

(Des Kim Im Yong (300w.), Lee Hea Ok (540w.), Chun Hee Han (1190w.), Won In Jae (others). Litho (300, 390, 540w.) or photo (others))

1994 (1 Oct)–**97**. Transport. T **1284/1285** and similar horiz designs. P 13½×13.

2121	**1284**	300w. multicoloured (18.11.94)	2·10	30
2122	**1285**	330w. multicoloured (11.11.95)	2·10	40
2122a	–	340w. multicoloured (12.9.97)	2·10	50
2122b	–	380w. multicoloured (12.9.97)	2·30	55
2123		390w. multicoloured	3·00	50
		a. Booklet pane. No. 2123×10 (1.6.95)	31·00	
2124	**1285**	400w. multicoloured (16.10.95)	2·10	40
		a. Booklet pane. No. 2124×10 (27.3.96)	22·00	
2126	–	540w. multicoloured (1.11.94)	3·50	55
2127	**1285**	560w. multicoloured (1.11.95)	3·50	65
2130	–	1190w. multicoloured	7·75	1·30
2131	**1285**	1340w. multicoloured (25.10.95)	6·75	1·70
2132		1340w. multicoloured (12.9.97)	5·75	1·80
2132a	–	1380w. multicoloured (12.9.97)	6·25	2·00
2121/2132a Set of 12			42·00	9·25

Designs: As T **1284**—390w. Airplane (different); 540w. Train; 1190w. River cruiser. As T **1285**—340, 380, 1340, 1380w. Airplane facing left.

The booklet panes have their top and bottom edges imperforate, giving stamps with one side imperf.

Numbers have been left for additions to this series.

(Des Chang Chung Hack. Photo)

1994 (4 Oct). Wild Flowers (5th series). Vert designs as T **1166**. Multicoloured. P 13½×13.

2133		130w. *Gentiana jamesii*	60	25
2134		130w. *Geranium eriostemon* var. *megalanthum*	60	25
2135		130w. *Leontopodium japonicum*	60	25
2136		130w. *Lycoris aurea*	60	25
2133/2136 Set of 4			2·20	90

1286 "Water Melon
and Field Mice"
(detail of folding
screen, Shin
Saimdang)

1287 "600"

1290 Spheres around
Reactor

1291 Scales of
Justice

(Des Kim Kyo Man. Photo)

(Des Lee Hea Ok. Photo)

1995 (7 Apr). Completion of Hanaro Research Reactor. P 13½×13.

1994 (19 Nov). Philatelic Week. P 13×13½ .

2151	**1290**	130w. multicoloured	70	15

2137	**1286**	130w. multicoloured	60	25
MS2138	90×60mm. No. 2137×2................................	1·50	130

(Des Lee Keun Moon. Photo)

1995 (25 Apr). Centenary of Judicial System. P 13×13½.

2152	**1291**	130w. multicoloured	70	15

(Des Yoon Hyun Chul. Photo)

1994 (29 Nov). 600th Anniv of Seoul as Capital (2nd issue).
P 13×13½.

2139	**1287**	130w. multicoloured	60	10

1292 Tiger

(Des Lee Keun Moon. Photo)

1995 (25 Apr). Centenary of Law Education. P 13½×13.

2153	**1292**	130w. multicoloured	70	15

1288 Pigs travelling in Snow   **1289** Family in Forest

(Des Yoo Ae Ro. Photo)

1994 (1 Dec). Lunar New Year ("Year of the Pig"). P 13½×13.

2140	**1288**	130w. multicoloured	60	10
2141	**1289**	130w. multicoloured	60	10
MS2142	Two sheets, each 90×60 mm. (a) No.
2140×2; (b) No. 2141×2..	3·00	2·75

1293 Dooly the Little
Dinosaur (Kim Soo Jeung)

1294 Kochuboo (Kim Yong
Hwan)

(Des Yi Won Soo (440w.). Photo)

1995 (4 May). Cartoons (1st series). T **1293** and similar horiz design.
P 13½×13.

2154	**1293**	130w. multicoloured	70	25
2155	**1294**	440w. multicoloured	1·60	65
MS2156	Two sheets, each 90×60mm. (a) No. 2154;
(b) No. 2155..	4·75	4·50

(Des Won In Jae. Photo)

1995 (23 Jan). Protection of Wildlife and Plants (2nd series). Horiz
designs as T **1270**. Multicoloured. P 13½×13.

2143	130w. Plancy's green pond frog
(*Rana plancyi*).............................	60	25
2144	130w. Common toad (*Bufo bufo*).........	60	25
MS2145	Two sheets, each 125×86mm. Imperf.
(a) No. 2143×2; (b) No. 2144×2	3·25	3·00

See also Nos. 2196/**MS**2198,2234/**MS**2236, 2280/**MS**2282, 2322/
MS2325, 2402/**MS**2404, 2498/**MS**2500, 2594/**MS**2596, 2697/**MS**2699
and 2754/**MS**2756.

(Des Kim Sang Rak. Photo)

1995 (31 Mar). Fungi (3rd series). Vert. designs as T **1246**.
Multicoloured. P 13×13½.

2146	130w. Shaggy ink caps (*Coprinus
comatus*)	70	25
2147	130w. Chicken mushroom (*Laetiporus
sulphureus*)..............................	70	25
2148	130w. *Lentinus lepideus*	70	25
2149	130w. Cracked green russula (*Russula
virescens*)................................	70	25
2146/2149	*Set of 4*..	2·50	90
MS2150	Four sheets, each 90×60mm. (a) No.
2146×2; (b) No. 2147×2; (c) No. 2148×2; (d) No.
2149×2	6·50	6·00

1295 Gate of
Eternal Youth,
Changdokkung
Palace

1296 Fish Water
Gate, Chuhamru
Pavilion,
Changdokkung
Palace

1297 Pomosa Temple Gate, Pusan City

1298 Yangban Residence Gate, Hahoe Village

(Des Lee Hea Ok. Litho)

1995 (22 May). Korean Beauty (5th series). Gates. P 13×13½.

2157	**1295**	130w. multicoloured	75	25
		a. Strip or block of 4. Nos. 2157/60	3·25	
2158	**1296**	130w. multicoloured	75	25
2159	**1297**	130w. multicoloured	75	25
2160	**1298**	130w. multicoloured	75	25
2157/2160		Set of 4	2·75	90

Nos. 2157/60 were issued together in *se-tenant* strips and blocks of four stamps within the sheet.

1299 Lion and Emblem

(Des Lee Young Hee. Photo)

1995 (4 July). 78th Convention of Lions Clubs International. P 13½×13

2161	**1299**	130w. multicoloured	65	15

(Des Chang Chung Hack. Photo)

1995 (24 July). Wild Flowers (6th series). Vert. designs as T **1166**. Multicoloured. P 13×13½.

2162	130w. *Halenia corniculata*	60	25
2163	130w. *Erythronium japonicum*	60	25
2164	130w. *Iris odaesanensis*	60	25
2165	130w. *Leontice microrrhyncha*	60	25
2162/2165	Set of 4	2·20	90

1300 National Flag

1301 Telescope

(Des Won In Jae. Photo)

1995 (14 Aug). 50th Anniv of Liberation. T **1300** and another horiz design. Multicoloured. P 13½×13 (130w.) or 13×13½ (440w.).

2166	130w. Type **1300**	60	25
	a. Booklet pane. No. 2166×	6·25	
2167	440w. Anniversary emblem (96×19mm)	1·90	55
MS2168 Two sheets, each 125×85 mm. (a) No. 2166×2; (b) No. 2167		4·75	4·25

The booklet pane has its top and bottom edges imperforate, giving stamps with one side imperf.

(Des Choi Mi. Litho)

1995 (13 Sept). Inauguration of Mt. Bohyun Optical Astronomy Observatory. P 13×13½.

2169	**1301**	130w. multicoloured	65	15

1302 Turtle's Back Song

1303 Song from *Standards of Musical Science*

(Des Chung Yung Nam. Photo)

1995 (25 Sept). Literature (1st series). P 13×13½ (2170) or 13½×13 (2171).

2170	**1302**	130w. multicoloured	60	15
2171	**1303**	130w. multicoloured	60	15
MS2172 Two sheets, each 90×60 mm. (a) No. 2170×2; (b) No. 2171×2		3·00	2·75

See also Nos. 2212/**MS**2214, 2269/**MS**2271, 2301/**MS**2303, 2344/**MS**2348 and 2412/**MS**2417.

1304 "50 Th" incorporating Man with Wheat

1305 Open Bible

(Des Won In Jae. Recess and litho)

1995 (16 Oct). 50th Anniv of Food and Agriculture Organization. P 13½×13.

2173	**1304**	150w. black and violet	75	25

(Des Chun Hee Han. Litho)

1995 (18 Oct). Centenary of Korean Bible Society. P 13½×13.

2174	**1305**	150w. multicoloured	75	25

1306 Families in Houses

1307 Dove of Flags

(Des Cho Sung Jin. Litho)

1995 (20 Oct). Population and Housing Census. P 13×13½.

2175	**1306**	150w. multicoloured	75	25

(Des Won In Jae. Photo)

1995 (24 Oct). 50th Anniv of United Nations Organization. P 13½×13.
2176 **1307** 150w. multicoloured.................................. 75   25

1308 Wilhelm Rontgen

1309 Water Pepper and Mantis (detail of folding screen. Shin Saim Dang)

(Des Cho Jong Hyun. Photo)

1995 (8 Nov). Centenary of Discovery of X-Rays by Wilhelm Rontgen. P 13½×13.
2177 **1308** 150w. multicoloured.................................. 75   25

(Des Lee Hea Ok. Photo)

1995 (18 Nov). Philatelic Week. P 13×13½ .
2178 **1309** 150w. multicoloured.................................. 75   25
MS2179 90×60 mm. No. 2178×2.............................. 1·70   1·50

1310 Rat and Snowman

1311 Cranes and Pine Tree

(Des Won In Jae. Photo)

1995 (1 Dec). Lunar New Year ("Year of the Rat"). P 13×13½ (2180) or 13½×13 (2181).
2180 **1310** 150w. multicoloured.............................. 75   25
2181 **1311** 150w. multicoloured.............................. 75   25
MS2182 Two sheets, each 90×60 mm. (a) No. 2180×2; (b) No. 2181×2.. 3·25   3·00

1312 Miroku Bosatsu, Koryu Temple, Kyoto

1313 Cable Route

(Des Kim Im Yong. Photo)

1995 (18 Dec). 30th Anniv of Resumption of Korea–Japan Diplomatic Relations. P 13×13½.
2183 **1312** 420w. multicoloured.................................. 2·10   70

(Des Kim Kyo Man. Litho)

1996 (8 Feb). Inauguration of Korea–China Submarine Cable. P 13½×13.
2184 **1313** 420w. multicoloured.................................. 2·10   70

1314 "30" and Molecule

1315 Satellite and Launching Pad

(Des Cho Jong Hyun. Photo)

1996 (10 Feb). 30th Anniv of Korea Institute of Science and Technology. P 13½×13.
2185 **1314** 150w. multicoloured 75   25

(Des Bang Lai Ki. Photo)

1996 (5 Mar). Protection of Wildlife and Plants (3rd series). Horiz designs as T **1270**. Multicoloured. P 13½×13.
2186   150w. Black pond turtle (*Geoclemys reevesii*).. 75   25
2187   150w. Ground skink (*Scincella laterale*).. 75   25
MS2188 Two sheets, each 125×86mm. (a) No. 2186×2; (b) No. 2187×2 .... 3·25   3·00

(Des Kim Im Yong. Photo)

1996 (18 Mar). Launch of Mugunghwa 2 Telecommunications Satellite. P 13½×13.
2189 **1315** 150w. multicoloured 75   25

1316 So Chae P'il (founder) and Leader from First Issue

1317 Anniversary Emblem and Cadets

(Des Won In Jae. Recess and litho)

1996 (6 Apr). Centenary of Tongnip Shinmun (first independent newspaper). P 13½×13.
2190 **1316** 150w. multicoloured 75   25

(Des Kim Im Yong. Photo)

1996 (22 Apr). Wild Flowers (7th series). Vert. designs as T **1166**. Multicoloured. P 13×13½.
2191   150w. *Cypripedium macranthum* 75   25
2192   150w. *Trillium tschonoskii* 75   25
2193   150w. *Viola variegata* 75   25
2194   150w. *Hypericum ascyron* 75   25
2191/2194 Set of 4... 2·75   90

(Des Chun Hee Han. Litho)

1996 (1 May). 50th Anniv of Korean Military Academy. P 13½×13.
2195   **1317**   150w. multicoloured   75   25

1318 Gobau (Kim Song Hwan)

1319 Battle between Kkach'i and Caesarius (Lee Hyun Se) (from film *Armageddon*)

1996 (4 May). Cartoons (2nd series). Photo. P 13½×13.
2196   **1318**   150w. multicoloured   75   25
2197   **1319**   150w. multicoloured   75   25
MS2198 Two sheets, each 90×60 mm. (a) No. 2196;
(b) No. 2197 ....   3·00   2·75

1320 Anniversary Emblem

1321 Globe and Congress Emblem

(Des Chun Hee Han. Litho)

1996 (10 May). 50th Anniv of Korean Girl Scouts. P 13½×13.
2199   **1320**   150w. multicoloured   75   25

(Des Kim Hyun. Litho)

1996 (8 June). 35th World Congress of International Advertising Association, Seoul. P13×13½.
2200   **1321**   150w. multicoloured   75   25

1322 Syringes and Drugs   **1323** Skater

(Des Jeon Chong Kwan. Photo)

1996 (26 June). International Anti-drug Day. P 13½×13.
2201   **1322**   150w. multicoloured   75   25

(Des Kang Bu Shin. Photo)

1996 (1 July). World University Students' Games, Muju and Chonju. T **1323** and similar multicoloured design. P 13½×13 (2202). 13×13½ (2203).
2202   150w. Type **1323**   75   25
2203   150w. Games emblem (vert)   75   25

1324 Torch Bearer

(Des Kim Hyun (2204), Lee Keun Moon (2205). Photo)

1996 (20 July). Olympic Games, Atlanta. T **1324** and similar vert design. Multicoloured. P 13×13½.
2204   150w. Type **1324**   75   25
2205   150w. Games emblem............................   75   25

1325 Match Scene   **1326** South Korean Team scoring Goal

(Des Won In Jae. Photo)

1996 (1 Aug). World Cup Football Championship (2002), South Korea and Japan (1st issue). Two sheets, each 134×78 mm. Multicoloured. P 13½×13.
MS2206 Two sheets, (a) 400w.×4. Type **1325**;
(b) 400w.×4, Type **1326** ....   21·00   18·00
See also Nos. 2238/**MS**2240, 2284/**MS**2288, 2368/**MS**2372, 2441/**MS**2451, 2501/**MS**2506, **MS**2598 and 2643/66.

(Des Kim Sang Rak. Photo)

1996 (19 Aug). Fungi (4th series). Vert designs as T **1246**. Multicoloured. P 13×13½ .
2207   150w. *Amanita inaurata*   75   25
2208   150w. *Paxillus atrotomentosus*   75   25
2209   160w. *Rhodophyllus crassipes*   75   25
2210   150w. *Sarcodon imbricatum*   75   25
2207/2210   *Set of 4* ....   2·75   90
MS2211 Four sheets, each 90×60mm. (a) No.
2207×2; (b) No. 2208×2; (c) No. 2209×2; (d)
No. 2210×2 ....   6·75   6·75

1327 Requiem for a Deceased Sister

1328 Ode to Knight Kip'a

(Des Chung Yung Nam. Photo)

1996 (16 Sept). Literature (2nd series). P 13½×13.
2212 **1327** 150w. multicoloured 75 25
2213 **1328** 150w. multicoloured 75 25
MS2214 Two sheets, each 90×61 mm. (a) No.
2212×2; (b) No. 2213×2·00 .... 3·25 3·00

1329 Alphabet

(Des Ahn Sang Soo. Recess and litho)

1996 (9 Oct). 550th Anniv of Han-Gûl (Korean alphabet created by King Sejong). P 13×13½.
2215 **1329** 150w. black and bluish grey 75 25
MS2216 90×60 mm. No. 2215×2 .... 1·70 1·50

1330 Castle

1331 Front Gate, University Flag and Emblem

(Des Won In Jae. Recess and photo)

1996 (10 Oct). Bicentenary of Suwon Castle. P 13½×13.
2217 **1330** 400w. multicoloured .... 2·10 80

(Des Kim Kyo Man. Litho)

1996 (15 Oct). 50th Anniv of Seoul National University. P 13½×13.
2218 **1331** 150w. multicoloured 75 25

1332 Five-direction Pouch

1333 Chinese Phoenix Pouch (Queen's Court pouch)

1334 Princess Pokon's Wedding Pouch

1335 Queen Yunbi's Pearl Pouch

(Des Na Je O. Photo)

1996 (1 Nov). Korean Beauty (6th series). Pouches. P 13×13½.
2219 **1332** 150w. multicoloured 75 25
a. Horiz strip of 4. Nos. 2219/22 .... 3·25
2220 **1333** 150w. multicoloured 75 25
2221 **1334** 150w. multicoloured 75 25
2222 **1335** 150w. multicoloured 75 25
2219/2222 Set of 4 .... 2·75 90
Nos. 2219/22 were issued together in horizontal se-tenant strips of four stamps within the sheet.

1336 "Poppy and Lizard" (detail of folding screen, Shin Saimdang)

(Des Lee Hea Ok. Photo)

1996 (16 Nov). Philatelic Week. P 13×13½.
2223 **1336** 150w. multicoloured 75 25
MS2224 90×60 mm. No. 2223×2 .... 1·70 1·50

1337 Children riding Ox

1338 Boy Piper and resting Ox

(Des Lee Hea Ok (2225), Kim Son Ik (2226). Photo)

1996 (2 Dec). Lunar New Year ("Year of the Ox"). P 13½×13.
2225 **1337** 150w. multicoloured 75 25
2226 **1338** 150w. multicoloured 75 25
MS2227 Two sheets, each 90×60 mm. (a) No.
2225×2; (b) No. 2226×2 .... 3·25 3·00

1339 Figure Skating

1340 Coins forming "100"

(Des Kim Hyun (2228), Kim Ok Nam (2229). Photo)

1997 (24 Jan). World University Students Games, Muju and Chonju (2nd issue). T **1339** and similar vert design. Multicoloured. P 13×13½.
2228 150w. Type **1339** 65 25
2229 150w. Skiing 65 25
MS2230 Two sheets, each 60×90 mm. (a) No.
2228×2; (b) No. 2229×2 .... 2·75 2·40

(Des Lee Gi Seog. Litho)

1997 (19 Feb). Centenary of Foundation of Hansong Bank (first commercial bank in Korea). P 13½×13.
2231 **1340** 150w. multicoloured 65 25

1341 "Auspicious Turtles"

1342 Globe, Pen and Open Book (painting) (Jeon Chong Kwan)

(Des Lee Hea Ok. Photo)

1997 (10 Apr). Interparliamentary Union Conference, Seoul. P 13×13½.
2232 **1341** 150w. multicoloured 70 25

1997 (23 Apr). World Book and Copyright Day. Litho. P 13×13½.
2233 **1342** 150w. multicoloured .... 1·20 25

1343 A Long, Long Journey in Search of Mummy (Kim Chong Nae)

1344 Run, Run, Hannie

(Lee Chin Ju)

1997 (3 May). Cartoons (3rd series). Photo. P 13½×13.
2234 **1343** 150w. multicoloured 70 25
2235 **1344** 150w. multicoloured 70 25
MS2236 Two sheets, each 90×60 mm. (a) No. 2234;
(b) No. 2235 .... 2·30 2·00

1345 Torch Bearer

(Des Park Eun Kyung. Litho)

1997 (10 May). Second East Asian Games, Pusan. P 13×13½.
2237 **1345** 150w. multicoloured 70 25

1346 Jules Rimet (founder)

1347 "Chukkuk" (Lee Chul Joo)

(Des Won In Jae. Photo)

1997 (31 May). World Cup Football Championship (2002), South Korea and Japan (2nd issue). P 13×13½.
2238 **1346** 150w. multicoloured 70 25
2239 **1347** 150w. multicoloured 70 25
MS2240 Two sheets, each 134×78 mm. (a) No. 2238×2; (b) No. 2239×3 .... 5·25 4·75

(Des Bang Lai Ki. Photo)

1997 (5 June). Protection of Wildlife and Plants (4th series). Horiz designs as T **1270**. Multicoloured. P 13½×13.
2241 150w. Chinese sticklebacks (*Pungitius sinensis*) 70 25
2242 150w. Spotear brook perch (*Coreoperca kawamebari*) 70 25
MS2243 Two sheets, each 125×86 mm. (a) No. 2241×2; (b) 2242×2 .... 2·75 2·40

(Des Kim Im Yong. Photo)

1997 (19 June). Wild Flowers (8th series). Vert designs as T **1166**. Multicoloured. P 13×13½.
2244 150w. *Belamcanda chinensis* 70 25
2245 150w. *Hylomecon vernale* 70 25
2246 150w. *Campanula takesimana* 70 25
2247 150w. *Magnolia sieboldii* 70 25
2244/2247 Set of 4 .... 2·50 90

1348 Emblem and "97" forming Face

1349 Seoul South Gate and Emblem

(Ko Ji Young and Lee Yun. Photo)

1997 (1 July). Second Art Biennale, Kwangju. P 13×13½.
2248 **1348** 150w. multicoloured 70 25

(Des Kim Sang Rak. Photo)

1997 (21 July). Fungi (5th series). Vert designs as T **1246**. Multicoloured. P 13×13½.
2249 150w. *Inocybe fastigiata* 70 25
2250 150w. *Panaeolus papilionaceus* 70 25
2251 150w. *Ramaria flava*.............................. 70 25
2252 150w. Fly agaric (*Amanita muscaria*) ... 70 25
2249/2252 Set of 4 .... 2·50 90
MS2253 Four sheets, each 90×60 mm. (a) No. 2249×2; (b) No. 2250×2; (c) No. 2251×2; (d) No. 2252×2 .... 5·50 5·00

1997 (5 Sept). 85th World Dental Congress, Seoul. P 13½×13.
2254 **1349** 170w. multicoloured 70 25

1350 Harbour and Score

1351 Main Building, Pyongyang

1997 (1 Oct). Centenary of Mokpo Port. P 13½×13.
2255 **1350** 170w. multicoloured............................... 70 25

(Des Kim Kyo Man. Recess and photo)

1997 (10 Oct). Centenary of Founding of Soongsil Academy in Pyongyang (now situated in Seoul). P 13½×13.
2256 **1351** 170w. multicoloured............................... 70 25

1352 Concentric Squares

1353 Green Silk

1354 Pattern of Squares

1355 Pattern of Squares and Triangles

(Des No. Jae O. Photo)

1997 (3 Nov). Korean Beauty (7th series). Patchwork Pojagi (wrapping cloths). P 13×13½.
2257 **1352** 170w. multicoloured............................... 70 25
     a. Strip of 4. Nos. 2257/60.............. 3·00
2258 **1353** 170w. multicoloured............................... 70 25
2259 **1354** 170w. multicoloured............................... 70 25
2260 **1355** 170w. multicoloured............................... 70 25
2257/2260 Set of 4... 2·50 90
    Nos. 2257/60 were issued together in se-tenant strips of four stamps within the sheet.

1356 "Hollyhock and Frog" (detail of folding screen, Shin Saimdang)

(Des Lee Hea Ok. Photo)

1997 (18 Nov). Philatelic Week. P 13×13½.
2261 **1356** 170w. multicoloured............................... 70 25
MS2262 90×60 mm. Nos. 2261×2..................... 1·40 1·10

1357 Tiger's Head (folk painting)

1358 "Magpie and Tiger"

(Des Kwon Myung Kwang (2263), Lee Hea Ok (2264). Photo)

1997 (1 Dec). Lunar New Year ("Year of the Tiger"). P 13×13½.
2263 **1357** 170w. multicoloured............................... 70 25
2264 **1358** 170w. multicoloured............................... 70 25
MS2265 Two sheets, each 90×60 mm. (a) No.
    2263×2; (b) No. 2264×2...................... 2·75 2·40

1359 Buddha, Sokkuram Shrine

1360 Pulguk Temple

1997 (9 Dec). World Heritage Sites (1st series). Recess and litho. P 13×13½.
2266 **1359** 170w. multicoloured............................... 1·30 90
    a. Pair. Nos. 2266/7.......................... 7·00 5·00
2267 **1360** 380w. multicoloured............................... 5·25 3·50
MS2268 144×88 mm. Nos. 2266/7................. 6·50 6·00
    Nos. 2266/**MS**2268 were issued together in sheetlets containing Nos. 2266/7 in a block of 12 stamps (Nos. 2266×9 and 2267×3) separated by a gutter (which has one of its outer edges perforated).
    See also Nos. 2317/**MS**2319, 2365/**MS**2367, 2457/**MS**2459 and 2533/**MS**2535.

1361 Poem to Sui General Yu Zhong Wen (Ulchi Mundok)

1362 Record of
Travel to Five Indian
Kingdoms (Hye Ch'o)

(Des Chun Hee Han. Photo)

1997 (12 Dec). Literature (3rd series). P 13½.×13 (2269) or 13×13½.
(2270).
2269 **1361** 170w. multicoloured.................................. 65 25
2270 **1362** 170w. multicoloured.................................. 65 25
MS2271 Two sheets, each 90×60 mm. (a) No.
2269×2; (b) No. 2270×2...................................... 2·75 2·40

1363 Neon Lights on Globe
and Nuclear Power Plant

(Des Lee Gi Seog. Photo)

1998 (26 Jan). Centenary of Introduction of Electricity to Korea.
P 13½×13.
2272 **1363** 170w. multicoloured.................................. 65 15

1364 Pres. Kim Dae Jung
and Flag

(Des Lee Hea Ok. Litho)

1998 (25 Feb). Inauguration of 15th President of South Korea.
P 13½×13.
2273 **1364** 170w. multicoloured.................................. 1·10 40
MS2274 120×110 mm. No. 2273 .... 6·00 5·75

(Des Chun Hee Han. Litho)

1998 (21 Mar). Protection of Wildlife and Plants (5th series). Vert
designs as T **1270**. Multicoloured. P 13×13½.
2275 340l. Korean leopard (*Panthera
pardus orientalis*).......................... 2·00 30
a. Block or horiz strip of 4. Nos.
2275/8 .... 8·25
2276 340l. Asiatic black bears (*Selenarctos
thibetanus*) .... 2·00 30
2277 340l. European otters (*Lutra lutra*) ..... 2·00 30
2278 340l. Siberian musk deers (*Moschus
moschiferus*)............................. 2·00 30

2275/2278 *Set of 4*.. 7·25 1·10
MS2279 129×123 mm. Nos. 2275/8 .... 8·25 7·00
Nos. 2275/**MS**2279 were issued together in sheetlets containing
Nos. 2275/8 in a block of eight stamps (giving blocks and horizontal
strips of the four designs *se-tenant* separated by a gutter from the
miniature sheet (which has one of its outer edges perforated).

1365 Aktong-i (Lee Hi Jae)

1366 Challenger (Park Ki Jong)

(Des Lee Hea Ok. Photo (170w.), recess and litho (340w.))

1998 (4 May). Cartoons (4th series). Photo. P 13½×13.
2280 **1365** 170w. multicoloured................................ 80 25
2281 **1366** 340w. multicoloured................................ 1·70 1·20
MS2282 Two sheets, each 90×60 mm. (a) No. 2280;
(b) No. 2281.. 3·25 2·75

1367 Assembly Building and   **1368** Player with Ball
Firework Display

(Des Kim So Jeong. Photo)

1998 (30 May). 50th Anniv of National Assembly. P 13.
2283 **1367** 170w. multicoloured................................ 65 15

(Des Kim Hyun. Photo)

1998 (30 May). World Cup Football Championship (2002), Korea and
Japan (3rd series). T **1368** and similar vert designs. Multicoloured.
P 13×13½.
2284 170w. Type **1368**.. 90 25
a. Strip of 4. Nos. 2284/7........ 3·75
2285 170w. Two players chasing ball............ 90 25
2286 170w. Players heading ball................... 90 25
2287 170w. Player kicking ball over head 90 25
2284/2287 *Set of 4* .... 3·25 90
MS2288 134×78 mm. Nos. 2284/7................................ 4·00 3·25
Nos. 2284/7 were issued together in *se-tenant* strips of four stamps
within the sheet.

1369 Writing on Stone
Tablets

1370 Pony Express

1371 Man using Telephone and Post Box

1372 Old and Modern Forms of Communication

(Des Park Eun Kyung. Litho)

1998 (1 June). Information Technology. P 13½×13.

2289	**1369**	170w. multicoloured	80	25
	a. Strip of 4. Nos. 2289/92	4·25	
2290	**1370**	170w. multicoloured	80	25
2291	**1371**	170w. multicoloured	80	25
2292	**1372**	170w. multicoloured	1·60	50
2289/2292 *Set of 4*	3·50	1·10

Nos. 2289/92 were issued together in *se-tenant* strips of four stamps within the sheet.

(Des Kim Sang Rak. Photo)

1998 (4 July). Fungi (6th series). Vert. designs as T **1246**. Multicoloured. P 13×13½.

2293	170w. *Pseudocolus schellenbergiae*	90	40
	a. Block or horiz strip of 4. Nos. 2293/6	4·00	
2294	170w. *Cyptotrama asprata*	90	40
2295	170w. *Laccaria vinaceoavellanea*	90	40
2296	170w. *Phallus rugulosus*	90	40
2293/2296 *Set of 4*	3·25	1·40
MS2297 114×144 mm. Nos. 2293/6	5·00	4·50

Nos. 2293/**MS**2297 were issued together in sheetlets containing Nos. 2293/6 in a block of 12 stamps (giving blocks and horizontal strips of the four designs *se-tenant*) separate by a gutter from the miniature sheet (which has one of its outer edges perforated).

1373 Flag and Runners

1374 "Grapes" (Lady Shin Saimdang)

(Des Lee Hea Ok. Photo)

1998 (14 Aug). 50th Anniv of Proclamation of Republic. P 13½×13.

2298	**1373**	170w. multicoloured	65	25

(Des Lee Hea Ok. Photo)

1998 (19 Aug). Philatelic Week. P 13×13½.

2299	**1374**	170w. multicoloured	65	25
MS2300 90×60 mm. No. 2299×2	1·70	1·40

1375 Thinking of Mother

1376 Would You Leave Me Now?

(Des Lee Hea Ok. Recess and litho)

1998 (14 Sept). Literature (4th series). Sogyo Songs. P 13½×13 (2301) or 13×13½ (2302).

2301	**1375**	170w. multicoloured	65	25
2302	**1376**	170w. multicoloured	65	25
MS2303 Two sheets, each 90×60 mm. (a) No. 2301; (b) No. 2302	2·20	1·80

1377 Film Strips and Masks

(Des Shin Myung Sub. Photo)

1998 (24 Sept). Third Pusan International Film Festival. P 13×13½.

2304	**1377**	170w. multicoloured	65	25

1378 Myungnyundang Hall

(Des Park Eun Kyung. Recess and litho)

1998 (25 Sept). 600th Anniv of Sungkyunkwan University. P 13.

2305	**1378**	170w. multicoloured	65	25

1379 National Constabulary, Badge and Lake Ch'onji

1380 Hot-air Balloon

(Des Lee Gi Seog. Litho)

1998 (1 Oct). 50th Anniv of Korean Armed Forces. P 13×13½.

2306 **1379** 170w. multicoloured 65   25

(Des Kim Ik Sang. Litho)

1998 (9 Oct). World Stamp Day. P 13×13½.

2307 **1380** 170w. multicoloured 65   25

1381 Peach   **1382** Double Crane

1383 Carp   **1384** Peach

1385 Toad   **1386** Dragon and Cloud

1387 Monkey   **1388** House

(Des Kim Im Yong. Photo)

1998 (20 Nov). Korean Beauty (8th series). Porcelain Water Droppers. P 13×13½.

2308	**1381**	170w. multicoloured	1·10	40
		a. Block of 8. Nos. 2308/15	9·00	
2309	**1382**	170w. multicoloured	1·10	40
2310	**1383**	170w. multicoloured	1·10	40
2311	**1384**	170w. multicoloured	1·10	40
2312	**1385**	170w. multicoloured	1·10	40
2313	**1386**	170w. multicoloured	1·10	40
2314	**1387**	170w. multicoloured	1·10	40
2315	**1388**	170w. multicoloured	1·10	40
2308/2315		*Set of 8*	8·00	3·00

Nos. 2308/15 were issued together in *se-tenant* blocks of eight stamps within the sheet.

1389 Rabbits

(Des Lee Hea Ok. Photo)

1998 (1 Dec). Lunar New Year ("Year of the Rabbit"). P 13×13½.

2316 **1389** 170w. multicoloured 65   25

1390 Tripitaka Koreana (scriptures engraved on wooden blocks)

1391 Changgyong P'anjon (woodblock repository)

(Des Won In Jae. Recess and litho)

1998 (9 Dec). World Heritage Sites (2nd series). Haein Temple. P 13×13½ (380w.) or compound perf 13 and 13½ (170w.).

2317	**1390**	170w. multicoloured	1·10	55
		a. Pair. Nos. 2317/18	4·50	2·30
2318	**1391**	380w. multicoloured	3·25	1·60
MS2319		144×98 mm. Nos. 2317 (p 13½×13) and		
		2318	21·00	11·00

Nos. 2317/**MS**2319 were issued together in sheetlets containing Nos. 2317/18 in a block of ten stamps (Nos. 2317×6 and 2318×4) separated by a gutter from the miniature sheet (which has one of its outer edges perforated). The horizontal line of perforation between the two rows of 170w. stamps in perforated 13½, giving stamps from the top row perforated 13×13×13½×13 and stamps from the bottom row perforated 13½×13×13×13. The 170w. stamp in the miniature sheet in perforated 13½×13 in the conventional way.

1392 Maize, Compass and Ship's Wheel

(Des Lee Gi Seog. Litho)

1999 (1 May). Centenary of Kunsan Port. P 13½×13.
2320 **1392** 170w. multicoloured 65 30

1393 Masan and Score of *I Want to Go* by Lee Eun Sang

(Des Lee Keun Moon. Litho)

1999 (1 May). Centenary of Masan Port. P 13½.
2321 **1393** 170w. multicoloured 65 30

1394 Rai-Fi (Kim San Ho)

1395 Tokgo T'ak (Lee Sang Mu)

1396 Im Kkuk Jung (Lee Du Ho)

(Des Park Eun Kyung. Photo)

1999 (3 May). Cartoons (5th series). P 13½×13 (vert) or 13½×13 (horiz).
2322 **1394** 170w. multicoloured 65 30
2323 **1395** 170w. multicoloured 65 30
2324 **1396** 170w. multicoloured 65 30
2322/2324 *Set of 3* .... 1·70 80
MS2325 Three sheets, each 88×58 mm.
Multicoloured. (a) 340w. Type **1394**; (b) 340w.
Type **1395**; (c) 340w. Type **1396** .... 6·00 5·75

(Des Lee Gi Seog. Litho)

1999 (5 June). Protection of Wildlife and Plants (6th series). Vert. designs as T **1270**. Multicoloured. P 13×13½.
2326 170w. Peregrine falcon (*Falco peregrinus*) .... 1·30 30
 a. Block or horiz strip of 4. Nos. 2326/9 .... 8·25
2327 170w. Grey frog hawk (*Accipiter soloensis*) .... 1·30 30
2328 340w. Steller's sea eagle (*Haliaeetus pelagicus*) .... 2·75 65
2329 340w. Eagle owl (*Bubo bubo*) .... 2·75 65
2326/2329 *Set of 4* .... 7·25 1·70
MS2330 136×133 mm. Nos. 2326/9 .... 8·25 7·75
 Nos. 2326/**MS**2330 were issued together in sheetlets containing Nos. 2326/9 in a block of eight stamps (giving blocks and horizontal strips of the four designs *se-tenant*) separated by a gutter from the miniature sheet (which has one of its outer edges perforated).

1397 Five clasped Hands

1398 Goethe (after Joseph Stieler)

(Des In Mi Aeh. Photo)

1999 (12 June). 109th International Olympic Committee Congress, Seoul. P 13×13½.
2331 **1397** 170w. multicoloured 65 30

(Des Lee Hea Ok. Recess and litho)

1999 (12 Aug). 250th Birth Anniv of Johann Wolfgang von Goethe (poet and playwright). P 13×13½.
2332 **1398** 170w. multicoloured 80 30
MS2333 110×94 mm. **1398** 480w. multicoloured...... 2·75 2·40

1399 "Kumgang Mountain" (Kyomjae Chong Son)

(Des Lee Hea Ok. Litho)

1999 (13 Aug). Philatelic Week. P 13×13½.
2334 **1399** 170w. multicoloured 65 30
MS2335 120×90 mm. **1399** 340w. multicoloured...... 1·70 1·60

1400 Mogul Tank Locomotive No. 101 (first locomotive in Korea)

(Des Lee Gi Seog. Recess and litho)

1999 (18 Sept). Centenary of Railway in Korea. P 13×13½.
2336 **1400** 170w. multicoloured .... 1·00 30

1401 Flint Tools and Paleolithic Ruins, Chungok-ri, Yonch'on

(Des Won In Jae and Lee Hea Ok. Litho)

1999 (2 Oct). New Millennium (1st series). T **1401** and similar horiz designs. Multicoloured. P 13×13½.
2337	Type **1401**	90	30
	a. Sheetlet. Nos. 2337/42	5·75	
2338	170w. Comb-patterned pottery, burnt-out and reconstructed Neolithic dwellings, Amsa-dong, Seoul	90	30
2339	170w. Shell bracelets, bone spear heads and Neolithic shell mounds, Tongsam-dong, Pusan	90	30
2340	170w. Dolmen, Pukon-ri, Kanghwa-do Island	90	30
2341	170w. Bronze and stone daggers and Bronze-age earthenware, Son-gguk-ri, Puyo	90	30
2342	170w. Rock carvings, Pan'gudae	90	30
2337/2342 Set of 6		4·75	1·60

Nos. 2337/42 were issued together in *se-tenant* sheetlets of six stamps.
See also Nos. 2357/62, 2374/8, 2388/92, 2397/401, 2406/10, 2420/5, 2431/6, 2460/5, 2487/91 and 2511/15.

1402 Bird carrying Letter

(Des Chang Hyun-ju. Photo)

1999 (9 Oct). 125th Anniv of Universal Postal Union. P 13×13½.
2343 **1402** 170w. multicoloured 65 30

1403 Little Odes on the Kwandong Area (Chong Ch'ol)

1404 Alas! How foolish I am! (Hwang Jin-i)

1405 Story of Hong Kil-dong (Ho Kyun)

1406 Story of Ch'unhyang

(Des Lee Wal-jong and Chung Young-nam. Litho)

1999 (20 Oct). Literature (5th series). P 13½×13 (2344, 2347) or 13×13½. (2345/6).
2344	**1403** 170w. multicoloured	65	30
2345	**1404** 170w. multicoloured	65	30
2346	**1405** 170w. multicoloured	65	30
2347	**1406** 170w. multicoloured	65	30
2344/2347 Set of 4		2·25	1·10
MS2348 Four sheets. (a) 90×60 mm. No. 2344; (b) 90×60 mm. No. 2345; (c) 60×90 mm. No. 2346; (d) 60×90 mm. No. 2347		5·50	5·00

1407 Chrysanthemum, Bird and Duck

1408 Birds in Tree and Snake on Korean Character

1409 Pot Plant with Butterfly on Korean Character

1410 Fish on Korean Character

1411 Plant behind Tub of Fishes

1412 Crab on Korean Character

1413 Bird on Korean Character

1414 Chest and Plant behind Deer

1416 Crown and Bowl

1417 Man on Horseback and Cave Paintings

1418 Gold Ornament and Jade Jewellery

1419 Stone Crafts

1420 Carved Stone Face

1999 (13 Nov). Korean Beauty (9th series). Litho. P 13×13½.

2349	**1407**	340w. multicoloured	1·50	65
		a. Sheetlet of 8. Nos. 2349/56	12·50	
2350	**1408**	340w. multicoloured	1·50	65
2351	**1409**	340w. multicoloured	1·50	65
2352	**1410**	340w. multicoloured	1·50	65
2353	**1411**	340w. multicoloured	1·50	65
2354	**1412**	340w. multicoloured	1·50	65
2355	**1413**	340w. multicoloured	1·50	65
2356	**1414**	340w. multicoloured	1·50	65
2349/2356		Set of 8	11·00	4·75

Nos. 2349/56 were issued together in *se-tenant* sheetlets of 8 stamps.

1999 (20 Nov). New Millennium (2nd series). Litho. P 13×13½.

2357	**1415**	170w. multicoloured	80	30
		a. Sheetlet. Nos. 2357/62	5·00	
2358	**1416**	170w. multicoloured	80	30
2359	**1417**	170w. multicoloured	80	30
2360	**1418**	170w. multicoloured	80	30
2361	**1419**	170w. multicoloured	80	30
2362	**1420**	170w. multicoloured	80	30
2357/2362		Set of 6	4·25	1·60

Nos. 2357/62 were issued together in *se-tenant* sheetlets of six stamps.

1415 Ornament and Bird-shaped Vase

1421 Dragon

1999 (1 Dec). Lunar New Year. "Year of the Dragon". Photo. P 13×13½.

2363	**1421**	170w. multicoloured..................................	60	30
MS2364		90×61 mm. No. 2363×2..........................	1·50	1·20

1422 Building

1423 Man and Musicians

1999 (9 Dec). World Heritage Sites (3rd series). Recess and litho. P 13×13½.

2365	**1422**	170w. multicoloured..............................	80	35
		a. Pair. Nos. 2365/6	3·00	1·10
2366	**1423**	340w. multicoloured..............................	2·00	70
MS2367		144×96 mm. Nos. 2365/6.........................	11·50	4·50

Nos. 2365/**MS**2367 were issued together in sheetlets containing Nos. 2365/6 in a block of eight stamps (Nos. 2365×4 and 2366×4) separated by a gutter from the miniature sheet (which has one of its outer edges perforated).

1424 Player   **1425** Emblem

1999 (31 Dec). World Cup Football Championship (2002), Japan and Korea (4th series). T **1424** and similar vert designs. Multicoloured. Photo. P 13×13½.

2368		170w. Type **1424**.................................	70	35
		a. Horiz strip of 4. Nos. 2368/71	3·00	
2369		170w. Players tackling	70	35
2370		170w. Player receiving ball	70	35
2371		170w. Goalkeeper catching ball...........	70	35
2368/2371		Set of 4...	2·50	1·20
MS2372		134×78 mm. Nos. 2368/71	3·50	3·25

Nos. 2368/71 were issued together in horizontal se-tenant strips of four stamps within the sheet, each strip forming a composite design.

2000 (3 Jan). Centenary of South Korea's Membership of Universal Postal Union. Photo. P 13½×13.

2373	**1425**	170w. multicoloured.............................	60	30

1426 Sunset, Altar and Tablet

2000 (3 Jan). New Millennium (3rd series). T **1426** and similar square designs. Multicoloured. Litho. P 13½.

2374		170w. Type **1426**.............................	80	35
		a. Sheetlet of 5. Nos. 2374/8		
		plus label	4·25	
2375		170w. Cave painting of wrestlers..........	80	35
2376		170w. Inscribed bronze disc and		
		warrior..	80	35
2377		170w. Silhouettes of archers and		
		inscribed standing stone...........	80	35
2378		170w. Junk and warrior	80	35
2374/2378		Set of 5...	3·50	1·60

Nos. 2374/8 were issued together in se-tenant sheetlets of five stamps and one label with an enlarged illustrated margin.

1427 Pashi Steam Locomotive

1428 Teho Steam Locomotive

1429 Mika Steam Locomotive

1430 Hyouki Steam Locomotive

(Des Lee Gi Seog. Photo)

2000 (1 Feb). Railways (1st series). P 13½×13.

2379	**1427**	170w. black, violet and dull mauve	80	30
		a. Block of 4. Nos. 2379/82..............	3·50	
2380	**1428**	170w. black, violet and mauve	80	30
2381	**1429**	170w. black, violet and bluish grey......	80	30
2382	**1430**	170w. black, violet and bistre	80	30
2379/2382		Set of 4..	3·00	1·10

Nos. 2379/82 were issued together in se-tenant blocks of four stamps within the sheet.

See also Nos. 2477/80, 2585/8, 2682/5 and 2741/4.

(Des Lee Gi Seog. Photo)

2000 (25 Feb). Protection of Wildlife and Plants (7th series). Vert. designs as T **1270**. Multicoloured. P 13×13½.

2383	170w. *Lilium cernum*	1·00	30
	a. Block or horiz strip of 4. Nos. 2383/6	4·25	
2384	170w. *Sedirea japonica*	1·00	30
2385	170w. *Hibiscus hamabo*	1·00	30
2386	170w. *Cypripedium japonicum*	1·00	30
2383/2386 *Set of 4*		3·50	1·10
MS2387 136×133 mm. Nos. 2383/6		4·25	4·00

Nos. 2383/**MS**2387 were issued together in sheetlets containing Nos. 2383/6 in a block of eight stamps (giving two blocks or horizontal strips of four designs se-tenant) separated by a gutter from the miniature sheet.

Nos. 2383/**MS**2387 are impregnated with the scent of flowers.

1434 Hand holding Rose

(Des Mo Ji Won. Photo)

2000 (20 Apr). "Share Love" (good neighbour campaign). P 13½ (outer square perforated 13½).

2395	**1434**	170w. multicoloured	1·20	40

No. 2395 was perforated in a heart-shape design contained within an outer perforated square.

No. 2395 is impregnated with the scent of roses.

1431 State Civil Service Examination and Text   **1432** Children playing and House (Kim Chin Sook)

(Des Kim So Jeong (2388, 2390), Lee Hea Ok (2389, 2392), and Park Eun Kyung (2391). Photo)

2000 (2 Mar). New Millennium (4th series). T **1431** and similar square designs. Multicoloured. P 13½.

2388	170w. Type **1431**	80	40
	a. Sheetlet. Nos. 2388/92, plus label	4·25	
2389	170w. Man carving wood blocks	80	40
2390	170w. Pieces of metal type	80	40
2391	170w. An-Hyang (scholar) and Korean script	80	40
2392	170w. Mun Ik-jom (scholar), spinning wheel and cotton plant	80	40
2388/2392 *Set of 5*		3·50	1·80

Nos. 2388/92 were issued together in *se-tenant* sheetlets of five stamps and one label.

1435 "2000"

1436 King Sejong and Korean Script

(Des Mo Ji Won. Litho)

2000 (22 Apr). CYBER KOREA 21. P 13½×13.

2396	**1435**	170w. multicoloured	60	40

(Des Kwon Myung Kwang. Photo)

2000 (1 May). New Millennium (5th series). T **1436** and similar square designs. Multicoloured. P 13½.

2397	170w. Type **1436**	80	50
	a. Sheetlet. Nos. 2397/401 plus label	4·25	
2398	170w. Lady Shin Saimdang (caligrapher poet and painter) and detail of "Ch'ochung-do" (painting)	80	50
2399	170w. Yi Hwang and Yi I (founders of Confucian Academy)	80	50
2400	170w. Admiral Yi Sun-shin and model of "turtle" ship	80	50
2401	170w. Sandae-nori (mask-dance drama)	80	50
2397/2401 *Set of 5*		3·50	2·20

Nos. 2397/401 were issued together in *se-tenant* sheetlets of five stamps and one label.

(Des Kim Sung Am. Photo)

2000 (22 Mar). World Water Day. Winning Design in Children's Painting Competition. P 13½. x 13.

2393	**1432**	170w. multicoloured	60	40

1433 Globe and Satellite

(Des Kim Sung Am. Photo)

2000 (23 Mar). 50th Anniv of World Meteorological Organization. P 13½×13½.

2394	**1433**	170w. multicoloured	60	40

1437 Goindol (Park Soo Dong)

1438 Youngsim-I
(Bae Gum Taek)

(Des Park Eun Kyung. Photo)

2000 (4 May). Cartoons (6th series). P 13½.

2402	**1437**	170w. multicoloured	60	50
2403	**1438**	170w. multicoloured	60	50

MS2404 Two sheets, each 90×60 mm. (a) No. 2402;
(b) No. 2403 .... 1·80   2·60

1439 Seedling on Map of
Korean Peninsula

1440 Anatomical Diagram
from Tongui Pogam
(medical treatise by Huh Joon)

(Des Lee Gi Seog. Photo)

2000 (12 Jun). Korean Summit, Pyongyang. P 13½×13.

2405	**1439**	170w. multicoloured	80	65

(Des Ahn Jung Un. Photo)

2000 (1 July). Millennium (6th series). T **1440** and similar square
designs. Multicoloured. P 13½.

2406	Type **1440**	80	40
	a. Sheetlet. Nos. 2406/10 plus label	4·25	
2407	170w. "Dancer with Musicians" (illustration by Kim Hong Do) ...	80	40
2408	170w. "Plum Blossoms and Bird" (painting, Chong Yak Yong) and house in Kangjin where he served his exile	80	40
2409	170w. Map of Korea by Kim Chong Ho and wheel chart	80	40
2410	170w. Chon Bong Joan (revolutionary) and Tonghak Peasant Uprising monument	80	40

2406/2410 Set of 5 .... 3·50   1·80

Nos. 2406/10 were issued together in *se-tenant* sheetlets of five
stamps and one label

1441 Numbers and
Mathematical
Symbols

(Des Park Eun Kyung. Photo)

2000 (13 July). International Mathematics Olympiad (high school
mathematics competition). P 13½.

2411	**1441**	170w. multicoloured	60	40

1442 Yolha Diary   **1443** Fisherman's
(Park Ji Won)   Calender

1444 The Nine-Cloud Dream   **1445** Tears of Blood

1446 From the Sea to a Child

(Des Lee Hye Ock. Photo)

2000 (1 Aug). Literature (6th series). P 13×13½ (2412/13) or 13½×13
(others).

2412	**1442**	170w. multicoloured	70	40
		a. Sheetlet. Nos. 2412/16	3·75	
2413	**1443**	170w. multicoloured	70	40
2414	**1444**	170w. multicoloured	70	40
2415	**1445**	170w. multicoloured	70	40
2416	**1446**	170w. multicoloured	70	40

2412/2416 Set of 5 .... 3·25   1·80

MS2417 Five sheets. (a) 60×90 mm. No. 2412;
(b) 60×90 mm. No. 2413; (c) 90×60 mm. No. 2414;
(d) 90×60 mm. No. 2415; (e) 90×60 mm. No. 2416   5·00   4·50

1447 Mountain

2000 (2 Aug). Philately Week. Litho. P 13½×13.
2418	**1447**	340w. multicoloured	1·30	70
MS2419 120×90 mm. No. 2418			1·70	1·50

1448 Porcelain

1449 "Bongjongsa" Temple (Paradise Pavillion)

1450 Hahoe Tal Masks

1451 Royal Palace

1452 Landscape Painting

1453 Water Clock

2000 (1 Sept). Millennium (7th series). Photo. P 13.
2420	**1448**	170w. multicoloured	80	40
		a. Sheetlet. Nos. 2420/25	5·00	
2421	**1449**	170w. multicoloured	80	40
2422	**1450**	170w. multicoloured	80	40
2423	**1451**	170w. multicoloured	80	40
2424	**1452**	170w. multicoloured	80	40
2425	**1453**	170w. multicoloured	80	40
2420/2425 Set of 6			4·25	2·20

Nos. 2420/5 were issued together in *se-tenant* sheetlets of six stamps

1454 Taekwondo

2000 (15 Sept). Olympics Games, Sydney. Photo. P 13×13½.
2426	**1454**	170w. multicoloured	75	50

1455 Former Kyunngi High School Building, Hwadong

(Des Kim So Jeong. Recess and litho)

2000 (2 Oct). Centenary of Public Secondary Schools. P 13.
2427	**1455**	170w. multicoloured	75	50

1456 "Returning to the Retirement House" (illustration from "Album of the Gathering of Old Statesmen")

1457 Emblem

(Des Park Eun Kyung. Photo)

2000 (20 Oct). Third Asia-Europe Meeting, Seoul. P 13½×13.
2428	**1456**	170w. multicoloured	75	50

(Des Chang Dong Ryun. Photo)

2000 (25 Oct). Icograde Millennium Congress, Seoul. P 13×13½.
2429	**1457**	170w. black and orange-yellow	75	50

1458 Mr. Gobau

(Des Lee Gi Seok. Litho)

2000 (1 Nov). 50th Anniv of Mr. Gobau (cartoon character). P 13½.
2430	**1458**	170w. multicoloured	75	50

1459 18th-Century Painting (Sin Yun Bok)

(Des Lee Gi Seok. Photo)

2000 (1 Nov). Millennium (8th series). T **1459** and similar horiz designs. Multicoloured. P 13.

2431	170w. Type **1459**	80	40
	a. Sheetlet of 6 Nos. 2431/6	5·00	
2432	170w. Calligraphy by Kim Jeong Hui...	80	40
2433	170w. Bongdon-Chiseong Hwaseong Fortress, Suwon	80	40
2434	170w. Myeongdong Cathedral	80	40
2435	170w. Wongaska theatre actors	80	40
2436	170w. The KITSat-satellite	80	40
2431/2436 Set of 6		4·25	2·20

Nos. 2431/6 were issued together in *se-tenant* sheetlets of six stamps.

1460 Decorated Comb

(Des Kim Im Yong. Photo)

2000 (16 Nov). Korean Beauty (10th series). T **1460** and similar horiz designs. Multicoloured. P 13½×13.

2437	170w. Type **1460**	75	40
	a. Strip of 4 Nos. 2437/40	3·25	
2438	170w. Woman's ceremonial headdress	75	40
2439	170w. Butterfly-shaped hairpin	75	40
2440	170w. Hairpin with dragon decoration and jade hairpin with Chinese phoenix decoration	75	40
2437/2440 Set of 4		2·75	1·40

Nos. 2437/40 were issued in *se-tenant* strips of four within the sheet.

1461 Seoul World Cup Stadium

1462 Busan Sports Complex Main Stadium

1463 Daegu Sports Complex Stadium

1464 Incheon Munhak Stadium

1465 Gwangu World Cup Stadium

1466 Daejeon World Cup Stadium

1467 Ulsan Munsu Football Stadium

1468 Suwon World Cup Stadium

1469 Jeonju World Cup Stadium

1470 Jeju World Cup Stadium

(Des Kim Sung Am. Photo)

2000 (24 Nov). World Cup Football Championship (2002), South Korea and Japan (5th series). P 13½×13.

2441	**1461**	170w. multicoloured	1·20	40
		a. Block of 10. Nos. 2341/50	12·50	
2442	**1462**	170w. multicoloured	1·20	40
2443	**1463**	170w. multicoloured	1·20	40
2444	**1464**	170w. multicoloured	1·20	40
2445	**1465**	170w. multicoloured	1·20	40
2446	**1466**	170w. multicoloured	1·20	40
2447	**1467**	170w. multicoloured	1·20	40
2448	**1468**	170w. multicoloured	1·20	40
2449	**1469**	170w. multicoloured	1·20	40
2450	**1470**	170w. multicoloured	1·20	40
2441/2450 Set of 10			11·00	3·50

MS2451 Five sheets each 60×90 mm. (a) 170w. No. 2441/2; (b) 170w. Nos. 2443/4; (c) 170w. Nos. 2445/6; (d) 170w. Nos. 2447/8; (e) 170w. Nos. 2449/50 .... 15·00   14·50

Nos. 2441/50 were issued together in *se-tenant* blocks of ten stamps within the sheet.

1471 Snake

1472 President Kim Dae Jung and Children

(Des Lee Hye Ock. Photo)

2000 (1–22 Dec). Lunar New Year. "Year of the Snake".

(a) Ordinary gum. P 13½.

2452	**1471**	170w. multicoloured	80	40
MS2453	107×69 mm. No. 2452×2		1·50	1·30

(b) Self-adhesive gum. Die-cut Perf 10½×10.

2454	**1471**	170w. multicoloured	1·00	40

(Des Lee Gi Seog. Photo)

2000 (9 Dec). Award of Nobel Peace Prize to President Kim Dae Jung. P 13×13½.

2455	**1472**	170w. multicoloured	80	40
MS2456	118×70 mm. No. 2455×2		2·50	2·20

No. 2455 was issued in *se-tenant* sheetlets of 20 stamps.

1473 Repository, Jeongjok Mountain and Taejo Sillok (script)

(Des Won In Jae. Recess and litho)

2000 (9 Dec). World Heritage Sites (4th series). T **1473** and similar horiz design. Multicoloured. P 13×13½.

2457		340w. Type **1473**	2·00	1·20
		a. Sheetlet of 6. Nos. 2457/8,		
		each×3	17·00	
2458		340w. King Sejong and script	2·00	1·20
MS2459	143×89 mm. No. 2457/8		5·00	3·00

Nos. 2457/**MS**2459 were issued together in sheetlets containing Nos. 2457/8 in a block of six stamps (Nos. 2457×3 and 2458×3) separated by a gutter from the miniature sheet (which has one of its outer edges perforated).

1474 Bicycle with coloured wheels (re-unification of Korea)

(Des Kim Sung Am. Photo)

2001 (2 Jan). Millennium (9th series). T **1474** and similar horiz designs. Multicoloured. P 13.

2460		170w. Type **1474**	80	45
		a. Sheetlet of 6. Nos. 2460/5	5·00	
2461		170w. Rainbow (environmental protection)	80	45
2462		170w. Human DNA and figure (eradication of incurable diseases)	80	45
2463		170w. Satellite and mobile telephone (communications technology)	80	45
2464		170w. Space (space travel)	80	45
2465		170w. Solar panels, solar-powered car and windmills (alternative energy sources)	80	45
2460/2465 *Set of* 6			4·25	2·40

Nos. 2460/5 were issued together in *se-tenant* sheetlets of six stamps.

1475 "Oksunn Peaks" (Kim Hong Do)

(Des Kim So Jeong. Photo)

2001 (10 Jan). Visit Korea Year 2001. P 13½.

2466	**1475**	170w. multicoloured	70	40

1476 Plough   **1477** Harrow   **1478** Sowing basket and Namtae

1479 Short-handled Hoes   **1480** Manure Barrel and Fertilizer Ash Container   **1481** Water Dipper

1482 Winnower and Thresher   **1483** Square Straw Drying Mat and Wicker Tray   **1484** Pestle, Mortar and Grinding Stones

1485 Rice Basket and Carrier

(Des Lee Gi Seog. Photo)

2001 (20 Jan). Agricultural Implements. P 13×13½.

2467	**1476**	170w. multicoloured	1·50	40
		a. Strip of 10. Nos. 2468/77	16·00	
2468	**1477**	170w. multicoloured	1·50	40
2469	**1478**	170w. multicoloured	1·50	40
2470	**1479**	170w. multicoloured	1·50	40
2471	**1480**	170w. multicoloured	1·50	40
2472	**1481**	170w. multicoloured	1·50	40
2473	**1482**	170w. multicoloured	1·50	40
2474	**1483**	170w. multicoloured	1·50	40
2475	**1484**	170w. multicoloured	1·50	40
2476	**1485**	170w. multicoloured	1·50	40
2467/2476 *Set of* 10			13·50	3·50

Nos. 2467/76 were issued in *se-tenant* strips of ten stamps within the sheet.

1486 2000 Series Diesel-electric Locomotive

1487 7000 Series Diesel-electric Locomotive

1488 Diesel Urban Commuter Train

1489 Diesel Saemaul Train

(Des Lee Gi Seog. Photo)

2001 (1 Feb). Railways (2nd series). P 13½×13.

2477	**1486**	170w. multicoloured	70	45
		a. Block of 4. Nos. 2477/80	3·00	
2478	**1487**	170w. multicoloured	70	45
2479	**1488**	170w. multicoloured	70	45
2480	**1489**	170w. multicoloured	70	45
2477/2480 Set of 4			2·50	1·60

Nos. 2477/80 were issued in *se-tenant* blocks of four stamps within the sheet.

(Des Lee Gi Seog. Photo)

2001 (26 Feb). Protection of Wildlife and Plants (8th series). Vert designs as T **1270**. Multicoloured. P 13½×13½.

2481	170w. *Jeffersonia dubia*	90	55
	a. Block or horiz strip of 4. Nos. 2481/4	3·75	
2482	170w. *Diapensia lapponica*	90	55
2483	170w. *Rhododendron aureum*	90	55
2484	170w. *Sedum orbiculatum*	90	55
2481/2484 Set of 4		3·25	2·00
MS2485 170w. 125×108 mm. Nos. 2481/4		3·75	3·50

Nos. 2481/**MS**2485 were issued together in sheetlets containing Nos. 2481/4 in a block of eight stamps (giving two blocks or horizontal strips of four designs *se-tenant* separated by a gutter from the miniature sheet.

Nos. 2481/**MS**2485 are impregnated with the scent of the Ume tree.

1490 Incheon Airport and Emblem

(Des Kim So Jeong. Photo)

2001 (29 Mar). Inauguration of Incheon Airport. P 13×13½.

2486	**1490**	170w. multicoloured	70	40

1491 Kim Ku (leader of Independence Movement)   **1492** Emblem

(Des Kim So Jeong. Photo)

2001 (2 Apr). Millennium (10th series). T **1491** and similar vert designs. Multicoloured. P 13½.

2487	170w. Type **1491**	80	40
	a. Sheetlet of 5. Nos. 2487/91	4·25	
2488	170w. Statue commemorating the March 1st Independence Movement	80	40
2489	170w. Interim Korean Government Headquarters, Shanghai and Members.	80	40
2490	170w. Ahn Ik Tae (composer) and music score	80	40
2491	170w. Yun Dong Ju (poet) and Seosi (poem)	80	40
2487/2491 Set of 5		3·50	1·80

Nos. 2487/91 were issued in *se-tenant* sheetlets of five stamps and one label with an enlarged illustrated mar

(Des Park Eun Kyung. Photo)

2001 (27 Apr). International Olympic Fair, Seoul. P 13½×13.

2492	**1492**	170w. multicoloured	70	40
MS2493 105×70 mm. No. 2492×2			2·00	1·80

1493 Bears hugging

(Des Kim So Jeong (2494, 2496), Pack Eun Kyung (2495, 2497). Photo)

2001 (30 Apr–2 July). Greetings Stamps. T **1493** and similar square designs. Multicoloured. P 13½.

2494	170w. Type **1493**	2·00	80
2495	170w. Flower	2·00	80
2496	170w. Trumpets (Congratulations) (1.6)	2·00	80
2497	170w. Cake (2.7)	2·00	80
2494/2497 Set of 4		7·25	3·00

Nos. 2494/5 were issued with *se-tenant* sheets of 20 stamps and 20 plain labels. These sheets could be personalised by the addition of a photograph or a company logo on the labels for the cost of 7000w. per sheet.

1494 Iljimae (Ko Woo Young)

1495 Kkeobeongi (Kil Chang Duk)

(Des Park Eun Kyung. Photo)

2001 (4 May). Cartoons (7th series). P 13×13½.
2498	**1494**	170w. multicoloured	70	40
2499	**1495**	170w. multicoloured	70	40

MS2500 Two sheets, each 90×60 mm. (a) No. 2498; (b) No. 2499 ... 2·00 1·80

1496 Players and Mountains (Switzerland, 1954)

(Des Kim Sung Am. Photo)

2001 (31 May). World Cup Football Championship (2002), Japan and South Korea (6th issue). T **1496** and similar horiz designs. Multicoloured. P 13½×13.
2501	170w. Type **1496**	90	40
	a. Strip of 5. Nos. 2501/2505	4·75	
2502	170w. Players and Ancient settlement (Mexico, 1986)	90	40
2503	170w. Players and Coliseum (Italy, 1990)	90	40
2504	170w. Players and buildings (United States of America, 1994)	90	40
2505	170w. Players and Eiffel Tower (France, 1998)	90	40

2501/2505 Set of 5 ... 4·00 1·80

MS2506 Five sheets, each 60×90 mm. (a) No. 2501×2; (b) No. 2502×2; (c) No. 2503×2; (d) No. 2504×2; (e) No. 2505×2 ... 10·00 9·75

Nos. 2501/5 were issued together in *se-tenant* strips of five stamps within the sheet.

1497 Baechu Kimchi (Chinese Cabbage)

1498 Bossam Kimch

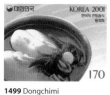

1499 Dongchimi

1500 Klakdugi

(Des Kim Hyun. Photo)

2001 (15 June). Korean Foods (1st series). P 13×13½.
2507	**1497**	170w. multicoloured	80	40
		a. Block of 4. Nos. 2507/10	3·50	
2508	**1498**	170w. multicoloured	80	40
2509	**1499**	170w. multicoloured	80	40
2510	**1500**	170w. multicoloured	80	40

2507/2510 Set of 4 ... 3·00 1·40

Nos. 2507/10 were issued together in *se-tenant* blocks of four stamps within the sheet.

See also Nos. 2599/2602, 2705/2708, 2758/61 and 2810/13.

1501 Raising Flag (Liberation, 1945)

(Des Park Eun Kyung. Photo)

2001 (2 July). Millennium (11th series). T **1501** and similar square designs. Multicoloured. P 13½.
2511	170w. Type **1501**	80	40
	a. Sheetlet. Nos. 2511/15 plus label	4·25	
2512	170w. Soldiers embracing (statue) (Korean War)	80	40
2513	170w. Seoul-Busan Expressway	80	40
2514	170w. Working in fields (Saemaul Undong movement)	80	40
2515	170w. Athletes forming emblem (Olympic Games, Seoul, 1988)	80	40

2511/2515 Set of 5 ... 3·50 1·80

Nos. 2511/15 were issued together in *se-tenant* sheetlets of five stamps and one label.

1502 Red Queen

1503 Pink Lady

467

(Des Park Eun Kyung. Photo)

2001 (18 July). Philakorea 2002 International Stamp Exhibition, Seoul (1st issue). Roses. P 13½.

2516	**1502**	170w. multicoloured..............................	70	40
2517	**1503**	170w. multicoloured..............................	70	40

MS2518 Two sheets, each 115×73 mm. (a) No.
2516×2; (b) No. 2517×2.. 4·00   3·75
See also Nos. 2604/**MS**2606 and 2639/**MS**2640.

1504 Roses in Heart

(Des Kim So Jeong. Photo)

2001 (18 July). Philately Week. T **1504** and similar square design. P 13½.

2519	**1504**	170w. multicoloured................................	70	40

MS2520 108×69 mm. No. 2519×2.................................... 1·80   1·60

1505 Goryeo
Dynasty Porcelain
Vase and Exhibition
Emblem

(Des Park Eun Kyung. Photo)

2001 (10 Aug). World Ceramics Expo, Icheon, Yeoju, and Gwangju. P 13×13½.

2521	**1505**	170w. multicoloured................................	70	40

1506 Conference Emblem

(Des Kim Sung Am. Photo)

2001 (22 Aug). International Statistical Institute (ISI) Conference, Seoul. P 13½×13.

2522	**1506**	170w. multicoloured................................	70	40

1507 Joseon Coin and Stamping
Machine

(Des Park Eun Kyung. Recess and litho)

2001 (28 Sept). 50th Anniv of Korea Minting and Security Printing Corporation (KOMSEP). P 13½.

2523	**1507**	170w. multicoloured................................	70	40

1508 Multicoloured
Ball (Oullim Globe)

(Des Kim So Jeong. Photo)

2001 (8 Oct). International Council of Societies of Industrial Design (ICSID) Conference, Seoul. P 13×13½.

2524	**1508**	170w. multicoloured................................	70	40

1509 Children
encircling Globe

(Des Mo Ji Won. Photo)

2001 (9 Oct). United Nations Year of Dialogue among Civilizations. P 13×13½.

2525	**1509**	170w. multicoloured................................	70	40

1510 Conference Emblem

(Des Park Eun Kyung. Photo)

2001 (19 Oct). International Organisation of Supreme Audit Institutions (INTOSAI) Conference, Seoul. P 13½×13.

2526	**1510**	170w. bright ultramarine and vermilion	70	40

1511 *Dendrobium
moniliforme*

(Des Kim So Jeung. Photo)

2001 (12 Nov). Orchids (1st series). T **1511** and similar vert designs. Multicoloured. P 13½×13.

2527	170w. Type **1511**	80	40
	a. Strip of 4. Nos. 2527/30	3·50	
2528	170w. *Gymnadenia camtschatica*	80	40
2529	170w. *Habenaria radiata*	80	40
2530	170w. *Orchis cyclochila*	80	40
2527/2530 *Set of 4*		3·00	1·40

Nos. 2527/30 were issued in *se-tenant* strips of four stamps within the sheet, each stamp impregnated with the scent of orchid.
See also Nos. 2670/3, 2727/30, 2789/92 and 2836/9.

1512 Snowflakes and Horse

(Des Park Eun Kyung. Photo)

2001 (3 Dec). New Year. Year of the Horse. T **1512** and similar vert design. P 13×13½.

2531	**1512** 170w. multicoloured	70	40
MS2532	90×60 mm. No. 2531×2	1·80	1·60

1513 Seonjeongjeon Conference Hall, Changdeok Palace

(Des Kim Sung Am. Recess and litho)

2001 (10 Dec). World Heritage Sites (5th series). T **1513** and similar horiz design. Multicoloured. P 13×13½.

2533	170w. Type **1513**	1·00	40
	a. Sheetlet of 6. Nos. 2533/4, each×4	16·00	
2534	340w. Injeongjeon coronation hall, Changdeok Palace (52×36 mm)	2·00	80
MS2535	144×96 mm. Nos. 2533/4	3·75	1·50

Nos. 2533/**MS**2535 were issued together in sheetlets containing Nos. 2533/4 in a block of eight stamps (Nos. 2533/4, each×4) separated by a gutter from the miniature sheet (which has one of its outer edges perforated).

1514 *Limenitis populi*

2002 (15 Jan—15 Mar). Fauna. P 13×13½.

2536	60w. *Eophona migratoria* (15.3)	80	40
2546	160w. Type **1514**	80	40
2547	210w. *Falco tinnunculus*	1·10	40
2548	280w. *Ficedula zanthopygia*	1·50	50

Numbers have been left for additions to this series.

1515 Airplane, Locomotive and Lorry

2002 (15 Jan)–**03**. Transport. Photo. P 13½×13.

2550	**1515** 280w. multicoloured	1·50	50
2551	310w. multicoloured	1·60	55
2551a	420w. multicoloured (1.7.03)	1·40	95
2552	1380w. multicoloured	4·50	2·50
2553	1410w. multicoloured	4·75	2·75
2554	1580w. multicoloured (1.1.03)	5·00	4·00
2555	1610w. multicoloured (1.1.03)	5·00	4·00

Numbers have been left for additions to this series.

1516 Kylin Roof Tile

2002 (15 Jan)–**03**. Roof Tiles. T **1516** and similar multicoloured design. Photo. P 13½×13.

2565	1290w. Type **1516**	4·00	2·50
2566	1310w. Ridge-end tile	4·50	2·75
2567	1490w. As No. 2565, background colour altered (1.1.03)	4·50	3·50
2568	1510w. As No. 2565, background colour altered (1.1.03)	4·50	3·50

Numbers have been left for additions to this series.

Nos. 2580/3 and Type **1517** have been left for "My Own Stamp" not yet received.

1518 Chungmu (signalling) Kites

(Des Kim Sung Am. Photo)

2002 (31 Jan). 50th Anniv of Membership of International Telecommunications Union. P 13×13½.

2584	**1518** 190w. multicoloured	80	40

1519 EL8000 Electric Locomotive

1520 EL8100 Electric Locomotive

1521 Express Rail Car

1522 Express Electric Rail Car

(Des Lee Gi Seog. Photo)

2002 (4 Feb). Railways (3rd series). P 13½×13.

2585	**1519**	190w. multicoloured	80	40
		a. Block of 4 Nos. 2585/8	3·50	
2586	**1520**	190w. multicoloured	80	40
2587	**1521**	190w. multicoloured	80	40
2588	**1522**	190w. multicoloured	80	40
2585/2588 *Set of 4*			3·00	1·40

Nos. 2585/8 were issued in *se-tenant* blocks of four stamps within the sheet.

1523 Safflower
(*Carthamus tinctorius*)

(Des Lee Gi Seog. Photo)

2002 (25 Feb). Traditional Dye Plants (1st series). T **1523** and similar vert designs. Multicoloured. P 13½×13.

2589	190w. Type **1523**	80	40
	a. Strip or block of 4. Nos. 2589/92	3·50	
2590	190w. *Lithospermum erythrorhizon*	80	40
2591	190w. Ash tree (*Fraxinus rhynchophylla*)	80	40
2592	190w. Indigo plant (*Persicaria tinctoria*)	80	40
2589/2592 *Set of 4*		3·00	1·40

Nos. 2589/92 were issued in *se-tenant* strips or blocks of four stamps within the sheet.

See also Nos. 2686/9, 2745/8 and 2801/4.

1524 Flowers

(Des Mo Ji-won. Photo)

2002 (26 Apr). International Flower Exhibition, Anmyeondo. P 13½.

2593	**1524**	190w. multicoloured	50	40

1525 "Mengkkong-i-Seodang Village School" (Yoon Seung-woon)

1526 "Wogdoggle Dugdoggle" (Hwang Mi-na)

(Des Park Eun Kyung. Photo)

2002 (4 May). Cartoons (8th series). P 13×13½.

2594	**1525**	190w. multicoloured	80	40
2595	**1526**	190w. multicoloured	80	40
MS2596 Two sheets, each 90×60 mm. (a) No. 2594; (b) No. 2595			2·40	2·10

1527 Campervan, Caravan and Tent

(Des Park Eun Kyung. Photo)

2002 (16 May). 64th International Camping and Caravanning Rally. P 13½×13.

2597	**1527**	190w. multicoloured	80	40

1528 Footballer (Europe)

(Des Kim Sung-am. Photo)

2002 (31 May). World Cup Football Championships, Japan and South Korea (7th issue). Six sheets, each 60×90 mm. containing T **1528** and similar circular designs. Multicoloured. P 13.
MS2598 (a) 190w.×2, Type **1528**×2; (b) 190w.×2, Central & North America×2; (c) 190w.×2, Asia×2; (d) 190w.×2, South America×2; (e) 190w.×2, Africa×2; (f) 170×240 mm. The stamps of Nos. **MS**2598a/e plus label...................... 20·00   20·00

1529 Jeolpyeon

1530 Sirutteok

1531 Injeolmi

1532 Songpyeon

(Des Kim Hyun. Photo)

2002 (15 June). Korean Foods (2nd series). P 13×13½.
2599	**1529**	190w. multicoloured...............	80	40
		a. Strip or block of 4. Nos. 2599/602......................	3·50	
2600	**1530**	190w. multicoloured...............	80	40
2601	**1531**	190w. multicoloured...............	80	40
2602	**1532**	190w. multicoloured...............	80	40
2599/2602	Set of 4.............................		3·00	1·40

Nos. 2599/602 were issued together in se-tenant strips or blocks of four stamps within the sheet.

1533 Woman's Face

(Des Roh Jung-hwa. Photo)

2002 (1 July). Women's Week. P 13×13½.
2603	**1533**	190w. multicoloured...............	80	40

1534 Child holding Flags

(Des Mo Ji-won. Photo)

2002 (1 July). Philakorea 2002 International Stamp Exhibition, Seoul (2nd issue). T **1534** and similar diamond-shaped design. Multicoloured. P 13.
2604	190w. Type **1534**.....................	80	40
2605	190w. Children and globe..................	80	40
MS2606	Two sheets, each 115×73 mm. (a) No. 2604×2; (b) No. 2605..................	4·00	3·75

1535 Heung-injimun Fortress, Seoul

(Des Lee Gi-sok (2607/10); Kim Sung-am (2611/18); Park Eun-Kyung (2619/24); Kim So-jeong (2625/30); Roh Jung-hwa (2631/4); Mo Ji-won (2635/8). Photo)

2002 (1 Aug). Hometowns. T **1535** and similar horiz designs. Multicoloured. P 13×13½.
2607	190w. Type **1535**.....................	90	40
	a. Pair. Nos. 2607/8..................	1·90	85
2608	190w. Two masked dancers, Seoul	90	40
2609	190w. Basalt cliffs, Incheon..................	90	40
	a. Pair. Nos. 2609/10..................	1·90	85
2610	190w. Dancers wearing white, Chamseongdan altar, Incheon	90	40
2611	190w. Freedom House, Paju, Gyeonggi	90	40
	a. Pair. Nos. 2611/12..................	1·90	85
2612	190w. Yangjubyeol Sandaenori dancers one with raised arm, Gyeonggi..................	90	40
2613	190w. Ulsanbawi rock, Mt. Seoraksan, Gangwon..................	90	40
	a. Pair. Nos. 2613/14..................	1·90	85
2614	190w. Two dancers one holding fan, Gangwon..................	90	40
2615	190w. Sail boat, Chungnam..................	90	40
	a. Pair. Nos. 2615/16..................	1·90	85
2616	190w. Weaver, Chungnam	90	40
2617	190w. Tower, Expo Science Park, Daejeon..................	90	40
	a. Pair. Nos. 2617/18..................	1·90	85
2618	190w. Scientist, Daedeok Science Town, Daejeon..................	90	40
2619	190w. Mt. Mai peaks, Jeonbuk..............	90	40
	a. Pair. Nos. 2619/20..................	1·90	85
2620	190w. Iri folk band drummers, Jeonbuk..................	90	40
2621	190w. Odong island, Jeonnam..............	90	40
	a. Pair. Nos. 2621/2..................	1·90	85
2622	190w. Ganggang Sullae circle dance, Jeonnam..................	90	40
2623	190w. May 18th monument, Gwangju	90	40
	a. Pair. Nos. 2623/4..................	1·90	85
2624	190w. Gossaum Nori tug of war, Gwangju..................	90	40
2625	190w. Beopju temple, Mt. Songni, Chungbuk..................	90	40
	a. Pair. Nos. 2625/6..................	1·90	85
2626	190w. Taekgyeon martial art, Chungbuk..................	90	40
2627	190w. Gwangbong Seokjoyeorae statue, Daegu..................	90	40
	a. Pair. Nos. 2627/8..................	1·90	85
2628	190w. Dalseong forest, Daegu..............	90	40
2629	190w. Taejeondae cliffs, Busan..............	90	40
	a. Pair. Nos. 2629/30..................	1·90	85
2630	190w. Three Dongnaeyaryu festival dancers, Busan..................	90	40
2631	190w. Dokdo islands, Gyeongbuk........	90	40
	a. Pair. Nos. 2631/2..................	1·90	85

2632	190w. Andongchajeon Nori log tying game, Gyeongbuk.........................	90	40
2633	190w. Haegeumgang island, Gyeongnam...............................	90	40
	a. Pair. Nos. 2633/4	1·90	85
2634	190w. Goseong Ogwangdae clown dance, Gyeongnam	90	40
2635	190w. Cheonjeonnigakseok rock wall, Ulsan..	90	40
	a. Pair. Nos. 2635/6	1·90	85
2636	190w. Three Cheoyongmu masked dancers, Ulsan......................	90	40
2637	190w. Mt. Halla and Baeknokdam crater, Jeju............................	90	40
	a. Pair. Nos. 2637/8	1·90	85
2638	190w. House, Jeju.............................	90	40
2607/2638 *Set of 32*		26·00	11·50

2651	190w. No.8	90	40
2652	190w. No.9	90	40
2653	190w. No.10.....................................	90	40
2654	190w. No.11.....................................	90	40
2655	190w. Goalkeeper	90	40
2656	190w. No.13.....................................	90	40
2657	190w. No. 14....................................	90	40
2658	190w. No. 15....................................	90	40
2659	190w. No.16.....................................	90	40
2660	190w. No.17.....................................	90	40
2661	190w. No.18.....................................	90	40
2662	190w. No.19.....................................	90	40
2663	190w. No.20.....................................	90	40
2664	190w. No.21.....................................	90	40
2665	190w. No.22.....................................	90	40
2666	190w. Goalkeeper (*different*)	90	40
2643/2666 *Set of 24*		19·00	8·75

Nos. 2643/66 were issued in *se-tenant* sheetlets of 24 stamps.

1536 Exhibition Emblem and Talchum Masked Dancer

(Des Kim Sung-am. Photo)

2002 (2 Aug). Philakorea 2002 International Stamp Exhibition, Seoul (3rd issue). P 13½×13.

2639	**1536**	190w. multicoloured.................................	80	40
MS2640 90×60 mm. No.2639×2. Imperf			2·00	1·50

1539 Stadium, Runner, Tower, Seagull and Diver

(Des Kim So-jeong. Photo)

2002 (28 Sept). 14th Asian Games, Busan. P 13×13½.

2667	**1539**	190w. multicoloured.................................	80	40
MS2668 120×70 mm. No. 2667×2..........................			2·00	1·80

1537 Children and Dog

(Des Roh Jung-hwa. Photo)

2002 (2 Aug). Philately Week. P 13½.

2641	**1537**	190w. multicoloured................................	80	40
MS2642 108×69 mm. Nos. 2641×2..........................			2·00	1·60

1540 Stylized Torch

(Des Roh Jung-hwa. Photo)

2002 (26 Oct). Eighth Far East and South Pacific Games for the Disabled (FESPIC), Busan. P 13×13½.

2669	**1540**	190w. multicoloured................................	80	40

1538 Guus Hiddink (coach)

(Des Lee Gi-seog. Photo)

2002 (7 Aug). South Korea—Semi-Finalists, World Cup Football Championships, Japan and South Korea (7th issue). T **1538** and similar horiz designs showing team members. Multicoloured. P 13½×13.

2643	190w. Type **1538**	90	40
	a. Sheetlet. Nos. 2643/67................	23·00	
2644	190w. No.1 player	90	40
2645	190w. No.2	90	40
2646	190w. No.3	90	40
2647	190w. No.4	90	40
2648	190w. No.5	90	40
2649	190w. No.6	90	40
2650	190w. No.7	90	40

1541 *Cymbidium kanran*

(Des Kim So Jeung. Photo)

2002 (12 Nov). Orchids (2nd series). T **1541** and similar vert designs. Multicoloured. P 13½×13.

2670	190w. Type **1541**	80	40
	a. Strip or block of 4. Nos. 2670/3	3·50	
2671	190w. *Gastrodia elata*................	80	40
2672	190w. *Pogonia japonica*..............	80	40
2673	190w. *Cephalanthera falcata*	80	40
2670/2673 *Set of 4*		3·00	1·40

Nos. 2670/3 were issued in *se-tenant* strips or blocks of four stamps within the sheet, each stamp impregnated with the scent of orchid.

1542 Taekwondo

(Des Kim Dong-seong and Lou Wei. Photo)

2002 (20 Nov). Tenth Anniv of South Korea—China Diplomatic Relations. Martial Arts. T **1542** and similar horiz design. Multicoloured. P 13×13½.

2674	190w. Type **1542**.......................................	80	40
	a. Pair. Nos. 2674/5	1·70	85
2675	190w. Wushu...	80	40

Nos. 2674/5 were issued in se-tenant horizontal or vertical pairs within the sheet.

1543 Sheep

(Des Park Eun-Kyung. Photo)

2002 (2 Dec). New Year. Year of the Sheep. Phosphorescent security markings. P 13×13½.

2676	**1543** 190w. multicoloured..................................	80	40
MS2677	90×60 mm. No. 2676×2	1·80	1·60

Nos. 2676/**MS**2677 have phosphor applied to the white snowflakes and the sheep. The outline of a lamb is visible against the sheep if the stamp is tilted or when viewed under a UV lamp.

1544 Gongsimdon Observatory Tower

(Des Shin Hyun-tae. Eng Kim Seong-am. Recess and litho)

2002 (9 Dec). Hwaseong Fortress—UNESCO World Heritage Site. Sheet 145×232 mm. containing T **1544** and similar horiz design. Multicoloured. P 13×13½.

MS2678	190w.×5 Type **1544**; 280w.×5	
	Banghwasuryu Pavilion (52×36 mm) .... 10·00	9·75

1545 Dabo Pagoda, Bulguk Temple, Gyeongju

(Des Kim So-jeong, Hoang Thuy Lieu and Vu Kim Lien. Photo)

2002 (21 Dec). Tenth Anniv of South Korea—Vietnam Diplomatic Relations.

T **1545** and similar vert design. Multicoloured. P 13½×13.

2679	190w. Type **1545**......................................	80	40
	a. Pair. Nos. 2679/80	1·70	85
2680	190w. One Pillar Pagoda, Hanoi	80	40

Nos. 2679/80 were issued in se-tenant pairs within the sheet.

1546 American and Korean Flags Combined

(Des Jaime Nascimento Da Silva. Photo)

2003 (13 Jan). Centenary of Korean Emigration to United States of America. P 13½×13.

2681	**1546**	190w. multicoloured	80	40

1547 Gondola Freight Car

1548 Box Car

1549 Tanker

1550 Hopper

(Des Lee Gi Seog. Photo)

2003 (4 Feb). Railways (4th series). P 13½×13.

2682	**1547**	190w. multicoloured................................	80	40
		a. Block of 4 Nos. 2682/5	3·50	
2683	**1548**	190w. multicoloured................................	80	40
2684	**1549**	190w. multicoloured................................	80	40
2685	**1550**	190w. multicoloured................................	80	40
2682/2685	Set of 4...		3·00	1·40

Nos. 2682/5 were issued in se-tenant blocks of four stamps within the sheet.

1551 *Rubia akane*

(Des Lee Gi Seog. Photo)

2003 (22 Feb). Traditional Dye Plants (2nd series). T **1551** and similar vert designs. Multicoloured. P 13½×13.

2686	190w. Type **1551**	80	40
	a. Block or strip of 4. Nos. 2686/9.	3·50	
2687	190w. *Rhus javanica*	80	40
2688	190w. *Sophora japonica*	80	40
2689	190w. *Isatis tinctoria*	80	40
2686/2689 *Set of 4*		3·00	1·40

Nos. 2686/9 were issued in *se-tenant* blocks or strips of four stamps within the sheet.

1552 Roh Moo Hyun

(Des Lee Gi Seog. Photo)

2003 (25 Feb). Inauguration of President Roh Moo Hyun. Sheet 115×70 mm. P 13×13½.

2689*a* **1552**	190w. multicoloured. P 13×13½.	80	40
MS2690 1552 190w. multicoloured		2·00	1·80

1553 Flag

(Des Kim So Jeong. Photo)

2003 (6 Mar). P 13×13½.

2691	**1553**	10w. multicoloured	20	10

1554 Unhye (embroidered shoes)

(Des Kim So Jeong. Eng Hong Yong Sun and Ka Sung Hyeon. Recess)

2003 (19 Mar). Traditional Culture (1st issue). T **1554** and similar octagonal designs. Each chocolate, blackish-brown and indigo. P 12½.

2692	190w. Type **1554**	80	40
	a. Strip of 4. Nos. 2692/5	3·50	

2693	190w. Mokhwa (ankle boots)	80	40
2694	190w. Jipsin (straw shoes)	80	40
2695	190w. Namaksin (wooden clogs)	80	40
2692/2695 *Set of 4*		3·00	1·40

Nos. 2692/5 were issued in horizontal *se-tenant* strips of four stamps within the sheet.

See also Nos. 2700/3, 2712/15, 2720/3, 2762/5 and 2771/4.

1555 Tortoise-shaped Celadon Jug

(Des Park Eun Kyung. Photo)

2003 (11 Apr). P 14×13.

2696	**1555**	400w. multicoloured	1·20	95

1556 "Goblin's Cap"   **1557** "Sword of Fire"
(Shin Moon Soo)   (Kim Hye Rin)

(Des Park Eun Kyung. Photo)

2003 (2 May). Cartoons (9th series). P 13×13½.

2697	**1556**	190w. multicoloured	80	40
2698	**1557**	190w. multicoloured	80	40
MS2699 Two sheets, each 90×60 mm. (a) No. 2697; (b) No. 2698		3·00	2·75

(Des Kim So Jeong. Eng Hong Yong Sun and Ka Sung Hyeon. Recess)

2003 (19 May). Traditional Culture (2nd issue). Octagonal designs as T **1554**. Each brownish-black and light brown. P 12½.

2700	190w. Eoyeon (royal sedan chair)	80	40
	a. Strip of 4. Nos. 2700/3	3·50	
2701	190w. Choheon (single-wheeled sedan chair)	80	40
2702	190w. Saingyo (wedding sedan chair)	80	40
2703	190w. Namyeo (small open sedan chair)	80	40
2700/2703 *Set of 4*		3·00	1·40

Nos. 2700/3 were issued in horizontal *se-tenant* strips of four stamps within the sheet.

1558 Palmido Lighthouse

(Des Roh Jung Hwa. Photo)

2003 (30 May). Centenary of Lighthouse Building. P 13½×13.
2704   **1558**   190w. multicoloured 80   40

1559 Yugwa

1560 Yeot Gangjeong

1561 Yakgwa

1562 Dasik

(Des Kim Hyun. Photo)

2003 (13 June). Korean Foods (3rd series). P 13×13½.
2705   **1559**   190w. multicoloured 80   40
     a. Strip or block of 4. Nos. 2705/8   3·50
2706   **1560**   190w. multicoloured 80   40
2707   **1561**   190w. multicoloured 80   40
2708   **1562**   190w. multicoloured 80   40
2705/2708 *Set of 4* .... 3·00   1·40
     Nos. 2705/8 were issued together in *se-tenant* strips or blocks of four stamps within the sheet.

1563 *Malus asiatica*

(Des Kim So Jeong. Photo)

2003 (1 July). Fruit and Flower. Self-adhesive booklet stamps. T **1563** and similar multicoloured design. Die-cut perf 11½.
2709   190w. Type **1563** .... 1·00   40
     a. Booklet pane. No. 2709×20 ...... 21·00
2710   190w. *Aquilegia flabellata* (*horiz*) .... 1·00   40
     a. Booklet pane. No. 2710×20 ...... 21·00

1564 Porcelain Vase

(Des Mo Ji Won. Photo)

2003 (11 July). P 13×13½.
2711   **1564**   500w. ulticoloured .... 1·60   1·10

(Des Kim So Jeong. Eng Hong Yong Sun and Ka Sung Hyeon. Recess)

2003 (25 July). Traditional Culture (3rd issue). Octagonal designs as T **1554**. Each agate and chocolate. P 12½.
2712   190w. Jojokdeung lantern 80   40
     a. Strip of 4. Nos. 2712/15 ....   3·50
2713   190w. Deungjan (lamp-oil container).   80   40
2714   190w. Juchilmokje yukgakjedeung
            (hexagonal portable lantern)....   80   40
2715   190w. Chot-dae (brass candlestick)..... 80   40
2712/2715 *Set of 4* .... 3·00   1·40
     Nos. 2712/ 15 were issued in horizontal *se-tenant* strips of four stamps within the sheet.

1565 Origami figure ("Expression of Gratitude")

(Des Kim Sung am. Photo)

2003 (1 Aug). Philately Week. P 13½.
2716   **1565**   190w. multicoloured 80   40
MS2717 109×69 mm. Nos. 2716×2 Imperf .... 2·00   1·80

1566 Leaves and Clasped Hands

(Des Mo Ji Won. Photo)

2003 (21 Aug). Summer Universiade (games), Daegu. P 13×13½.
2718   **1566**   190w. multicoloured 80   40
MS2719 91×60 mm. Nos. 2718×2 .... 1·80   1·60

(Des Kim So Jeong. Eng Hong Yong Sun and Ka Sung Hyeon. Recess)

2003 (25 Sept). Traditional Culture (4th issue). Octagonal designs as T **1554**. Each indigo and deep claret. P 12½.
2720   190w. Gujok-ban (table with
            decorated top)...........................   80   40
     a. Strip of 4. Nos. 2720/3 ....   3·50
2721   190w. Punghyeol-ban (tray table)........ 80   40
2722   190w. Ilju-ban (single stemmed table)   80   40
2723   190w. Haeju-ban (straight-sided
            table)..   80   40
2720/2723 *Set of 4* .... 3·00   1·40
     Nos. 2720/3 were issued in horizontal *se-tenant* strips of four stamps within the sheet.

1567 Faces

(Des Roh Jung Hwa. Photo)

2003 (28 Oct). Centenary of Korean YMCA (Young Men's Christian Association) Movement. P 13½×13.
2724 **1567** 190w. multicoloured 80 40

1568 Stylised
Teacher and Pupil

(Des Kim So Jeong. Photo)

2003 (31 Oct). Centenary of Soong Eui Girl's School. P 13×13½.
2725 **1568** 190w. multicoloured 80 40

1569 Hearts as TB
Symbol

(Des Mo Ji Won. Photo)

2003 (6 Nov). 50th Anniv of National Tuberculosis Association. P 13.
2726 **1569** 190w. scarlet vermilion, dull
                 ultramarine and grey 80 40

1570 *Cremastra*
appendiculata

(Des Kim So Jeung. Photo)

2003 (12 Nov). Orchids (3rd series). T **1570** and similar vert designs. Multicoloured. P 13½×13.
2727   190w. Type **1570** 80 40
             a. Strip of 4. Nos. 2727/30 .... 3·50
2728   190w. *Cymbidium lancifolium* 80 40
2729   190w. *Orchis graminifolia*....................... 80 40
2730   190w. *Bulbophyllum drymoglossum*..... 80 40
2727/2730 *Set of 4*.. 3·00 1·40
Nos. 2727/30 were issued in *se-tenant* strips of four stamps within the sheet, each stamp impregnated with the scent of orchid.

1571 Monkey

(Des Park Eun Kyung. Photo)

2003 (1 Dec). New Year. "Year of the Monkey". Phosphorescent security markings. P 13×13½.
2731 **1571** 190w. multicoloured 80 40
MS2732 90×60 mm. No. 2731×2..................................... 1·80 1·60
Nos. 2731/**MS**2732 have phosphor applied to the white snowflakes and the monkey.

1572 Dolmen, Ganghwa

(Des Kim Sung Am. Recess and litho)

2002 (9 Dec). Ganghwa, Hwasoon and Gochang—UNESCO World Heritage Sites. Sheet 145×232 mm. containing T **1572** and similar horiz design. Multicoloured. P 13×13½.
MS2733 190w.×5 Type **1572**; 280w.×5 Dolmen
      (52×36 mm) .... 10·00 9·75

1573 Cheomseongdae,
Gyeongju

(Des Park Eun Kyung and Bharati Mirchandani. Photo)

2003 (10 Dec). 30th Anniv of South Korea—India Diplomatic Relations. Observatories. T **1573** and similar vert design. Multicoloured. P 13½×13.
2734   190w. Type **1573**..................................... 80 40
             a. Pair. Nos. 2734/5 .... 1·70 85
2735   190w. Jantar Mantar, Jaipur................... 80 40
Nos. 2734/5 were issued in *se-tenant* pairs within the sheet.

1574 *Calystegia soldanella*

(Des Lee Bok-sik and Lee Gi-seog. Photo)

2004 (16 Jan). Dokdo Island. T **1574** and similar horiz designs. Multicoloured. P 13×13½.

2736	190w. Type **1574**	60	40
	a. Strip of 4. Nos. 2736/9	2·50	
2737	190w. *Aster spathulifolius*	60	40
2738	190w. *Calonectris leucomelas* (inscr "laucomelas")	60	40
2739	190w. *Larus crassirostris*	60	40
2736/2739	*Set of* 4	2·20	1·40

Nos. 2736/9 were issued in *se-tenant* strips of four stamps within the sheet, each strip forming a composite design.

1575 Emblems

(Des Roh Jung-hwa. Photo)

2004 (30 Jan). 50th Anniv of National UNESCO Commission. P 13½.

2740	**1575**	190w. multicoloured	60	40

1576 Multiple Tie Tamper

1577 Ballast Regulator

1578 Track Inspection Car

1579 Ballast Cleaner

(Des Lee Gi Seog. Photo)

2004 (4 Feb). Railways (5th series). P 13½×13.

2741	**1576**	190w. multicoloured	60	40
		a. Block of 4 Nos. 2741/4	2·50	
2742	**1577**	190w. multicoloured	60	40
2743	**1578**	190w. multicoloured	60	40
2744	**1579**	190w. multicoloured	60	40
2741/2744	*Set of* 4		2·20	1·40

Nos. 2741/4 were issued in *se-tenant* blocks of four stamps within the sheet.

1580 *Juglans regia*

(Des Lee Gi Seog. Photo)

2004 (25 Feb). Traditional Dye Plants (3rd series). T **1580** and similar vert designs. Multicoloured. P 13½×13.

2745		190w. Type **1580**	60	40
		a. Block or strip of 4. Nos. 2745/8.	2·50	
2746		190w. *Acer ginnala*	60	40
2747		190w. *Pinus densiflora*	60	40
2748		190w. *Punica granatum*	60	40
2745/2748	*Set of* 4		2·20	1·40

Nos. 2745/8 were issued in *se-tenant* blocks or strips of four stamps within the sheet.

1581 Heart enclosing Water Droplet

(Des Shin Jae-yong. Litho)

2004 (22 Mar). International Water Day. P 13½.

2749	**1581**	190w. multicoloured	60	40

1582 Satellite, Dish and Weather Symbols

(Des Kim So-jeong. Photo)

2004 (25 Mar). Centenary of Meteorological Service. P 13½.

2750	**1582**	190w. multicoloured	60	40

1583 Locomotive

(Des Park Eun-kyung. Photo)

2004 (1 Apr). Inauguration of High Speed Trains. P 13½.
2751 **1583** 190w. multicoloured 60 40

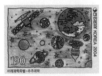

1584 "Space Exploration"
(Radhika Kakrania)

(Des Shin Jae-yong. Photo)

2004 (21 Apr). Science Day. Winning Entries in International Stamp
Design Competition. T **15**84 and similar multicoloured design.
P 13½.
2752 190w. Type **1584** 60 40
2753 190w. "Mysteries of Life" (Kim dong-
min) (vert) 60 40

1585 "Wicked Boy   **1586** "Nation of
Simsultong" (Lee   Winds" (Kim Jin)
Jeong-moon)

(Des Park Eun Kyung. Photo)

2004 (4 May). Cartoons (10th series). P 13½.
2754 **1585** 190w. multicoloured 60 40
2755 **1586** 190w. multicoloured 60 40
MS2756 Two sheets, each 90×60 mm. (a) No. 2754;
(b) No. 2755 .... 1·20 1·00

1587 Emblem

(Des Shin Jae-yong. Photo)

2004 (21 May). Centenary of FIFA (Fédération Internationale de
Football). P 13.
2757 **1587** 190w. multicoloured 60 40

1588 Gujeolpan   **1589** Hwayangjeok

1590 Bibimbap   **1591** Sinsello

(Des Kim Hyun. Photo)

2004 (15 June). Korean Foods (4th series). P 13×13½.
2758 **1588** 190w. multicoloured 60 40
a. Strip or block of 4. Nos.
2758/61 .... 2·50
2759 **1589** 190w. multicoloured 60 40
2760 **1590** 190w. multicoloured 60 40
2761 **1591** 190w. multicoloured 60 40
2758/2761 Set of 4 .... 2·20 1·40
Nos. 2758/61 were issued together in se-tenant strips or blocks of
four stamps within the sheet.

(Des Roh Jung-hwa. Eng Hong Yong Sun and Ka Sung Hyeon.
Recess)

2004 (24 June). Traditional Culture (5th issue). Octagonal designs as
T **1554**. Each blackish purple and bottle green. P 12½.
2762 190w. Work box 60 40
a. Strip of 4. Nos. 2762/5 .... 2·50
2763 190w. Thimble 60 40
2764 190w. Bobbin 60 40
2765 190w. Needle case 60 40
2762/2765 Set of 4 .... 2·50 1·40
Nos. 2762/5 were issued in horizontal se-tenant strips of four
stamps within the sheet.

1592 Symbols of Science   **1593** Symbols of Art

(Des Mo Ji-won. Litho)

2004 (16 July). 50th Anniv of National Academies of Science and Art.
P 13.
2766 **1592** 190w. multicoloured 60 40
a. Horiz. pair. Nos. 2766/7 .... 1·30 85
2767 **1593** 190w. multicoloured 60 40
Nos. 2766/7 were issued in horizontal se-tenant pairs within the
sheet, each pair forming a composite design.

1594 Animals Celebrating

(Des Mo Ji-won. Photo)

2004 (22 July). Philately Week. P 13½.
2768 **1594** 190w. multicoloured 60   40
MS2769 109×69 mm. Nos. 2768×2 .... 1·00   95

1595 Acropolis

(Des Park Eun-kyung. Photo)

2004 (13 Aug). Olympic Games, Athens. P 13.
2770 **1595** 190w. multicoloured 60   40

(Des Mo Ji-won. Eng Hong Yong Sun and Ka Sung Hyeon. Recess)

2004 (20 Aug). Traditional Culture (6th issue). Octagonal designs as T **1554**. Each maroon and Prussian blue. P 12½.
2771   190w. Golden crown 60   40
         a. Strip of 4. Nos. 2771/4 .... 2·50
2772   190w. Bamboo hat 60   40
2773   190w. Gauze hat 60   40
2774   190w. Horsehair hat 60   40
2771/2774 *Set of 4* .... 2·20   1·40
    Nos. 2771/4 were issued in horizontal *se-tenant* strips of four stamps within the sheet.

1596 Geumcheongyo Bridge

1596a Jeongotgyo

1596b Jincheon Nongdari

1596c Seungseongyo

(Des Lee Gi-seok. Photo)

2004 (24 Sept). Bridges (1st series). P 13½ (with three irregular perfs on each vert side).
2775 **1596** 190w. multicoloured 60   40
         a. Block of 4. Nos. 2775/8 .... 2·50
2776 **1596a** 190w. multicoloured 60   40
2777 **1596b** 190w. multicoloured 60   40
2778 **1596c** 190w. multicoloured 60   40
2775/2778 *Set of 4* .... 2·20   1·40
    Nos. 2775/8 were issued in *se-tenant* blocks of four stamps within the sheet.
    See also Nos. 2826/9 and 2875/8.

1597 Emblem

(Des Roh Jung-hwa. Photo)

2004 (1 Oct). International Council of Museums (ICOM) Conference, Seoul. P 13.
2779 **1597** 190w. multicoloured 60   40

1598 Obaegnahan Mountain

1598a Seonjakjiwat

1598b Baengnokdam

1598c Oreum

(Des Lee Gi-seok. Photo)

2004 (18 Oct). Mountains (1st series). P 13½.

2780	**1598**	190w. multicoloured	60	40
		a. Block of 4. Nos. 2780/3	2·50	
2781	**1598a**	190w. multicoloured	60	40
2782	**1598b**	190w. multicoloured	60	40
2783	**1598c**	190w. multicoloured	60	40
2780/2783 *Set of 4*			2·20	1·40

Nos. 2780/3 were issued in *se-tenant* blocks of four stamps within the sheet.

See also Nos. 2830/3 and 2895/8.

1599 White
Hibiscus

2004 (1 Nov). *Hibiscus syriacus*. Photo. P 13½×13.

2784		190w. Type **1599**	50	40
2785		220w. Three white blooms and two buds	60	50
2786		240w. Red hibiscus	65	50
2787		310w. Five red blooms	80	65
2784/2787 *Set of 4*			2·30	1·80

1600 White Porcelain
with Iron-painted
Plum and Bamboo
Design

2004 (1 Nov). Photo. P 13×13½.

2788	**1600**	1520w. multicoloured	5·50	4·50

1601 *Goodyera
maximowicziana*

(Des Kim So Jeung. Photo)

2004 (12 Nov). Orchids (4th series). T **1601** and similar vert designs. Multicoloured. P 13½×13.

2789		190w. Type **1601**	60	50
		a. Strip of 4. Nos. 2789/92	2·50	
2790		190w. *Sarcanthus scolpendrifolius*	60	50
2791		190w. *Calanthe sieboldii*	60	50
2792		190w. *Bletilla striata*	60	50
2789/2792 *Set of 4*			2·20	1·80

Nos. 2789/92 were issued in *se-tenant* strips of four stamps within the sheet, each stamp impregnated with the scent of orchid.

1602 Hen and Chicks

(Des Park Eun-kyung. Photo)

2004 (1 Dec). New Year. Year of the Rooster. Multicoloured. P 13×13½.

MS2793 90×60 mm. 220w.×2; Type **1602**×2		1·20	1·00

1603 Daeneungwon Tumuli Park

(Des Kim So-jeong. Eng Shin Hyun-tae and Shin In-chul. Recess and Litho)

2004 (9 Dec). Gyenongju—UNESCO World Heritage Site. Sheet 145×232 mm. containing T **1603** and similar horiz design. Multicoloured. P 13×13½.

MS2794 310w.×10 Type **1603**×5; Anapji×5 (each, 52×36 mm)		8·00	7·25

1604 Girella punctata

(Des Lee Bok-sik and Lee Gi-seog. Photo)

2005 (18 Jan). Marado Island. T **1604** and similar horiz designs. Multicoloured. P 13×13½.

2795		190w. Type **1604**	60	50
		a. Horiz. pair. Nos. 2795/6	1·30	1·10
		b. Strip of 4. Nos. 2795/8	2·50	
2796		190w. *Epinephelus septemfasciatus*	60	50
2797		190w. *Chromis notata*	60	50
2798		190w. *Sebastiscus marmoratus*	60	50
2795/2798 *Set of 4*			2·20	1·80

Nos. 2795/6 were issued in horizontal *se-tenant* pairs, each pair forming a composite design, within strips of four stamps.

1605 Cells and Wheelchair User

(Des Roh Jung-hwa. Photo)

2005 (12 Feb). Stem Cell Research. P 13×13½.

2799	**1605**	220w. multicoloured	70	50

1606 Emblem, Heart and Flying Figure

(Des Shin Jae-yong. Photo)

2005 (23 Feb). Centenary of Rotary International. P 13×13½.
2800 **1606** 220w. multicoloured 70   50

1607 Clerodendron trichotomum

(Des Lee Gi Seog. Photo)

2005 (25 Feb). Traditional Dye Plants (4th series). T **1607** and similar vert designs. Multicoloured. P 13½×13.
2801   220w. Type **1607** 70   50
       a. Block or strip of 4. Nos. 2801/4 . 3·00
2802   220w. Gardenia jasminoides 70   50
2803   220w. Taxus cuspidata........................ 70   50
2804   220w. Smilax china 70   50
2801/2804 Set of 4... 2·50 1·80
    Nos. 2801/4 were issued in se-tenant blocks or strips of four stamps within the sheet.

1608 Vase, Mask and Dove

(Des Mo Ji-won. Photo)

2005 (10 Mar). Tourism. Visit Gyeonggi. P 13½×13.
2805 **1608** 220w. multicoloured 70   50

1609 Children

(Des Shin Jae-yong. Photo)

2005 (22 Apr). 50th Anniv of Information and Communication Day. T **1609** and similar multicoloured design. P 13½×13 (horiz) or 13×13½ (vert).
2806   220w. Type **1609** 70   50
2807   220w. Boy, computer screen and
       sheep (vert)................................ 70   50

1610 Inchon Memorial Hall

(Des Mo Ji-won. Photo)

2005 (4 May). Centenary of Korea University. P 13×13½.
2808 **1610** 220w. agate, silver and magenta......... 70   50

1611 Eschrichtius robustus

(Des Park Eun-kyung. Photo)

2005 (27 May). International Whaling Commission Meeting, Ulsan. P 13×13½.
2809 **1611** 220w. multicolourd 70   50

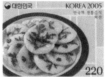 

1612 Hwajeon (pan-fried rice with flower petals)   **1613** Bindaetteok (pan-fried ground mung beans)

1614 Jeongol (casserole)   **1615** Neobani (boiled beef).

(Des Kim Hyun. Photo)

2005 (15 June). Korean Foods (5th series). P 13×13½.
2810 **1612** 220w. multicoloured.............................. 70   50
       a. Strip or block of 4. Nos. 2810/13 3·00
2811 **1613** 220w. multicoloured.............................. 70   50
2812 **1614** 220w. multicoloured.............................. 70   50
2813 **1615** 220w. multicoloured.............................. 70   50
2810/2813 Set of 4... 2·50 1·80
    Nos. 2810/13 were issued together in se-tenant strips or blocks of four stamps within the sheet.

1616 Ancient Sword and Armoured Mounted Soldier

(Des Kim So-jeong. Photo)

2005 (1 July). Goguryeo (1st issue). T **1616** and similar horiz design. P 13½×13 (with one irregular Perf. on each vert side).

2814	310w. Type **1616**	80	65
	a. Vert pair. Nos. 2814/15	1·70	1·40
2815	310w. Oneyo fortress..............................	80	65

Nos. 2814/15 were issued in vertical *se-tenant* pairs within the sheet.

The irregular perforations show the outline of Goguryeo area when seen across the sheet.

See also Nos. 2869/70.

No. 2816 is vacant.

1617 Girl icing Birthday Cake

(Des Park Eun-kyung. Photo)

2005 (29 July). Philately Week. P 13½.

2817	**1617** 220w. multicoloured..............................	70	50

No. 2817 was issued both in sheets and small sheets of two stamps with enlarged margins.

1618 Buncheong Jar

(Des Kim so-jeong. Photo)

2005 (1 Aug). P 13½.

2818	**1618** 1720w. multicoloured	6·00	5·75

1619 Provisional Government Building and Charter

(Des Lee Gi-seog. Photo)

2005 (12 Aug). 60th Anniv of Liberation. T **1619** and similar horiz designs. Multicoloured. P 13×13½.

2819	480w. Type 1619..................................	1·00	80
	a. Strip of 4. Nos. 2819/22	5·25	
2820	520w. Declaration of Independence...	1·20	95
2821	580w. Freedom fighters taking oath of allegiance	1·40	1·10
2822	600w. Anniversary emblem...................	1·50	1·20
2819/2822 *Set of 4*..		4·50	3·75

Nos. 2819/22 were issued together in *se-tenant* strips of four stamps within the sheet.

No. 2823 is vacant.

1620 Colours and Hand holding Cutlery

(Des Shin Jae-yong. Photo)

2005 (18 Aug). Fusion Culture. P 13½.

2824	**1620** 220w. multicoloured..............................	70	50

1621 *Strix aluco*

(Des Kim So-jeong. Photo)

2005 (1 Sept). P 14×13.

2825	**1621** 50w. multicoloured................................	50	40

1622 Hangang Bridge

1623 Expogyo Bridge

1624 Tongyeong Bridge

1625 Banghwa Bridge

(Des Lee Gi-seog. Photo)

2005 (23 Sept). Bridges (2nd series). P 13½ (with three indentations on each vert side).

2826	**1622**	220w. multicoloured..................................	80	65
		a. Block of 4. Nos. 2826/9	3·50	
2827	**1623**	220w. multicoloured..................................	80	65
2828	**1624**	220w. multicoloured..................................	80	65
2829	**1625**	220w. multicoloured..................................	80	65
2826/2829	*Set of 4*..		3·00	2·30

Nos. 2826/9 were issued together in *se-tenant* blocks of four stamps within the sheet.

1626 Cheonwangbong Peak   **1627** Baraebong peak

1628 Ikki Falls   **1629** Piagol Valley

(Des Park Eun-kyung. Photo)

2005 (18 Oct). Mountains (2nd series). Mount Jirisan. P 13×13½.

2830	**1626**	220w. multicoloured..................................	80	65
		a. Horiz strip of 4. Nos. 2830/3.......	3·50	
2831	**1627**	220w. multicoloured..................................	80	65
2832	**1628**	220w. multicoloured..................................	80	65
2833	**1629**	220w. multicoloured..................................	80	65
2830/2833	*Set of 4*..		3·00	2·30

Nos. 2830/3 were issued together in horizontal *se-tenant* strips of four stamps within the sheet.

1630 Emblem

2005 (27 Oct). Centenary of Korean Red Cross. P 13½.

2834	**1630**	220w. multicoloured	80	65

1631 Buddha

(Des Roh Jeonghwa. Photo)

2005 (28 Oct). Relocation and Reopening of National Museum. P 13½.

2835	**1631**	220w. multicoloured.............................	80	65

1632 *Epipactis thunbergii*

(Des Kim So-jeong. Photo)

2005 (11 Nov). Orchids (5th series). T **1632** and similar vert designs. Multicoloured. P 13½×13.

2836	220w. Type **1632**	80	65
	a. Horiz. strip of 4. Nos. 2836/9......	3·50	
2837	220w. *Cymbidium goeringii*	80	65
2838	220w. *Cephalanthera erecta*...................	80	65
2839	220w. *Spiranthes sinensis*	80	65
2836/2839 *Set of 4*...		3·00	2·30

Nos. 2836/9 were issued together in horizontal *se-tenant* strips of four stamps within the sheet.

1633 Nurimaru APEC House, Dongbaek Island

(Des Roh Junghwa. Photo)

2005 (18 Nov). APEC Economic Leaders' Meeting, Busan. T **1633** and similar vert design. P 13×13½.

2840	220w. Type **1633**	80	65
	a. Horiz. pair. Nos. 2840/1	1·70	1·40
2841	220w. "The Sun, the Moon and Five Peaks" (traditional painting)	80	65

Nos. 2840/1 were issued in horizontal *se-tenant* pairs within the sheet.

1634 Puppy

(Des Park Eun-kyung. Photo)

2005 (1 Dec). New Year. Year of the Dog. P 13½.

2842	**1634**	220w. multicoloured..................................	80	65

No. 2842 was issued both in sheets and small sheets of two stamps with enlarged margins.

1635 Jikjisimcheyojeol (oldest book created using moveable type)

(Des Kim So-jeong. Eng Shin In-chul. Recess and litho)

2005 (9 Dec). Registration of Korean Cultural Treasures as UNESCO World Heritage. Sheet 145×232 mm. containing T **1635** and similar horiz design. Multicoloured. P 13×13½.

MS2843 Type **1635**×5; 310w. Seungjeongwon Ilgi (Diaries of the Royal Secretariat)×5 (52×36 mm) .... 8·00   7·75

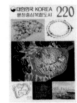

1636 Plans and Design Layout

(Des Park Eun-kyung. Photo)

2005 (27 Dec). Construction of Multifunctional Administrative City, Chungcheong. P 13½.

2844 **1636** 220w. multicoloured 80   65

1637 Phoca vitulina largha

(Des Lee Bok-sik and Lee Gi-seog. Photo)

2006 (18 Jan). Baengnyeongdo Island. T **1637** and similar horiz designs. Multicoloured. P 13×13½.

2845   220w. Type **1637** 80   65
2846   220w. *Phalacrocorax pelagicus* 80   65
2847   220w. *Orithyia sinica* 80   65
2848   220w. *Ammodytes personatus* 80   65
2845/2848 *Set of 4* .... 3·00   2·30

Nos. 2845/8 were issued in sheets with enlarged illustrated margins, the whole forming a composite design of the island.

1638 Fruit, Horses, Flowers and Stone Grandfather

(Des Roh Junghwa. Photo)

2006 (27 Jan). First Anniv of Jeju as Designated Island of World Peace. P 13½.

2849 **1638**   220w. multicoloured 80   65

1639 *Crinum asiaticum*

2006 (2 Mar). P 14×13.

2850 **1639** 100w. ulticoloured 80   65

1640 Car (automobile industries)

2006 (15 Mar). Korean Industries. T **1640** and similar horiz designs. Multicoloured. P 13½.

2851   220w. Type **1640** 80   65
         a. Block of 8. Nos. 2851/8 .... 6·75
2852   220w. Computer chips (semi-
            conductors) 80   65
2853   220w. Chemical symbols
            (petrochemical) 80   65
2854   220w. TV screen and mobile
            telephone (electronics) 80   65
2855   220w. Robotic arms (engineering)....... 80   65
2856   220w. Ships (ship building) 80   65
2857   220w. Rolls of steel (steel industry)...... 80   65
2858   220w. Fabric (textile industry) 80   65
2851/2858 *Set of 8* .... 5·75   4·75

Nos. 2851/8 were issued together in *se-tenant* blocks of eight stamps within the sheet.

1641 Rainbow, Children and Computer (Lee Annr Rulloda)

2006 (21 Apr). "Ubiquitous World" (pervasive computing). Winning Designs in Children's Painting Competition. T **1641** and similar multicoloured design. P 13½.

2859   220w. Type **1641** 80   65
2860   220w. "Green IT" (Kim Jeonghee)
            (horiz).. 80   65

1642 Iguanodon

(Des Shin Jaeyong. Photo)

2006 (14 Apr). Gyeongnam Goseong Dinosaurs World Expo. T **1642** and similar horiz design. Multicoloured. Self-adhesive gum. Die-cut Perf. 11½.

2861	220w. Type **1642**	80	65
	a. Pair. Nos. 2861/2	1·70	1·40
2862	220w. Megaraptor	80	65

Nos. 2861/2 were issued in horizontal *se-tenant* pairs within the sheet.

1643 Myeongjingwan Building

(Des R. Junghwa. Litho)

2006 (8 May). Centenary of Dongguk University. P 13½.
2863	**1643**	220w. multicoloured	80	65

1644 Second Foundation Campus

(Des R. Junghwa. Photo)

2006 (22 May). Centenary of Sookmyung Women's University. P 13½.
2864	**1644**	220w. multicoloured	80	65

A sheet containing a 220w. stamp showing the Korean flag×14 and various photographs of the National football team, was on sale from the Philatelic bureau for 6000w.

No. 2865 and Type **1645** are vacant.

1646 *Parus major*

(Des Kim So-jeong. Photo)

2006 (5 June). P 13×14.
2866	**1646**	90w. multicoloured	80	65

1647 Football, Emblem and Mascot

(Des Mo Jiwon. Photo)

2006 (9 June). World Cup Football Championship, Germany. T **1647** and similar horiz design. Multicoloured. P 13×14.
2867	220w. Type **1647**	80	65
2868	220w. Players	80	65

(Des Kim So-jeong. Photo)

2006 (3 July). Goguryeo (2nd issue). Horiz. designs as T **1616**. Multicoloured. P 13½×13 (with one irregular Perf. on each vert side).

2869	80w. Janggunchong	1·50	1·20
	a. Vert. pair. Nos. 2869/70	3·25	2·50
2870	480w. Gods	1·50	1·20

Nos. 2869/70 were issued in vertical *se-tenant* pairs within the sheet.

The irregular perforations show the outline of Goguryeo area when seen across the sheet.

1648 Fingerprints as Heart

(Des Shin Jae-yong. Photo)

2006 (3 Aug). Philately Week. Marriage. T **1648** and similar horiz design. Multicoloured. P 13½.
2871	220w. Type **1648**	80	65
	a. Pair. Nos. 2871/2	1·70	1·40
2872	220w. As No. 2871 but with country inscription and face value at top	80	65

Nos. 2871/2 were issued in *se-tenant* pairs within the sheet.

The background (except for No. 2871 and the heart and the two larger roses) of No. 2871 and the heart and the two larger roses of No. 2872, were printed in optically variable ink which causes the colour to have a silver tinge when viewed from different angles.

Nos. 2871/2 were issued both in sheets and together in sheetlets of two stamps with enlarged illustrated margins.

1649 Tail Stole

(Des Park Eun-kyung. Photo)

2006 (5 Sept). Extreme Sports (1st issue). Skateboarding. Sheet 75×106 mm. containing T **1649** and similar vert designs. Multicoloured. Self-adhesive. Die-cut.
MS2873	220w.×4 Type **1649**; Drop in; Backside spin; Backside grab	3·50	3·25

The stamps of No. **MS**2873 were die-cut around to simulate perforations and form a composite background design

1650 Ginseng Root

(Des Mo Jiwon. Photo)

2006 (22 Sept). World Ginseng Expo, Geumsan. P 13½.
2874 **1650** 220w. multicoloured 80 65

1651 Olympic Bridge

1652 Seohae Bridge

1653 Jindo Bridge

1654 Changseon-Samcheonpo Bridge

(Des Lee Gi-seog. Photo)

2006 (28 Sept). Bridges (3rd series). P 13½ (with three indentations on each vert side).
2875 **1651** 220w. multicoloured 80 65
    a. Block of 4. Nos. 2875/8 .... 3·50
2876 **1652** 220w. multicoloured 80 65
2877 **1653** 220w. multicoloured 80 65
2878 **1654** 220w. multicoloured 80 65
2875/2878 Set of 4.. 3·00 2·30
   Nos. 2875/8 were issued together in *se-tenant* blocks of four stamps within the sheet.

1655 Script

1656 Building Façade

(Des Lee Gi-seog. Photo)

2006 (9 Oct). 560th Anniv of Hangeul (Korean script) Day. P 13½.
2879 **1655** 220w. multicoloured 80 65

(Des Shin Jae-yong. Photo)

2006 (10 Oct). Centenary of Sahmyook University. P 13½.
2880 **1656** 220w. multicoloured 80 65

1657 Flower

2006 (1 Nov). My Own Stamp. P 13½.
2881 **1657** 250w. multicoloured .... 1·00 80
   No. 2881 was issued with a *se-tenant* label attached at right which could be personalised by the addition of photograph or logo.

1658 *Ninox scutulata*   **1659** Swans

(Des Lee Gi-seog. Photo)

2006 (1 Nov). P 13½.
2882 **1658** 250w. multicoloured .... 1·00 80

(Des Kim So-jeong. Photo)

2006 (1 Nov). P 13½.
2883 **1659** 340w. multicoloured .... 1·30 1·00

1660 Buncheong Ware Vase

(Des Roh Junghwa. Photo)

2006 (1 Nov). P 13½.
2884 **1660** 1750w. multicoloured .... 7·00 6·50

1661 'Lineage'

2006 (9 Nov). Online Computer Games. Self adhesive. Die-cut.

2885	250w. Type **1661**	1·00	80
	a. Sheetlet of 10. Nos. 2885/94	10·50	
2886	250w. 'Maple Story'	1·00	80
2887	250w. 'Ragnarok'	1·00	80
2888	250w. 'Gersang'	1·00	80
2889	250w. 'Legend of Mir III'	1·00	80
2890	250w. 'Kartrider'	1·00	80
2891	250w. 'Mu'	1·00	80
2892	250w. 'Pangya'	1·00	80
2893	250w. 'Fortress2 Blue'	1·00	80
2894	250w. 'Mabinogi'	1·00	80
2885/2894 *Set of* 10		9·00	7·25

Nos. 2885/94 were issued in sheetlets of ten stamps.

1662 Daecheongbong Peak

1663 Sibiseonnyeotang Valley

1664 Janggunbong Peak

1665 Ulsanbawi Rock

(Des Park Eun-kyung. Photo)

2006 (16 Nov). Mountains (3rd series). Mount Seoraksan. P 13×13½.

2895	**1662**	250w. multicoloured	1·00	80
		a. Block of 4. Nos. 2895/8	4·25	
2896	**1663**	250w. multicoloured	1·00	80

2897	**1664**	250w. multicoloured	1·00	80
2898	**1665**	250w. multicoloured	1·00	80
2895/2898 *Set of* 4		3·50	3·00

Nos. 2895/8 were issued together in *se-tenant* blocks of four stamps within the sheet.

1666 Pig

(Des Park Eun-kyung. Photo)

2006 (1 Dec). New Year. Year of the Pig. P 13½.

2899	**1666**	250w. multicoloured	1·00	80

No. 2899 was issued both in sheets and small sheets of two stamps with enlarged margins.

1667 Script, Singer and Drummer

(Des Kim So-jeong. Eng Shin Incheol. Recess and litho)

2006 (8 Dec). UNESCO Masterpiece of Oral and Intangible Heritage of Humanity. Pansori Songs and Singers. T **1667** and similar horiz design. Multicoloured. P 13½.

2900	480w. Type **1667**	2·00	1·60
	a. Pair. Nos. 2900/1	4·25	3·50
2901	480w. Singer, musician and audience		
	(51×35 mm)	2·00	1·60

Nos. 2900/1 were issued together in *se-tenant* blocks of four stamps within the sheet and also in small sheets of two stamps with enlarged illustrated margins.

1668 Faces and Hands holding Flowers (Kim Han-yun)

2006 (14 Dec). Caring Neighbourhood and Donation Culture. T **1688** and similar vert design. Multicoloured. P 13×13½.

2902	250w. Type **1668**	1·00	80
2903	250w. Man watering tree seedling	1·00	80

STAMP BOOKLETS

The following checklist covers, in simplified form, booklets issued by the Post Office. It is intended that it should be used in conjunction with the main listings and details of stamps and panes listed there are not repeated.

Some booklets exist in more than one version, differing in the inscription on the margin of the pane. Such differences are not covered in this list.

PHILATELIC CENTRE BOOKLETS. From 1989 most stamps were also sold in booklets by the Philatelic Centre, at a premium over the price of the contents, to collectors. Until July 1995 these were in a common format and contained a strip or block torn from the sheet and mounted by the selvedge, with a further example stuck on the front and tied by a "First Day" cancellation. From August 1995 the stamp on the front was removed; these more closely resemble Post Office booklets but can be identified by the inscription "KOREAN PHILATELIC CENTER" on the back. As these are collector souvenirs they are not included in the list below.

Prices are for complete booklets

Booklet No.	Date	Contents and Cover Price	Price
SB1	20.7.56	Reconstruction (T **101**)	
		5 panes, No. 235a (600h.)	9·00
SB2	25.7.58	*King Sejong* (T **106**)	
		5 panes, No. 281a (1200h.)	12·00
SB3	20.4.74	*Manchurian Cranes* (T **465**)	
		5 panes, No. 1065×6 (300w.)	40·00
SB4	30.9.81	*Hibiscus syriacus* (T **706**)	
		1 pane. No. 1371×16 (640w.)	20·00
		a. Cover additionally inscr "PHILATOKYO '81"	30·00
SB5	15.3.83	*Kyongju Observatory* (T **708**)	
		1 pane, No. 1374×10	20·00
SB6	24.1.94	*U.P.U. Congress* (T **1268**)	
		1 pane. No. 2088a (3000w.)	16·00
SB7	13.6.94	*"Philakorea 1994"* (T **1273**)	
		1 pane, No. 2101a (9100w.)	42·00
SB8	16.8.94	*"Philakorea 1994"* (T **1278**)	
		1 pane, No. 2107a (1300w.)	6·50
SB9	16.8.94	*"Philakorea 1994"* (T **1279**)	
		1 pane, No. 2108a (1300w.)	6·50
SB10	16.8.94	*"Philakorea 1994"* (T **1280**)	
		1 pane, No. 2109a (1300w.)	6·50
SB11	22.8.94	*U.P. U. Congress* (T **1282**)	
		1 pane, No. 2112a (1300w.)	6·50
SB12	22.8.94	*U.P.U. Congress*	
		1 pane, No. 2113a (1300w.)	6·50
SB13	22.8.94	*U.P.U. Congress*	
		1 pane, No. 2114a (1300w.)	6·50
SB14	22.8.94	*U.P.U. Congress*	
		1 pane, No. 2115a (3700w.)	6·50
SB15	28.2.95	*Narcissi* (T **1225**)	
		1 pane, No. 2034b (2600w.)	20·00
SB16	20.3.95	*Celadon Pitcher* (T **1238**)	
		1 pane, No. 2049ab (9300w.)	37·00
SB17	1.6.95	*Airplane*	
		1 pane, No. 2123a (3900w.)	32·00
SB18	14.8.95	*50th Anniv of Liberation* (T **1299**)	
		1 pane, No. 2166a (1300w.)	6·50
SB19	20.3.96	*Painted Porcelain Jar* (T **1226**)	
		1 pane, No. 2035a (3000w.)	30·00
SB20	27.3.96	*Airplane* (T **1285**)	
		1 pane. No. 2124a (4000w.)	23·00

NORTH KOREAN OCCUPATION OF SOUTH KOREA

North Korean troops invaded South Korea on 25 June 1950 and occupied a large part of the country from July to 15 September. Then a landing of UN forces at Inchon, behind their lines, forced them out of South Korea

1 ("Democratic People's Republic of Korea")

2 ("Korean People's Inferior Republic Postage Stamp")

1950. Nos 116 and 118/19 of South Korea optd with T **1**, in red.

1	10w. turquoise-green		65·00
2	20w. brown		25·00
3	30w. turquoise green		31·00

Type **2** is a local overprint which was placed on sale at some post offices after the North Koreans had withdrawn. The different character arrowed changed the word "democratic" to "inferior".

INDIAN CUSTODIAN FORCES IN KOREA

Overprints for use by the Indian contingent of the U.N Forces in Korea. The listing is repeated from the *British Commonwealth* Catalogue.

भारतीय
संरक्षा कटक
कोरिया

307 Ajanta Panel   **314** Bhuvanesvara   (K **1**)

1953. Stamps of India optd with Type K **1**

K1	**307**	3p. slate violet	1·75	4·50
K2	–	6p. purple brown (No. 310)	1·50	4·50
K3	–	9p. yellow-green (No. 311)	1·75	4·50
K4	–	1a. turquoise (No. 333)	1·50	4·50
K5	–	2a. carmine (No. 313)	1·50	4·50
K6	–	2½a. lake (No. 333a)	1·50	4·75
K7	–	3a. brown-orange (No. 314)	1·50	4·50
K8	**314**	4a. bright blue	2·00	4·75
K9	–	6a. violet (No. 317)	8·50	4·75
K10	–	8a. turquoise-green (No. 318)	2·00	9·50
K11	–	12a. dull blue (No. 319)	2·25	17·00
K12	–	1r. dull violet and green (No. 320) .	3·25	17·00
K1/K12	*Set of* 12		26·00	80·00

Designs: As T **307**—9p. Trimurti; 1a. Bodhissattva; 2a. Nataraja. As T **307** but horiz—6p. Konarak horse. As T **314**—2½a. Bodh Gaya Temple; 3a. Sanchi Stupa, East Gate. As T **314** but horiz—6a. Gol Gumbad, Bijapur; 8a. Kandaraya Mahadeva Temple; 12a. Golden Temple, Amritsar. 22×38 mm—1r. Victory Tower, Chittorgarh.

NORTH KOREA

The Soviet Union declared war on Japan on 8 August 1945 and its forces, which entered Korea on 10 August, soon occupied all of the country north of the 38th parallel. A Provisional People's Committee was set up on 9 February 1946, with Kim Il Sung as Prime Minister. Japanese stamps continued in use until 1946.

100 Cheun = 1 Won

GUM All stamps of North Korea up to No. N1506 are *without* gum, except where otherwise stated.

> **REPRINTS.** Collectors should beware of official imitations ("reprints") of most issues from 1946 to 1956, made in 1957–58 by the North Korean Postal Administration for sale to collectors. These "reprints" could be, and have been, used for postage, but as that was not their primary purpose we do not list them.

Six stamps listed in earlier editions of the catalogue have been removed from the list below, until there is proof of their existence. They were originally listed in Japanese or Chinese publications in 1955–57, but so far no examples of them have been seen by European collectors. If and when they are seen, they will be restored to the list. The stamps were previously listed as Nos. NK1, NK3, NK7, NK8, NK15 and NK21.

A. RUSSIAN OCCUPATION

1 Hibiscus **2** Diamond Mountains **3** Diamond Mountains

T **2.** "50" 2 mm high

T **3.** "50" 3 mm high

1946 (12 Mar)–**55**. Litho.
N1	1	20ch. red (perf 11)	75·00	50·00
N2	2	50ch. apple-green (p 11, white paper)		
		(shades)	50·00	40·00
		a. Yellow-green (thin buff paper)		
N3		50ch. carmine-rose (roul) (1947?)	60·00	70·00
N4	3	50ch. rose-red (pin-perf 12) (shades).		
		(1948)	39·00	39·00
		a. P 11×imp or imp×p 11	21·00	21·00
		b. Imperf (1950)	13·50	13·50
		c. Perf 10 (1955)	60·00	46·00
N5		50ch. violet (p 11) (1950?)	34·00	34·00
		a. P 11×imperf or imperf×p 11	27·00	27·00
		b. Imperf (1950)	12·50	14·50
		c. Perf 10 (1955)	65·00	46·00

No. N4 has lines of coloured dots along the horizontal pin perforations. No. N5 is crudely printed from worn plates.
Reprints of No. N1 are in *yellow-green*, perf 8½ to 10 or imperforate, 23 mm high instead of 22 mm, with other differences in the design. Reprints of No. N4 are in vermilion, perf 10×10½, 11 or imperforate, on gummed paper,

4 Gen Kim Il Sung and Flag **5** Peasants

1946 (15 Aug). First Anniv of Liberation from Japan. Litho. Pin-perf.
N6	4	50ch. brown (shades)	£250	£190

1947 (22 Apr)–**55**. Typo. Pin-perf 12.
N7	5	1wn. turquoise-green	6·75	5·75
N8		1wn. violet (shades) (1949)	21·00	21·00
N9		1wn. deep blue/*buff* (1950)	8·50	6·75
N10		1wn. deep blue (imperf) (1950)	4·25	3·25
		a. Perf 11×imperf (1950)	40·00	29·00
		b. Perf 10 (1955)	60·00	55·00

Nos. N7/9 have lines of coloured dots along the horizontal pin perforations.
Reprints of Type **5** are in light blue, finely printed and perf 8½ to 10½ or imperforate.

PERF 10. In 1955 a new perforating machine was acquired and many back issues, previously issued imperforate, were reissued perforated by this machine. Most of these stamps perf 10 are scarce

6 **7** **8**

1948 (5 June). Second Anniv of the Labour Law. Litho. P 11.
N11	6	50ch. deep blue	£300	£300

Reprints are perf 10½ or imperforate, on gummed paper, with many slight differences of design.

1948 (15 Aug). Third Anniv of Liberation from Japan. Litho. P 11.
N12	7	50ch. rose-red	£180	£600

Reprints are perf 10½, or imperforate, on gummed paper, with many slight differences of design.

1948 (20 Aug). Promulgation of Constitution. Litho. P 11.
N13	8	50ch. indigo and red	£225	£110

B. KOREAN PEOPLE'S DEMOCRATIC REPUBLIC

This Republic was proclaimed on 9 September 1948. The last Soviet troops left Korea by 30 December 1948.

9 North Korean Flag **10**

1948 (19 Sept). Establishment of People's Republic. Litho. Roul.
N16	9	25ch. violet	4·50	4·50
N17		50ch. grey-blue	8·00	7·75

No. N16 sometimes has a vertical row of dots between rows of stamps and No. N17 sometimes has a horizontal row. No. N17 may be found with rouletting combined with rough perforation.
Reprints of No. N16 are in blue, on gummed paper, perf 9 to 10½; or impeforate, size 20½×28 mm instead of 24×31 mm

1949 (9 Feb). Litho. Rouletted.
N18   **10**   6wn. red and blue (shades) ....   3·00   3·50
                   a. Perf 10 (1956).................................   17·00   16·00
    Reprints are perf 10½×10, size 19×26½ mm instead of 24×33½
mm, with colours reversed apart from those of the flag.

11   Kim Il Sung University,   **11a**
            Pyongyang

1949. Litho. Rouletted.
N19   **11**   1wn. violet (9.8).................................   £110   60·00
N20   **11a**   1wn. blue (Sept?).................................   £150   41·00
    Reprints of No. N19 are in greyish purple, perf 8½, 10 or imperforate,
finely printed on gummed paper.

12   North Korean   **13**   Order of the
         Flags   National Flag

1949 (15 Aug). Fourth Anniv of Liberation from Japan. Litho. P 11 or
roul (No. N23).
N22   **12**   1wn. red, green & blue (20½×31 mm)   £140   50·00
                   a. Imperf×perf 11 ....   £140   50·00
N23   1wn. red, grn & turq (20×29½ mm)...   —   £275
    The design of No. N23 differs in many details from that of No. N22,
e.g., the dates at top are smaller and upright.

1950 (4 Apr)–**56**.
                  (a) Litho. Roul. Size 23½×37½ mm.
N24   **13**   1wn. sage-green...............................   5·50   1·40
                   a. Bright green ....   7·25   1·60
N25   1wn. brown-orange (1950)...............   70·00   55·00

                  (b) Litho. Roul. Size 20×32½ mm
N26   **13**   1wn. red-orange (1950) ....   22·00   18·00

                  (c) Typo. Imperf. Size 22×35½ mm
N27   **13**   1wn. deep green (1951).................   5·50   2·00
                   a. Perf 10 (1956)...............................   20·00   13·00

                  (d) Typo. Imperf. Size 22½×36½ mm
N28   **13**   1wn. pale olive green (1951?)..............   9·25   5·75
    Reprints of Type **13** are in pale blue-green on white paper, 22×35
mm, perf 10 or imperforate; or in red-orange on white paper, 20×32½
mm, perf 9, 10×imperf or imperforate. Numeral "1" tall and thin.

14   Liberation   **15**   Soldier
         Monument,   and Flags
         Pyongyang

16 Peasant and   **17** Tractor
        Worker

1950 (20 June)–**56**. Fifth Anniv of Liberation from Japan.
                  (a) Litho. Thin paper. Roul×imperf
N29   **14**   1wn. Red, deep blue and pale blue...   1·60   1·10
                   a. Perf 10 (1955).................................   8·00   8·75
N30   1wn. brownish orange ....   9·25   8·75
N31   **15**   2wn. black, blue and red ....   1·60   1·20
                   a. Perf 10 (1955).................................   8·00   8·75

                  (b) Litho. Thin soft paper. Roul
N32   **16**   6wn. bright green (20×30 mm)..........   2·20   1·60
N33   **17**   10wn. brown (20×28 mm)..................   3·25   2·40

                  (c) Typo. Thick paper. Imperf×roul
N34   **16**   6wn. red (22×33 mm) ....   22·00   16·00
N35   **17**   10wn chestnut (22×30 mm) ....   28·00   19·00

                  (d) Typo. Thin paper. Imperf
N36   **16**   6wn. red (22×33 mm) ....   17·00   13·50
                   a. Perf 10 (1956).................................   17·00   14·50
N37   **17**   10wn. red-brown (22×30 mm)..............   25·00   16·00
    Reprints of No. N29 are 22 mm wide instead of 23 mm with thin
numeral "1" 2 mm high instead of 2½ mm; reprints of No. N31 are perf
10 or imperforate, clearly printed, with three vertical lines at each
side of lower central inscription; reprints of No. N32 are perf 10×10½,
11 or imperforate, on opaque white paper; reprints of Type **17** are
perf 10 or imperforate, 22×31 mm. on white paper.

18 Capitol,   **19**   **20** Kim Gi Ok
        Seoul   and Aeroplane

(Des Ham Hyon. Litho)

1950 (10 July). Capture of Seoul by North Korean Forces. Roul.
N38   **18**   1wn. red, blue and turquoise-green .   50·00   44·00

1951 (5 Apr)–**56**. Order of Admiral Li Sun Sin. Typo. Imperf.
N39   **19**   6wn. orange (shades) ....   8·50   7·00
                   a. Perf 10 or 9 (1956) ....   15·00   16·00
    Reprints are perf 10 or imperforate, but are clearly printed on
white paper instead of yellowish local paper.

1951 (17 Apr). Air Force Hero Kim Gi Ok. Typo. Imperf.
N40   **20**   1wn. blue (shades)...............................   10·50   6·75
    Reprints are perf 10 to 10½, with design 22×33½ mm instead of
23×36½ mm, on white paper.

21 Russian   **22** Kim   **23** N. Korean and
        and N. Korean   Ki U (hero)   Chinese Soldiers
        Flags

1951 (15 Aug–**55**. Sixth Anniv of Liberation from Japan. Litho. Roul.

N41	**21**	1wn. deep blue	4·50	3·25
		b. Perf 10 (1955)	11·00	7·75
N42		1wn. carmine-red	4·50	3·25
		b. Perf 10 (1955)	11·00	7·75
N43	**22**	1wn. deep blue	4·50	3·25
		b. Perf 10 (1955)	11·00	7·75
N44		1wn. carmine-red	5·00	3·25
		b. Perf 10 (1955)	12·50	12·00
N45	**23**	2wn. deep blue	9·25	6·50
		b. Perf 10 (1955)	11·00	7·75
N41A/46A	Set of 6		37·00	28·00
N41b/46b	Set of 6		65·00	47·00

All values exist on buff and on white paper.

Reprints of No. N41 are in medium blue, perf 10½×10 or imperforate, 22 mm high instead of 23 mm; reprints of Nos. N43/4 have no lines of shading between the characters above the portrait; reprints of No. N45 are 22½ mm wide instead of 23 mm, with Korean word after "2" in four parts instead of three.

24 Order of   **25**   **26** Woman
Soldier's   Partisan, Li Su Dok
Honour

1951 (15 Nov)–**56**. Litho. Imperf.

N47	**24**	40wn. carmine red (17×24 mm)	12·50	5·75
		a. Perf 10 (1956)	20·00	13·50
N48		40wn. carmine-red (16½×25 mm)	12·50	5·75
		a. Perf 10 (1956)	20·00	13·50

Alternate stamps in the sheet of No. N47 have the "eggs" flaw, as shown in Type **24**, at lower left of the medal.

1951 (15 Nov)–**56**. Co-operation of Chinese People's Volunteers. Litho. Imperf.

N49	**25**	10wn. blue (shades)	7·25	6·50
		a. Perf 10 (1956)	16·00	15·00

Reprints are in brighter blue, clearly printed on white instead of cream or buff paper, with inscription at foot outlined against criss-cross shading.

1952 (10 Jan)–**55** Partisan Heroes. Litho. Imperf.

N50	**26**	70wn. brown (shades)	5·50	1·60
		a. Perf 10 (1955)	12·50	12·00

27   **28** General   **29** Munition
              Peng Teh-huai   Worker

1952 (20 Jan)–**57**. Peace Propaganda. Litho. Imperf.

N51	**27**	20wn. deep blue, pale turquoise-green		
		and red (shades)	8·00	2·75
		a. Perf 10 (1955)	15·00	8·75
		b Perf 9 (1957)	8·00	6·50
		c. Perf 9½×8½ (1957)	12·50	8·00

Reprints are perf 10 or imperforate. The bottom of the flagpole does not touch the rim of the circle and there are other differences of design.

1952 (Apr ?). Honouring Commander of Chinese People's Volunteers. Litho. Imperf.

N52	**28**	10wn. slate-purple	16·00	6·50

1952 (20 Apr)–**55**. Labour Day. Litho. Imperf.

N53	**29**	10wn. rose red	42·00	40·00
		a. Perf 10 (1955)	46·00	43·00

30   **31**   **32**

1952 (1 June)–**55**. Sixth Anniv of Labour Law. Litho. Imperf.

N54	**30**	10wn. blue	25·00	20·00
		a. Perf 10 (1955)	21·00	16·00

Reprints are on thick gummed paper, with no printed broken lines between stamps.

1952 (4 June)–**56**. Anti-US Imperialism Day. Litho. Imperf.

N55	**31**	10wn. rose-red	31·00	30·00
		a. Perf 10 (1956)	35·00	34·00

Reprints are on thick gummed paper, with no printed broken lines between stamps.

1952 (25 July)–**56**. North Korean and Chinese Friendship. Litho. Imperf.

N56	**32**	20wn. deep blue	15·00	14·50
		a. Perf 10 (1956)	14·50	13·50

Reprints are in medium blue on thick gummed paper, with shading on sandbags below machine-gun.

33   **34**

1952 (25 July)–**55**. Seventh Anniv of Liberation from Japan. Litho. Imperf.

N57	**33**	10wn. carmine	31·00	30·00
		a. Perf 10 (1955)	34·00	32·00
N58	**34**	10wn. red (1.8.52)	24·00	23·00
		a. Perf 10 (1955)	29·00	25·00

Reprints of No. N57 are clearly printed in vermilion on thick gummed paper; those of No. N58 are in rose-red, 31 mm wide instead of 29½ mm.

35   **36**   **37**

1952 (20 Oct)–**55**. International Youth Day. Litho. With gum. Imperf.

N59	**35**	10wn. deep green	17·00	17·00
		a. Perf 10 (1955)	19·00	18·00

Reprints are on thinner ungummed paper, size 20×27 mm instead of 20½×28 mm.

1953 (20 Jan)–**55**. Fifth Anniv of People's Army. Litho. Imperf.

N60	**36**	10wn. deep carmine	32·00	31·00
		a. Perf 10 (1955)	37·00	33·00
N61	**37**	40wn. brown-purple	21·00	20·00
		a. Perf 10 (1955)	29·00	25·00

Reprints of Nos. N60/1 are on thick gummed paper; the star on the 10wn. has thin points and there is no line between "4" and "0" on the 40wn.

38

39

1953 (1 Mar)–**55**. International Women's Day. Litho. With gum. Imperf.

N62	**38**	10wn. deep carmine	22·00	19·00
		a. Perf 10 (1955)	22·00	19·00
N63	**39**	40wn. yellow-green	24·00	21·00
		a. Perf 10 (1955)	24·00	21·00

Reprints are without gum; the colours are rose and dull green and there are differences of design.

40

41

1953 (15 Apr)–**55**. Labour Day. Litho. Imperf.

N64	**40**	10wn. yellow-green	16·00	15·00
		a. Perf 10 (1955)	22·00	21·00
N65	**41**	40wn. brown-orange	16·00	15·00
		a. Perf 10 (1955)	22·00	21·00

Reprints of the 10wn. are in dull green, perf 10, 9×8½ or imperforate; those of the 40wn. are in orange-brown, perf 10 or imperforate. There are differences of design.

42

43

1953 (1 June)–**55**. Anti-US Imperialism Day. Litho. With gum. Imperf.

N66	**42**	10wn. greenish blue	31·00	30·00
		a. Perf 10 (1955)	37·00	33·00
N67	**43**	40wn. red	31·00	30·00
		a. Perf 10 (1955)	37·00	33·00

Reprints are in light blue and vermilion, on very white paper; there are differences of design.

1953 (10 June)–**55**. Fourth World Youth Festival, Bucharest. Litho. With gum. Imperf.

N68	**44**	10wn. blue and pale blue green	18·00	17·00
		a. Perf 10 (1955)	21·00	19·00
N69	**45**	20wn. grey-green and pink	15·00	8·75
		a. Perf 10 (1955)	19·00	17·00

Reprints of No. N68 are perf 10 or imperforate, in indigo and pale green.

1953 (28 July)–**55**. Armistice and Victory Issue. Litho. With gum. Imperf.

N70	**46**	10wn brown and yellow	£110	£100
		a. Perf 10 (1955)	90·00	85·00

47

48

49 Liberation Monument, Pyongyang

1953 (5 Aug). Eighth Anniv of Liberation from Japan. Litho. Imperf.

N71	**47**	10wn. red-orange	£400	£375

Reprints are perf 10 or imperforate, and have shading on left side of spire.

1953 (25 Aug)–**55**. Fifth Anniv of People's Republic. Litho. Imperf.

N72	**48**	10wn. blue and red	20·00	19·00
		a. Perf 10 (1955)	28·00	27·00

Reprints are perf 10, in light blue and orange-red and are dated "1948–1955".

1953 (25 Dec)–**55**. Litho. With gum. Imperf.

N73	**49**	10wn. slate	19·00	9·75
		a. Perf 10 (1955)	19·00	11·00

Reprints are in grey and the base of the "1" cuts across only one ray.

료금수리 (50)　　(◯5원 채상심 (51))　　5 (51a)

1953 (Dec ?). No. N18 optd "Fee Collected" in Korean characters. T **50**.

N74	**10**	6wn. red and blue	£250	£250

1954 (Jan). Nos. N18 and N39 surch with T **51**.

N75	**10**	5wn. on 6wn. red and blue	29·00	19·00
N76	**19**	5wn. on 6wn. orange	75·00	55·00
		a. Surch as T **51**. but diameter 11 mm	£130	90·00
		b. Surch with T **51a**	£250	£225

44

45

46

52

53

54

1954 (25 Jan)–**55**. Post-war Economic Reconstruction. Litho. With gum. Imperf.
N77 **52**   10wn. pale blue.. 31·00   18·00
          a. Perf 10 (1955)................................. 41·00   37·00
Reprints are perf 10, have no gum and the sky above the scaffolding is heavily shaded.

1954 (25 Jan)–**55**. Sixth Anniv of People's Army. Litho. With gum. Imperf.
N78 **53**   10wn. dull red £110   £110
          a. Perf 10 (1955)................................. £120   £110
Reprints are in vermilion, on very white paper, and the right-hand border of the design is straight and unbroken.

1954 (25 Feb)–**55**. International Women's Day. Litho. With gum. Imperf.
N79 **54**   10wn. carmine-red.................................... 25·00   24·00
          a. Perf 10 (1955)................................. 27·00   26·00
Reprints are in vermilion, and the design is slightly larger, with minor differences.

      55   **56**

1954 (15 Apr)–**55**. Labour Day. Litho. With gum. Imperf.
N80 **55**   10wn. scarlet .... 20·00   19·00
          a. Perf 10 (1955)................................. 24·00   23·00
Reprints are in vermilion, perf 8×9, 9, 10 or imperforate, with slight differences of design.

1954 (10 June)–**55**. Anti-US Imperialism Day. Litho. With gum. Imperf.
N81 **56**   10wn. dull carmine-red .... 37·00   33·00
          a. Perf 10 (1955)................................. 41·00   37·00

  57 Taedong Gate,   **58**
  Pyongyang

1954 (June)–**56**. Litho. Imperf.
N82 **57**   5wn. lake (shades).................................... 4·25   1·50
          a. Perf 10 (1956)................................. 8·75   7·75
N83   5wn. red-brown (1.9.54)....................... 4·25   1·50
          a. Perf 10 (1956)................................. 8·75   7·75
Nos. N82/a are on gummed paper.

1954 (20 July)–**55**. National Young Activists' Conference. Litho. With gum. Imperf.
N84 **58**   10wn. red, blue and slate...................... 5·25   5·00
          a. Perf 10 (1955)................................. 7·25   7·00
In the reprints the man's thumb is upright, the girl's chin does not touch his shoulder and only part of the crane is visible.

  59 Soldier   **60** North Korean Flag

1954 (1 Aug)–**55**. Ninth Anniv of Liberation from Japan. Litho. With gum. Imperf.
N85 **59**   10wn. vermilion .... 12·00   11·50
          a. Perf 10 (1955)................................. 12·00   11·50
In the reprints only the top of the left-hand chimney appears below the rifle muzzle.

1954 (25 Aug)–**55**. Sixth Anniv of People's Republic. Litho. With gum. Imperf.
N86 **60**   10wn. blue and scarlet............................ 9·75   9·25
          a. Perf 10 (1955)................................. 11·50   11·00
Reprints are perf 10, have no gum and the ribbon is entirely scarlet.

  61 Hwanghae   **62** Hwanghae Iron Works
  Iron Works   and Workers

1954 (1 Nov)–**56**. Economic Reconstruction. Litho. Imperf.
N87 **61**   10wn. pale blue....................................... 8·75   1·20
          a. Perf 10 (1955)................................. 16·00   5·50
N88 **62**   10wn. chocolate...................................... 8·75   1·20
          a. Perf 10 (1955)................................. 16·00   5·50
          b. Perf 9×8½ (1956) .... 42·00   16·00

      63   **64**

1955 (25 Jan). Seventh Anniv of People's Army. Litho. With gum. Imperf.
N89 **63**   10wn. rose red .... 11·50   9·75
          a. Perf 10.. 12·00   11·00

1955 (25 Feb). International Women's Day. Litho. With gum. Imperf.
N90 **64**   10wn. deep blue...................................... 11·50   9·75
          a. Perf 10.. 15·00   13·00
Reprints are in lighter blue and the shading on the face of the woman at the left and on the dress of the woman at right is solid.

65 66 67 Admiral
Li Sun Sin

1955 (16 Apr). Labour Day. Litho. With gum. Imperf.
N91 65 10wn. bright green .... 8·25 7·75
     a. Perf 10.................................. 11·00 10·50
N92 66 10wn. carmine .... 8·25 7·75
     a. Perf 10.................................. 11·00 10·50
In reprints of No. N91 the cloud at right is clearly outlined; those of No. N92 have no gum and differ slightly in design.

1955 (14 May)–**56**. Litho. Imperf.
N93 67 1wn. blue/*pale green* (shades)............. 4·75 60
     a. Perf 10 (1956)............................ 7·25 7·00
N94 2wn. rose/*buff*............................... 5·25 60
     a. Perf 10 (1956)............................ 8·75 8·25

     Redrawn with larger "2" (14.11.56)
N95 67 2wn. rose-red.............................. 10·00 1·10
     a. Perf 9 to 10½............................ 11·00 9·75
In reprints of Nos. N93/4 the design is 19×28½ mm instead of 20×29½ mm.

68 69 Liberation
Monument and
Flags

1955 (30 May). Ninth Anniv of Labour Law. Litho. With gum. Imperf.
N96 68 10wn. rose................................. 12·50 11·50
     a. Perf 10................................. 15·00 14·50
Reprints are 26½ mm high instead of 27 mm.

1955 (10–20 July). Tenth Anniv of Liberation from Japan. Litho. P 10.
N97 69 10wn. dull green (22×32 mm) .... 4·25 3·75
     a. Imperf.................................. 5·75 3·25
N98 10wn. pale red, blue and chestnut
     (29½×42½ mm) (20.7) .... 3·75 3·25
     a. Imperf.................................. 4·25 3·00
Reprints of No. N97 are in grey-green on thick gummed paper, with slight differences of design; those of No. N98 have a brown star on obelisk and thicker top inscription.

70 71 72 Son Rock

1955 (16-20 July). Soviet Union Friendship Month. Litho. P 10.
N99 70 10wn. rose-red (22×32½ mm) .... 2·75 1·50
     b. Imperf.................................. 3·25 2·20
N100 10wn. vermilion and cobalt (29½×43
     mm) (20.7)............................... 3·50 2·20
     b. Imperf.................................. 4·75 2·75
N101 71 20wn. scarlet and slate-blue (18½×32
     mm) .... 4·75 3·25
     b. Imperf.................................. 6·25 3·75
     c. Inscr below flag in two colours 70·00 65·00
     ca. Imperf................................ £110 £110
N102 20wn. vermilion and new blue
     (25×43 mm) (20.7)....................... 2·75 1·70
     b. Imperf.................................. 4·75 2·75
N99/102 Set of 4................................. 12·50 7·75
N99b/102b Set of 4.............................. 17·00 10·50
No. N101a occurred once in the sheet.
In reprints of No. N102 there are 5 red dots in the laurel instead of 8 and the characters and numerals in red are very uneven.

1956 (20 Jan). Haegumgang Maritime Park. Litho. P 10.
N103 72 10wn. new blue/*bluish*................... 6·00 3·25
     a. Imperf.................................. 6·50 3·50

73 74

1956 (20Jan). Eighth Anniv of People's Army. Litho. P 10.
N104 73 10wn. Venetian red/*yellow-green* .... 14·00 12·50
     a. Imperf.................................. 14·00 13·50
Reprints have shading in the sky and on the face.

1956 (29 Apr). Labour Day. Litho. P 10.
N105 74 10wn. blue................................. 11·50 8·00
     a. Imperf.................................. 11·50 9·25
Reprints are on thick gummed paper and the tablet containing "1956" is joined to the ribbon at the right.

75 Machinist 76 Taedong Gate, 77 Woman
Pyongyang Harvester

78 Moranbong Theatre, 79 Miner
Pyongyang

1956 (8 May–14 Nov). Litho. P 10.

N106	**75**	1wn. deep brown (28.7)	2·00	95
		a. Perf 8×9 or 9	16·00	3·00
		b. Imperf	3·75	3·25
N107	**76**	2wn. pale blue	8·50	1·90
		a. Imperf	9·25	2·50
N108	**77**	10wn rose (14.11)	1·60	1·10
		a. Rouletted	4·00	2·75
		b. Imperf	3·75	3·00
N109	**78**	40wn. light green	11·00	5·50
		a. Imperf	25·00	18·00
N106/109	Set of 4 (cheapest)		21·00	8·50

Reprints of No. N107 are in greyish blue on thick gummed paper and the central character to the right of "2" projects to the left of the others.

1956 (7 June). Tenth Anniv of Labour Law. Litho. P 10.

N110	**79**	10wn sepia	3·25	1·40
		a. Perf 9	16·00	15·00
		b. Imperf	12·50	8·50

80 Boy Bugler and Girl Drummer   **81** Workers

1956 (7 June). Tenth Anniv of Children's Union. Litho. P 10.

N111	**80**	10wn. sepia	5·50	3·50
		a. Imperf	26·00	8·50

1956 (10 July). Tenth Anniv of Sex Equality Law. P 10.

N112	**81**	10wn. deep brown	3·25	2·10
		a. Perf 9	11·00	7·00
		b. Imperf	8·25	5·25

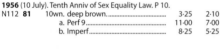

82 Industrial Plant   **83** Liberation Tower   **84** Kim Il Sung University

1956 (10 July). Tenth Anniv of Nationalization of Industry. Litho. P 10.

N113	**82**	10wn. deep brown	50·00	33·00
		a. Imperf	70·00	41·00

1956 (24 July). 11th Anniv of Liberation from Japan. Litho. P 10.

N114	**83**	10wn. rose-red	4·25	1·80
		a. Imperf	15·00	5·00

1956 (30 Sept). Tenth Anniv of Kim Il Sung University. Litho. P 10.

N115	**84**	10wn. deep brown	3·50	3·25
		a. Perf 8½×9½	9·50	4·00
		b. Imperf	4·50	3·50

85 Boy and Girl   **86** Pak Ji Won

1956 (3 Nov). Fourth Democratic Youth League Congress. Photo. P 10.

N116	**85**	10wn deep brown.	3·50	2·00
		a. Imperf	6·00	4·75

1957 (4 Mar). 220th Birth Anniv of Pak Ji Won, "Yonam" (statesman). Photo. P 10.

N117	**86**	10wn. blue	2·00	1·00
		a. Imperf	4·00	2·75

87 Tabo Pagoda, Pulguksa   **88** Ulmil Pavilion, Pyongyang   **89** Furnaceman

1957 (20 Mar). Litho. P 10.

N118	**87**	5wn. light blue	1·80	1·20
		a. Rouletted	2·20	1·60
		b. Perf 11 (with gum)	3·00	2·10
		c. Imperf	4·50	2·10
N119	**88**	40wn. dull blue-green	2·75	1·80
		a. Perf 8×8½	5·75	2·75
		b. Perf 11	6·25	3·00
		c. Imperf	5·50	3·50

No. N118c. exists with or without gum.

The stamp formerly listed as NK120 is a cut-out from postal stationery, sold at Pyongyang post office for use on letters.

1957 (4 July). Production and Economy Campaign. Litho. With or without gum. P 10.

N121	**89**	10wn. bright blue	4·25	2·75
		a. Perf 11	5·50	3·50
		b. Imperf	8·50	5·50

90 Furnaceman   **91** Voters and Polling Booth

1957 (10-13 Aug). Second General Election. Litho. P 10.

N122	**90**	1wn. red-orange (13.8)	1·10	45
		b. Imperf	3·00	1·40
N123		2wn. pale brown (13.8)	1·10	45
		b. Imperf	3·00	1·40
N124	**91**	10wn. vermilion	6·50	1·80
		b. Imperf	12·00	8·00
N122/124	Set of 3		7·75	2·40
N122b/124b	Set of 3		16·00	9·75

92 Ryongwangjong, Pyongyang   93 Lenin and Flags

99 Weighing a Baby   100 Bandaging a Hand

1957 (1 Nov). Red Cross. Litho. P 10.

N132	**99**	1wn. carmine	7·50	1·20
		a. Imperf	14·50	5·25
N133		2wn. carmine (shades)	7·50	1·20
		a. Rouletted	15·00	6·75
		b. Imperf	14·50	5·25
N134	**100**	10wn. carmine	20·00	3·50
		a. Imperf	31·00	11·00
N132/134	Set of 3		32·00	5·25

No. N133 exists with and without gum, No. N133a with gum; other values without gum only.

94 Kim Il Sung at Pochonbo   95 Lenin   96 Pouring Steel

1957 (28 Sept). 1530th Anniv of Pyongyang. Litho. P 10.

N125	**92**	10wn. blue-green	1·30	35
		a. Imperf	5·25	2·50

1957 (30 Sept–16 Oct). 40th Anniv of Russian Revolution. Litho. P 10.

N126	**93**	10wn. blue-green	1·00	55
		a. Pin-perf 13	7·25	3·00
		b. Imperf	5·00	2·30
N127	**94**	10wn. rose-red (3.10)	1·00	55
		a. Rouletted	7·25	3·00
		b. Imperf	5·00	2·30
N128	**95**	10wn. grey-blue	1·00	55
		a. Imperf	5·00	2·30
N129	**96**	10wn. red orange (16.10)	2·50	55
		a. Rouletted	17·00	3·50
		b. Imperf	19·00	3·50
N126/129	Set of 4		5·00	2·00

No. N126 exists with gum.

101 Koryo Celadon Jug (12th-century)   102 Koryo Incense-burner (12th-century)   103 Woljong Temple Pagoda

1958 (14 Jan). Korean Antiquities. Litho. P 10.

N135	**101**	10wn. light blue	6·25	95
		a. Imperf	15·00	5·25
N136	**102**	10wn. grey-green	6·25	95
		a. Imperf	15·00	5·25

The imperforate stamps exist with or without gum.

1958 (23 Jan–21 Feb). Litho. 5wn. with gum, 10wn. without gum. P 10½ (5wn.) or 10 (10wn.).

N137	**103**	5wn. green (21.2)	1·50	80
		a. Rouletted	4·50	3·25
		b. Imperf	5·00	3·75
N138		10wn. light blue	2·50	1·40
		a. Rouletted	6·00	4·50
		b. Imperf	7·00	4·75

97 Congress Emblem   98 Liberation Monument, Spassky Tower and Flags

104 Soldier   105 Soldier, Flag and Hwanghae Iron Works

1957 (3 Oct). Fourth World Trade Unions Federation Congress, Leipzig. Litho. P 10.

N130	**97**	10wn. ultramarine & light grey-green	1·60	65
		a. Imperf	5·50	3·00

No. N130a exists with or without gum.

1958 (4–21 Feb). Tenth Anniv of People's Army. P 10.

(a) Photo. No. gum

N139	**104**	10wn. blue	3·25	60
		a. Perf 11	7·50	4·25
		b. Rouletted	8·75	4·75
		c. Imperf	9·50	5·00

(b) Litho. With or without gum.

N140	**105**	10wn. carmine pink (21.2)	6·00	80
		a. Imperf	11·50	6·75

1957 (16 Oct). Russian Friendship Month. Litho. P 10.

N131	**98**	10wn. pale emerald	2·20	60
		a. Imperf	5·50	3·50

106 Lisunov Li-2 Airliner
over Pyongyang

1958 (4 Feb). AIR. Photo. P 10.
N141 **106** 20wn. blue...................................... 7·00 1·20
    a. Perf 11.. 11·50 3·75
    b. Rouletted...................................... 12·50 5·50
    c. Imperf.. 12·50 5·50

107 Sputniks   **108** Sputnik
circling Globe

1958 (26 Mar). International Geophysical Year. T **107/8** and similar
design. Photo. P 10.
N142 **107** 10wn dull turquoise-blue...................... 5·25 3·25
    a. Imperf.. 25·00 14·50
N143 **108** 20wn. dull turquoise-blue...................... 5·25 3·25
    a. Imperf.. 25·00 14·50
    b. Rouletted...................................... 20·00 19·00
N144   – 40wn. dull turquoise-blue...................... 5·25 3·25
    a. Imperf.. 25·00 14·50
N145 **107** 70wn. dull turquoise-blue...................... 11·50 9·75
    a. Imperf.. 34·00 19·00
N142/N145 *Set of 4*.. 25·00 18·00
  Design: Horiz—40wn. Sputnik over Pyongyang Observatory.
Nos. 142/4 exist with or without gum.

109 Furnaceman   **110** Hwanghae Iron
Works

1958 (12 May). Young Socialist Constructors Congress, Pyongyang.
Litho. P 10.
N146 **109** 10wn. blue...................................... 3·75 70
    a. Imperf.. 6·50 3·25

1958 (22 May). Opening of Hwanghae Iron Works. Litho. P 10.
N147 **110** 10wn. light blue .... 5·50 80
    a. Imperf.. 9·00 4·25

111
Commemorative
Badge
    112 Federation
Emblem
    113 Conference Emblem

1958 (27 May). Farewell to Chinese People's Volunteers (1st issue).
Litho. P 10.
N148 **111** 10wn. claret-purple and light blue....... 2·75 70
    a. Perf 11.. 4·75 1·80
    b. Rouletted...................................... 4·75 1·80
    c. Imperf.. 4·75 1·80
  See also No. N158.

1958 (5 June). Fourth International Democratic Women's Federation
Congress. Litho. P 10
N149 **112** 10wn. new blue.............................. 1·30 50
    a. Imperf.. 6·00 2·75

1958 (4 July). First World Trade Unions Young Workers' Federation
Conference, Prague. Litho. P 10.
N150 **113** 10wn. red-brown & green (shades)....... 2·30 95
    a. Perf 11.. 5·50 1·70
    b. Imperf.. 4·75 1·60

114 Flats, East Ward,   **115** Workers Flats,
Pyongyang   Pyongyang

1958 (24 July–20 Aug). Rehousing Progress. Litho. P l0.
N151 **114** 10wn. new blue.............................. 2·75 70
    a. Perf 11.. 6·25 2·40
    b. Imperf.. 5·50 2·40
N152 **115** 10wn. turquoise-green (21.8)............... 2·75 70
    a. Imperf.. 5·50 2·40

116 Hungnam Fertiliser
Plant
    117 Pyongyang Railway
Station

118 Arms of
People's Republic
    119 Textile
Worker
    120 Yongp'ung Dam,
Pyongyang

1958 (21 Aug–10 Sept). Tenth Anniv of Korean People's Republic.
Litho. (Nos. N153/5) or photo (others). P 10.
N153 **116** 10wn. deep blue-green.......................... 3·50 65
    a. Perf 11.. 9·50 2·00
    b. Imperf.. 13·50 3·00
N154 **117** 10wn. deep grey-green.......................... 12·50 2·00
    a. Perf 11.. 19·00 3·00
    b. Imperf.. 20·00 6·75
N155 **118** 10wn. cinnamon and buff (7.9)............... 2·20 65
    b. Imperf.. 9·50 4·50
N156 **119** 10wn. blackish brown (10.9).................. 10·00 2·30
    b. Imperf.. 23·00 8·00

N157 **120**	10wn. blackish brown (10.9)...................	12·00	4·50
	b. Imperf..	18·00	5·25
N153/157 *Set of 5*		36·00	9·00
N153b/157b *Set of 5*		75·00	25·00

121 Volunteer and Troop Train

122 Transplanting Rice

1958 (10 Sept). Farewell to Chinese People's Volunteers (2nd issue). Photo. P 10.

N158 **121**	10wn. blackish brown..............................	30·00	9·75
	a. Imperf..	46·00	21·00

1958 (10 Sept). Photo. P 10.

N159 **122**	10wn. blackish brown..............................	1·10	30
	a. Imperf..	3·00	1·80

123 Winged Horse of Chollima

124 N. Korean and Chinese Flags

1958 (16 Sept). National Production Executives' Meeting, Pyongyang. Litho. With or without gum. P 10.

N160 **123**	10wn. red..	1·90	30
	a. Imperf..	5·25	1·40

1958 (8 Oct). North Korean–Chinese Friendship Month. Litho. With or without gum. P 10.

N161 **124**	10wn. red, ultramarine & turq-grn	1·60	40
	a. Rouletted..	4·00	1·20
	b. Imperf..	3·50	1·20

125 Farm Workers

126 General Ulji Mun Dok

127 Women with Banner

1959 (5 Jan). National Co-operative Farming Congress, Pyongyang. Litho. With or without gum. P 10.

N162 **125**	10wn. deep turquoise-blue	1·40	35
	a. Imperf..	3·25	1·10

1959 (11 Feb). Litho. With gum. P 10.

N163 **126**	10wn. Venetian red and light yellow...	2·75	65
	a. Imperf..	4·25	1·90
See also Nos. N165/7 and 216/19.			

Currency Revaluation

1 (old) Won = 1 Chon
100 Chon = 1 (new) Won

1959 (29 Mar). National Conference of Women Socialist Constructors, Pyongyang. Litho. With or without gum. P 10.

N164 **127**	10ch. chocolate and rose-red	2·75	70

1959 (1 Apr). T **126** and similar portraits. Litho. With gum. P 10.

N165	2ch. deep blue/*pale green*	1·20	20
	a. Imperf. With or without gum	3·00	60
N166	5ch. purple/*buff*....................................	1·40	25
	a. Imperf. With or without gum	3·50	60
N167	10ch. brown red/*cream*..........................	2·40	30
	a. Imperf. With or without gum	3·75	60
N165/167 *Set of 3*..		4·50	70
Portraits:—2ch. Gen. Kang Gam Chan; 5ch. Gen. Chon Bong Jun.			

128 Rocket and Moon

129 Irrigation'

1959 (4 May). Launch of Soviet Moon Rocket. Litho. P 10 with gum; P 10½ without gum.

N168 **128**	2ch. slate-purple/*pale buff*...................	8·50	3·00
	a. Imperf. With gum	47·00	16·00
N169	10ch. blue/*pale green*.............................	16·00	4·00
	a. Imperf. With gum	47·00	16·00

1959 (27 May). Land Irrigation Project. Litho. P 10.

N170 **129**	10ch. multicoloured................................	5·75	1·30
	a. Imperf..	9·00	3·50

130 Inscribed Tree at Partisan H.Q., Chongbong

131 Kim Il Sung Statue

132 Mt. Paekdu

133 "Flying Horse" Tractor

1959 (4 June). Partisan Successes against Japanese, 1937–39. Litho. With gum (No. N172) or no gum (others). P 10. (Nos. N171, 173) or 11 (Nos. N171/2).

N171 **130**	5ch. blk, buff, grey & dp bluish grn...	3·75	70
	a. Imperf...	11·00	2·50
	b. Rouletted..	11·00	2·50

N172	**131**	10ch. blue and light turquoise	1·90	45
N173	**132**	10ch. deep violet-blue	3·25	90
		a. Imperf	8·25	3·00
N171/173		Set of 3	8·00	1·80

1959 (12 June). "Great Perspectives" (1st issue: Development of industrial Mechanization). Various horiz designs as T **133**. Litho. With or without gum. P 10½.

N174		1ch. Red, deep olive and yellow-green	1·70	25
		a. Rouletted	7·75	4·25
		b. Imperf	7·50	4·25
N175		2ch. multicoloured	8·50	2·00
		a. Rouletted	20·00	9·50
		b. Imperf	18·00	8·75
N176		2ch. carmine, pink and slate-violet	1·60	30
		a. Rouletted	9·75	2·50
		b. Imperf	9·50	2·50
N177		5ch. yellow-orange, olive-brn & ochre	1·60	60
		a. Rouletted	8·25	4·50
		b. Imperf	8·00	4·25
N178		10ch. deep blue, apple green and brown	2·00	60
		a. Rouletted	8·25	4·50
		b. Imperf	8·00	4·25
N179		10ch. green, pale green and lake-brown	3·75	65
		a. Imperf	8·75	4·25
N174/179		Set of 6	17·00	3·75

Designs:—No. N175, Electric shunting locomotive; N176, "Red Star 58" bulldozer; N177, "Flying Horse" excavator; N178, "SU-50" universal lathe; N179, "Victory 58" lorry.

See also Nos. N189a/200 and N275/9.

134 Armistice Building, Pamnunjom

135 Protest Meeting

136 "Hoisting link between North and South Korea"

137 Emigration "Pickets"

1959 (25 June). Campaign for the Withdrawal of US forces from South Korea. Litho. With gum. P 11.

N180	**134**	10ch. light blue and ultramarine	1·20	30
		a. Imperf	2·50	65
		b. Perf 10	9·00	4·75
N181	**135**	20ch. deep blue and blue	1·50	50
N182	**136**	70ch. brown, cream & brown-pur	20·00	8·00
		a. Imperf	41·00	13·00
		b. Rough perf 11×rouletted	65·00	40·00

1959 (25 June). Campaign Against Emigration of South Koreans. Litho. With gum. P 11.

N183	**137**	20ch. brown and sepia	4·50	1·30

138 Korean Type of "1234"

139 Books breaking Chains

140 Emblems of Peace, Labour, and Letters

141 Korean Alphabet of 1443

1959 (1 Aug). International Book Exhibition, Leipzig. Litho. With gum (Nos. N184, N186) or no gum (others). P 11.

N184	**138**	5ch. sepia	20·00	6·50
N185	**139**	5ch. red and slate green	6·25	1·90
N186	**140**	10ch. bright blue	6·25	1·90
N187	**141**	10ch. deep violet-blue & pale blue	9·25	3·25
N184/187		Set of 4	38·00	12·00
MSN187a		152×122 mm. Nos. 184/7. Imperf. No gum	85·00	44·00

142 Pig Farm

143 Rotary Cement Kiln

1959 (20 Sept). Animal Husbandry. T **142** and similar design. Litho. With gum (5ch.) or no gum (2ch.). P 11.

N188		2ch. orange-brown, green and buff	3·00	65
N189		5ch. cream, light blue and brown	3·75	95

Design: Horiz—2ch. Cow girl with cattle.

1959 (20 Sept)–**60**. "Great Perspectives" (2nd issue: Production Targets). Various designs as T **143**. Litho. With gum (Nos. N190, N192) or no gum (others). P 10½ (2ch.) or 11 (others).

N189a		1ch. cinnamon, red-brown & turq-bl	40	25
		ab. Imperf	1·70	55
N190		2ch. multicoloured	75	30
		a. Imperf	1·60	55
N191		5ch. multicoloured	70	35
		a. Imperf	3·00	1·20
N192		10ch. multicoloured	1·30	50
		a. Imperf	3·75	1·60
N193		10ch. brown-purple, greenish yellow and pale turquoise-blue	1·30	50
		a. Imperf	1·60	60
N194		10ch. yellow, green and red	1·30	50
		a. Imperf	2·50	1·20
N195		10ch. multicoloured	1·30	50
		a. Imperf	1·90	60

N196   10ch. blue, light blue & turquoise-
        green... 1·30   50
        a. Imperf.................................... 3·00   1·00
N197   10ch. multicoloured...................... 1·30   50
N198   10ch. grey-green, buff and deep
        brown .... 1·30   50
N199   10ch. chestnut and orange.................. 1·30   50
        a. Imperf.................................... 3·00   1·00
N200   10ch. multicoloured (8.60)................. 1·30   50
N189a/200 Set of 12...................................... 12·00   4·75
  Designs: Vert—No. N190, Electric power lines and dam; N191,
Loading fertilizers into truck. Horiz—No. N189a. Type **143**; N192,
Factory, electric power lines and dam; N193, Harvesting; N194, Sugar-
beet, factory and pieces of sugar. N195, Steel furnace; N196, Trawlers;
N197, Pig-iron workers; N198, Coal miners; N199, Girl picking apples;
N200, Textile worker.

144 Sika Deer

145 Congress Emblem

1959 (24 Oct)–**62**. Game Preservation. T **144** and similar designs.
  Litho. With gum (N205/6), no gum (others). P 11.
N201   5ch. yell, brn, grn & pl bl (11.11.60)..   5·00   60
N202   5ch. yellow, red-brn & bl (24.1.62) ....   5·00   60
N203   5ch. sepia, green and brown
        (24.1.62) ....   5·00   60
N204   5ch. brown, black & lt blue (24.1.62)   5·00   60
N205   10ch. yell-orge, blk vio-bl & pale grey   5·00   65
N206   10ch. red, brn red & grn/crm (25.3.60)   13·50   1·80
N201/206 Set of 6..   35·00   4·25
  Designs: Horiz—No. N201, Chinese water deer; N202, Siberian
weasel; N203, Steppe polecat; N204, European otter; N206, Ring-
necked pheasant. Vert—N205. Type **144**.

1959 (4 Nov). Third Korean Trade Unions Federation Congress. Litho.
  With gum. P 11.
N207 **145**   5ch. brown-purple, red, vio-bl & lt bl   70   25

146 Chungnyon-ho (freighter)

1959 (5 Nov). Transport. T **146** and similar horiz design. Litho. With
  gum. P 11.
N208   5ch. dull purple (Electric train)..........   18·00   2·00
N209   10ch. slate-green...............................   4·50   1·30

147 Soldier, Tractor and Plough

1960 (8 Feb). 12th Anniv of People's Army. Litho. With gum. P 11.
N210 **147**   5ch. slate-violet and ultramarine ......   70·00   55·00

148 Knife Dance

149 Women of Three Races

1960 (25 Feb). Korean National Dances. T **148** and similar vert
  designs. Multicoloured. Litho. P 11.
N211   5ch. Type **148**..............................   4·25   25
N212   5ch. Drum dance..............................   4·25   25
N213   10ch. Farmers' dance..........................   4·25   30
N211/213 Set of 3..   11·50   70

1960 (8 Mar). 50th Anniv of International Women's Day. T **149** and
  similar design. Litho. With gum. P 11.
N214   5ch. mauve and light blue..................   1·20   15
N215   10ch. emerald green and orange........   1·20   30
  Design: Vert.—10ch. Woman operating lathe.

150 Kim Jong Ho (geographer)

151 Grapes

152 Lenin

1960 (16 Mar–June). T **150** and similar vert portrait designs. Litho.
  With gum. P 11.
N216   1ch. deep grey and pale green.........   1·30   10
N217   2ch. dull ultramarine and pale
        yellow ....   1·60   10
N218   5ch. greenish blue and greenish
        yellow ....   5·75   25
N219   10ch. brown and yellow-ochre
        (June)..   1·60   15
N216/219 Set of 4..   9·25   55
  Portraits:—2ch. Kim Hong Do (painter); 5ch. Pak Yon (musician);
10ch. Chong Da San (scholar).

1960 (8 Apr). Wild Fruits. Various vert designs as T **151** with fruits in
  natural colours. Litho. With gum. P 11.
N220   5ch. olive and turquoise-blue.........   2·75   65
N221   5ch. drab and light blue ....   2·75   65
N222   5ch. brown-olive and blue ....   2·75   65
N223   10ch. olive and orange......................   3·25   90
N224   10ch. grey-green and pink.................   3·25   90
N220/224 Set of 5..   13·50   3·50
  Designs—No. N220, T **151**; N221, Fruit of *Actinidia arguta planch*;
N222, Pine-cone; N223, Hawthorn berries; N224, Horse-chestnut.
Nos. N221/2 also exist without gum.

1960 (22 Apr). 90th Birth Anniv of Lenin. Litho. With gum. P 11.
N225 **152**   10ch. reddish purple   90   20

153 Koreans and American Soldier (caricature)

154 Arch of Triumph Square, Pyongyang

1960 (20 June). Campaign Day for Withdrawal of US Forces from South Korea. Litho. With gum. P 11.

N226	**153**	10ch. deep blue	4·50	50

1960 (29 June). T **154** and similar horiz designs. Litho. P 11.

N227	10ch. blue-green	75	15
N228	20ch. slate	1·50	25
N229	40ch. blackish green	2·50	55
N230	70ch. emerald	4·50	1·20
N231	1wn. blue	5·75	2·10
N227/231 *Set of 5*		13·50	3·75

Designs (Views of Pyongyang):—20ch. River Taedong promenade; 40ch. Youth Street; 70ch. People's Army Street; 1wn. Sungri Street.

155 Russian Flag on Moon (14.9.59)

156 "Mirror Rock"

157 Lily

1960 (15 July). Russian Cosmic Rocket Flights. T **155** and similar vert design. Litho. With gum (5ch.) or no gum (10ch.). P 11.

N232	5ch. turquoise blue	7·50	7·25
N233	10ch. multicoloured	11·00	3·50

Design:—5ch. "Lunik 3" approaching Moon (4.10.59).

1960 (15 July)–**61**. Diamond Mountains Scenery (1st issue). T **156** and similar designs. Multicoloured. Litho. P 11.

N234	5ch. Type **156**	1·30	20
N235	5ch. Devil-faced Rock	1·30	20
N236	10ch. Dancing Dragon Bridge (horiz)	4·75	30
N237	10ch. Nine Dragon Falls	4·25	30
N238	10ch. Mt. Diamond on the Sea (horiz) (8.2.61)	1·70	15
N234/238 *Set of 5*		12·00	1·00

See also Nos. N569/72, N599/601 and N1180/4.

1960 (15 July)–**61**. Flowers T **157** and similar vert designs. Multicoloured. Litho. With gum. P 11.

N239	5ch. Type **157**	1·50	25
N240	5ch. Rhododendron	1·50	25
N241	10ch. Hibiscus	2·50	40
N242	10ch. Blue campanula	2·50	40
N243	10ch. Mauve campanula (1.6.61)	2·50	40
N239/243 *Set of 5*		9·50	1·50

Nos. N239/41 and N243 also exist without gum.

158 Guerrillas in the Snow

159 Korean and Soviet Flags

1960 (26 July). Revolutionary Leadership of Kim Il Sung. T **158** and similar horiz designs. Photo. P 11.

N244	5ch. carmine-red	65	15
N245	10ch. blue	1·20	15
N246	10ch. carmine-red	1·20	15
N247	10ch. blue	1·20	15
N248	10ch. carmine-red	1·20	15
N244/248 *Set of 5*		5·00	70

Designs: No. N245, Kim Il Sung talks to guerrillas; N246, Kim Sung at Pochonbo; N247, Kim Il Sung on bank of Amnok River; N248, Kim Il Sung returns to Pyongyang.

1960 (6 Aug). 15th Anniv of Liberation from Japan. Litho. P 11.

N249	**159**	10ch. rose-red, blue and red-brown...	1·00	20

160 "North Korean–Soviet" Friendship

161 Okryu Bridge, Pyongyang

1960 (6 Aug). North Korean–Soviet Friendship Month. Litho. P 11.

N250	**160**	10ch. brown-lake/*cream*	60	20

1960 (11 Aug). Pyongyang Buildings. T **161** and similar horiz designs. Litho. P 11.

N251	**161**	10ch. grey-blue	3·25	30
N252	10ch. dull violet	2·75	15
N253	10ch. turquoise	1·00	15
N251/253 *Set of 3*		6·25	55

Designs: No. N252, Grand Theatre, Pyongyang; No. N253, Okryu Restaurant.

162 Tokro River Dam

163

164 Quayside Welcome

1960 (9 Sept). Inauguration of Tokro River Hydro-electric Power Station. Litho. With gum. P 11.

N254	**162**	5ch. slate-blue...........................	1·20	20

1960 (16 Sept). 15th Anniv of World Federation of Trade Unions. Litho. P 11.

N255	**163**	10ch. pale blue, ultramarine & blue ...	65	20

1960 (26 Sept). Repatriation of Korean Nationals from Japan. Litho. P 11.

N256	**164**	10ch. maroon...........................	3·25	25

165 Lenin and
Workers

166 Football

1960 (5 Oct). Korean–Soviet Friendship. Litho. With gum. P 11.
N257 **165** 10ch. brown and flesh 70 20

1960 (5 Oct). Liberation Day Sports Meeting, Pyongyang. T **166** and
similar sporting designs. Multicoloured. Litho. P 11.
N258 5ch. Running (vert)................................. 85 15
N259 5ch. Weightlifting (vert) 85 15
N260 5ch. Cycling (vert)................................. 2·50 20
N261 5ch. Gymnastics (vert)......................... 85 15
N262 5ch. Type **166** .... 1·30 20
N263 10ch. Swimming................................... 1·00 50
N264 10ch. Moranbong Stadium,
Pyongyang...................................... 85 50
N258/264 *Set of 7*.. 7·50 1·70

167 Friendship
Monument,
Pyongyang

168 Federation
Emblem

169 White-
backed
Woodpecker

1960 (20 Oct). Tenth Anniv of Entry of Chinese Volunteers into Korean
War. T **167** and similar design. Litho. With gum. P 11.
N265 5ch. magenta 60 15
N266 10ch. ultramarine.................................. 60 15
Design: Horiz—5ch. Chinese and North Korean soldiers
celebrating.

1960 (11 Nov). 15th Anniv of World Democratic Youth Federation.
Litho. P 11.
N267 **168** 10ch. yellow, black, green and blue ... 55 20

1960 (15 Dec)–**61**. Birds. T **169** and similar designs. Litho. P 11.
N268 2ch. bl, orge, brn & yell-grn (22.4.61) 7·50 80
N268a 5ch. orange-brn, red-brn, blk & lt bl 11·00 65
N269 5ch. brown, yellow & lt blue (1.6.61) 13·50 1·80
N270 10ch. brown, brn & lt bl-grn (15.3.61) 9·25 80
N268/270 *Set of 4*.. 37·00 3·75
Designs: Horiz—5ch. (N268a), Mandarins; 10ch. Black-naped
oriole. Vert—5ch. (N269), Scops owl.

170 Korean Wrestling

171 Cogwheel and Corn
("Mechanization of Rural
Economy")

1960 (15 Dec)–**61**. Sports and Games. T **170** and similar designs.
Multicoloured. Litho. P 11.
N271 5ch. Type **170**.............................. 80 15
N272 5ch. Riding on swing (vert) (6.1.61).. 80 15
N273 5ch. Archery................................. 3·25 40
N274 10ch. Jumping on see-saw (vert)........ 80 15
N271/274 *Set of 4*.. 5·00 75

1961 (1 Jan). "Great Perspectives" (3rd issue: Targets of Seven-
Year Plan, 1961–67). T **171** and similar designs inscr "1961".
Multicoloured. Litho. P 11.
N275 5ch. Type **171**.............................. 1·10 15
N276 5ch. Cogwheel and textiles................. 2·10 15
N277 10ch. Hammer, sickle and torch on
flag (vert) 55 15
N278 10ch. Cogwheels around power
station.. 1·10 15
N279 10ch. Cogwheel and molten steel 80 15
N275/279 *Set of 5*.. 5·00 70

172 Cultivated
Ginseng

173 Aldehyde Shop

1961 (5 Jan–15 Mar). T **172** and similar vert design. Multicoloured.
Litho. P 11.
N280 5ch. Type **172** (15.3)............................ 3·50 25
N281 10ch. Wild ginseng (perennial herb).. 3·50 25

1961 (8 Feb). Construction of Vinalon Factory. T **173** and similar horiz
designs. Litho. With gum. P 11.
N282 5ch. brown-red and pale yellow........ 1·00 15
N283 10ch. dp turquoise-green & pale
yellow .... 2·30 25
N284 10ch. deep violet-blue & pale yellow. 2·30 25
N285 20ch. purple and pale yellow.............. 3·00 50
N282/284 *Set of 4*.. 7·75 1·00
Designs: No. N283, Glacial acetic acid shop; N284, Polymerization
and saponification shop; N285, Spinning shop.
See also Nos. N338/41.

174 Construction Work

175 Museum Building

1961 (8 Feb). Construction of Children's Palace, Pyongyang. Litho.
With gum. P 11.
N286 **174** 2ch. red/*yellow*............................ 60 20

1961 (8 Feb). Completion of Museum of Revolution, Pyongyang.
Litho. With gum. P 11.
N287 **175** 10ch. red.................................... 50 20

176 Cosmic Rocket

177 Wheat Harvester

503

1961 (21 Feb). Launching of Soviet Venus Rocket. Litho. P 11.
N288 **176**   10ch. red, yellow and blue .... 6·25   25

1961 (21 Feb). Agricultural Mechanisation. T **177** and similar horiz designs. Litho. With gum. P 11.
N289   5ch. violet (Tractor-plough) 70   15
N290   5ch. blue-green (Disc-harrow) 70   15
N291   5ch. deep green (Type **177**) 70   15
N292   10ch. violet-blue (Maize-harvester).. 1·00   15
N293   10ch. plum (Tractors) .... 1·00   15
N289/293 *Set of 5* .... 3·75   70

178   **179** Agriculture

1961 (1 Mar). Opening of Training Institute. Litho. P 11.
N294 **178**   10ch. red-brown/*buff* 90   20

1961 (1 Mar.) 15th Anniv of Land Reform Law. Litho. With gum. P 11.
N295 **179**   10ch. dull green/*yellow* 85   20

180   **181** Mackerel

1961 (15 Mar). 15th Anniv of National Programme. Litho. With gum. P 11.
N296 **180**   10ch. purple/*yellow* 50   20

1961 (3 Apr). Marine Life. T **181** and similar horiz designs. Litho. P 11.
N297   5ch. multicoloured .... 2·75   25
N298   5ch. black and light blue .... 6·50   80
N299   10ch. blue, black and light greenish blue... 7·50   35
N300   10ch. blue, yellow, black and olive-grey.. 2·75   25
N301   10ch. brown, green and lemon .... 2·75   25
N297/301 *Set of 5* .... 20·00   1·70
    Designs:—No. N297, Type **181**; N298, Common dolphin; N299, Whale sp.; N300, Tunny; N301, Pollack.

182 Tractor-crane   **183** Tree-planting

1961 (22 Apr–20 May). T **182** and similar designs. Litho. With gum. P 11.
N302   1ch. purple-brown. .... 1·30   15
N303   2ch. deep brown (27.4) .... 1·30   15
N304   5ch. bottle green (20.5) .... 1·90   15

N305   10ch. deep violet (20.5).......................... 1·80   25
N302/305 *Set of 4*.. 5·75   65
    Designs: Horiz—2ch. Heavy-duty lorry; 5ch. Eight-metres turning lathe. Vert—10ch. 3000-ton press.
    See also Nos. N378/9c.

1961 (27 Apr). Re-afforestation Campaign. Litho. With gum. P 11.
N306 **183**   10ch. green... 1·60   30

184 "Peaceful Unification" Banner   **185** Pioneers visiting Battlefield

1961 (9 May). Propaganda for Peaceful Reunification of Korea. Litho. P 11.
N307 **184**   10ch. multicoloured .... 20·00   2·00

1961 (1 June). 15th Anniv of Children's Union. T **185** and similar designs. Multicoloured. Litho. P 11.
N308   5ch. Pioneers bathing .... 1·30   25
N309   10ch. Pioneer bugler.............................. 3·25   50
N310   10ch. Type **185**..................................... 1·30   25
N308/310 *Set of 3*.. 5·25   90

186 "Labour Law"   **187** Apples

1961 (21 June). 15th Anniv of Labour Law. Litho. With gum. P 11.
N311 **186**   10ch. deep blue/*yellow* 85   25

1961 (11 July). Fruit. T **187** and similar horiz designs. Multicoloured. Litho. P 11.
N312   5ch. Peaches .... 1·10   15
N313   5ch. Plums .... 1·10   15
N314   5ch. Type **187**....................................... 1·10   15
N315   10ch. Persimmons.................................... 1·10   15
N316   10ch. Pears... 1·10   15
N312/316 *Set of 5*.. 5·00   70

188 Yuri Gagarin and "Vostok 1"   **189** Power Station

1961 (11 July). Worlds First Manned Space Flight. Litho. P 11.
N317 **188**   10ch. ultramarine and pale blue.......... 1·90   55
N318   10ch. reddish violet and pale blue...... 1·90   55

1961 (11 July). 15th Anniv of Nationalisation of Industries Law. Litho. With gum. P 11.
N319 **189**   10ch. lake brown .... 15·00   80

190 Women at Work   **191** Children
planting Tree

1961 (27 July). 15th Anniv of Sex Equality Law. Litho. With gum.
P 11.
N320 **190**   10ch. brown-red 60   20

1961 (29 Aug). Children. T **191** and similar vert designs. Multicoloured.
Litho. P 11.
N321   5ch. Type **191** .... 1·30   15
N322   5ch. Reading book................................ 65   15
N323   10ch. Playing with ball 65   20
N324   10ch. Building a house 65   20
N325   10ch. Waving flag................................. 65   20
N321/325 Set of 5.. 3·50   80

192 Poultry and   **193** Soldiers on March
Stock breeding   (statue)

1961 (29 Aug). Improvement in Living Standards. T **192** and similar
designs. Multicoloured. Litho. P 11.
N326   5ch. Type **192** .... 1·00   15
N327   10ch. Fabrics and textile factory.......... 1·60   25
N328   10ch. Trawler and fish (horiz).............. 1·50   25
N329   10ch. Grain-harvesting (horiz)............. 85   15
N326/329 Set of 4.. 4·50   70

1961 (8 Sept). 25th Anniv of Fatherland Restoration Association.
T **193** and similar horiz designs. Litho. With gum. P 11.
N330   –   10ch. bluish violet.................................. 65   30
N331   –   10ch. reddish violet............................... 65   30
N332 **193**   10ch. ultramarine and buff.................... 95   30
N330/332 Set of 3... 2·00   80
    Designs: Marshal Kim Il Sung—No. N330, Seated under tree; No.
N331, Working at desk.

194 Party Emblem   **195** Miner
and Members

1961 (11 Sept). Fourth Korean Workers' Party Congress. Pyongyang.
T **194** and similar designs. Litho. With gum. P 11.
N333 **194**   10ch. deep bluish green 55   30
N334   –   10ch. purple 55   30
N335   –   10ch. brown-red 55   30
N333/335 Set of 3.. 1·50   80
    Designs: Vert—No. N334, "Chollima" statue, Pyongyang. Horiz—
No. N335, Marshal Kim Il Sung.

1961 (12 Sept). Miners' Day. Litho. With gum. P 11.
N336 **195**   10ch. bistre-brown. .... 11·00   80

196 Pak In Ro   **197** Aldehyde Shop
(1561–1642)

1961 (12 Sept). 400th Birth Anniv of Pak In Ro (poet). Litho. P 11.
N337 **196**   10ch. indigo/pale blue 95   20

1961 (17 Oct). Completion of Vinalon Factory. T **197** and similar horiz
designs. Litho. With gum. P 11.
N338   5ch. brown-red and pale yellow........ 1·00   15
N339   10ch. deep brown and pale yellow .... 1·60   15
N340   10ch. deep ultramarine and pale
    yellow .... 1·60   15
N341   20ch. purple and pale yellow.............. 2·50   30
N338/341 Set of 4.. 6·00   70
    Designs:—No. N339, Glacial-acetic shop; N340, Polymerization
and saponification shop; N341, Spinning shop.

198 Korean and   **199** Basketball   **(200)**
Chinese Flags

1961 (26 Oct). North Korean Friendship Treaties with China and the
USSR T **198** and similar vert design. Litho. P 11.
N342   –   10ch. mult (Korean and Soviet flags) . 80   30
N343 **198**   10ch. red, blue and yellow 80   30

1961 (4 Nov). Physical Culture Day. Sports designs as T **199**. Litho.
With gum. P 11.
N344   2ch. brownish grey (Table tennis)...... 1·00   15
N345   5ch. Prussian blue (Flying model
    glider) .... 1·70   15
N346   10ch. indigo (Type **199**)....................... 1·70   25
N347   10ch. greenish blue (Rowing)............... 1·70   25
N348   10ch. reddish purple (High jumping)... 1·70   25
N349   20ch. claret (Sports emblem)............... 1·30   40
N344/349 Set of 6.. 8·25   1·30

1961 (25 Nov). Centenary of Publication of Map "Taidong Yu Jido" by
Kim Jung Ho. No. N216 surch with T **200** in violet.
N350 **150**   5ch. on 1ch. deep grey & pale green 65·00   50·00

201 General Rock   **202** "Agriculture and Industry"   **203** Winged Horse and Congress Emblem

1961 (29 Nov). Mt. Chilbo Scenery. T **201** and similar designs. Litho. With gum. P 11.

N351	5ch. slate-blue (Type **201**)	90	15
N352	5ch. brown (Chonbul Peak) (horiz)	90	15
N353	10ch. bright violet (Mansa Peak)	1·70	25
N354	10ch. dp bl (Tiled House Rock) (horiz)	1·70	25
N355	10ch. ultram (Rainbow Rock) (horiz)	1·70	25
N351/355 *Set of 5*		6·25	95

1961 (29 Nov). Litho. With gum. P 11.

N356 **202**	10ch. grey-green	65	20

1961 (29 Nov). Fifth World Federation of Trade Unions Congress, Moscow. Litho. With gum. P 11.

N357 **203**	10ch. blue, purple and violet	40	20

204 "Red Banner" Class Electric Locomotive   **205** Ice Hockey

1961 (29 Nov). Railway Electrification. Litho. With gum. P 11.

N358 **204**	10ch. violet and yellow	18·00	2·10

1961 (12 Dec). Winter Sports. T **205** and similar horiz designs. Litho. With gum. P 11.

N359	10ch. sepia and grey-green	1·30	25
N360	10ch. sepia and bluish green	1·30	25
N361	10ch. sepia and violet blue	1·30	25
N362	10ch. sepia and light blue	1·30	25
N359/362 *Set of 4*		4·75	90

Designs:—No. N359, Figure skating; N360, Speed skating; N361, Type **205**; N362, Skiing.

206 Grain Harvest   **207** Tiger

1962 (1 Jan)."Six Heights" of Production Targets (1st series). T **206** and similar horiz designs inscr "1962". Litho. With gum. P 11.

N363	5ch. red, violet and slate		25
N364	5ch. chocolate and grey	6·75	65
N365	10ch. yellow, black and deep blue	1·00	25
N366	10ch. red, yellow and blue	3·25	25

N367	10ch. brown-black and light blue	3·00	30
N368	10ch. yellow, buff and blue	1·00	25
N363/368 *Set of 6*		14·50	2·50

Designs:—No. N363, Ladle and molten steel; N364, Coal trucks; N365, Type **206**; N366, Fabrics and mill; N367, Trawler and catch; N368, Construction of flats.
See also Nos. N440/5.

1962 (24 Jan). Animals. T **207** and similar designs. Litho. P 11.

N369	**207**	2ch. multicoloured	3·75	25
N370	–	2ch. olive-sepia & yellowish green	2·75	15
N371	–	5ch. dull yellow and blue-green	1·70	15
N372	–	10ch. deep brown and bright green	3·00	30
N369/372 *Set of 4*			10·00	75

Animals: Horiz—2ch. (No. 370), Racoon-dog; 5ch. Chinese ferret-badger; 10ch. Asiatic black bear.

208 Kayagum Player   **209** *Luehdorfia puziloi*

1962 (2 Feb). Musical Instruments and Players (1st series). T **208** and similar vert designs. Multicoloured. Litho. P 11.

N373	10ch. Type **208**	2·75	30
N374	10ch. Man playing haegum (two-stringed bowed instrument)	2·75	30
N375	10ch. Woman playing wolgum (banjo)	2·75	30
N376	10ch. Man playing chotdae (flute)	2·75	30
N377	10ch. Woman playing wagonghu (harp)	2·75	30
N373/377 *Set of 5*		12·50	1·40

See also Nos. N473/7.

1962 (13 Mar–15 Sept). New designs as T **182** inscr "1962". Litho. With gum (Nos. N379 and N379b), No. gum (others). P 11.

N378	5 ch. grey-green (15.9)	1·20	15
N379	10ch. ultramarine	2·10	20
N379a	10ch. brown	—	12·50
N379b	5wn. sepia (5.9)	18·00	4·00
N379c	10wn. brown-purple (30.7)	23·00	8·00

Designs: Vert.—5ch. Hydraulic press; 10ch. (2), Three-ton hammer; 10wn. Tunnel drill. Horiz—5wn. Hobbing machine.

1962 (13 Mar). Butterflies. T **209** and similar multicoloured designs. Litho. P 11.

N380	5ch. Type **209**	4·25	20
N381	10ch. *Sericinus telamon* (purple background)	4·25	20
N382	10ch. Keeled apollo (lilac background)	4·25	20
N383	10ch. Peacock (green background)	4·25	20
N380/383 *Set of 4*		15·00	70

210 G. S. Titov and "Vostok 2"

1962 (13 Mar). Second Soviet Manned Space Flight. Litho. P 11.
N384 **210**   10ch. red, blue, green and yellow .... 3·00   30

211 Marshal Kim Il Sung and   **212** Kim Chaek
(inset) addressing Workers

1962 (14 Apr). Marshal Kim Il Sung's 50th Birthday. T **211** and similar
   horiz design. Recess. With gum. P 11 (No. N387) or 12½ (others).
N385 **211**   10ch. rose red 65   25
N386   –   10ch. green 65   25
N387   –   10ch. blue.. 65   25
N385/387 Set of 3.. 1·80   70
   Design:—No. N387, Kim Il Sung in fur hat and (inset) inspecting
battle-front.

1962 (23 Apr). Korean Revolutionaries (1st issue). T **212** and similar
   vert portraits. Recess. With gum. P 12½.
N388   10ch. sepia (Type **212**) 85   15
N389   10ch. blue (Kang Gon)................................ 85   15
N390   10ch. carmine (An Gil)............................... 85   15
N391   10ch. purple (Ryu Gyong Su) 85   15
N392   10ch. bluish green (Kim Jong Suk)...... 85   15
N393   10ch. indigo (Kim Jong Suk)................... 85   15
N394   10ch. chocolate (Choe Chun Guk)....... 85   15
N388/394 Set of 7... 5·25   95
   See also Nos. N478/82 and N733/5.

213 Mother with Children   **214** Black-faced
                                        Spoonbill

1962 (23 May). National Mothers' Meeting, Pyongyang. Litho. P 11.
N395 **213**   10ch. multicoloured 65   20

1962 (23 May). Birds. Vert designs as T **214** inscr "1962". Multicoloured.
   Litho. P 11.
N396   5ch. Type **214**.. 2·30   30
N397   5ch. Brown hawk owl .... 8·00   40
N398   10ch. Eastern broad-billed roller .... 4·75   50
N399   10ch. Black paradise flycatcher.............. 4·75   50
N400   20ch. Whistling swan............................... 5·75   80
N396/400 Set of 5... 23·00   2·30

215 Victory Flame   **216** Croaker

1962 (23 May). 25th Anniv of Battle of Pochonbo. Litho. P 11.
N401 **215**   10ch. yellow, red. purple and black 90   20

1962 (28 June). Fishes. T **216** and similar horiz designs. Multicoloured.
   Litho. P 11.
N402   5ch. Type **216**.. 2·10   15
N403   5ch. Hairtail... 2·10   15
N404   10ch. Gizzard shad (head pointing to
                 right) .... 3·00   25
N405   10ch. Japanese sea bass (dull
                 ultramarine background) .... 3·00   25
N406   10ch. Japanese croaker (apple green
                 background)................................... 3·00   25
N402/406 Set of 5... 12·00   95

217 Waterdropper   **218** Radial Drill   **219** Chong Da San

1962 (30 July). Antiques. T **217** and similar designs. Litho. With gum.
   P 11.
N407   4ch. black and pale blue .... 1·30   15
N408   5ch. black and ochre.............................. 1·30   15
N409   10ch. black and green .... 1·70   20
N410   10ch. black and brown-orange............ 1·70   20
N411   10ch. black and purple........................... 1·70   20
N412   10ch. black and orange-brown............ 1·70   20
N413   10ch. black and yellow .... 1·70   20
N414   40ch. black and grey .... 5·00   50
N407/414 Set of 8.. 14·50   1·60
   Designs: Vert—4ch. Brush pot; 40ch. Porcelain decanter.
Horiz—N409, Inkstand; N410, Brushstand; N411, Turtle paper-weight;
N412, Inkstone; N413, Document case.

1962 (30 July)–**63**. Various designs as T **218**. Recess. With gum.
   P 12½.
N415   2ch. bronze-green (11.2.63)................ 45   10
N415a   2ch. brown (1963).................................. —   6·25
N416   4ch. blue (15.6.63) .... 3·00   10
N417   5ch. indigo (shades) (30.7.62)............ 85   10
N418   5ch. brown-purple (9.4.63) 95   10
N419   10ch. slate-purple (26.12.62).................. 1·30   10
N420   40ch. indigo (13.9.63) .... 6·50   25
N421   90ch. slate-blue (15.5.63) .... 2·75   40
N422   1wn. purple-brown (16.10.63) .... 8·25   65
N415/422 Set of 8 (excl No. N415a) .... 22·00   1·60
   Designs: Vert—2ch. Vertical milling machine; 5ch. (N417), T **218**;
5ch. (N418), Hydraulic hammer; 1wn. Spindle drill. Horiz—4ch.
"Victory April 15" motor-car; 10ch. All-purpose excavator; 40ch.
Trolley-bus; 90ch. Planing machine.
   See also Nos. N513/15 and N573.

1962 (30 July). Birth Bicentenary of Chong Da San (philosopher).
   Recess. P 12½.
N423 **219**   10ch. dull purple.. 55   20

220 Voter   **221** Pyongyang

1962 (3 Oct). Election of Deputies to National Assembly. T **220** and similar vert design. Multicoloured. Litho. P 11.

N424	10ch. Type **220**	1·30	25
N425	10ch. Family going to poll	1·30	25

1962 (15 Oct) 1535th Anniv of Pyongyang. Litho. With gum. P 11.

N426 **221**	10ch. black and pale blue	85	20

222 Globe and "Vostok 3" and "4"	**223** Spiraea	**224** *Uibang Ryuchui*

1962 (12 Nov). First "Team" Manned Space Flight. Litho. P 11.

N427 **222**	10ch. deep blue, red & light blue	3·00	65

1962 (30 Nov). Korean Plants. T **223** and similar vert designs. Plants in natural colours, frame and inscription colours below. Litho. P 11.

N428	5ch. pale yellow-green & dull blue-grn	1·50	15
N429	10ch. dull blue-green and scarlet	1·50	15
N430	10ch. turquoise-blue and purple	1·50	15
N431	10ch. pale green and deep olive	1·50	15
N428/431 *Set of 4*		5·50	55

Plants:—No. N429, Ginseng; N430, Campanula; N431, *Rheumcoreanum makai* (*Polyonaceae*).

1962 (26 Dec). 485th Anniv of Publication of *Uibang Ryuchui* (medical encyclopaedia). Litho. P 11.

N432 **224**	10ch. yellow, black, blue & lavender	5·00	40

225 Science Academy	**226** Fisherwomen

1962 (26 Dec). Tenth Anniv of Korean Science Academy. Litho. P 11.

N433 **225**	10ch. dull ultramarine & pale turq-grn	1·30 20

1962 (30 Dec). Litho. P 11.

N434 **226**	10ch. blue	1·30	20

227 European Mink	**228** Harvesting

1962 (30 Dec). Animals. T **227** and similar designs. Litho. P 11.

N435	4ch. red-brown and apple green	2·10	35
N436	5ch. blue, cinnamon and light green	2·10	35
N437	10ch. grey-blue and pale yellow	2·50	35
N438	10ch. sepia and pale turquoise-green	2·50	35
N439	20ch. red brown and pale blue	5·00	60
N435/439 *Set of 5*		13·00	1·80

Animals: Horiz—5ch. Chinese hare. Vert—10ch. (N437), Eurasian red squirrel; 10ch. (N438), Common goral; 20ch. Siberian chipmunk.

1963 (1 Jan). "Six Heights" of Production Targets (2nd series). T **228** and similar horiz designs inscr "1963". Multicoloured. Litho. P 11.

N440	5ch. Miner	1·00	25
N441	10ch. Type **228**	75	15
N442	10ch. Furnaceman	75	15
N443	10ch. Construction worker	75	15
N444	10ch. Textiles loom operator	1·00	15
N445	40ch. Fisherman and trawler	2·50	55
N440/445 *Set of 6*		6·00	1·30

229 Soldier	**230** Peony

1963 (1 Feb). 15th Anniv of Korean People's Army. T **229** and similar vert designs. Recess. With gum. P 12½.

N446	5ch. sepia (Airman)	50	10
N447	10ch. rose (Type **229**)	85	15
N448	10ch. blue (Sailor)	1·30	15
N446/448 *Set of 3*		2·40	35

1963 (21 Mar). Korean Flowers. T **230** and similar vert designs. Multicoloured. Litho. P 11.

N449	5ch. Type **230**	85	15
N450	10ch. Rugosa rose	1·30	15
N451	10ch. Azalea	1·30	15
N452	10ch. Campion	1·30	15
N453	40ch. Orchid	3·75	50
N449/453 *Set of 5*		7·75	1·00

231 "Sandang-ch'um" (Korean folk dance)	**232** Revolutionaries

1963 (15 Apr). International Music and Dancing Contest, Pyongyang. T **231** and similar vert design. Multicoloured. Litho. P 11.

N454	10ch. Type **231**	3·25	25
N455	10ch. Dancer with fan	3·25	25

1963 (19 Apr). Third Anniv of South Korean Rising of April, 1960. Litho. P 11.

N456 **232**	10ch. multicoloured	60	20

233 Karl Marx

234 Children in Chemistry Class

1963 (23 Apr). 145th Birth Anniv of Marx. Recess. With gum. P 12½.
N457 **233** 10ch. ultramarine 55 20

1963 (15 June). Child Care and Amenities. T **234** and similar vert designs. Multicoloured. Litho. P 11.
N458 2ch. Type **234** .... 1·10 25
N459 5ch. Children running 90 15
N460 10ch. Boy conducting choir................... 2·50 25
N461 10ch. Girl chasing butterfly .... 5·00 30
N458/461 *Set of 4* .... 8·50 85

235 Armed Koreans and American Soldier (caricature)

236 *Cyrtoclytus capra*

1963 (25 June). Campaign Month for Withdrawal of US Forces from South Korea. Litho. P 11.
N462 **235** 10ch. multicoloured 85 20

1963 (24 July). Korean Beetles. T **236** and similar horiz designs. Multicoloured; colours of beetles given below for identification. Litho. P 11.
N463 5ch. Type **236** .... 1·70 25
N464 10ch. dp blue, orange-red, yellow &
grn. .... 2·50 25
N465 10ch. bright red and blue..................... 2·50 25
N466 10ch. deep blue, light blue and
purple .... 2·50 25
N463/466 *Set of 4* .... 8·25 90
Designs:—No. N464, *Cicindela chinensis* (tiger beetle); N465, *Purpuricenus lituratus*; N466, *Agapanthia pilicornis*.

237 Soldier with Flag

238 North Korean Flag

1963 (27 July). Tenth Anniv of Victory in Korean War. Litho. P 11.
N467 **237** 10ch. multicoloured 90 20

1963 (15 Aug). 15th Anniv of People's Republic. T **238** and similar vert design inscr "1948 1963". Multicoloured. Litho. P 11.
N468 10ch. Type **238**.. 50 25
N469 10ch. North Korean Badge..................... 50 25

239 Namdae Gate, Kaesong

240 Ajaeng (bowed "zither")

1963 (13 Sept). Ancient Korean Buildings (1st issue). T **239** and similar horiz designs. Recess. With gum. P 12½.
N470 5ch. black... 40 15
N471 10ch. slate-blue....................................... 70 20
N472 10ch. chocolate.. 70 20
N470/472 *Set of 3*.. 1·60 50
Buildings:—No. N471, Taedong Gate, Pyongyang; N472, Potong Gate, Pyongyang.
See also Nos. N537/8.

1963 (13 Sept). Musical Instruments and Players (2nd series) T **240** and similar vert designs. Multicoloured. Litho. With gum (Nos. N473, N476) or no gum (others). P 11.
N473 5ch. Type **240**.. 1·70 15
N474 5ch. Pyongyon (jade chimes) .... 1·70 15
N475 10ch. Saenap (brass bowl) .... 2·10 20
N476 10ch. Rogo (drums in frame)................. 2·10 20
N477 10ch. Piri ("wooden pipe") .... 2·10 20
N473/477 *Set of 5*.. 8·75 80

1963 (10 Oct). Korean Revolutionaries (2nd issue). Portrait designs as T **212**. Recess. With gum. P 12½.
N478 5ch. brown (Kwon Yong Byok) 35 10
N479 5ch. brown-purple (Ma Dong Hui) ... 35 10
N480 10ch. rose (Li Je Sun) 40 15
N481 10ch. greenish slate (Pak Dal) 40 15
N482 10ch. maroon (Kim Yonq Bom)........... 40 15
N478/482 *Set of 5*.. 1·70 60

241 Nurse with Children

242 Hwajang Hall

1963 (30 Nov). Child Welfare. T **241** and similar design. Multicoloured. Litho. P 11.
N483 10ch. Type **241**.. 50 20
N484 10ch. Children in playground 50 20

1963 (30 Nov). Mount Myohyang Resort. T **242** and similar designs. Multicoloured. Litho. P 11.
N485 5ch. Type **242**.. 65 15
N486 10ch. Mountain stream and chalet..... 1·30 15
N487 10ch. Kwanum Pavilion and stone
pagoda (horiz) .... 1·30 15
N488 10ch. Rope bridge across river (horiz) 3·25 15
N485/488 *Set of 4*.. 5·75 55

243 Furnaceman   244 Children hoeing

1963 (5 Dec). Seven Year Plan. T **243** and similar designs. Recess. With gum. P 12½.
N489	5ch. deep rose-red	40	15
N490	10ch. slate	3·00	40
N491	10ch. Venetian red	3·00	40
N492	10ch. grey-lilac	1·80	15
N489/492 *Set of 4*		7·50	1·00

Designs: Vert— No. N490, Construction workers. Horiz—No. N491, Power technicians; N492, Miners.

1963 (10 Dec). "Hung Bo" (fairy tale). T **244** and similar horiz designs. Multicoloured. Litho. P 11.
N493	5ch. Type **244**	45	25
N494	10ch. Tying up broken leg of swallow	1·40	25
N495	10ch. Barn swallow dropping gourd seed	1·40	25
N496	10ch. Sawing through giant gourd	75	25
N497	10ch. Treasure inside gourd	75	25
N493/497 *Set of 5*		4·25	1·10

245 Marksman   246 Sinuiju Chemical Fibre Factory

1963 (15 Dec). Marksmanship. T **245** and similar horiz designs. Multicoloured. Litho. P 11.
N498	5ch. Type **245**	50	15
N499	10ch. Marksman with small-bore rifle	75	15
N500	10ch. Marksman with standard rifle	75	15
N498/500 *Set of 3*		1·80	40

1964 (10 Jan). Chemical Fibres Factories. T **246** and similar horiz design. Recess. With gum. P 12½.
N501	10ch. slate (Type **246**)	1·00	15
N502	10ch. slate-purple (Chongjin Chemical Fibre Factory)	1·00	15

247 Strikers   248 Korean Alphabet

1964 (14 Jan). 35th Anniv of Wonsan General Strike. Recess. With gum. P 12½.
N503 **247**	10ch. brown	85	20

1964 (15 Jan). 520th Anniv of Korean Alphabet. Litho. P 11.
N504 **248**	10ch. deep green, buff & lt brown	85	25

249 Lenin   250 Whale-catcher

1964 (22 Jan). 40th Anniv of Lenin's Death. Recess. With gum. P 12½.
N505 **249**	10ch. rose-red	55	20

1964 (10 Feb). Fishing Industry. T **250** and similar horiz designs. Multicoloured. Litho. P 11.
N506	5ch. Type **260**	85	15
N507	5ch. Trawler No. 051	85	15
N508	10ch. Trawler No. 397	1·70	40
N509	10ch. Trawler No. 738	1·70	40
N506/509 *Set of 4*		4·50	1·00

251 Insurgents   252 Warring Peasants

1964 (10 Feb). 45th Anniv of Rising of 1st March. Recess. With gum. P 12½.
N510 **251**	10ch. slate-purple	45	20

1964 (15 Feb). 10th Anniv of Kabo Peasants' War. Recess. With gum. P 12½.
N511 **252**	10ch. slate purple	45	20

253 Students' Palace, Pyongyang   254 "Changbaek" Excavator

1964 (3 Mar). Recess. With gum. P 12½.
N512 **253**	10ch. deep bronze-green	45	20

1964 (20 Mar–25 June). T **254** and similar designs. Recess. With gum. P 12½.
N513	–	5ch. slate-violet (28.4)	1·10	15
N514 **254**		10ch. grey-green	1·70	15
N515	–	10ch. slate-blue (25.6)	1·70	15
N513/515 *Set of 3*			4·00	40

Designs: Vert—5ch. 200 Metre drill. Horiz—10ch. (N515), 400 h.p. Diesel engine.

See also Nos. N415/22 and N573

255 "On the March"   256 Electric Train

1964 (12 May). Fifth Korean Democratic Youth League Congress, Pyongyang. Litho. P 11.
N516 **255**   10ch. multicoloured   45   20

1964 (21 May). Inauguration of Pyongyang–Sinuiju Electric Railway. Litho. P 11.
N517 **256**   10ch. multicoloured ....   10·00   30

257 Rejoicing in Chongsan-ri
Village   **258** Drum Dance

1964 (4 June). Popular Movement at Chongsan-ri. Recess. With gum. P 12½.
N517*a* **257**   5ch. Chestnut £250

1964 (15 June). Korean Dances. T **258** and similar vert designs. Litho. P 11.
N518   2ch. magenta, buff and black.............   2·10   40
N519   5ch. red, black and pale yellow..........   2·50   40
N520   10ch. multicotoured............................   3·00   40
N518/520 *Set of 3*............................   6·75   1·10
Designs:—5ch. Dance of ecstasy; 10ch. Tabor dance.

259 "For the Sake of the   **260** Nampo Smelting Works
Fatherland"

1964 (15 June). Li Su Bok Commemoration. Recess. With gum. P 12½.
N521 **259**   5ch. carmine-red...........................   65   15

1964 (15 June–15 Oct). T **260** and similar horiz design. Recess. With gum. P 12½.
N522   5ch. bronze-green............................   3·75   15
N523   10ch. deep slate (15.10) ....   4·00   25
Design:—10ch. Hwanghae iron works.

261 Torch, Chollima Statue   **262** Korean People and Statue
and Cogwheel   of Kang Ho Yong (war hero)

1964 (15 June). Asian Economic Seminar, Pyongyang. T **261** and similar horiz design. Multicoloured. Litho. P 11.
N524   5ch. Type **261**.............................   40   15
N525   10ch. Flags, statue and cogwheel   55   20

1964 (25 June). Struggle for Reunification of Korea. Litho. P 11.
N526 **262**   10ch. multicoloured   70   15

263 Hawk Fowl   **264** Skiing

1964 (5 Aug). Domestic Poultry. T **263** and similar designs. Multicoloured. Litho. P 11.
N527   2ch. Type **263**.............................   85   15
N528   4ch. White fowl.............................   85   15
N529   5ch. Ryongyon fowl ....   1·30   15
N530   5ch. Black fowl.............................   1·30   15
N531   40ch. Helmet guineafowl ....   4·25   1·30
N527/531 *Set of 5*............................   7·75   1·70

1964 (5 Aug). Winter Olympic Games, Innsbruck. T **264** and similar designs. Litho. P 11.
N532   5ch. red, blue and buff...................   65   10
N533   10ch. deep blue, blue-green and buff   1·10   15
N534   10ch. blue, red and buff...................   1·10   15
N532/534 *Set of 3*............................   2·50   35
Designs:—No. N533, Ice skating; N534, Skiing (slalom).

265 *Tobolsk*   **266** Tonggun Pavilion, Uiju
(passenger ship) and
Flags

1964 (13 Aug). Fifth Anniv of Agreement for Repatriation of Koreans in Japan. T **265** and similar vert design. Litho. P 11.
N535   10ch. red, blue and light blue.............   1·60   25
N536   30ch. red, green, yellow & ultramarine   1·60   15
Design:—30ch. Return of repatriates.

1964 (22 Aug). Ancient Korean Buildings (2nd series). T **266** and similar horiz design. Recess. With gum. P 12½.
N537   5ch. dull purple.............................   35   15
N538   10ch. emerald.............................   40   15
Design:—10ch. Inpung Pavilion, Kanggye City.

267 Cycling   **268** Burning of the *General
Sherman*

1964 (5 Sept). Olympic Games, Tokyo. T **267** and similar designs. Centres litho, backgrounds photo. P 11
N539   2ch. orange-brown and slate-blue...   35   15
N540   5ch. red-brown and light green ....   1·00   15
N541   10ch. orange and blue   40   15

N542	10ch. orange and deep bluish green	40	15
N543	40ch. brown and ultramarine	85	50
N539/543	*Set of 5*...	2·75	1·00

Designs. Horiz—2ch. Rifle-shooting; 10ch. blue, Running. Vert—10ch. green, Wrestling; 40ch. Volleyball
Nos. N539/43 exist imperforate (Price £15 un, £4 used).

1964 (28 Sept). The "General Sherman" Incident, 1866. Recess. With gum. P 12½.

N544	**268**	30ch. red-brown	3·00	40

269 Organising Guerrillas

270 Students Attacking

1964 (28 Sept). Guerrilla Operations in the 1930s against the Japanese. T **269** and similar horiz designs. Recess. With gum. P 12½.

N545	2ch. reddish violet...................	40	15
N546	5ch. ultramarine	55	15
N547	10ch. black.............................	65	15
N545/547	*Set of 3*.................................	1·40	40

Designs:—5ch. Kim Il Sung addressing guerrillas; 10ch. Battle at Xiaowangqing.

1964 (15 Oct). Kwangju Students Rising, 1929. Recess. With gum. P 12½.

N548	**270**	10ch. bluish violet...................	2·20	15

271 Weightlifting

272 Lynx

1964 (15 Oct). GANEFO Athletic Games, Djakarta, Indonesia, (1963). T **271** and similar designs. Litho. Multicoloured. P 11.

N549	2ch. Type **271**...........................	40	15
N550	5ch. Athlete breasting tape................	40	15
N551	5ch. Boxing (horiz).......................	40	15
N552	10ch. Football (horiz)	75	15
N553	10ch. Globe emblem (horiz).................	65	15
N549/553	*Set of 5*.................................	2·30	70

Nos. N549/53 exist imperforate (Price £12 un. £4 used).

1964 (20 Nov). Animals. T **272** and similar horiz designs. Recess. With gum. P 12½.

N554	2ch. blackish brown............................	1·50	25
N555	5ch. blackish brown (Leopard cat) ...	3·75	25
N556	10ch. brown (Leopard).........................	4·50	25
N557	10ch. sepia (Yellow-throated marten)	4·50	25
N554/557	*Set of 4*..................................	13·00	90

273 Vietnamese Attack

274 Prof. Kim Bong Han and Emblems

1964 (20 Dec). Support for People of Vietnam. Litho. P 11.

N558	**273**	10ch. multicoloured................................	55	15

1964 (20 Dec). Kyongrak Biological System. T **274** and similar horiz designs. Photo. P 11.

N559	2ch. brown-purple and olive-green	90	15
N560	5ch. blue-green, orange & deep blue..	1·30	15
N561	10ch. rose-red. greenish yell & dp blue..	1·70	15
N559/561	*Set of 3*..................................	3·50	40

Designs (33×23½ mm)—5ch. "Bonghan" duct; 10ch. "Bonghan" corpuscle. Each with emblems as in Type **274**.

275 Farmers, Tractor and Lorry

276 Chung Jin gets a Pistol

1964 (30 Dec). Agrarian Programme. T **275** and similar horiz designs. Multicoloured. Litho. P 11.

N562	5ch. Type **275**..............................	25	10
N563	10ch. Peasants with scroll and book	40	15
N564	10ch. Peasants—one writing in book	40	15
N562/564	*Set of 3*.................................	95	35

1964 (30 Dec). The Struggle to capture Japanese Arms. Recess. With gum. P 12½.

N565	**276**	4ch. brown.	60	15

277 Girl with Korean Products

278 Three Fairies Rock

1964 (30 Dec). Economic Seven Year Plan. T **277** and similar multicoloured designs. Litho. With gum (5ch.) or no gum (others). P 11.

N566	5ch. Type **277**..............................	75	10
N567	10ch. Farm girl..............................	75	15
N568	10ch. Couple on winged horse (23½×23½ mm)............................	50	15
N566/568	*Set of 3*.................................	1·80	35

Nos. N566/8 exist imperforate (Price £15 un).

1964 (30 Dec). Diamond Mountains Scenery (2nd issue). T **278** and similar vert designs, inscr "1964". Multicoloured. Litho. Without gum (2, 4ch.). or with gum (others). P 11.

N569	2ch. Type **278**..............................	1·00	15
N570	4ch. Ryonju Falls..........................	3·50	20
N571	10ch. The Ten Thousand Rocks, Manmulsang............................	1·00	15
N572	10ch. Chinju Falls..........................	3·50	20
N569/572	*Set of 4*.................................	8·00	65

279 "Horning-500" Machine

280 Soldiers Advancing, Fusong

1965 (1 Jan). Recess. With gum. P 12½.
N573 **279**   10ch. slate violet.............................. 1·50   25

1965 (20 Jan). Guerrilla Operations against the Japanese, 1934–40. T **280** and similar horiz designs. Recess. With gum. P 12½.
N574 **280**   10ch. deep reddish violet............... 45   15
N575 –   10ch. deep slate-violet................... 45   15
N576 –   10ch. deep bluish green 45   15
N574/576 *Set of 3*.. 1·20   40
Designs:—No. N575, Soldiers descending hill, Hongqihe; No. N576, Soldiers attacking hill post. Luozigou.

281 Tuman River   **282** Union Badge

1965 (27 Feb). Korean Rivers. T **281** and similar designs. Multicoloured. Litho. P 11.
N577   2ch. Type **281**............................... 60   10
N578   5ch. Taedong (vert) .... 2·10   15
N579   85ch. Amnok.................................... 85   15
N577/579 *Set of 3*.. 3·25   35

1965 (25 Mar). First Congress of Landworkers' Union, Pyongyang. Litho. With gum. P 11.
N580 **282**   10ch. multicoloured................... 70   15

283 Furnacemen and Workers   **284** Colliery Scene

1965 (25 Mar). Ten Major Tasks of Seven Year Plan. Litho. With gum. P 11.
N581 **283**   10ch. multicoloured................... 55   15

1965 (31 Mar–10 May). 35th Annivs of Strikes and Peasants' Revolt. T **284** and similar horiz designs. Recess. With gum. P 12½.
N582   10ch. deep olive-brown............... 1·70   15
N583   10ch. brown (10.5) .... 2·10   15
N584   40ch. maroon............................... 1·40   25
N582/584 *Set of 3*.. 4·75   50
Designs:—No. N582, Type **284** (Miners' Strike, Sinhung Colliery); N583, Strikers at Pyongyang Rubber Factory; N584, Revolt of Tanchon peasants.

285 Embankment   **286** Hand holding
Construction   Torch

1965 (31 Mar). Sunhwa River Works. Litho. With gum. P 11.
N585 **285**   10ch. multicoloured................... 40   15

1965 (10 Apr). Fifth Anniv of South Korean Rising of 19 April. T **286** and similar vert design inscr "4,19". Multicoloured. Litho. With gum. P 11.
N586   10ch. Type **286**........................... 35   15
N587   40ch. Student-hero, Kim Chio.............. 70   15
Nos. N586/7 exist imperforate (Price £4.25 un).

287 Power Station under   **288** African and Asian
Construction

1965 (10 Apr). Construction of Thermal Power Station, Pyongyang. Litho. With gum. P 11.
N588 **287**   5ch. chocolate and cobalt 75   15
No. N588 exists imperforate (Price £3·75 un).

1965 (18 Apr). 10th Anniv of First Afro-Asian Conference, Bandung. Litho. With gum. P 11.
N589 **288**   10ch. multicoloured................... 50   15

289 Rejoicing Koreans   **290** Workers in Battle

1965 (27 Apr). Tenth Anniv of General Association of Koreans in Japan. T **289** and similar horiz design inscr "1955–1965". Photo. With gum. P 11.
N590   10ch. blue and red............................. 45   15
N591   40ch. deep slate-blue, blue and red...
          (Patriot and flag)........................ 70   25
Nos. N590/1 exist imperforate (Price £17 un).

1965 (20 June). Second Afro-Asian Conference, Algiers. T **290** and similar vert design. Photo. With gum. P 11.
N592   10ch. black, yellow and red. .... 1·10   15
N593   40ch. black, yellow and red .... 1·80   40
Design:—40 ch. Korean and African soldiers.
Nos. N592/3 exist imperforate (Price £7·50 un).
The Algiers Conference did not take place.

291 "Victory 64" 10-ton   **292** Kim Chang Gol
Lorry

1965 (20 June). Recess. With gum. P 12½.
N594 **291** 10ch. deep bluish green .... 1·70 25

1965 (20 June). War Heroes (1st series). T **292** and similar horiz designs. Recess. With gum. P 11.
N595 **292** 10ch. slate-green...................................... 40 15
N596 – 10ch. red-brown...................................... 40 15
N597 – 40ch. reddish purple .... 1·30 50
N595/597 *Set of 3*.. 1·90 70
Portraits:—No. N596, Cho Gun Sil and machine-gun; No. N597, An Hak Ryong and machine-gun.
See also Nos. N781/3 and N842/3.

297 Workers and Map   **298** Engels

1965 (15 Aug). 20th Anniv of Liberation from Japan. Litho. With gum. P 11.
N606 **297** 10ch. multicoloured................................. 40 15

1965 (10 Sept). 145th Birth Anniv of Engels. Recess. With gum. P 12½.
N607 **298** 10ch. brown. 40 15

293 Marx and Lenin    **294** Lake Samil

1965 (20 June). Postal Ministers' Congress, Peking. Photo. With gum. P 11.
N598 **293** 10ch. black, yellow and red .... 2·00 30

1965 (20 June). Diamond Mountains Scenery (3rd issue). T **294** and similar horiz designs. Multicoloured. Litho. With gum. P 11.
N599 2ch. Type **294**............................ 85 15
N600 5ch. Chipson Peak .... 1·40 15
N601 10ch. Kwanum Falls .... 3·75 30
N599/601 *Set of 3*.. 5·50 55
Nos. N599/601 exist imperforate (Price £21 un).

299 Pole Vaulting   **301** Korean Fighters

1965 (24 Sept). Sports. Various multicoloured designs as T **299**. Litho. With gum. P 11.
N608 2ch. Type **299**............................ 50 10
N609 4ch. Throwing the javelin .... 2·10 25
N610 10ch. Throwing the discus 60 15
N611 10ch. High jumping (horiz)............... 60 15
N612 10ch. Putting the shot (horiz) 60 15
N608/612 *Set of 5*.. 4·00 70
Nos. N608/12 exist imperforate, without gum (Price £15 un, £5·75 used).

1965 (10 Oct). 20th Anniv of Korean Workers' Party. T **301** and similar horiz designs. Each black, yellow and red. Photo With gum. P 13×13½.
N613 10ch. Type **301**............................ 1·10 40
a. Horiz block of 6. Nos. 613/18..... 7·00
N614 10ch. Party emblem .... 1·10 40
N615 10ch. Lenin and Marx .... 1·10 40
N616 10ch. Workers marching................. 1·10 40
N617 10ch. Fighters .... 1·10 40
N618 40ch. Workers.............................. 1·10 40
N613/618 *Set of 6*.. 6·00 2·20
MSN619 191×99 mm. Nos. N613/18................... 40·00 23·00
Nos. N613/18 each have a red banner in the background and were issued together in blocks of six (3×2), forming a composite design, within the sheet.

295 Amnok River, Kusimuldong   **296** Footballer and Games' Emblem

1965 (20 June). Scenes of Japanese War. T **295** and similar horiz design. Photo. With gum. P 11.
N602 5ch. slate-green and pale grey-blue 50 15
N603 10ch. turquoise and pale blue............. 85 15
Design.—10 ch. Lake Samji.

1965 (1 Aug). "GANEFO" Football Games, Pyongyang. T **296** and similar vert design. Multicoloured. Litho. With gum. P 11.
N604 10ch. Type **296**............................ 1·30 20
N605 10ch. Games' emblem and
Moranbong Stadium.................. 1·30 20
Nos. N604/5 exist imperforate, without gum (Price £10 un, £4.75 used).

302 Kim Chaek Iron Works

1965 (25 Nov). T **302** and similar horiz design. Recess. With gum. P 12½.
N620 10ch. deep dull purple (T **302**)............ 5·00 15
N621 10ch. bistre-brn (Chongjin Steel
Works)................................. 5·00 15

303 Grass Carp   **304** Building House

1965 (10 Dec). Freshwater Fishes. T **303** and similar vert designs. Multicoloured. Photo. With gum. P 11×13½ (4ch.) or 13½ (others).

N622	2ch. Rainbow trout	1·00	15
N623	4ch. Dolly Varden trout	1·10	15
N624	10ch. Brown trout (surfacing water)...	2·10	15
N625	10ch. Carp diving (date at left)	2·10	15
N626	10ch. Type **303**	2·10	15
N627	40ch. Crucian carp	3·25	40
N622/627	Set of 6	10·50	1·00

Nos. N622/7 exist imperforate, without gum (Price £17 un, £6·50 used).

1965 (15 Dec). Kim Hong Do's Drawings. T **304** and similar vert designs. Recess. With gum. P 12½.

N628	2ch. green (Type **304**)	60	15
N629	4ch. maroon (Weaving)	1·30	15
N630	10ch. brown (Wrestling)	1·10	15
N631	10ch. slate-blue (School class)	1·10	15
N632	10ch. crimson (Dancing)	1·70	15
N633	10ch. violet (Blacksmiths)	1·50	15
N628/633	Set of 6	6·50	80

305 Children in Workshop   **306** Whale-catcher

1965 (15 Dec). Life at Pyongyang Children's and Students' Palace. T **305** and similar square designs. Multicoloured. Litho. With gum. P 13½.

N634	2ch. Type **305**	25	10
N635	4ch. Boxing	25	10
N636	10ch. Chemistry	1·00	20
N637	10ch. Playing violin and accordion	1·00	20
N634/637	Set of 4	2·30	55

1965 (15 Dec). Korean Fishing Boats. T **306** and similar horiz design. Recess. With gum. P 12½.

N638	10ch. indigo (Type **306**)	1·70	35
N639	10ch. slate-green (Fishing Fleet Service Vessel)	1·70	35

307 Great Tit   **308** Silkworm Moth (*Bombyx mori*) and Cocoon

1965 (30 Dec). Korean Birds. T **307** and similar multicoloured designs. Litho. With gum. P 13½ (No. N643) or 11 (others).

N640	4ch. Black-capped kingfisher (vert)..	2·40	35
N641	10ch. Type **307**	3·25	55
N642	10ch. Pied wagtail (facing left)	3·25	55
N643	10ch. Azure-winged magpie (facing right)	3·25	55
N644	40ch. Black-tailed hawfinch	8·50	1·10
N640/644	Set of 5	19·00	2·75

Nos. 640/4 exist imperforate, without gum (Price £29 un, £8 used).

1965 (30 Dec). Korean Sericulture. T **308** and similar vert designs. Recess. With gum. P 12½.

N645	2ch. bronze-green	42·00	1·50
N646	10ch. brown	42·00	1·50
N647	10ch. light purple	42·00	1·50
N645/647	Set of 3	£110	4·00

Moths and cocoons:—No. N646, Ailanthus silk moth (*Samia cynthia*); No. N647, Chinese oak silk moth (*Antheraea pernyi*).

309 Hooded Crane   **310** Japanese Common Squid

1965 (30 Dec). Wading Birds. T **309** and similar vert designs. Recess. With gum. P 12½.

N648	2ch. olive-brown.	4·50	40
N649	10ch. deep violet-blue	5·00	65
N650	10ch. slate-purple	5·00	65
N651	40ch. slate green	9·25	1·40
N648/651	Set of 4	21·00	2·75

Birds:—No. N649, Japanese white-necked crane; N650, Manchurian crane; N651, Grey heron.

1965 (31 Dec). Molluscs. T **310** and similar horiz design. Multicoloured. Litho. With gum. P 11.

N652	5ch. Type **310**	2·10	30
N653	10ch. Giant Pacific octopus	3·00	45

Nos. N652/3 exist imperforate, without gum (Price £8·50 un, £3·25 used).

311 Spotbill Duck   **312** Circus Theatre, Pyongyang

1965 (31 Dec). Korean Ducks. T **311** and similar horiz designs. Multicoloured. Litho. With gum. P 11.

N654	2ch. Type **311**	3·25	40
N655	4ch. Ruddy shelduck	3·25	45
N656	10ch. Mallard	5·00	90
N657	40ch. Baikal teal	7·25	1·60
N654/657	Set of 4	17·00	3·00

Nos. N654/7 exist imperforate, without gum (Price £29 un, £6·50 used).

1965 (31 Dec). Korean Circus. T **312** and similar designs. Photo. With gum except No. N661. P 11.

N658	2ch. new blue, black & orange-brown	65	20
N659	10ch. new blue, vermilion and black	1·70	30
N660	10ch. vermilion, black & yellow-green	1·70	30
N661	10ch. red-orange, sepia & yellow-green	1·70	30

N662		10ch. carmine-red, orge-yell & turq...	1·70	30
N658/662 *Set of 5*			6·75	1·30

Designs: Vert—Nos. N659, Trapeze artistes; N660, Performer with hoops on seesaw; N661, Tightrope dancers; N662, Performer with revolving cap on stick.

313 "Marvel of Peru" (*Mirabilis jalapa*) **314** "Finn" Class Dinghy **315** Cuban, Korean and African

1965 (31 Dec). Korean Flowers. T **313** and similar vert designs. Multicoloured. Litho. 4ch. without gum. P 11; others with gum. P 13½.

N663		4ch. Type **313**	2·20	25
N664		10ch. Peony	3·50	40
N665		10ch. Moss rose	3·50	40
N666		10ch. Magnolia	3·50	40
N663/666 *Set of 4*			11·50	1·30

Nos. N663/6 exist imperforate, without gum (Price £17 un, £4 used).

1965 (31 Dec). Sailing. T **314** and similar vert designs. Multicoloured. Litho. With gum. P 13½.

N667		2ch. Type **314**	75	25
N668		10ch. "5.5m" class	1·20	40
N669		10ch. "Dragon" class	1·20	40
N670		40ch. "Star" class	2·50	85
N667/670 *Set of 4*			5·00	1·70

Nos. N667/70 exist imperforate, without gum (Price £8·50 un, £3·25 used).

1966 (3 Jan). African, Asian and Latin-American Friendship Conference, Havana. Litho. With gum. P 11.

N671	**315**	10ch. multicoloured	40	15

316 Hosta **317** Farmer and Wife

1966. Wild Flowers. T **316** and similar vert designs. Multicoloured. Litho. With gum. P 11.

(a) First Series (15 Jan).

N672		2ch. Type **316**	1·10	25
N673		4ch. Dandelion	1·10	25
N674		10ch. Pink convolvulus	1·60	25
N675		10ch. Lily-of-the-valley	1·60	25
N676		40ch. Catalpa blossom	4·75	65

(b) Second Series (10 Feb).

N677		2ch. Polyanthus	1·10	25
N678		4ch. Lychnis	1·10	25
N679		10ch. Adonis	1·60	25
N680		10ch. Orange lily	1·60	25
N681		90ch. Rhododendron	7·50	80
N672/681 *Set of 10*			21·00	3·00

Nos. N672/6 exist imperforate, without gum (Price £21 un, £7·25 used).

1966 (5 Mar). 20th Anniv of Land Reform Law. Litho. With gum. P 11.

N682	**317**	10ch. multicoloured	40	15

318 Troops advancing, Dashahe **319** Silla Bowl

1966 (25 Mar). Paintings of Guerrilla Battles, 1937–39. T **318** and similar horiz designs. Recess. With gum except No N684. P 12½.

N683		10ch. crimson	50	15
N684		10ch. deep turquoise-green	50	15
N685		10ch. brown-purple	50	15
N683/685 *Set of 3*			1·40	40

Designs and battles:—Nos. N683., T **318**; N684, Troops firing from trees, Taehongdan; N685, Troops on hillside, Jiansanfeng.

1966 (30 Apr). Art Treasures of Silla Dynasty. T **319** and similar vert designs. Recess. With gum. P 12½.

N686		2ch. ochre	1·70	30
N687		5ch. black (Earthenware jar)	1·70	30
N688		10ch. reddish violet (Censer)	1·70	30
N686/688 *Set of 3*			4·50	80

320 Hands holding Torch, Rifle and Hammer **321** Torch and Patriots

1966 (1 May). 80th Anniv of Labour Day. Litho. With gum. P 11.

N689	**320**	10ch. multicoloured	45	15

1966 (5 May). 30th Anniv of Association for Restoration of Fatherland. Photo. P 11.

N690	**321**	10ch. brown-red and yellow	50	15

322 Harvester

1966 (30 May). Aid for Agriculture. T **322** and similar horiz design. Multicoloured. Litho. P 11.

N691		5ch. Type **322**	35	15
N692		10ch. Labourer	45	15

323 Young Pioneers **324** Kangson Steel Works

1966 (6 June). 20th Anniv of Korean Children's Union. Litho. P 11.

N693	**323**	10ch. multicoloured	45	15

1966 (10 June). Korean Industries. T **324** and similar horiz design. Recess. With gum. P 12½.
N694   10ch. grey (Type **324**)............................ 5·00   20
N695   10ch. red (Pongung Chemical Works) 5·00   20

325 Saury   **326** Professor Kim Bong Han

1966 (10 June). Korean Fishes. T **325** and similar horiz designs. Photo. With gum except Nos. N699/700. P 11.
N696   2ch. blue, yellow-green & dull
       purple .... 1·20   25
N697   5ch. purple-brn, yell-grn &
       cinnamon .... 1·50   25
N698   10ch. blue, buff and dull green .... 2·75   50
N699   10ch. purple-brown and yellow-
       green .... 2·75   50
N700   40ch. green, pale buff and light blue 6·25   85
N696/700 *Set of 5*... 13·00   2·10
   Fishes:—5ch. Cod; 10ch. (N698), Salmon; (N699), *Pleurogrammus azonus*; 40ch. "Pink" salmon.
   Nos. N696/700 exist imperforate, without gum (Price £17 un £4 used).

1966 (30 June). Kyongrak Biological System. T **326** and similar horiz designs. Photo. With gum. P 11.
N701   2ch. lt bl, dp bluish grn & greenish
       yell.. 85   25
       a. Vert block of 8. Nos. N701/8 ...... 7·00
N702   4ch. multicoloured.............................. 85   25
N703   5ch. multicoloured.............................. 85   25
N704   10ch. multicoloured.............................. 85   25
N705   10ch. multicoloured.............................. 85   25
N706   10ch. multicoloured.............................. 85   25
N707   15ch. multicoloured.............................. 85   25
N708   40ch. multicoloured.............................. 85   25
N701/708 *Set of 8*.. 6·00   1·80
MSN709 117×141 mm. Nos. N701/8............................ 24·00   23·00
   Designs:—No. N704, Kyongrak Institute; N708. Figure of Man; 702/3, 705/7, Diagram of system.
   Nos. N701/8 were issued together in *se-tenant* blocks of 8 (2×4) within the sheet, each block forming a composite design.

327 Leonov in Space   **328** Footballers
("Voskhod 2")

1966 (30 June). Cosmonauts Day. T **327** and similar horiz designs. Multicoloured. Photo. P 11.
N710   5ch. Type **327**............................ 25   15
N711   10ch. "Luna 9".............................. 85   40
N712   40ch. "Luna 10"............................ 1·60   65
N710/712 *Set of 3*... 2·40   1·10
   Nos. N710/12 exist imperforate (Price £6·75 un, £3·25 used).

1966 (11 July). World Cup Football Championship. T **328** and similar designs. Multicoloured. Litho. P 11.
N713   10ch. Type **328**............................ 1·70   40
N714   10ch. Jules Rimet Cup, football &
       boots.................................... 1·70   40
N715   10ch. Goalkeeper saving goal (vert)... 1·70   40
N713/715 *Set of 3*.. 4·50   1·10
   Nos. N713/15 exist imperforate (Price £10 un, £4 used).

329 Defence of Seoul   **330** Women in Industry

1966 (27 July) Korean War of 1950–53. T **329** and similar horiz designs. Recess. With gum. P 12½.
N716 **329**   10ch. grey-green 65   15
N717   –   10ch. bright purple.......................... 65   15
N718   –   10ch. reddish purple........................ 65   15
N716/718 *Set of 3*.. 1·80   40
   Designs:—No. N717, Battle on Mt. Napal; No. N718, Battle for Height 1211.

1966 (30 July). 20th Anniv of Sex Equality Law. Litho. P 11.
N719 **330**   10ch. multicoloured................... 45   15

331 Industrial Workers   **332** Water-jar Dance

1966 (10 Aug). 20th Anniv of Nationalisation of Industry. Litho. P 11.
N720 **331**   10ch. multicoloured................... 1·30   20

1966 (10 Aug). Korean Dances. T **332** and similar vert designs. Multicoloured. Litho. 5ch., 40ch. with or without gum; others without. P 11.
N721   5ch. Type **332**............................ 1·30   20
N722   10ch. Bell dance .... 2·10   35
N723   10ch. "Dancer in a Mural Painting"...... 2·10   35
N724   15ch. Sword dance .... 2·10   40
N725   40ch. Gold Cymbal dance .... 3·75   70
N721/725 *Set of 5*.. 10·00   1·80
   Nos. N721/5 exist imperforate, without gum (Price £17 un, £5·75 used).

333 Korean   **334** Crop-spraying
attacking US Soldier

1966 (15 Aug). Korean Reunification Campaign. T **333** and similar vert designs. Recess. With gum. P 12½.
N726 **333**   10ch. bronze-green 85   20
N727   10ch. bright purple.......................... 85   20
N728   10ch. slate-lilac............................... 5·00   1·10
N726/728 *Set of 3*.. 6·00   1·40
   Designs:—No. N727, Korean with young child; N728, Korean with shovel, industrial scene and electric train.

1966 (30 Sept). Industrial Uses of Aircraft. T **334** and similar horiz designs. Photo. With gum except 2, 5ch. P 11.

N729	2ch. blue-green and brown-purple	50	10
N730	5ch. olive-brown & deep bluish green......................	7·25	80
N731	10ch. sepia and new blue.....................	1·70	30
N732	40ch. brown and new blue..................	1·70	30
N729/732	Set of 4..	10·00	1·40

Designs (each with aircraft):—5ch. Forest-fire observation; 10ch. Geological survey; 40ch. Detection of fish shoals.

Nos. N729/32 exist imperforate, without gum (Price £25 un, £6·50 used).

1966 (30 Sept). Korean Revolutionaries (3rd issue). Portrait designs as T **212**. Recess. With gum. P 12½.

N733	10ch. reddish violet (O Jung Hub)......		
N734	10ch. deep green (Kim Gyong Sok)....		
N735	10ch. ultramarine (Li Dong Gol)..........		

335 Kim Il Sung University   **336** Judo

1966 (1 Oct). 20th Anniv of Kim Il Sung University. Recess. With gum. P 12½.

| N736 | **335** | 10ch. slate-violet .... | 65 | 15 |

1966 (30 Oct). "GANEFO" Games, Phnom-Penh. T **336** and similar horiz designs. Litho. P 11.

N737	5ch. black, green & light greenish blue...	60	20
	a. Vert strip of 3. Nos. 737/9	1·90	
N738	10ch. black, myrtle green and deep green (Basketball).........................	60	20
N739	10ch. black and red (Table tennis)	60	20
N737/739	Set of 3..	1·60	55

Nos. N737/9 were issued together in vertical *se-tenant* strips of 3 within the sheet.

Nos. N737/9 exist imperforate (Price £6·75 un, £3·25 used).

337 Hoopoe   **338** Building Construction

1966 (30 Oct). Korean Birds. T **337** and similar multicoloured designs inscr "1966". Litho. P 11.

N740	2ch. Common rosefinch (horiz)	1·80	30
N741	5ch. Type **337**................................	2·10	35
N742	10ch. Black-breasted thrush (blue background) (horiz).....................	2·50	55
N743	10ch. Crested lark (green background) (horiz).....................	2·50	55
N744	40ch. White-bellied black woodpecker	5·75	1·10
N740/744	Set of 5...	13·00	2·50

Nos. N740/4 exist imperforate (Price £25 un, £7·25 used).

1966 (20 Nov). "Increased Production with Economy". T **338** and similar horiz designs. Multicoloured. Litho. With gum. (Nos. N745/7). P 11.

N745	5ch. Type **338**.................................	35	10
N746	10ch. Furnaceman and graph..............	60	15
N747	10ch. Machine-tool production..........	60	15
N748	40ch. Miners and pit-head...................	1·80	50
N745/748	Set of 4...	3·00	80

339 Parachuting   **340** Samil Wolgan (Association Magazine)

1966 (30 Nov). National Defence Sports. T **339** and similar horiz designs. Recess. With gum. P 12½.

N749	2ch. sepia...	1·00	20
N750	5ch. orange-vermilion........................	65	15
N751	10ch. deep violet-blue	3·50	60
N752	40ch. grey-green	2·10	40
N749/752	Set of 4..	6·50	1·20

Designs:—5ch. Show jumping; 10ch. Motor cycle racing; 40ch. Radio receiving and transmitting competition.

1966 (1 Dec). 30th Anniv of Samil Wolgan Magazine. Photo. P 11.

| N753 | **340** | 10ch. multicoloured................................ | 1·20 | 20 |

341 Red Deer   **342** Blueberries

1966 (20 Dec). Korean Deer. T **341** and similar vert designs. Multicoloured. Litho. P 11.

N754	2ch. Type **341**..................................	85	25
N755	5ch. Sika deer......................................	1·30	25
N756	10ch. Indian muntjac (erect)	2·10	25
N757	10ch. Reindeer (grazing).......................	2·10	25
N758	70ch. Fallow deer..................................	6·25	80
N754/758	Set of 5...	11·50	1·60

Nos. N754/8 also exist imperforate (Price £29 un, £8 used).

1966 (30 Dec). Wild Fruit. T **342** and similar vert designs. Multicoloured. Litho. P 11.

N759	2ch. Type **342**..................................	50	15
N760	5ch. Wild pears....................................	75	20
N761	10ch. Wild raspberries	1·00	20
N762	10ch. Schizandra	1·00	20
N763	10ch. Wild plums..................................	1·00	20
N764	40ch. Jujube..	2·75	45
N759/764	Set of 6...	6·25	1·30

Nos. N759/64 exist imperforate (Price £12·50 un, £3·25 used).

343 Onpo Rest Home   **344** Soldier

1966 (30 Dec). Korean Rest Homes. T **343** and similar horiz designs. Recess. With gum. P 12½.

N765	2ch. bluish violet.................................	40	15
N766	5ch. turquoise-green..........................	40	15
N767	10ch. deep bluish green	65	20
N768	40ch. black..	1·30	30
N765/768	Set of 4...	2·50	70

Rest homes:—5ch. Mt. Myohyang; 10ch. Songdowon; 40ch. Hongwon.

1967 (8 Feb). 19th Anniv of Army Day. Photo. P 11.
N769 **344** 10ch. dp bluish green, yellow & red ... 40 15

345 Sow   **346** Battle Scene

1967 (28 Feb). Domestic Animals. T **345** and similar horiz designs. Multicoloured. Litho. Without gum: 40ch. also with gum. P 11.
N770 5ch. Type **345**.................................. 1·30 40
N771 10ch. Goat.. 1·70 40
N772 40ch. Ox... 4·25 1·00
N770/772 Set of 3.. 6·50 1·60
Nos. N770/2 exist imperforate, without gum (Price £21 un, £7·25 used).

1967 (6 Mar). 30th Anniv of Battle of Pochonbo. Photo. With gum. P 11.
N773 **346** 10ch. orange, brown-red 6 green........ 65 20

347 Students

1967 (1 Apr). Compulsory Technical Education for Nine Years. Photo. P 11.
N774 **347** 10ch. multicoloured 40 15

348 Table Tennis Player

1967 (11 Apr). 29th International Table Tennis Championships, Pyongyang. T **348** and similar horiz designs showing players in action. Litho. 5ch. with or without gum. P 11.
N775 5ch. multicoloured 60 15
N776 10ch. multicoloured .... 1·00 20
N777 40ch. multicoloured .... 1·50 35
N775/777 Set of 3.. 2·75 65
Nos. N775/7 exist imperforate (Price £7·50 un, £2·75 used).

349 Anti-aircraft Defences

350 Workers

1967 (25 Apr). Paintings of Guerrilla War against the Japanese. T **349** and similar horiz designs. Recess. With gum. P 11.
N778 **349** 10ch. slate-blue................................... 40 15
N779 – 10ch. slate-purple................................ 3·75 40
N780 – 10ch. reddish violet............................. 40 15
N778/780 Set of 3.. 4·00 65
Paintings:—No. N779, Blowing-up railway bridge; N780, People helping guerrillas in Wangyugou.

1967 (25 Apr). War Heroes (2nd series). Horiz designs as T **292** showing portraits and combat scenes. Recess. With gum. P 11.
N781 10ch. slate....................................... 50 15
N782 10ch. reddish violet........................ 50 15
N783 10ch. ultramarine............................ 1·30 20
N781/783 Set of 3.. 2·10 45
Portraits:—No. N781, Li Dae Hun and grenade-throwing; N782, Choe Jong Un and soldiers charging; N783, Kim Hwa Ryong and air dog-fight.

1967 (1 May). Labour Day. Litho. P 11.
N784 **350** 10ch. multicoloured 40 15

351 Card Game

1967 (1 June). Korean Children. T **351** and similar horiz designs. Multicoloured. Litho. P 11.
N785 5ch. Type **351**.. 1·10 20
N786 10ch. Children modelling tractor 60 15
N787 40ch. Children playing with ball .... 1·20 30
N785/787 Set of 3.. 2·50 60

352 Victory Monument

1967 (4 June). Unveiling of Battle of Pochonbo Monument. Litho. P 11.
N788 **352** 10ch. multicoloured 50 15

353 Attacking Tank   **354** *Polygonatum japonicum*

1967 (25 June). Monuments to War of 1950–53. T **353** and similar vert designs. Photo. 2ch. with or without gum. P 11.

N789	2ch. dp yellow-green & turquoise-grn	25	10
N790	5ch. sepia and bluish green	65	10
N791	10ch. brown and light buff	50	15
N792	40ch. brown and light greenish blue	1·30	50
N789/792	Set of 4	2·40	75

Monuments:—5ch. Soldier-musicians; 10 ch. Soldier; 40 ch. Soldier with children.

1967 (20 July). Medicinal Plants. T **354** and similar vert designs. Multicoloured background colours of 10ch. values given to aid identification. Photo. Nos. 793/5, 797 with or without gum. P 11.

N793	2ch. Type **354**	1·20	20
N794	5ch. Hibiscus manihot	1·20	20
N795	10ch. Scutellaria baicalensis (turquoise-blue)	1·40	25
N796	10ch. Pulsatilla koreana (violet-blue)	1·40	25
N797	10ch. Rehmannia glutinosa (ol-yell)	1·40	25
N798	40ch. Tanacetum boreale	3·75	85
N793/798	Set of 6	9·25	1·80

355 Servicemen   **356** Freighter *Chollima*

1967 (25 July). People's Army. T **355** and similar horiz designs. Multicoloured. Photo. 5ch. with or without gum. P 11.

N799	5ch.	25	10
N800	10ch. Soldier and Farmer	35	15
N801	10ch. Officer decorating soldier	35	15
N799/801	Set of 3	85	35

1967 (30 July). Recess. With gum. P 11.

N802	**356** 10ch. deep emerald	1·50	30

357 "Reclamation of Tideland"   **358** *Erimaculus isenbeckii*

1967 (5 Aug). "Heroic Struggle of the Chollima Riders". Paintings. T **357** and similar designs. Recess. Without gum (5ch.) or with gum (others). P 11.

N803	5ch. agate	50	15
N804	**357** 10ch. slate	65	20
N805	10ch. myrtle-green	1·10	20
N803/805	Set of 3	2·00	50

Paintings: Vert—5ch. "Drilling Rock Precipice"; 10ch. (N805), "Felling Trees".

1967 (10 Aug). Crabs. T **358** and similar horiz designs. Multicoloured. Photo. P 11.

N806	2ch. Type **358**	1·00	20
N807	5ch. Neptunus trituberculatus	1·30	20
N808	10ch. Paralithodes camtschatica	1·80	35
N809	40ch. Chionoecetes opilio	3·25	65
N806/809	Set of 4	6·50	1·30

 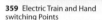 

359 Electric Train and Hand switching Points   **360** Tongrim Waterfall

(Des Kim Han. Litho)

1967 (15 Aug). Propaganda for Reunification of Korea. P 11.

N810	**359** 10ch. multicoloured	3·25	75

1967 (10 Oct). Korean Waterfalls. T **360** and similar vert designs. Multicoloured. Litho. 2ch. with or without gum. P 11.

N811	2ch. Type **360**	3·50	55
N812	10ch. Sanju waterfall, Mt. Myohyang	4·25	75
N813	40ch. Sambang waterfall, Mt. Chonak	6·75	1·40
N811/813	Set of 3	13·00	2·40

361 Chollima Flying Horse and Banners   **362** Lenin

1967 (1 Nov). "The Revolutionary Surge Upwards". T **361** and horiz designs incorporating the Chollima Flying Horse. Recess. P 11.

N814	5ch. ultramarine	4·25	35
N815	10ch. brown-red	75	15
N816	10ch. myrtle-green	75	15
N817	10ch. slate-lilac	75	15
N818	**361** 10ch. red	65	15
N814/818	Set of 5	6·50	85

Designs: Horiz—5ch. Ship, diesel train and lorry (Transport); No. N815, Bulldozers (Building construction); N816, Tractors (Rural development); N817, Heavy presses (Machine-building industry).

1967 (7 Nov). 50th Anniv of Russian October Revolution. Photo, P 11.

N819	**362** 10ch. chocolate, yellow and red	50	15

363 Voters and Banner

1967 (23 Nov). Korean Elections. T **363** and similar design. Multicoloured. Litho. P 11.

N820	10ch. Type **363**	45	15
N821	10ch. Woman casting vote (vert)	45	15

364 European Black Vulture   **365** Chongjin

1967 (1 Dec). Birds of Prey. T **364** and similar designs. Multicoloured. Photo. With gum. P 11.

N822	2ch. Type **364**	3·00	60
N823	10ch. Booted eagle (horiz)	5·75	1·10
N824	40ch. White-bellied sea eagle	7·50	1·50
N822/824	*Set of 3*	14·50	3·00

1967 (20 Dec). North Korean Cities. T **365** and similar horiz designs. Recess. With gum. P 11.

N825	5ch. bronze-green	90	20
N826	10ch. reddish lilac (Hamhung)	90	20
N827	10ch. slate-violet (Sinuiju)	90	20
N825/827	*Set of 3*	2·40	55

366 Soldier brandishing Red Book   **367** Whaler firing Harpoon

1967 (30 Dec). "Let us carry out the Decisions of the Workers' Party Conference". T **366** and similar horiz designs. Multicoloured. Photo (No. N829) or litho (others). P 11.

N828	10ch. Type **366**	40	15
N829	10ch. Militiaman holding bayonet	40	15
N830	10ch. Foundryman and bayonet	40	15
N828/830	*Set of 3*	1·10	40

1967 (30 Dec). Recess. With gum. P 11.

N831	**367**	10ch. blue	1·10	40

368 Airman, Soldier and Sailor   **369** Dredger *September 2*

370 Ten-storey Flats, East Pyongyang   **371** Palace of Students and Children, Kaesong

1968 (3 Feb). 20th Anniv of People's Army. T **368** and similar vert designs. Multicoloured. Litho. With gum. P 11.

N832	10ch. Type **368**	40	20
	a. Sheetlet of 10. Nos. N832/41	16·00	
N833	10ch. Soldier below attack in snow	40	20
N834	10ch. Soldier below massed ranks	40	20
N835	10ch. Soldier holding flag	40	20
N836	10ch. Soldier holding book	40	20
N837	10ch. Soldier and armed workers with flag	40	20
N838	10ch. Furnaceman and soldier	40	20
N839	10 ch. Soldier saluting	40	20
N840	10ch. Charging soldiers	40	20
N841	10ch. Soldier, sailor and airman below flag	40	20
N832/841	*Set of 10*	3·50	1·80

Nos. N832/41 were issued together in *se-tenant* sheetlets of 10.

1968 (10 Feb). War Heroes (3rd series). Horiz designs as T **292** showing portraits and combat scenes. Recess. With gum. P 11.

N842	10ch. bluish violet	40	15
N843	10ch. purple	40	15

Portraits:—No. N842, Han Gye Ryol firing Bren gun; N843, Li Su Bok charging up hill.

1968 (5 Mar–5 Oct). Litho. With gum. P 11.

N844	**369**	5ch. green (5.6)	1·00	20
N845	**370**	10ch. bright blue	45	15
N846	**371**	10ch. greenish blue (5.10)	45	15
N844/846	*Set of 3*		1·70	45

372 Marshal Kim Il Sung   **374** Matsu-take Mushroom

373 Kim Il Sung with Mother

521

1968 (15 Apr). Marshal Kim Il Sung's 56th Birthday. Litho. With gum. P 11.

N847	**372**	40ch. multicoloured	85	50

1968 (15 Apr). Childhood of Kim Il Sung. T **373** and similar multicoloured designs. Litho. P 11.

N848		10ch. Type **373**	50	15
N849		10ch. Kim Il Sung with his father	50	15
N850		10ch. Setting out from home, aged 13	50	15
N851		10ch. Birthplace at Mangyongdae	50	15
N852		10ch. Mangyong Hill	50	15
N848/852		*Set of 5*	2·30	70

1968 (10 Aug). Mushrooms. T **374** and similar vert designs. Photo. With gum. P 11.

N853		5ch. orange-brown and emerald	25·00	1·40
N854		10ch. ochre, light brown and emerald	42·00	1·50
N855		10ch. yellow-brown and light green	42·00	1·50
N853/855		*Set of 3*	£100	4·00

Designs:—No. N854, Black mushroom; N855, Cultivated mushroom.

377 Proclaiming the Ten Points   **378** Livestock

1968 (5 Dec). Kim Il Sung's Ten Point Political Programme. T **377** and similar design. Multicoloured. Multicoloured.

N867		2ch. Type **377**	20	10
N868		10ch. Soldier and artisan (horiz)	30	10

1968 (10 Dec). Development of Agriculture. T **378** and similar horiz designs. Multicoloured. Photo. With gum. P 11.

N869		5ch. Type **378**	35	10
N870		10ch. Fruit-growing	35	15
N871		10ch. Wheat-harvesting	35	15
N869/871		*Set of 3*	95	35

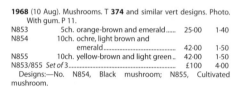

375 Leaping Horseman   **376** Domestic Products

379 Yesso Scallop   **380** Kim Il Sung at Head of Columns

1968 (2 Sept). 20th Anniv of Korean People's Democratic Republic. T **375** and simitar vert designs. Multicoloured. Litho. With gum. P 11.

N856		10ch. Type **375**	1·40	30
		a. Block of 8. Nos. N856/63	13·50	
N857		10ch. Four servicemen	1·40	30
N858		10ch. Soldier with bayonet	1·40	30
N859		10ch. Advancing with banners	1·40	30
N860		10ch. Statue	1·40	30
N861		10ch. Korean flag	1·40	30
N862		10ch. Soldier and peasant with flag	1·40	30
N863		10ch. Machine-gunner with flag	1·40	30
N856/863		*Set of 8*	10·00	2·20

Nos. N856/63 were issued together in *se-tenant* blocks of eight within the sheet.

1968 (5 Nov). Development of Light Industries. T **376** and similar vert designs. Multicoloured. Photo. With gum. P 11.

N864		2ch. Type **376**	35	15
N865		5ch. Textiles	1·40	15
N866		10ch. Tinned produce	50	15
N864/866		*Set of 3*	2·00	40

1968 (20 Dec). Shellfish. T **379** and similar horiz designs. Multicoloured. Photo. With gum. P 11.

N872		5ch. Type **379**	1·70	20
N873		5ch. *Meretrix chione* (venus clam)	1·70	20
N874		10ch. *Modiolus hanleyi* (mussel)	3·00	35
N872/874		*Set of 3*	5·75	70

1968 (30 Dec). Battle of Pochonbo Monument. Various details of Monument as T **380**. Multicoloured. Photo. P 11.

(a) Vert. design

N875		10ch. Type **380**	35	20

(b) Horiz. (43×28 mm)

N876		10ch. Head of right-hand column	35	20
N877		10ch. Tail of right-hand column	35	20
N878		10ch. Head of left-hand column	35	20
N879		10ch. Tail of left-hand column	35	20

(c) Horiz. (56×28 mm)

N880		10ch. Centre of right-hand column	35	20
N881		10ch. Centre of left-hand column	35	20
N875/881		*Set of 7*	2·20	1·30

The centrepiece of the monument is flanked by two columns of soldiers, headed by Kim Il Sung.

No. N882 *is vacant.*

381 Museum of the Revolution, Pochonbo   **382** Grand Theatre, Pyongyang

1968 (30 Dec). Recess. P 11.

N883	**381**	2ch. grey-green	30	10
N884	**382**	10ch. chocolate	90	20

Various stamps from 1969 to 1973 previously listed with an asterisk and unpriced have now been deleted as they are not in the *List of Korean Stamps* (1946–1982), recently published by the Korean Stamp Corporation of the Democratic People's Republic of Korea.

These items were reported in *Korean Stamps*, the journal of the Philatelists' Union of North Korea. They will be reinstated if anyone is able to show us examples.

383 Irrigation

1969 (25 Feb). Rural Development. T **383** and similar horiz designs. Multicoloured. Photo. P 11.

N885	2ch. Type **383**	25	10
N886	5ch. Agricultural mechanisation	25	10
N887	10ch. Electrification	50	15
N888	40ch. Applying fertilizers and spraying trees	85	20
N885/888	*Set of 4*	1·70	50

384 Grey Rabbits

1969 (10 Mar). Rabbits. T **384** and similar horiz designs. Multicoloured. Photo. With or without gum. P 11.

N889	2ch. Type **384**	1·50	25
N890	10ch. Black rabbits	1·70	25
N891	10ch. Brown rabbits	1·70	25
N892	10ch. White rabbits	1·70	25
N893	40ch. Doe and young	4·50	50
N889/893	*Set of 5*	10·00	1·40

385 "Age and Youth"

1969 (1 Apr). Public Health Service. T **385** and similar horiz designs. Photo. P 11.

N894	2ch. brown and ultramarine	50	10
N895	10ch. blue and vermilion	1·00	20
N896	40ch. green and yellow	2·10	40
N894/896	*Set of 3*	3·25	65

Designs: —10ch. Nurse with syringe; 40ch. Auscultation by woman doctor.

386 Sowing Rice Seed

1969 (10 Apr). Agricultural Mechanisation. T **386** and similar horiz designs. Recess. P 11.

N897	10ch. bronze-green (Type **386**)	75	20
N898	10ch. salmon (Rice Harvester)	75	20
N899	10ch. black (Weed-spraying machine)	75	20
N900	10ch. red-brown (Threshing machine)	75	20
N897/900	*Set of 4*	2·75	70

387 Ponghwa

1969 (15 Apr). Revolutionary Historical Sites. T **387** and similar horiz design. Multicoloured. Litho. P 11.

N901	10ch. Type **387**	55	15
N902	10ch. Mangyongdae, birthplace of Kim Il Sung	55	15

388 Kim crosses into Manchuria, 1926, aged 13

1969 (15 Apr). Kim Il Sung in Manchuria. T **388** and similar horiz designs. Multicoloured. Litho. No. N907 with gum. P 11.

N903	10ch. Type **388**	50	20
N904	10ch. Leading strike of Yuwen Middle School boys, 1927	50	20
N905	10ch. Leading anti-Japanese demonstration in Kirin, 1928	50	20
N906	10ch. Presiding at meeting of Young Communist League, 1930	50	20
N907	10ch. Meeting of young revolutionaries	50	20
N903/907	*Set of 5*	2·30	90

389 Birthplace at Chilgol

390 Pegaebong Bivouac

395 Statue of Marshal Kim Il Sung

396 Teaching at Myongsin School

1969 (21 Apr). Commemoration of Mrs. Kang Ban Sok, mother of Kim Il Sung. T **389** and similar designs. Multicoloured. Photo. P 11.

N908	10ch. Type **389**	40	15
N909	10ch. With members of Women's Association	40	15
N910	10ch. Resisting Japanese police	3·50	75
N908/910	Set of 3	3·75	95

1969 (21 Apr). Bivouac Sites in the Guerrilla War against the Japanese. T **390** and similar multicoloured designs. Photo. P 11.

N911	5ch. Type **390**	25	10
N912	10ch. Mupo site (horiz)	40	15
N913	10ch. Chongbong site	40	15
N914	40ch. Konchang site (horiz)	1·40	55
N911/914	Set of 4	2·20	85

1969 (4 June). Memorials on Pochonbo Battlefield. T **395** and similar vert designs inscr "1937.6.4". Multicoloured. Photo. P 11.

N922	5ch. Machine-gun post	35	15
N923	10ch. Type **395**	35	15
N924	10ch. "Aspen-tree" monument	35	15
N925	10ch. Glade, Konjang Hill	35	15
N922/925	Set of 4	1·30	55

1969 (10 July). Commemoration of Kim Hyong Jik, father of Kim Il Sung. T **396** and similar design. Multicoloured. Photo. P 11.

N926	10ch. Type **396**	45	15
N927	10ch. Secret meeting with Korean National Association members	45	15

391 Chollima Statue

392 Museum of the Revolution, Pyongyang

1969 (1 May–10 Sept). Litho. P 11.

N915	**391**	10ch. blue	40	15
N916	**392**	10ch. myrtle green (10.9)	40	15

397 Relay Runner

398 Pres. Nixon attacked by Pens

1969 (10 Sept). 20th Anniv of Sports Day. Photo. P 11

N928	**397**	10ch. multicoloured	55	15

1969 (18 Sept). Anti-US Imperialism Journalists' Conference, Pyongyang. Litho. P 11.

N929	**398**	10ch. multicoloured	1·20	15

393 Mangyong Chickens

394 Marshal Kim Il Sung and Children

1969 (1 June). Korean Poultry. T **393** and similar horiz design. Recess. P 11.

N917	10ch. new blue (Type **393**)	1·30	25
N918	10ch. bluish violet (Kwangpo ducks)	3·75	45

1969 (1 June). Kim Il Sung's Educational System. T **394** and similar horiz designs. Multicoloured. Photo. P 11.

N919	2ch. Type **394**	10	10
N920	10ch. Worker with books	25	15
N921	40ch. Students with books	1·00	55
N919/921	Set of 3	1·20	70

399 Fighters and Battle

1969 (1 Oct). Implementation of Ten-point Programme of Kim Il Sung. T **399** and similar design. Multicoloured. Photo. P 11.

N930	5ch. Type **399** (Reunification of Korea)	40	15
N931	10ch. Workers upholding slogan (vert)	40	15

400 Bayonet Attack over US Flag

1969 (1 Oct). Anti-American Campaign. Photo. P 11.
N932 **400**   10ch. multicoloured   50   15

401 Armed Workers

1969 (1 Oct). Struggle for the Reunification of Korea. T **401** and similar multicoloured designs. Litho. P 11.
N933   10ch. Workers stabbing US soldier
            (vert)   25   15
N934   10ch. Kim II Sung and crowd with
            flags (vert)   25   15
N935   50ch. Type **401**   70   25
N933/935 *Set of 3* ....   1·10   50

402 Yellowtail

1969 (20 Dec). Korean Fishes. T **402** and similar horiz designs. Multicoloured. Photo. P 11.
N936   5ch. Type **402**   85   15
N937   10ch. Dace ....   1·30   20
N938   40ch. Mullet...................................   3·00   45
N936/938 *Set of 3* ....   4·75   70

403 Freighter *Taesungsan*   **405** Dahuangwai (1935)

1969 (20 Dec). Recess. P 11.
N939 **403**   10ch. slate-purple ....   1·00   20

1970 (10 Feb). Guerrilla Conference Places. T **405** and similar horiz designs. Photo. P 11.
N940   2ch. turquoise-blue and green   35   10
N941   5ch. bistre-brown and yellow-green   35   10
N942   10ch. light green and green   35   10
N940/942 *Set of 3*   95   25
    Designs:—5ch. Yaoyinggou (barn) (1935); 10ch. Xiaohaerbaling (tent) (1940).

406 Lake Chon   **407** Vietnamese
                          Soldier and
                          Furnaceman

1970 (10 Mar). Mt. Paekdu, Home of Revolution (1st issue). T **406** and similar horiz designs inscr "1970". Photo. P 11.
N943 **406**   10ch. black, buff and olive-green........   50   20
N944   –   10ch. black, blue-green & dull yell......   50   20
N945   –   10ch. reddish purple, new blue and
                orange-yellow   50   20
N946   –   10ch. black, slate-blue and flesh..........   50   20
N943/946 *Set of 4*..   1·80   70
    Designs:—No. N944, Piryu Peak; N945, Pyongsa (Soldier) Peak; N946, Changgun (General) Peak.
    See also Nos. N979/81

1970 (10 Mar). Help for Vietnamese People. Photo. P 11.
N947 **407**   10ch. green, red-brown and claret......   40   15

408 Receiving his Father's Revolvers from his Mother

1970 (15 Apr). Revolutionary Career of Kim II Sung. T **408** and similar horiz designs. Multicoloured. Litho. P 11.
N948   10ch. Type **408**...........................   90   25
N949   10ch. Receiving smuggled weapons
            from his mother   90   25
N950   10ch. Talking to farm workers   90   25
N951   10ch. At Kalun meeting, 1930................   90   25
N948/951 *Set of 4*..   3·25   90

409 Lenin   **410** March of
                    Koreans

1970 (22 Apr). Birth Centenary of Lenin. T **409** and similar vert design. Photo. P 11.
N952 **409**   10ch. sepia and cinnamon.....................   45   15
N953   10ch. orange-brown & light green   45   15
    Design:—No. N953, Lenin making a speech.

1970 (27 Apr). 15th Anniv of Association of Koreans in Japan. Recess. P 11.
N954 **410**   10ch. red.......................................   30   15
N955   10ch. maroon..............................   30   15

411 Uniformed   **412** Students and Newspapers
Factory Worker

1970 (5 May). Workers' Militia. T **411** and similar design. Photo. P 11.

| N956 | **411** | 10ch. green, orange-brown & mve..... | 30 | 10 |
| N957 | – | 10ch. green, red-brown & light blue .. | 30 | 10 |

Design: Horiz—No. N957, Militiaman saluting.

1970 (25 June). Peasant Education. T **412** and similar horiz designs. Multicoloured. Photo. P 11.

N958	2ch. Type **412**...............................	50	10
N959	5ch. Peasant with book	25	10
N960	10ch. Students in class	25	10
N958/960	*Set of 3*..	90	25

413 "Electricity Flows"

414 Soldier with Rifle

1970 (25 June). Commemoration of Army Electrical Engineers. Photo. P 11.

| N961 | **413** | 10ch. purple brown. .... | 50 | 15 |

1970 (25 June). Campaign Month for Withdrawal of US Troops from South Korea. T **414** and similar design. Recess. P 11.

| N962 | 5ch. violet .... | 15 | 10 |
| N963 | 10ch. purple (Soldier and partisan).... | 40 | 10 |

415 Rebel wielding Weapons

416 Labourer ("Fertilisers")

1970 (25 June). Struggle in South Korea against US Imperialism. Recess. P 11.

| N964 | **415** | 10ch. slate-violet .... | 30 | 15 |

1970 (10 Sept). Encouragement of Increased Productivity. T **416** and similar horiz designs. Photo. P 11.

N965	10ch. deep bluish green, pink & red-brn	50	15
N966	10ch. green, brown-red & bistre-brown	1·00	20
N967	10ch. blue, yellow-green & orange-brn	50	15
N968	10ch. bistre-brown, orge-brn & yell-grn	50	15
N969	10ch. bluish violet. It yell-ol & yell-brn	65	15
N965/969	*Set of 5*..	2·75	70

Designs:—No. N965, T **416;** N966, Furnaceman ("Steel"); N967, Operative ("Machines"); N968, Labourer ("Building Construction"); N969, Miner ("Mining").

417 Railway Guard

418 Agriculture

1970 (10 Sept). "Speed the Transport System". Photo. P 11.

| N970 | **417** | 10ch. turquoise, red-orge & yell-grn .. | 1·70 | 35 |

1970 (5 Oct). Executive Decisions of the Workers' Party Congress. T **418** and similar horiz designs embodying book. Recess. P 11.

N971	5ch. red...	35	10
N972	10ch. deep olive (Industry).................	1·50	25
N973	40ch. myrtle-green (The Armed Forces)	1·50	25
N971/973	*Set of 3*..	3·00	55

419 Chollima Statue and Workers' Party Banner

1970 (10 Oct). 25th Anniv of Korean Workers' Party. Photo. P 11.

| N974 | **419** | 10ch. red, bistre-brown and buff......... | 35 | 15 |

420 Kim Il Sung and the People

421 Emblem of League

1970 (2 Nov). Fifth Congress of Workers' Party. Miniature sheet (153×192 mm) comprising ten stamps as T **420** (10ch. values with symbol and inscr in panel at right). Litho. P 11.

MSN975 Multicoloured, comprising 40ch. T **420** and nine 10ch. stamps showing Family and new housing; Advance with Kim Il Sung's programme; People's army; Furnaceman and industry; Anti-US Imperialism; Peasants and agriculture; Students with books; Schoolgirl with book; Collaboration with Freedom Fighters....................................... 18·00   8·00

There was a second printing of this sheet which only measures 135×170 mm.

1971 (17 Jan). 25th Anniv of League of Socialist Working Youth. Photo. P 11.

| N976 | **421** | 10ch. carmine, buff & greenish blue... | 30 | 15 |

422 Log Cabin, Nanhutou

423 Tractor Driver

1971 (28 Feb). 35th Anniv of Nanhutou Guerrilla Conference. Photo. P 11.

| N977 | **422** | 10ch. multicoloured................................. | 30 | 15 |

1971 (5 Mar). 25th Anniv of Land Reform Law. Photo. P 11.

| N978 | **423** | 2ch. red, green and black..................... | 30 | 15 |

1971 (10 Mar). Mt. Paekdu, Home of Revolution (2nd issue). Designs similar to T **406** but inscr "1971". Photo.

N979	2ch. black, olive-green and turq-grn	50	15
N980	5ch. flesh, black and slate	3·00	60
N981	10ch. black, orge-red & greenish grey	85	20
N979/981	Set of 3...	4·00	85

Designs: Horiz—2ch. General view; 10ch. Western peak. Vert—5ch. Waterfall.

424 Popyong Museum **425** Miner

1971 (1 Apr). Museums of the Revolution. T **424** and similar horiz designs. Photo. P 11.

N982	**424**	10ch. chocolate and yellow	25	15
N983	–	10ch. ultramarine and red-orange......	25	15
N984	–	10ch. bronze-green & light orange	25	15
N982/984	Set of 3...		70	40

Designs:—No. N983, Mangyongdae Museum; N984, Chunggang Museum.

1971 (1 Apr). Six Year Plan for Coal Industry. Litho. P 11.

N985	**425**	10ch. multicoloured	65	25

426 Kim Il Sung **428** Hands holding Hammer and Rifle

427 Kim Il Sung founding Anti-Japanese Guerrilla Army

1971 (15 Apr). Founding of Anti-Japanese Guerrilla Army. T **426/7** and similar horiz designs as T **427.** Multicoloured. Litho. P 11.

N986	10ch. Type **426**..	50	20
N987	10ch. Type **427**	50	20
N988	10ch. Kim Il Sung addressing the people	50	20
N989	10ch. Kim Il Sung and members of Children's Corps	50	20
N986/989	Set of 4...	1·80	70

1971 (1 May). 85th Anniv of Labour Day. Photo. P 11.

N990	**428**	1wn. red, chocolate and buff	3·00	55

429 Soldiers and Map **430** Monument

1971 (5 May). 35th Anniv of Association for Restoration of Fatherland. Photo. P 11.

N991	**429**	10ch. red, buff and black	50	20

1971 (23 May). Battlefields in Musan Area, May, 1939. T **430** and similar multicoloured designs. Photo. P 11.

N992	5ch. Type **430**...	15	10
N993	10ch. Machine-guns in perspex cases (horiz)...	35	15
N994	40ch. Huts among birch trees (horiz).	90	55
N992/994	Set of 3...	1·30	70

431 Koreans Marching **432** Pioneer Emblem

1971 (25 May). Solidarity of Koreans in Japan. Photo. P 11.

N995	**431**	10ch. chocolate..	30	15

1971 (6 June). 25th Anniv of Korean Children's Union. Photo. P 11.

N996	**432**	10ch. red, yellow and greenish blue...	30	15

433 Marchers and Banners **434** Foundryman

1971 (21 June). Sixth Congress of League of Socialist Working Youth. T **433** and similar vert design. Photo. P 11.

N997	5ch. red, yellow-buff and black..........	25	10
N998	10ch. red, yellow-green and black......	35	15

Design:—10ch. Marchers and banner under globe.

1971 (24 June). 25th Anniv of Labour Law. Photo. P 11.

N999	**434**	5ch. black, brown-purple and buff...	30	15

435 Young Women   **436** Schoolchildren

1971 (30 July). 25th Anniv of Sex Equality Law. Photo. P 11.
N1000 **435**   5ch. multicoloured 30   15

1971 (1 Aug). 15th Anniv of Compulsory Primary Education. Photo. P 11.
N1001 **436**   10ch. multicoloured 55   15

437 Choe Yong Do and   **438** Two Foundrymen
Combat Scene

1971 (1 Aug). Heroes of the Revolutionary Struggle in South Korea. T **437** and similar horiz designs. Photo. P 11.
N1002   5ch. black and grey-green 35   10
N1003   10ch. red and brown 35   10
N1004   10ch. black and orange-red 35   10
N1002/1004 *Set of 3* 95   25
Designs—No. N1003, Revolutionary with book; N1004, Kim Jong Tae and scene of triumph.

1971 (10 Aug). 25th Anniv of Nationalisation of Industry Law. Photo. P 11.
N1005 **438**   5ch. black, yellow-green and buff .... 2·10   35

439 Struggle in Korea   **440** Kim Il Sung University

1971 (12 Aug). The Anti-Imperialist and Anti-US imperialist Struggles. T **439** and similar horiz designs. Photo. P 11.
N1006   10ch. vermilion, black &
     yellow-brown 35   15
N1007   10ch. orange brown, black & lt blue... 50   15
N1008   10ch. vermilion, black and salmon.... 65   15
N1009   10ch. black, olive green & yellow-grn 35   15
N1010   10ch. orange, black and red 65   15
N1011   40ch. green, black and flesh 65   20
N1006/1011 *Set of 6* .... 2·75   85
Designs:—No. N1007, Struggle in Vietnam: N1008, Soldier with rifle and 'plane marked "EC"; N1009, Struggle in Africa; N1010, Cuban Soldier and Central America; N1011, Bayoneting US soldier.

1971 (1 Oct). 25th Anniv of Kim Il Sung University. Photo. P 11.
N1012 **440**   10ch. grey, orange-red & yellow 30   10

441 Iron-ore Ladle (Mining)

1971 (2 Nov). Tasks of Six Year Plan. T **441** and similar horiz designs. Multicoloured. Photo. P 11.
N1013   10ch. Type **441** .... 2·10   35
N1014   10ch. Workers and text 40   15
N1015   10ch. Railway track (Transport) .... 2·10   35
N1016   10ch. Hand and wrench (Industry) 85   25
N1017   10ch. Mechanical scoop
     (Construction) .... 2·10   35
N1018   10ch. Manufactured goods (Trade) 40   15
N1019   10ch. Crate on hoists (Exports) 35   10
N1020   10ch. Lathe (Heavy Industries) .... 2·10   35
N1021   10ch. Freighter (Shipping) 85   25
N1022   10ch. Household equipment (Light
     Industries) 40   15
N1023   10ch. Corncob and wheat
     (Agriculture) 50   15
N1013/1023 *Set of 11* .... 11·00   2·30
See also Nos. N1089/1112.

442 Technicians

1971 (2 Nov). Cultural Revolution. T **442** and similar horiz designs. Multicoloured. Photo. P 11.
N1024   2ch. Type **442** 25   10
N1025   5ch. Mechanic 35   10
N1026   10ch. Schoolchildren 40   10
N1027   10ch. Chemist 65   10
N1028   10ch. Composer at piano .... 1·10   10
N1024/1028 *Set of 5* .... 2·50   45

443 Workers with Red Books

1971 (2 Nov). Ideological Revolution. T **443** and similar horiz designs. Multicoloured. Photo. P 11.
N1029   10ch. Type **443** 25   10
N1030   10ch. Workers reading book 25   10
N1031   10ch. Workers' lecture 25   10
N1032   10ch. Worker and pneumatic drill....... 25   10
N1029/1032 *Set of 4* 90   35

444 Korean Family

1971 (2 Nov). Improvement in Living Standards. Photo. P 11.
N1033 **444** 10ch. multicoloured.................................. 25 10

445 Furnaceman **446**

1971 (2 Nov). Implementation of Decisions of Fifth Workers' Party Conference. Photo. P 11.
N1034 **445** 10ch. multicoloured................................. 1·40 25

No. N1035 *is vacant.*

1971 (2 Nov). Solidarity with South Korean Revolutionaries. T **446** and similar designs. Photo. P 11.
N1036 **446** 10ch. red-brown, turq-blue & blk........ 40 15
N1037 – 10ch. reddish brn, flesh & orge-red 40 15
N1038 – 10ch. multicoloured.......................... 40 15
N1039 – 10ch. multicoloured.......................... 40 15
N1036/1039 *Set of 4*.. 1·40 55
Designs: Vert— No. N1037, US soldier attacked by poster boards; N1038, Hands holding rifles aloft. Horiz—N1039, Men advancing with rifles.

447 6000-ton Press **448** Title-page and Militants

1971 (2 Nov). T **447** and similar designs but horiz. Litho. P 11.
N1040 2ch. red-brown 90 15
N1041 5ch. ultramarine.................................... 1·30 25
N1042 10ch. brown-olive.................................. 1·50 25
N1043 10ch. dull blue-green .... 1·50 25
N1040/1043 *Set of 4*.. 4·75 80
Designs:—No. N1041, Refrigerated freighter *Ponghwasan;* N1042, 300 h.p. bulldozer; N1043, "Sungrisan" lorry.

1971 (1 Dec). 35th Anniv of "Samil Wolgan" Magazine. Photo. P 11.
N1044 **448** 10ch. rose-red, green and black........... 60 15

Nos. N1045/50 *are vacant.*

452 Poultry Chicks

1972 (1 Feb). Poultry Breeding. T **452** and similar horiz designs. Photo. P 11.
N1051 5ch. greenish yell, Prussian bl & brn 35 10
N1052 10ch. orange-brown, bistre & brown 50 10
N1053 40ch. blue, orange and deep blue...... 85 50
N1051/1053 *Set of 3*.. 1·50 65
Designs:—10ch. Chickens and battery egg house; 40ch. Eggs and fowls suspended from hooks.

453 Scene from *Village Shrine*

1972 (1 Apr). Films of Guerrilla War. T **453** and similar horiz designs. Photo. P 11.
N1054 **453** 10ch. olive-grey & deep bluish grn..... 1·00 20
N1055 – 10ch. Prussian bl, mar & red-orge .... 1·00 20
N1056 – 10ch. dull purple, dp blue & yellow .... 1·00 20
N1054/1056 *Set of 3*.. 2·75 55
Designs:—No. N1055, Patriot with pistol (*A Sea of Blood*); N1056, Guerrilla using bayonet (*The Lot of a Self-defence Corps Member*).

454 Kim Il Sung **455** Bugler sounding "Charge"
acknowledging Greetings

1972 (15 Apr). 60th Birthday of Kim Il Sung. T **454** and similar designs showing scenes in the life of Kim Il Sung, dated "1912–1972". Multicoloured. Litho. P 11.
N1057 5ch. Type **454**.. 25 10
a. Strip of 3. Nos. N1057/8 and
1071.. 1·50
N1058 5ch. In campaign H.Q. 25 10
N1059 5ch. Military conference (horiz)......... 25 10
a. Pair. Nos. N1059 and 1070.......... 90
N1060 10ch. In wheatfield (horiz) 40 10
a. Block of 10. Nos. 1060/9............. 11·00
N1061 10ch. Directing construction (horiz) .. 2·75 50
N1062 10ch. Talking to foundry workers
(horiz).. 25 10
N1063 10ch. Aboard whaler (horiz)................. 75 10
N1064 10ch. Visiting a hospital (horiz) .... 1·00 10
N1065 10ch. Viewing orchard (horiz)............... 25 10

N1066	10ch. With survey party on Haeju-Hasong railway line (horiz)	2·75	50
N1067	10ch. Meeting female workers at silk factory (horiz)	1·40	15
N1068	10ch. Village conference (horiz)	25	10
N1069	10ch. Touring chicken factory (horiz)	50	10
N1070	40ch. Relaxing with children	60	25
N1071	1wn. Giant portrait and marchers	90	50
N1057/1071 *Set of 15*		11·50	2·40

MSN1072 100×79 mm. 3wn. Kim Il Sung by Lake Chon (horiz). Imperf ..... 8·50 6·00

Nos. N1057/8 and N1071; N1059 and N1070; and N1060/9 were respectively issued together *se-tenant* within their sheets.

1972 (25 Apr). 40th Anniv of Guerrilla Army. Photo. P 11.

N1073	**455**	10ch. multicoloured	60	15

456 Pavilion of Ryongpo   **457** Volleyball

1972 (27 July). Historic Sites of the 1950–53 War. T **456** and similar horiz designs. Multicoloured. Litho. P 11.

N1074	2ch. Type **456**	20	10
N1075	5ch. Houses at Onjong	20	10
N1076	10ch. Headquarters, Kosanjin	20	10
N1077	40ch. Victory Museum, Chonsung	40	15
N1074/1077 *Set of 4*		90	40

1972 (1 Oct). Olympic Games, Munich. T **457** and similar designs. Multicoloured. Litho. P 11.

N1078	2ch. Type **457**	35	10
N1079	5ch. Boxing (horiz)	40	10
N1080	10ch. Judo	50	15
N1081	10ch. Wrestling (horiz)	50	15
N1082	40ch. Rifle-shooting	1·30	55
N1078/1082 *Set of 5*		2·75	95

458 Chollima Street, Pyongyang

1972 (1 Nov). Chollima Street, Pyongyang. T **458** and similar horiz designs. Litho. P 11.

N1083	5ch. salmon and black	2·20	55
N1084	10ch. yellow and black	85	20
N1085	10ch. light emerald and black	85	20
N1083/1085 *Set of 3*		3·50	35

Designs:—No. N1083, Bridge and skyscraper blocks; N1084, Type **458**; N1085, Another view looking up street.

459 Dredger

1972 (1 Nov). Development of Natural Resources. T **459** and similar horiz designs. Multicoloured. Photo. P 11.

N1086	5ch. Type **459**	50	10
N1087	10ch. Forestry	65	10
N1088	40ch. Reclaiming land from the sea	85	20
N1086/1088 *Set of 3*		1·80	35

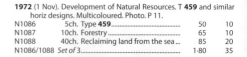

460 Ferrous Industry

1972 (1 Nov). Tasks of the Six-Year Plan. The Metallurgical Industry. T **460** and similar horiz design inscr "1971–1976". Multicoloured. Litho. P 11.

N1089	10ch. Type **460**	2·10	15
N1090	10ch. Non-ferrous Industry	60	15

461 Iron Ore Industry

1972 (1 Nov). Tasks of the Six-Year Plan. The Mining Industry. T **461** and similar horiz design inscr "1971–1976". Multicoloured. Litho. P 11.

N1091	10ch. Type **461**	85	15
N1092	10ch. Coal mining industry	3·25	45

462 Electronic and Automation Industry

1972 (2 Nov). Tasks of the Six-Year Plan. The Engineering Industry. T **462** and similar horiz designs inscr "1971–1976". Multicoloured. Photo. P 11.

N1093	10ch. Type **462**	85	15
N1094	10ch. Single purpose machines	60	15
N1095	10ch. Machine tools	60	15
N1093/1095 *Set of 3*		1·80	40

463 Clearing Virgin Soil

1972 (2 Nov). Tasks of the Six-Year Plan. Rural Economy. T **463** and similar horiz designs inscr "1971–1976". Multicoloured. Litho. P 11.

N1096	10ch. Type **463**	65	15
N1097	10ch. Irrigation	65	15
N1098	10ch. Harvesting	65	15
N1096/1098	*Set of 3*	1·80	40

464 Automation

1972 (2 Nov). Tasks of the Six-Year Plan. T **464** and similar horiz designs inscr "1971–1976". Multicoloured. Photo. P 11.

N1099	10ch. Type **464**	1·00	25
N1100	10ch. Agricultural mechanisation	65	15
N1101	10ch. Lightening of household chores	65	15
N1099/1101	*Set of 3*	2·10	50

465 Chemical Fibres and Materials

1972 (2 Nov). Tasks of the Six-Year Plan. The Chemical Industry. T **465** and similar horiz design inscr "1971–1976". Multicoloured. Photo. P 11.

N1102	10ch. Type **465**	85	15
N1103	10ch. Fertilisers, insecticides and weed killers	85	15

466 Textiles

1972 (2 Nov). Tasks of the Six-Year Plan. Consumer Goods. T **466** and similar horiz designs inscr "1971–1976". Multicoloured. Photo. P 11.

N1104	10ch. Type **466**	90	20
N1105	10ch. Kitchen ware and overalls	65	15
N1106	10ch. Household goods	65	15
N1104/1106	*Set of 3*	2·00	45

467 Fish, Fruit and Vegetables

1972 (2 Nov). Tasks of the Six-Year Plan. The Food Industry. T **467** and similar horiz designs. Multicoloured. Photo. P 11.

N1107	10ch. Type **467**	90	20
N1108	10ch. Tinned foods	90	20
N1109	10ch. Food packaging	90	20
N1107/1109	*Set of 3*	2·40	55

468 Electrifying Railway Lines

1972 (2 Nov). Tasks of the Six-Year Plan. Transport. T **468** and similar horiz designs. Multicoloured. Litho. P 11.

N1110	10ch. Type **468**	65	15
N1111	10ch. Laying new railway track	65	15
N1112	10ch. Freighters	60	15
N1110/1112	*Set of 3*	1·70	40

469 Soldier with Shell   **470** "Revolution of 19 April 1960"

1972 (2 Nov). North Korean Armed Forces. T **469** and similar horiz designs. Multicoloured. Litho. P 11.

N1113	10ch. Type **469**	50	15
N1114	10ch. Marine	50	15
N1115	10ch. Air Force pilot	50	15
N1113/1115	*Set of 3*	1·40	40

1972 (2 Nov). The Struggle for Reunification of Korea. T **470** and similar vert designs. Multicoloured. Photo. P 11.

N1116	10ch. Type **470**	25	15
N1117	10ch. Marchers with banners	25	15
N1118	10ch. Insurgents with red banner	25	15
N1119	10ch. Attacking US and South Korean soldiers	25	15
N1120	10ch. Workers with posters	25	15
N1121	10ch. Workers acclaiming revolution	5·00	90
N1122	10ch. Workers and manifesto	25	15
N1116/1122	*Set of 7*	5·75	1·60

471 Single-spindle Automatic Lathe   **472** Casting Vote

1972 (1 Dec). Machine Tools. T **471** and similar designs. Litho. P 11.
N1123   5ch. green and maroon 35   15
N1124   10ch. ultramarine and grey-green 50   15
N1125   40ch. dull green and brown .... 1·20   20
N1123/1125 *Set of 3*.. 1·80   45
Designs: Horiz:—10ch. "Kusong-3" lathe. Vert—40ch. 2000-ton crank press.

1972 (12 Dec). National Elections. T **472** and similar vert design. Multicoloured. Photo. P 11.
N1126   10ch. Type **472**.. 40   15
N1127   10ch. Election campaigner 40   15

Nos. N1128/9 *are vacant.*

475 Soldier

1973 (8 Feb). 25th Anniv of Founding of Korean People's Army. T **475** and similar horiz designs. Multicoloured. Photo. P 11.
N1130   5ch. Type **475**... 25   10
N1131   10ch. Sailor 40   10
N1132   40ch. Airman .... 1·00   65
N1130/1132 *Set of 3*.. 1·50   75

476 Wrestling Site

477 Monument to Socialist Revolution and Construction, Mansu Hill

1973 (15 Apr). Scenes of Kim Il Sung's Childhood, Mangyongdae. T **476** and similar designs. Photo. P 11.
N1133   2ch. Type **476**... 15   15
N1134   5ch. Warship rock.................................... 15   15
N1135   10ch. Swinging site (vert)...................... 25   15
N1136   10ch. Sliding rock.................................... 25   15
N1137   40ch. Fishing site 85   25
N1133/1137 *Set of 5*.. 1·50   75

1973 (15 Apr). Museum of the Korean Revolution. T **477** and similar designs. Litho. P 11.
N1138 **477** 10ch. multicoloured............................ 35   10
N1139   –   10ch. multicoloured............................ 35   10
N1140   –   40ch. multicoloured............................ 75   15
N1141   –   3wn. brown-olive and pale yellow..... 3·75   80
N1138/1141 *Set of 4*.. 4·75   1·00

Designs: As T **477**—10ch. (No. N1139), similar monument but men in military clothes (Monument to Anti-Japanese Struggle); 40ch. Statue of Kim Il Sung. 60×29 mm—3wn. Museum building.

478 Karajibong Camp

1973 (25 Apr). Secret Camps by the Tuman-Gang in the Guerrilla War, 1932. T **478** and similar horiz design. Multicoloured. Litho. P 11.
N1142   10ch. Type **478**....................................... 20   10
N1143   10ch. Soksaegol Camp............................ 20   15

479

480 Wrecked US Tanks

1973 (1 June). Menace of Japanese Influence in South Korea. Litho. P 11.
N1144 **479** 10ch. multicoloured................................ 30   10

1973 (23 June). Five-Point Programme for Reunification of Korea. T **480** and similar vert designs. Multicoloured. Litho. P 11.
N1145   2ch. Type **480**... 60   10
N1146   5ch. Electric train and crane lifting
              tractor... 3·75   50
N1147   10ch. Leaflets falling on crowd............. 25   10
N1148   10ch. Hand holding leaflet and map
              of Korea.. 60   10
N1149   40ch. Banner and globe.......................... 90   25
N1145/1149 *Set of 5*.. 5·50   95

481 Lorries

482 Volleyball

1973 (1 July). Lorries and Tractors. T **481** and similar design. Multicoloured. Photo. P 11.

N1150	10ch. Type **481**	50	15
N1151	10ch. Tractors and earth-moving machine	50	15

1973 (27 July). Socialist Countries' Junior Women's Volleyball Games, Pyongyang. Litho. P 11.

N1152 **482**	10ch. multicoloured	55	15

483 Battlefield

1973 (27 July). 20th Anniv of Victory in Korean War. T **483** and similar horiz design. Photo. P 11.

N1153 **483**	10ch. myrtle-green, claret & black	35	15
N1154 –	10ch. orange-brown, grey-blue & black (Urban fighting)	35	15

484 "The Snow Falls"

1973 (1 Aug). Mansudae Art Troupe. T **484** and similar horiz designs showing dances. Multicoloured. Litho. P 11.

N1155	10ch. Type **484**	75	15
N1156	25ch. "A Bumper Harvest of Apples"	1·70	40
N1157	40ch. "Azalea of the Fatherland"	2·10	45
N1155/1157 *Set of 3*		4·00	90

485 Schoolchildren   **486** *Fervour in the Revolution*

1973 (1 Sept). Ten Years Compulsory Secondary Education. Litho. P 11.

N1158 **485**	10ch. multicoloured	40	15

1973 (1 Sept). The Works of Kim Il Sung (1st series). T **486** and similar horiz designs. Litho. P 11.

N1159 **486**	10ch. lake-brown, claret & yellow	20	15
N1160 –	10ch. lake-brown, ol-grn & lemon	20	15
N1161 –	10ch. lake-brown, ol-brn & lemon	20	15
N1159/1161 *Set of 3*		55	40

Designs: No. N1160, Selected works; N1161, *Strengthen the Socialist System*.

See also Nos. N1217/18.

487 Celebrating Republic   **488** Pobwang Peak

1973 (9 Sept). 25th Anniv of People's Republic. T **487** and similar designs. Multicoloured. Litho. P 11.

N1162	5ch. Type **487**	20	10
N1163	10ch. Fighting in Korean War	20	10
N1164	40ch. Peace and reconstruction	2·20	60
N1162/1164 *Set of 3*		2·30	70

1973 (1 Oct). Mt. Myohyang. T **488** and similar multicoloured designs. Photo. P 11.

N1165	2ch. Type **488**	30	10
N1166	5ch. Inhodae Pavilion	35	15
N1167	10ch. Taeha Falls (vert)	1·60	40
N1168	40ch. Ryongyon Falls (vert)	4·50	70
N1165/1168 *Set of 4*		6·00	1·20

489 Party Memorial Building

1973 (10 Oct). Party Memorial Building. Photo. P 11.

N1169 **489**	1wn. brown, grey & orange-buff	1·80	45

490 Football and Handball   **491** Weightlifting

1973 (1 Nov). National People's Sports Meeting. T **490** and similar designs. Multicoloured. Litho. P 11.

N1170	2ch. Type **490**	75	15
N1171	5ch. High jumper and woman sprinter	35	10
N1172	10ch. Skaters and skier	60	15
N1173	10ch. Wrestling and swinging	40	10
N1174	40ch. Parachutist and motor cyclists	4·25	70
N1170/1174 *Set of 5*		5·75	1·10

1973 (1 Nov). Junior Weightlifting Championships of Socialist Countries. Litho. P 11.

N1175 **491**	10ch. blue, purple-brown & lt grn	50	15

492 Chongryu Cliff   **493** Rainbow Bridge

1973 (1 Nov). Scenery of Moran Hill, Pyongyang. T **492** and similar vert designs. Multicoloured. Litho. P 11.

N1176	2ch. Type **492**	1·00	20
N1177	5ch. Moran Waterfall	4·25	80
N1178	10ch. Pubyok Pavilion	1·10	20
N1179	40ch. Ulmil Pavilion	1·30	25
N1176/1179 *Set of 4*		7·00	1·30

1973 (1 Nov). Diamond Mountains Scenery (4th issue). T **493** and similar designs. Multicoloured. Litho. P 11.

N1180	2ch. Type **493**	2·00	35
N1181	5ch. Suspension footbridge, Okryudong (horiz)	2·00	35
N1182	10ch. Chonnyo Peak	1·00	20
N1183	10ch. Chilchung Rock and Sonji peak (horiz)	1·00	20
N1184	40ch. Sujongand Pari Peaks (horiz)	1·20	25
N1180/1184 *Set of 5*		6·50	1·20

494 Magnolia Flower   **495** South Korean Revolutionaries

1973 (1 Nov). Litho. P 11.

N1185	**494** 10ch. multicoloured	1·80	40

1973 (2 Nov). South Korean Revolution. T **495** and similar vert design. Multicoloured. Photo. P 11.

N1186	10ch. Type **495**	20	15
N1187	10ch. Marching revolutionaries	20	15

496 Cock sees Butterflies

1973 (1 Dec). Scenes from "Cock Chasing Butterflies" Fairy Tale. T **496** and similar horiz designs. Multicoloured. Litho. P 11.

N1188	2ch. Type **496**	2·10	35
N1189	5ch. Butterflies discuss how to repel cock	2·10	35
N1190	10ch. Cock chasing butterflies with basket	3·00	40
N1191	10ch. Cock chasing butterfly up cliff	3·00	45
N1192	40ch. Cock chasing butterflies over cliff	3·25	55
N1193	90ch. Cock falls into sea and butterflies escape	5·00	60
N1188/1193 *Set of 6*		17·00	2·40

Nos. N1194/5 *are vacant.*

497 Yonpung

1973 (1 Dec). Historical Sites of War and Revolution (40ch.). T **497** and similar horiz designs. Multicoloured. Litho. P 11.

N1196	2ch. Type **497**	15	10
N1197	5ch. Hyangha	15	10
N1198	10ch. Changgol	15	15
N1199	40ch. Paeksong	85	20
N1196/1199 *Set of 4*		1·20	50

498 Science Library, Kim Il Sung University

1973 (1 Dec). New Buildings in Pyongyang. T **498** and similar designs. Photo. P 11.

N1200	2ch. violet	75	15
N1201	5ch. yellow-green	25	15
N1202	10ch. brown.	35	15
N1203	40ch. yellow-brown and buff	85	20
N1204	90ch. buff	1·40	40
N1200/1204 *Set of 5*		3·25	95

Designs: 24×39 mm—5ch. Building No. 2, Kim Il Sung University. 60×24 mm—10ch. Victory Museum; 40ch. People's Palace of Culture. As T **498**—90ch. Indoor stadium.

499 Red Book   **500** Oriental Great Reed Warbler

1973 (27 Dec). Socialist Constitution of North Korea. T **499** and similar horiz designs. Multicoloured. Litho. P 11.

N1205	10ch. Type **499**	35	15
N1206	10ch. Marchers with red book and banners	35	15
N1207	10ch. Marchers with red book and emblem	35	15
N1205/1207 *Set of 3*		95	40

1973 (28 Dec). Korean Songbirds. T **500** and similar horiz designs. Multicoloured. Photo. P 11.

N1208	5ch. Type **500**	2·50	45
N1209	10ch. Grey starling	3·75	70
N1210	10ch. Daurian starling	3·75	70
N1208/1210 Set of 3		9·00	1·70

Nos. N1211/16 *are vacant.*

503 Chollima Statue

1974 (10 Jan). The works of Kim Il Sung (2nd issue). T **503** and similar horiz design. Multicoloured. Litho. P 11.

N1217	10ch. Type **503**	90	20
N1218	10ch. Bayonets threatening US soldier	15	15

504 Train in Station

1974 (20 Jan). Opening of Pyongyang Metro. T **504** and similar horiz designs. Multicoloured. Litho. P 11.

N1219	10ch. Type **504**	90	15
N1220	10ch. Escalators	90	15
N1221	10ch. Station Hall	90	15
N1219/1221 Set of 3		2·40	40

505 Capital Construction Front

506 Marchers with Banners

1974 (20 Feb). Five Fronts of Socialist Construction. T **505** and similar multicoloured designs. Litho. P 11.

N1222	10ch. Type **505**	20	15
N1223	10ch. Agricultural front	35	15
N1224	10ch. Transport front	1·80	35
N1225	10ch. Fisheries front	1·10	20
N1226	10ch. Industrial front (vert)	35	15
N1222/1226 Set of 5		3·50	90

1974 (25 Feb). 10th Anniv of Publication of Theses on the Socialist Rural Question in Our Country. T **506** and similar vert designs. Multicoloured. Litho. P 11.

N1227	10ch. Type **506**	25	10
	a. Horiz strip of 3. Nos. 1227/9.	80	
N1228	10ch. Book and rejoicing crowd	25	10
N1229	10ch. Tractor and banners	25	10
N1227/1229 Set of 3		70	25

Nos. 1227/9 were issued together in *se-tenant* horizontal strips of three within the sheet, forming a composite design.

507 Manure Spreader　　　　**508** Archery (Grenoble)

1974 (25 Feb). Farm Machinery. T **507** and similar horiz designs. Photo. P 11.

N1230	2ch. yellow-green, black and red	60	15
N1231	5ch. red, black and blue	60	15
N1232	10ch. red, black and yellow-green	60	15
N1230/1232 Set of 3		1·60	40

Designs:—5ch. "Progress" tractor; 10ch. "Mount Taedoksan" tractor.

1974 (10 Mar). North Korean Victories at International Sports Meetings. T **508** and similar multicoloured designs. Litho. P 12 (2ch., 60ch.) or 11 (others).

N1233	2ch. Type **508**	1·30	25
N1234	5ch. Gymnastics (Varna)	25	15
N1235	10ch. Boxing (Bucharest)	35	15
N1236	20ch. Volleyball (Pyongyang)	25	15
N1237	30ch. Rifle shooting (Sofia)	65	20
N1238	40ch. Judo (Tbilisi)	1·00	25
N1239	60ch. Model aircraft flying (Vienna) (horiz)	1·70	35
N1240	1wn.50 Table tennis (Peking) (horiz)	3·00	65
N1233/1240 Set of 8		7·75	1·90

509 Book and rejoicing Crowd

1974 (1 Apr). The First Country with No Taxes. Litho. P 11.

N1241	**509**	10ch. multicoloured	40	10

510 Drawing up Programme in Woods

1974 (15 Apr). Kim Il Sung during Anti-Japanese Struggle. T **510** and similar horiz designs. Multicoloured. Litho. P 12.

N1242	10ch. Type **510**	35	15
N1243	10ch. Giving directions to Pak Dal	35	15
N1244	10ch. Presiding over Nanhutou Conference	35	15
N1245	10ch. Supervising creation of strong-point	35	15
N1242/1245 Set of 4		1·30	55

511 Sun Hui loses her Sight

1974 (30 Apr). Scenes from *The Flower Girl* (revolutionary opera). T **511** and similar horiz designs. Multicoloured. Litho. P 12.

N1246	2ch. Type **511**	1·00	20
N1247	5ch. Death of Ggot Bun's mother	1·00	20
N1248	10ch. Ggot Bun throws boiling water at landlord	2·10	35
N1249	40ch. Ggot Bun joins revolutionaries	2·75	45
N1246/1249 Set of 4		6·25	1·10
MSN1250 111×62 mm. 50ch. Ggot Bun amid flowers of revolution. Imperf		3·75	1·50

512 Leopard Cat   **513** *Rosa acucularis lindly*

1974 (10 May). 15th Anniv of Pyongyang Zoo. T **512** and similar square designs. Multicoloured. Litho. P 11.

N1251	2ch. Type **512**	75	15
N1252	5ch. Lynx	75	15
N1253	10ch. Red fox	75	15
N1254	10ch. Wild Boar	75	15
N1255	20ch. Dhole	75	15
N1256	40ch. Brown bear	85	40
N1257	60ch. Leopard	1·50	40
N1258	70ch. Tiger	2·10	45
N1259	90ch. Lion	2·75	55
N1251/1259 Set of 9		9·75	2·25
MSN1260 140×100 mm. Diamond-shaped designs: 10ch. Wildcat; 30ch. Lynx; 50ch. Leopard; 60ch. Tiger. Imperf		29·00	8·00

1974 (20 May) Roses. T **513** and similar vert designs. Multicoloured. Litho. P 11.

N1261	2ch. Type **513**	75	15
N1262	5ch. Yellow sweet briar	85	20
N1263	10ch. Pink aromatic rose	1·00	20
N1264	10ch. Aronia sweet briar (yellow centres)	1·00	20
N1265	40ch. Multi-petal sweet briar	2·50	35
N1261/1265 Set of 5		5·50	1·00

514 Kim Il Sung greeted by Children (½-size illustration)

1974 (1 June). 30th Anniv of Korean Children's Union. Sheet 126×95 mm. Litho. Imperf.

MSN1266	**514** 1wn.20 multicoloured	4·50	3·25

515 Weigela   **516** Postwoman and Construction Site

1974 (30 June). Flowering Plants of Mt. Paekdu. T **515** and similar vert designs. Multicoloured. Litho. P 11.

N1267	2ch. Type **515**	60	15
N1268	5ch. Amaryllis	60	15
N1269	10ch. Red lily	60	15
N1270	20ch. Orange lily	85	20
N1271	40ch. Azalea	1·10	20
N1272	60ch. Yellow lily	1·80	35
N1267/1272 Set of 6		5·00	1·10

1974 (1 July). Centenary of Universal Postal Union, and Admission of North Korea to Union. T **516** and similar horiz designs. Multicoloured. Litho. P 12.

N1273	10ch. Type **516**	1·80	30
N1274	25ch. Chollima monument	20	20
N1275	40ch. Globe and Antonov An-12 transport planes	1·30	30
N1273/1275 Set of 3		3·00	70

517 Common Pond Frog

1974 (10 July). Amphibians. T **517** and similar horiz designs. Multicoloured. Litho. P 11.

N1276	2ch. Type **517**	3·00	30
N1277	5ch. Oriental fire-bellied toad	3·25	30

N1278	10ch. Bullfrog	3·75	45
N1279	40ch. Common toad	5·50	65
N1276/1279 Set of 4		14·00	1·50

No. N1280 is vacant.

518 "Women of Namgang Village"

1974 (10 July). Korean Paintings. T **518** and similar multicoloured designs. Litho. P 11.

N1281	2ch. Type **518**	75	15
N1282	5ch. "An Old Man on the Rakdong River" (60×49 mm)	85	20
N1283	10ch. "Morning in the Nae-kumgang" (bridge)	1·80	35
N1284	20ch. "Mt. Kumgang" (60×49 mm)	1·70	30
N1281/1284 Set of 4		4·50	90
MSN1285 116×115 mm. 1wn.50, "Evening Glow in Kangson". Imperf.		6·25	4·50

519 "Elektron 1" and "Elektron 2", 1964

1974 (10 July). Cosmonauts Day. T **519** and similar horiz designs. Multicoloured. Litho. P 11.

N1286	10ch. Type **519**	15	10
N1287	20ch. "Proton 1", 1965	25	15
N1288	30ch. "Venera 3", 1966	50	15
N1289	40ch. "Venera 5" and "Venera 6", 1969	60	20
N1286/1289 Set of 4		1·40	55
MSN1290 80×120 mm. 1wn. Dogs Belka and Strelka. Imperf		29·00	2·75

520 Satellite

1974 (10 July). Fourth Anniv of Launching of First Chinese Satellite. Sheet 80×120 mm. Litho. Imperf.

MSN1291 **520** 50ch. multicoloured		3·75	1·40

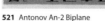

521 Antonov An-2 Biplane   **522** *Rhododendron redowskianum*

1974 (1 Aug). Civil Aviation. T **521** and similar horiz designs. Multicoloured. Litho. P 11.

N1292	2ch. Type **521**	85	15
N1293	5ch. Lisunov Li-2 airliner	85	15
N1294	10ch. Ilyushin Il-14P airliner	1·10	20
N1295	40ch. Antonov An-24 airliner	1·50	45
N1296	60ch. Ilyushin Il-18 airliner	2·75	70
N1292/1296 Set of 5		6·25	1·50
MSN1297 96×68 mm. 90ch. Airliner. Imperf.		6·25	4·75

1974 (10 Aug). Plants of Mount Paekdu. T **522** and similar vert designs. Multicoloured. Litho. P 12.

N1298	2ch. Type **522**	50	10
N1299	5ch. *Dryas octopetala*	50	15
N1300	10ch. *Potentilla fruticosa*	60	15
N1301	20ch. *Papaver somniferum*	75	15
N1302	40ch. *Phyllodoce caerulea*	1·00	30
N1303	60ch. *Oxytropis anertii*	2·20	55
N1298/1303 Set of 6		5·00	1·30

523 "Sobaek River in the Morning"

1974 (15 Aug). Modern Korean Paintings (1st series). T **523** and similar multicoloured designs. Litho. P 11.

N1304	10ch. Type **523**	1·30	20
N1305	20ch. "Combatants of Mt. Laohei" (60×40 mm)	1·50	25
N1306	30ch. "Spring in the Fields"	1·80	25
N1307	40ch. "Tideland Night"	5·75	85
N1308	60ch. "Daughter" (60×54 mm)	2·10	60
N1304/1308 Set of 5		11·00	1·90

See also Nos. N1361/5, N1386/96 and N1485/9.

524 (illustration reduced. Actual size 71 mm wide)

1974 (1 Sept). Bologna Exhibition for 50th Anniv of L'Unità (organ of the Italian communist party). Sheet 148×98 mm. Litho. Imperf.
MSN1309 **524** 1wn.50. multicoloured........................ 6·25   2·10

525 Log cabin, Unha Village

1974 (9 Sept). Historic Sites of the Revolution. T **525** and similar horiz design. Multicoloured. Litho. P 11.
N1310   5ch. Munmyong 20   10
N1311   10ch. Type **525**.. 20   10

526 Sesame

1974 (30 Sept). Oil-producing Plants. T **526** and similar horiz designs. Multicoloured. Litho. P 11.
N1312   2ch. Type **526**.. 90   20
N1313   5ch. *Perilla frutescens*........................... 1·00   20
N1314   10ch. Sunflower .... 1·20   25
N1315   40ch. Castor bean .... 1·70   55
N1312/1315 *Set of 4*.. 4·25   1·10

527 Kim Il Sung as Guerrilla Leader

1974 (10 Oct). Kim Il Sung. T **527** and similar multicoloured designs. Litho. P 12.
N1316   10ch. Type **527**....................................... 35   15
N1317   10ch. Commander of the People's Army (52×35 mm) 35   15
N1318   10ch. "The commander is also a son of the people" (52×35 mm)........ 35   15
N1319   10ch. Negotiating with the Chinese anti-Japanese unit (52×35 mm) 35   15
N1316/1319 *Set of 4*.. 1·30   55

528

1974 (10 Oct). Grand Monument on Mansu Hill. T **528** and similar horiz designs. Multicoloured. Litho. P 11.
N1320   10ch. Type **528**.. 25   15
N1321   10ch. As Type **528** but men in civilian clothes.. 25   15
N1322   10ch. As Type **528** but men facing left.. 25   15
N1323   10ch. As No. N1322 but men in civilian clothes.............................. 25   15
N1320/1323 *Set of 4*... 90   55

529 Factory ship *Chilbosan*

1974 (20 Nov). Deep-sea Fishing. T **529** and similar horiz designs. Multicoloured. Litho. P 11.
N1324   2ch. Type **529**.. 1·20   30
            a. Block of 6. Nos. N1324/9 .... 7·50
N1325   5ch. Trawler support ship *Paekdusan* and trawler.................... 1·20   30
N1326   10ch. Freighter *Moranbong*.................. 1·20   30
N1327   20ch. Whale-catcher .... 1·20   30
N1328   30ch. Trawler.. 1·20   30
N1329   40ch. Stern trawler.................................. 1·20   30
N1324/1329 *Set of 6*... 6·50   1·60
      Nos. 1324/9 were issued together in *se-tenant* blocks of six within the sheet.

Nos. N1330/48 *are vacant.*

539 Kim Il Sung crosses River Agrok

1975 (3 Feb). 50th Anniv of Kim Il Sung's crossing of River Agrok.
P 12.
N1349 **539** 10ch. multicoloured 40 15

540 Pak Yong Sun "World Table Tennis Queen"

1975 (16 Feb). Pak Yong Sun, Winner of 33rd World Table Tennis
Championships, Calcutta. Litho. P 11×12.
N1350 **540** 10ch. multicoloured .... 1·50 15
MSN1351 80×119 mm. 80ch. "Table Tennis Crown".
Imperf .... 2·75 80

541 Common Zebra

1975 (20 Feb). Pyongyang Zoo. T **541** and similar multicoloured
designs. Litho. P 12 (Nos. 1352, 1354/5, 1356) or 11 (others).
N1352 10ch. Type **541**.............................. 85 15
N1353 10ch. African buffalo......................... 85 15
N1354 20ch. Giant panda (horiz)...................... 2·10 25
N1355 25ch. Bactrian camel............................ 1·70 40
N1356 30ch. Indian elephant............................ 3·25 45
N1352/1356 Set of 5 .... 8·00 1·30

542 "Blue Dragon"

1975 (20 Mar). 7th-century Mural Paintings from Koguryo Tombs,
Kangso. T **542** and similar multicoloured designs. Litho. P 12.
N1357 10ch. Type **542**.............................. 90 15
N1358 15ch. "White Tiger".......................... 1·30 25
N1359 25ch. "Red Phoenix" (vert) .... 1·50 30
N1360 40ch. "Snake-turtle".......................... 2·10 40
N1357/1360 Set of 4.................................. 5·25 1·00

543 "Spring in the Guerilla Base" (1968)

1975 (30 Mar). Modern Korean Paintings (2nd series). Anti-Japanese
Struggle. T **543** and similar multicoloured designs. Litho. P 12.
N1361 10ch. Type **543**.............................. 50 15
N1362 10ch. "Revolutionary Army landing at
Unggi" (1969).............................. 50 15
N1363 15ch. "Sewing Team Members" (1961) 85 20
N1364 20ch. "Girl Watering Horse" (1969) ..... 1·50 25
N1365 30ch. "Kim Jong Suk giving Guidance
to Children's Corps" (1970)......... 1·20 25
N1361/1365 Set of 5.................................. 4·00 90
Each design includes the year of the painting, as noted above (see
also Nos. N1386/96).

544 Cosmonaut **545** Victory Monument

1975 (12 Apr). Cosmonauts' Day. T **544** and similar multicoloured
designs. Litho. P 12.
N1366 10ch. Type **544**.............................. 15 10
N1367 30ch. "Lunokhod" moon vehicle
(horiz)....................................... 65 15
N1368 40ch. "Soyuz" spacecraft and "Salyut"
space laboratory (horiz)............. 90 25
N1366/1368 Set of 3.................................. 1·50 45

1975 (15 Apr). Commemoration of Battle of Pochonbo. Sheet 140×98
mm. Litho. Imperf.
MSN1369 **545** 1wn. multicoloured .... 5·75 3·00

546 The Beacon lit at Pochonbo, 1937

1975 (15 Apr). Kim Il Sung during the Guerrilla War against the Japanese, 1937–40. T **546** and similar horiz designs. Multicoloured. Litho. P 12.

N1370	10ch. Type **546**	35	15
N1371	10ch. "A Bowl of Parched-rice Powder", 1938	35	15
N1372	10ch. Guiding the Nanpaizi meeting, November 1938	35	15
N1373	10ch. Welcoming helpers	35	15
N1374	10ch. Lecturing the guerrillas	35	15
N1375	15ch. Advancing into the homeland, May 1939	40	15
N1376	25ch. By Lake Samji, May 1939	60	25
N1377	30ch. At Sinsadonq, May 1939	75	30
N1378	40ch. Xiaohaerbaling meeting, 1940	1·10	40
N1370/1378 *Set of 9*		4·25	1·70

547 Vase of Flowers and Kim Il Sung's Birthplace

1975 (15 Apr). 63rd Birthday of Kim Il Sung. P 12.

N1379	10ch. Type **547**	20	10
N1379a	40ch. Kim Il Sung's birthplace, Mangyongdae	65	15

548 South Korean Insurgent   **549** "Kingfisher at a Lotus Pond"

1975 (19 Apr). 15th Anniv of April 19th Rising. Litho. P 11.

N1380	**548** 10ch. multicoloured	30	10

1975 (10 May). Paintings of Li Dynasty. T **549** and similar vert designs. Multicoloured. Litho. P 12.

N1381	5ch. Type **549**	2·10	30
N1382	10ch. "Crabs"	1·30	25
N1383	15ch. "Rose of Sharon"	2·10	35
N1384	25ch. "Lotus and Water Cock"	3·00	50
N1385	30ch. "Tree Peony and Red Jungle-fowl"	4·25	75
N1381/1385 *Set of 5*		11·50	1·90

1975 (10 May). Modern Korean Paintings (3rd series). Fatherland Liberation War. Dated designs similar to T **543**. Multicoloured. Litho. P 12.

N1386	5ch. "On the Advance Southward" (1966) (vert)	25	15
N1387	10ch. "The Assigned Post" (girl sentry) (1968) (vert)	35	15
N1388	15ch. "The Heroism of Li Su Bok" (1965)	40	15
N1389	25ch. "Retaliation" (woman machine-gunner) (1970)	75	25
N1390	30ch. "The awaited Troops" (1970)	90	25
N1386/1390 *Set of 5*		2·40	90

1975 (20 May). Modern Korean Paintings (4th series). Socialist Construction. Dated designs similar to T **543**. Multicoloured. Litho. P 12.

N1391	10ch. "Pine Tree" (1966) (vert)	1·00	20
N1392	10ch. "The Blue Signal Lamp" (1960) (vert)	3·75	55
N1393	15ch. "A Night of Snowfall" (1963)	1·10	20
N1394	20ch. "Smelters" (1968)	1·30	25
N1395	25ch. "Tideland Reclamation" (1961)	1·30	25
N1396	30ch. "Mount Paekgum" (1966)	1·30	25
N1391/1396 *Set of 6*		8·75	1·50

550 Flag and Building   **551** Marathon Runners

1975 (25 May). 20th Anniv of "Chongryon" Association of Koreans in Japan. Litho. P 11½×12.

N1397	**550** 10ch. multicoloured	40	10
N1398	3wn. multicoloured	9·50	85

1975 (8 June). Marathon Race of Socialist Countries. Sheet 105×74 mm. Litho. Imperf.

MSN1399	**551** 1wn. multicoloured	4·25	1·40

552 "Feet first" entry (man)   **553**

1975 (20 June). Diving. T **552** and similar vert designs. Multicoloured. Litho. P 11.

N1400	10ch. Type **552**	15	10
N1401	25ch. Piked somersault (man)	65	30
N1402	40ch. "Head first" entry (woman)	1·30	40
N1400/1401	Set of 3	1·90	70

1975 (25 June). Campaign against US Imperialism. Litho. P 12.

N1403	**553**	10ch. multicoloured	40	15

554 Memorial Fish

1975 (25 June). Fresh-water Fish. T **554** and similar horiz designs. Multicoloured. Litho. P 11.

N1404	10ch. Type **554**	85	15
N1405	10ch. Whitefish (fish swimming to right)	85	15
N1406	15ch. *Opsariichthys bidens*	1·30	20
N1407	25ch. Naere	1·80	30
N1408	30ch. Catfish (fish swimming to right)	2·50	40
N1409	30ch. Snakehead (fish swimming to left)	2·50	40
N1404/1409	Set of 6	8·75	1·40

1975 (10 July). 10th Socialist Countries' Football Tournament, Pyongyang. T **555** and similar horiz designs. Litho. P 11.

N1410	5ch. multicoloured	50	10
N1411	10ch. multicoloured	50	15
N1412	15ch. multicoloured	60	15
N1413	20ch. multicoloured	75	25
N1414	50ch. multicoloured	1·40	50
N1410/1414	Set of 5	3·50	1·00
MSN1415	112×80 mm. 1wn. multicoloured. Imperf	6·25	4·00

1975 (10 July). Birds. T **556** and similar vert designs. Multicoloured. Litho. P 12.

N1416	10ch. Type **556**	1·70	35
N1417	15ch. Sulphur-crested cockatoo	2·00	40
N1418	20ch. Blyth's parakeet	2·75	50
N1419	25ch. Rainbow lory	3·00	65
N1420	30ch. Budgerigar	3·25	70
N1416/1420	Set of 5	11·50	2·30

557 Flats   **558** White Peach Blossom

1975 (20 July). New Buildings in Pyongyang. T **557** and similar horiz designs. Multicoloured. Litho. P 12 (90ch.) or 11 (others).

N1421	90ch. Saesallim (formerly Sarguson) St.	5·00	90
N1422	1wn. Type **557**	5·00	95
N1423	2wn. Potonggang Hotel	10·00	2·00
N1421/1423	Set of 3	18·00	3·50

1975 (20 Aug). Blossoms of Flowering Trees. T **558** and similar vert designs. Multicoloured. Litho. P 11.

N1424	10ch. Type **558**	60	15
N1425	15ch. Red peach blossom	60	15
N1426	20ch. Red plum blossom	1·00	25
N1427	25ch. Apricot blossom	1·20	25
N1428	30ch. Cherry blossom	1·70	40
N1424/1428	Set of 5	4·50	1·10

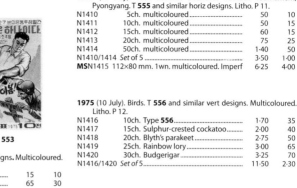

555   **556** Blue and Yellow Macaw   **559** Sejongbong   **560** Azalea

1975 (20 Aug). Landscapes in Diamond Mountains. T **559** and similar vert designs. Multicoloured. Litho. P 12.

N1429	5ch. Type **559**	50	10
N1430	10ch. Chonsondae	75	15
N1431	15ch. Pisamun	1·00	25
N1432	25ch. Manmulsang	1·30	30
N1433	30ch. Chaehabong	1·50	35
N1429/1433	Set of 5	4·50	1·00

1975 (30 Aug). Flowers of the Azalea Family. T **560** and similar horiz designs. Multicoloured. Litho. P 11.

N1434	5ch. Type **560**	65	15
N1435	10ch. White Azalea	65	25
N1436	15ch. Wild Rhododendron	1·00	25
N1437	20ch. White Rhododendron	1·00	25
N1438	25ch. Rhododendron	1·30	30
N1439	30ch. Yellow Rhododendron	1·70	40
N1434/1439	Set of 6	5·75	1·40

561 Gliders

1975 (9 Sept). Training for National Defence. T **561** and similar multicoloured designs. Litho. P 12.

N1440	5ch. Type **561**	60	10
N1441	5ch. Radio-controlled model airplane	60	10
N1442	10ch. "Free fall" parachutist (vert)	75	20
N1443	10ch. Parachutist landing on target (vert)	75	20
N1444	20ch. Parachutist with bouquet of flowers (vert)	1·30	30
N1440/1444	Set of 5	3·50	80
MSN1445	90×68 mm. 50ch. Three parachutists in circle. Imperf	2·75	75

562 Wild Apple   **563** Torch of Juche

1975 (30 Sept). Fruit Tree Blossom. T **562** and similar vert designs. Multicoloured. Litho. P 12.

N1446	10ch. Type **562**	65	25
N1447	15ch. Wild pear	65	25
N1448	20ch. Hawthorn	1·00	30
N1449	25ch. Chinese quince	1·30	40
N1450	30ch. Flowering quince	1·40	50
N1446/1450	Set of 5	4·50	1·50

1975 (10 Oct). 30th Anniv of Korean Workers' Party. T **563** and similar vert designs. Multicoloured. Litho. P 12.

N1451	2ch. "Victory" and American graves	15	10
N1452	2ch. Sunrise over Mt. Paekdu-san	15	10
N1453	5ch. Type **563**	15	10
N1454	5ch. Chollima Statue and sunset over Pyongyang	15	10
N1455	10ch. Korean with Red Book	15	10
N1456	10ch. Chollima Statue	15	10
N1457	25ch. Crowds and burning building	50	25
N1458	70ch. Flowers and map of Korea	1·60	80
N1451/1458	Set of 8	2·75	1·50
MSN1459	Two sheets (a) 85×120 mm. 90ch. Kim Il Sung delivering speech; (b) 120×85 mm. 1wn. Kim Il Sung leading crowd	6·25	4·75

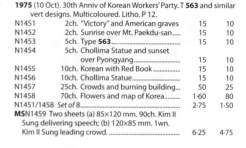

564 Welcoming Crowd

1975 (14 Oct). 30th Anniv of Return of Kim Il Sung to Pyongyang. Litho. P 12.

N1460	**564**	20ch. multicoloured	35	15

565 Workers Holding "Juche" Torch   **566** Hyonmu Gate

1975 (1 Nov). 30th Anniv of Rodong Sinmun (Journal of the Central Committee of the Workers' Party). Litho. P 11.

N1461	**565**	10ch. multicoloured	60	15
MSN1462		95×68 mm. **565** 1wn. multicoloured. Imperf	3·00	2·10

1975 (20 Nov). Ancient Wall-Gates of Pyongyang. T **566** and similar multicoloured designs. Litho. P 12.

N1463	10ch. Type **566**	15	10
N1464	10ch. Taedong Gate	15	10
N1465	15ch. Potong Gate	25	15
N1466	20ch. Chongum Gate	40	25
N1467	30ch. Chilsong Gate (vert)	60	40
N1463/1467	Set of 5	1·40	90

567

1975 (30 Nov). Views of Mt. Chilbo. T **567** and similar horiz designs.
Litho. P 12.

N1468	**567**	10ch. multicoloured	50	15
N1469		10ch. multicoloured	50	20
N1470		15ch. multicoloured	75	25
N1471		20ch. multicoloured	90	30
N1472		30ch. multicoloured	1·00	35
N1468/1472	*Set of 5*		3·25	1·10

568 Right-hand Section of Monument

1975 (20 Dec). Historic Site of Revolution in Wangjaesan. T **568** and
similar multicoloured designs. P 11 (15ch.) or 12 (others).

N1473	10ch. Type **568**	15	10
N1474	15ch. Left-hand section of monument	25	10
N1475	25ch. Centre section of monument (38×60 mm)	40	15
N1476	30ch. Centre section. close-up (60×38 mm)	50	25
N1473/1476	*Set of 4*	1·20	55

569 Marchers with Flags

1976 (17 Jan). 30th Anniv of Korean League of Socialist Working
Youth. T **569** and similar horiz design. Multicoloured. Litho.
P 12.

N1477	2ch. Flags and Emblem	20	15
N1478	70ch. Type **569**	1·30	65

570 Geese

1976 (5 Feb). Ducks and Geese. T **570** and similar horiz designs.
Multicoloured. Litho. P 11 (10ch.) or 12 (others).

N1479	10ch. Type **570**	85	15
N1480	20ch. "Perennial" duck	1·80	25
N1481	40ch. Kwangpo duck	3·25	45
N1479/1481	*Set of 3*	5·25	75

571 "Oath"   **572** "Rural Road at Evening"

1976 (8 Feb). Korean People's Army (sculptural works). T **571** and
similar multicoloured designs. Litho. P 12**.**

N1482	5ch. Type **571**	25	10
N1483	10ch. "Union of Officers with Men" (horiz)	35	10
N1484	10ch. "This Flag to the Height"	35	10
N1482/1484	*Set of 3*	85	25

1976 (10 Feb). Modern Korean Paintings (5th series). Social Welfare.
T **572** and similar multicoloured designs. Litho. P 12.

N1485	10ch. Type **572**	60	15
N1486	15ch. "Passing on Technique" (1970)	65	20
N1487	25ch. "Mother (and Child)" (1965)	90	20
N1488	30ch. "Medical Examination at School" (1970) (horiz)	1·70	35
N1489	40ch. "Lady Doctor of Village" (1970) (horiz)	2·00	45
N1485/1489	*Set of 5*	5·25	1·20

Each design includes the year of the painting, as noted.

573 Worker holding Text of Law

1976 (5 Mar). 30th Anniv of Agrarian Reform Law. Litho. P 12.

N1490	**573**	10ch. multicoloured	30	15

574 Telephones and Satellite

1976 (12 Mar). Centenary of First Telephone Call. T **574** and similar vert designs. Multicoloured. Litho. With gum. P 13.

N1491	2ch. Type **574**	60	10
N1492	5ch. Satellite and antenna	60	10
N1493	10ch. Satellite and telecommunications systems	65	15
N1494	15ch. Telephone and linesman	1·40	35
N1495	25ch. Satellite and map of receiving stations	2·10	45
N1496	40ch. Satellite and cable-laying barge	3·25	60
N1491/1496	Set of 6	7·75	1·60

MSN1497 94×70 mm. 50ch. Old telephone and satellite. Without gum................ 2·50 60

Limited quantities of Nos. N1491/6 exist without gum. Nos. N1491/**MS**N1497 were also issued in sheetlets of seven stamps and one *se-tenant* label (Price £12·50 un).

575 Cosmos   **576** Fruit and Products

1976 (20 Mar). Flowers. T **575** and similar horiz designs. Multicoloured. Litho. P 12.

N1498	5ch. Type **575**	40	15
N1499	10ch. Dahlia	40	15
N1500	20ch. Zinnia	60	20
N1501	40ch. China aster	1·00	40
N1498/1501	Set of 4	2·20	80

1976 (7 Apr). Pukchong Meeting of Presidium of Korean Workers' Party. T **576** and similar vert design. Multicoloured. Litho. P 11½×12.

N1502	5ch. Type **576**	85	20
N1503	10ch. Fruit and orchard scene	85	20

577 "Pulgungi" Type Electric Locomotive

1976 (10 Apr). Railway Locomotives. T **577** and similar horiz designs. Multicoloured. Litho. P 12.

N1504	5ch. Type **577**	50	15
N1505	10ch. "Chaju" type underground train	1·00	20
N1506	15ch. "Saebyol" type diesel locomotive	1·20	30
N1504/1506	Set of 3	2·40	60

GUM AND IMPERFORATE STAMPS. All of the following stamps were issued with gum, except where otherwise stated. Limited quantities of imperforate stamps, miniature sheets, and sheetlets were also issued for most of the following sets.

578 Satellite   **580** Bat and Ribbon

579 Kim Il Sung beside Car

1976 (12 Apr). Space Flight. T **578** and similar vert designs. Litho. P 13½.

N1507	**578** 2ch. multicoloured	15	10
N1508	5ch. multicoloured	15	10
N1509	10ch. multicoloured	25	15
N1510	15ch. multicoloured	40	15
N1511	25ch. multicoloured	60	25
N1512	40ch. multicoloured	1·00	30
N1507/1512	Set of 6	2·30	95

MSN1513 77×98 mm. 50ch. Moon vehicle................ 1·30 55

Limited quantities of Nos. N1507/**MS**N1513 exist without gum.

1976 (15 Apr). 64th Birthday of Kim Il Sung. P 12.

N1514 **579** 10ch. multicoloured................ 50 20

MSN1515 120×80 mm. 40ch. Kim Il Sung and rejoicing crowd................ 4·50 1·30

1976 (25 Apr). 3rd Asian Table Tennis Championships. T **580** and similar vert designs. Multicoloured. Litho. Without gum. P 12.

N1516	5ch. Type **580**	35	10
N1517	10ch. Three women players with flowers	35	15
N1518	20ch. Player defending	60	30
N1519	25ch. Player making attacking shot	1·00	40
N1516/1519	Set of 4	2·10	90

MSN1520 74×99 mm. 50ch. Player making backhand shot. Imperf................ 2·50 80

581 Kim Il Sung announcing Establishment of Association

1976 (5 May). 40th Anniv of Association for the Restoration of the Fatherland. Litho. Without gum. P 12.
N1521 **581** 10ch. multicoloured.................................. 25 15

582 Golden Pheasant

583 Monument and Map of River

1976 (5 May). Pheasants. T **582** and similar horiz designs. Multicoloured. Litho. P 13½.
N1522	2ch. Type **582**..................................	1·00	25
N1523	5ch. Lady Amherst's pheasant..........	1·10	25
N1524	10ch. Silver pheasant..........................	1·30	30
N1525	15ch. Reeves's pheasant......................	1·50	40
N1526	25ch. Temminck's pheasant................	2·00	60
N1527	40ch. Ring-necked pheasant (albino)	2·30	80
N1522/1527	*Set of* 6....................................	8·25	2·30

MSN1528 77×58 mm. 50ch. Ring-necked pheasant 5·00 2·10
Limited quantities of Nos. N1522/**MS**N1528 exist without gum. Nos. N1522/**MS**N1528 were also issued together (p 12, on dull paper) in sheetlets of seven stamps and one *se-tenant* label (Price £11 un).

1976 (21 May). Potong River Monument. Without gum. P 11.
N1529 **583** 10ch. pale purple-brown and dull
yellowish green............................. 25 15

584 Running

1976 (17 July). Olympic Games, Montreal. T **584** and similar horiz designs. Multicoloured. Litho. P 13.
N1530	2ch. Type **584**................................	15	15
N1531	5ch. Diving..	35	15
N1532	10ch. Judo...	75	15
N1533	15ch. Gymnastics..............................	1·30	25
N1534	25ch. Gymnastics..............................	1·70	35
N1535	40ch. Fencing....................................	3·50	85
N1530/1535	*Set of* 6....................................	7·00	1·70

MSN1536 109×85 mm. 50ch. Runner with torch,
and Olympic Stadium .... 4·25 2·10
Nos. N1530/**MS**N1536 were also issued together (p 12, on dull paper) in sheetlets of seven stamps and one *se-tenant* label (Price £12·50 un). A limited number of these sheetlets and of No. **MS**N1536 were issued in 1977 overprinted "amphilex 77 AMSTERDAM".

585 Bronze Medal (Hockey, Pakistan) **586** Boxing (Ku Yong Jo)

1976 (2 Aug). Olympic Medal Winners (1st issue). T **585** and similar vert designs. Multicoloured. Litho. P 13.
N1537	2ch. Type **585**................................	1·10	15
N1538	5ch. Bronze medal (shooting, Rudolf Dollinger)	35	10
N1539	10ch. Silver medal (boxing, Li Byong Uk).................	35	15
N1540	15ch. Silver medal (cycling, Daniel Morelon).................	3·00	45
N1541	25ch. Gold medal (marathon, Waldemar Cierpinski)................	1·30	30
N1542	40ch. Gold medal (boxing, Ku Yong Jo)	1·70	35
N1537/1542	*Set of* 6.................................	7·00	1·40

MSN1543 109×84 mm. 50ch. Three medals.............. 2·10 2·10
Nos. N1536/**MS**N1543 were also issued together (p 13½, on dull paper) in sheetlets of seven stamps and one *se-tenant* label but with the stamps printed with different winners' names (Price £19 un). A limited number of these sheetlets and of No. **MS**N1543 were issued in 1977 overprinted "amphilex 77 AMSTERDAM".

1976 (2 Aug). Olympic Medal Winners (2nd issue). T **586** and similar vert designs. Multicoloured. Litho. P 13.
N1544	2ch. Type **586**................................	35	10
N1545	5ch. Gymnastics (Nadia Comaneci)	35	10
N1546	10ch. Pole vaulting (Tadeusz Slusarski).................	35	15
N1547	15ch. Hurdling (Guy Drut)...................	40	15
N1548	25ch. Cycling (Bernt Johansson)..........	3·75	55
N1549	40ch. Football (East Germany).............	2·20	40
N1544/1549	*Set of* 6.................................	6·75	1·30

MSN1550 104×84 mm. 50ch. Ku Yong Jo (boxing
champion)................................. 2·50 55
Nos. N1544/**MS**N1550 were also issued in sheetlets of seven stamps and five *se-tenant* labels (Price £9·25 un).

> **APPENDIX.** Further commemorative issues which appeared during 1976–83 are recorded in the Appendix to this country.

587 UPU Headquarters, Berne

1976 (5 Aug). International Festivities. T **587** and similar horiz designs. Multicoloured. Litho. P 13½.

N1551	2ch. Type **587**	60	10
N1552	5ch. Footballers (World Cup)	60	10
N1553	10ch. Olympic Stadium	65	15
N1554	15ch. Olympic Village	1·40	25
N1555	25ch. Junk and satellite	1·20	35
N1556	40ch. Satellites	1·20	60
N1551/1556	*Set of 6*	5·00	1·40
MSN1557	85×105 mm. 50ch. World map	2·10	1·40

Nos. N1551/**MS**N1557 were also issued together (on dull paper) in sheetlets of seven stamps and one *se-tenant* label (Price £8·50 un). A limited number of these sheetlets and of No. **MS**N1557 were issued in 1977 overprinted "amphilex 77 AMSTERDAM".

588 Azure-winged Magpies

1976 (8 Aug). Embroidery. T **588** and similar multicoloured designs. Litho. P 12.

N1558	2ch. Type **588**	2·00	40
N1559	5ch. White magpie	1·40	30
N1560	10ch. Roe deer	50	15
N1561	15ch. Black-naped oriole and magnolias	2·10	40
N1562	25ch. Fairy with flute (horiz)	1·20	25
N1563	40ch. Tiger	2·50	65
N1558/1563	*Set of 6*	8·75	1·90
MSN1564	94×105 mm. 50ch. Tiger (52×82 mm). P 10½	10·00	90

Limited quantities of Nos. N1558/63 exist without gum. Nos. N1558/**MS**N1564 were also issued together (p 13) in sheetlets of seven stamps and one *se-tenant* label (Price £20 un).

589 Roman "5" and Flame   **590** Trophy and Certificate

1976 (10 Aug). Fifth Summit Conference of Non-aligned States, Colombo. Litho. Without gum. P 12.

N1565	**589** 10ch. multicoloured	25	15

1976 (15 Aug). World Model Plane Championships, 1975. T **590** and similar horiz designs. Multicoloured. Litho. Without gum. P 12.

N1566	5ch. Type **590**	25	10
N1567	10ch. Trophy and medals	40	10
N1568	20ch. Model airplane and emblem	60	20
N1569	40ch. Model glider and medals	1·00	50
N1566/1569	*Set of 4*	2·00	80

591 "Pulgungi" Type Diesel Shunting Locomotive

1976 (14 Sept). Locomotives. T **591** and similar horiz designs. Multicoloured. Litho. P 12.

N1570	2ch. Type **591**	60	15
N1571	5ch. "Saebyol" type diesel locomotive	85	20
N1572	10ch. "Saebyol" type diesel shunting locomotive	90	20
N1573	15ch. Electric locomotive	1·10	25
N1574	25ch. "Kumsung" type diesel locomotive	1·50	30
N1575	40ch. "Pulgungi" type electric locomotive	1·80	35
N1570/1575	*Set of 6*	6·00	1·30
MSN1576	100×68 mm. 50ch. "Kumsong" type diesel locomotive. Imperf	7·50	3·75

Nos. N1570/**MS**N1576 were also issued together in sheetlets of seven stamps and one *se-tenant* label (Price £18 un).

592 House of Culture

1976 (7 Oct). House of Culture. Without gum. P 12.

N1577	**592** 10ch. light brown and black	20	15

593 Kim Il Sung visiting Tosongrang

1976 (10 Oct). Revolutionary Activities of Kim Il Sung. T **593** and
similar horiz designs. Multicoloured. Litho. P 13.

N1578	2ch. Type **593**..............................	25	10
N1579	5ch. Kim Il Sung visits peasants.........	25	10
N1580	10ch. Kim Il Sung on hilltop	35	10
N1581	15ch. Kim Il Sung giving house to farmhand.......................................	40	15
N1582	25ch. Kim Il Sung near front line..........	1·00	20
N1583	40ch. Kim Il Sung walking in rain	1·00	35
N1578/1583 Set of 6...		3·00	90
MSN1584 105×85 mm. 50ch. Kim Il Sung with child at roadside. P 10½		1·80	1·40

594 Kim Il Sung with Union Members

1976 (17 Oct). 50th Anniv of Down-with-Imperialism Union. Litho.
Without gum. P 12.

N1585 **594** 20ch. multicoloured 50 20

Nos. N1586/8 are vacant.

604 Searchlights and **605** Spring Costume
Kim Il Sung's Birthplace

1977 (1 Jan). New Year. Litho. Without gum. P 12.
N1589 **604** 10ch. multicoloured 25 15

1977 (10 Feb). National Costumes of Li Dynasty. T **605** and similar
vert designs. Multicoloured. Litho. P 12.

(a) POSTAGE.

N1590	10ch. Type **605**...........................	65	15
N1591	15ch. Summer costume..........................	90	20
N1592	20ch. Autumn costume.........................	1·00	25

(b) AIR. Inscr "AIR MAIL"

N1593	40ch. Winter costume..............................	1·70	40
N1590/1593 Set of 4...		3·75	90

Nos. N1590/3 were also issued together in sheetlets of four stamps
(Price £6·75 un).

606 Two Deva Kings (Koguryo **607** Worker with Five-Point
Dynasty) Programme

1977 (26 Feb). Korean Cultural Relics. T **606** and similar multicoloured
designs. Litho. P 13½.

(a) POSTAGE

N1594	2ch. Type **606**..................................	60	15
N1595	5ch. Gold-copper decoration, Koguryo Dynasty..........................	60	15
N1596	10ch. Copper Buddha, Koryo Dynasty......................................	85	20
N1597	15ch. Gold-copper Buddha, Paekje Dynasty......................................	1·00	20
N1598	25ch. Gold crown, Koguryo Dynasty	1·20	30
N1599	40ch. Gold-copper sun decoration, Koguryo Dynasty (horiz).............	1·40	35

(b) AIR. Inscr "AIR MAIL"

N1600	50ch. Gold crown, Silla Dynasty..........	1·50	50
N1594/1600 Set of 7...		6·50	1·70

Nos. N1594/1600 were also issued together in sheetlets of seven
stamps and one label (Price £8·50 un).

1977 (5 Mar). Five-Point Programme for Remaking Nature. Litho.
Without gum. P 12.
N1601 **607** 10ch. multicoloured 30 15

608 Pine Branch and Map of Korea

1977 (23 Mar). 60th Anniv of Korean National Association. Litho.
Without gum. P 12.
N1602 **608** 10ch. multicoloured 55 20

609 Championship Emblem and
Trophy

1977 (5 Apr). 34th World Table Tennis Championships. T **609** and similar horiz designs. Multicoloured. Litho. Without gum. P 12.

(a) POSTAGE

N1603	10ch. Type **609**	25	10
N1604	15ch. Pak Yong Sun	40	15
N1605	20ch. Pak Yong Sun with trophy	65	20

(b) AIR. Inscr "AIR MAIL"

N1606	40ch. Pak Yong Ok and Yang Ying	1·30	40
N1603/1606	Set of 4	2·30	75

610 Kim Il Sung founds Guerrilla Army at Mingyuegou

1977 (15 Apr). 65th Birthday of Kim Il Sung. T **610** and similar horiz designs. Multicoloured. Litho. P 12.

N1607	2ch. Type **610**	15	10
N1608	5ch. In command of army	15	10
N1609	10ch. Visiting steel workers in Kangson	35	10
N1610	15ch. Before battle	25	10
N1611	25ch. In schoolroom	35	15
N1612	40ch. Viewing bumper harvest	50	15
N1607/1612	Set of 6	1·60	65
MSN1613	85×94 mm. 50ch. "Kim Il Sung among the Artists". P 11½	1·30	90

611 "Chollima 72" trolleybus

612 Red Flag and Hand holding Rifle

1977 (20 Apr). Trolleybuses. T **611** and similar horiz design. Litho. Without gum. P 12.

N1614	5ch. dull blue, bright lilac & black	1·50	30
N1615	10ch. rosine, pale sage green & black	1·50	30

Design:—10ch. "Chollima 74" trolleybus.

1977 (25 Apr). 45th Anniv of Korean People's Revolutionary Army. Litho. Without gum. P 12.

N1616	**612** 40ch. pale red, pale yellow & black	85	25

613 Proclamation and Watchtower

1977 (4 June). 40th Anniv of Pochonbo Battle. Litho. Without gum. P 13.

N1617	**613** 10ch. multicoloured	25	15

614 Koryo White Ware Teapot

615 Postal Transport

1977 (10 June). Korean Porcelain. T **614** and similar vert designs. Multicoloured. Litho. P 13.

(a) POSTAGE

N1618	10ch. Type **614**	75	15
N1619	15ch. White vase, Li Dynasty	1·00	20
N1620	20ch. Celadon vase, Koryo Dynasty	1·30	30

(b) AIR. Inscr "AIR MAIL"

N1621	40ch. Celadon vase with lotus decoration, Koryo Dynasty	1·80	40
N1618/1621	Set of 4	4·25	95

Nos. N1618/21 were also issued together in sheetlets of four stamps (Price £5 un).

1977 (28 June). Postal Service T **615** and similar horiz designs. Multicoloured. Litho. Without gum. P 13.

N1623	2ch. Type **615**	1·50	30
N1624	10ch. Postwoman delivering letters...	60	15
N1625	30ch. Mil Mi-8 helicopter	1·50	40
N1626	40ch. Ilyushin Il-18 airliner and world map	1·70	45
N1623/1626	Set of 4	4·75	1·20

616 Rapala arata

617 Grey Cat

1977 (25 July). Butterflies and Dragonflies. T **616** and similar horiz designs. Multicoloured. Litho. P 12.

(a) POSTAGE

N1627	2ch. Type **616**	65	10
N1628	5ch. Colias aurora	1·00	15
N1629	10ch. Poplar admiral (Limenitis populi)	1·30	20
N1630	15ch. Anax partherope (dragonfly)	1·70	35
N1631	25ch. Sympetrum pedemontanum (dragonfly)	2·20	45

(b) AIR. Inscr "AIR MAIL"

N1632	50ch. Papilio maackii	2·75	60
N1627/1632	Set of 6	8·75	1·70

Nos. N1627/32 were also issued together in sheetlets of six stamps (Price £17 un).

1977 (10 Aug). Cats. T **617** and similar vert designs. Multicoloured. Litho. P 11½×12.

N1634	2ch. Type **617**	1·70	30

N1635	10ch. Black and white cat	2·20	40
N1636	25ch. Ginger cat	3·75	55
N1634/1636	Set of 3	7·00	1·10

Nos. N1634/6 were also issued together in sheetlets of three stamps (Price £11 un).

618

619 Kim Il Sung and Pres. Tito

1977 (10 Aug). Dogs. T **618** and similar vert designs. Multicoloured. Litho. P 11½×12.

(a) POSTAGE

N1638	5ch. Type **618**	1·30	25
N1639	15ch. Chow	1·50	25

(b) AIR. Inscr "AIR MAIL"

N1640	50ch. Pungsang dog	2·30	45
N1638/1640	Set of 3	4·50	85

Nos. N1638/40 were also issued together in sheetlets of three stamps (Price £10 un).

1977 (25 Aug). Visit of President Tito. P 12.

N1642	**619**	10ch. multicoloured	15	10
N1643		15ch. multicoloured	15	10
N1644		20ch. multicoloured	25	15
N1645		40ch. multicoloured	40	25
N1642/1645		Set of 4	85	55

620 Girl and Symbols of Education

1977 (1 Sept). Fifth Anniv of 11-year Compulsory Education. Litho. Without gum. P 13.

N1646	**620**	10ch. multicoloured	25	15

621 Chinese Mactra
(*Mactra sulcataria*)

622 Students and "Theses"

1977 (5 Sept). Shellfish and Fish. T **621** and similar vert designs. Multicoloured. Litho. P 11½×12.

(a) POSTAGE

N1647	2ch. Type **621**	50	10
N1648	5ch. Bladder moon (*Natica fortunei*)	65	20
N1649	10ch. *Arca inflata*	1·00	20
N1650	25ch. Thomas's rapa whelk (*Rapana thomasiana*)	1·40	35

(b) AIR

N1651	50ch. *Sphoeroides porphyreus*	2·30	65
N1647/1651	Set of 5	5·25	1·30

Nos. N1647/51 were also issued together in sheetlets of five stamps and one label (Price £8·50 un).

1977 (5 Sept). Kim Il Sung's "Theses on Socialist Education". T **622** and similar vert design. Multicoloured. Litho. Without gum. P 11½×12.

N1653	10ch. Type **622**	25	10
N1654	20ch. Students, crowd and text	30	15

623 "Juche" Torch

624 Jubilant Crowd

1977 (14 Sept). Seminar on the Juche Idea. T **623** and similar vert designs. Multicoloured. Litho. Without gum. P 12.

N1655	2ch. Type **623**	25	10
N1656	5ch. Crowd and red book	25	10
N1667	10ch. Chollima Statue and flags	25	10
N1658	15ch. Handclasp and red flag on world map	25	10
N1659	25ch. Map of Korea and anti-US slogans	35	15
N1660	40ch. Crowd and Mount Paekdu-san	40	15
N1655/1660	Set of 6	1·60	65
MSN1661	117×78 mm. 50ch. Emblem of Juche seminar	1·30	55

1977 (11 Nov). Election of Deputies to Supreme People's Assembly. Litho. Without gum. P 13.

N1662	**624**	10ch. multicoloured	25	15

625 Footballers

1977 (10 Dec). World Cup Football Championship. Argentina. T **625** and similar horiz designs. Litho. Without gum. P 13.

N1663	**625**	10ch. multicoloured	1·10	25
N1664	–	15ch. multicoloured	1·50	35

N1665	– 40ch. multicoloured	2·50	50
MSN1666	132×82 mm. 50ch. Footballers	2·20	55
N1663/1665	Set of 3	4·50	1·00

Nos. N1663/**MS**N1666 were also issued together in sheetlets of four stamps (Price £12·50 un). A small number of these sheetlets were issued in July 1978 overprinted with the results.

626 Kim Il Sung with Rejoicing Crowds

1977 (15 Dec). Re-election of Kim Il Sung. Litho. Without gum. P 11½×12.

N1667	**626**	10ch. multicoloured	30	15

See also Nos. N2165/80.

627 Chollima Statue and Symbols of Communication

1977 (16 Dec). 20th Anniv of Socialist Countries' Communication Organization. Litho. Without gum. P 11½×12.

N1668	**627**	10ch. multicoloured	30	15

Nos. N1669/86 *are vacant.*

638 Chollima Statue and City Skyline

1978 (1 Jan). New Year. Litho. Without gum. P 13.

N1687	**638**	10ch. multicoloured	30	15

639 Skater in 19th-century Costume

640 Post-rider and "Horse-ticket"

1978 (18 Feb). Winter Olympic Games, Sapporo-Innsbruck. T **639** and similar vert designs. Multicoloured. Litho. P 13.

(a) POSTAGE

N1688	2ch. Type **639**	60	15
N1689	5ch. Skier	60	15
N1690	10ch. Woman skater	60	15
N1691	15ch. Hunter on skis	65	20
N1692	20ch. Woman (in 19th century costume) on skis	65	20
N1693	25ch. Viking with longbow	3·25	50

(b) AIR. Inscr "AIR MAIL"

N1694	40ch. Skier	1·80	35
N1688/1694	Set of 7	7·25	1·50
MSN1695	Two sheets (a) 78×97 mm. 50ch. Innsbruck skyline; (b) 97×78 mm. 60ch. Skater	3·00	1·30

Nos. N1688/**MS**N1695 were also issued together in sheetlets of nine stamps and one *se-tenant* label (Price £17 un).

1978 (12 Mar). Postal Progress. T **640** and similar vert designs. Multicoloured. Litho. P 13.

(a) POSTAGE

N1696	2ch. Type **640**	35	10
N1697	5ch. Postman on motor cycle	2·10	45
N1698	10ch. Electric train and post-van	2·10	45
N1699	15ch. Mail steamer and Mil Mi-8 helicopter	1·20	25
N1700	25ch. Tupolev Tu-154 jetliner and satellite	1·10	25

(b) AIR. Inscr "AIR MAIL"

N1701	40ch. Dove and UPU headquarters	65	20
N1696/1701	Set of 6	6·75	1·50
MSN1702	Two sheets, each 97×79 mm. (a) 50ch. Dove and UPU) symbol, (b) 60ch. Dove and UPU headquarters	6·25	3·25

Nos. N1696/**MS**N1702 were also issued together in sheetlets of eight stamps (p 13½) (Price £11 un).

641 Self-portrait

642 "Chungsong" Tractor

1978 (20 Mar). 400th Birth Anniv of Rubens. Litho. P 13.
N1703 **641** 2ch. multicoloured 35 15
N1704   5ch. multicoloured 35 15
N1705   40ch. multicoloured .... 2·10 45
N1703/1705 *Set of 3* .... 2·50 70
MSN1706 96×79 mm. 50ch. multicoloured .... 2·50 1·70
  Nos. N1703/**MS**N1706 were also issued together in sheetlets of four stamps (Price £6·75 un).

1978 (1 Apr). Farm Machines. T **642** and similar horiz design. Litho. Without gum. P 11½×12.
N1707   10ch. bright rose-red and black........... 65 20
N1708   10ch. lake-brown and black 65 20
  Design:—10ch. (No. N1708) Sprayer.

643 Show Jumping   **644** Soldier

1978 (1 Apr). Olympic Games, Moscow, 1980 (1st issue). Equestrian Events. T **643** and similar vert designs. Multicoloured. Litho. P 13.
N1709   2ch. Type **643**.......................... 35 10
N1710   5ch. Jumping bar 35 10
N1711   10ch. Cross-country 65 15
N1712   15ch. Dressage........................ 65 25
N1713   25ch. Water splash.................. 1·00 40
N1714   40ch. Dressage (different).......... 1·70 75
N1709/1714 *Set of 6*............................ 4·25 1·60
MSN1715 75×111 mm. 50ch. Jumping triple bar ..... 2·50 55
  Nos. N1709/**MS**N1715 were also issued together in sheetlets of seven stamps and one *se-tenant* label (Price £9·25 un).
  See also Nos. N1861/**MS**N1866, N1873/**MS**N1880 and N1887/**MS**N1893.

1978 (25 Apr). Korean People's Army Day. T **644** and similar vert design. Multicoloured. Litho. Without gum. P 11½×12.
N1716   5ch. Type **644**........................... 25 10
N1717   10ch. Servicemen saluting.................... 25 10

645 *Mangyongbong* (freighter)

1978 (5 May). Korean Ships. T **645** and similar horiz designs. Multicoloured. Litho. P 13.
(a) POSTAGE
N1718   2ch. Type **646**.......................... 2·10 50
N1719   5ch. *Hyoksin* (freighter) 35 15
N1720   10ch. *Chongchongang* (gas carrier) 65 15
N1721   30ch. *Sonbong* (tanker) .... 1·30 40

(b) AIR
N1722   50ch. *Taedonggang* (freighter).............. 1·50 85
N1718/1722 *Set of 5*............................ 5·25 1·80
  Nos. N1718/22 were also issued together in sheetlets of five stamps and one *se-tenant* label (Price £11·50 un).

646 Uruguayan Footballer

1978 (1 June). World Cup Football Championship Winners. T **646** and similar multicoloured designs. Litho. P 13.
(a) POSTAGE
N1724   5ch. Type **646**........................ 60 10
N1725   10ch. Italian player................... 60 10
N1726   15ch. West German player.............. 60 15
N1727   25ch. Brazilian player 60 15
N1728   40ch. English player .... 1·00 35
(b) AIR
N1729   50ch. Hands holding World Cup (vert) .... 1·70 50
N1724/1729 *Set of 6*............................ 4·50 1·20
MSN1730 110×74 mm. AIR. 50ch. Italian and North Korean players .... 3·75 1·00
  Nos. N1724/9 were also issued together in sheetlets of six stamps (Price £11 un).

647 Footballers (1930 Winners, Uruguay)

1978 (1 June). History of the World Cup Football Championship. T **647** and similar vert designs. Multicoloured. Litho. P 13.
(a) POSTAGE
N1731   20ch. Type **647**........................ 1·00 35
N1732   20ch. Italy, 1934 .... 1·00 35
N1733   20ch. France, 1938 .... 1·00 35
N1734   20ch. Brazil, 1950.................... 1·00 35
N1735   20ch. Switzerland, 1954 .... 1·00 35
N1736   20ch. Sweden, 1958 .... 1·00 35
N1737   20ch. Chile, 1962 .... 1·00 35
N1738   20ch. England, 1966 .... 1·00 35
N1739   20ch. Mexico, 1970 .... 1·00 35
N1740   20ch. W. Germany, 1974.............. 1·00 35
N1741   20ch. Argentina, 1978................ 1·00 35
(b) AIR
N1742   50ch. Footballers and emblem.......... 2·50 1·00
N1731/1742 *Set of 12*............... 12·00 4·25
MSN1743 73×98 mm. 50ch. World Cup and championship emblem.................. 2·10 60
  Nos. N1731/41 and **MS**N1743 were also issued together in sheetlets of twelve stamps (Price £17 un).

648 *Sea of Blood* (opera)

1978 (2 June). Art from the Period of Anti-Japanese Struggle. T **648** and similar horiz designs. Multicoloured. Litho. P 13.

N1744	10ch. Type **648**	35	15
N1745	15ch. Floral kerchief embroidered with map of Korea	50	15
N1746	20ch. "Tansimjul" (maypole dance)	65	25
N1744/1746 *Set of 3*		1·40	50
MSN1747 100×69 mm. 40ch. Notation of Song of Korea		1·60	60

649 Red Flag and "7" Electricity and Coal

1978 (15 June). Second Seven Year Plan. T **649** and similar horiz designs. Multicoloured. Litho. Without gum. P 11½×12.

N1748	5ch. Type **649**	35	10
N1749	10ch. Steel and non-ferrous metal	35	10
N1750	15ch. Engineering and chemical fertilizers	50	15
N1751	30ch. Cement and fishing	75	25
N1752	50ch. Grain and tideland reclamation	1·00	50
N1748/1752 *Set of 5*		2·75	1·00

650 Gymnastics (Alfred Flatow)

1978 (16 June). History of Olympic Games and Winners. T **650** and similar horiz designs. Multicoloured. Litho. P 13.

N1753	20ch. Type **650**	90	35
N1754	20ch. Runners (Michel Theato)	90	35
N1755	20ch. Runners (Wyndham Halswelle)	90	35
N1756	20ch. Rowing (William Kinnear)	90	35
N1757	20ch. Fencing (Paul Anspach)	1·70	50
N1758	20ch. Runners (Ugo Frigerio)	90	35
N1759	20ch. Runners (Ahmed El Quafi)	90	35
N1760	20ch. Cyclists (Robert Charpentier)	2·10	50
N1761	20ch. Gymn astics (Joseph Stalder)	90	35
N1762	20ch. Boxing (László Papp)	1·20	40
N1763	20ch. Runners (Ronald Delany)	90	35
N1764	20ch. High jump (Jolanda Balas)	90	35
N1765	20ch. High jump (Valery Brumel)	90	35
N1766	20ch. Gymnastics (Vera Caslavska)	90	35
N1767	20ch. Rifle shooting (Li Ho Jun)	90	35
N1753/1767 *Set of 15*		14·00	5·00
MSN1768 105×95 mm. 50ch. Boxing (Ku Yong Jo)		1·70	85

Nos. N1753/**MS**N1768 were also issued together in sheetlets of 16 stamps (Price £21 un).

651 Douglas DC-8-63 Jetliner and Comte AC-4 Gentleman

1978 (25 July). Aircraft. T **651** and similar horiz designs. Multicoloured. Litho. P 13.

N1769	2ch. Type **651**	75	15
N1770	10ch. Ilyushin Il-62M jetliner and Avia BH-25	1·00	15
N1771	15ch. Douglas DC-8-63 jetliner and Savoia Marchetti S-71	1·10	25
N1772	20ch. Tupolev Tu-144 jetliner and Kalinin K-5	1·30	25
	a. Gold (face value and inscr) omitted		
N1773	25ch. Tupolev Tu-154 jetliner and Antonov An-2 biplane	1·30	25
N1774	30ch. Ilyushin Il-18 airliner and early airplane	1·30	25
N1775	40ch. Concorde supersonic jetliner and Wibault 283 trimotor	3·00	75
N1769/1775 *Set of 7*		8·75	1·80
MSN1776 102×75 mm. 50ch. Airbus Industrie A300B2 jetliner and Focke Wulf A-17 Mowe		2·75	60

Nos. N1769/**MS**N1776 were also issued together in sheetlets of eight stamps (Price £13·50 un).

652 White-bellied Black Woodpecker

653 Demonstrators and Korean Map

1978 (5 Aug). White-bellied Black Woodpecker (*Drycopus richardsi Tristram*) Preservation. T **652** and similar vert designs. Multicoloured. Litho. P 11½×12.

N1777	5ch. Type **652**	1·10	40
N1778	10ch. Woodpecker and eggs	1·30	50
N1779	15ch. Woodpecker feeding young	1·70	65
N1780	25ch. Woodpecker feeding young (different view)	2·10	85
N1781	50ch. Adult woodpecker on tree trunk	3·25	1·20
N1777/1781 *Set of 5*		8·50	3·25

Nos. N1777/81 were also issued together in sheetlets of five stamps and one *se-tenant* label (Price £10 un).

1978 (9 Sept). 30th Anniv of Democratic People's Republic of Korea. T **653** and similar vert designs. Multicoloured. Litho. Without gum. P 13.

N1783	10ch. Type **653**	25	15
N1784	10ch. Flag and soldiers	25	15
N1785	10ch. Flag and "Juche"	25	15
N1786	10ch. Red Flag	25	15
N1787	10ch. Chollima Statue and city skyline	25	15
N1788	10ch. "Juche" torch and men of three races	25	15
N1783/1788 *Set of 6*		1·40	80

654 Cat and Pup

668 Red Flag and Pine Branch

655 Footballers

1978 (16 Oct). Animal Paintings by Li Am. T **654** and similar vert designs. Multicoloured. Litho. P 13.

N1789	10ch. Type **654**	3·00	65
N1790	15ch. Cat up a Tree	3·00	65
N1791	40ch. Wild Geese	3·00	65
N1789/1791	Set of 3	8·00	1·80

Nos. N1789/91 were also issued together in sheetlets of three stamps and one se-tenant label (Price £12·50 un).

1978 (15 Dec). World Cup Winner, World Cup Football Championship, Argentina. T **655** and similar horiz designs. Multicoloured. Litho. Without gum. P 13.

N1792	**655**	10ch. multicoloured	90	20
N1793	–	15ch. multicoloured	1·10	25
N1794	–	25ch. multicoloured	1·30	40
N1792/1794		Set of 3	3·00	75
MSN1795	94×69 mm. 50ch. multicoloured		2·10	1·70

Nos. N1792/**MS**N1795 were also issued together in sheetlets of four stamps (Price £11 un).

Nos. N1796/1811 are vacant.

1979 (1 Jan). New Year. Litho. Without gum. P 12.

| N1812 | **668** | 10ch. multicoloured | 30 | 15 |

1979 (1 Jan). International Year of the Child (1st issue). T **669** and similar multicoloured designs. Litho. P 13.

(a) Paintings of Kim Il Sung and children

N1813	5ch. Type **669**	10	10
N1814	10ch. Kim Il Sung and Children's Corps members in classroom....	25	10
N1815	15ch. New Year gathering	40	25
N1816	20ch. Kim Il Sung and children in snow	60	35
N1817	30ch. Kim Il Sung examines children's schoolbooks (vert)	85	40

(b) Designs showing children

N1818	10ch. Tug of war	25	10
N1819	15ch. Dance "Growing up Fast"	40	15
N1820	20ch. Children of many races and globe	50	25
N1821	25ch. Children singing	85	40
N1822	30ch. Children in toy spaceships	85	40
N1813/1822	Set of 10	4·50	2·30

MSN1823 Two sheets (a) 90×72 mm. 50ch. Kim Il Sung visits a kindergarten (vert); (b) 124×85 mm. 50ch. As No. N1820 ... 5·00 4·25

Nos. N1813/22 were issued with se-tenant labels. See also Nos. N1907/**MS**N1918.

670 Rose

671 Warriors on Horseback

1979 (5 Jan). Roses. T **670** and similar vert designs. Multicoloured. Litho. P 13½.

N1824	1wn. Red rose
N1825	3wn. White rose
N1826	5wn. Type **670**
N1827	10wn. Deep pink rose

See also Nos. N1837/42.

1979 (10 Jan). Story of Two Generals. T **671** and similar horiz designs. Multicoloured. Litho. Without gum. P 12.

N1828	5ch. Type **671**	25	10
N1829	10ch. Farm labourer blowing feather	40	15
N1830	10ch. Generals fighting on foot	40	15
N1831	10ch. Generals on horseback	40	15
N1828/1831	Set of 4	1·30	50

669 Kim Il Sung with Children's Corps Members, Maanshan

672 Red Guard and Industrial Skyline

674 Crowd of Demonstrators

673 Clement-Bayard Airship *Fleurus*

1979 (14 Jan). 20th Anniv of Worker-Peasant Red Guards. Litho. Without gum. P 12.
N1832 **672** 10ch. multicoloured 30 15

1979 (27 Feb). Airships. T **673** and similar horiz design. Multicoloured. Litho. Without gum. P 13.
N1833   10ch. Type **673**............................. 1·30 30
N1834   20ch. N.1 *Norge*................................ 1·30 30
MSN1835 80×79 mm. 50ch. *Graf Zeppelin*.................. 2·20 60
    Nos. N1833/**MS**N1835 were also issued together in sheetlets of three stamps (Price £10 un).

1979 (1 Mar). 60th Anniv of March First Popular Uprising. Litho. Without gum. P 12.
N1836 **674** 10ch. bright blue & bright rose-red.... 30 15

1979 (18 Apr) Roses. As Nos N1824/7 and similar vert designs. Multicoloured. Litho P 13.

              (a) POSTAGE
N1837   5ch. Type **670**............................. 25 10
N1838   10ch. As No. N1827...................... 35 10
N1839   15ch. As No. N1824...................... 35 10
N1840   20ch. Yellow rose......................... 60 15
N1841   30ch. As No. N1825...................... 75 25
           (b) AIR. Inscr "AIR MAIL"
N1842   50ch. Deep pink rose (different) .... 1·10 50
N1837/1842 *Set of 6*.. 3·00 1·10
    Nos. N1837/42 were also issued together in sheetlets of six stamps (Price £6.75 un).

675 Table Tennis Trophy

676 Marchers with Red Flag

1979 (25 Apr). 35th World Table Tennis Championship, Pyongyang. T **675** and similar vert designs. Multicoloured. Litho. P 13.
N1843   5ch. Type **675**............................. 25 10
N1844   10ch. Women's doubles.......... 25 10
N1845   15ch. Women's singles 40 15
N1846   20ch. Men's doubles................ 65 15
N1847   30ch. Men's singles .... 1·00 35
N1843/1847 *Set of 5*.. 2·30 75
MSN1848 84×108 mm. 50ch. Chollima Statue and championship emblem... 2·50 1·70
    Limited quantities of Nos. N1843/**MS**N1848 exist without gum.
    Nos. N1843/**MS**N1848 were also issued together in sheetlets of six stamps (Price £5 un).

1979 (28 Apr). Socialist Construction under Banner of Juche Idea. T **676** and similar vert designs. Multicoloured. Litho. Without gum. P 12.
N1849   5ch. Type **676**............................. 30 15
N1850   10ch. Map of Korea.................... 30 15
N1851   10ch. Juche torch 30 15
N1849/1851 *Set of 3*.. 80 40

677 Badge   **678** Emblem, Satellite orbiting Globe and Aerials

1979 (2 May). Order of Honour of the Three Revolutions. Litho. Without Gum. P 12.
N1852 **677** 10ch. royal blue............................... 25 10

1979 (17 May). World Telecommunications Day. Litho. Without gum. P 12.
N1853 **678** 10ch. multicoloured 40 15

679 Advancing Soldiers and Monument

1979 (23 May). 40th Anniv of Battle in Musan Area. Without gum. P 12.
N1854 **679** 10ch. bright magenta, new bl & bl...... 30 15

680 Exhibition Entrance

1979 (29 May). International Friendship Exhibition. Litho. Without gum. P 12.
N1855 **680** 10ch. multicoloured 25 15

681 "Peonies"

1979 (8 June). 450th Death Anniv (1978) of Albrecht Dürer (artist) (1st issue). T **681** and similar vert designs. Multicoloured. Litho. P 13.

N1856	15ch. Type **681**	85	25
N1857	20ch. "Columbines"	1·40	35
N1858	25ch. "A Great Tuft of Grass"	1·40	35
N1859	30ch. "Wing of a Bird"	2·10	55
N1856/1859 Set of 4		5·25	1·40
MSN1860 92×67 mm. 50ch. As No. N1859		3·25	85

Nos. N1857/**MS**N1860 were also issued together in sheetlets of four stamps (Price £11 un).

See also Nos. N2012/**MS**N2013.

682 Fencing

1979 (1 July). Olympic Games, Moscow (2nd issue). T **682** and similar horiz designs. Multicoloured. Litho. With gum (10, 40ch.) or without gum (others). P 12×11½.

N1861	5ch. Type **682**	1·50	35
N1862	10ch. Gymnastics	60	15
N1863	20ch. Yachting	85	35
N1864	30ch. Athletics	1·00	40
N1865	40ch. Weightlifting	1·30	60
N1861/1865 Set of 5		4·75	1·70
MSN1866 106×77 mm. 50ch. Equestrian event.			
P 11½		3·25	1·70

Nos. N1861/**MS**N1866 were also issued together in sheetlets of six stamps (p 11½) (Price £11 un).

683 Hunting   **684** Judo

1979 (1 Aug). Horse-riding (people of Koguryo Dynasty). T **683** and similar horiz designs. Multicoloured. Litho. P 13.

(a) POSTAGE

N1867	5ch. Type **683**	85	35
N1868	10ch. Archery contest	85	35
N1869	15ch. Man beating drum on		
	horseback	35	10
N1870	20ch. Man blowing horn	35	10
N1871	30ch. Man and horse armoured with		
	chainmail	40	15

(b) AIR. Inscr "AIR MAIL"

N1872	50ch. Hawking	2·75	55
N1867/1872 Set of 6		5·00	1·40

Nos. N1867/72 were also issued together in sheetlets of six stamps (Price £7·50 un).

1979 (5 Aug). Olympic Games, Moscow (3rd issue). T **684** and similar vert designs. Multicoloured. Litho. With gum (5, 15, 20, 30ch.) or without gum (others). P 11½×12 (5, 30ch.) or 11½ (others).

N1873	5ch. Type **684**	40	10
N1874	10ch. Volleyball	40	10
N1875	15ch. Cycling	1·70	40
N1876	20ch. Basketball	65	25
N1877	25ch. Canoeing	65	25
N1878	30ch. Boxing	1·00	35
N1879	40ch. Shooting	90	35
N1873/1879 Set of 7		5·25	1·60
MSN1880 79×108 mm. 50ch. Gymnastics. P 11½		1·30	50

Nos. N1873/**MS**N1880 were also issued together in sheetlets of eight stamps (p 11½) (Price £9·25 un).

685 Warrior's Costume   **686** Wrestling

1979 (6 Aug). Warriors' Costume of Li Dynasty. T **685** and similar vert designs. P 12×11½.

(a) POSTAGE

N1881	**685**	5ch. multicoloured	25	15
N1882	–	10ch. multicoloured	25	15
N1883	–	15ch. multicoloured	40	15
N1884	–	20ch. multicoloured	60	20
N1885	–	30ch. multicoloured	1·00	30

(b) AIR. Inscr "AIR MAIL"

N1886	–	50ch. multicoloured	1·30	50
N1881/1886 Set of 6			3·50	1·30

Nos. N1881/6 were also issued together in sheetlets of six stamps (p 11½×12) (Price £5 un).

1979 (5 Sept). Olympic Games, Moscow (4th issue). T **686** and similar vert designs. Multicoloured. Litho. P 12×11½.

N1887	10ch. Type **686**	40	15
N1888	15ch. Handball	40	15
N1889	20ch. Archery	2·10	50
N1890	25ch. Hockey	2·10	60
N1891	30ch. Sailing	1·00	35
N1892	40ch. Football	2·00	50
N1887/1892 Set of 6		7·25	2·00
MSN1893 77×106 mm. 50ch. Equestrian events		3·25	1·40

Nos. N1887/**MS**N1893 were also issued together in sheetlets of seven stamps (Price £13·50 un).

687 Monument   **668** Bottle-feeding Fawn

1979 (10 Sept). Chongbong Monument. Litho. Without gum. P 12.

N1894	**687**	10ch. multicoloured............................	30	15

1979 (5 Oct). Sika Deer. T **688** and similar horiz designs. Multicoloured. P 13½.

(a) POSTAGE

N1895	5ch. Type **688**............................	25	15
N1896	10ch. Doe and fawn.........................	25	15
N1897	15ch. Stag drinking from stream........	25	15
N1898	20ch. Stag....................................	35	15
N1899	30ch. Stag and doe.........................	40	35

(b) AIR. Inscr "AIR MAIL"

N1900	50ch. Antlers and sika deer..............	65	50
N1895/1900	*Set of 6*...................................	1·90	1·30

Nos. N1895/1900 were also issued together in sheetlets of six stamps (Price £4·25 un).

689 Moscovy Ducks

690 Girl with Model Viking Ship

1979 (9 Oct). Central Zoo, Pyongyang. T **689** and similar vert designs. Multicoloured. Litho. P 12.

(a) POSTAGE

N1901	5ch. Type **689**............................	35	15
N1902	10ch. Ostrich................................	65	25
N1903	15ch. Common turkey......................	90	35
N1904	20ch. Dalmatian pelican...................	1·10	40
N1905	30ch. Vulturine guineafowl...............	1·30	50

(b) AIR. Inscr "AIR MAIL"

N1906	50ch. Mandarins............................	2·00	85
N1901/1906	*Set of 6*...................................	5·75	2·30

Nos. N1901/6 were also issued together in sheetlets of six stamps (Price £7·25 un).

1979 (13 Oct). International Year of the Child (2nd issue). T **690** and similar vert designs. Multicoloured. Litho. P 12.

N1907	20ch. Type **690**............................	1·50	40
N1908	20ch. Boys with model steam railway locomotive...................................	3·25	40
N1909	20ch. Boy and model biplane..............	1·70	40
N1910	20ch. Boy and model spaceman..........	1·30	40
N1911	30ch. Boy with model speedboat........	2·50	60
N1912	30ch. Boy sitting astride toy electric train......................................	3·25	60
N1913	30ch. Boy and model airplane............	2·50	60
N1914	30ch. Boy and flying spaceman..........	1·90	60
N1907/1914	*Set of 8*...................................	16·00	3·50

MSN1915 Four sheets, each 77×104 mm. P 12×11½. (a) 80ch. Boy and Concorde; (b) 80ch. Girl and satellite; (c) 80ch. Boy and model liner; (d) 80ch. Children with model train.................. | 29·00 | 6·75

Nos. N1907/**MS**N1915d were also issued in four sheetlets, each sheetlet consisting of three designs (the three ship designs, three train designs etc.) and one label bearing the IYC emblem (Price for 4 sheetlets: £50 un).

691 Footballers

1979 (15 Nov). International Year of the Child (3rd issue). T **691** and similar horiz designs. Multicoloured. Litho. P 12.

N1916	20ch. Type **691**............................	1·30	50
N1917	30ch. Footballers (different)..............	2·10	75
MSN1918	104×78 mm. 80ch. Footballers (different) P 11½×12............................	6·75	2·10

Nos. N1916/**MS**N1918 were also issued together in sheetlets of three stamps (Price £10 un).

692 Devil Stinger (*Inimicus japonicus*)

1979 (4 Dec). Marine Life. T **692** and similar horiz designs. Multicoloured. Litho. P 12.

N1919	20ch. Type **692**............................	1·10	40
N1920	30ch. *Sebastes schlegeli* (fish).........	1·30	50
N1921	50ch. Northern sealion (*Eumetopias jubatus*)...............................	2·20	85
N1919/1921	*Set of 3*...................................	4·25	1·60

Nos. N1919/21 were also issued together in sheetlets of three stamps (Price £6·75 un).

693 Cross-country Skiing (Sergei Saveliev)

694 Bee collecting Nectar

1979 (9 Dec). Winter Olympic Games, Lake Placid. T **693** and similar multicoloured designs. Litho. P 12.

N1922	10ch. Figure skating (Irina Rodnina and Aleksandr Zaitsev) (horiz)	60	20
N1923	20ch. Ice hockey (Russian team) (horiz)...................................	1·00	30
N1924	30ch. Ladies' 5 km. relay (horiz).........	1·40	55
N1925	40ch. Type **693**............................	2·00	85
N1926	50ch. Ladies' speed skating (Tatiana Averina)..................................	3·00	1·10
N1922/1926	*Set of 5*...................................	7·25	2·75

MSN1927 81×68 mm. 60ch. Ice dancing (Ludmila Pakhomova and Aleksandr Gorshkov). P 12×11½ | 6·25 | 4·75

The 10, 20 and 30ch. were also issued together in sheetlets of three stamps, as were the 40, 50 and 60ch. (Price for 2 sheetlets: £11·50 un.)

1979 (22 Dec). The Honey Bee. T **694** and similar vert designs. Multicoloured. Litho. P 12.

N1928	20ch. Type **694**	1·70	35
N1929	30ch. Bee and flowers	2·00	40
N1930	50ch. Bee hovering over flower	2·20	50
N1928/1930	*Set of* 3	5·25	1·10

Nos. N1928/30 were also issued together in sheetlets of three stamps (p 12×11½).

695 Kim Jong Suk's Birthplace, Hoeryong

1979 (24 Dec). Historic Revolutionary Sites. T **695** and similar horiz design. Litho. P 12.

N1931	10ch. multicoloured	35	15
N1932	10ch. brown-ochre, new blue and black	35	15

Design:—No. N1932, Sinpa Revolutionary Museum.

696 Mt. Paekdu   **697** Student and Books

1980 (1 Jan). New Year. Litho. P 12.

N1933	**696**	10ch. multicoloured	75	15

1980 (10 Jan). Studying. Litho. P 12.

N1934	**697**	10ch. multicoloured	35	15

698 Conveyor Belt

1980 (20 Jan). Unryul Mine Conveyor Belt. Litho. P 11½×12.

N1935	**698**	10ch. multicoloured	75	15

699 Children of Three Races

1980 (28 Jan). International Day of the Child. T **699** and similar horiz designs. Multicoloured. Litho. P 12.

N1936	10ch. Type **699**	40	15
N1937	10ch. Girl dancing to accordion	65	15
N1938	10ch. Children in fairground airplane	60	15
N1939	10ch. Children as astronauts	40	15
N1940	10ch. Children on tricycles	1·70	40
N1941	10ch. Children with toy train	2·50	60
N1942	10ch. "His loving care for the children, the future of the fatherland" (59½×38 mm)	40	15
N1936/1942	*Set of* 7	6·00	1·60
MSN1943	69×89 mm. 50ch. "Father Marshal visiting Kindergarten..." (52×44 mm). P 13½	3·00	1·40

Nos. N1936/41 were also issued together in sheetlets of six stamps (Price £10 un).

700 Monument

1980 (5 Feb). Chongsan-ri Historic Site. T **700** and similar horiz design. Multicoloured. Litho. P 12.

N1944	5ch. Type **700**	15	15
N1945	10ch. Meeting place of General Membership	25	15

701 Monument

1980 (16 Feb). Monument marking Kim Jong Suk's Return. Litho. P 12.

N1946	**701**	10ch. multicoloured	25	15

702 Vasco Nuñez de Balboa

1980 (18 Feb). Conquerors of the Earth. T **702** and similar vert designs. Multicoloured. Litho. P 13½.

N1947	10ch. Type **702**	65	25
N1948	20ch. Francisco de Orellana	1·00	35
N1949	30ch. Haroun Tazieff	1·40	50
N1950	40ch. Edmund Hillary and Sherpa Tenzing	2·10	85
N1947/1950	*Set of* 4	4·75	1·80
MSN1951	75×105 mm. 70ch. Ibn Battuta	3·50	1·70

Nos. N1947/**MS**N1951 were also issued together in sheetlets of five stamps and one label (Price £7·50 un).

703 Museum

1980 (23 Feb). Ryongpo Revolutionary Museum. Litho. P 11½×12.
N1952 **703** 10ch. new blue and black 25   10

704 Rowland Hill and Stamps

1980 (1 Mar). Death Centenary (1979) of Sir Rowland Hill. T **704** and
similar horiz design. Multicoloured. Litho. P 12.
N1953   30ch. Type **704**.. 3·75   1·10
N1954   50ch. Rowland Hill and stamps
            (different).. 5·50   1·40
Nos. N1953/4 were also issued together in sheetlets of two stamps
(Price £21 un).

705 N. Korean Red Cross
Flag

706 Fernando Magellan

1980 (17 Apr). World Red Cross Day. T **705** and similar vert designs.
Multicoloured. Litho. P 12×11½.
N1955   10ch. Type **705**.. 1·00   35
N1956   10ch. Henri Dunant (founder)............... 1·00   35
N1957   10ch. Nurse and child .... 1·00   35
N1958   10ch. Polikarpov Po-2 biplane and
            ship.. 1·30   50
N1959   10ch. Mil Mi-4 helicopter....................... 1·50   50
N1960   10ch. Children playing at nurses .... 1·00   35
N1961   10ch. Red Cross over map of Korea
            and forms of transport .... 3·50   1·30
N1955/1961 Set of 7.. 9·25   3·25
MSN1962 83×93 mm. 50ch. Nurse with syringe........ 5·00   2·50
Nos. N1955/**MS**N1962 were also issued together in sheetlets of
eight stamps (Price £17 un).

1980 (30 Apr). Conquerors of the Sea. T **706** and similar vert designs.
Multicoloured. Litho. P 13½.
N1963   10ch. Type **706**.. 2·10   75
N1964   20ch. Fridtjof Nansen............................. 2·10   75
N1965   30ch. Auguste and Jacques Piccard ... 3·00   1·00
N1966   40ch. Jacques-Yves Cousteau .... 3·50   1·00
N1963/1966 Set of 4.. 9·75   3·50
MSN1967 75×105 mm. 70ch. James Cook.................. 6·75   1·80
Nos. N1963/**MS**N1967 were also issued together in sheetlets of five
stamps and one label (Price £18 un).

707 Korean Stamps and Penny Black

1980 (6 May) "London 1980" International Stamp Exhibition. T **707**
and similar horiz designs. Multicoloured. Litho. P 13½.
(a) POSTAGE
N1968   10ch. Type **707**.. 3·00   1·00
N1969   20ch. Korean cover and British
            Guiana 1c. black on magenta.... 3·00   1·00
N1970   30ch. Early Korean stamp and
            modern cover .... 2·10   75
N1971   50ch. Korean stamps............................. 2·20   85
(b) AIR. Inscr "AIR MAIL"
N1972   40ch. Korean stamp and miniature
            sheet .... 3·50   1·30
N1968/1972 Set of 5.. 12·50 4·50
MSN1973 110×138 mm. 20ch. Type **707**; 30ch. As
No. N1969; 50ch. As No. N1970 .... 9·25   3·25

708 Wright Brothers   **709** Space Station on
                                    Planet

1980 (10 May). Conquerors of Sky and Space. T **708** and similar vert
designs. Multicoloured. Litho. P 13½.
N1974   10ch. Type **708**.. 85   30
N1975   20ch. Louis Blériot.................................. 1·30   50
N1976   30ch. Anthony Fokker............................ 1·70   65
N1977   40ch. Secondo Campini and Sir Frank
            Whittle... 2·50   85
N1974/1977 Set of 4.. 5·75   2·10
MSN1978 76×106 mm. 70ch. Count Ferdinand
Zeppelin... 3·25   1·00
Nos. N1974/**MS**N1978 were also issued together in sheetlets of five
stamps and one label (Price £11·50 un).

1980 (20 May). Conquerors of the Universe. T **709** and similar vert
designs. Multicoloured. Litho. P 12.
N1979   10ch. Orbiting space station 35   15
N1980   20ch. Type **709**.. 50   25
N1981   30ch. Prehistoric animals and
            spaceships.. 1·30   50
N1982   40ch. Prehistoric animal and birds
            and spaceship.................................. 1·70   60
N1979/1982 Set of 4.. 3·50   1·40
MSN1983 77×106 mm. 70ch. Planetary scene.
P 12×11½.. 3·25   1·70
Nos. N1979/**MS**N1983 were also issued together in sheetlets of five
stamps and one label (Price £6·75 un).

710 Flag and Banners   **711** Hospital

1980 (25 May). 25th Anniv of General Association of Korean Residents in Japan (Chongryon). Litho. P 12½×12.
N1984 **710** 10ch. multicoloured 25   15

1980 (30 May). Pyongyang Maternity Hospital. Litho. P 12.
N1985 **711** 10ch. violet-blue, dp magenta & blk   60   20

712 Health Centre   **713** Hand holding Rifle

1980 (2 June). Changgangwon Health Centre. Litho. P11½×12.
N1986 **712** 2ch. black and new blue 35   15

1980 (6 July). 50th Anniv of Revolutionary Army. Litho. P 12.
N1987 **713** 10ch. multicoloured 35   15

714 Workers'   **715** Party Emblem
Hostel, Samjiyon

1980 (25 July–1 Aug). T **714** and similar horiz designs. Litho.
P 11½×12 (N1989), 12×11½ (N1995) or 11½ (others).
N1988   10ch. buff, new blue and black 40   15
N1989   10ch. black and emerald 65   25
N1990   10ch. black and dull scarlet 65   25
N1991   10ch. black and orange yellow............ 65   25
N1992   10ch. multicoloured (1.8) 40   15
N1993   10ch. multicoloured (1.8) 40   15
N1994   10ch. multicoloured (1.8) .... 1·70 50
N1995   10ch. green and black (1.8)................... 1·30 40
N1996   10ch. grey, new blue and black (1.8)   5·00 85
N1997   10ch. multicoloured (1.8) .... 5·75 85
N1988/1997 Set of 10.. 15·00 3·50
Designs—No. N1989, "Taedonggang" rice transplanter; N1990, "Changsan-ri" rice harvester; N1991, Maize harvester; N1992, Revolutionary building, Songmun-ri; N1993, Revolutionary building, Samhwa; N1994, Sundial of 1438; N1995, 16th-century "turtle" ship; N1996, Pungsan dog; N1997, Japanese quail.

1980 (30 July). Sixth Korean Workers' Party Congress. T **715** and similar horiz designs. Multicoloured. Litho. P 12.
N1998   10ch. Type **715**..................................... 25   15
N1999   10ch. Students and laurel leaf on
                    globe...................................... 25   15
N2000   10ch. Group with accordion................. 65   15
N2001   10ch. Group with banner,
                    microscope, book and trophy... 40   25
N2002   10ch. Worker with book and flag .... 1·30 40
N2003   10ch. Worker with spanner and flag   1·30 40
N2004   10ch. Marchers with torch and flags   25   15
N2005   10ch. Emblem, marchers and map 35   20
N1998/2005 Set of 8.. 4·25 1·70
MSN2006 Two sheets, each 94×77 mm. (a) 50ch.
"The great Leader inspires and encourages
Colliers on the Spot" (41×50 mm). P 13½;
(b) 50ch. "Leading the Van in the arduous March"
(38×60 mm). P 11½...................................... 2·50 1·70

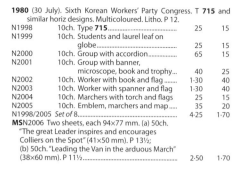

716 Dribbling Ball   **717** Irina Rodnina and Aleksandr Zaitsev

1980 (5 Aug). World Cup Football Championship, 1978–1982. T **716** and similar vert designs. Multicoloured. Litho. P 12.
N2007   20ch. Type **716**..................................... 3·50 1·30
                    a. Vert strip. Nos. N2007/8 plus
                        label...................................... 8·00 3·25
N2008   30ch. Tackling.. 4·25 1·70
MSN2009 147×118 mm. 40ch. Tackling (different);
60ch. Moving in to tackle .... 7·25 2·75
Nos. N2007/8 were issued together with se-tenant intervening stamp-size label in vertical strips within sheets of 10 stamps and five labels.
Nos. N2007/**MS**N2009 were also issued together in sheetlets of four stamps (Price £17 un).

1980 (10 Aug). Winter Olympic Gold Medal Winners. T **717** and similar horiz design. Multicoloured. Litho. P 13½.
N2010   20ch. Type **717**..................................... 6·75 2·30
MSN2011 67×94 mm. 1wn. Natalia Linitshchnuk
and Gennadi Karponosov......................... 7·25 2·50
Nos. N2010/**MS**N2011 were also issued together in sheetlets of two stamps (Price £14·50 un).

718 "Soldier with Horse"   **719** Kepler, Astrolabe and
                                        Satellites

1980 (18 Aug). 450th Death Anniv (1978) of Albrecht Dürer (artist) (2nd issue). T **718** and similar vert design. Multicoloured. Litho. P 12.

N2012	20ch. Type **718**	7·25	2·75
MSN2013	81×106 mm. 1wn. "Horse and Rider"	11·00	3·75

Nos. N2012/**MS**N2013 were also issued together in sheetlets of two stamps (Price £25 un).

1980 (25 Aug). 350th Death Anniv of Johannes Kepler (astronomer). T **719** and similar vert design. Multicoloured. Litho. P 12.

N2014	20ch. Type **719**	3·75	1·70
MSN2015	93×75 mm. 1wn. Kepler, astrolabe and satellites (different). P 12×11½	6·75	2·10

Nos. N2014/**MS**N2015 were also issued together in sheetlets of two stamps (Price £15 un).

720 German 1m. and Russian 30k. Zeppelin Stamps

1980 (25 Sept). Third International Stamp Fair, Essen. T **720** and similar horiz designs. Multicoloured. Litho. P 13½.

N2016	10ch. Type **720**	1·20	40
N2017	20ch. German 2m. and Russian 35k. Zeppelin stamps	2·50	90
N2018	30ch. German 4m. and Russian 1r. Zeppelin stamps	3·50	1·30
N2016/2018 *Set of 3*		6·50	2·30
MSN2019	137×82 mm. 50ch. Russian 2r. Polar Flight stamp and Korean 50ch. IYC stamp	8·50	3·50

Nos. N2016/**MS**N2019 were also issued together in sheetlets of four stamps (Price £20 un). A quantity of these sheetlets was overprinted in the margin for the Universal Postal Union Congress Stamps Exhibition, Hamburg. 1984.

721 Shooting (Aleksandr Melentev)

1980 (20 Oct). Olympic Medal Winners. T **721** and similar horiz designs. Multicoloured. Litho. P 12.

N2020	10ch. Type **721**	40	15
N2021	20ch. Cycling (Robert Dill Bundi)	4·50	1·60
N2022	25ch. Gymnastics (Stoyan Deltchev)	65	35
N2023	30ch. Wrestling (Chang Se Hong and Li Ho Pyong)	65	35
N2024	35ch. Weightlifting (Ho Bong Chol)	65	35
N2025	40ch. Running (Maria Koch)	70	40
N2026	50ch. Modern pentathlon (Anatoli Starostin)	1·00	50
N2020/2026 *Set of 7*		7·75	3·25
MSN2027	Two sheets. (a) 100×76 mm. 70ch. Boxing (Teofilo Stevenson); (b) 107×163 mm. 70ch. Ancient Greek rider on horse. P 13½	5·75	3·75

Nos. N2020/**MS**N2027a were also issued together in sheetlets of eight stamps (Price £16 un).

722 Tito   **723** Convair CV 340 Airliner

1980 (4 Dec). President Tito of Yugoslavia Commemoration. Litho. P 12.

N2028	**722** 20ch. multicoloured	50	15

1980 (10 Dec). 25th Anniv of First Post-war Flight of Lufthansa. T **723** and similar vert design. Multicoloured. Litho. P 13½.

N2029	20ch. Type **723**	6·25	2·50
MSN2030	90×75 mm. 1wn. Airbus "A 300"	8·50	3·25

Nos. N2029/**MS**N2030 were also issued together in sheetlets of two stamps (Price £21 un).

724 *The Rock*et

1980 (16 Dec). 150th Anniv of Liverpool–Manchester Railway. T **724** and similar horiz design. Multicoloured. Litho. P 12.

N2031	20ch. Type **724**	7·25	2·75
MSN2032	105×60 mm. 1wn. Locomotive drawing carriage and horsebox	8·50	3·25

Nos. N2031/**MS**N2032 were also issued together in sheetlets of two stamps (Price £21 un)

725 Steam and Electric Locomotives

1980 (24 Dec). Centenary of First Electric Train. T **725** and similar horiz design. Multicoloured. Litho. P 13½.

N2033	20ch. Type **725**	7·25	2·50
MSN2034	106×86 mm. 1wn. Opening ceremony of first electric railway	14·50	5·00

Nos. N2033/**MS**N2034 were also issued together in sheetlets of two stamps (Price £22 un).

726 Hammarskjöld

727 Bobby Fischer and Boris Spassky

1980 (26 Dec). 75th Birth Anniv of Dag Hammarskjöld (former Secretary General of United Nations). T **726** and similar vert design. Multicoloured. Litho. P 12×11½.

N2035	20ch. Type **726**.....................	4·25	3·00

MSN2036 87×68 mm. 1wn. Hammarskjöld
(different).. 5·50 3·25
Nos. N2035/**MS**N2036 were also issued together in sheetlets of two stamps (p 12) (Price £12·50 un).

1980 (28 Dec). World Chess Championship, Merano. T **727** and similar vert design. Multicoloured. Litho. P 13½.

N2037	20ch. Type **727**.........................	8·00	2·50

MSN2038 84×84 mm. 1wn. Viktor Korchnoi and
Anatoly Karpov... 10·00 2·50
Nos. N2037/**MS**N2038 were also issued together in sheetlets of two stamps (Price £21 un).

728 Stolz

729 Chollima Statue

1980 (30 Dec). Birth Centenary of Robert Stolz (composer). T **728** and similar vert design. Multicoloured. Litho. P 13½.

N2039	20ch. Type **728**.........................	3·75	1·30

MSN2040 94×76 mm. 1wn. Stolz examining stamp
with magnifying glass...................................... 6·25 1·80
Nos. N2039/**MS**N2040 were also issued together in sheetlets of two stamps (Price £12·50 un).

1981 (1 Jan). New Year. Litho. Without gum. P 12.

N2041	**729**	10ch. multicoloured	40	15

730 Russian Fairy Tale

731 Changgwang Street

1981 (30 Jan). International Year of the Child (1979) (4th issue). Fairy Tales. T **730** and similar vert designs. Multicoloured. Litho. P 13½.

N2042	10ch. Type **730**..............................	1·80	60
N2043	10ch. Icelandic tale	1·80	60
N2044	10ch. Swedish tale	1·80	60
N2045	10ch. Irish tale	1·80	60
N2046	10ch. Italian tale............................	1·80	60
N2047	10ch. Japanese tale........................	1·80	60
N2048	10ch. German tale...........................	1·80	60
N2042/2048 Set of 7..		11·50	3·75

MSN2049 95×117 mm. 70ch. Korean tale................... 4·75 3·50
Nos. N2042/**MS**N2049 were also issued together in sheetlets of eight stamps (Price £17 un).

1981 (16 Feb). Changgwang Street, Pyongyang. Litho. Without gum. P 12.

N2050	**731**	10ch. multicoloured	40	15

732 Footballers

1981 (20 Feb). World Cup Football Championship, Spain (1982) (1st issue). T **732** and similar vert designs. Multicoloured. Litho. P 13½.

N2051	10ch. Type **732**..............................	3·50	1·00
N2052	20ch. Hitting ball past defender..........	3·50	1·00
N2053	30ch. Disputing possession of ball	3·50	1·00
N2051/2053 Set of 3..		9·50	2·75

MSN2054 95×103 mm. 70ch. Three players................. 8·50 3·50
Nos. N2051/**MS**N2054 were also issued together in sheetlets of four stamps (Price £17 un). A quantity of these sheetlets was overprinted in August 1982 with the results down to fourth place.
See also Nos. N2055/**MS**N2060 and N2201/**MS**N2207.

733 Map, Emblem and World Cup

1981 (28 Feb). World Cup Football Championship, Spain (1982) (2nd issue). T **733** and similar horiz designs. Multicoloured. Litho. P 13½.

N2055	10ch. Type **733**	2·20	85
N2056	15ch. Footballers	2·20	85
N2057	20ch. Heading ball	2·20	85
N2058	25ch. Footballers (different)	2·20	85
N2059	30ch. Footballers (different)	2·20	85
N2055/2059 *Set of 5*		10·00	3·75
MSN2060 96×92 mm. 70ch. Footballers (different)		8·50	3·50

Nos. N2055/**MS**N2060 were also issued together in sheetlets of six stamps (Price £17 un).

734 Workers with Book and Marchers with Banner

735 Footballers

1981 (15 Mar). Implementation of Decisions of Sixth Korean Workers' Party Congress. T **734** and similar multicoloured designs. Litho. P 12.

N2061	2ch. Type **734**	15	10
N2062	10ch. Worker with book	20	10
N2063	10ch. Workers and industrial plant	35	15
N2064	10ch. Electricity and coal (horiz)	1·60	35
N2065	10ch. Steel and non-ferrous metals (horiz)	35	15
N2066	10ch. Cement and fertilizers (horiz)	35	15
N2067	30ch. Fishing and fabrics (horiz)	50	15
N2068	40ch. Grain and harbour (horiz)	65	25
N2069	70ch. Clasped hands	1·20	50
N2070	1wn. Hand holding torch	1·70	75
N2061/2070 *Set of 10*		6·25	2·40

1981 (27 Mar). Gold Cup Football Championship, Uruguay. T **735** and similar horiz design. Multicoloured. Litho. P 13½.

N2071	20ch. Type **735**	3·75	1·50
MSN2072 99×84 mm. 1wn. Goalkeeper diving for ball		6·25	3·25

736 Dornier Do-X Flying Boat

1981 (28 Apr). Naposta '81 International Stamp Exhibition, Stuttgart. T **736** and similar horiz designs. Multicoloured. Litho. P 12.

N2073	10ch. Type **736**	3·50	65
N2074	20ch. Airship LZ-120 *Bodensee*	3·50	65
N2075	30ch. "Götz von Berlichingen"	2·10	60
N2073/2075 *Set of 3*		8·25	1·70
MSN2076 135×80 mm. 70ch. Mercedes-Benz "W 196" car. P 11½×12		6·25	3·00

737 Telecommunications Equipment

1981 (17 May). World Telecommunications Day. Litho. P 12×11½.

N2077	**737** 10ch. multicoloured	2·50	40

738 *Iris pseudacorus*

1981 (20 May). Flowers. T **738** and similar horiz designs. Multicoloured. Litho. P 12.

N2078	10ch. Type **738**	1·10	15
N2079	20ch. *Iris pallasii*	1·40	25
N2080	30ch. *Gladiolus gandavensis*	2·00	40
N2078/2080 *Set of 3*		4·00	70

Nos. N2078/80 were also issued together in sheetlets of three stamps.

739 Austrian "WIPA 1981" and Rudolf Kirchschläger Stamps

1981 (22 May). WIPA 1981 International Stamp Exhibition, Vienna. T **739** and similar multicoloured designs. Litho. P 13½.

N2081	20ch. Type **739**	2·50	75
N2082	30ch. Austrian Maria Theresa and Franz Joseph stamps	3·25	1·20
MSN2083 133×87 mm. 50ch. Kim Il Sung and choir (38×60 mm). P 11½		6·25	3·00

740 Rings Exercise   **741** Armed Workers

1981 (25 May). Centenary of International Gymnastic Federation. T **740** and similar multicoloured designs. Litho. P 12.

N2084	10ch. Type **740**	50	25
N2085	15ch. Horse exercise	60	25
N2086	20ch. Backwards somersault	1·00	25
N2087	25ch. Floor exercise	1·10	35
N2088	30ch. Exercise with hoop	1·30	40
N2084/2088 *Set of 5*		4·00	1·40

MSN2089 104×77 mm. 70ch. Exercise with wand

(horiz). P 11½×12		2·50	1·10

Nos. N2084/**MS**N2089 were also issued together in sheetlets of six stamps (p 12×11½) (Price £11 un).

1981 (15 June). 50th Anniv of Mingyuehgou Meeting. Litho. P 12.

N2090	**741**	10ch. multicoloured	30	15

742 Farm Building, Sukchon   **743** Woman and Banner

1981 (25 June). 20th Anniv of Agricultural Guidance System and Taean Work System T **742** and similar horiz design. Litho. P 12×12½.

N2091	10ch. yellowish green, gold and		
	black	30	15
N2092	10ch. deep bright blue, gold and		
	black	30	15

Design:—No. N2092, Taean Revolutionary Museum.

1981 (5 July). 55th Anniv of Formation of Women's Anti-Japanese Association. Litho. P 12.

N2093	**743**	5wn. multicoloured	5·25	1·10

743a Scene from Opera   **744** Joan of Arc

1981 (17 July). Tenth Anniv of Opera *Sea of Blood*. Litho. P 12.

N2094	**743a**	10wn. multicoloured	14·50	6·25

1981 (20 July). 550th Death Anniv of Joan of Arc. T **744** and similar vert designs. Multicoloured. Litho. P 12.

N2095	10ch. Type **744**	3·25	85
N2096	10ch. Archangel Michael	3·50	85
	a. Sheetlet of 2. Nos. N2096/7	8·50	1·90
N2097	70ch. Joan of Arc in armour	3·50	85
N2095/N2097 *Set of 3*		9·25	2·30

MSN2098 96×124 mm. No. N2097. P 11½   6·25   2·10

Nos. N2096/7 were issued together in *se-tenant* sheetlets of two stamps.

745 Torch, Mountains and Flag   **746** "Young girl by the Window"

1981 (25 July). 55th Anniv of Down with Imperialism Union. Litho. P 12.

N2099	**745**	1wn.50 multicoloured	1·60	75

1981 (25 July). 375th Birth Anniv of Rembrandt (artist). T **746** and similar vert designs. Multicoloured. Litho. P 13½.

N2100	10ch. Type **746**	75	35
N2101	20ch. "Rembrandt's Mother"	1·70	60
N2102	30ch. "Saskia van Uylenburgh"	1·70	1·00
N2103	40ch. "Pallas Athene"	3·00	1·30
N2100/2103 *Set of 4*		6·50	3·00

MSN2104 91×105 mm. 70ch. "Self-portrait"   6·25   3·25

747 Emblems and Banners over Pyongyang

1981 (26 Aug). Symposium of Non-aligned Countries on Food Self-sufficiency, Pyongyang. T **747** and similar horiz designs. Multicoloured. Litho. P 12.

N2105	10ch. Type **747**	25	15
N2106	50ch. Harvesting	65	35
N2107	90ch. Factories, tractors and marchers with banners	1·30	65
N2105/2107	*Set of 3*	2·00	1·00

748 St. Paul's Cathedral   **749** "Four Philosophers" (detail)

(Des Wurthner. Litho)

1981 (18 Sept). Wedding of Prince of Wales (1st issue). T **748** and similar vert designs. Multicoloured. P 13½.

N2108	10ch. Type **748**	2·50	85
N2109	20ch. Great Britain Prince of Wales Investiture stamp	2·50	85
N2110	30ch. Lady Diana Spencer	2·50	85
N2111	40ch. Prince Charles in military uniform	2·50	85
N2108/2111	*Set of 4*	9·00	3·00
MSN2112	93×96 mm. 70ch. Engagement day portrait of couple.	10·50	6·25

See also Nos. N2120/**MS**N2124.

1981 (20 Sept). Paintings by Rubens. T **749** and similar vert designs. Multicoloured. Litho. P 12.

N2113	10ch. Type **749**	85	40
N2114	15ch. "Portrait of Helena Fourment"	1·30	60
N2115	20ch. "Portrait of Isabella Brandt"	1·70	65
N2116	25ch. "Education of Maria de Medici"	2·10	85
N2117	30ch. "Helena Fourment and her Child"	2·50	90
N2118	40ch. "Helena Fourment in her Wedding Dress"	3·00	1·30
N2113/2118	*Set of 6*	10·50	4·25
MSN2119	92×110 mm. 70ch. "Portrait of Nikolaas Rubens". P 11½	6·25	3·00

(Des Wurthner. Litho)

1981 (29 Sept). Wedding of Prince of Wales (2nd issue). T **750** and similar vert designs. Multicoloured. P 13½.

N2120	10ch. Type **750**	3·75	1·30
	a. Sheetlet of 4. Nos. N2120/3	16·00	
N2121	20ch. Couple on balcony after wedding	3·75	1·30
N2122	30ch. Couple outside St. Paul's Cathedral	3·75	1·30
N2123	70ch. Full-length wedding portrait of couple	3·75	1·30
N2120/2123	*Set of 4*	13·50	4·75
MSN2124	85×106 mm. 70ch. Royal couple and Queen Elizabeth on balcony	13·00	7·25

Nos. N2120/3 were issued together in *se-tenant* sheetlets of four stamps.

1981 (9 Oct). Philatokyo '81 International Stamp Exhibition. Multicoloured. Litho. P 12.

(a) Horiz designs, 41×29 mm			
N2125	10ch. Korean 2ch. Seminar on Juche Idea stamp	1·30	35
N2126	10ch. Korean 10 and 70ch. stamps	3·00	1·20

(b) T **751** and similar vert designs			
N2127	10ch. Type **751**	3·00	1·20
N2128	20ch. Korean Fairy Tales stamps	2·50	60
N2129	30ch. Japanese stamps	4·25	1·30
N2125/2129	*Set of 5*	12·50	4·25
MSN2130	93×105 mm. 70ch. Medals, building and pigeon carrying letter. P 12×11½	8·00	2·20

Nos. N2127/**MS**N2130 were also issued together in sheetlets of four stamps (p 12×11½) (Price £23 un).

752 League Members and Flags

1981 (20 Oct). Seventh League of Socialist Working Youth Congress, Pyongyang. Litho. P 12.

N2131	**752** 10ch. multicoloured	25	10
N2132	80ch. multicoloured	85	40

750 Royal Couple   **751** Rowland Hill and Stamps   **753** Government Palace, Sofia, Bulgarian Arms and Khan Asparuch   **754** Dimitrov

1981 (20 Oct). 1300th Anniv of Bulgarian State. Litho. P 12.
N2133 **753** 10ch. multicoloured 35 10

1981 (5 Nov). Birth Centenary of Georgi Dimitrov (Bulgarian statesman). Litho. P 12.
N2134 **754** 10ch. multicoloured 35 10

755 Emblem, Boeing 747-200 Jetliner, City Hall and Mercedes "500"

1981 (14 Nov). Philatelia '81 International Stamp Fair, Frankfurt-am-Main. Litho. P 13½.
N2135 **755** 20ch. multicoloured .... 3·25 50

756 Concorde, Airship *Graf Zeppelin* and Count Ferdinand von Zeppelin

757 Rising Sun

1981 (1 Dec). Philexfrance 82 International Stamp Exhibition, Paris. Litho. P 13½.

(a) T **756** and similar vert designs.
N2136 10ch. Type **756** .... 3·75 60
N2137 20ch. Concorde, Breguet Provence airliner and Santos-Dumont's biplane 14 bis .... 4·50 1·10
N2138 30ch. "Mona Lisa" (Leonardo da Vinci) and stamps .... 2·50 40
MSN2139 99×105 mm. 60ch. French Rembrandt and Picasso stamps .... 8·00 2·50

(b) *Size* 32×53 mm
N2140 10ch. Hotel des Invalides, Paris .... 1·40 60
       a. Sheetlet of 4. Nos. N2140/3 .... 5·75
N2141 20ch. President Mitterrand of France ... 1·40 60
N2142 30ch. International Friendship Exhibition building .... 1·40 60
N2143 70ch. Kim Il Sung .... 1·40 60
N2136/8, N2140/3 *Set of 7* .... 14·50 4·00
Nos. N2140/3 were issued together in *se-tenant* sheetlets of four stamps.

1982 (1 Jan). New Year. Litho. P 12.
N2144 **757** 10ch. multicoloured 40 10

758 Emblem and Flags   **759** "The Hair-do"

1982 (16 Feb). "Prospering Korea". T **758** and similar vert designs. Multicoloured. Litho. P 12.
N2145 2ch. Type **758** 15 10
N2146 10ch. Industry 35 15
N2147 10ch. Agriculture 35 15
N2148 10ch. Mining 60 15
N2149 10ch. Arts 35 15
N2150 10ch. Al Islet lighthouse, Uam-ri .... 3·50 60
N2151 40ch. Buildings 65 25
N2145/2151 *Set of 7* .... 5·25 1·40

1982 (30 Mar). Birth Centenary of Pablo Picasso (artist). T **759** and similar vert designs. Multicoloured. Litho. P 12.
N2152 10ch. Type **759** .... 1·10 25
N2153 10ch. "Paulo on a Donkey" .... 2·50 50
       a. Sheetlet of 6. Nos. N2153, N2155, N2157 and N2159/61 .... 16·00
N2154 20ch. "Woman leaning on Arm" .... 1·30 35
N2155 20ch. "Harlequin" .... 2·50 50
N2156 25ch. "Child with Pigeon" .... 2·75 65
N2157 25ch. "Reading a Letter" .... 2·50 50
N2158 35ch. "Portrait of Gertrude Stein" .... 2·10 40
N2159 35ch. "Harlequin" (different) .... 2·50 50
N2160 80ch. "Minotaur" .... 2·50 50
N2161 90ch. "Mother and Child" .... 2·50 50
N2152/2161 *Set of 10* .... 20·00 4·25
MSN2162 Two sheets, each 78×96 mm. P 11½
(a) No. N2160; (b) No. N2161 .... 7·50 4·25
Nos. N2153, N2155, N2157 and N2159/61 were issued together in *se-tenant* sheetlets of six stamps.

760 Fireworks over Pyongyang   **761** Soldier saluting

1982 (15 Apr). 70th Birthday of Kim Il Sung. Multicoloured. Litho.
P 12.

(a) T **760** and similar vert design

N2163	10ch. Kim Il Sung's birthplace, Mangyongdae	25	10
N2164	10ch. Type **760**	25	10

(b) Horiz designs as T **626**

N2165	10ch. "The Day will dawn on downtrodden Korea"	25	10
N2166	10ch. Signalling start of Pochonbo Battle	25	10
N2167	10ch. Kim Il Sung starting Potong River project	25	10
N2168	10ch. Embracing bereaved children	25	10
N2169	10ch. Kim Il Sung as Supreme Commander	25	10
N2170	10ch. "On the Road of Advance"	25	10
N2171	10ch. Kim Il Sung kindling flames of Chollima movement at Kangson Steel Plant	25	10
N2172	10ch. Kim Il Sung talking to peasants	25	10
N2173	10ch. Kim Il Sung fixing site of reservoir	25	10
N2174	20ch. Kim Il Sung visiting Komdok Valley	25	10
N2175	20ch. Kim Il Sung visiting Red Flag Company	25	10
N2176	20ch. Kim Il Sung teaching Juche farming methods	25	10
N2177	20ch. Kim Il Sung visiting iron works	25	10
N2178	20ch. Kim Il Sung talking with smelters	25	10
N2179	20ch. Kim Il Sung at chemical plant	25	10
N2180	20ch. Kim Il Sung with fishermen	25	10
N2163/2180 *Set of* 18		4·00	1·60

MSN2181 Two sheets. P 13½ (a) 93×82 mm. 60ch.
Kim Il Sung as a boy (35×47 mm); (b) 60ch. "Long
live Comrade Kim Il Sung..." (35×46 mm) .... 4·25   2·10
Nos. 2165/80 were each issued with *se-tenant* label depicting Kim
Il Sung's birthplace and a text relevant to the stamp.

1982 (25 Apr). 50th Anniv of People's Army. Litho. P 12.
N2182 **761** 10ch. multicoloured 35   10

762 "The Bagpiper"   **763** Surveyors
(Dürer)

1982 (28 Apr). Fourth Essen International Stamp Fair. Litho. P 12.
N2183 **762** 30ch. multicoloured .... 5·50   65

1982 (30 Apr). Implementation of Four Nature-remaking Tasks. Litho.
P 12.
N2184 **763** 10ch. multicoloured 60   10

764 Princess as Baby   **765** Tower of Juche
Idea, Pyongyang

1982 (1 May). 21st Birthday of Princess of Wales. T **764** and similar
vert designs showing Princess at various ages. Litho. P 13½.

N2185	10ch. multicoloured	65	25
N2186	20ch. multicoloured	1·50	40
N2187	30ch. multicoloured	1·80	60
N2188	50ch. multicoloured	1·90	1·00
	a. Sheetlet of 4. Nos. 2188/91	7·75	
N2189	60ch. multicoloured	1·90	1·00
N2190	70ch. multicoloured	1·90	1·00
N2191	80ch. multicoloured	1·90	1·00
N2185/2191 *Set of* 7		10·50	4·75

MSN2192 Two sheets, each 88×100 mm. (a) 40ch.
Princess with her brother; (b) No. N2191 .... 11·00   5·00
Nos. N2188/91 were issued together in *se-tenant* sheetlets of four
stamps.

1982 (21–22 May). T **765** and similar vert design. Litho. P 12.

N2193	2wn. multicoloured	2·75	85
N2194	3wn. yellow-orange and black (22.5)	3·25	90

Design: 26×37½ mm—3wn. Arch of Triumph.

766 Tiger

1982 (30 May). Tigers. T **766** and similar designs showing tigers.
Litho. P 12.

N2195	20ch. multicoloured	2·20	65
N2196	30ch. multicoloured	3·00	65
N2197	30ch. multicoloured (horiz)	3·75	1·10
	a. Sheetlet of 3. Nos. 2197/9	12·00	
N2198	40ch. multicoloured (horiz)	3·75	1·10
N2199	80ch. multicoloured (horiz)	3·75	1·10
N2195/2199 *Set of* 5		15·00	4·25

MSN2200 105×54 mm. 80ch. multicoloured (horiz).
P 11½×12 .... 7·75   2·50
Nos. N2197/9 were issued together in *se-tenant* sheetlets of three
stamps.

767 Group 1 Countries

1982 (12 June). World Cup Football Championship, Spain (3rd issue).
T **767** and similar horiz designs. Multicoloured. Litho. P 13½.

N2201	10ch. Type **767** 45	75	25
N2202	20ch. Group 2 countries	1·50	60
N2203	30ch. Group 3 countries	2·20	90
N2204	40ch. Group 4 countries	2·50	1·10
N2205	50ch. Group 5 countries	3·00	1·30
N2206	60ch. Group 6 countries	3·75	1·40
N2201/2206	Set of 6	12·50	5·00
MSN2207	133×92 mm. 1wn. World Cup, footballers and emblem	10·00	5·00

768 Rocket Launch

769 Charlotte von Stein

1982 (20 June). The Universe. T **768** and similar vert designs.
Multicoloured. Litho. P 12½×11½.

N2208	10ch. Type **768**	2·10	85
	a. Sheetlet. Nos. N2208/10 plus label	7·00	
N2209	20ch. Spaceship over globe	2·10	85
N2210	80ch. Spaceship between globe and moon	2·50	85
N2208/2210	Set of 3	6·00	2·30
MSN2211	71×103 mm. 80ch. Spaceship over crags	4·25	1·70

Nos. N2208/10 were issued together in *se-tenant* sheetlets of three
stamps and one label. Nos. N2208/9 were also issued separately in
large sheets.

1982 (25 July). 150th Death Anniv of Johann von Goethe (writer).
T **769** and similar vert designs. Multicoloured. Litho. P 12.

N2212	10ch. Type **769**	65	35
N2213	10ch. Goethe's mother	2·10	60
	a. Sheetlet. Nos. N2213, N2215, N2217 and N2219/20 plus label	11·00	
N2214	20ch. Goethe's sister	1·00	40
N2215	20ch. Angelika Kauffman	2·10	60
N2216	25ch. Charlotte Buff	1·30	50
N2217	25ch. Anna Amalia	2·10	60
N2218	35ch. Lili Schönemann	1·70	55
N2219	35ch. Charlotte von Lengefeld	2·10	60
N2220	80ch. Goethe	2·10	60
N2212/2220	Set of 9	13·50	4·25
MSN2221	126×84 mm. 80ch. Goethe (different). P 12×11½	5·00	2·10

Nos. N2213, N2215, N2217 and N2219/20 were issued together in
se-tenant sheetlets of five stamps and one label.

770 Player holding aloft World Cup

1982 (30 Aug). World Cup Football Championship Results. T **770** and
similar horiz designs. Multicoloured. Litho. P 13½.

N2222	20ch. Type **770**	1·70	40
N2223	30ch. Group of players with World Cup	2·50	65
N2224	30ch. Type **770**	3·50	90
	a. Sheetlet. Nos. N2224/6 plus label	11·00	
N2225	40ch. As No. N2203	3·50	90
N2226	80ch. King Juan Carlos of Spain and two players with World Cup	3·50	90
N2222/2226	Set of 5	13·00	3·25
MSN2227	105×78 mm. No. N2226	5·75	2·75

Nos. N2224/6 were issued together in *se-tenant* sheetlets of three
stamps and one label.

771 Princess and Prince William of Wales

772 Royal Couple with Prince William

1982 (21 Sept). First Wedding Anniv of Prince and Princess of Wales.
T **771** and similar horiz designs. Multicoloured. Litho. P 13½.

N2228	30ch. Type **771**	6·50	3·25
MSN2229	135×102 mm. 80ch. Prince and Princess of Wales with Prince William	11·00	4·25

No. N2228 was issued in sheetlets of four stamps and two labels.

1982 (29 Sept). Birth of Prince William of Wales. T **772** and similar
multicoloured designs. Litho. P 13½.

N2230	10ch. Couple with Prince William (different)	90	65
N2231	10ch. Princess of Wales holding bouquet	2·75	1·00
	a. Sheetlet of 4. Nos. N2231, N2233, N2235 and N2240	11·50	
N2232	20ch. Couple with Prince William (different)	1·80	85
N2233	20ch. Prince Charles carrying baby, and Princess of Wales	2·75	1·00
N2234	30ch. Type **772**	3·00	1·30
N2235	30ch. Prince Charles carrying baby, and Princess of Wales (different)	2·75	1·00
N2236	40ch. Princess with baby	3·75	1·90
N2237	40ch. Prince and Princess of Wales (horiz)	3·25	1·50
	a. Sheetlet of 3. Nos. N2237, N2239 and N2241	10·00	
N2238	50ch. Princess with baby (different)	4·75	2·10
N2239	50ch. Prince and Princess of Wales in evening dress (horiz)	3·25	1·50

N2240	80ch. Couple with Prince William (different).................................	2·75	1·00
N2241	80ch. Prince Charles holding baby, and Princess of Wales (horiz).....	3·25	1·50
N2230/2241 Set of 12		31·00	14·00

MSN2242 Two sheets, each 115×90 mm. (a) 80ch. Princess of Wales holding Prince William, and royal family; (b) 80ch Princess of Wales holding Prince William, and godparents .... 27·00 10·00
Nos. N2231, N2233, N2235 and N2240 were issued together in se-tenant sheetlets of four stamps, while Nos. N2237, N2239 and N2241 were issued together in se- tenant sheetlets of three stamps.

773 Airship *Nulli Secundus II*, 1908

1982 (21 Nov). Bicentenary of Manned Flight (1st issue). T **773** and similar multicoloured designs. Litho. P 13½.

N2243	10ch. Type **773**.......................................	1·50	50
N2244	10ch. Pauley and Durs Egg's dirigible balloon *The Dolphin*, 1818..........	2·75	85
	a. Sheetlet. Nos. N2244, N2246, N2248 and N2250/1 plus label	14·50	
N2245	20ch. Tissandier brothers' airship, 1883...	1·80	60
N2246	20ch. Guyton de Morveau's balloon with oars, 1784........................	2·75	85
N2247	30ch. Parseval airship PL-VII, 1912	2·50	65
N2248	30ch. Sir George Cayley's airship design, 1837.................................	2·75	85
N2249	40ch. Count Lennox's balloon *Eagle*, 1834...	2·75	65
N2250	40ch. Carmille Vert's balloon *Poisson Volant*, 1859................................	2·75	85
N2251	80ch. Dupuy de Lôme's airship, 1872.	2·75	85
N2243/2251 Set of 9...		20·00	6·00

MSN2252 71×100 mm. 80ch. Massé's oar-powered balloon, 1784 (vert).......................... 5·00 2·50
No. N2243 is wrongly inscribed "Baldwin's Airship".
Nos. N2244, N2246, N2248 and N2250/1 were issued together in se-tenant sheetlets of five stamps and one label.

774 "Utopic Balloon Post" (Balthasar Antoine Dunker)

1982 (10 Dec). Bicentenary of Manned Flight (2nd issue). T **774** and similar vert designs. Multicoloured. Litho. P 13½.

N2253	10ch. Type **774**.......................................	1·30	50
N2254	10ch. Montgolfier balloon at Versailles, 1783	4·25	1·00

	a. Sheetlet. Nos. N2254, N2256, N2258 and N2260/1 plus label.	22·00	
N2255	20ch. "... and they fly into heaven and have no wings..."	2·50	1·00
N2256	20ch. Montgolfier Brothers' balloon, 1783..	4·25	1·00
N2257	30ch. Pierre Testu-Brissy's balloon ascent on horseback, 1798	3·75	1·70
N2258	30ch. Charles's hydrogen balloon landing at Nesle................................	4·25	1·00
N2259	40ch. Test flight of Gaston Tissandier's balloon *Zenith*, 1875........................	5·00	2·10
N2260	40ch. Blanchard and Jeffries' flight over English Channel, 1785	4·25	1·00
N2261	80ch. Henri Giffard's balloon *Le Grand Ballon Captif at* World Fair, 1878	4·25	1·00
N2253/N2261 Set of 9		30·00	9·25

MSN2262 130×96 mm. 80ch. Night flight of balloon 5·00 2·50
Nos. N2254, N2256, N2258 and N2260/1 were issued together in se-tenant sheetlets of five stamps and one label.

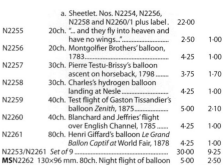

775 Turtle with Scroll   **776** Flag, Red Book and City

1982 (25 Dec). Tale of the Hare. T **775** and similar horiz designs. Multicoloured. Litho. P 12.

N2263	10ch. Type **775**.......................................	1·10	25
N2264	20ch. Hare riding on turtle...................	1·50	35
N2265	30ch. Hare and turtle before Dragon King	1·80	50
N2266	40ch. Hare back on land	2·75	60
N2263/2266 Set of 4...		6·50	1·50

1982 (27 Dec). Tenth Anniv of Socialist Constitution. Litho. P 12.
N2267 **776** 10ch. multicoloured.............................. 40 15

777 Tower of Juche Idea   **778** Children reading *Saenal*

1983 (1 Jan). New Year. Litho. P 12.
N2268 **777** 10ch. multicoloured.............................. 30 15

1983 (15 Jan). 55th Anniv of *Saenal* Newspaper. Litho. P 11½×12.
N2269 **778** 10ch. multicoloured.............................. 75 25

779 "Man in Oriental Costume"

1983 (25 Jan). Paintings by Rembrandt. T **779** and similar vert designs. Multicoloured. Litho. P 12×11½ (N2270, N2272, N2274, N2276) or 12 (others).

N2270	10ch. Type **779**	90	35
N2271	10ch. "Child with dead Peacocks" (detail)	2·50	85
	a. Sheetlet. Nos. N2271. N2273, N2275 and N2277/8 plus label	13·00	
N2272	20ch. "The Noble Slav"	1·80	50
N2273	20ch. "Old Man in Fur Hat"	2·50	85
N2274	30ch. "Dr. Tulp's Anatomy Lesson" (detail)	3·25	90
N2275	30ch. "Portrait of a fashionable Couple"	2·50	85
N2276	40ch. "Two Scholars disputing"	2·75	60
N2277	40ch. "Woman with Child"	2·50	85
N2278	80ch. "Woman holding an Ostrich Feather Fan"	2·50	85
N2270/2278	Set of 9	19·00	6·00
MSN2279	102×69 mm. 80ch. "Self-portrait". P 12×11½	4·25	2·10

Nos. N2271 N2273, N2275 and N2277/8 were issued together in *se-tenant* sheetlets of five stamps and one label.

780 Airships *Gross Basenach II* and *Graf Zeppelin* over Cologne

1983 (10 Feb). "Luposta" International Air Mail Exhibition, Cologne. T **780** and similar multicoloured designs. Litho. P 11.

N2280	30ch. Type **780**	4·25	1·30
	a. Pair. Nos. N2280/1	8·75	2·75
N2281	40ch. Parseval airship PL-II over Cologne	4·25	1·30
MSN2282	86×95 mm. 80ch. "Virgin and Child" (Stephan Lochner) (vert). P 13½	4·25	2·10

Nos. N2280/1 were issued together in *se-tenant* pairs within the sheet, each pair forming a composite design.

781 Banner and Monument

782 Karl Marx

1983 (11 Mar). 50th Anniv of Wangjaesan Meeting. Litho. P 12×11½.

N2283	**781**	10ch. multicoloured	30	15

1983 (14 Mar). Death Centenary of Karl Marx. Litho. P 12.

N2284	**782**	10ch. multicoloured	1·10	40

783 Scholar, Marchers and Map of Journey

784 "Madonna of the Goldfinch"

1983 (16 Mar). 60th Anniv of Thousand-ri Journey for Learning. Litho. P 12.

N2285	**783**	10ch. multicoloured	1·40	15

1983 (20 Mar). 500th Birth Anniv of Raphael. T **784** and similar vert designs. Multicoloured. Litho. P 13½.

N2286	10ch. Type **784**	1·80	50
N2287	20ch. "The School of Athens" (detail).	2·10	65
	a. Sheetlet. Nos. N2287 and N2290/1 plus label	6·50	
N2288	30ch. "Madonna of the Grand Duke"	3·00	75
N2289	50ch. "Madonna of the Chair"	3·50	85
N2290	60ch. "Madonna of the Lamb"	2·10	65
N2291	80ch. "The beautiful Gardener"	2·10	65
N2286/2291	Set of 6	13·00	3·75
MSN2292	80×106 mm. 80ch. "Sistine Madonna"	5·00	2·10

Nos. N2287 and N2290/1 were issued together in *se-tenant* sheetlets of three stamps and one label.

785 Department Store No. 1   **786** Emblem and Crowd

1983 (7 Apr). Pyongyang Buildings. T **785** and similar horiz designs. Multicoloured. Litho. P 12.

N2293	2ch. Chongrvu Restaurant................	25	10
N2294	10ch. Part of Munsu Street....................	40	10
N2295	10ch. Ice rink...................................	50	15
N2296	40ch. Type **785**..................................	95	55
N2297	70ch. Grand People's Study House	1·70	75
N2293/2297 *Set of 5*...............................		3·50	1·50

1983 (9 Apr). Fifth Anniv of International Institute of Juche Idea. Litho. P 12.

N2298 **786**	10ch. multicoloured.................................	30	15

788 Satellite, Masts and Dish Aerial

1983 (30 Apr). World Communications Year (1st issue). Litho. P 12.

N2309 **788**	10ch. multicoloured.................................	2·10	40

See also Nos. N2349/**MS**N2354.

789 Emblem, Giant Panda and Stamp

1983 (21 May). Tembal '83 International Thematic Stamp Exhibition, Basel. T **789** and similar horiz design. Multicoloured. Litho. P 12.

N2310	20ch. Type **789**........................	2·50	85
N2311	30ch. Emblem, flag and Basel Town Post stamp	2·75	90

787 Judo

1983 (20 Apr). Olympic Games, Los Angeles (1st issue). T **787** and similar horiz designs. Multicoloured. Litho. P 11.

N2299	20ch. Type **787**...........................	1·30	60
N2300	20ch. Wrestling	2·50	60
	a. Sheetlet. Nos. N2300, N2302, N2304 and N2306/7 plus label	13·00	
N2301	30ch. Judo (different) (value in gold)	1·30	60
N2302	30ch. Judo (different) (value in black)	2·50	60
N2303	40ch. Boxing.......................................	1·30	60
N2304	40ch. Li Ho Jun (1972 shooting gold medallist)......................................	2·50	60
N2305	50ch. Weightlifting	1·30	60
N2306	50ch. Wrestling (different)	2·50	60
N2307	80ch. Boxing (different).........................	2·50	60
N2299/2307 *Set of 9*..		16·00	4·75
MSN2308 95×74 mm. 80ch. Judo (different). P 13½		5·00	1·80

Nos. N2300, N2302, N2304 and N2306/7 were issued together in *se-tenant* sheetlets of five stamps and one label.

See also Nos. N2359/**MS**N2365.

790 *Colourful Cow* (kogge), 1402

1983 (30 May). Old Ships. T **790** and similar horiz designs. Multicoloured. Litho. P 11.

N2312	20ch. Type **790**...	1·60	65
N2313	20ch. "Turtle" ship, 1592	3·75	1·10
	a. Sheetlet. Nos. N2313, N2315 and N2317/8 plus 2 labels..........	16.00	
N2314	35ch. *Great Harry* (warship), 1555........	2·10	75
N2315	35ch. Admiral Li Sun Sin and "turtle" ship...................................	3·75	1·10
N2316	50ch. *Eagle of Lubeck* (galleon), 1567	3·00	1·00
N2317	50ch. *Merkur* (full-rigged sailing ship), 1847..	3·75	1·10
N2318	80ch. *Herzogin Elisabeth* (cadet ship)	3·75	1·10
N2312/2318 *Set of 7*...............................		20·00	6·00
MSN2319 104×82 mm. 80ch. *Cristoforo Colombo* (cadet ship). P 13½.		7·25	5·00

Nos. N2313, N2315 and N2317/18 were issued together in *se-tenant* sheetlets of four stamps and two labels.

791 *Locomotion*, 1825

1983 (20 June). Railway Locomotives. T **791** and similar horiz designs. Multicoloured. Litho. P 12.

N2320	20ch. Type **791**	1·70	65
N2321	20ch. *Drache*, 1848	6·25	1·70
	a. Sheetlet. Nos. N2321, N2323 and N2325/6 plus 2 labels	65·00	
N2322	35ch. *Der Adler*, 1835	3·25	1·50
N2323	35ch. Korean steam locomotive	6·25	1·70
N2324	60ch. *Austria*, 1837	4·25	2·10
N2325	50ch. Bristol and Exeter railway locomotive, 1853	6·25	1·70
N2326	80ch. Caledonian railway locomotive, 1859	6·25	1·70
N2320/2326	Set of 7	31·00	10·00
MSN2327	106×64mm. 80ch. *Ilmarinen*, 1860	50·00	4·25

Nos. N2321, N2323 and N2325/6 were issued together in *se-tenant* sheetlets of four stamps and two labels.

792 Map, Hand and Weapons

793 Emblem, Tower of Juche Idea and Fireworks

1983 (23 June). Tenth Anniv of Publication of Five-point Policy for Korea's Reunification. Litho. P 12.

N2328	**792**	10ch. multicoloured	60	15

1983 (2 July). World Conference of Journalists against Imperialism and for Friendship and Peace, Pyongyang. T **793** and similar horiz designs. Multicoloured. Litho. P 12.

N2329	10ch. Type **793**	35	10
N2330	40ch. Emblem and rainbow and clasped hands	60	25
N2331	70ch. Emblem, map and hand with raised forefinger	90	40
N2329/2331	Set of 3	1·70	70

794 Worker and Banners

1983 (10 July). "Let's Create the Speed of the '80s". Litho. P 12.

N2332	**794**	10ch. multicoloured	40	15

795 Soldier and Rejoicing Crowd

1983 (27 July). 30th Anniv of Victory in Liberation War. Litho. P 12.

N2333	**795**	10ch. multicoloured	35	10

796 *Gorch Fock* (cadet barque) and Korean 1978 2ch. Stamp

1983 (4 Aug). Bangkok 1983 International Stamp Exhibition. T **796** and similar horiz design. Multicoloured. Litho. P 12.

N2334	40ch. Type **796**.	4·25	1·70
MSN2335	105×71 mm. 80ch. Bangkok, Penny Black and Korean I.Y.C stamp. P 11½×12	6·75	3·25

797 Skiing

1983 (20 Aug). Winter Olympic Games, Sarajevo (1984). T **797** and similar multicoloured designs. Litho. P 12.

N2336	10ch. Type **797**	90	40
N2337	20ch. Figure skating (vert)	3·25	85
	a. Sheetlet of 3. Nos. N2337 and N2340/1	10·00	
N2338	30ch. Skating (pair)	2·50	1·30
N2339	50ch. Ski jumping	3·00	1·40
N2340	60ch. Ice hockey (vert)	3·25	85
N2341	80ch. Speed skating (vert)	3·25	85
N2336/2341	Set of 6	14·50	5·00
MSN2342	74×87 mm. 80ch. Shooting (biathlon) (vert). P 12×11½	5·00	2·10

Nos. N2337 and N2340/1 were issued together in *se-tenant* sheetlets of three stamps.

798 Workers and Soldier with Books   **799** Archery

1983 (9 Sept). 35th Anniv of Korean People's Democratic Republic. Litho. P 13½.
N2343 **798** 10ch. multicoloured 55   15

1983 (20 Sept). Folk Games. T **799** and similar vert designs. Multicoloured. Litho. P 12.

N2344	10ch. Type **799**	3·75	60
N2345	10ch. Flying kites	90	35
	a. Sheetlet of 2 Nos. N2345 and N2347	1·90	75
N2346	40ch. See-sawing	90	35
N2347	40ch. Swinging	90	35
N2344/2347	Set of 4	5·75	1·50

Nos. N2345 and N2347 were issued together in *se-tenant* sheetlets of two stamps.

800 Girls holding Hands   **801** Envelopes and Forms of Transport

1983 (25 Oct). Korean-Chinese Friendship. Litho. P 12.
N2348 **800** 10ch. multicoloured 65   20

1983 (30 Oct). World Communications Year (2nd issue). T **801** and similar vert designs. Multicoloured. Litho. P 13½.

N2349	30ch. Mail van, motor cyclist and hand holding magazines	6·25	1·40
N2350	30ch. Satellite, globe and dish aerial	1·70	60
	a. Sheetlet of 3. Nos. N2350 and N2352/3	5·25	
N2351	40ch. Type **801**	6·25	1·40
N2352	40ch. Television cameraman	1·70	60
N2353	80ch. Telephone and aerial	1·70	60
N2349/2353	Set of 5	16·00	4·25
MSN2354	96×75 mm. 80ch. W.C.Y. emblem and satellite	4·50	2·10

Nos. N2350 and N2352/3 were issued together in *se-tenant* sheetlets of three stamps.

802 Portrait   **803** Sprinting

1983 (10 Nov). Paintings by Rubens. T **802** and similar horiz designs. Multicoloured. Litho. P 13½.

N2355	40ch. Type **802**	1·80	75
N2356	40ch. Portrait (different)	2·30	1·00
	a. Sheetlet of 2 Nos. N2356/7	4·75	2·10
N2357	80ch. "The Sentencing of Midas"	2·30	1·00
N2355/2357	Set of 3	5·75	2·50
MSN2358	129×95 mm. 80 ch "The Bear Hunt"	3·25	1·20

Nos. N2356/7 were issued together in *se-tenant* sheetlets of two stamps.

1983 (30 Nov). Olympic Games, Los Angeles (2nd issue). T **803** and similar vert designs. Multicoloured. Litho. P 11½. (N2360, N2363/4) or 13½ , (others)

N2359	10ch. Type **803**	90	25
N2360	20ch. Show jumping	2·50	85
	a. Sheetlet of 3 Nos. N2360 and N2363/4	7·75	
N2361	30ch. Cycling	3·75	85
N2362	60ch. Handball	2·50	85
N2363	50ch. Fencing	2·50	85
N2364	80ch. Gymnastics	2·50	85
N2359/2364	Set of 6	13·00	4·00
MSN2365	109×75 mm. 80ch. Judo	4·25	1·80

Nos. N2360 and N2363/4 were issued together in sheetlets of three stamps.

Six "de luxe" miniature sheets, each 1wn., exist from limited printings. A similar six sheets were issued in December 1983 for the Winter Olympic Games, Sarajevo.

804 "St. Catherine"   **804a** Cat

1983 (12 Dec). 450th Death Anniv (1984) of Antonio Correggio (artist). T **804** and similar vert designs. Multicoloured Litho. P 13½.

N2366	20ch. Type **804**	2·10	65
N2367	20ch. "Morning" (detail)	2·50	85
	a. Sheetlet. Nos. N2367, N2369 and N2371/2	10·50	
N2368	35ch. "Madonna"	2·10	65
N2369	35ch. "Morning" (different)	2·50	85
N2370	50ch. "Madonna with St. John"	2·10	65
N2371	50ch. "St. Catherine" (different)	2·50	85
N2372	80ch. "Madonna and Child"	2·50	85

N2366/2372 *Set of 7*.................................... 15·00   4·75
MSN2373 58×73 mm. 80ch. "Madonna and Child
  with Music-making Angels"............................ 5·50   2·10
  Nos. N2367, N2369 and N2371/2 were issued together in *se-tenant*
sheetlets of four stamps.

1983 (20 Dec). Cats. T **804a** and similar horiz designs showing
  different cats' heads. Multicoloured, frame colour given. Litho.
  P 13½.
N2373a   10ch. bright emerald .... 1·40   20
N2373b   10ch. gold... 1·40   20
N2373c   10ch. ultramarine................................. 1·40   20
N2373d   10ch. vermilion .... 1·40   20
N2373e   10ch. silver.. 1·40   20
N2373a/2373e *Set of 5* .... 6·25   90

805 Kimilsungflower   **806** Worker and Workers'
                      Party Flag

1984 (1 Jan). New Year. Litho. P 12.
N2374 **805**   10ch. multicoloured 85   15

1984 (16 Feb). "Under the Leadership of the Workers' Party". T **806**
  and similar horiz design. Multicoloured. Litho. P 12.
N2375   10ch. Type **806**............................. 35   10
N2376   10ch. Ore-dressing plant No. 3,
              Komdok General Mining
              Enterprise, and Party flag 50   10

807 Farm Worker. Rice and Maize

1984 (25 Feb). 20th Anniv of Publication of *Theses on the Socialist
  Rural Question in Our Country*. Litho. P 12.
N2377 **807**   10ch. multicoloured 30   10

808 Changdok School, Chilgol

1984 (15 Apr). 72nd Birthday of Kim Il Sung. T **808** and similar horiz
  design. Litho. P 12.
N2378   5ch. green, black and deep
              ultramarine 40   15
N2379   10ch. multicoloured................................. 40   15
  Design:—10ch. Birthplace, Mangyongdae, and rejoicing crowd.

809 "Spanish Riding School"   **810** "La Donna Velata"
(Julius von Blaas)

1984 (27 Apr). España 84 International Stamp Exhibition, Madrid.
  T **809** and similar vert designs. Multicoloured. Litho. P 13½.
N2380   10ch. Type **809**............................. 2·20   65
N2381   20ch. "Ferdinand of Austria" (Rubens) 2·20   65
MSN2382 73×96 mm. 80ch. "Spanish Riding
  School" (Julius von Blaas) (different)........................... 5·75   2·50

1984 (30 Apr). 500th Birth Anniv (1983) of Raphael (artist). T **810** and
  similar vert designs. Multicoloured. Litho. P 12.
N2383   10ch. "Portrait of Agnolo Doni"............ 1·90   75
N2384   20ch. Type **810**............................. 1·90   75
N2385   30ch. "Portrait of Jeanne d'Aragon"..... 1·90   75
N2383/2385 *Set of 3*.. 6·00   2·50
MSN2386 79×105 mm. 80ch. "St Sebastian".
  P 12×11½.. 5·25   2·50

811 Map and Second Stage Pumping   **812** Construction
Station   Site

1984 (30 Apr). 25th Anniv of Kiyang Irrigation System. Litho. P 12.
N2387 **811**   10ch. multicoloured 65   20

1984 (20 May). Construction on Five District Fronts. Litho. P 12.
N2388 **812**   10ch. carmine-vermilion, blk & yell 65   25

813 Bobsleighing (East Germany)

1984 (20 May). Winter Olympic Games Medal Winners. T **813** and similar multicoloured designs. Litho. P 13½.

N2389	10ch. Ski jumping (Matti Nykäenen)	3·00	65
	a Sheetlet of 3. Nos. N2389.		
	N2391 and N2393...........................	9·50	
N2390	20ch. Speed skating (Karin Enke)	2·10	60
N2391	20 ch Slalom (Max Julen)........................	3·00	65
N2392	30ch. Type **813**..................................	2·10	60
N2393	30ch. Downhill skiing (Maria Walliser)	2·30	65
N2394	40ch. Cross-country skiing (Thomas		
	Wassberg).......................................	3·75	75
	a. Sheetlet of 2. Nos. N2394/5	7·75	1·60
N2395	80ch. Cross-country skiing (Marja-		
	Liisa Hämäläinen)	3·75	75
N2389/2395 *Set of 7*..		18·00	4·25
MSN2396 106×86 mm. 80ch. Biathlon (Peter			
Angerer) (vert)		4·50	2·10

Nos. N2389, N2391 and N2393 were issued together in *se-tenant* sheetlets of three stamps, and Nos. N2394/5 in *se-tenant* sheetlets of two stamps.

814 Type "E" Goods Locomotive

1984 (26 May). Essen International Stamp Fair. T **814** and similar horiz designs. Multicoloured. Litho. P 12.

N2397	20ch. Type "202" express locomotive.	5·50	1·20
N2398	30ch. Type **814**..................................	5·50	1·20
MSN2399 94×86 mm. 80ch. Type "D" locomotive.....		9·25	2·20

815 "Mlle. Fiocre in the Ballet *La Source*"

1984 (10 June). 150th Birth Anniv of Edgar Degas (artist). T **815** and similar horiz designs. Multicoloured. Litho. P 12.

N2400	10ch. Type **815**..................................	2·00	50
N2401	20ch. "The Dance Foyer at the Rue le		
	Peletier Opera"...............................	3·00	55
N2402	30ch. "Race Meeting"	5·00	90
N2400/2402 *Set of 3*..		9·00	1·80
MSN2403 108×89 mm. 80ch. "Dancers at the Barre"			
P 11½..		4·50	2·10

816 Map of Pyongnam Irrigation System and Reservoir

817 Korean Stamp and Building

1984 (16 June). Irrigation Experts' Meeting, Pyongyang. Litho. P 12.

N2404	**816** 2ch. multicoloured.................................	55	15

1984 (19 June). Universal Postal Union Congress Stamp Exhibition, Hamburg. T **817** and similar vert design. Multicoloured. Litho. P 12.

N2405	20ch. Type **817**..	3·75	65
MSN2406 106×76 mm. 80ch. *Gorch Fock* (cadet			
barque) and Korean "turtle" ship stamp. P 12×11½		6·25	3·25

818 Crowd and Banners

819 Nobel experimenting

1984 (25 June). Proposal for Tripartite Talks. Litho. P 12.

N2407	**818** 10ch. multicoloured.................................	55	15

1984 (30 June). 150th Anniv (1983) of Alfred Bernhard Nobel (inventor). T **819** and similar vert designs. Multicoloured. Litho. P 13½.

N2408	20ch. Type **819**..	3·75	65
N2409	30ch. Portrait of Nobel	4·25	65
MSN2410 109×99 mm. 80ch. Portrait of Nobel			
(different)..		6·25	3·25

Nos. N2408/9 were each issued with *se-tenant* label depicting Nobel's laboratory and house respectively.

820 Drinks, Tinned Food. Clothes and Flats

1984 (10 July). Improvement of Living Standards. Litho. P 12.

N2411	**820** 10ch. multicoloured.................................	65	15

821 Sunhwa School, Mangyongdae

1984 (17 Aug). School of Kim Hyong Jik (Kim Il Sung's father). Litho. P 12.

N2412	**821** 10ch. multicoloured.................................	60	15

822 Armed Crowd with Banners

1984 (17 Aug). 65th Anniv of Kuandian Conference. Litho. P 12.
N2413 **822** 10ch. multicoloured 65   15

823 *Thunia bracteata*

1984 (20 Aug). Flowers. T **823** and similar horiz designs. Multicoloured. Litho. P l2.
N2414   10ch. *Cattleya loddigesii* 90   10
N2415   20ch. Type **823** .... 1·40   35
N2416   30ch. *Phalaenopsis amabilis* .... 1·80   50
N2414/2416 *Set of 3* .... 3·75   85
MSN2417 67×94mm. 80ch. Kimilsung flower .... 4·50   1·70

824 Swordfish and Trawler

1984 (25 Aug). Fishing Industry. T **824** and similar horiz designs. Multicoloured. Litho. P 12.
N2418   5ch. Type **824** 90   25
N2419   10ch. Marlin and trawler .... 1·30   40
N2420   40ch. *Histiophorus orientalis* and
                 game fishing launch .... 3·50   1·20
N2418/2420 *Set of 3* .... 5·25   1·70

825 Revolutionary Museum. Chilgol

826 Kim Hyok, Cha Gwang Su and Youth

1984 (29 Aug). Litho. P 12.
N2421 **825** 10ch. multicoloured 55   15

1984 (31 Aug). "Let's All become the Kim Hyoks and Cha Gwang Sus of the '80s". Litho. P 12.
N2422 **826** 10ch. multicoloured 55   15

827 Inauguration of a French Railway Line, 1860

1984 (7 Sept). Centenary (1983) of "Orient Express". T **827** and similar horiz designs. Multicoloured. Litho. P 13½.
N2423   Type **827** .... 1·60   35
N2424   20ch. Opening of a British railway
                 line, 1821 .... 3·00   65
N2425   30ch. Inauguration of Paris-Rouen
                 line, 1843 .... 4·25   1·10
N2423/2425 *Set of 3* .... 8·00   1·90
MSN2426 105×85 mm. 80ch. Interiors of Wagons-lits Car, 1905 .... 7·50   3·00

828 Clock Face

829 Grand Theatre, Hamhung

1984 (15 Sept). Centenary of Greenwich Meridian. T **828** and similar vert design. Multicoloured. Litho. P 12.
N2427   10ch. Type **828** .... 3·25   1·30
MSN2428 112×81 mm. 80ch. Chollima statue, buildings and clock. P 12×11½ .... 5·00   2·10

1984 (21 Sept). Litho. P 12.
N2429 **829** 10ch. royal blue 55   15

830 Turning on Machinery

831 "Dragon Angler"

1984 (25 Sept). Automation of Industry. Litho. P 12.
N2430 **830** 40ch. multicoloured 75   40

1984 (30 Sept). Paintings. T **831** and similar multicoloured designs.
Litho. P 12 (10ch.) or13½ (others).

N2431	10ch. Type **831**	1·10	20
N2432	20ch. "Ox Driver" (Kim Du Ryang)		
	(47×35 mm)	1·40	40
N2433	30ch. "Bamboo" (Kim Jin U)		
	(47×35 mm)	2·10	60
N2431/2433	*Set of 3*	4·25	1·10

No. N2434 has been left for a reported but unseen miniature
sheet.

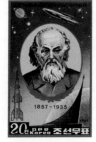

832 Tsiolkovsky

1984 (5 Oct). K. E. Tsiolkovsky (space scientist) T **832** and similar vert
designs. Multicoloured. Litho. P 12.

N2435	20ch. Type **832**	1·10	35
N2436	30ch. "Sputnik" orbiting Earth	1·60	60
MSN2437	100×70 mm. 80ch. Rocket launch.		
	P 12×11½	5·00	1·30

833 *Pongdaesan*

1984 (6 Oct). Container Ships. T **833** and similar horiz designs.
Multicoloured. P 12.

N2438	10ch. Type **833**	1·30	25
N2439	20ch. *Ryongnamsan*	1·40	50
N2440	30ch. *Rungrado*	1·80	75
N2438/2440	*Set of 3*	4·00	1·40
MSN2441	97×107 mm. 80ch. *Kumgangsan*	6·25	1·90

834 Caracal

1984 (13 Oct). Animals. T **834** and similar multicoloured designs.
Litho. P 13½.

N2442	10ch. Spotted hyenas	75	15
N2443	20ch. Type **834**	1·10	35
N2444	30ch. Black-backed jackals	1·60	60
N2445	40ch. Foxes	2·10	85
N2442/2445	*Set of 4*	5·00	1·80
MSN2446	80×104 mm. 80ch. Lanner falcon (vert)	7·50	2·50

835 Marie Curie   **836** Chestnut-eared
                                 Aracari

1984 (21 Oct). 50th Anniv of Marie Curie (physicist). T **835** and similar
vert design. Multicoloured. Litho. P 12.

N2447	10ch. Type **835**	2·50	35
MSN2448	78×103 mm. 80ch. Portrait of Marie Curie.		
	P 12×11½	5·00	2·10

1984 (5 Nov). Birds. T **836** and similar vert designs. Multicoloured.
Litho. P 11½.

N2449	10ch. Hoopoe	1·40	25
N2450	20ch. South African crowned cranes	1·80	50
N2451	30ch. Saddle-bill stork	2·50	65
N2452	40ch. Type **836**	3·50	90
N2449/2452	*Set of 4*	8·25	2·10
MSN2453	104×74 mm. 80ch. Black kite	9·25	2·50

837 Cosmonaut

1984 (15 Nov). Space Exploration. T **837** and similar horiz designs.
Multicoloured. Litho. P 12.

N2454	10ch. Type **837**	65	15
N2455	20ch. Cosmonaut on space-walk	1·00	35
N2456	30ch. Cosmonaut (different)	1·40	50
N2454/2456	*Set of 3*	2·75	90
MSN2457	77×90 mm. 80ch. Moon vehicle	4·50	1·70

838 *Arktika*

1984 (26 Nov). Russian Ice-breakers. T **838** and similar horiz designs.
Multicoloured. Litho. P 13½.

N2458	20ch. Type **838**	1·60	50
N2459	30ch. *Ermak*	2·20	65
MSN2460	97×67 mm. 80ch. *Lenin*	6·25	2·10

839 Mendeleev

1984 (1 Dec). 150th Birth Anniv of Dmitri Mendeleev (chemist).
T **839** and similar vert design. Multicoloured. Litho. P 13½.
N2461   10ch. Type **839** .... 1·20   25
MSN2462 95×65 mm. 80ch. Seated statue of
Mendeleev .... 5·00   2·10

840 Kim Il Sung in U.S.S.R.   **841** Freesia

1984 (30 Dec). Kim Il Sung's Visits to Eastern Europe. T **840** and similar
vert designs. Multicoloured. Litho. P 12.
N2463   10ch. Type **840** 85   20
                       a. Sheetlet of 4. Nos. N2463/6 .... 3·75
N2464   10ch. In Poland 85   20
N2465   10ch. In German Democratic
                       Republic 85   20
N2466   10ch. In Czechoslovakia 85   20
N2467   10ch. In Hungary 85   20
                       a. Sheetlet of 3. Nos. N2467/9 .... 2·75
N2468   10ch. In Bulgaria 85   20
N2469   10ch. In Rumania 85   20
N2464/2469 Set of 7 .... 5·25   1·30
MSN2470 80×105 mm. 10ch. In China. P 11½ .... 1·70   1·70
Nos. N2463/6 were issued together in se-tenant sheetlets of four
stamps and Nos. N2467/9 in se-tenant sheetlets of three.

1985 (1 Jan). New Year. Litho. P 12.
N2471 **841**   10ch. multicoloured 90   25

842 Journey Route, Steam
Locomotive and Memorials

1985 (22 Jan). 60th Anniv of 1000 ri Journey by Kim Il Sung. T **482** and
similar horiz design. Multicoloured. Litho. P I2.
N2472   5ch. Type 842 .... 1·60   25
                       a. Horiz. pair Nos. N2472/3 .... 2·30   40
N2473   10ch. Boy trumpeter and school-
                       children following route 60   10
Nos. N2472/3 were issued together in horizontal se-tenant pairs
within the sheet, each pair forming a composite design.

843 Cugnots Steam Car, 1769   **844** Camp,
                                                                         Mt Paekdu

1985 (25 Jan). History of the Motor Car (1st series). T **843** and similar
horiz designs. Multicoloured. Litho. P 11½.
N2474   10ch. Type **843** .... 1·60   20
N2475   15ch. Goldsworthy Gurney steam
                       omnibus, 1825 .... 1·60   25
N2476   20ch. Gottlieb Daimler diesel car,
                       1885 .... 1·60   35
N2477   25ch. Benz three-wheeled diesel car,
                       1886 .... 1·70   50
N2478   30ch. Peugeot diesel car, 1891 .... 2·20   60
N2474/2478 Set of 5 .... 7·75   1·70
MSN2479 92×75 mm. 80ch. black and gold (Wind
car) .... 5·00   2·20
See also Nos. N2562/**MS**N2567.

1985 (16 Feb). Korean Revolution Headquarters. Litho. P 12.
N2480 **844**   10ch. multicoloured 55   30

845 Taechodo   **846** Hedgehog challenges
Lighthouse   Tiger

1985 (23 Feb). Lighthouses. T **845** and similar vert designs. Litho.
P 12×11½.
N2481   10ch. Type **845** .... 2·20   20
N2482   20ch. Sodo .... 2·50   40
N2483   30ch. Pido .... 3·00   65
N2484   40ch. Suundo .... 3·50   1·00
N2481/2484 Set of 4 .... 10·00   2·00

1985 (6 Mar). "The Hedgehog defeats the Tiger" (fable). T **846** and
similar horiz designs. Litho. Multicoloured. P 11½.
N2485   10ch. Type **846** 75   15
N2486   20ch. Tiger goes to stamp on rolled-
                       up hedgehog .... 1·10   35
N2487   30ch. Hedgehog clings to tiger's nose 1·60   60
N2488   35ch. Tiger flees .... 1·70   65
N2489   40ch. Tiger crawls before hedgehog ... 2·00   85
N2485/2489 Set of 5 .... 6·50   2·30

847 *Pleurotus cornucopiae*

848 West Germany v. Hungary, 1954

1985 (16 Mar). Fungi. T **847** and similar vert designs. Multicoloured. Litho. P 11½.

N2490	10ch. Type **847**	1·40	20
N2491	20ch. Oyster fungus (*Pleurotus ostreatus*)	1·70	40
N2492	30ch. *Catathelasma ventricosum*	2·50	65
N2490/2492	*Set of 3*	5·00	1·10

1985 (20 Mar). World Cup Football Championship Finals. T **848** and similar designs. Litho. P 13½.

N2493	10ch. black, buff and orange-brown..	75	20
N2494	10ch. multicoloured	75	20
N2495	20ch. black, buff and orange-brown..	1·10	35
N2496	20ch. multicoloured	1·10	35
N2497	30ch. black, buff and orange-brown..	1·60	60
N2498	30ch. multicoloured	1·60	60
N2499	40ch. black, buff and orange-brown..	2·00	85
N2500	40ch. multicoloured	2·00	85
N2493/2500	*Set of 8*	9·75	3·50

MSN2501 Two sheets. (a) 105×75 mm. 80ch. black, cinnamon and gold; (b) 94×95 mm. 80ch, multicoloured .... 10·00 4·25

Designs: Vert—No. N2493, Type **848**; N2496, West Germany v. Netherlands, 1974; N2499, England v. West Germany, 1966; **MS**N2501(b), Azteca Stadium, Mexico (venue of 1986 final). Horiz— N2494, Brazil v. Italy., 1970; N2495, Brazil v. Sweden, 1958; N2497, Brazil v. Czechoslovakia. 1962; N2498, Argentina v. Netherlands, 1968; N2500, Italy v. West Germany, 1982; **MS**N2501 (a), North Korea's quarter-final place, 1966.

849 Date and Kim Il Sung's Birthplace

850 Horn Player

1985 (15 Apr). 73rd Birthday of Kim Il Sung. Litho. P 12.

N2502	**849** 10ch. multicoloured	55	15

1985 (7 May). Fourth-century Musical Instruments. T **850** and similar vert design. Multicoloured. Litho. P 11½.

N2503	10ch. Type **850**	1·70	20
N2504	20ch. So (pipes) player	1·70	35

851 Chongryon Hall, Tokyo

852 Common Marmoset (*Callithrix jacchus*)

1985 (25 May). 30th Anniv of Chongryon (General Association of Korean Residents in Japan). Litho. P 11½.

N2505	**851** 10ch. deep brown	55	15

1985 (7 June). Mammals. T **852** and similar vert design. Multicoloured. Litho. P 11½.

N2506	5ch. Type **852**	1·10	20
N2507	10ch. Ring-tailed lemur (*Lemur catta*)	1·10	20

853 National Emblem

854 Buenos Aires and Argentina 1982 Stamp

1985 (20 June). Sheets 51×70 mm. Litho. P 11½

MSN2508 **853** 80ch. multicoloured		1·90	65

1985 (5 July). Argentina '85 International Stamp Exhibition, Buenos Aires. T **854** and similar multicoloured designs. Litho. P 12.

N2509	10ch. Type **854**	90	20
N2510	20ch. Iguacu Falls and Argentina 1984 and North Korea 1978 stamps (horiz)	3·00	35
MSN2511 73×100 mm. 80ch. Gaucho. P 12×11½		6·25	5·00

855 Dancer and Gymnast

856 Peace Pavilion, Youth Park

1985 (27 July). 12th World Youth and Students' Festival, Moscow T **855** and similar vert designs. Litho. P 12.

N2512	10ch. Type **855**	75	15
N2513	20ch. Spassky Tower. Moscow, and Festival emblem	1·10	35
N2514	40ch. Youths of different races	2·00	85

1985 (1 Aug). Pyongyang Buildings. T **856** and similar vert design. Litho. P 12.

N2515	2ch. greenish black and grey-green	25	10
N2516	40ch. reddish brown and light brown	60	25

Design:—40ch. Multi-storey flats, Chollima Street.

857 Liberation Celebrations

1985 (15 Aug). 40th Anniv of Liberation. T **857** and similar designs. Litho. P 11½.

N2517	5ch. Indian red. black and ultramarine	20	10
N2518	10ch. multicoloured	50	15
N2519	10ch. chestnut, brownish blk & bl-grn	50	15
N2520	10ch. multicoloured	50	15
N2521	10ch. yellow-ochre, black & orge-verm	50	15
N2522	10ch. vermilion, reddish orange & blk	50	15
N2523	40ch. multicoloured	1·20	75
N2517/2523	Set of 7	3·50	1·40
MSN2524	68×50 mm. 90ch. multicoloured	2·75	1·90

Designs: Horiz—No. N2517, Soldiers with rifles and flag; N2518, Crowd with banners and Flame of Juche; N2519, Korean and Soviet soldiers raising arms; N2520, Japanese soldiers laying down weapons; N2521, Type **857**; N2523, Students bearing banners. Vert—N2522, Liberation Tower, Moran Hill, Pyongyang; **MS**N2524, Monument.

858 Halley and Comet   859 Camellia japonica

1985 (25 Aug). Appearance of Halley's Comet. T **858** and similar horiz designs. Multicoloured. Litho. P 13½.

N2525	10ch. Type **858**	90	15
N2526	20ch. Diagram of comet's flight and space probe	1·40	35
MSN2527	144×128 mm. 80ch. ultramarine and gold (Comet's trajectory)	5·00	2·20

1985 (10 Sept). Flowers. T **859** and similar vert designs. Multicoloured. Litho. P 12.

N2528	10ch. Hippeastrum hybridum	90	35
N2529	20ch. Type **859**	1·40	40
N2530	30ch. Cyclamen persicum	1·80	60
N2528/2530	Set of 3	3·75	1·20

860 "Hunting"   861 Party Founding Museum

1985 (30 Sept). Koguryo Culture. T **860** and similar multicoloured designs. Litho. P 13½.

N2531	10ch. "Hero" (vert)	75	15
N2532	15ch. "Heroine" (vert)	90	35
N2533	20ch. "Flying Fairy"	1·10	35
N2534	25ch. Type **860**	1·40	50
N2531/2534	Set of 4	3·75	1·20
MSN2535	90×80 mm. 50ch. "Pine Tree" (28×48 mm). P 12	4·25	1·30

Nos. N2531/4 were issued both in separate sheets and together in se-tenant sheetlets of four stamps.

1986 (10 Oct). 40th Anniv of Korean Workers' Party. T **861** and similar vert designs. Multicoloured. Litho. P 11½.

N2536	5ch. Type **861**	20	10
N2537	10ch. Soldier with gun and workers...	50	15
N2538	10ch. Soldiers and flag	50	15
N2539	40ch. Statue of worker, peasant and intellectual holding aloft party emblem	1·20	75
N2536/2539	Set of 4	2·20	1·00
MSN2540	60×75 mm. 90ch. People with flowers	2·20	90

862 Arch of Triumph, Pyongyang

863 Colosseum, Rome, and N. Korea 1975 10ch. Stamp

1985 (14 Oct). 40th Anniv of Kim Il Sungs Return. Litho. P 12.

N2541	**862** 10ch. reddish brown & bright green	55	15

1985 (25 Oct). Italia '85 International Stamp Exhibition, Rome. T **863** and similar multicoloured designs. Litho. P 11½.

N2542	10ch. Type **863**	75	25
N2543	20ch. "The Holy Family" (Raphael) (vert)	1·10	40
N2544	30ch. Head of "David" (statue, Michelangelo) (vert)	1·60	60
N2542/2444	Set of 3	3·00	1·10
MSN2545	67×47 mm. 80ch. Pantheon, Rome	5·00	2·20

864 Mercedes Benz Type "300"

1985 (25 Oct). South-West German Stamp Fair, Sindelfingen. T **864** and similar horiz designs. Multicoloured. Litho. P 12.

N2546	10ch. Type **864**	1·10	15
N2547	15ch. Mercedes Benz Type "770"	1·70	25
N2548	20ch. Mercedes Benz "W 150"	1·80	35
N2549	30ch. Mercedes Type ""600"	2·50	60
N2546/2549	Set of 4	6·50	1·20
MSN2550	84×57 mm. 80ch. Mercedes Benz "W31". P 11½×12	5·50	1·50

865 Tackle **866** Dancers

1985 (1 Nov). World Cup Football Championship. Mexico (1st issue). T **865** and similar vert designs. Multicoloured. Litho.P 13½.
N2551	20ch. Type **865**	1·50	40
N2552	30ch. Three players	1·70	60
MSN2553	106×76 mm. 80ch. Goalkeeper and Mexican monuments	5·00	1·90

See also Nos. N2558/MSN2560 and N2577/MSN2583.

1985 (9 Nov). International Youth Year. T **866** and similar horiz designs. Multicoloured. Litho. P 11½.
N2554	10ch. Type **866**	75	20
N2555	20ch. Sports activities	1·10	35
N2556	30ch. Technology	1·60	60
N2554/2556	Set of 3	3·00	1·00
MSN2557	75×60 mm. 80ch. Young people	5·75	2·10

867 Players

1985 (20 Nov). World Cup Football Championship. Mexico (2nd issue). T **867** and similar horiz designs. Multicoloured. Litho. P 12.
N2558	20ch. Type **867**	1·50	40
N2559	30ch. Goalkeeper and players	1·70	60
MSN2560	102×80 mm. 80ch. Goalkeeper and bullfighter. P 11½	5·00	2·10

868 Juche Torch **869** Amédée Bollée Limousine, 1901

1986 (1 Jan). New Year. Litho. P 12.
N2561	**868** 10ch. multicoloured	55	15

1986 (20 Jan). History of the Motor Car (2nd series). T **869** and similar horiz designs. Multicoloured. Litho. P 11½.
N2562	10ch. Type **869**	90	15
N2563	20ch. Stewart Rolls. Henry Royce and "Silver Ghost", 1906	1·60	35
N2564	25ch. Giovanni Agnelli and Fiat car, 1912	1·70	50
N2565	30ch. Ettore Bugatti and 'Royal' coupe, 1928	2·00	60
N2566	40ch. Louis Renault and fiacre,1906...	3·00	85
N2562/2566	Set of 5	8·25	2·20
MSN2567	75×60 mm. 80ch. Gottlieb Daimler, Karl Benz and Mercedes "S",1927	5·75	1·50

870 Gary Kasparov **871** Cemetery Gate

1986 (5 Feb). World Chess Championship, Moscow. T **870** and similar vert design. Multicoloured. Litho. P 12.
N2568	20ch. Type **870**	3·00	35
MSN2569	60×82 mm. 80ch. Anatoly Karpov and Kasparov	5·75	2·50

1986 (10 Feb). Revolutionary Martyrs' Cemetery, Pyongyang. T **7871** and similar horiz design. Multicoloured. Litho. P 12.
N2570	5ch. Type **871**	25	10
N2571	10ch. Bronze sculpture (detail)	65	15

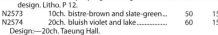

872 Tongdu Rock, Songgan **873** Buddhist Scriptures Museum

1986 (16 Feb). 37th Anniv of Pres. Kim II Sungs Visit to Songgan Revolutionary Site. Litho. P 12.
N2572	**872** 10ch. multicoloured	55	15

1986 (20 Feb). Mt. Myohyang Buildings. T **873** and similar horiz design. Litho. P 12.
N2573	10ch. bistre-brown and slate-green...	50	15
N2574	20ch. bluish violet and lake	60	15

Design:—20ch. Taeung Hall.

874 Amphiprion frenatus

1986 (12 Mar). Fishes. T **874** and similar horiz design. Multicoloured. Litho. P 11½.
N2575	10ch. Pennant coralfish (Heniochus acuminatus)	1·20	15
N2576	20ch. Type **874**	1·70	40

875 Footballers and Flags of Italy. Bulgaria and Argentina

1986 (21 Mar). World Cup Football Championship, Mexico (3rd issue). T **875** and similar horiz designs showing footballers and flags of participating countries. Multicoloured. Litho. P 12.

N2577	10ch. Type **875**	75	15
N2578	20ch. Mexico, Belgium, Paraguay and		
	Iraq	1·10	35
N2579	25ch. France, Canada, U.S.S.R. and		
	Hungary	1·40	50
N2580	30ch. Brazil, Spain, Algeria and		
	Northern Ireland	1·60	60
N2581	35ch. West Germany, Uruguay,		
	Scotland and Denmark	1·70	65
N2582	40ch. Poland, Portugal, Morocco and		
	England	2·00	85
N2577/2582 *Set of 6*		7·75	2·75
MSN2583 100×70 mm. 80ch. Ball, boots, footballers			
and trophy		5·00	2·30

876 Singer, Pianist and Emblem **877** Daimler "Motorwagen", 1886

1986 (5 Apr). Fourth Spring Friendship Art Festival, Pyongyang. Litho. P 12.

N2584	**876**	1wn. multicoloured	1·70	1·10

1986 (8 Apr). 60th Anniv of Mercedes-Benz (car manufacturers). T **877** and similar horiz designs. Multicoloured. Litho. P 11½.

N2585	10ch. Type **877**	65	15
N2586	10ch. Benz "velo", 1894	65	15
N2587	20ch. Mercedes car, 1901	1·00	35
N2588	20ch. Benz limousine, 1909	1·00	35
N2589	30ch. Mercedes "tourenwagen", 1914	1·40	50
N2590	30ch. Mercedes-Benz "1.70"		
	6-cylinder, 1931	1·40	50
N2591	40ch. Mercedes-Benz "380", 1933	1·80	90
N2592	40ch. Mercedes-Benz "540 K", 1936	1·80	90
N2585/2592 *Set of 8*		8·75	3·50
MSN2593 75×60 mm. 80ch. Mercedes-Simplex "			
phaeton", 1904		5·75	2·30

878 Mangyong Hill **879** Crowd

1986 (15 Apr). 74th Birthday of Kim Il Sung. Litho. P 12.

N2594	**878**	10ch. multicoloured	50	10

1986 (5 May). 50th Anniv of Association for the Restoration of the Fatherland. Litho. P 12.

N2595	**879**	10ch. multicoloured	40	10

880 Dove carrying Letter **881** "Mona Lisa"(Leonardo da Vinci)

1986 (18 June). International Peace Year. T **880** and similar vert designs. Multicoloured. Litho. P 12.

N2596	10ch. Type **880**	50	35
N2597	20ch. United Nations Headquarters,		
	New York	1·00	65
N2598	30ch. Dove, globe and broken		
	missiles	1·50	1·00
N2596/2598 *Set of 3*		2·75	1·80
MSN2599 72×90 mm. 80ch. Sculpture. P 12×11½		3·75	1·30

1986 (9 July). Litho. P 13½.

N2600	**881**	20ch. multicoloured	1·20	40

882 Pink Iris **883** Kim Un Suk

1986 (20 July). Irises. T **882** and similar vert design. Multicoloured. Litho. P 11½.

N2601	20ch. Type **882**	1·50	40
N2602	30ch. Violet iris	1·70	60
MSN2603 84×64 mm. 80ch. Magenta iris		5·00	2·10

1986 (30 July). Tennis Players. T **883** and similar vert designs. Multicoloured. Litho. P 13½.

	(a) POSTAGE		
N2604	10ch. Type **883**	2·20	50
	a. Block of 4. Nos. N2604/7	9·00	
N2605	20ch. Ivan Lendl	2·20	50
N2606	30ch. Steffi Graf	2·20	50
	(b) AIR MAIL		
N2607	50ch. Boris Becker	2·20	50
N2604/2607 *Set of 4*		8·00	1·80

Nos. N2604/7 were issued together in *se-tenant* blocks of 4 within the sheet.

884 Sulphur-crested Cockatoo   **885** First Issue of *L 'Unità*

1986 (4 Aug). Stampex 86 Stamp Exhibition, Adelaide, Australia.
T**884** and similar horiz design. Multicoloured. Litho. P 11½.

N2608	10ch. Type **884**	1·80	35
MSN2609	75×60 mm. 80ch. Kangaroo	5·00	2·10

1986 (26 Aug). National *L'Unità* (Italian Communist Party newspaper)
Festival, Milan. T **885** and similar multicoloured designs. Litho.
P 11½.

N2610	10ch. Type **885**	70	40
N2611	20ch. Milan Cathedral	1·30	85
N2612	30ch. "Pietà" (Michelangelo) (vert)	1·80	1·30
N2610/2612 *Set of 3*		3·50	2·30
MSN2613 85×65 mm. 80ch. Enrico Berlinguer			
(former General Secretary of Italian Communist			
Party) (vert)		2·50	1·00

886 Ice-breaker   **887** Reprint of First Stamp
Express II and Sweden
1872 20ö. Stamp

1986 (28 Aug). "Stockholmia 86" International Stamp Exhibition,
Stockholm. T **886** and similar multicoloured design. Litho.
P 11½.

N2614	10ch. Type **886**	2·50	25
MSN2615 86×60 mm. 80ch. U.P.U. emblem, mail			
coach and Swedish stamps (horiz)		4·50	1·80

1986 (12 Sept). 40th Anniv of First North Korean Stamps (1st issue).
T **887** and similar horiz designs. Multicoloured. Litho. P 12.

(a) POSTAGE

N2616	10ch. Type **887**	50	40
N2617	15ch. Imperforate reprint of first		
	stamp	75	60

(b) AIR MAIL

N2618	50ch. 1946 50ch. violet stamp	2·50	1·70
N2616/2618 *Set of 3*		3·50	2·40
See also Nos. N2619/21			

888 Postal Emblems and 1962 and 1985 Stamps

1986 (5 Oct). 40th Anniv of First North Korean Stamps (2nd issue).
T **888** and similar multicoloured designs. Litho. P 12.

(a) POSTAGE

N2619	10ch. Type **888**	2·20	40
N2620	15ch. General Post Office and 1976		
	and 1978 stamps	1·20	25

(b) AIR MAIL

N2621	50ch. Kim Il Sung, first stamp and		
	reprint (vert)	1·80	65
N2619/2621 *Set of 3*		4·75	1·20

1st **ARG**

2nd **FRG**

3rd **FRA**

4th **BEL**

(889)

1986 (14 Oct). World Cup Football Championship Results. Nos.
N2577/**MS**N2583 optd with T **889**.

N2622	10ch. multicoloured	1·20	15
N2623	20ch. multicoloured	1·40	40
N2624	25ch. multicoloured	1·70	50
N2625	30ch. multicoloured	1·80	60
N2626	35ch. multicoloured	2·10	75
N2627	40ch. multicoloured	2·50	85
N2622/2627 *Set of 6*		9·75	3·00
MSN2628 100×70 mm. 80ch. multicoloured		5·75	1·70

890 Flag and Man   **891** Gift Animals House
with raised Fist

1986 (17 Oct). 60th Anniv of Down-with-Imperialism Union. Litho.
P 11½.

N2629	**890**	10ch. multicoloured	40	25

1986 (18 Oct). First Anniv of Gift Animals House, Central Zoo,
Pyongyang. Litho P 12.

N2630	**891**	2wn. multicoloured	4·25	1·40

892 Schoolchildren   **893** Communications Satellite

1986 (4 Nov). 40th Anniv of United Nations Educational. Scientific
and Cultural Organization. T **892** and similar multicoloured
design. Litho. P 12.

N2631	10ch. Type **892**	50	35
N2632	50ch. Anniversary emblem. Grand		
	People's Study House and		
	telecommunications (horiz)	2·50	1·70

1986 (15 Nov). 15th Anniv of Intersputnik. Litho. P 12.

N2633	**893**	5wn. multicoloured	9·25	4·25

894 Oil tanker leaving Lock

1986 (20 Nov). West Sea Barrage. T **894** and similar horiz designs. Litho. P 12.

N2634	10ch. multicoloured	65	15
N2635	40ch. green, black and gold	1·70	35
N2636	1wn.20 multicoloured	3·50	85
N2634/2636 *Set of 3*		5·25	1·20

Designs:—20ch. Aerial view of dam; 1wn.20 Aerial view of lock.

895 Common Morel (*Morchella esculenta*)

896 Machu Picchu, Peru, and N. Korea Taedong Gate Stamp

1986 (23 Nov). Minerals and Fungi. T **895** and similar vert designs. Multicoloured. Litho. P 13½.

(a) POSTAGE

N2637	10ch. Lengenbachite	2·10	40
	a. Block of 6. Nos. N2637/42	13·00	
N2638	10ch. Common funnel cap (*Clitocybe infundibuliformis*)	2·10	40
N2639	15ch. Rhodochrosite	2·10	40
N2640	15ch. Type **895**	2·10	40

(b) AIR MAIL

N2641	50ch. Annabergite	2·10	40
N2642	50ch. Blue russula (*Russula cyanoxantha*)	2·10	40
N2637/2642 *Set of 6*		11·50	2·20

Nos. N2637/42 were issued together in *se-tenant* blocks of six stamps within the sheet.

1986 (25 Nov). North Korean Three-dimensional Photographs and Stamps Exhibition, Lima, Peru. T **896** and similar vert design. Multicoloured. Litho. P 13½.

N2643	10ch. Type **896**	1·70	35
MSN2644 110×75 mm. 80ch. Korean and Peruvian children		5·00	1·80

897 Pine Tree

898 *Pholiota adiposa*

1987 (1 Jan). New Year. T **897** and similar vert design. Multicoloured. Litho. P 12.

N2645	10ch. Type **897**	90	20
N2646	40ch. Hare	1·20	40

1987 (5 Jan). Fungi. T **898** and similar vert designs. Multicoloured. Litho. P 11½.

N2647	10ch. Type **898**	1·80	40
N2648	20ch. Chanterelle (*Cantharellus cibarius*)	1·90	40
N2649	30ch. *Boletus impolitus*	2·30	45
N2647/2649 *Set of 3*		5·50	1·10
MSN2650 50×70 mm. 80ch. *Gomphidius rutilus*		5·75	2·30

899 Kim Ok Song (composer)

1987 (29 Jan). Musicians' Death Anniversaries. T **899** and similar vert designs. Multicoloured. Litho. P 13½.

N2651	10ch. Maurice Ravel (composer. 50th anniv)	1·70	30
	a. Block of 6. Nos. N2651/6	10·50	
N2652	10ch. Type **899** (22nd anniv)	1·70	30
N2653	20ch. Giovanni Lully (composer, 300th anniv)	1·70	30
N2654	30ch. Franz Liszt (composer, centenary (1986))	1·70	30
N2655	40ch. Violins (250th anniv of Antonio Stradivari (violin maker))	1·70	30
N2656	40ch. Christoph Gluck (composer, bicentenary)	1·70	30
N2651/2656 *Set of 6*		9·25	1·60

Nos. N2651/6 were issued together in *se-tenant* blocks of six stamps within the sheet.

900 Kim Jong Il (½-size illustration)

1987 (16 Feb). Kim Jong Il's Birthday. Sheet 85×105 mm. Litho. P 13½.

MSN2657 **900** 80ch. multicoloured		1·80	65

901 East Pyongyang Grand Theatre   **902** *Gorch Fock* (German cadet barque)

1987 (23 Feb). Buildings. T **901** and similar designs. Litho. P 12.

N2658	5ch. brown-olive	40	10
N2659	10ch. chocolate	50	15
N2660	3wn. deep blue	4·50	1·60
N2658/2660	*Set of 3*	4·75	1·70

Designs Vert—10ch. Pyongyang Koryo Hotel. Horiz—3wn. Rungnado Stadium.

1987 (25 Feb). Sailing Ships. T **902** and similar multicoloured designs. Litho. P 13½.

(a) POSTAGE

N2661	20ch. Type **902**	85	30
N2662	30ch. *Tovarishch* (Russian three-masted cadet barque) (vert)	1·20	40

(b) AIR MAIL

N2663	50ch. *Belle Poule* (cadet schooner) (vert)	1·70	65
N2664	50ch. *Sagres II* (Portuguese cadet barque) (vert)	1·70	65
N2665	1wn. Koryo period merchantman	3·75	1·30
N2666	1wn. *Dar Mlodziezy* (Polish cadet full-rigged ship) (vert)	3·75	1·30
N2661/2666	*Set of 6*	11·50	4·25

903 Road Signs

1987 (27 Feb). Road Safety. T **903** and similar horiz designs showing different road signs. Litho. P 12.

(a) POSTAGE

N2667	10ch. new blue, bright scarlet & black	1·30	10
N2668	10ch. bright scarlet and black	1·30	10
N2669	20ch. new blue, bright scarlet & black	1·70	30

(b) AIR MAIL

N2670	50ch. bright scarlet and black	1·80	75
N2667/2670	*Set of 4*	5·50	1·10

904 Fire Engine

1987 (27 Feb). Fire Engines. T **904** and similar horiz designs showing different machines. Litho. P 12.

(a) POSTAGE

N2671	10ch. multicoloured	2·20	40
N2672	20ch. multicoloured	2·50	45
N2673	30ch. multicoloured	3·25	55

(b) AIR MAIL

N2674	50ch. multicoloured	4·25	75
N2671/2674	*Set of 4*	11·00	2·00

905 *Apatura ilia* and Spiraea

1987 (12 Mar). Butterflies and Flowers. T **905** and similar horiz designs. Multicoloured. Litho. P 12.

N2675	10ch. Type **905**	90	25
N2676	10ch. *Ypthima argus* and fuchsia	90	25
N2677	20ch. *Neptis philyra* and aquilegia	1·30	30
N2678	20ch. *Papilio protenor* and chrysanthemum	1·30	30
N2679	40ch. *Parantica sita* and celosia	2·10	65
N2680	40ch. *Vanessa indica* and hibiscus	2·10	65
N2675/2680	*Set of 6*	7·75	2·20

906 Association Monument, Pyongyang   **907** Doves. Emblem and Tree

1987 (23 Mar). 70th Anniv of Korean National Association (independence movement). Litho. P 11½.

N2681	**906** 10ch. bright scarlet, silver and black	40	20

1987 (6 Apr). Fifth Spring Friendship Art Festival, Pyongyang. Litho. P 11½.

N2682	**907** 10ch. multicoloured	40	20

908 Mangyong Hill   **909** Bay

1987 (15 Apr). 75th Birthday of Kim Il Sung. T **908** and similar multicoloured designs. Litho. P 12.

N2683	10ch. Type **908**..	35	10
N2684	10ch. Kim Il Sung's birthplace, Mangyongdae (horiz)	35	10
N2685	10ch. "A Bumper Crop of Pumpkins" (62×41 mm).............................	35	10
N2686	10ch. "Profound Affection for the Working Class".............................	35	10
N2683/2686	Set of 4..................................	1·30	35

1987 (20 Apr). Horses. T **909** and similar vert designs. Multicoloured. Litho. P 13½.

N2687	10ch. Type **909**..	40	20
	a. Block of 4. Nos. N2687/90..........	4·50	
N2688	10ch. Bay (different)	40	20
N2689	40ch. Grey rearing	1·70	1·20
N2690	40ch. Grey on beach	1·70	1·20
N2687/2690	Set of 4..................................	3·75	2·50

Nos. N2687/90 were issued together in *se-tenant* blocks of four stamps within the sheet.

910 "Sputnik 1" (first artificial satellite)   **911** Musk Ox

1987 (30 Apr). Transport. T **910** and similar multicoloured designs. Litho. P 13½.

N2691	10ch. Electric train "Juche" (horiz)........	50	10
	a. Pair. Nos. N2691/2	1·10	25
N2692	10ch. Electric locomotive *Mangyong-dae* (horiz)......................................	50	10
N2693	10ch. Type **910** (30th anniv of flight).	50	10
	a. Pair. Nos. N2693/4	1·50	45
N2694	20ch. Laika (30th anniv of first animal in space)..................................	90	30
N2695	20ch. Tupolev Tu-144 supersonic jetliner (horiz)	90	30
	a. Pair. Nos. N2695/6	1·90	65
N2696	20ch. Concorde supersonic jetliner (11th anniv of first commercial flight) (horiz)...................................	90	30
N2697	30ch. Count Ferdinand von Zeppelin (70th death anniv and LZ-4 airship) (horiz)	1·30	40
	a. Pair. Nos. N2697/8	5·25	2·00
N2698	80ch. Zeppelin and diagrams and drawings of airships (horiz)........	3·75	1·50
N2691/2698	Set of 8..................................	8·25	2·75

Nos. N2691/2, N2693/4, N2695/6 and N2697/8 were each issued together in *se-tenant* pairs within their sheets.

1987 (30 May). Capex '87 International Stamp Exhibition, Toronto. T **911** and similar multicoloured designs. Litho. P 11.

N2699	10ch. Type **911**	85	15
N2700	40ch. Jacques Cartier, his ship *Grande Hermine* and ice-breaker (horiz)	2·20	55
N2701	60ch. Ice hockey (Winter Olympics, Calgary, 1988) (horiz)	2·20	85
N2699/2701	Set of 3..................................	4·75	1·40

912 Trapeze Artistes

1987 (31 May). International Circus Festival, Monaco. T **912** and similar multicoloured designs. Litho. P 12.

N2702	10ch. Type **912**..	50	15
N2703	10ch. "Brave Sailors" (North Korean acrobatic act) (vert)......................	50	15
N2704	20ch. Clown and elephant (vert)	90	30
N2705	20ch. North Korean artiste receiving "Golden Clown" award................	90	30
N2706	40ch. Performing horses and cat act	2·75	45
N2707	50ch. Prince Rainier and his children applauding	1·80	65
N2702/2707	Set of 6..................................	6·50	1·80

913 Attack on Watch Tower   **914** Sports

1987 (4 June.) 50th Anniv of Battle of Pochonbo. Litho. P 11½.

N2708	**913** 10ch. lake-brown, black and ochre.....	40	20

1987 (18 June). Angol Sports Village. T **914** and similar horiz designs. Litho. P 12.

N2709	5ch. reddish brown and gold	15	10
N2710	10ch. deep violet-blue and gold	25	10
N2711	40ch. olive-brown and gold	85	30
N2712	70ch. deep turquoise-blue and gold	1·40	45
N2713	1wn. red and gold...............................	2·20	75
N2714	1wn.20 bluish violet...............................	2·75	1·10
N2709/2714	Set of 6..................................	6·75	2·50

Designs: Exteriors of—10ch. Indoor swimming pool; 40ch. Weightlifting gymnasium; 70ch. Table tennis gymnasium; 1wn. Football stadium; 1wn.20 Handball gymnasium.

915 Mandarins

1987 (4 Aug). Mandarins (*Aix galericulata*) T **915** and similar horiz designs. Multicoloured. Ltlho. P 13½.

N2715	20ch. Type **915**..	1·70	45
N2716	20ch. Mandarins on shore......................	1·70	45
N2717	20ch. Mandarins on branch....................	1·70	45
N2718	40ch. Mandarins in water........................	2·50	65
N2715/2718	Set of 4..................................	6·75	1·80

916 Exhibition Site and 1987 3wn. Stamp

1987 (29 Aug). Olymphilex '87 Olympic Stamps Exhibition, Rome. T **916** and similar vert design. Multicoloured. Litho. P 13½.

N2719	10ch. Type **916**..............................	1·30	20
MSN2720	95×80 mm 80ch. Exhibition emblem and 5ch. and 1wn. Angol Sports Village stamps.............	4·25	1·60

917 Underground Station and Guard

918 White Stork

1987 (23 Sept). Railway Uniforms. T **917** and similar horiz designs. Multicoloured. Litho. P 13½.

N2721	10ch. Type **917**..........................	50	10
N2722	10ch. Underground train and station supervisor	50	10
N2723	20ch. Guard and train	75	15
N2724	30ch. Guard and train	1·10	30
N2725	40ch. "Orient Express" guard................	1·40	40
N2726	40ch. German ticket controller and steam train...................................	1·40	40
N2721/2726	*Set of 6*.................................	5·00	1·30

1987 (26 Sept). Hafnia 87 International Stamp Exhibition, Copenhagen. T **918** and similar vert design. Multicoloured. Litho. P 13½.

N2727	40ch. Type **918**...........................	2·20	55
N2728	60ch. *Danmark* (cadet full-rigged ship) and "Little Mermaid". Copenhagen	2·50	65

919 Ice Skating

920 Victory Column

1987 (16 Oct). Winter Olympic Games, Calgary (1988). T **919** and similar multicoloured designs. Litho. P 13½.

N2729	40ch. Type **919**..................................	1·20	40
N2730	40ch. Ski jumping................................	1·20	40
N2731	40ch. Skiing (value on left) (horiz)......	1·20	40
N2732	40ch. Skiing (value on right) (horiz)....	1·20	40
N2729/2732	*Set of 4*.................	4·25	1·40
MSN2733	73×100 mm. 80ch. Skiing	3·75	1·40

1987 (5 Nov). 750th Anniv of Berlin and Philatelia '87 International Stamp Exhibition, Cologne. T **920** and similar multicoloured designs. Litho. P 12.

N2734	10ch. Type **920**...........................	50	10
N2735	20ch. Reichstag (horiz)	85	30
N2736	30ch. Pfaueninsel Castle	1·30	40
N2737	40ch. Charlottenburg Castle (horiz) ...	1·40	55
N2734/2737	*Set of 4*.................	3·75	1·20
MSN2738	77×94 mm. 80ch. Olympic stadium (horiz). P 11½×12.............................	3·75	1·40

921 Garros and Blériot XI Airplane

1987 (10 Nov). Birth Centenary of Roland Garros (aviator) and Tennis as an Olympic Sport. T **921** and similar vert designs. Multicoloured. Litho. P 13½.

N2739	20ch. Type **921**...........................	1·80	30
N2740	20ch. Ivan Lendl (tennis player)..........	3·00	40
N2741	40ch. Steffi Graf (tennis player)..........	3·75	55
N2739/2741	*Set of 3*..	7·75	1·10
MSN2742	80×101 mm. 80ch. Steffi Graf (different)...	5·00	1·40

922 Kim Jong Suk (½-size illustration)

1987 (24 Dec). 70th Birth Anniv of Kim Jong Suk (revolutionary). Sheet 80×100 mm. Litho. P 13½.

MSN2743	**922** 80ch. multicoloured	1·60	75

923 Pyongyang Buildings   **924** Banner and Newspaper

1988 (1 Jan). New Year. T **923** and similar horiz design. Multicoloured. Litho. P 12.
N2744   10ch. Type **923**..   25   10
N2745   40ch. Dragon   85   30

1988 (Jan). 60th Anniv of *Saenal* Newspaper. Litho. P 11½.
N2746 **924**   10ch. multicoloured.................................   60   20

925 Birthplace.   **926** Henry Dunant (founder)
Mt. Paekdu

1988 (16 Feb). Kim Jong Il's Birthday. T **925** and similar vert design. Multicoloured. Litho. P 12.
N2747   10ch. Type **925**...   35   10
MSN2748 109×85 mm. 80ch. Kim Jong II (41×63
mm). P 11½..   1·80   65

1988 (17 Feb). 125th Anniv of International Red Cross. T **926** and similar horiz designs. Multicoloured. Litho. P 12.
N2749   10ch. Type **926**..   75   10
             a. Sheetlet of 4 Nos. N2749/52......   4·50
N2750   20ch. North Korean Red Cross
             emblem and map.......................   1·20   30
N2751   20ch. International Committee head-
             quarters. Geneva ....   1·20   30
N2752   40ch. Pyongyang Maternity Hospital,
             doctor and baby ....   1·20   40
N2749/2752 *Set of 4*..   4·00   1·00
MSN2753 70×100 mm. 80ch. Red Cross and Red
Crescent flags and anniversary emblem.
P 11½×12...   2·50   95
Nos. N2749/52 were issued together in *se-tenant* sheetlets of four stamps.

927 *Santa Maria*

1988 (10 Mar). 500th Anniv (1992) of Discovery of America by Christopher Columbus. T **927** and similar multicoloured designs. Litho. P 13½×13.
N2754   10ch. Type **927**.............................   1·70   20
             a. Horiz. strip of 3. Nos. N2764/6   5·25
N2755   20ch. *Pinta* ....   1·70   30
N2756   30ch. *Nina* ....   1·70   45
N2754/2756 *Set of 3*...   4·50   85
MSN2757 80×102 mm. 80ch. "Columbus on the
Deck of his Flagship" (detail, Karl von Piloty)
P 13×13½...   3·50   95
Nos. N2754/6 were issued together in horizontal *se-tenant* strips of three stamps within the sheet, each strip forming a composite design of Columbus's ships leaving Palos.

928 Montgolfier Balloon   **929** Dancers
and Modern Hot-air
Balloons

1988 (29 Mar). Juvalux 88 International Youth Stamp Exhibition, Luxembourg. T **928** and similar vert design. Litho. P 13½.
N2758   40ch. Type **928**.............................   1·10   40
N2759   60ch. Early railway locomotive and
             railway map of Luxembourg.
             1900..   2·10   55

1988 (7 Apr). Sixth Spring Friendship Art Festival, Pyongyang. T **929** and similar vert design. Multicoloured. Litho. P 12.
N2760   10ch. Singer (poster)   25   10
N2761   1wn.20 Type **929**.........................   3·25   1·30

930 Inaugural   **931** Birthplace.
Congress Emblem   Mangyongdae

1988 (9 Apr). Tenth Anniv of International Institute of the Juche Idea. Litho. P 12.
N2762 **930**   10ch. multicoloured....................   40   10

1988 (15 Apr). 76th Birthday of Kim Il Sung. T **931** and another multicoloured vert design. Litho. P 12.
N2763   10ch. Type **931**..............................   40   10
MSN2764 1 32×95 mm. 80ch. Kim Il Sung and
schoolchildren (40×62 mm). P 11½. ....   1·40   65

932 *Urho* (ice-breaker)

1988 (2 May). Finlandla 88 International Stamp Exhibition, Helsinki. T **932** and similar horiz design. Multicoloured. Litho. P13½.

N2765	40ch. Type **932**................................	1·80	40
N2766	60ch. Matti Nykaenen (Olympic Games ski-jumping medallist)	1·70	55

933 Postcard for 1934 Championship

934 Emblem

1988 (19 May). World Cup Football Championship, Italy (1st issue). T **933** and similar multicoloured designs. Litho. P 13½.

N2767	10ch. Football match	65	15
N2768	20ch. Type **933**................................	1·10	30
N2769	30ch. Player tackling (horiz)	1·70	40
N2767/2769 Set of 3..		3·00	75
MSN2770 100×75 mm. 80ch Winning Italian team.			
1982 (horiz)..		2·50	95

See also Nos. N2924/7.

1988 (27 May). 13th World Youth and Students' Festival, Pyongyang (1st issue). T **934** and similar vert design. Multi-coloured. Litho. P 12.

N2771	5ch. Type **934**................................	10	10
N2772	10ch. Dancer	50	10
N2773	10ch. Gymnast and gymnasium, Angol Sports Village	25	10
N2774	10ch. Map of Korea, globe and doves	35	10
N2775	10ch. Finger pointing at shattered nuclear rockets............................	90	20
N2776	1wn. 20. Three differently coloured hands and dove	2·75	1·00
N2771/2776 Set of 6..		4·25	1·40

See also Nos. N2860/3 and N2879/80.

935 Fairy   **936** Mallards

1988 (20 June). Eight Fairies of Mt. Kumgang (tale). T **935** and similar vert designs. Multicoloured. Litho. P 12.

N2777	10ch. Type **935**................................	25	10
N2778	10ch. Fairy at pool and fairies on rainbow................................	40	10
N2779	20ch. Fairy and woodman husband...	60	20
N2780	25ch. Couple with baby	75	20
N2781	30ch. Couple with son and daughter	85	30
N2782	35ch. Family on rainbow	1·00	35
N2777/2782 Set of 6..		3·50	1·10

1988 (26 June). Praga 88 International Stamp Exhibition, Prague. T **936** and similar vert design. Multicoloured. Litho. P 13½.

N2783	20ch. Type **936**................................	1·50	30
N2784	40ch. Vladimir Remek (Czechoslovak cosmonaut)	1·10	40

937 Red Crossbill (*Loxia curvirostra*)

1988 (9 July). Birds. T **937** and similar vert designs. Multicoloured. Litho. P 12.

N2785	10ch. Type **937**................................	75	20
N2786	15ch. Stonechat (*Saxicola torquata*) ...	1·00	30
N2787	20ch. European nuthatch (*Sitta europaea*)...........................	1·50	40
N2788	25ch. Great spotted woodpecker (*Dendrocopos major*)	1·70	45
N2789	30ch. Common kingfisher (*Alcedo atthis*)	2·00	55
N2790	35ch. Bohemian waxwing (*Bombycilla garrula*)......................	2·10	65
N2785/2790 Set of 6..		8·25	2·30

938 Fair Emblem

1988 (25 July). 40th International Stamp Fair, Riccione. T **938** and similar multicoloured design. Litho. P 12.

N2791	20ch. Type **938**	50	40

MSN2792 101×75 mm. 80ch. Drum dancer (vert).
P 12×11½ .... 2·10   75

N2803	30ch. *Viktoria Luise*	90	40
N2804	40ch. LZ-3	1·30	45
N2801/2804 *Set of 4*		3·00	1·10

MSN2805 102×80 mm. 1wn. Portrait of Zeppelin (vert). P 13½ .... 3·25   1·40

939 Emu

1988 (30 July). Bicentenary of Australian Settlement. T **939** and similar multicoloured designs. Litho. P 13½.

N2793	10ch. Type **939**	85	20
N2794	15ch. Satin bowerbirds	1·10	30
N2795	25ch. Laughing kookaburra (vert)	1·80	45
N2793/2795 *Set of 3*		3·50	85

MSN2796 101×73 mm. 80ch. H.M.S. *Resolution* (Cook's ship) .... 3·00   1·00

942 Kim Il Sung and Jambyn Batmunkh   **943** Hero and Labour Hero of the D.P.R.K. Medals

1988 (30 Aug). Kim Il Sung's Visit to Mongolia. Litho. P 12.

N2806	**942**	10ch. multicoloured	25	10

1988 (1 Sept). National Heroes Congress. Litho. P 12.

N2807	**943**	10ch. multicoloured	25	10

940 *5-28* (floating crane)

1988 (12 Aug). Ships. T **940** and similar multicoloured designs. Litho. P 12.

N2797	10ch. Type **940**	50	20
N2798	20ch. *Hwanggumsan* (freighter)	85	30
N2799	30ch. *Changjasan Chongnyon-ho* (freighter)	1·00	40
N2800	40ch. *Samjiyon* (liner)	1·30	45
N2797/2800 *Set of 4*		3·25	1·20

944 Tower of Juche Idea   **945** "Sunflowers" (Vincent van Gogh)

1988 (9 Sept). 40th Anniv of Democratic Republic. T **944** and similar vert designs. Multicoloured. Litho. P 12.

N2808	5ch. Type **944**	15	10
N2809	10ch. Smelter and industrial buildings	25	10
N2810	10ch. Soldier and Mt Paekdu	25	10
N2811	10ch. Map of Korea and globe	25	10
N2812	10ch. Hand holding banner, globe and doves	25	10
N2808/2812 *Set of 5*		1·00	45

MSN2813 118×105 mm. 1wn.20 Kim Il Sung designing national flag and emblem (41×63 mm).
P 11½ .... 3·00   1·10

941 *Hansa*

1988 (21 Aug). 150th Birth Anniv of Count Ferdinand von Zeppelin (airship pioneer). T **941** and similar multicoloured designs. Litho. P 11.

N2801	10ch. Type **941**	35	10
N2802	20ch. *Schwaben*	65	30

1988 (18 Sept). Filacept 88 Stamp Exhibition, The Hague. T **945** and similar multicoloured design. Litho. P 13½.

N2814	40ch. Type **945**	2·20	1·70
N2815	60ch. "The Chess Game" (Lucas van Leyden) (horiz)	3·25	2·40

946 Emblem   947 Chaju "82" 10-ton Truck

1988 (23 Sept). 16th Session of Socialist Countries' Post and Telecommunications Conference, Pyongyang. Litho. P 11½.

N2816	**946**	10ch. multicoloured	25	10

1988 (25 Sept). Tipper Trucks. T **947** and similar horiz design. Litho. P 13½.

N2817	20ch. Type **947**	50	40
N2818	40ch. Kumsusan-ho 40-ton truck	1·00	75

948 "Owl"   949 "Chunggi" Type Steam Locomotive No. 35·

1988 (5 Oct). Paintings by O Un Byol. T **948** and similar vert designs. Multicoloured. Litho. P 11½.

N2819	10ch. Type **948**	2·20	30
N2820	15ch. "Dawn" (red junglefowl)	1·10	30
N2821	20ch. "Beautiful Rose received by Kim Il Sung"	85	25
N2822	25ch. "Sun and Bamboo"	1·00	25
N2823	30ch. "Autumn" (fruit tree)	1·20	30
N2819/2823	*Set of 5*	5·75	1·30

1988 (28 Oct). Railway Locomotives. T **949** and similar horiz designs. Multicoloured. Litho. P 12.

N2824	10ch. Type **949**	65	15
N2825	20ch. "Chunggi" type steam locomotive No. 22	90	20
N2826	30ch. "Chongiha" type electric locomotive No. 3	1·10	30
N2827	40ch "Chunggi" type steam locomotive No. 307	1·30	40
N2824/2827	*Set of 4*	3·50	95

950 Pirmen Zurbriggen (downhill skiing)   951 Yuri Gagarin

1988 (1 Nov). Winter Olympic Games, Calgary. Medal Winners. T **950** and similar multicoloured designs. Litho. P 13½.

N2828	10ch. Type **950**	25	10
N2829	20ch. Yvonne van Gennip (speed skating)	50	40
N2830	30ch. Marjo Matikainen (cross-country skiing)	75	55
N2831	40ch. U.S.S.R. (ice-hockey) (horiz)	1·00	75
N2828/2831	*Set of 4*	2·30	1·60

MSN2832 Two sheets, each 105×95 mm (a) 80ch. Katarina Witt (figure skating); (b) 80ch. As sheet (a) but with names of winners printed in margin   4·25   1·60

1988 (12 Nov). First Man and Woman in Space. T **951** and similar vert design. Multicoloured. Litho. P 13½.

N2833	20ch. Type **951**	40	30
	a. Pair Nos. N2833/4	1·40	1·00
N2834	40ch. Valentina Tereshkova	90	65

Nos. N2833/4 were issued together in *se-tenant* pairs within the sheet

952 Nehru   953 Chollima Statue

1988 (15 Dec). Birth Centenary of Jawaharlal Nehru (Indian statesman) and "India 89" International Stamp Exhibition, New Delhi. T **952** and similar vert design. Litho. P 12.

N2835	**952**	20ch. maroon, black and gold	85	20

MSN2836 90×74 mm. 60ch. multicoloured (Dancer). P 12×11½   1·70   55

1989 (1 Jan). New Year. T **953** and similar multicoloured designs. Litho. P 12.

N2837	10ch. Type **953**	25	10
N2838	20ch. "The Dragon Angler" (17th-century painting)	85	20
N2839	40ch. "Tortoise and Serpent" (Kangso tomb painting) (horiz)	1·20	40
N2837/2839	*Set of 3*	2·10	65

954 Archery

1989 (10 Jan). National Defence Training. T **954** and similar horiz designs. Multicoloured. Litho. P 12.

N2840	10ch. Type **954**	1·20	30
N2841	15ch. Rifle shooting	40	10
N2842	20ch. Pistol shooting	50	20
N2843	25ch. Parachuting	65	25
N2844	30ch. Launching model glider	75	30
N2840/2844 *Set of 5*		3·25	1·00

955 Dobermann Pinscher

1989 (23 Jan). Animals presented to Kim Il Sung. T **955** and similar multicoloured designs. Litho. P 13½.

N2845	10ch. Type **955**	65	20
N2846	20ch. Labrador	90	25
N2847	25ch. German shepherd	1·20	30
N2848	30ch. Rough collies (horiz)	1·30	35
N2849	35ch. Serval (horiz)	1·70	40
N2845/2849 *Set of 5*		5·25	1·40
MSN2850 95×75 mm 80ch. *Felis libica* (horiz)		3·75	95

956 Begonia "Kimjongil"

957 Agriculture

1989 (16 Feb). Birthday of Kim Jong Il. Sheet 78×100 mm. Litho. P 13½.

MSN2851 **956** 80ch. multicoloured	1·80	65

1989 (25 Feb). 25th Anniv of Publication of *Theses on the Socialist Rural Question in our Country* by Kim Il Sung. Litho. P 12.

N2852 **957**	10ch. multicoloured	50	15

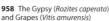

958 The Gypsy (*Rozites caperata*)   **959** Korean Girl
and Grapes (*Vitis amurensis*)

1989 (27 Feb). Fungi and Fruits. T **958** and similar horiz designs. Multicoloured. Litho. P 12.

N2853	10ch. Caesar's mushroom (*Amanita*	65	15
N2854	20ch. Caesar's mushroom (*Amanita caesarea*) and magnolia vine (*Schizandra chinensis*)	1·10	30
N2855	25ch. *Lactarius hygrophoides* and *Eleagnus crispa*	1·50	35
N2856	30ch. Horse mushroom (*Agaricus arvensis*) and *Lycium chinense*	1·70	40
N2857	35ch. Horse mushroom (*Agaricus arvensis*) and *Lycium chinense*	2·10	40
N2858	40ch. Elegant boletus (*Suillius grevillei*) and *Juglans cordiformis*	2·20	45
N2853/2858 *Set of 6*		8·25	1·80
MSN2859 100×78 mm. 1wn. *Gomphidius roseus* and *Diospyros lotus* (48×30 mm). P 11½×12		4·50	1·40

1989 (18 Mar). 13th World Youth and Students' Festival, Pyongyang (2nd issue). T **959** and similar vert designs. Multicoloured. Litho. P 12.

N2860	10ch. Type **959**	25	10
N2861	20ch. Children of different races	45	30
N2862	30ch. Fairy and rainbow	65	45
N2863	40ch. Young peoples and Tower of Juche Idea	90	65
N2860/2863 *Set of 4*		2·00	1·40

960 *Parnassius eversmanni*   **961** Dancers (poster)

1989 (23 Mar). Insects. T **960** and similar horiz designs. Multicoloured. Litho. P 12.

N2864	10ch. Type **960**	1·00	30
	a. Sheetlet. Nos. N2864/9	6·25	
N2865	15ch. *Colias heos*	1·00	30
N2866	20ch. *Dilipa fenestra*	1·00	30
N2867	25ch. *Buthus martensis*	1·00	30
N2868	30ch. *Trichogramma ostriniae*	1·00	30
N2869	40ch. *Damaster constricticollis*	1·00	30
N2864/2869 *Set of 6*		5·50	1·60
MSN2870 82×65 mm. 80ch. *Parnassius nomion*		3·25	1·10

1989 (6 Apr). Spring Friendship Art Festival, Pyongyang. Litho. P 12.

N2871 **961**	10ch. multicoloured	60	15

962 Birthplace, Mangyongdae

963 Battle Plan and Monument to the Victory

1989 (15 Apr). 11th Birthday of Kim Il Sung. Litho. P 11½.
N2872 **962** 10ch. multicoloured 35   10

1989 (19 May). 50th Anniv of Battle of the Musan Area. Litho. P 12.
N2873 **963** 10ch. ultramarine, flesh & brt scarlet   85   20

964 Modern Dance

965 Hands supporting Torch

1989 (30 May). Chamo System of Dance Notation. T **964** and similar horiz designs. Multicoloured. Litho. P 12.
N2874   10ch. Type **964**   60   20
N2875   20ch. Ballet   75   30
N2876   25ch. Modern dance (different) ....   1·00   35
N2877   30ch. Traditional dance..........................   1·10   40
N2874/2877 Set of 4..   3·00   1·10
MSN2878 85×105 mm 80ch. Dancers ....   3·00   75

1989 (8 June). 13th World Youth and Students' Festival, Pyongyang (3rd issue). T **965** and similar vert design. Litho. P 11½.
N2879   5ch. deep bright blue............................   15   10
N2880   10ch. lake-brown.....................................   25   10
Design:—10ch. Youth making speech.

1989 (21 June). "Badger measures the Height" (cartoon film). T **966** and similar vert designs. Multicoloured. Litho. P 11½.
N2881   10ch. Cat. bear and badger race to
                        flag pole..   1·10   20
N2882   40ch. Cat and bear climb pole while
                        badger measures shadow.........   1·70   40
N2883   50ch. Type **966** ....   2·00   45
N2881/2883 Set of 3..   4·25   95

1989 (29 June). Astronomy. T **967** and similar multicoloured design. Litho. P 12.
N2884   20ch. Type **967**...   1·30   25
MSN2885 102×85 mm. 80ch. Planet Saturn (horiz).
                        P 11½×12..   5·50   75

968 "Liberty guiding the People" (Eugene Delacroix)

969 Pele (footballer) and 1978 25ch. Stamp

1989 (7 July). Philexfrance 89 International Stamp Exhibition, Paris. Sheet 107×88 mm. P 12×11½.
MSN2886 **968** 70ch. multicoloured ....   1·80   95

1989 (28 July). Brasiliana 89 International Stamp Exhibition, Rio de Janeiro. Litho. P 12.
N2887 **969** 40ch. multicoloured ....   1·30   45

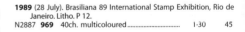

970 Nurse and Ambulance

1989 (12 Aug). Emergency Services. T **970** and similar horiz designs. Multicoloured. Litho. P 12.
N2888   10ch. Type **970**......................................   25   10
N2889   20ch. Surgeon and ambulance   40   20
N2890   30ch. Fireman and fire engine.............   3·00   30
N2891   40ch. Fireman and engine (different)   3·00   40
N2888/2891 Set of 4..   6·00   90

966 Victorious Badger

967 Kyongju Observatory and Star Chart

971 Kaffir Lily (*Clivia miniata*)

972 Air Mail Letter and Postal Transport

1989 (19 Aug). Plants presented to Kim Il Sung. T **971** and similar vert designs. Multicoloured. Litho. P 12.

N2892	10ch. Type **971**	40	10
N2893	15ch. Tulips (*Tulipa gesneriana*)	50	15
N2894	20ch. Flamingo lily (*Anthurium andreanum*)	75	20
N2895	25ch. *Rhododendron obtusum*	90	25
N2896	30ch. Daffodils (*Narcissus pseudo-narcissus*)	1·10	30
N2892/2896 *Set of 5*		3·25	90
MSN2897 84×104 mm. 80ch. *Gerbera hybrida*		3·00	75

1989 (27 Aug). 150th Anniv of the Penny Black and "Stamp World London 90" International Stamp Exhibition (1st issue). T **972** and similar vert designs. Multicoloured. Litho. P 12.

N2898	5ch. Type **972**	40	10
N2899	10ch. Post box and letters	60	15
N2900	20ch. Stamps, tweezers and magnifying glass	65	20
N2901	30ch. First North Korean stamps	85	30
N2902	40ch. Universal Postal Union emblem and headquarters, Berne	1·10	40
N2903	50ch. Sir Rowland Hill and Penny Black	1·50	55
N2898/2903 *Set of 6*		4·50	1·50

See also Nos. N2956/**MS**N2957.

973 *Bistorta incana*

974 Tree, Mt Paekdu

1989 (8 Sept). Alpine Flowers. T **973** and similar horiz designs. Multicoloured. Litho. P 11½.

N2904	10ch. *Iris setosa*	50	15
N2905	15ch. *Aquilegia japonica*	65	20
N2906	20ch. Type **973**	85	25
N2907	25ch. *Rodiola elongata*	90	30
N2908	30ch. *Sanguisorba sitchensis*	1·00	35
N2904/2908 *Set of 5*		3·50	1·10
MSN2909 62×49 mm. 80ch. *Trollius japonicus*		2·75	85

1989 (21 Sept). Slogan-bearing Trees (1st series). T **914** and similar vert designs. Multicoloured. Litho. P 12.

N2910	10ch. Type **974**	25	10
N2911	3wn. Tree, Oun-dong, Pyongyang	8·50	6·50
N2912	5wn. Tree, Mt. Kanbaek	14·50	10·50
N2910/2912 *Set of 3*		21·00	15·00

See also No. N2931.

975 Skipping   **976** Marchers

1989 (30 Sept). Children's Games. T **975** and similar vert designs. Multicoloured. Litho. P 12.

N2913	10ch. Type **975**	25	10
	a. Block of 4. Nos. N2913/16	4·00	
N2914	20ch. Windmill	1·70	30
N2915	30ch. Kite	75	35
N2916	40ch. Whip and top	1·00	40
N2913/2916 *Set of 4*		3·25	1·00

Nos. N2913/16 were issued together in *se-tenant* blocks of four stamps within the sheet.

1989 (1 Oct). International March for Peace and Reunification of Korea. Sheet 100×77 mm. Litho. P 11½×12.

MSN2917 **976** 80ch. dp pur-brn. silver & blk ... 2·10   1·40

977 Diesel Train and Sinpa Youth Station

1989 (19 Oct). Railway Locomotives. T **977** and similar horiz designs. Multicoloured. Litho. P 11½×12.

N2918	10ch. Type **977**	50	10
N2919	20ch. "Pulgungi" type electric locomotive	75	20
N2920	25ch. Diesel locomotive	85	30
N2921	30ch. Diesel locomotive (different)	1·00	35
N2922	40ch. Steam locomotive	1·30	40
N2923	50ch. Steam locomotive (different)	1·30	45
N2918/2923 *Set of 6*		5·25	1·60

978 Players and Map of Italy

1989 (28 Oct). World Cup Football Championship, Italy (2nd issue). T **978** and similar horiz designs. Multicoloured. Litho. P 12.

N2924	10ch. Type **978**	90	20
N2925	20ch. Free kick	50	20
N2926	30ch. Goal mouth scrimmage	75	30
N2927	40ch. Goalkeeper diving for ball	1·00	35
N2924/2927 *Set of 4*		2·75	95

979 Magellan (navigator) and his Ship *Vitoria*

980 Mangyong Hill and Pine Branches

1989 (25 Nov). Descobrex '89 International Stamp Exhibition, Portugal. Litho. P 12.

N2928	**979**	30ch. multicoloured	1·50	30

1990 (1 Jan). New Year. T **980** and similar horiz design. Multi-coloured. Litho. P 11½.

N2929	10ch. Type **980**	25	10
N2930	20ch. Koguryo mounted archers	1·10	20

1990 (12 Jan). Slogan-bearing trees (2nd series). Vert design as T **974** Multicoloured. Litho. P 11½.

N2931	5ch. Tree. Mt. Paekdu	35	10

981 Ryukwoli

982 Birthplace. Mt Paekdu

1990 (17 Jan). Dogs. T **981** and similar vert designs. Multicoloured. Litho. P 12.

N2932	20ch. Type **981**	1·30	30
	a. Sheetlet of 4. Nos. N2932/5	5·50	
N2933	30ch. Palryuki	1·30	30
N2934	40ch. Komdungi	1·30	30
N2935	60ch. Oulruki	1·30	30
N2932/2935 *Set of 4*		4·75	1·10

Nos. N2932/5 were issued together in *se-tenant* sheetlets of four stamps.

1990 (16 Feb). Birthday of Kim Jong II. Litho. P 12.

N2936	**982**	10ch. purple-brown	35	10

983 Stone Instruments and Primitive Man

1990 (21 Feb). Evolution of Man. T **983** and similar horiz design. Multicoloured. Litho. P 12.

N2937	10ch. Type **983**	2·50	20
N2938	40ch. Palaeolithic and Neolithic man	3·25	30

984 Rungna Bridge. Pyongyang

1990 (27 Feb). Bridges. T **984** and similar horiz designs. Multicoloured. Litho. P 11½.

N2939	10ch. Type **984**	50	10
N2940	20ch. Potong bridge, Pyongyang	75	20
N2941	30ch. Sinuiji-Ryucho Island Bridge	1·00	30
N2942	40ch. Chungsongui Bridge, Pyongyang	1·30	40
N2939/2942 *Set of 4*		3·25	90

985 Infantryman

986 *Atergatis subdentatus*

(Des Li Song Taek. Litho)

1990 (18 Mar). Warriors' Costumes. T **985** and similar vert designs. Multicoloured. P 12.

N2943	20ch. Type **985**	40	30
N2944	30ch. Archer	65	55
N2945	50ch. Military commander in armour	1·20	95
N2946	70ch. Officer's costume (10th–14th centuries)	1·60	1·20
N2943/2946 *Set of 4*		3·50	2·75

Nos. N2943/5 depict costumes from the 3rd century B.C. to the 7th century A.D.

(Des Kim Jong Gil. Litho)

1990 (25 Mar). Crabs. T **986** and similar horiz designs. Multicoloured. P 12.

N2947	20ch. Type **986**	50	20
N2948	30ch. *Platylambrus validus*	75	30
N2949	50ch. *Uca arcuata*	1·30	45
N2847/2849 *Set of 3*		2·30	85

987 Dancers (poster)

988 Monument at Road Fork. Mangyongdae

1990 (7 Apr). Spring Friendship Art Festival, Pyongyang. Litho. P 12.

N2950	**987**	10ch. multicoloured	35	10

(Des Kim Hui Won. Litho)

1990 (16 Apr). 76th Birthday of Kim II Sung. T **988** and another design. P 11½.

N2951 **988** 10ch. yellowish green and gold 35   10
MSN2952 85×105 mm. 80ch. multicoloured (Kim II Sung) (38×60 mm) .... 2·10   75

993 "Self-portrait" (Rembrandt)

994 K. H. Rummenigge (footballer)

1990 (2 June). Belgica 90 International Stamp Exhibition, Brussels. T **993** and similar vert designs. Litho. P 12.

N2965   10ch. Type **993** 35   10
N2966   20ch. "Self-portrait" (Raphael) 60   20
N2967   30ch. "Self-portrait" (Rubens) 75   30
N2965/2967 Set of 3 .... 1·50   55

989 Gymnocalycium sp.

990 Exhibition Emblem

(Des Kim Hui Won. Litho)

1990 (21 Apr). Cacti. T **989** and similar vert designs. Multicoloured. P 12.

N2953   10ch. Type **989** 50   10
N2954   30ch. Pyllocactus hybridus 90   30
N2955   50ch. Epiphyllum truncatum .... 1·50   45
N2953/2955 Set of 3 .... 2·50   75

(Des Cho Jong Gu. Litho)

1990 (3 May). Stamp World London 90 International Stamp Exhibition (2nd issue). T **990** and similar vert design. P 11½.

N2956 **990** 20ch. vermilion and black 60   20
MSN2957 49×66 mm. 70ch. grey, blk & gold .... 2·00   1·90
Design:—70ch. Sir Rowland Hill.

1990 (20 June). Düsseldorf '90 International Youth Stamp Exhibition. T **994** and similar vert designs. Multicoloured. Litho. P 12.

N2968   20ch. Steffi Graf (tennis player) 85   20
N2969   30ch. Exhibition emblem 75   30
N2970   70ch. Type **994** .... 1·70   65
N2968/2970 Set of 3 .... 3·00   1·00

995 Workers' Stadium, Peking, and Games Mascot

996 Ball

1990 (14 July). 11th Asian Games, Peking (Nos. N2971/2) and Third Asian Winter Games, Samjiyon (N2973). T **995** and similar vert designs. Multicoloured. Litho. P 12.

N2971   10ch. Type **995** 25   10
N2972   30ch. Chollima Statue and sportsmen   75   40
N2973   40ch. Sportsmen and Games emblem   1·10   45
N2971/2973 Set of 3 .... 1·90   85

991 Congo Peafowl (Afropavo congensis)

992 Dolphin and Submarine

(Des Cho Gyong Ho. Litho)

1990 (10 May). Peafowl. T **991** and similar vert designs. Multicoloured. P 11½×12.

N2958   10ch. Type **991** .... 1·00   20
N2959   20ch. Common peafowl (Pavo cristatus) .... 1·80   45
MSN2960 96×82 mm. 70ch. Common peafowl displaying tail. P 11½ .... 3·25   95

1990 (24 May). Bio-engineering. T **992** and similar horiz designs. Multicoloured. Litho. P 12.

N2961   10ch. Type **992** .... 1·40   45
    a. Sheetlet of 4. Nos. N2961/4 .... 5·75
N2962   20ch. Bat and dish aerial .... 1·40   45
N2963   30ch. Owl and Tupolev Tu-154 jetliner   1·40   45
N2964   40ch. Squid, rockets and Concorde supersonic jetliner .... 1·40   45
N2961/2964 Set of 4 .... 5·00   1·60
Nos. N2961/4 were issued together in se-tenant sheetlets of four stamps.

1990 (8 Aug). West Germany. Winners of World Cup Football Championship. T **996** and similar vert designs. Multicoloured. Litho. P 13½.

N2974   15ch. Emblem of F.I.F.A. (International Federation of Football Associations) 40   10
N2975   20ch. Jules Rimet 60   20
N2976   25ch. Type **996** 65   30
N2977   30ch. Olympic Stadium, Rome (venue of final) 75   35
N2978   35ch. Goalkeeper 90   40
N2979   40ch. Emblem of West German Football Association .... 1·10   45
N2974/2979 Set of 6 .... 4·00   1·60
MSN2980 106×92 mm. 80ch. German Football Association emblem and trophy (horiz) .... 2·10   1·40

997 Kakapo and Map of New Zealand

1990 (24 Aug). New Zealand 1990 International Stamp Exhibition, Auckland. Litho. P 12.
N2981 **997** 30ch. multicoloured .... 1·50 55

1001 Praying Mantis (*Mantis religiosa*)

1990 (20 Sept.) Insects. T **1001** and similar horiz designs. Multicoloured. Litho. P 12.
N2989 20ch. Type **1001** 50 20
N2990 30ch. Ladybird (*Coccinella septem punctata*) 75 30
N2991 40ch. *Pheropsophus jessoensis* .... 1·10 35
N2992 70ch. *Phyllium siccifolium*...................... 1·70 55
N2989/2992 *Set of 4*.. 3·75 1·30

998 "Summer at Chipson Peak"

1990 (24 Aug). Europa 90 International Stamp Fair, Riccione. Sheet 90×70 mm. P 11½.
MSN2982 **998** 80ch. multicoloured . ... 2·10 75

1002 Footballers   **1003** Concert Emblem

1990 (11 Oct). North-South Reunification Football Match, Pyongyang. T **1002** and similar horiz designs. Multicoloured. Litho. P 12.
N2993 10ch. Type **1002** 75 10
    a. Pair Nos. N2993/4 .... 1·60 35
N2994 20ch. Footballers (different) 75 20
MSN2995 105×80 mm. 1wn. Teams parading.
    P 11½×12... 2·20 85
Nos. N2993/4 were issued together in *se-tenant* pairs within sheets of 8 stamps and one label showing map of Korea and a ball.

1990 (17 Oct). National Reunification Concert. Litho. P 12.
N2996 **1003** 10ch. multicoloured 35 10

999 Head of Procession

999 Head of Procession   **1000** Marchers descending Mt. Paekdu

1990 (3 Sept). Koguryo Wedding Procession. T **999** and similar horiz designs. Multicoloured. Litho. P 12.
N2983 10ch. Type **999**.. 1·30 40
    a. Horiz. strip of 4 Nos. N2983/6 ... 5·50
N2984 30ch. Bridegroom .... 1·30 40
N2985 50ch. Bride in carriage............................ 1·30 40
N2986 1wn. Drummer on horse .... 1·30 40
N2983/2986 *Set of 4*.. 4·75 1·40
Nos. N2983/6 were issued together in horizontal *se-tenant* strips of four within the sheet, each strip forming a composite design.

1004 Ox   **1005** Chinese and North Korean Soldiers

1990 (15 Sept). Rally for Peace and Reunification of Korea. T **1000** and similar multicoloured design. Litho. P 12.
N2987 10ch. Type **1000** 25 10
MSN2988 106×70 mm. 1wn. Crowd watching dancers.. 2·20 85

1990 (18 Oct). Farm Animals. T **1004** and similar vert designs. Litho. P 12.
N2997 10ch. chestnut and emerald 25 10
N2998 20ch. slate-lilac and orange-yellow.... 45 20
N2999 30ch. greenish slate and vermilion...... 60 30

N3000	40ch. blue-green and orange-yellow	85	35
N3001	50ch. lake-brown and blue....................	1·10	40
N2997/3001	*Set of 5*....................	3·00	1·20

Designs:—20ch. Pig; 30ch. Goat; 40ch. Sheep; 50ch. Horse.

Nos. N2997/3001 were issued both in separate sheets of 50 stamps and together in *se-tenant* sheetlets of 10 stamps (Price for *se-tenant* strip of 5: £3.50 un).

1990 (23 Oct). 40th Anniv of Participation of Chinese Volunteers in Korean War. T **1005** and similar multicoloured designs. Litho. P 12.

N3002	10ch. Type **1005**....................	25	10
N3003	20ch. Populace welcoming volunteers (horiz)....................	45	20
N3004	30ch. Rejoicing soldiers and battle scene (horiz)....................	60	25
N3005	40ch. Post-war reconstruction (horiz)	85	30
N3002/3005	*Set of 4*....................	1·90	75
MSN3006	95×75 mm. 80ch. Friendship Tower, Moran Hill, Pyongyang. P 12½×11½....................	1·70	70

1006 Anniversary Emblem

1007 Sturgeon (*Acipenser mikadoi*)

1990 (24 Oct). 40th Anniv of United Nations Development Programme. Litho. P 13½.

N3007	**1006** 1wn. brt new blue, silver & black........	3·00	2·10

1990 (20 Nov). Fishes. T **1007** and similar horiz designs. Litho. P 12.

N3008	10ch. dp purple-brn & yellowish grn	25	10
N3009	20ch. yellowish green and new blue	60	20
N3010	30ch. deep ultramarine & bright purple....................	80	30
N3011	50ch. violet and yellowish green........	1·10	40
N3012	50ch. violet and yellowish green........	1·40	50
N3008/3012	*Set of 5*....................	3·75	1·40

Designs:—20ch. Sea bream (*Sparus macrocephalus*); 30ch. Flying fish (*Cypsilurus agoö*); 40ch. Fat greenling (*Hexagrammos otakii*); 50ch. Ray (*Myliobatus tobijei*).

Nos. N3008/12 were issued both in separate sheets of 50 stamps and together in *se-tenant* sheetlets of ten stamps (Price for *se-tenant* strip of 5: £4·50 un).

1008 Sheep

1009 Moorhen (*Gallinula chloropus*)

1990 (1 Dec). New Year. Litho. P 12.

N3013	**1008** 40ch. multicoloured....................	85	30

1990 (18 Dec). Birds. T **1009** and simitar vert designs. Litho. P 12.

N3014	10ch. pale blue, dp bluish green & blk....................	50	10
N3015	20ch. reddish brown, olive-bistre & blk....................	85	30
N3016	30ch. bottle green, olive-grey & black....................	1·10	50
N3017	40ch. reddish brown, dull orange & blk....................	1·60	60
N3018	60ch. ochre, deep brown and black...	2·20	80
N3014/3018	*Set of 5*....................	5·75	2·10

Designs:—20ch. Jay (*Garrulus glandarius*); 30ch. Three-toed woodpecker (*Picoides tridactylus*); 40ch. Whimbrel (*Numenius phaeopus*); 50ch. Water rail (*Rallus aguaticus*).

Nos. N3014/18 were issued both in separate sheets of 50 stamps and together in *se-tenant* sheetlets of ten stamps (Price for *se-tenant* strip of 5: £6.50 un).

1010 Giant Panda

1011 Changsan

1991 (10 Jan). Phila Nippon '91 International Stamp Exhibition, Tokyo. T **1010** and similar vert designs. Multicoloured. Litho. P 11½×12.

N3019	10ch. Type **1010**....................	25	10
N3020	20ch. Two giant pandas feeding..........	45	20
N3021	30ch. Giant panda clambering onto branch....................	60	25
N3022	40ch. Giant panda on rock....................	95	30
N3023	50ch. Two giant pandas....................	1·10	40
N3024	60ch. Giant panda in tree fork..............	1·30	50
N3019/3024	*Set of 6*....................	4·25	1·60
MSN3025	115×85 mm. 1wn. Giant panda. P 11½..	6.00	1·50

Nos. N3019/24 were isued both in separate sheets and together in *se-tenant* sheetlets of six stamps.

1991 (16 Jan). Revolutionary Sites. T **1011** and similar horiz design. Litho. P 12.

N3026	5ch. Type **1011**....................	15	10
N3027	10ch. Oun....................	25	20

1012 Black-faced Spoonbills (*Platalea minor*)

1013 *Clossiana angarensis*

1991 (5 Feb). Endangered Birds. T **1012** and similar vert designs. Multicoloured. Litho. P 12.

N3028	10ch. Type **1012**	25	10
N3029	20ch. Grey herons (Ardea cinerea)	60	20
N3030	30ch. Great egrets (Egretta alba)	85	30
N3031	40ch. Manchurian cranes (Grus japonensis)	1·20	40
N3032	50ch. Japanese white-necked cranes (Grus vipio)	1·60	50
N3033	70ch. White storks (Ciconia boyciana)	2·20	70
N3028/3033	Set of 6	6·00	2·00

Nos. N3028/33 were issued both in separate sheets of nine stamps and together in se-tenant sheetlets of six stamps.

1991 (20 Feb). Alpine Butterflies. T **1013** and similar horiz designs. Multicoloured. Litho. P 13½.

N3034	10ch. Type **1013**	15	10
N3035	20ch. Erebia embla	35	30
N3036	30ch. Camberwell beauty (Nymphalis antiopa)	50	40
N3037	40ch. Comma (Polygonia c-album)	70	50
N3038	50ch. Eastern pale clouded yellow (Colias erate)	95	70
N3039	60ch. Thecla betulae	1·20	80
N3034/3039	Set of 6	3·50	2·50

Nos. N3034/9 were issued both in separate sheets and together in se-tenant sheetlets of six stamps.

1014 Hedgehog Fungus (Hydnum repandum)   **1015** Kumchon

1991 (26 Feb). Fungi. T **1014** and similar vert designs. Multicoloured. Litho. P 12.

N3040	10ch. Type **1014**	15	10
N3041	20ch. Phylloporus rhodoxanthus	45	20
N3042	30ch. Calvatia craniiformis	60	30
N3043	40ch. Cauliflower clavaria (Ramana botrytis)	80	40
N3044	50ch. Russula integra	1·00	50
N3040/3044	Set of 5	2·75	1·40

Nos. N3040/4 were issued both in separate sheets of nine stamps and together in se-tenant sheetlets of ten stamps.

1991 (15 Mar). Revolutionary Sites. T **1015** and similar horiz design. Multicoloured. Litho. P 12.

N3045	10ch. Type **1015**	15	10
N3046	40ch. Samdung	70	50

1016 Dr. Kye Ung Sang (researcher)   **1017** Emblem and Venue

1991 (27 Mar). Silkworm Research. T **1016** and similar vert designs. Multicoloured. Litho. P 12.

N3047	10ch. Type **1016**	15	10
N3048	20ch. Chinese oak silk moth (Antheraea pernyi)	35	30
N3049	30ch. Attacus ricini	50	40
N3050	40ch. Antheraea yamamai	70	50
N3051	50ch. Silkworm moth (Bombyx mori)	95	70
N3052	60ch. Aetias artemis	1·10	80
N3047/3052	Set of 6	3·50	2·50

Nos. N3047/52 were issued both in separate sheets of 21 stamps and together in se-tenant sheetlets of six stamps.

1991 (3 Apr). Ninth Spring Friendship Art Festival, Pyongyang. Litho. P 12.

N3053	**1017** 10ch. multicoloured	20	10

1018 Emperor Penguins   **1019** People's Palace of Culture (venue)

1991 (20 Apr). Antarctic Exploration. T **1018** and similar vert designs. Multicoloured. Litho. P 12.

N3054	10ch. Type **1018**	45	20
N3055	20ch. Research station	45	20
N3056	30ch. Elephant seals	50	30
N3057	40ch. Research ship	95	40
N3058	50ch. Southern black-backed gulls	1·60	60
N3054/3058	Set of 5	3·50	1·50
MSN3059	75×105 mm. 80ch. National flag and map of Antarctica. P 12×11½	1·60	90

Nos. N3054/8 were issued both in separate sheets of 21 stamps and all together with 80ch. value in se-tenant sheetlets (p 12) of six stamps.

1991 (29 Apr). 85th Interparliamentary Union Conference, Pyongyang. T **1019** and similar horiz design. Litho. P 12.

N3060	10ch. dp bluish green, blue-grn & silver	25	10
N3061	1wn.50 multicoloured	2·75	2·10

Design:—1wn. 50, Conference emblem and azalea.

1020 Map and Kim Jong Ho

1991 (8 May). 130th Anniv of Publication of Kim Jong Ho's Map Taidong Yu Jido. Litho. P 12.

N3062	**1020** 90ch. black, pale cinnamon & silver	1·90	1·30

1021 Cynognathus

1991 (21 May). Dinosaurs. T **1021** and similar horiz designs. Multicoloured. Litho. P 12.

N3063	10ch. Type **1021**	35	10
N3064	20ch. Brontosaurus	70	40
N3065	30ch. Stegosaurus and Allosaurus	1·00	50
N3066	40ch. Pterosauria	1·40	80
N3067	50ch. Ichthyosaurus	1·70	90
N3063/3067	*Set of 5*	4·75	2.40

Nos. N3063/7 were issued both in separate sheetlets of six stamps and together in *se-tenant* sheets of 30 stamps and six labels.

1022 Sprinting

1991 (18 June). Olympic Games, Barcelona (1992) (1st issue). T **1022** and similar horiz designs. Multicoloured. P 12.

N3068	10ch. Type **1022**	15	10
N3069	10ch. Hurdling	15	10
N3070	20ch. Long jumping	45	20
N3071	20ch. Throwing the discus	45	20
N3072	30ch. Putting the shot	60	30
N3073	30ch. Pole vaulting	60	30
N3074	40ch. High jumping	95	50
N3075	40ch. Throwing the javelin	95	50
N3068/3075	*Set of 8*	3·75	2·00

MSN3076 Two sheets, each 105×85 mm.
P 11½×12. (a) 80ch. Breasting the tape;
(b) 80ch. Running .... 3·50   1·90
Nos. N3068/75 were issued both in separate sheets of nine stamps and all together with the 80ch. values in *se-tenant* sheetlets (p 12) of ten stamps.
See also Nos. N3142/**MS**N3148.

1023 Cats and Tree Sparrows

(Des Kim Hui Won. Litho)

1991 (21 July). Cats. T **1023** and similar horiz designs. Multicoloured. P 13½.

N3077	10ch. Type **1023**	50	40
N3078	20ch. Cat and rat	1·00	60
N3079	30ch. Cat and butterfly	1·60	80
N3080	40ch. Cats with ball	2·10	1·10
N3081	50ch. Cat and frog	2·75	1·30
N3077/3081	*Set of 5*	7·25	3·75

1024 "Wisteria Flowers and Pups" (detail)

(Des Li Yong Jin. Litho)

1991 (27 Aug). Riccione '91 Stamp Fair and Exhibition, Italy. Sheet 116×80 mm. P 11½×12.
MSN3082 **1024** 80ch. multicoloured .... 3·50   95

1025 Wild Horse   **1026** Pennant Coralfish
(*Equus caballus*)   (*Heniochus acuminatus*)

(Des Li Song Taek. Litho)

1991 (2 Sept). Horses. T **1025** and similar vert designs. Multicoloured. P 13½.

N3083	10ch. Type **1025**	15	10
N3084	20ch. Hybrid of wild ass and wild horse	50	20
N3085	30ch. Przewalski's horse (*Equus przewalskii*)	70	30
N3086	40ch. Wild ass (*Equus asinus*)	95	50
N3087	50ch. Wild horse (*Equus caballus*) (different)	1·20	60
N3083/3087	*Set of 5*	3·25	1·50

Nos. N3083/7 were issued both in separate sheets of 18 stamps and together in *se-tenant* sheetlets of five stamps.

(Des Cho Jong Gu. Litho)

1991 (20 Sept). Fishes. T **1026** and similar horiz designs. Multicoloured. P 12.

(a) POSTAGE.

N3088	10ch. Type **1026**	15	10
N3089	20ch. Big-spotted trigger fish (*Balistoides conspicillum*)	45	20
N3090	30ch. Anemone fish (*Amphiprion frenatus*)	60	30
N3091	40ch. Blue surgeon fish (*Paracanthurus hepatus*)	95	50

(b) AIR. Inscr "AIR MAIL"

N3092	50ch. Angel fish (*Pterophyllum eimekei*)	1·30	70
N3088/3092	*Set of 5*	3·00	1·60

MSN3093 88×60 mm. 80ch. Tetras (*Hyphessobrycon innesi*) (51×31 mm) .... 3·00   95
Nos. N3088/92 were issued both in separate sheets of 24 stamps and together in *se-tenant* sheetlets of five stamps commemorating "Phila Nippon '91" international stamp exhibition.

599

1027 Rhododendrons   **1028** Panmunjom

(Des Kim Dong Han. Litho)

1991 (16 Oct). Flowers. T **1027** and similar vert designs. Multicoloured. P 12.

N3094	10ch. Begonia	25	10
N3095	20ch. Gerbera	35	30
N3096	30ch. Type **1027**	50	40
N3097	40ch. Phalaenopsis	70	50
N3098	50ch. *Impatiens sultanii*	95	70
N3099	60ch. Streptocarpus	1·10	80
N3094/3099	*Set of 6*	3·50	2·50

Nos. N3097/9 commemorate "CANADA 92" international youth stamp exhibition, Montreal.

Nos. N3094/9 were issued both in separate sheets and together in *se-tenant* sheetlets of six stamps.

(Des Kim Hui Won. Litho)

1991 (27 Oct). P 12.
N3100 **1028** 10ch. multicoloured 20   10

1029 Magnolia   **1030** Players

(Des An Choi. Litho)

1991 (1 Nov). National Flower. P 11½.
N3101 **1029** 10ch. multicoloured 20   10

1991 (3 Nov). Women's World Football Championship, China. T **1030** and similar vert designs. Multicoloured. P 12.

N3102	10ch. Type **1030**	25	10
N3103	20ch. Dribbling the ball	35	30
N3104	30ch. Heading the ball	50	40
N3105	40ch. Overhead kick	70	50
N3106	50ch. Tackling	95	70
N3107	60ch. Goalkeeper	1·10	80
N3102/3107	*Set of 6*	3·50	2·50

Nos. N3102/7 were issued both in separate sheets and together in *se-tenant* sheetlets of six stamps.

1031 Squirrel Monkeys (*Saimin sciureus*)

1992 (1 Jan). Monkeys. T **1031** and similar multicoloured designs. Litho. P 12.

N3108	10ch. Type **1031**	45	20
N3109	20ch. Pygmy marmosets (*Cebuella pygmaea*)	80	40
N3110	30ch. Red-handed tamarins (*Saguinas midas*)	1·40	50
N3108/3110	*Set of 3*	2·40	1·00

MSN3111 65×91 mm. 80ch. Monkey leaping (33×51 mm). P 12×11½ .... 2·30   1·70

Nos. N3108/10 were issued both in separate sheets of 21 stamps and together in *se-tenant* sheetlets of three stamps.

1032 Eagle Owl (*Bubo bubo*)

(Des An Choi and Kim Jong Kil. Litho)

1992 (5 Jan). Birds of Prey. T **1032** and similar horiz designs. Multicoloured. P 13½.

N3112	10ch. Type **1032**	35	10
N3113	20ch. Common buzzard (*Buteo buteo*)	80	40
N3114	30ch. African fish eagle (*Haliaeëtus vocifer*)	1·10	50
N3115	40ch. Steller's sea eagle (*Haliaeëtus pelagicus*)	1·50	80
N3116	50ch. Golden eagle (*Aquila chrysaëtos*)	1·90	90
N3112/3116	*Set of 5*	5·00	2·40

MSN3117 78×59 mm. 80ch. Common kestrel (*Falco tinnunculus*) (41×31 mm). P 11½ .... 2·20   95

Nos. N3112/16 were issued both in separate sheets and together in *se-tenant* sheetlets of ten stamps and two labels commemorating "Granada '92" international stamp exhibition.

1033 Birthplace, Mt. Paekdu

1992 (16 Feb). 50th Birthday of Kim Jong Il, Mt. Paekdu. T **1033** and similar multicoloured designs. Litho. P 12.

N3118	10ch. Type **1033**	15	10
N3119	20ch. Mountain summit	35	30
N3120	30ch. Lake Chon (crater lake)	50	40
N3121	40ch. Lake Samji	70	50
N3118/3121	*Set of 4*	1·50	1·20

MSN3122 162×87 mm. 80ch. "Snowstorm on Mt. Paekdu" (41×63 mm). P 11½ .... 1·70   95

1034 Service Bus   **1035** Dancers and Emblem

1992 (20 Feb). Transport. T **1034** and similar horiz designs showing buses and trams. Litho. P 12.

N3123	10ch. multicoloured	15	10
N3124	20ch. multicoloured	35	30
N3125	30ch. multicoloured	50	40
N3126	40ch. multicoloured	70	50
N3127	50ch. multicoloured	95	70
N3128	60ch. multicoloured	1·10	80
N3123/3128	Set of 6	3·50	2·50

Nos. 3123/8 were issued both in separate sheets and together in *se-tenant* sheetlets of six stamps commemorating Essen international stamp fair.

1992 (7 Apr). Spring Friendship Art Festival, Pyongyang. Litho. P 12.

N3129	**1035** 10ch. multicoloured	20	10

1036 Birthplace, Mangyongdae

1992 (15 Apr). 80th Birthday of Kim II Sung. Revolutionary Sites. T **1036** and similar multicoloured designs. Litho. P 12.

(a) POSTAGE

N3130	10ch. Type **1036**	15	10
N3131	10ch. Party emblem and Turubong monument	15	10
N3132	10ch. Map and Ssuksom	15	10
N3133	10ch. Statue of soldier and Tongchang	15	10
N3134	40ch. Cogwheels and Taean	70	50
N3135	40ch. Chollima Statue and Kangson	70	50

(b) AIR. Inscr "AIR MAIL"

N3136	1wn.20 Monument and West Sea Barrage	2·40	1·90
N3130/3136	Set of 7	4·00	3·00
MSN3137	160×106 mm. 80ch. "April Spring Friendship Art Festival" (41×63 mm). P 11½	1·70	95

1037 Kang Ban Sok

1992 (21 Apr). Birth Centenary of Kang Ban Sok (mother of Kim II Sung). Sheet 80×103 mm. Litho. P 13½.

MSN3138	**1037** 80ch. multicoloured	1·70	95

1038 Soldiers on Parade

(Des Jon Kum Hui, Kim Hui Won and Cho Jong Gu. Litho)

1992 (25 Apr). 60th Anniv of People's Army. T **1038** and similar horiz designs. Multicoloured. P 12.

N3139	10ch. Type **1038**	15	10
N3140	10ch. Couple greeting soldier	15	10
N3141	10ch. Army, air force and navy personnel	15	10
N3139/3141	Set of 3	40	25

Nos. N3139/41 were issued both in separate sheets and together in *se-tenant* sheetlets of eight stamps (four examples of No. N3141 and two examples each of the other designs) and one label.

1039 Hurdling

(Des Kim Hui Won. Litho)

1992 (10 May). Olympic Games, Barcelona (2nd issue). T **1039** and similar horiz designs. Multicoloured. P 12.

N3142	10ch. Type **1039**	15	10
N3143	20ch. High jumping	35	30
N3144	30ch. Putting the shot	50	40
N3145	40ch. Sprinting	70	50
N3146	50ch. Long jumping	95	70
N3147	60ch. Throwing the javelin	1·10	80
N3142/3147	Set of 6	3·50	2·50
MSN3148	105×85 mm. 80ch. Running. P 11½×12	1·70	95

Nos. N3142/7 were issued both in separate sheets and all together with 80ch. value in *se-tenant* sheetlets (p 12) of seven stamps and one label.

1040 Planting Crops

1041 White-bellied Black Woodpecker (*Drycopus javensis*)

(Des Kim Jong Kil. Litho)

1992 (1 June). Evolution of Man. T **1040** and similar horiz designs showing life in the New Stone Age (10, 20ch.) and the Bronze Age (others). Multicoloured. P 12.

(a) POSTAGE.

N3149	10ch. Type **1040**	45	10
N3150	20ch. Family around cooking pot	70	30
N3151	30ch. Ploughing fields	1·10	40
N3152	40ch. Performing domestic chores	1·40	50

(b) AIR. Inscr "Air Mail"

N3153	50ch. Building a dolmen	2·40	70
N3149/3153	Set of 5	5·50	1·80

Nos. N3149/53 were issued both in separate sheets and together in *se-tenant* sheetlets of five stamps and one label.

(Des Cho Jong Gu. Litho)

1992 (28 June). Birds. T **1041** and similar vert designs. Multicoloured. P 11½.

N3154	10ch. Type **1041**	15	10
N3155	20ch. Ring-necked pheasant (*Phasianus colchicus*)	45	30
N3156	30ch. White stork (*Ciconia boyciana*)	50	40
N3157	40ch. Blue-winged pitta (*Pitta brachyura*)	80	50
N3158	50ch. Pallas's sandgrouse (*Syrraptes paradoxus*)	1·00	70

N3159	60ch. Black grouse (*Lyrurus tetrix*)	1·40	80
N3154/3159 *Set of 6*..		4·00	2·50

MSN3160 98×63 mm. 80ch. Daurian starling
(*Sturnus sturnus*).................................... 1·70 1·50

Nos. N3154/9 were issued both in separate sheets and all together with 80ch. value in *se-tenant* sheetlets of seven stamps and one label.

1042 Map and
Hands holding Text

1043 *Bougainvillea spectabilis*

(Des An Chol. Litho)

1992 (4 July). 20th Anniv of Publication of North–South Korea Joint Agreement. P 11 ½.

N3161	**1042** 1wn. 50, multicoloured...........................	2·75	2·10
MSN3162 112×76 mm. No. N3161×2		6·00	4·50

(Des Kim Hun Il. Litho)

1992 (15 July). Flowers. T **1043** and similar vert designs. Multicoloured. P 12.

N3163	10ch. Type **1043**	15	10
N3164	20ch. *Ixora chinensis*	35	30
N3165	30ch. *Dendrobium taysuwie*	50	40
N3166	40ch. *Columnea gloriosa*	70	50
N3167	50ch. *Crinum*	95	70
N3168	60ch. *Ranunculus asiaticus*	1·10	80
N3163/3168 *Set of 6*..		3·50	2·50

Nos. N3163/8 were issued both in separate sheets and together in *se-tenant* sheetlets of six stamps and two labels commemorating "Genova '92" international thematic stamps exhibition.

1044 Venus, Earth, Mars
and Satellite

1045 470 Dinghy

(Des Ri Yong Jin. Litho)

1992 (10 Aug). The Solar System. T **1044** and similar vert designs. Multicoloured. P 11½.

N3169	50ch. Type **1044**	95	70
	a. Horiz strip of 5. Nos. N3169/73.	5·00	
N3170	50ch. Jupiter..	95	70
N3171	50ch. Saturn (with rings)	95	70
N3172	50ch. Uranus (green planet with ring) ...	95	70
N3173	50ch. Neptune and Pluto	95	70
N3169/3173 *Set of 5*..		4·25	3·25

MSN3174 90×71 mm. 80ch. Planet Earth..................... 1·70 1·40

Nos. N3169/73 were issued together in horizontal *se-tenant* strips of five both within large sheets and in sheetlets of five stamps and five ²/₅ stamp-size labels, each strip forming a composite design.

(Des Kim Dong Han. Litho)

1992 (27 Aug). Riccione '92 Stamp Fair. T **1045** and similar vert designs. Multicoloured. P 12.

N3175	10ch. Type **1045**	15	10
N3176	20ch. Sailboard...	35	30
N3177	30ch. Sailing dinghy.................................	50	40

N3178	40ch. Finn dinghy (different).................	70	50
N3179	50ch. 420 dinghy (different).................	95	70
N3180	60ch. Fair emblem..................................	1·10	80
N3175/3180 *Set of 6*..		3·50	2·50

Nos. N3175/80 were issued both in separate sheets of 24 stamps and in *se-tenant* sheetlets of six stamps containing two examples each of either 10, 30 and 50ch. values or 20, 40 and 60ch.

1046 Moreno
Mannini (defender)

1047 Black-belts warming up

1992 (31 Aug). Sampdoria, Italian Football Champion 1991.T **1046** and similar multicoloured designs. Litho. P 12.

N3181	20ch. Type **1046**.......................................	35	30
	a. Sheetlet of 6. Nos. N3181/6.	5·75	
N3182	30ch. Gianluca Vialli (forward)..............	50	40
N3183	40ch. Pietro Vierchowod (defender)...	70	50
N3184	50ch. Fausto Pari (defender).................	95	70
N3185	60ch. Roberto Mancini (forward)........	1·20	80
N3186	1wn. Paolo Mantovani (club		
	president)...	1·90	1·50
N3181/3186 *Set of 6*..		5·00	3·75

MSN3187 92×66 mm. 1wn. Vialli and Riccardo
Garrone (president of club sponsor) (51×33 mm).
P 11½×12... 1·90 1·50

Nos. N3181/6 were issued together in *se-tenant* sheetlets of six stamps.

(Des Jon Kum Hui. Litho)

1992 (1 Sept). Eighth World Taekwondo Championship, Pyongyang. T **1047** and similar multicoloured designs. P 12.

(a) POSTAGE

N3188	10ch. Type **1047**.......................................	15	10
N3189	30ch. "Roundhouse" kick.........................	50	40
N3190	50ch. High kick	95	70
N3191	70ch. Flying kick	1·30	95
N3192	90ch. Black-belt breaking tiles with		
	fist	1·70	1·30
N3188/3192 *Set of 5*..		4·25	3·00

(b) AIR. Inscr "AIR MAIL"

MSN3193 93×75 mm. 1 wn. 20, Fight scene (33×51
mm). P 12×11½ .... 2·30 1·70

Nos. N3188/92 were issued both in separate sheets and together in *se-tenant* sheetlets of five stamps and one label.

1048 Common Toad (*Bufo bufo*)

(Des Kim Hun II and Jong Hyon II. Litho)

1992 (10 Sept). Frogs and Toads. T **1048** and similar horiz designs. Multicoloured. P 12.

(a) POSTAGE.

N3194	40ch. Type **1048**.......................................	70	50
N3195	40ch. Moor frog (*Rana arvalis*).............	70	50
N3196	40ch. *Rana chosenica*..............................	70	50
N3197	70ch. Common pond frog (*Rana		
	nigromaculata*)	1·40	95
N3198	70ch. Japanese tree toad (*Hyla		
	japonica*)...	1·40	95

(b) AIR. Inscr "AIR MAIL"

N3199	70ch. *Rana coreana*..................	1·40	95
N3194/3199	*Set of 6*..................	5·75	4·00

Nos. N3194/9 were issued both in separate sheets and together in *se-tenant* sheetlets containing eight stamps of either the 40 (three examples of No. 3195 and two each of the others) or 70ch. (three examples of No. 3198 and two each of the others) values and one label.

1049 *Rhododendron mucronulatum*

(Des Kim Hui Won. Litho)

1992 (5 Oct). World Environment Day. T **1049** and similar horiz designs. Multicoloured. P 12.

(a) POSTAGE.

N3200	10ch. Type **1049**	25	10
N3201	30ch. Barn swallow (*Hirundo rustica*)..	50	40
N3202	40ch. *Stewartia koreana* (flower).........	70	50
N3203	50ch. *Dictyoptera aurora* (beetle)......	95	70
N3204	70ch. *Metasequoia glyptostroboides* (tree).....................	1·30	95
N3205	90ch. Chinese salamander (*Hynobius leechii*).............	1·70	1·30

(b) AIR. Inscr "AIR MAIL"

N3206	1wn.20 Ginkgo biloba (tree)............	2·30	1·70
N3207	1wn.40 Spotted sculpin (*Cottus poecilopus*)............	2·75	1·90
N3200/3207	*Set of 8*............	9·50	6·75

Nos. N3200/7 were issued both in separate sheets of 21 stamps and together in *se-tenant* sheetlets of eight stamps.

1050 Fin Whale (*Balaenoptera physalus*)

1051 Mother and Chicks

(Des An Choi. Litho)

1992 (20 Oct). Whales and Dolphins. T **1050** and similar horiz designs. Multicoloured. P 12.

(a) POSTAGE.

N3208	50ch. Type **1050**	1·30	70
N3209	50ch. Common dolphin (*Delphinus delphis*)............	1·30	70
N3210	50ch. Killer whale (*Orcinus orca*)	1·30	70
N3211	50ch. Hump-backed whale (*Megaptera nodosa*)............	1·30	70
N3212	50ch. Bottle-nosed whale (*Berardius bairdii*)............	1·30	70

(b) AIR. Inscr "AIR MAIL"

N3213	50ch. Sperm whale (*Physeter catodon*)............	1·30	70
N3208/3213	*Set of 6*............	7·00	3·75

Nos. N3208/13 were issued both in separate sheets of 25 stamps and together in *se-tenant* sheetlets of three stamps, containing either Nos. N3208/10 or Nos. N3211/13.

(Des Cho Jong Gu. Litho)

1992 (7 Dec). New Year. T **1051** and similar horiz designs showing roosters in various costumes. Multicoloured. P 11½.

N3214	10ch. Type **1051**	15	10
N3215	20ch. Lady............	35	30
N3216	30ch. Warrior............	50	40
N3217	40ch. Courtier............	70	50
N3218	50ch. Queen............	95	70
N3219	60ch. King............	1·10	80

N3214/3219	*Set of 6*............	3·50	2·50
MSN3220	112×80 mm. 1wn.20 Sultan............	2·50	1·50

Nos. N3214/19 were issued both in separate sheets of 12 stamps and together in *se-tenant* sheetlets of four stamps, containing either Nos. N3214/16 or Nos. N3217/19, each with the 1wn. 20 value.

1052 Choe Choi Su (boxing)

1053 Golden Mushroom (*Flammulina velutipes*)

(Des Ri Yong Jin. Litho)

1992 (20 Dec). Gold Medal Winners at Barcelona Olympics. T **1052** and similar horiz designs. P 12.

N3221	10ch. Type **1052**	15	10
N3222	20ch. Pae Kil Su (gymnastics)............	35	30
N3223	50ch. Ri Hak Son (freestyle wrestling)	95	70
N3224	1wn. Kim Il (freestyle wrestling).........	1·10	80
N3221/3224	*Set of 4*............	2·30	1·70
MSN3225	128×120 mm. Nos. N3221/4; 30ch. Flags of Spain and North Korea, flame, gold medal and archer; 40ch. Church of the Holy Family (Barcelona), games mascot and emblem	4·00	3·00

No. N3226 is vacant.

(Des Jon Kum Hui. Litho)

1993 (10 Jan). Fungi. T **1053** and similar vert designs. Multicoloured. P 11½.

N3227	10ch. Type **1053**	15	10
N3228	20ch. Shaggy caps (*Coprinus comatus*)	35	30
N3229	30ch. *Ganoderma lucidum*	50	40
N3230	40ch. Brown mushroom (*Lentinus edodes*)............	70	50
N3231	50ch. *Volvaria bombycina*	95	70
N3232	60ch. *Sarcodon aspratus*............	1·10	80
N3227/3232	*Set of 6*............	3·50	2·50
MSN3233	59×60 mm. 1wn. Scarlet caterpillar fungus (*Cordyceps militaris*)............	2·20	1·50

Nos. N3227/32 were issued both in separate sheets and together in *se-tenant* sheetlets of four stamps, containing either 10, 40 and 60ch. or 20, 30 and 50ch., each with the 1wn. value.

1054 *Keumkangsania asiatica*

1055 League Members and Flag

(Des Kim Hui Won. Litho)

1993 (20 Jan). Plants. T **1054** and similar multicoloured designs. P 12.

N3234	10ch. Type **1054**	15	10
N3235	20ch. Echmosophora koreensis	35	30
N3236	30ch. Abies koreana	50	40
N3237	40ch. Benzoin angustifolium	70	50
N3238	50ch. Abeliophyllum distichum	95	70
N3239	60ch. Abelia mosanensis	1·10	80
N3234/3239	Set of 6	3·50	2·50

MSN3240 73×93 mm. 1wn. Pentactina rupicola
(27×38 mm). P 11½ .... 1·90   1·50

Nos. N3234/9 were issued both in separate sheets of 16 stamps and together in se-tenant sheetlets of six stamps.

(Des Ri Yong Jin and An Cho. Litho)

1993 (25 Jan). Eighth League of Socialist Working Youth Congress. T **1055** and similar vert design. P 12.

N3241	10ch. Type **1055**	15	10
N3242	40ch. Flame, League emblem and text	70	50

1056 Phophyong Revolutionary Site Tower and March Corps Emblem

1057 Tower of Juche Idea and Grand Monument, Mt. Wangjae

(Des Ri Kwang Hyok. Litho)

1993 (29 Jan). 70th Anniv of 1000-ri Journey for Learning. P 12.
N3243 **1056** 10ch. multicoloured 20   10

(Des Kim Hui Won. Litho)

1993 (11 Feb). 60th Anniv of Wangjaesan Meeting. P 12.
N3244 **1057** 5ch. multicoloured 10   10

1058 "Kimjongil" (begonia)

1059 Pilot Fish (Naucrates ductor)

(Des Kim Dong Han (N3245), Kim Hui Won (**MS**N3246). Litho)

1993 (16 Feb). 51st Birthday of Kim Jong Il. T **1058** and similar multicoloured design. P 12.
N3245   10ch. Type **1058** 20   10
MSN3246 170×95 mm. 1wn. Kim Il Sung writing paean to Kim Jong Il on his 50th birthday (50×41 mm). P 13½ .... 1·90   1·20

(Des An Choi. Litho)

1993 (25 Feb). Fishes. T **1059** and similar horiz designs. Multicoloured. P 11½.

N3247	10ch. Type **1059**	15	10
N3248	20ch. Japanese stingray (Dasyatis akajei)	35	30
N3249	30ch. Moonfish (Lampris guttatus)	50	40
N3250	40ch. Coelacanth (Latimeria chalumnae) (wrongly inscr "Laitimeria")	70	50
N3251	50ch. Grouper (Epinephelus moara)	1·00	70
N3247/3251	Set of 5	2·40	1·80

MSN3252 96×70 mm. 1wn. 20, Mako shark (Isurus oxyrhynchus) .... 2·75   1·50

No. **MS**N3252 commemorates "NAPOSTA '93" stamp fair, Dortmund.

Nos. N3247/51 were issued both in separate sheets and together in se-tenant sheetlets of two stamps, comprising the 10ch. and 1wn. 20 (as in No. **MS**N3252), the 20 and 50ch. or the 30 and 40ch.

1060/64 Spring on the Hill" (½-size illustration)

(Des Kim Jong Kil. Litho)

1993 (20 Mar). 18th-century Korean Painting. P 12×11½.

N3253	**1060** 40ch. multicoloured	70	50
	a. Sheetlet. Nos. N3253/7	3·75	
N3254	**1061** 40ch. multicoloured	70	50
N3255	**1062** 40ch. multicoloured	70	50
N3256	**1063** 40ch. multicoloured	70	50
N3257	**1064** 40ch. multicoloured	70	50
N3253/3257	Set of 5	3·25	2·30

Nos. N3253/7 were issued in se-tenant sheetlets of five stamps, forming the composite design illustrated.

1065 Violinist, Dancers and Emblem

1066 Books

(Des Cho Jong Gu. Litho)

1993 (5 Apr). Spring Friendship Art Festival, Pyongyang. P 12.
N3258 **1065** 10ch. multicoloured 20   10

(Des Kim Hui Won. Litho)

1993 (15 Apr). 81st Birthday of Kim Il Sung and Publication of his Reminiscences With the Century. T **1066** and similar multicoloured design. P 12.
N3259 **1066** 10ch. Type **1066** 20   10
MSN3260 140×105 mm. 1wn. Kim Il Sung writing (62×41 mm). P 11½ .... 2·00   1·30

1067 Kwangbok Street

(Des Han Pom Jo. Litho)

1993 (20 Apr). Pyongyang. T **1067** and similar horiz designs. Multicoloured. P 12.

N3261	10ch. Type **1067**	15	10
N3262	20ch. Chollima Street	35	30
N3263	30ch. Munsu Street	50	40
N3264	40ch. Moranbong Street	70	50
N3265	50ch. Thongil Street	1·00	70
N3261/3265	Set of 5	2·40	1·80
MSNN3266	115×74 mm. 1wn. Changgwang Street	1·90	1·50

1068 *Trichogramma dendrolimi* (fly)

1069 Ri In Mo

(Des Jon Kum Hui, Kim Hui Won and Kim Jong Kil. Litho)

1993 (10 May). Insects. T **1068** and similar horiz designs. Multicoloured. P 12.

N3267	10ch. Type **1068**	15	10
N3268	20ch. *Brachymeria obscurata* (fly)	35	30
N3269	30ch. *Metrioptera brachyptera* (cricket)	50	40
N3270	50ch. European field cricket (*Gryllus campestris*)	95	70
N3271	70ch. *Geocoris pallidipennis* (beetle)	1·40	95
N3272	90ch. *Cyphononyx dorsalis* (wasp) fighting spider	1·70	1·30
N3267/3272	Set of 6	4·50	3·50

Nos. N3267/72 were issued both in separate sheets and together in se-tenant sheetlets of three stamps, comprising the 10, 30 and 90ch. or the 20, 50 and 70ch.

1993 (19 May). Return from Imprisonment of Ri In Mo (war correspondent). T **1069** and similar multicoloured design. Litho. P 11½.

N3273	10ch. Type **1069**	20	10
MSNN3274	110×80 mm. 1wn.20 Ri In Mo and flowers (47×35 mm). P 13¼	2·50	1·50

1070 Footballers

1071 Grey-headed Green Woodpecker (*Picus canus*)

(Des Kim Hun II. Litho)

1993 (25 May). World Cup Football Championship, U.S.A. T **1070** and similar horiz designs showing various footballing scenes. P 11½.

N3275	10ch. multicoloured	15	10
N3276	20ch. multicoloured	35	30
N3277	30ch. multicoloured	50	40
N3278	50ch. multicoloured	1·00	70
N3279	70ch. multicoloured	1·40	95
N3280	90ch. multicoloured	1·70	1·30
N3275/3280	Set of 6	4·50	3·50

Nos. N3275/80 were issued both in separate sheets and in se-tenant sheetlets of three stamps comprising the 10, 30 and 90ch. or the 20, 50 and 70ch.

1993 (29 May). Birds. T **1071** and similar vert designs. Multicoloured. Litho. P 12.

N3281	10ch. Type **1071**	15	10
N3282	20ch. King bird of paradise (*Cicinnurus regius*)	35	30
N3283	30ch. Lesser bird of paradise (*Paradisea minor*)	50	40
N3284	40ch. Paradise whydah (*Steganura paradisea*)	70	50
N3285	50ch. Magnificent bird of paradise (*Diphyllodes magnificus*) (wrongly inscr "Diphyllobes")	1·00	70
N3286	60ch. Greater bird of paradise (*Paradisea apoda*)	1·10	80
N3281/3286	Set of 6	3·50	2·50

Nos. N3283/4 also commemorate "indopex '93" international stamp exhibition, Surabaya.

Nos. N3281/6 were issued both in separate sheets and together in three se-tenant sheetlets, comprising 10ch.×2 and 60ch.×2; 20ch.×2 and 50ch.×2; or 30 and 40ch.

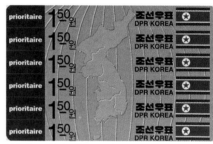

1072 Korean Peninsula (⅔-size illustration)

(Litho PostLine Security Printing, Sweden)

1993 (29 May). Self-adhesive. Rouletted.

N3287	**1072** 1wn. 50, multicoloured	2·50	1·90
	a. Card. No. N3287×6	16·00	

No. N3287 is for any one of the six stamps forming the composite design illustrated. No. N3287a. is for the full card of six.

The individual stamps are peeled directly from the card backing. Each stamp is a horizontal strip with a label indicating the main class of mail covered by the rate at the left, separated by a vertical line of rouletting. The outer edges of the card are imperforate.

Nos. N3288/92 are vacant.

1073 Kim Myong Nam (weightlifting, 1990)

(Des Ri Kwang Hyok and Kim Chung Song. Litho)

1993 (15 June). World Champions. T **1073** and similar horiz designs. Multicoloured. P 12.

N3293	10ch. Type **1073**	15	10
N3294	20ch. Kim Kwang Suk (gymnastics, 1991)	35	30
N3295	30ch. Pak Yong Sun (table tennis. 1975, 1977)	50	40
N3296	50ch. Kim Yong Ok (radio direction-finding, 1990)	1·00	70
N3297	70ch. Han Yun Ok (taekwondo, 1987, 1988, 1990)	1·40	95
N3298	90ch. Kim Yong Sik (free-style wrestling, 1986, 1989)	1·70	1·20
N3293/3298	*Set of 6*	4·50	3·25

Nos. N3293/8 were issued both in separate sheets and together in two *se-tenant* sheetlets of six stamps, comprising two each of the 10, 30 and 90ch. or 20, 50 and 70ch.

1074 Cabbage and Chilli Peppers

1075 State Arms

(Des Jong Chang Mo. Litho)

1993 (25 June). Fruits and Vegetables. T **1074** and similar vert designs. Multicoloured. P 12.

N3299	10ch. Type **1074**	15	10
N3300	20ch. Squirrels and horse chestnuts	35	30
N3301	30ch. Grapes and peach	50	40
N3302	40ch. Birds and persimmon	70	50
N3303	50ch. Tomatoes, aubergine and cherries	1·00	70
N3304	60ch. Radish, onion and garlic	1·10	80
N3299/3304	*Set of 6*	3·50	2·50

Nos. N3299/3304 were issued both in separate sheets and together in two *se-tenant* sheetlets of three stamps comprising the 10, 40 and 60ch. or 20, 30 and 50ch.

(Des Kim Dong Han. Litho)

1993 (5 July). P 12.

N3305	**1075** 10ch. vermilion	20	10

1076 Soldiers and Civilians

1077 Choe Yong Do

1993 (27 July). 40th Anniv of Victory in Liberation War. T **1076** and similar multicoloured designs. Litho.

(a) P 12.

N3306	10ch. Type **1076**	20	10
N3307	10ch. Officer and soldier	20	10
N3308	10ch. Guided missiles on low-loaders on parade	20	10
N3309	10ch. Anti-aircraft missiles on lorries on parade	20	10
N3310	10ch. Self-propelled missile launchers (tracked vehicles) on parade	20	10
N3311	10ch. Machine gun emplacement (30×48 mm)	20	10
N3312	10ch. Soldier holding flag (bronze statue) (30×48 mm)	20	10
N3313	40ch. Soldiers and flags ("Let us become Kim Jims and Ri Su Boks of the 90s") (30×48 mm)	80	50

Nos. N3311/13 were issued both in separate sheets of 21 stamps and together in *se-tenant* sheetlets of three stamps.

(b) P 11½

N3314	10ch. Kim Il Sung at strategic policy meeting	20	10
	a. Sheetlet of 2. Nos. N3314 and N3319	65	45
N3315	10ch. Kim Il Sung directing battle for Height 1211	20	10
	a. Sheetlet of 2. Nos. N3315 and N3320	65	45
N3316	10ch. Kim Il Sung at munitions factory	20	10
	a. Sheetlet of 2. Nos. N3316 and N3321	65	45
N3317	10ch. Kim Il Sung with tank commanders	20	10
	a. Sheetlet of 2. Nos. N3317 and N3322	65	45
N3318	10ch. Kim Il Sung with triumphant soldiers	20	10
	a. Sheetlet of 2. Nos. N3318 and N3323	65	45
N3319	20ch. Kim Il Sung with artillery unit	40	30
N3320	20ch. Kim Il Sung encouraging machine gun crew	40	30
N3321	20ch. Kim Il Sung studying map of Second Front	40	30
N3322	20ch. Kim Il Sung with airmen	40	30
N3323	20ch. Musicians ("Alive is art of Korea")	40	30
N3306/3323	*Set of 18*	4·75	3·00

Nos. N3314/23 were issued together in five sheetlets, each of two stamps.

(c) Four sheets. P 12×11½ (**MS**N3324b) or 13½ (others)

MSN3324 (a) 150×90 mm. 80ch. Kim Il Sung beside tank (39×50 mm): (b) 131×75 mm. 80ch. Kim Il Sung and victory celebrations (33×51 mm); (c) 134×98 mm. 1wn. Kim Il Sung making speech (47×35 mm); (d) 190×93 mm. 1wn. Kim Il Sung taking salute (38×49 mm) .... 7·75 4·25

(Des Hwang In Jae. Litho)

1993 (1 Aug). National Reunification Prize Winners. T **1077** and similar vert designs. Multicoloured. P 12.

N3325	10ch. Type **1077**	20	10
N3326	20ch. Kim Ku	40	30
N3327	30ch. Hong Myong Hui	60	40
N3328	40ch. Ryo Un Hyong	80	50
N3329	50ch. Kim Jong Thae	1·10	75
N3330	60ch. Kim Chaek	1·30	85
N3325/3330	*Set of 6*	4·00	2·50

1078 *Robinia* sp.

1079 Newton

(Des Kim Hui Won. Litho)

1993 (14 Aug). Taipei '93 International Stamp Exhbition, Taipeh.
T **1078** and similar vert designs. Multicoloured. P 12.

N3331	20ch. Type **1078**......................	40	30
N3332	30ch. *Hippeastrum*....................	60	40
MSN3333 75×105 mm. 1wn. Deer (33×51 mm).			
P 12×11½............................		2·10	1·60

(Des O Ok Ryon. Litho)

1993 (1 Sept). 350th Birth Anniv (1992) of Sir Isaac Newton
(mathematician and scientist). T **1079** and similar vert designs.
Multicoloured. P 12.

N3334	10ch. Type **1079**......................	20	10
N3335	20ch. Apple tree and formula of law		
	of gravitation	40	30
N3336	30ch. Satellite, reflecting telescope,		
	dish aerial, globe and rocket.....	70	40
N3337	50ch. Formula of binomial theorem..	1·10	75
N3338	70ch. Newton's works and statue........	1·60	1·00
N3334/3338 *Set of 5*.................		3·50	2·30

Nos. N3334/8 were issued both in separate sheets of 21 stamps
and together in two *se-tenant* sheetlets of three stamps, comprising
the 10, 20 and 70ch. or the 10, 30 and 50ch.

1080 King Tongmyong
shooting Bow

1081 First North Korea and
Thailand Stamps

(Des Kim Jong Kil. Litho)

1993 (10 Sept). Restoration of King Tongmyong of Koguryo's Tomb.
T **1080** and similar multicoloured designs. P 12.

N3339	10ch. Type **1080**......................	20	10
N3340	20ch. King Tongmyong saluting		
	crowd................................	40	30
N3341	30ch. Restoration monument...............	70	40
N3342	40ch. Temple of the Tomb of King		
	Tongmyong (horiz)	90	60
N3343	50ch. Tomb (horiz)....................	1·10	75
N3339/3343 *Set of 5*.................		3·00	1·90
MSN3344 95×105 mm. 80ch. Kim Il Sung visiting			
tomb (41×63 mm). P 11½............		1·90	1·60

(Des Ri Yong Jin. Litho)

1993 (1 Oct). Bangkok 1993 International Stamp Exhibition, Thailand.
Sheet 76×81 mm. P 11½.

MSN3345 **1081** 1wn. 20, multicoloured.......................	2·50	2·10

1082 *Cyrtopodium
andresoni*

(Des Ri Yong Jin. Litho)

1993 (15 Oct). Orchids. T **1082** and similar vert designs. Multicoloured.
P 12.

N3346	10ch. Type **1082**......................	20	10
N3347	20ch. *Cattleya*........................	40	30
N3348	30ch. *Cattleya intermedia* "Oculata"....	70	40
N3349	40ch. *Potinaria* "Maysedo godonsiu"	90	60
N3350	50ch. Kim Il Sung flower	1·10	75
N3346/3350 *Set of 5*.................		3·00	1·90

Nos. N3346/50 were issued both in separate sheets of 25 stamps
and together in *se-tenant* sheetlets of 25.

모택동탄생100돐
毛泽东诞生100周年
1893-1993

(**1083**)

1993 (16 Nov). Birth Centenary of Mao Tse-tung (1st issue). No.
MSN3006 optd in the margin with T **1083** in gold and black.

MSN3351 95×75 mm. 80ch. multicoloured.................	1·90	1·60

See also Nos. N3352/**MS**N3357.

1084 Mao Tse-tung at
Yanan, 1944

1085 Phungsan

1993 (26 Dec). Birth Centenary of Mao Tse-tung (2nd issue). T **1084**
and similar vert designs. Multicoloured. Litho. P 11½.

N3352	10ch. Type **1084**......................	20	10
N3353	20ch. Seated portrait (Peking. 1960)	40	30
N3354	30ch. Casting a vote, 1953	70	40
N3355	40ch. With pupils at Shaoshan		
	Secondary School, 1959.............	90	60
N3352/3355 *Set of 5*.................		2·00	1·30
MSN3356 110×70 mm. 1wn. Mao Tse-tung and Pres.			
Kim Il Sung of North Korea (47×35 mm). P 13½...		2·10	1·60
MSN3357 169×130 mm. Nos. N3352/**MS**N3356;			
25ch. Mao Tse-tung proclaming foundation of			
Chinese People's Republic, 1949 (47×35 mm).			
25ch. Mao Tse-tung with son Mao An-ying			
(47×35 mm). P 11½ (vert) or 12½ (horiz)		5·25	4·25

(Des Ri Yong Jin. Litho)

1994 (1 Jan). New Year. Dogs. T **1085** and similar vert designs.
Multicoloured. P 12.

N3358	10ch. Type **1085**......................	20	10
N3359	20ch. Yorkshire terriers...............	40	30
N3360	30ch. Gordon setter...................	70	40
N3361	40ch. Pomeranian	80	60

N3362	50ch. Spaniel with pups.........................	1·20	85
N3358/3362	*Set of 5*....................................	3·00	2·00
MSN3363 80×66 mm. 1wn. Pointer. P 13½..................		2·10	1·60

Nos. N3358/62 were each issued both in separate sheets of 25 stamps and in five sheetlets each containing two examples of one value together with one example of the stamp in No. **MS**N3363 (perf 12).

1086 Purple Hyosong Flower

1087 Red and Black Dragon-eye

(Des Jon Kum Hui. Litho)

1994 (16 Feb). 52nd Birthday of Kim Jong II. T **1086** and similar vert designs. Multicoloured. P 13½.

N3364	10ch. Type **1086**........................	20	10
N3365	40ch. Yellow hyosong flower (*Primula polyantha*).......................	90	60
MSN3366 156×82 mm. 1wn. Kim II Sung and Kim Jong II surrounded by flowers (44×53 mm).............		2·10	1·60

Nos. N3364/5 were issued both in separate sheets of 25 stamps and together in *se-tenant* sheetlets of eight stamps and one label.

(Des Kim Hun II. Litho)

1994 (18 Feb). Goldfishes (*Carassius auratus*). T **1087** and similar horiz designs. Multicoloured. P 12.

N3367	10ch. Type **1087**........................	20	10
	a. Sheetlet of 4. Nos. N3367/70......	3·75	
N3368	30ch. Red and white bubble-eye	70	40
N3369	50ch. Red and white long-finned wenyu	1·10	75
N3370	70ch. Red and white fringetail	1·60	1·00
N3367/3370 *Set of 4*...		3·25	2·00

Nos. N3367/70 were issued together in *se-tenant* sheetlets of four stamps.

1088 Crowd with Banners

1089 Wheat, Banner and Woman writing

(Des Kim Hui Won (20ch.), Paek Nam Sik (1wn. 20). Litho)

1994 (19 Feb). 20th Anniv of Publication of *Programme for Modelling the Whole Society on the Juche Idea* by Kim Jong II. T **1088** and similar vert design. Multicoloured. P 12.

| N3371 | 20ch. Type **1088**........................ | 25 | 10 |
| **MS**N3372 145×95 mm. 1wn. 20, Kim Jong II making speech (41×63 mm). P 11½.. | | 2·50 | 1·60 |

(Des Cho Jong Gu. Litho)

1994 (25 Feb). 30th Anniv of Publication of *Theses on the Socialist Rural Question in Our Country* by Kim II Sung. T **1089** and similar vert designs. Multicoloured. P 12.

| N3373 | 10ch. Type **1089**........................ | 20 | 10 |
| N3374 | 10ch. Electricity generating systems and pylon .... | 20 | 10 |

N3375	10ch. Lush fields, grain and tractor.....	20	10
N3376	40ch. Modern housing, books, food crops and laboratory technician...............................	90	60
N3377	40ch. Revellers...........................	90	60
N3373/3377 *Set of 5*...		2·20	1·40
MSN3378 Two sheets, each 134×111 mm. P 11½. (a) 1wn. Kim II Sung in field (138×59 mm): (b)1wn. Peasants with Kim II Jong (41×63 mm)		4·50	3·00

1090 *Mangyongbong-92* (passenger ship)

1091 National Flag

(Des Ri Kwang Hyok. Litho)

1994 (25 Mar). Ships. T **1090** and similar horiz designs. Multicoloured. P 11½.

N3379	20ch. Type **1090**........................	40	30
N3380	30ch. *Osandok* (cargo ship)............	80	40
N3381	40ch. *Ryongaksan* (factory stern trawler)................................	90	60
N3382	50ch. Stern trawler.......................	1·10	75
N3379/3382 *Set of 4*...		3·00	1·80
MSN3383 131×112 mm. Nos. N3379/82; 2×80ch. *Maekjon-1* (passenger ship)................................		6·25	5·25

(Des Ri Yong Jin. Litho)

1994 (30 Mar). P 13½.

| N3384 | **1091** 10ch. carmine-vermilion & dp brt bl | 25 | 10 |

1092 Birthplace and Magnolia (national flower)

1093 *Chrysosplenium sphaerospermum*

(Des Kim Hun II. Litho)

1994 (15 Apr). 82nd Birthday of Kim II Sung. T **1092** and similar vert designs. Multicoloured. P 12.

N3385	10ch. Type **1092**........................	20	10
N3386	40ch. Birthplace, Manyongdae, and Kim II Sung flower..................	90	60
MSN3387 162×103 mm. 5×40ch. Composite design of Lake Chon (crater lake of Mt. Paekdu) and score of "Song of General Kim II Sung". P 13½		4·50	3·00

Nos. N3385/6 were each issued both in sheets of 25 stamps and in sheetlets of eight stamps.

(Des Ri Yong Jin (**MS**N3393), Kim Chung Song and Ri Yong Jin (others). Litho)

1994 (25 Apr). Alpine Plants on Mt. Paekdu. T **1093** and similar vert designs. Multicoloured. P 13½.

| N3388 | 10ch. Type **1093**........................ | 20 | 10 |
| N3389 | 20ch. *Campanula cephalotes* .... | 40 | 30 |

N3390	40ch. *Trollius macropetalus*...............	90	60
N3391	40ch. *Gentiana algida*.........................	90	60
N3392	50ch. *Sedum kamtschaticum*............	1·10	75
N3388/3392 *Set of 5*..		3·25	2·10
MSN3393 78×64 mm. 1wn. *Dianthus repens*..........		2·10	1·60

Nos. N3388/**MS**N3393 were also issued together in *se-tenant* sheetlets of three stamps, containing either Nos. N3388, N3390 and **MS**N3393 or N3389 and N3391/2.

1094 National Olympic Committee Emblem

1095 Red Cross Launch ("Relief on the Sea")

(Des Kim Hui Won. Litho)

1994 (2 May). Centenary of International Olympic Committee. T **1094** and similar vert designs. Multicoloured. P 12.

N3394	10ch. Type **1094**	20	10
N3395	20ch. Pierre de Coubertin (founder)...	40	30
N3396	30ch. Olympic flag and flame..............	70	40
N3397	50ch. Emblem of Centennial Olympic		
	Congress, Paris.............................	1·10	75
N3394/3397 *Set of 4*..		2·20	1·40
MSN3398 Two sheets, each 75×105 mm. P 13½.			
(a) 1wn. Torch carrier; (b) 1wn. Juan Antonio			
Samaranch (I.O.C. President) and entrance to			
new headquarters..		4·50	3·75

Nos. N3394/7 were each issued in sheetlets of eight stamps.

(Des Kim Hui Won. Litho)

1994 (5 May). 75th Anniv of International Red Cross and Red Crescent Federation. T **1095** and similar vert designs. Multicoloured. P 12.

N3399	10ch. Tram, pedestrians on		
	footbridge and traffic lights		
	("Prevention of Traffic		
	Accident").....................................	20	10
	a. Horiz strip of 4. Nos. N3399/		
	3402...	2·30	
N3400	20ch. Type **1095**......................................	40	30
N3401	30ch. Planting tree ("Protection of		
	Environment")...............................	70	40
N3402	40ch. Dam ("Prevention of Drought		
	Damage")..	90	60
N3399/3402 *Set of 4*..		2·00	1·30

Nos. N3399/3402 were issued together in *se-tenant* sheetlets containing two examples of No. N3399a.

(1096)

1097 Northern Fur Seal (*Callorhinus ursinus*)

1994 (29 May). No. N3287 surch with T **1096.**

| N3403 | **1072** 1wn.60 on 1wn.50 multicoloured .... | 4·50 | 3·75 |
| | a. Card. No. N3403×6 .... | 28·00 | |

No. N3403 is for any one of the six stamps forming No. 3403a (see note below No. N3287). Each stamp also has an additional fluorescent obliteration and surcharge.

(Des Kim Hun Il and Kim Chung Song. Litho)

1994 (10 June). Marine Mammals. T **1097** and similar horiz designs. Multicoloured. P 11½.

N3404	10ch. Type **1097**	20	10
N3405	40ch. Southern elephant seal		
	(*Mirounga leonina*).......................	90	60
N3406	60ch. Southern sealion		
	(*Otaria byronia*)	1·40	95
N3404/3406 *Set of 3*...		2·30	1·50
MSN3407 Two sheets. (a) 80×130 mm. 20ch.			
Californian sealion (*Zalophus californianus*); 30ch.			
Ringed seal (*Phoca hispida*); 50ch. Walrus			
(*Odobenus rosmarus*). (b) 80×88 mm. 1wn. Harp			
seal (*Pagophilus groenlandicus*)		4·75	4·25

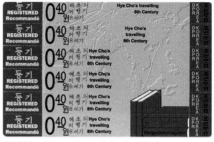

1098 Map of Asia and Books (½-size illustration)

(Litho PostLine Security Printing, Sweden)

1994 (17 June). 8th-century Travels of Hye Cho. Self-adhesive. Rouletted.

| N3408 | **1098** 40ch. multicoloured................................. | 70 | 50 |
| | a. Card. No. N3408×6............................ | 4·50 | |

No. N3408 is for any one of the six stamps forming the composite design illustrated (see note below No. N3287).

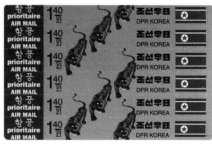

1099 Tiger (½-size illustration)

(Litho PostLine Security Printing, Sweden)

1994 (18 June). Korean Tiger. Self-adhesive. Rouletted.

| N3409 | **1099** 1wn.40 multicoloured............................ | 2·50 | 2·10 |
| | a. Card. No. N3409×6............................ | 16·00 | |

No. N3409 is for any one of the six stamps forming the composite design illustrated (see note below No. N3287).

1100 Kim Jong Il on Mt. Paekdu

(Des Kim Hui Won, An Chol and Kim Jong Kil. Litho)

1994 (19 June). 30th Anniv of Kim Jong Il's Leadership of Korean Workers' Party. Two sheets containing multicoloured designs as T **1100** showing various scenes featuring Kim Jong Il. P 12 (**MS**N3410a) or 11½ (**MS**N3410b).

MS N3410 Two sheets, (a) 148×182 mm. 40ch. Type **1100**; 40ch. With engineers surveying bay; 40ch. Visiting the set of *Star of Korea* (film); 40ch. Visiting Chongryu Restaurant; 40ch. Reviewing tank corps; 40ch. Shaking hands with international figures. (b) 145×95mm. 1wn. At desk (41×63 mm) .... 7·50   6·25

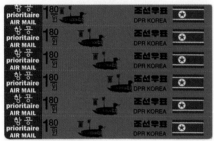

1101 "Turtle" Ship (½-size illustration)

(Litho PostLine Security Printing, Sweden)

1994 (20 June). Self-adhesive. Rouletted.

N3411 **1101** 1wn.80 multicoloured............................. 3·00   2·50
    a. Card. No. N3411×6..................... 19·00

No. N3411 is for any one of the six stamps forming the composite design illustrated (see note below No. N3287).

1102 Striped Bonnet   **1103** Trapeze
(*Phalium strigatum*)

(Des Ri Kwang Hyok and Jon Kum Hui (N3412/13), Jon Kum Hui (others). Litho)

1994 (25 June). Molluscs. T **1102** and similar vert designs. Multicoloured. P 12.

N3412   30ch. Type **1102** 70   40
N3413   40ch. Equilateral venus (*Gomphina veneriformis*) 95   60
MS N3414 103×75 mm. 1wn.20 Bladder moon (*Neverita didyma*). P 13½ .... 2·75   2·10
MS N3415 Two sheets, each 127×73 mm. P 12½. (a) Nos. N3413 and **MS**N3414; 10ch. *Cardium muticum* (cockle). (b) Nos. N3412 and **MS**N3414; 20ch. *Buccinum bayani* (whelk) .... 7·25   6·25

(Des An Chol. Litho)

1994 (7 July). Circus Acrobatics. T **1103** and similar horiz designs. Multicoloured. P 11½.

N3416   10ch. Type **1103** 20   10
      a. Sheetlet of 4. Nos. N3416/19....... 2·30
N3417   20ch. Reino (Swedish acrobat) performing rope dance.............. 40   30
N3418   30ch. Seesaw performer......................... 70   40
N3419   40ch. Unicycle juggler........................... 90   60
N3416/3419 *Set of 4*.. 2·00   1·30

Nos. N3416/19 were issued together in *se-tenant* sheetlets of four stamps.

1104 Korean Script and "100"

(Des Kim Jong Kil. Litho)

1994 (10 July). Birth Centenary of Kim Hyong Jik (father of Kim Il Sung). T **1104** and similar vert design. Multicoloured. P 13½.

N3420   10ch. Type **1104** 80   10
MS N3421 61×85 mm. 1wn. Kim Hyong Jik (30×48 mm). P 12×11½ .... 2·10   1·60

1105 Jon Pong Jun and Battle Scene   **1106** Inoue Shuhachi

(Des Kim Dong Han. Litho)

1994 (15 July). Centenary of Kabo Peasant War. P 12.

N3422 **1105** 10ch. multicoloured................................... 25   10

(Des Paek Nam Sik. Litho)

1994 (30 July). Award of First International Kim Il Sung Prize to Inoue Shuhachi (Director General of Juche Idea International Institute). Sheet 103×78 mm. P 13½.

MS N3423 **1106** 1wn.20 multicoloured....................... 2·50   1·60

1107 Workers and Banner   **1108** Onsong Fish

(Des Ri Yong Jin. Litho)

1994 (1 Aug). Revolutionary Economic Strategy. P 11½.

N3424 **1107** 10ch. multicoloured................................ 25   10

(Des Kim Chung Song. Litho)

1994 (10 Aug). Fossils. T **1108** and similar horiz designs. Multicoloured. P 12.

N3425   40ch. Type **1108** 90   60
N3426   40ch. Metasequoia 90   60
N3427   40ch. Mammoth teeth........................... 90   60

N3428   80ch. Archaeopteryx.................................. 1·80   1·20
N3425/3428 *Set of 4*.................................... 4·00   2·75
Nos. N3425/8 were issued both in separate booklets containing
a strip of seven stamps and together in three *se-tenant* sheetlets of
four stamps, each containing two examples of No. N3428 plus two
examples of one of the other designs.

1109 *Acorus calamus*   **1110** Ribbon
                              Exercise

(Des Kim Hun II. Litho)

1994 (25 Aug). Medicinal Plants. T **1109** and similar multicoloured
designs. P 12.
N3429   20ch. Type **1109**....................... 40   30
N3430   30ch. *Arctium lappa* 70   40
MSN3431 Two sheets. P 13½. (a) 133×86 mm.
80ch. *Lilium lancifolium*; 80ch. *Codonopsis
lanceolata*. (b) 56×83 mm. 1wn. Ginseng (*Panax
schinseng*) (vert) .... 5·50   4·25

(Des Ri Yong Jin. Litho)

1994 (7 Sept). Callisthenics. T **1110** and similar vert designs.
Multicoloured. P 12.
N3432   10ch. Type **1110** 20   10
         a. Horiz strip. Nos. N3432/6 plus
         label .... 3·50
N3433   20ch. Ball exercise 40   30
N3434   30ch. Hoop exercise 70   40
N3435   40ch. Ribbon exercise (different).......... 90   60
N3436   50ch. Club exercise .... 1·10   75
N3432/3436 *Set of 5*.................................... 3·00   1·90
Nos. N3432/6 were issued together in horizontal strips of five
stamps and one label within sheetlets containing three such strips,
each label differing.

1111 Chou En-lai at
Tianjun, 1919

(Des Kim Dong Han. Litho)

1994 (1 Oct). 96th Birth Anniv of Chou En-lai (Chinese statesman).
T **1111** and similar designs. Multicoloured (except **MS**N3441).
P 11½.
N3437   10ch. Type **1111** 20   10
N3438   20ch. Arrival in Northern Shanxi from
         Long March...................................... 40   30
N3439   30ch. At Conference of Asian and
         African Countries, Bandung,
         Indonesia, 1955 70   40

N3440   40ch. Surrounded by children in
         Wulumuqi, Xinjiang Province.... 90   60
N3437/3440 *Set of 4*.................................... 2·00   1·30
MSN3441 106×70 mm. 80ch. blackish green, silver
and black (Kim Il Sung proposing toast to Chou
En-lai during Korean visit, 1970) (46½×35 mm).
P 13½... 1·90   1·60
MSN3442 Two sheets, each 144×110 mm. P 11½
(vert designs) or 12×12½ (horiz designs). (a) Nos.
N3437, N3440 and **MS**N3441; 20ch. Leading
Nanchang Uprising, 1927 (46½×35 mm). (b) Nos.
N3438/9 and **MS**N3441; 20ch. At airport on return
from foreign visits (46½×35 mm) .... 6·75   5·25
Nos. N3437/40 were each issued with *se-tenant* ²/₅ stamp-size label
showing an associated building.

No. N3443 has been left for a reported issue for World Environment
Day which has not been seen by us.

1113 Kim Il Sung as   **1114** Player No. 4
Youth, 1927

1994 (8 Oct). Kim Il Sung Commemoration (1st issue). T **1113** and
similar designs. Litho.

(a) As T **1113**. Each lake, gold and black. P 12
N3444   40ch. Type **1113** 90   60
         a. Sheetlet of 3. Nos. N3444/6 .... 3·00
N3445   40ch. Kim Il Sung and Kim Jong Suk.. 90   60
N3446   40ch. Kim Il Sung as young man 90   60

(b) Horiz designs as T **1115**. Each deep dull purple, gold and black.
P 12
N3447   40ch. Kim Il Sung making speech,
         Pyongyang, 1945......................... 90   60
         a. Sheetlet of 3. Nos. N3447/9 .... 3·00
N3448   40ch. Kim Il Sung sitting at desk....... 90   60
N3449   40ch. Kim Il Sung at microphone 90   60
N3444/3449 *Set of 6*................................... 4·75   3·25

(c) Miniature sheet. P 12½×12
MSN3450 78×106 mm. 1wn. Kim Il Sung smiling
(35×46 mm) .... 2·10   1·60
Nos. N3444/6 and N3447/9 respectively were issued together in
se-tenant sheetlets of three stamps.
See also Nos. N3450/**MS**N3464.

1994 (13 Oct). World Cup Football Championship. U.S.A. T **1114** and
similar vert designs. Multicoloured. P 13½.
N3451   10ch. Type **1114** 20   10
N3452   20ch. Player No. 5 40   30
N3453   30ch. Player No. 6 70   40
N3454   40ch. Player No. 7 90   60
N3455   1wn. Player No. 8 .... 2·10   1·60
N3456   1wn.50 Player No. 9 .... 3·50   2·30
N3451/3456 *Set of 6*................................... 7·00   4·75
MSN3457 Two sheets. (a) 79×112 mm. 2wn.50
Stadium, players and trophy (41×38 mm); (b)
200×223 mm. 1wn.×6, Each depicting player,
trophy and different view .... 18·00   11·50
The designs in No. **MS**N3457b were also issued in separate
"de-luxe" miniature sheets.

1115 Kim Il Sung making Radio Broadcast, 1950

1116 National Flags and Flowers

1994 (15 Oct). Kim Il Sung Commemoration (2nd issue). T **1115** and similar designs. Litho.

(a) Each blackish olive, gold and black. P 12

N3458	40ch. Type **1115**	90	60
	a. Sheetlet of 3. Nos. N3458/60.....	3·00	
N3459	40ch. Kim Il Sung with four soldiers, 1951	90	60
N3460	40ch. Kim Il Sung and crowd of soldiers, 1953	90	60

(b) Multicoloured (N3463) or deep lilac, gold and black (others). P 12

N3461	40ch. Kim Il Sung with workers at Chongjin Steel Plant, 1959	90	60
	a. Sheetlet of 3. Nos. N3461/3	3·00	
N3462	40ch. Kim Il Sung on Onchon Plain	90	60
N3463	40ch. Kim Il Sung at desk using telephone	90	60
N3458/3463	Set of 6	4·75	3·25

(c) Miniature sheet. P 12½×12

MSN3464	78×106 mm. 1wn. Kim Il Sung and Kim Jong Il (35×47 mm)	2·10	1·60

Nos. N3458/60 and N3461/3 respectively were issued together in se-tenant sheetlets of three stamps.

(Des Ri Yong Jin. Litho)

1994 (25 Oct). Korean–Chinese Friendship. T **1116** and similar design. P 11½.

N3465	**1116** 40ch. multicoloured	90	60
MSN3466	79×100 mm. 1wn.20 black, grey and gold (Mao Tse-tung and Kim Il Sung) (53×44 mm). P 13½	2·50	2·10

1117 Ri Myon Sang and Score of Snow Falls

1118 State Arms

(Des Jon Kum Hui. Litho)

1994 (25 Nov). Composers. T **1117** and similar vert designs. Multicoloured. P 11½.

N3467	50ch. Type **1117**	1·10	75
N3468	50ch. Pak Han Kyu and score of Nobody Knows	1·10	75
N3469	50ch. Ludwig van Beethoven and score of piano sonata No. 14	1·10	75
N3470	50ch. Wolfgang Amadeus Mozart and score of symphony No. 39	1·10	75
N3467/3470	Set of 4	4·00	2·75

1994 (10 Dec). Litho. P 12.

N3471	**1118** 1wn. deep blue-green	2·40	1·60
N3472	3wn. olive-sepia	6·25	4·75

1119 P. Wiberg (Alpine combined skiing)

(Des J.-L. Puvilland)

1994 (20 Dec). Winter Olympic Games, Lillehammer, Gold Medal Winners. T **1119** and similar horiz designs. Multicoloured. Litho. P 13½.

N3473	10ch. Type **1119**	20	10
N3474	20ch. D. Compagnoni (slalom)	40	30
N3475	30ch. O. Baiul (figure skating)	70	40
N3476	40ch. D. Jansen (speed skating)	90	60
N3477	1wn. L. Yegorova (cross-country skiing)	2·10	1·60
N3478	1wn.50 B. Blair (speed skating)	3·25	2·30
N3473/3478	Set of 6	6·75	4·75

MSN3479 Seven sheets, each 102×75 mm (a/f) or 131×95 mm. (g). (a) 1wn. Norwegian skiing team and B. Daehlie (Alpine combined); (b) 1wn. Gordeyeva and Grinkov (pairs figure skating); (c) 1wn. Vreni Schneider (Alpine combined); (d) 1wn. G. Hackl (luge); (e) 1wn. J. Weissflog (ski jumping); (f) 1wn. Kono, Ogiwara and Abe (cross-country skiing); (g) 2wn.50 T. Moe (downhill) (50×35 mm)18·0011·50

Nos. N3473/8 were issued both in separate sheets of 21 stamps and together in se-tenant sheetlets of six stamps.

1120 Pig Couple

1121 Pison Waterfalls, Mt. Myohyang

(Des An Chol. Litho)

1995 (1 Jan). New Year. Year of the Pig. T **1120** and similar horiz designs. Multicoloured. P 11½.

N3480	20ch. Type **1120**	40	30
N3481	40ch. Pigs carrying bucket and spade	90	60
MSN3482	Two sheets, each 72×70 mm. (a) 1wn. Adult pig greeting young pigs; (b) 1wn. Pig couple carrying pumpkin	4·75	4·25

See also No. **MS**N3533.

(Des An Chol. Litho)

1995 (2 Jan). 20th Anniv of World Tourism Organization. T **1121** and similar vert designs. Multicoloured. P 12.

N3483	30ch. Tower of Juche Idea, Pyongyang	70	40
	a. Sheetlet. Nos. N3483/5 plus label	2·20	
N3484	30ch. Type **1121**	70	40
N3485	30ch. Myogilsang (cliff-face carving of Buddha), Mt. Kumgang	70	40
N3483/3485	Set of 3	1·90	1·10

Nos. N3483/5 were issued together in se-tenant sheetlets of three stamps and one label commemorating the Korea International Travel Company.

1122 Mangyongdae, Badaogou and Badge

1123 Monument bearing 50th Birthday Ode, Mt. Paekdu

(Des Kim Hun II. Litho)

1995 (22 Jan). 70th Anniv 1000-ri (250 mile) Journey by Kim II Sung to Restore Fatherland. P 11½.
N3486 **1122** 40ch. multicoloured 90 60

1995 (16 Feb). 53rd Birthday of Kim Jong II. T **1123** and similar multicoloured designs. Litho. P 12.
N3487 10ch. Type **1123** 20 10
MSN3488 Three sheets, (a) 75×90 mm. 20ch. Kim II Sung and Kim Jong II (horiz); 80ch. Kim Jong II on balcony overlooking West Sea Barrage (horiz). (b) 90×75 mm. 40ch. Kum Jong II in public park; 50ch. Kim Jong II before memorial in Taesongsan Revolutionary Martyrs' Cemetery, (c) 96×75 mm. 1wn. Kim Jong II on visit to Ryongsong Machine Complex, 1984 (31×50 mm) .... 6·25 5·25

1124 Reconstruction Monument

1125 Jamaedo Lighthouse

(Des Kim Jong Kil. Litho)

1995 (25 Feb). Completion of Reconstruction of King Tangun's Tomb. T **1124** and similar multicoloured designs. P 12.
N3489 10ch. Type **1124** 20 10
N3490 30ch. Bronze dagger on plinth............. 70 45
N3491 50ch. Monument inscribed with exploits of King Tangun .... 1·10 75
N3492 70ch. Gateway (horiz) .... 1·60 1·10
N3489/3492 Set of 4... 3·25 2·20
MSN3493 103×60 mm. 1wn.40 King Tangun.......... 3·75 2.50

(Des Kim Chung Song. Litho)

1995 (10 Mar). Lighthouses. T **1125** and similar vert design. Multicoloured. P 13½.
N3494 20ch. Type **1125** 40 20
N3495 1wn.20 Phido Lighthouse, West Sea Barrage... 2·50 1·20

1126 Cracked Green Russula (*Russula virescens*)

1127 Couple planting Tree

(Des Paek Nam Sik. Litho)

1995 (25 Mar). Fungi. T **1126** and similar vert designs. Multicoloured. P 13½.
N3496 20ch. Type **1126** 40 20
N3497 30ch. *Russula atropurpurea* 70 25
MSN3498 105×75 mm. 1wn. Caesar's mushroom (*Amanita caesarea*) .... 2·10 1·50

(Des Ri Yong Jin. Litho)

1995 (6 Apr). Tree Planting Day. P 11½.
N3499 **1127** 10ch. multicoloured............................... 20 10
No. N3499 was issued both in sheets of 36 and in sheetlets of six stamps.

1128 Birthplace, Mangyongdae

1129 Deng Xiaoping waving

(Des Kim Hun II. Litho)

1995 (15 April). 83rd Birth Anniv of Kim II Sung. T **1128** and similar multicoloured designs. P 11½.
N3500 10ch. Type **1128** 20 10
N3501 40ch. Tower of Juche Idea and Kim II Sung flower (vert)........................ 90 60
MSN3502 68×90 mm. 1wn. Kim II Sung and children (29×41 mm). P 13½ .... 2·20 1·50
Nos. N3500/1 were each issued both in sheets of 36 and in sheetlets of six stamps.

1995 (17Apr). 20th Anniv of Kim II Sung's Visit to China. T **1129** and similar designs. Litho. P 13½.
N3503 10ch. multicoloured 20 10
N3504 20ch. multicoloured 40 20
MSN3505 84×80 mm. 50ch. deep dull purple, gold and black. P 11½ .... 1·10 75
Designs: As T **1129** but vert—20ch. Deng Xiaoping of China sitting in armchair. 60×38 mm—50ch. Kim II Sung and Deng Xiaoping.

1130 Venue

1131 Emblem

1995 (18 Apr). 40th Anniv of Asian–African Conference, Bandung. T **1131** and similar vert designs. Litho. P 11½.

N3506	10ch. black, buff and carmine-red......	20	10
N3507	50ch. purple-brown, gold and black	1·10	45
MSN3508	88×85 mm. 1wn. lake-brown & black........	2·10	1·50

Designs:—50ch. Kim Il Sung receiving honorary Doctorate at Indonesia University; 1wn. Kim Il Sung and Kim Jong Il at conference tenth anniversary ceremony, Djakarta.

(Des Ri Yong Jin. Litho)

1995 (28 Apr). International Sports and Cultural Festival for Peace, Pyongyang. T **1131** and similar vert designs. Multicoloured. P 11½.

N3509	20ch. Type **1131**	40	20
N3510	40ch. Dancer	90	40
N3511	40ch. Inoki Kanji (leader of Sports Peace Party of Japan)..................	90	40
N3509/3511	*Set of 3*..................	2·00	90
MSN3512	87×70 mm. 1wn. Rikidozan (wrestler)	2·10	1·50

Nos. N3509/11 were issued in separate sheets of 36 stamps. Nos. N3509/10 and N3511 with the stamp in No. **MS**N3512 respectively were also issued together in *se-tenant* sheetlets of three stamps: 1×20ch. and 2×40ch. or 2×40ch. and 1×1wn.

1132 Amethyst

1133 Tree Sparrow (*Passer montanus*)

(Des Ri Choi Min. Litho)

1995 (2 May). Minerals. P 11½.

N3513	**1132** 2ch. multicoloured.................................	40	20
	a. Booklet pane. No. N3513×10	4·25	

No. N3513 was issued in large sheets, booklets of ten and sheetlets of six stamps.

The booklet pane has a white margin around the block.

(Des Ri Kwang Hyok. Litho)

1995 (12 May). White Animals. T **1133** and similar horiz design. Multicoloured. P 13½

N3514	40ch. Type **1133**	90	40
N3515	40ch. *Stichopus japonicus* (sea slug) ...	90	40

Nos. N3514/15 were issued both in separate sheets and together in *se-tenant* sheetlets of six stamps.

1134 Ostrea

1135 Chess

(Des Ri Kwang Hyok. Litho)

1995 (15 May). Fossils. T **1134** and similar vert design. Multicoloured. P 12.

N3516	50ch. Type **1134**	1·10	45
	a. Pair. Nos. N3516/17.......................	3·50	1·60
	b. Booklet pane. Nos. N3516×4 and N3517×3	11·00	
N3517	1wn. Cladophlebis (fern)	2·10	1·00

Nos. N3516/17 were issued together in *se-tenant* sheetlets of four stamps and booklets of seven stamps.

(Des Paek Nam Sik. Litho)

1995 (20 May). Traditional Games. T **1135** and similar horiz designs. Multicoloured. P 11½.

N3518	30ch. Type **1135**	70	25
N3519	60ch. Taekwondo	1·30	60
N3520	70ch. Yut...	1·60	65
N3518/3520	*Set of 3*......................	3·25	1·40

Nos. N3518/20 were each issued both in large sheets and in sheetlets of two stamps of the same value and one label. They were also issued together in booklets of ten stamps.

1136 National Flag and Korean Hall, Tokyo

1137 Weightlifting

(Des An Chol. Litho)

1995 (25 May). 40th Anniv of Association of Koreans in Japan. P 11½.

N3521	**1136** 1wn. multicoloured.................................	2·10	1·00

(Des Ri Kwang Hyok. Litho)

1995 (2 June). Olympic Games, Atlanta (1996). T **1137** and similar horiz designs. Multicoloured. P 11½.

N3522	50ch. Type **1137**	1·10	45
N3523	50ch. Boxing..	1·10	45
MSN3524	62×78 mm. 1wn. Clay-pigeon shooting...	2·10	1·50

Nos. N3522/3 were issued both in separate sheets and together in *se-tenant* sheetlets of four stamps.

1138 *Russula citrina*

1139 Kim Il Sung greeting Pres. Mugabe of Zimbabwe

(Des Paek Nam Sik. Litho)

1995 (1 July). Fungi. T **1138** and similar vert designs. Multicoloured. P 13½.

N3525	40ch. Type **1138**..	90	40
N3526	60ch. Black trumpets (*Craterellus cornucopioides*)............................	1·30	60
N3527	80ch. Shaggy caps (*Coprinus comatus*)	1·80	80
N3525/3527	*Set of 3*..................................	3·50	1·60

(Des Kim Dong Han and Jon Kum Hui (1wn.), Kim Dong Han (others). Litho)

1995 (8 July). First Death Anniv of Kim Il Sung. Four sheets containing designs as T **1139**. Inscriptions in black, frames in gold, centre colour as listed. P 13½.
MSN3528 Four sheets, (a) 109×85 mm. 10ch. chalky blue; 70ch. Sepia. (b) 130×66 mm. 20ch. turquoise-blue; 50ch. chocolate. (c) 129×66 mm. 30ch. steel blue; 40ch. deep reddish purple. (d) 80×107 mm. 1wn. plum .... 7·00 4·75
Designs: Vert—70ch. With King Norodom Sihanouk of Cambodia. Horiz—20ch. Kim Il Sung being awarded title of Honorary Doctor of Algeria University, 1975; 30ch. With Pres. Ho Chi Minn of Vietnam; 40ch. Greeting Che Guevara; 50ch. With Pres. Fidel Castro of Cuba; 1wn. Giving speech, 1981.

1140 Mt. Paekdu and Revolutionaries

1141 Markswoman

(Des Ri Yong Jin and Ri Chol Min. Litho)

1995 (15 Aug). 50th Anniv of Liberation. T **1140** and similar vert designs. Multicoloured. P 11½.
N3529 10ch. Type **1140** 20 10
N3530 30ch. Map of Korea and family........... 70 25
N3531 60ch. Medal .... 1·30 60
N3529/3531 Set of 3.. 2·00 85
MSN3532 Two sheets, each 120×110 mm. (a) 2×20ch. Revolutionary and crowd with banners; No. N3530×2. (b) No. N3530×2; 2×40ch. Revolutionaries.. 6·00 4·25

(Des An Chol. Litho)

1995 (1 Sept). Singapore '95 International Stamp Exhibition. Sheet 139×90 mm. Multicoloured. P 11½.
MSN3533 Nos. N3480/1, each×2...................... 2·40 1·70

(Des An Chol. Litho)

1995 (4 Sept). First Military World Games. Rome. P 11½.
N3534 **1141** 40ch. multicoloured.................................. 90 40
No. N3534 was issued in sheetlets of three stamps and one label depicting the Games emblem.

1142 Kim Il Sung with Prime Minister Chou En-lai of China, 1970

1143 Emblem and Banner

(Des Kim Tong Hwan. Litho)

1995 (1 Oct). Korean–Chinese Friendship. Three sheets containing designs as T **1142**. Inscriptions in black, frames in gold, centre colour listed below. P 12×12½ (horiz) or 12½×12 (vert).
MSN3535 Three sheets. (a) 95×130 mm. 50ch. brown-purple (Type **1142**); 50ch. bottle green (With Deng Ying-chao of China, 1979). (b) 85×100 mm. 80ch. grey-green (Greeting Mao Tse-tung of China, 1958) (vert). (c) 85×100 mm. 80ch. brown-purple (In Hamburg with Prime Minister Chou En-lai of China) (vert)......................... 5·75 4·00

(Des An Chol. Litho)

1995 (10 Oct). 50th Anniv of Korean Workers' Party. T **1143** and similar vert designs. Multicoloured. P 11½.
N3536 10ch. Type **1143** 20 10
N3537 20ch. Statue of worker, peasant and intellectual 40 20
N3538 30ch. Party monument 70 25
N3536/3538 Set of 3.. 1·20 50
MSN3539 108×75 mm. 1wn. Kim Il Sung (founder) (38×50 mm). P 13½.................................. 2·10 1·50

1144 Arch of Triumph, Pyongyang

1145 Great Tunny

(Des Ri Yong Jin. Litho)

1995 (14 Oct). 50th Anniv of Kim Il Sung's Return to Homeland. P 11½.
N3540 **1144** 10ch. multicoloured.............................. 20 10

(Des Jon Kum Hui (N3541/5); Kim Chung Song (N3546/50); Kim Jong Kil (N3551/5); Ri Chol Min (N3556/60), An Chol (3561/5). Litho)

1995 (20 Oct–5 Dec). Designs as T **1145**. Each chocolate and black. P 13½.

(a) Fishes (20 Oct)
N3541 40ch. Type **1145** 95 40
 a. Horiz. strip of 5. Nos. N3541/5 17·00
N3542 50ch. Pennant coralfish (with two bands).. 1·20 45
N3543 50ch. Needlefish .... 1·20 45
N3544 60ch. Bullrout... 1·40 60
N3545 5wn. Imperial butterfly fish .... 11·50 5·00

(b) Buildings on Kwangbok Street, Pyongyang (20 Oct)
N3546 60ch. Circus .... 1·40 65
 a. Horiz strip of 5. Nos. N3546/50. 9·00
N3547 70ch. Flats .... 1·60 65
N3548 80ch. Ryanggang Hotel.............................. 1·80 80
N3549 90ch. Tower apartment block (vert) ... 1·90 85
N3550 1wn. Sosan Hotel (vert)........................... 2·10 1·00

(c) Machines (2 Nov)
N3551 10ch. Kamsusan tipper truck.................. 30 10
 a. Horiz strip of 5. Nos. N3551/5 ... 25·00
N3552 20ch. Bulldozer... 60 20
N3553 30ch. Excavator.. 80 25
N3554 40ch. Earth mover (vert) .... 1·30 40
N3555 10wn. "Chollima 80" tractor (vert) .... 21·00 10·00

(d) Animals (20 Nov)
N3556 30ch. Giraffe (vert) 70 25
 a. Horiz strip of 5. Nos. N3556/60 11·50
N3557 40ch. Ostrich (vert)...................................... 90 40
N3558 60ch. Bluebuck (vert).................................. 1·30 60
N3559 70ch. Bactrian camel................................... 1·60 65
N3560 3wn. Indian rhinoceros .... 6·25 3·00

(e) Sculptures of Children (5 Dec)
N3561 30ch. Boy holding bird (vert) 70 25
 a. Vert. strip of 5. Nos. N3561/5..... 9·25
N3562 40ch. Boy with goose (vert)...................... 90 40
N3563 60ch. Girl with geese (vert)....................... 1·30 60
N3564 70ch. Boy and girl with football (vert) 1·60 75
N3565 2wn. Boy and girl arguing over football (vert) .... 4·50 2·00
N3541/3565 Set of 25 .... 60·00 28·00
Nos. N3541/5, N3546/50, N3551/5, N3556/60 and N3561/5 respectively were issued together in vertical (N3561/5) or horizontal se-tenant strips of five stamps within their sheets.

1146 Kim Hyong Gwon

1147 Guinea Pig

(Des Kim Jong Kil. Litho)

1995 (4 Nov). 90th Birth Anniv of Kim Hyong Gwon (uncle of Kim Il Sung). Sheet 90×70 mm. P 12½×12.
MSN3566 **1146** 1wn. black and gold.......................... 2·10   1·50

(Des Kim Hun Il. Litho)

1996 (1 Jan). Rodents. T **1147** and similar horiz designs. Multicoloured. P 11½.
N3567   20ch. Type **1147** 40   20
               a. Strip of 3. Nos. N3567/9............ 1·60
N3568   20ch. Squirrel... 40   20
N3569   30ch. White mouse................................. 70   25
N3567/3569 *Set of 3*... 1·40   60
Nos. N3567/9 were issued together in *se-tenant* sheetlets of eight stamps, consisting of two examples each of Nos. N3567/8 and four examples of N3569 plus one label depicting a landscape.

1148 Emblem, Badge and Flag

1149 Restoration Monument

(Des Ri Chol Min. Litho)

1996 (17 Jan). 50th Anniv of League of Socialist Working Youth. P 11½
N3570 **1148** 10ch. multicoloured................................. 20   10

(Des An Chol. Litho)

1996 (30 Jan). Reconstruction of Tomb of King Wanggon. T **1149** and similar multicoloured designs. P 11½.
N3571   30ch. Type **1149**...................................... 70   25
N3572   40ch. Entrance gate................................. 90   40
N3573   50ch. Tomb.. 1·10   45
N3571/3573 *Set of 3*... 2·40   1·00

1150 Teng Li-Chuang (singer)

1151 Kim Song Sun

1996 (1 Feb). Sheet 130×86 mm. Litho. P 13½.
MSN3574 **1150** 40ch. multicoloured....................... 1·20   60

(Des An Chol and Zhu Zuwei. Litho)

1996 (4 Feb). Third Asian Winter Games, Harbin, China. Speed Skaters. Sheet 130×81 mm containing T **1151** and similar vert design. Multicoloured. P 11½.
MSN3575 30ch. Type **1151**; 30ch. Ye Qiaobo.............. 1·50   1·00

1152 Jong Il Peak and Kim Jong Il Flower

1153 Pairs Skating

1154 Left-hand detail

(Des An Chol. Litho)

1996 (16 Feb). 54th Birthday of Kim Jong Il. T **1152** and similar multicoloured design. P 11½.
N3576   10ch. Type **1152** 20   10
MSN3577 96×78 mm. 80ch. Kim Jong Il and
            servicemen in snow (35×56 mm). P 13½ .... 1·80   1·20

(Des Ri Yong Jin. Litho)

1996 (17 Feb). Fifth Paektusan Prize Figure Skating Championships. T **1153** and similar vert designs. Multicoloured. P 11½.
N3578   10ch. Type **1153** 20   10
               a. Booklet pane. Nos. N3578/81 ... 2·50
N3579   20ch. Pairs skating (different) 40   20
N3580   30ch. Pairs skating (different) 70   25
N3581   50ch. Women's individual skating....... 1·10   45
N3578/3581 *Set of 4*... 2·20   90
MSN3582 100×116 mm. Nos. N3578/81 .... 2·40   1·70
No. N3581 was issued only in *se-tenant* booklets and miniature sheets.

1996 (2 Mar). "Folk Tales" (screen painting) by Ryu Suk. Sheet 206×84 mm containing T **1154** and similar vert designs. Multicoloured. P 11½.
MSN3583 8×20ch. Composite design of the
            painting.. 3·50   2·40

1155 Farm Worker

1156 1946 20ch. Stamp and Tower of Juche Idea

(Des Ri Yong Jin. Litho)

1996 (5 Mar). 50th Anniv of Agrarian Reform Law. P 11½.
N3584   **1155**   10ch. multicoloured 20   10
    No. N3584 was issued in sheetlets of five stamps and one label showing bars of music.

(Des Ri Yong Jin. Litho)

1996 (12 Mar). 50th Anniv of First North Korean Stamps. P 11½.
N3585   **1156**   1wn. multicoloured .... 2·10   1·00

1157 Yangzhou, China

(Des Ri Kwang Hyok. Litho)

1996 (20 Mar). Centenary of Founding of Chinese Imperial Post. Two sheets each 108×90 mm containing Type **1157** or similar horiz design. Multicoloured. P 11½.
MSN3586 Two sheets. (a) 50ch. Type **1157**; (b)
    50ch. Taihu Lake, Jiangsu....................................... 4·50   3·00

1158 Birthplace,   **1159** Gateway
Mangyongdae

(Des Ri Kwang Hyok. Litho)

1996 (15 Apr). 84th Birth Anniv of Kim Il Sung. T **1158** and similar multicoloured design. P 11½.
N3587   10ch. Type **1158** 20   10
MSN3588 105×115 mm. 1wn. "Eternal Image"
    (portrait of Kim Il Sung) (41×62 mm) .... 2·10   1·50

(Des Ri Yong Jin. Litho)

1996 (22 Apr). China '96 Asian International Stamp Exhibition, Peking. Landmarks in Zhejiang. T **1159** and similar horiz designs. Multicoloured. P 13½.
N3589   10ch. Type **1159** 20   10
N3590   10ch. Haiyin Pool 20   10
MSN3591 105×80 mm. 60ch. Pantuo Stone 160×38
    mm). P 11½ .... 1·30   85

1160 Hopscotch   **1161** Association
Pamphlets

(Des Paek Nam Sik. Litho)

1996 (2 May). Children's Games. T **1160** and similar horiz designs. Multicoloured. P 11½.
N3592   20ch. Type **1160** 40   20
N3593   40ch. Shuttlecock 90   40
N3594   50ch. Sledging .... 1·10   45
N3592/3594 Set of 3 .... 2·20   95
    Nos. N3592/4 were each issued both in large sheets and in sheetlets of two stamps of the same value and one label.

(Des Yun Chol Su. Litho)

1996 (5 May). 60th Anniv of Association for Restoration of the Fatherland. P 11½.
N3595   **1161**   10ch. multicoloured 20   10
    No. N3595 was issued both in large sheets and in sheetlets of five stamps and one label.

1162 Ri Po Ik

(Des Jon Kum Hui. Litho)

1996 (31 May). 120th Birth Anniv of Ri Po Ik (grandmother of Kim Il Sung). Sheet 80×90 mm. P 13½.
MSN3596 **1162** 1wn. grey, black and gold................. 2·10   1·50

1163 Arctic Fox (*Alopex*   **1164** Boy saluting
lagopus)

(Des Ri Kwang Hyok. Litho)

1996 (2 June). Polar Animals. T **1163** and similar horiz designs. Multicoloured. P 11½.
N3597   50ch. Type **1163** .... 1·20   50
        a. Sheetlet of 2. Nos. N3597/8 .... 2·50   1·10
N3598   50ch. Polar bear (*Thalarctos*
        maritimus) .... 1·20   50
N3599   50ch. Emperor penguins
        (*Aptenodytes forsteri*) .... 1·20   50
        a. Sheetlet of 2. Nos. N3599/3600 ... 3·00   1·50
N3600   50ch. Leopard seals (*Hydrurga*
        leptonyx) .... 1·20   50
N3597/3600 Set of 4.. 4·25   1·80
    Nos. N3597/8 and N3599/3600 respectively were issued together in *se-tenant* sheetlets of two stamps.

(Des Ri Yong Jin (N3601), Jon Kum Hui (**MS**N3602). Litho)

1996 (6 June). 50th Anniv of Korean Children's Union. T **1164** and similar vert design. P 11½.
N3601   10ch. Type **1164** 20   10
MSN3602 83×98 mm. 1wn. "There's Nothing to
    Envy in the World" (painting of Kim Il Sung with
    Union members) (33×51 mm). P 11½×12 .... 2·10   1·50

1165 Steam Locomotive

(Des Ri Yong Jin. Litho)

1996 (6 June). Railway Locomotives. T **1165** and similar horiz designs.
Multicoloured. P 11½.

N3603	50ch. Type **1165**	1·20	50
N3604	50ch. Electric locomotive (green)	1·20	50
N3605	50ch. Steam locomotive (different)	1·20	50
	a. Sheetlet. Nos. N3605/6 plus two labels	2·50	1·10
N3606	50ch. Electric locomotive (red and yellow)	1·20	50
N3603/3606	Set of 4	4·25	1·80

Nos. N3605/6 were issued together in sheetlets of two stamps and
two labels, one inscribed for Capex'96 international stamp exhibition
and the other showing a railway viaduct.

1166 Kim Chol Ju

(Des Jon Kum Hui. Litho)

1996 (12 June). 80th Birth Anniv of Kim Chol Ju (brother of Kim Il
Sung). Sheet 58×77 mm. P 13½.

MSN3607 **1166** 1wn.50 purple-brown, gold and black		3·75	2·50

1167 Open Book
and Characters

1168 Worker using Microphone

(Des Ri Chol Min. Litho)

1996 (15 June). 760th Anniv of Publication of Complete Collection of
Buddhist Scriptures printed from 80,00 Wooden Blocks. P 13½.

N3608	**1167** 40ch. multicoloured	95	45

(Des Kim Chol Ung. Litho)

1996 (24 June). 50th Anniv of Labour Laws. P 11½×11.

N3609	**1168** 10ch. multicoloured	30	15

1169 Eastern Broad-billed
Roller (*Eurystomas orientalis*)

1170 Ye Qiaobo

(Des Ri Kwang Hyok. Litho)

1996 (5 July). Birds (1st series). Sheet 110×92 mm containing T **1161**
and similar horiz designs. Multicoloured. P 11½.
MSN3610 10ch. Type **1169**; 40ch. Yellow-rumped
flycatcher (*Ficedula zanthopygia*); 50ch. European
cuckoo (*Cuculus canorus*) .... 3·25 2·30
See also No. MSN3622.

1996 (5 July). Third Asian Winter Games, Harbin, China (2nd issue).
As No. MSN3575 but with right-hand stamp changed. Litho.
P 11½.
MSN3611 30ch. Type **1151**; 30ch. Type **1170**............. 1·50 1·10

1171 Kumsusan Memorial Palace

(Des Ri Kwang Hyok (3612), Kim Tong Hwan, Jon Kum Hui and Ri
Kwang Hyok (**MS**3613). Litho)

1996 (8 July). Second Death Anniv of Kim Il Sung. T **1171** and similar
multicoloured designs. P 12.
N3612   10ch. Type **1171** 20 10
MSN3613 Three sheets. (a) 116×71 mm. 1wn.
Statue of Kim Il Sung, Kumsusan Memorial Palace
(29×41 mm). P 13½; (b) 80×106 mm. 1wn. Bars
of The Leader will always be with Us (44×53 mm).
P 13½; (c) 115×105 mm. 1wn. Crown visiting
statue of Kim Il Sung, Mansu Hill (34×51 mm).
P 12×11½......... 7·00 5·00

1172 Kim Il Sung meeting
Jiang Zemin of China, 1991

1173 Football and
Ancient Greek Athletes

(Des An Chol. Litho)

1996 (11 July). 35th Anniv of Korean–Chinese Treaty for Friendship, Co-operation and Mutual Assistance. T **1172** and similar designs. P 11½.

N3614	10ch. chocolate, gold and black	20	10
N3615	10ch. deep dull green, gold and black	20	10
MSN3616	70×80 mm. 80ch. deep ultramarine, gold and black	1·90	1·40

Designs: Vert—10 ch. Kim Il Sung meeting Pres. Mao Zedong of China, 1954. Horiz—80 ch. Kim Il Sung meeting Deng Xiaoping of China, 1982.

(Des Jo Jong Gu. Litho)

1996 (19 July). Centenary of Modern Olympic Games and Olympic Games, Atlanta. T **1173** and similar vert designs. Multicoloured. P 12.

N3617	50ch. Type **1173**	1·30	55
N3618	50ch. Tennis, Olympic Anthem and 1896 5 l. Greece stamp	1·30	55
N3619	50ch. Throwing the hammer and advertisement poster for first modern olympics	1·30	55
N3620	50ch. Baseball and Olympic stadium, Atlanta	1·30	55
N3617/3620	Set of 4	4·75	2·00

1174 Couple

1175 State Arms and Symbols of Industry and Communications

(Des An Chol. Litho)

1996 (30 July). 50th Anniv of Sex Equality Laws. P 11½.
N3621 **1174** 10ch. multicoloured 35   15

1996 (5 Aug). Birds (2nd series). Sheet 110×92 mm containing horiz designs as T **1169**. Multicoloured. P 11½.
MSN3622 10ch. Crested shelduck (*Tadorna cristata*); 40ch. Demoiselle crane (*Anthopoides virgo*); 50ch. Mute swan (*Cygnus olor*) .... 3·25   2·30

(Des Kim Chol Ung. Litho)

1996 (10 Aug). 50th Anniv of Nationalisation of Industries. P 11½.
N3623 **1175** 10ch. bistre and sepia 30   15

1176 Boy with Ball

1177 Pae Kil Su (men's pommel) (N. Korea)

(Des Kim Chung Song. Litho)

1996 (20 Aug). 50th Anniv of United Nations Childrens Fund. T **1176** and similar vert designs. Multicoloured. P 11½.

N3624	10ch. Type **1176**	25	10
N3625	20ch. Boy with building blocks	45	25
N3626	50ch. Boy eating melon	1·30	55
N3627	60ch. Girl playing accordion	1·50	70
N3624/3627	Set of 4	3·25	1·40

Nos. N3624/7 were issued both in separate sheets and together in two *se-tenant* sheetlets comprising either10ch. ×2, 60ch. plus label or 20ch. ×2, 50ch. plus label.

(Des Yu Yong Gwan and Ri Yong Jin. Litho)

1996 (24 Sept). First Asian Gymnastics Championships, Changsha, China. Sheet 162×127 mm. containing T **1177** and similar vert designs. Multicoloured. P 11½.
MSN3628 15ch. Type **1177**; 15ch. Li Jing (China); 15 ch. Chen Cui Ting on rings (China); 15ch. Kim Kwang Suk (asymmetrical bars) (N. Korea) .... 1·60   1·10

1178 University Buildings, Pyongyang

1179 Tiger

(Des Choe Chol Man. Litho)

1996 (1 Oct). 50th Anniv of Kim Il Sung University. P 11½.
N3629 **1178** 10ch. multicoloured 25   10

(Des Yu Yong Gwan (MSN3632), Kim Chung Song (others). Litho)

1996 (13 Oct). World Conservation Union Congress, Montreal, Canada. T **1179** and similar multicoloured designs. P 11½.

N3630	50ch. Type **1179**	1·40	55
N3631	50ch. White spoonbill	1·40	55
MSN3632	80×66 mm. 80ch. Dove-hand protecting sapling growing from globe (horiz)	2·30	1·60

Nos. N3630/1 were each issued both in large sheets and in sheetlets of three stamps of the same design and one label.

1180 Red Flag and Tower of Juche Idea

1181 Score of Theme Song from Red Mountain Ridge (film)

(Des Jon Kum Hui. Litho)

1996 (17 Oct). 70th Anniv of Down-with-Imperialism Union. P 11½.
N3633 **1180** 10ch. multicoloured 35   15

No. N3633 was issued both in large sheets and in sheetlets of five stamps and one label.

(Des Ri Yong Jin. Litho)

1996 (25 Oct). 44th Death Anniv of Huang Ji Guang (Chinese volunteer in Korean War). P 11½.
MSN3634 142×80 mm. 10ch. multicoloured (Type **1181**); 30ch. purple-brown, silver and black (Huang Ji Guang); 30ch. multicoloured (Huang Ji Guang blocking gun muzzle with his body) .... 1·80   1·30

1182 Archeozoic Era

1183 Japanese Eel (*Anguilla japonica*)

(Des Yun Chol Su and Ri Yong Jin. Litho)

1996 (1 Nov). History of the Earth. Sheet 160×70 mm. containing T **1182** and similar vert designs. Multicoloured. P 13½.
MSN3635 50ch. Type **1182**; 50ch. Proterozoic era; 50ch. Palaeozoic era; 50ch. Mesozoic era; 50ch. Cainozoic era.. 6·25   4·50

(Des An Chol and Yun Chol Su. Litho)

1996 (20 Nov). Freshwater Fishes. T **1183** and similar horiz designs. Multicoloured. P 11½.
N3636   20ch. Type **1183** 65   25
N3637   20ch. Mullet (*Liza haematocheila*)....... 65   25
MSN3638 74×53 mm. 80ch. Silver carp (*Hypophthalmichthys molitrix*) .... 2·30   1·50

1184 Soldiers and Supreme Commander's Flag

(Des Choe Chol Man. Litho)

1996 (24 Dec). Fifth Anniv of Appointment of Kim Jong Il as Supreme Commander of the People's Army. P 12.
N3639 **1184** 20ch. multicoloured 50   25
No. N3639 was issued both in large sheets and in sheetlets of ten stamps.

1185 "Ox Driver" (Kim Tu Ryang)

1186 Left-hand Detail

(Des An Chol. Litho)

1997 (1 Jan). New Year. Year of the Ox. T **1185** and similar horiz designs. Multicoloured. P 12.
N3640   70ch. Type **1185**.............................. 2·00   85
N3641   70ch. Bronze ritual plate of two bulls and a tiger.. 2·00   85
N3642   70ch. Boy with bull (ceramic)............... 2·00   85
N3643   70ch. Boy flautist sitting on bull (sculpture).. 2·00   85
N3640/3643 *Set of 4*.. 7·25   3·00
MSN3644 83×82 mm. 80ch. "People's support of the Front" (drawing, Jong Jong Yo) (60×38 mm). P 11½   2·20   1·60
Nos. N3640/1 and N3642/3 were issued both in separate sheets and together in two *se-tenant* sheetlets comprising Nos. N3640/1 plus label or Nos. N3642/3 plus label.

(Des Ri Kwang Hyok. Litho)

1997 (5 Jan). "Flowers and Butterflies" by Nam Kye U. T **1186** and similar vert designs. Multicoloured. P 12½×12.
N3645   50ch. Type **1186**.............................. 1·40   60
    a. Sheetlet of 3. Nos. N3645/7 .... 4·50
N3646   50ch. Centre detail............................ 1·40   60
N3647   50ch. Right-hand detail...................... 1·40   60
N3645/3647 *Set of 3*.. 3·75   1·60
Nos. N3645/7 were issued together in *se-tenant* sheetlets of three stamps, forming a composite design of the painting.

1187 Kitten with Dogs in Basket

1188 Bank of China

(Des Ri Kwang Hyok. Litho)

1997 (25 Jan). Paintings of Cats and Dogs. T **1187** and similar vert designs. Multicoloured. P 12½×12½.
N3648   50ch. Type **1187** .... 1·40   60
N3649   50ch. Pup in vine-wreathed basket, kitten and pumpkin........................ 1·40   60
MSN3650 Two sheets, each 96×114 mm. (a) 50ch.×2, Kitten in basket of vegetables, pup, fruit and roses; 50ch. Kittens in basket of flowers, pup and ball of wool; No. N3648. (b) 50ch. ×2, Kittens, pup and wool (as in sheet a); 50ch. Kitten pup and vegetables (as in sheet a); No. N3649...................... 6·75   4·00

1997 (Feb). Return of Hong Kong to China. Sheet 145×100 mm. containing T **1188** and similar vert designs. Multicoloured. P 13½.
MSN3651 20ch. Type **1188**; 20ch. Building with spire; 20ch. High-rise buildings..................... 3·75   3·00

1189 Birthplace, Mt. Paekdu

1190 Pair

(Des Kim Hui Won and An Chol. Litho)

1997 (16 Feb). 55th Birthday of Kim Jong Il. T **1189** and similar multicoloured designs. P 12.

N3652	**1189**	10ch. multicoloured	35	15

MSN3653 Two sheets, each 64×86 mm. (a) 1wn. Kim Jong Il inspecting farm equipment (47×35 mm); (b) 1wn. Kim Jong Il receiving flowers from soldier (47×35 mm).. 5·50 3·75

(Des Ri Yong Jin. Litho)

1997 (17 Feb). Sixth Paektusan Prize International Figure Skating Championships, Pyongyang. T **1190** and similar horiz design. Multicoloured. P 11½.

N3654	50ch. Type **1190**	1·40	60
N3655	50ch. Pair (mauve)	1·40	60
N3656	50ch. Pair (green)	1·40	60
N3654/3656	Set of 3	3·75	1·60

Nos. N3654/6 were issued both in separate sheets and in *se-tenant* sheetlets of four stamps containing two examples each of either Nos. N3654 and N3655 or Nos. N3655 and N3656.

1191 Kye Sun Hui

1192 Choe Un A

(Des Yu Yong Gwan and Kim Chung Song. Litho)

1997 (20 Feb). North Korean Gold Medal in Women's Judo at Olympic Games, Atlanta. Sheet 90×110 mm. P 11½.

N3657	**1191**	80ch. multicoloured	2·20	1·60

(Des Yu Yong Gwan and Kim Chung Song. Litho)

1997 (25 Feb). Choe Un A (competitor in World Go championships at seven years). Sheet 90×110 mm. P 11½.

N3658	**1192**	80ch. multicoloured	2·20	1·60

1193 *Prunus ansu*   **1194** Foundation Monument

(Des Kim Chol Ung. Litho)

1997 (4 Mar). Apricots. T **1193** and similar vert designs. Multicoloured. P 11½.

N3659	50ch. Type **1194**	1·50	65
N3660	50ch. *Prunus mandshurica*	1·50	65
N3661	50ch. Hoeryong white apricot (*Prunus armeniaca*)	1·50	65
N3662	50ch. Puksan apricot (*Prunus sibirica*)	1·50	65
N3659/3662	Set of 4	5·50	2·30

Nos. N3659/62 were issued both in separate sheets and together in *se-tenant* sheets containing two horizontal strips of the four designs.

(Des Jon Kum Hui. Litho)

1997 (23 Mar). 80th Anniv of Foundation of Korean National Association. P 12½×12.

N3663	**1194**	10ch. ochre and deep green	35	10

No. N3663 was issued both in large sheets and in sheetlets of eight stamps.

1195 Sapling   **1196** Birthplace, Mangyongdae

(Des Kim Chol Ung (10ch.), Kim Hui Won and Kim Chol Ung (1wn.). Litho)

1997 (6 Apr). 50th Anniv of Reforestation Day. P 11½.

N3664	**1195**	10ch. multicoloured	35	15

MSN3665 90×100 mm. 1wn. Kim Il Sung planting sapling on Munsu Hill .... 2·20 1·50

(Des Yu Yong Gwan and Yun Chol Su. Litho)

1997 (15 Apr). 85th Birth Anniv of Kim Il Sung. T **1196** and similar multicoloured designs. P 12 (N3666) or 13½. (N3667/8).

N3666	10ch. Type **1196**	25	10
N3667	20ch. Sliding Rock (horiz)	50	25
N3668	40ch. Warship Rock (horiz)	1·10	50
N3666/3668	Set of 3	1·70	75

MSN3669 Two sheets. (a) 110×90 mm. 1wn. Kim Il Sung in crowd (50×41 mm). P 13½; (b) 100×120 mm. 1wn. Kim Il Sung on flowered hill-top (33×51 mm). P 12×12½ .... 5·50 3·75

1197 Cap Badge and Modern Weapons   **1198** Map of Korea

(Des An Chol (10ch.), Kim Hui Won and An Chol (1 wn.). Litho)

1997 (25 Apr). 65th Anniv of People's Army. T **1197** and similar multicoloured design. P 11½.

N3670	10ch. Type **1197**	25	10

MSN3671 75×90 mm. 1wn. Soldiers applauding Kim Il Sung and Kim Jong Il (35×49 mm). P 12½×12 .... 2·75 1·90

(Des Choe Chol Man. Litho)

1997 (4 May). 25th Anniv of Publication of North–South Korea Joint Agreement. T **1198** and similar multicoloured design. P 11½.

N3672	10ch. Type **1198**	25	10

MSN3673 105×70 mm. 1wn. Kim Il Sung's Autograph Monument, Phanmunjom (60×38 mm). P 12×11½ .... 2·75 1·90

1199 Tower of Juche Idea, People and Flag

1200 Exhibition Centre

(Des Yu Yong Gwan and Yun Chol Su. Litho)

1997 (25 May). Posters reflecting Joint New Year Newspaper Editorials. T **1199** and similar vert designs. Multicoloured. P 12.

N3674	10ch. Type **1199**	25	10
N3675	10ch. Man with flag	25	10
N3676	10ch. Soldier, miner, farmer, intellectual and Bugler	25	10
N3674/3676	Set of 3	70	25

1997 (30 May). International Friendship Exhibition, Myohyang Mountains. Four sheets containing designs as T **1200**. Multicoloured. Litho. P 12.

MSN3677 Four sheets, each 105×120 mm. (a) 70ch. Type **1200**; (b) 70ch. Statue of Kim Il Sung in entrance hall; (c) "Native Home in Mangyongdae" (ivory sculpture from China) (horiz); (d) 70ch. Stuffed crocodile holding cups on salver and wooden ash tray (from Nicaragua) .... 7·50   5·25

1201 Memorial Post and Blazing Fortress

(Des Choe Chol Man. Litho)

1997 (4 June). 60th Anniv of Battle of Pochonbo. P 11½.
N3678 **1201** 40ch. multicoloured.................................. 1·10   50
No. N3678 was issued both in large sheets and in sheetlets of six stamps.

1202 Kim Il Sung transplanting Rice

(Des Yu Yong Gwan and Kim Chol Ung. Litho)

1997 (7 June). 50th Anniv of Kim Il Sung's Visit to Mirim Plain Paddy-fields. Two sheets, each 75×105 mm., containing designs as T **1202**. P 13½.
MSN3679 Two sheets. (a) 1wn. black and gold (Type **1202**); (b) 1wn. multicoloured (Kim Il Sung inspecting rice-transplanting machine)................... 6·25   4·25

1203 Signing Nanjing Treaty, 1842

(Des An Chol (**MS**N3680a), Ri Yong Jin (**MS**N3680b). Litho)

1997 (1 July). Return of Hong Kong to China. Two sheets containing multicoloured designs as T **1203**. P 12.
MSN3680 Two sheets. (a) 124×117 mm. 20ch. Type **1203**; 20ch. Signing China–Britain Joint Statement, Peking, 1984; 20ch. Deng Xiaoping and Margaret Thatcher; 20ch. Jiang Zemin and Tong Jianhua (Mayor of Hong Kong), 1996. (b) 124×95 mm. 97ch. Deng Xiaoping (circular, diameter 42 mm) (pair sold at 1wn.80) .... 5·00   3·50

1204 Redlichia chinensis

1205 Kim Il Sung at Kim Chaek Ironworks, June 1985

(Des Kim Chung Song. Litho)

1997 (5 July). Fossils. T **1204** and similar vert design. Multicoloured. P 11½.

N3681	50ch. Type **1204**	1·40	60
	a. Pair. Nos. 3681/2	4·50	2·00
N3682	1wn. Ptychoparia coreanica	2·75	1·30

Nos. 3681/2 were issued together in se-tenant pairs within sheetlets of four stamps.

(Des Kim Hui Won and Ri Yong Jin. Litho)

1997 (8 July). Third Death Anniv of Kim Il Sung. T **1205** and similar vert designs. Multicoloured. P 12.

N3683	50ch. Kim Il Sung at microphones (party conference, October 1985)	1·40	60
	a. Sheetlet. Nos. N3683/5	4·50	1·90
N3684	50ch. Type **1205**	1·40	60
N3685	50ch. Kim Il Sung and farmers holding wheat (Songsin Co-operative Farm, Sadong District, 1993)	1·40	60
N3686	50ch. Performing artists applauding Kim Il Sung, 1986	1·40	60
	a. Sheetlet. Nos. N3686/8	4·50	1·90
N3687	50ch. Kim Il Sung at Jonchon Factory, Jagang Province, 1991	1·40	60
N3688	50ch. Kim Il Sung receiving flowers at People's Army Conference, 1989	1·40	60
N3683/3688	Set of 6	7·50	3·25

Nos. N3683/8 were issued both in separate sheets and together in se-tenant sheetlets of three stamps, containing either N3683/5 or N3686/8.

1206 Blindman's Buff

1207 Spring

(Des Jo Mun Hui and Yun Chol Su. Litho)

1997 (26 July). Children's Games. T **1206** and similar horiz designs. Multicoloured. P 11½.

N3689	30ch. Type **1206**	85	35
N3690	60ch. Five stones	1·60	80
N3691	70ch. Arm wrestling	2·00	85
N3686/3691	*Set of 3*	4·00	1·80

Nos. N3689/91 were each issued both in large sheets and in sheetlets of two stamps of the same value and one label.

(Des Jon Kum Hui. Litho)

1997 (10 Aug). Women's National Costumes. T **1207** and similar vert designs. Multicoloured. P 11½.

N3692	10ch. Type **1207**	25	10
N3693	40ch. Summer	1·10	50
N3694	50ch. Autumn	1·40	60
N3695	60ch. Winter	1·60	80
N3692/3695	*Set of 4*	4·00	1·80

Nos. N3692/5 were issued both in separate sheets and together in three se-tenant sheetlets of four stamps, consisting of two examples each of Nos. N3692/3; N3693/4 or N3694/5.

1208 Aerial View

(Des Kim Chung Song. Litho)

1997 (25 Aug). Chongryu Bridge, Pyongyang. T **1208** and similar horiz design. Multicoloured. P 11½.

N3696	50ch. Type **1208**	1·40	60
N3697	50ch. Chongryu Bridge and birds	1·40	60

Nos. N3696/7 were issued both in separate sheets and together in se-tenant sheetlets of two stamps.

1209 Sun, Magnolias and Balloons

1210 Korean Text and Kim Il Sung University

1997 (3 Sept). 85th Anniv of Juche Era and Sun Day. T **1209** and circular design. Multicoloured. P 13½.

N3698	10ch. Type **1209**	25	10
MS	N3699 85×115 mm. 1wn. Kim Il Sung (circular, diameter 45 mm.)	2·75	2·00

No. **MS**N3699 exists in four different versions, differing in the design of the margin.

(Des Yun Chol Su. Litho)

1997 (5 Sept). 20th Anniv of Publication of Theses on Socialist Education. P 11½.

N3700	**1210** 10ch. multicoloured	25	10

No. N3700 was issued both in large sheets and in sheetlets of six stamps.

1211 Tupolev Tu-134

(Des Kim Hui Won and Kim Chol Ung. Litho)

1997 (14 Sept). 20th Anniv of Korean Membership of International Civil Aviation Organization. Three sheets, each 165×58 mm., containing designs as T **1211**. Multicoloured. P 13½.

MSN3701 Three sheets. (a) 2×20ch. Type **1211**; (b) 2×30ch. Tupolev Tu-154; (c) 2×50ch. Ilyushin Il-62 .... 5·75   4·00

1212 Chonbul Peak

1213 Podok Hermitage

(Des Kim Chol Ung. Litho)

1997 (22 Sept). Tenth Anniv of Korean Membership of World Tourism Organisation. Mt. Chilbo. T **1212** and similar horiz designs. Multicoloured. P 12.

N3702	50ch. Type **1212**	1·40	60
	a. Sheetlet of 3 and label	4·50	
N3703	50ch. Sea-Chilbo (coast)	1·40	60
N3704	50ch. Rojok Peak	1·40	60
N3702/3704	*Set of 3*	3·75	1·60

Nos. N3702/4 were issued both in separate sheets and together in sheetlets of three stamps and one label.

(Des Kim Chol Ung. Litho)

1997 (2 Oct). Kumganç Mountains. T **1213** and similar vert design. Multicoloured. P 12.

N3705	50ch. Type **1213**	1·40	60
N3706	50ch. Kumgang Gate	1·40	60

Nos. N3705/6 were issued both in separate sheets and together in se-tenant sheetlets of six stamps.

1214 School, Pupil and Mt. Paekdu

1215 Lion (*Panthera leo*)

(Des Choe Chol Man. Litho)

1997 (12 Oct). 50th Anniv of Mangyongdae Revolutionary School. P 11½.
N3707 **1214** 40ch. multicoloured .... 1·10 50
No. N3707 was issued both in large sheets and in sheetlets of four stamps.

(Des An Chol. Litho)

1997 (15 Oct). Animals presented as Gifts to Kim Il Sung. T **1215** and similar horiz designs. Multicoloured. P 11½.
N3708 20ch. Type **1215** (Ethiopia, 1987)........ 50 25
N3709 30ch. Jaguar (*Panthera onca*) (Japan, 1992)... 85 35
N3710 50ch. Barbary sheep (*Ammotragus lervia*) (Czechoslovakia, 1992)... 1·40 60
N3711 80ch. Scarlet macaw (*Ara macao*) (Austria, 1979)............................... 2·20 1·00
N3708/3711 *Set of 4*................................... 4·50 2·00
Nos. N3708/11 were issued both in separate sheets and together in *se-tenant* sheetlets of eight stamps.

1216 Bust

1217 Ten-pin Bowling

(Des Ri Yong Jin. Litho)

1997 (18 Oct). 47th Anniv of Participation in Korean War of the Chinese People's Volunteers. Qu Shao Yun. Sheet 145×80 mm. containing T **1216** and similar vert designs. Multicoloured. P 11½.
MSN3712 10ch. Statue; 30ch. Type **1216**; 30ch. Qu Shao Yun on fire .... 2·00 1·40

(Des Ri Yong Jin. Litho)

1997 (10 Nov). Sports. T **1217** and similar horiz designs. Multicoloured. P 13½.
N3713 50ch. Type **1217** .... 1·40 60
N3714 50ch. Golf.. 1·40 60
N3715 50ch. Fencing.. 1·40 60
N3713/3715 *Set of 3*.. 3·75 1·60
Nos. 3713/15 were issued both in separate sheets and together in *se-tenant* sheetlets of six stamps and two labels showing sports equipment.

1218 Snails

1219 Shanghai

(Des Jon Kum Hui. Litho)

1997 (15 Nov). Snails. T **1218** and similar vert designs. Multicoloured. P 12.
N3716 50ch. Type **1218** .... 1·50 60
a. Strip of 3. Nos. N3716/18........... 4·75
N3717 50ch. Two snails on leaf........................ 1·50 60
N3718 50ch. Snail laying eggs......................... 1·50 60
N3716/3718 *Set of 3*.. 4·00 1·60
Nos. N3716/1, were issued in *se-tenant* strips of three stamps within sheets of 16 stamps and sheetlets of six.

(Des An Chol. Litho)

1997 (19 Nov). International Stamp and Coin Exhibition, Shanghai. Sheet 145×100 mm. containing T **1219** and similar vert design. Multicoloured. P 11½.
MSN3719 30ch. Type **1219**; 50ch. Shanghai (different).. 2·20 1·60

1220 "Juche 87" and Temple

1221 Birthplace, Hoeryong

(Des Jo Jong Gu. Litho)

1997 (15 Dec). New Year. Year of the Tiger. T **1220** and similar vert designs. Multicoloured. P 13½. (10ch.) or 11½ (others).
N3720 10ch. Type **1220** 25 10
N3721 50ch. Tiger in rocket (24×34 mm) 60 35
N3722 50ch. Tiger steering ship (24×34 mm) 60 35
N3720/3722 *Set of 3*.. 1·30 70
MSN3723 (a) 112×75 mm. 80ch. Tiger driving train (24×34 mm); (b) 82×115mm. Nos. 3721/2; 80ch. As No. **MS**N3723a .... 4·50 3·25
Nos. N3720/**MS**N3723 were also issued together in *se-tenant* sheetlets of four stamps.

(Des Yun Chol Su. Litho)

1997 (24 Dec). 80th Birth Anniv of Kim Jong Suk (revolutionary). T **1221** and similar multicoloured design. P 13½.
N3724 10ch. Type **1221** 25 10
MSN3725 85×115 mm. 1wn. Kim Jong Suk (41×50 mm) .... 2·75 1·90

1222 Skiing

1223 Birthdate and Celebration Ribbon

(Des Kim Chung Song. Litho)

1998 (7 Feb). Winter Olympic Games, Nagano, Japan. T **1222** and similar vert design. Multicoloured. P 11½.
N3726 20ch. Type **1222** 25 10
N3727 40ch. Speed skating................................... 60 25
Nos. N3726/7 were issued together both in separate sheets and together in *se-tenant* sheetlets of four stamps.

(Des Yun Chol Su. Litho)

1998 (16 Feb). 56th Birth Anniv of Kim Jong Il. T **1223** and similar vert design. Multicoloured. P 11½.
N3728 10ch. Type **1223** 25 10
MSN3729 65×88mm. 3wn. Log cabin (birthplace, Mt. Paekdu)... 4·25 3·00

1224 Korean Tigers

1225 Route map, Birthplace as Mangyongdae and Trail Followers

(Des Jon Kum Hui. Litho)

1998 (6 Mar). Wildlife Paintings. T **1224** and similar vert designs. Multicoloured. P 12.

N3730	50ch. Type **1224**	75	35
N3731	50ch. White cranes	75	35
MSN3732 102×157 mm. 50ch. Nos. N3730/1; 50ch. Bears; 50ch. Racoon dogs		3·00	2·10

(Des Ri Yong Jin. Litho)

1998 (16 Mar). 75th Anniv of 1000-ri (250 mile) Journey by Kim Il Sung. P 11½.

N3733	**1225** 10ch. multicoloured	25	10

No. N3733 was issued both in large sheets and in sheetlets of ten stamps.

1226 Soldiers and Balloons

(Des Kim Chol Ung. Litho)

1998 (9 Apr). Fifth Anniv of Appointment of Kim Jong Il as Chairman of National Defence Commission. P 11½.

N3734	**1226** 10ch. Multicoloured	25	10

1227 Flags and Birthplace, Mangyongdae

1228 Kim Il Sung as Child

(Des Jon Tok Jae (N3735), Yun Chol Su (**MS**N3736). Litho)

1998 (15 Apr). 86th Birth Anniv of Kim Il Sung. T **1227** and circular designs as T **1228**. Multicoloured. P 11½ (10ch.) or 13 (others).

N3735	10ch. Type **1227**	25	10

MSN3736 Eight sheets, each 84×115 mm. (a) 80ch. Type **1228**; (b) 80ch. As student (wearing cap with rectangular badge); (c) 80ch. As commander of revolutionary army (wearing cap with star badge); (d) 80ch. In jacket and tie (three-quarter face); (e) 80ch. In army uniform; (f) 80ch. In Mao jacket; (g) 80ch. In jacket and tie (full-face); (h) 80ch. Wearing glasses ... 9·00 6·25

1229 United Front Tower and Moranbong Theatre

1230 Players and Championship Emblem

(Des Choe Chol Man. Litho)

1998 (21 Apr). 50th Anniv of North–South Conference, Pyongyang. P 13½.

N3737	**1229** 10ch. light brown, dull blue and black	25	10

(Des Ri Yong Jin. Litho)

1998 (5 May). World Cup Football Championship, France. T **1230** and similar horiz designs. Multicoloured. P 11½.

N3738	30ch. Type **1230**	35	15
N3739	50ch. Player winning ball and emblem	75	35
MSN3740 62×87 mm. 80ch. Tackling and emblem		1·10	80

Nos. N3738/9 were issued both in separate sheets and together with the 80ch. value in *se-tenant* sheetlets of six stamps.

1231 Cabbages

1232 "Countryside in May" (Jong Jong Yo)

(Des Jon Kum Hui. Litho)

1998 (20 May). Vegetables. T **1231** and similar vert designs. Multicoloured. P 13½.

N3741	10ch. Type **1231**	25	10
	a. Sheetlet of 8	7·25	
N3742	40ch. Radishes	50	25
N3743	50ch. Spring onions	60	35
N3744	60ch. Cucumbers	85	40
N3745	70ch. Pumpkins	1·00	45
N3746	80ch. Carrots	1·10	50
N3747	90ch. Garlic	1·20	60
N3748	1wn. Peppers	1·40	70
N3741/3748 *Set of 8*		6·25	3·00

Nos. N3741/8 were issued together in *se-tenant* sheetlets of eight stamps.

(Des Kim Chol Ung. Litho)

1998 (20 May). Paintings. T **1232** and similar multicoloured designs. P 12.

N3749	60ch. Type **1232**	1·00	35
N3750	1wn.40 "Dance" (Kim Yong Jun)	2·20	85
MSN3751 80×80 mm. 3wn. "Heart to Heart tale with a Peasant" (Yu Yong Gwan) (59×38 mm). P 11½		4·25	3·00

1233 Model of Automatic
Space Station (from U.S.S.R.)

(Des Ri Yong Jin. Litho)

1998 (20 May). International Friendship Exhibition, Myohyang Mountain (2nd series). T **1233** and similar vert designs. Multicoloured (except No. **MS**N3755). P 12.

N3752	1wn. Type **1233**	1·40	60
	a. Sheetlet Nos. N3752/3	2·75	1·90
	b. Sheetlet Nos. N3752 and N3754	2·75	1·90
N3753	1wn. Ceramic flower vase (from Egypt)	1·40	60
N3754	1wn. "Crane" (statuette, from Billy Graham (evangelist))	1·40	60
N3752/3754	Set of 3	3·75	1·60
MSN3755	86×100 mm. 1wn. claret and black (Kim Il Sung) (35×56 mm). P 13½.	1·40	95

Nos. N3752/4 were issued both in separate sheets and together in *se-tenant* sheetlets of two stamps, containing either Nos. N3752/3 or Nos. N3752 and N3754.

1234 Research Ship, Buoy and Dolphins in Globe and Hydro-meteorological Headquarters

1235 Stone Age Implement

(Des Jon Kum Hui. Litho)

1998 (22 May). International Year of the Ocean. T **1234** and similar multicoloured designs. P 13½.

N3756	10ch. Type **1234**	35	15
N3757	80ch. Sailing dinghies and mother with child	1·10	70
MSN3758	128×105 mm. 5wn. Vasco da Gama (vert)	6·75	4·75

Nos. N3756/7 were issued both in separate sheets and together in *se-tenant* sheetlets of four stamps and two labels.

(Des Yun Chol Su. Litho)

1998 (15 June). Korean Central History Museum, Pyongyang. T **1235** and similar designs. Multicoloured (except No. **MS**N3763). P 13½.

N3759	10ch. Type **1235**	25	10
N3760	2wn.50 Fossil skull of monkey	3·50	1·70
MSN3761	80×75mm. 4wn. claret, grey and black (Kim Il Sung visiting museum) (60×38 mm). P 11½.	5·75	4·00

1236 Commander of Hedgehog Unit and Squirrel

1237 Ri Sung Gi and Molecular Model

(Des Yun Chol Su. Litho)

1998 (15 June). Squirrels and Hedgehogs (cartoon film). T **1236** and similar vert designs. Multicoloured. P 11½.

N3762	20ch. Type **1236**	25	10
	a. Sheetlet of 6	9·75	
N3763	30ch. Commander of hedgehog unit receiving invitation to banquet	35	15
N3764	60ch. Weasel ordering mouse to poison bear	85	45
N3765	1wn.20 Squirrel with poisoned bear	1·90	85
N3766	2wn. Weasel and mice invade Flower Village	2·75	1·30
N3767	2wn.50 Hedgehog scout rescues squirrel	3·50	1·70
N3762/3767	Set of 6	8·75	4·00

Nos. N3762/7 were issued both in separate sheets and together in *se-tenant* sheetlets of six stamps.

(Des Kim Chung Song. Litho)

1998 (15 June). Second Death Anniv of Ri Sung Gi (inventor of vinalon material). T **1237** and similar multicoloured design. P 11½.

N3768	40ch. Type **1237**	60	25
MSN3769	80×65 mm. 80ch. Ri Sung Gi working in laboratory (vert)	1·10	80

A presentation pack containing three 10wn. gold stamps depicting Mao Tse-tung, Deng Xiaoping or Jiang Zemin and a 10wn. gold miniature sheet showing all three portraits was issued on 1 July 1998 to commemorate the first anniversary of the return of Hong Kong to China.

1238 Tiger Cub

1239 "Victory" (Liberation War Monument, Pyongyang) and Medal

(Des An Chol. Litho)

1998 (10 July). Young Mammals. T **1238** and similar horiz designs. Multicoloured. P 11½.

N3770	10ch. Type **1238**	25	10
	a. Booklet pane. Nos. N3770/3, each ×2	13·00	
N3771	50ch. Donkey foal	75	50
N3772	1wn.60 Elephant	2·40	1·70
N3773	2wn. Two lion cubs	2·75	2·00
N3770/3773	Set of 4	5·50	4·00

(Des Kim Chol Ung. Litho)

1998 (27 July). 45th Anniv of Victory in Liberation War. T **1239** and similar designs. P 13½.

N3774	**1239** 10ch. purple-brown and pink	25	15
MSN3775	Two sheets, each 62×87 mm. Multicoloured. (a) 2wn. "Gaz-67" jeep and route map of Kim Il Sung's wartime inspections (30×48 mm). P 12×11½; (b) 2wn. "Kim Il Sung inspecting Frontline" (painting) (48×30 mm). P 12½×12.	5·50	3·75

1240 "White Herons in Forest" 1241 Pouch

(Des Choe Chol Man (**MS**N3780), Kim Hui Won and Choe Chol Man (others). Litho)

1998 (10 Aug). Embroidery. T **1240** and similar vert designs. Multicoloured. P 12.

N3776	10ch. Type **1240**	25	15
	a. Booklet pane. Nos. N3776 ×2, N3777 ×2 and N3778/9	8·75	
N3777	40ch. "Carp"	1·90	1·30
N3778	1wn.20 "Hollyhock"	1·90	1·30
N3779	1wn.50 "Cockscomb"	2·20	1·60
N3776/3779	Set of 4	5·75	4·00
MSN3780	80×65 mm. 4wn. "Pine and Cranes"	5·75	4·00

Nos. N3776/9 were issued both in separate sheets and together with the 4wn. value in *se-tenant* sheetlets (perf 12×12½) of five stamps and a label showing an embroiderer.

(Des Jon Kum Hui and Ha Kyong Guk. Litho)

1998 (20 Aug). Traditional Costume Adornments. T **1241** and similar vert designs. Multicoloured. P 11½.

N3781	10ch. Type **1241**	25	10
	a. Booklet pane. Nos. N3781/4 ×2	12·00	
N3782	50ch. Tassels	75	50
N3783	1wn.50 Hairpin	2·10	1·50
N3784	1wn.90 Silver knife	2·75	1·90
N3781/3784	Set of 4	5·25	3·50

Nos. N3781/4 were issued both in separate sheets and together in two *se-tenant* sheetlets of 20 stamps containing ten examples each of either Nos. N3781 and N3784 or Nos. N2782/3.

1242 Rocket and State Flag 1243 Kim Jong Il Flower

(Des Kim Chol Ung. Litho)

1998 (31 Aug). Launch of First Korean Artificial Satellite "Kwangmyongsong 1". T **1242** and similar vert design. Multicoloured. P 13½.

N3785	40ch. Type **1242**	60	45
MSN3786	81×115 mm. 1wn.50 Rocket and satellite orbit (41×63 mm). P 11½×12	2·40	1·70

(Des Jon Kum Hui. Litho)

1998 (5 Sept). Re-election of Kim Jong Il as Chairman of National Defence Commission. T **1243** and circular design. Multicoloured. P 11½.

N3787	10ch. Type **1243**	25	15
MSN3788	69×94 mm. 1wn. Kim Jong Il (circular, diameter 42 mm). P 13	1·40	95

1244 Tower of Juche Idea and State Arms and Flag

(Des Jo Jong Gu. Litho)

1998 (9 Sept). 50th Anniv of Democratic Republic (1st issue). T **1244** and similar horiz designs. Multicoloured. P 13½. (10ch.) or 12½×12 (others).

N3789	10ch. Type **1244**	25	15
N3790	1wn. Painting "The Founding of the Democratic People's Republic of Korea, Our Glorious Fatherland" (Kim Il Sung waving from balcony) (48×30 mm)	1·40	95
	a. Horiz strip of 3. Nos. N3790/2	4·50	
N3791	1wn. Painting "Square of Victory" (Kim Il Sung and crowd with banners) (48×30 mm)	1·40	95
N3792	1wn. Poster "The Sacred Marks of the Great Leader Kim Il Sung will shine on this Land of Socialism" (Kim Il Sung with produce against panoramic background of Korea) (48×30 mm)	1·40	95
N3789/3792	Set of 4	4·00	2·75

Nos. N3790/2 were issued together in *se-tenant* horizontal strips of three within sheetlets of six stamps.
See also No. **MS**3794.

1245 "Let Us Push Ahead with the Forced March for Final Victory"

(Des Kim Chol Ung. Litho)

1998 (15 Sept). P 11½.

N3793	**1245** 10ch. multicoloured	25	15

1246 State Flag and Arms forming "50"

(Des Kim Gwang Sok, Ri Su Il, Choe Chol Man and Ha Gyong Guk. Litho)

1998 (20 Sept). 50th Anniv of Democratic Republic (2nd issue).Two sheets containing T **1246** or similar multicoloured design. P 13½ (40ch.) or 11½ (1wn.).

MSN3794	Two sheets. (a) 108×84 mm. 40ch. Type **1246**; (b) 108×125 mm. 1wn. Celebration Parade (31×38 mm)	2·20	1·60

1247 Cycling

1248 *Cyclamen persicum*

(Des Ri Yong Jin. Litho)

1998 (25 Sept). Olympic Games, Sydney, Australia (2000). T **1247** and similar vert designs. Multicoloured. P 13½.

N3795	20ch. Type **1247**	25	15
N3796	50ch. Football	75	50
N3797	80ch. Show jumping	1·10	80
N3798	1wn.50 Throwing the javelin	2·20	1·60
N3795/3798 *Set of 4*		4·00	2·75
MSN3799 57×80 mm. 2wn.50 Basketball		3·75	2·50

Nos. N3795/8 were issued both in separate sheets and together in two *se-tenant* sheetlets of three stamps, containing either the 20ch., 1wn.50 and 2wn.50 or the 50, 80ch. and 2wn.50.

(Des Kim Chung Song. Litho)

1998 (25 Sept). Plants presented as Gifts to Kim Jong Il. T **1248** and similar vert design. Multicoloured. P 11½.

N3800	20ch. Type **1248** (France, 1994)	35	25
N3801	2wn. *Dianthus chinensis* var. *laciniatus* (Japan, 1994)	2·75	1·90

1249 Oral Vaccination

1250 Leopard

(Des Ri Yong Jin. Photo)

1998 (20 Oct). National Vaccination Day. P 13½.

N3802	**1249** 40ch. multicoloured	60	45

No. N3802 was issued both in large sheets and in sheetlets of six stamps.

(Des Jo Jong Gu. Litho)

1998 (21 Oct). The Leopard (*Panthera pardus*). T **1250** and similar horiz designs. Multicoloured. P 13½.

N3803	1wn. Type **1250**	1·50	1·00
N3804	1wn. Leopard in snow	1·50	1·00
N3805	1wn. Leopard looking to left	1·50	1·00
N3806	1wn. Leopard's face	1·50	1·00
N3803/3806 *Set of 4*		5·50	3·50

Nos. N3803/6 were issued both in separate sheets and together in *se-tenant* blocks of four within sheetlets of 16 stamps.

1251 Canal

1252 Emblem and Milan Cathedral

(Des Yun Chol Su. Litho)

1998 (23 Oct). Land and Environment Conservation Day. T **1251** and similar horiz designs. Multicoloured. P 11½.

N3807	10ch. Type **1251**	25	10
N3808	40ch. Motorway, tower blocks and lorry	65	45
MSN3809 85×71 mm. 1wn. Kim Il Sung shovelling earth to signal start of Pothong River improvement. P 12×12½		1·50	1·00

(Des Yu Yong Gwan. Litho)

1998 (23 Oct). Italia 98 International Stamp Exhibition, Milan, Italy. Sheet 108×90 mm. P 12½×12.

MSN3810 **1252** 2wn. multicoloured		3·00	2·10

1253 Peng Dehuai and Kim Il Sung

1254 Liu Shaoqi

(Des Zhu Zu Wei and Ri Yong Jin. Litho)

1998 (24 Oct). Birth Centenary of Peng Dehuai (commander of Chinese People's Volunteers in Korean Liberation War). Sheet 131×112 mm. containing T **1253** and similar multicoloured designs. P 11½.

MSN3811 20ch. Type **1253**; 20ch. Mao Tse-tung (Chinese communist leader), Chou En-lai (Chinese statesman) and Peng Dehuai; 30ch. Peng Dehuai in marshal's uniform (27×38 mm); 30ch. "On the Front" (painting, He Kong De) (27×38 mm) ... 1·60   1·10

(Des An Chol. Litho)

1998 (24 Nov). Birth Centenary of Liu Shaoqi (Chairman of Chinese People's Republic, 1959–68). T **1254** and similar multicoloured designs. P 13½.

N3812	10ch. Type **1254**	25	10
N3813	20ch. Liu Shaoqi and Mao Tse-tung	40	20
N3814	30ch. Liu Shaoqi and his daughter, Xiao Xiao	55	40
N3815	40ch. Liu Shaoqi and his wife, Wang Guangmei	65	45
N3812/3815 *Set of 4*		1·70	1·00
MSN3816 100×70 mm. 1wn. Liu Shaoqi and Kim Il Sung (46½×35 mm). P 12×12½		1·50	1·00

1255 Victory in Yonsong Monument, Yonan Fortress and Banners

1256 Dish Aerial, Artificial Satellite, Globe and Relay Tower

(Des Jo Jong Gu. Litho)

1998 (25 Nov). 400th Anniv of Victory in Korean–Japanese War.
T **1255** and similar vert designs. Multicoloured. P 11½.
N3817	10ch. Type **1255**	25	10
	a. Strip of 3	3·25	
N3818	30ch. Naval Victory in Myongryang		
	Monument, General Ri Sun Sin		
	and "turtle" ship...............................	40	30
N3819	1wn.60 Monument to Hyujong in		
	Kwangwon province, Hyujong		
	(Buddhist priest), sword and		
	helmet	2·40	1·70
N3817/3819 *Set of 3*..		2·75	1·90

MSN3820 112×68 mm. 10wn. "Sea Battle off
Hansan Islet in 1592" (painting)..................... 15·00   12·00
Nos. N3817/9 were issued both in separate sheets and together in
se-tenant sheetlets of 15 stamps containing five horizontal *se-tenant*
strips of three.

(Des Ha Kyong Guk. Litho)

1998 (25 Nov). 15th Anniv of North Korean Membership of
Interspultnik. P 13½.
N3821   **1256** 1wn. deep yellowish green and
                        bright green .... 1·60   1·10

1257 Goat   **1258** "A Floral Carriage of
                                   Happiness" (sculpture) and
                                   Palace

(Des Kim Chol Man. Litho)

1998 (26 Nov). P 13½.
N3822	**1257**	10ch. black and yellowish green..........	30	20
N3823		1wn. black and deep claret..................	1·70	1·20

(Des Kim Chung Song. Litho)

1998 (26 Nov). Mangyongdae Schoolchildren's Palace. T **1258** and
similar horiz design. Multicoloured. P 11½.
N3824   40ch. Type **1258** 70   50
MSN3825 85×64 mm. 1wn. Quotation of Kim Il
Sung "Children are the treasure of our country.
Korea of the future is theirs"............................ 1·70   1·20
No. N3824 was issued both in large sheets and in sheetlets of four
stamps with an enlarged bottom margin showing the score of We are
the Happiest in the World.

1259 Emblem   **1260** Reeves's Turtle
                               (*Chinemys reevesii*)

(Des Jo Jong Gu. Litho)

1998 (10 Dec). 50th Anniv of Universal Declaration of Human Rights.
P 11½.
N3826   **1259** 20ch. multicoloured 30   20

(Des Choe Chol Man. Litho)

1998 (15 Dec). Reptiles and Amphibians. T **1260** and similar horiz
designs. Multicoloured. P 13½.
N3827	10ch. Type **1260**	30	20
	a. Block of 4. Nos. N3827/30...........	4·25	
N3828	40ch. Skink (*Eumeces coreensis*)	70	50
N3829	60ch. Loggerhead turtle (*Caretta*		
	caretta)	1·00	70
N3830	1wn.20 Leatherback turtle		
	(*Dermochelys coriacea*)	2·00	1·40
N3827/3830 *Set of 4*..		3·50	2·50

Nos. N3827/30 were issued together in *se-tenant* blocks of four
stamps, both in sheets and in sheetlets of 16 stamps, each block
forming a composite design. Booklets containing a strip of three
blocks were also issued.

1261 Thajong Rock   **1262** Ri Mong Ryong
                                      marrying Song Chun
                                      Hyang

(Des Kim Chol Ung. Litho)

1998 (15 Dec). Mt. Chilbo. T **1261** and similar vert designs.
Multicoloured. P 11½.
N3831	30ch. Type **1261**	40	30
N3832	50ch. Peasant Rock	85	60
N3833	1wn.70 Couple Rock	2·75	1·90
N3831/3833 *Set of 3*..		3·50	2·50

(Des An Chol. Litho)

1998 (20 Dec). Tale of Chun Hyang. T **1262** and similar vert designs.
Multicoloured. P 11½.
N3834	40ch. Type **1262**	70	50
	a. Booklet pane. Nos. N3834/6,		
	each ×2..	15·00	
N3835	1wn.60 Pyon Hak Do watching Chun		
	Hyang	2·50	1·90
N3836	2wn.50 Ri Mong Ryong and Chun		
	Hyang	4·00	3·00
N3834/3836 *Set of 3*..		6·50	4·75

MSN3837 110×95 mm. Nos. N3834/6; 2wn. Chun
Hyang in wedding veil .... 10·50   8·75

1263 Chollima   **1264** Rabbit meeting
    Statue   Lion

(Des Jo Jong Gu, Ri Yong Jin and Kim Chol Ung. Litho)

1998 (22 Dec). Pyongyang Monuments. T **1263** and similar vert
designs. Multicoloured. P 13×13½.
N3838	**1263**	10ch. scarlet...............................	20	15
N3839	A	10ch. scarlet...............................	20	15
N3840	B	10ch. scarlet-vermilion	20	15

N3841	A	20ch. reddish orange	30	20
N3842	**1263**	30ch. reddish orange	55	40
N3843	A	40ch. yellow....................................	70	50
N3844	B	40ch. yellow....................................	70	50
N3845	**1263**	70ch. bright apple green	1·10	85
N3846	B	70ch. bright apple green	1·10	85
N3847		1wn.20 bright yellowish green.........	2·00	1·50
N3848	**1263**	1wn.50 bright blue-green..................	2·50	1·90
N3849	A	2wn. new blue..............................	3·50	2·50
N3850	B	3wn. new blue..............................	5·00	3·75
N3851	**1263**	5wn. deep ultramarine.................	8·50	6·25
N3852	A	10wn. reddish violet	17·00	12·50
N3838/3852 *Set of 15*			39·00	29·00

Designs:— A, Arch of Triumph; B, Tower of Juche Idea.

(Des An Chol. Litho)

1999 (1 Jan). New Year. Year of the Rabbit. T **1264** and similar vert designs. P 11½.

N3853		10ch. Type **1264**	30	20
		a. Booklet pane. Nos. N3853/6.......	8·75	
N3854		1wn. Rabbit with mirror and lion	1·70	1·30
N3855		1wn.50 Lion in trap............................	2·50	1·90
N3856		2wn.50 Rabbit	4·00	3·00
N3853/3856 *Set of 4*			7·75	5·75

MSN3857 160×70 mm. 10ch. Type **1264**; 1wn. No. N3854; 1wn.50 No. N3855; 2wn.50 No. N3856........ 8·50 6·50

1265 Automatic Rifle and Star

1266 Log Cabin (birthplace, Mt. Paekdu)

(Des Yun Chol Su. Litho)

1999 (14 Jan). 40th Anniv of Worker–Peasant Red Guards. P 13½.
N3858 **1265** 10ch. multicoloured 30 20

(Des Ri Yong Jin. Litho)

1999 (16 Feb). 57th Birth Anniv of Kim Jong Il. P 11½.
N3859 **1266** 40ch. multicoloured 70 55

1267 Cranes, Rice Sheaf and "35"

1268 Korean Script and Crowd

(Des Kim Chol Ung. Litho)

1999 (25 Feb). 35th Anniv of Publication of Theses on the Socialist Rural Question in Our Country by Kim Il Sung. P 13½.
N3860 **1267** 10ch. multicoloured 30 20

(Des Jo Jong Gu. Litho)

1999 (1 Mar). 80th Anniv of 1 March Uprising. P 11½.
N3861 **1268** 10ch. black and olive-sepia 30 20

1269 16th-century "Turtle" Ship

1270 Birthplace, Mangyongdae

(Des Jon Kum Hui. Litho)

1999 (19 Mar). Australia '99 International Stamp Exhibition, Melbourne. P 13½.
N3862 **1269** 2wn. multicoloured.............................. 2·40 1·80
MSN3863 100×75 mm. **1269** 2wn. Multicoloured..... 2·75 2·00

(Des Jo Jong Gu. Litho)

1999 (15 Apr). 87th Birth Anniv of Kim Il Sung. T **1270** and similar vert design. P 11½.
N3864 **1270** 10ch. lake-brown, flesh and lavender-grey............................... 30 20
MSN3865 68×95 mm. 2wn. multicoloured (Kim Il Sung (41×62 mm)) .... 2·75 2·00

1271 Player

1272 Korean Sports Stamps and Emblem

(Des Jo Jung Gu. Litho)

1999 (26 Apr). 45th Table Tennis Championship, Belgrade, Yugoslavia. P 11½.
N3866 **1271** 1wn.50 multicoloured................................ 2·00 1·50

(Des Jo Jong Gu. Litho)

1999 (27 Apr). iBRA'99 International Stamp Exhibition, Nuremberg, Germany. P 11½.
N3867 **1272** 1wn. multicoloured .... 1·30 95

1273 *Benzoin obtusilobum*

(Des Choe Chol Man. Litho)

1999 (30 Apr). 40th Anniv of Central Botanical Garden, Mt. Taesong, Pyongyang. T **1273** and similar vert designs. Multicoloured. P 11½.

N3868		10ch. Type **1273**	30	20
		a. Booklet pane. Nos. N3868/71, each ×3..	9·25	
		b. Sheetlet of 4 stamps....................	3·25	
N3869		30ch. *Styrax obassia*	40	30
N3870		70ch. *Petunia hybrid*	1·00	75

N3871   90ch. *Impatiens hybrid* .... 1·30   95
N3868/3871   *Set of 4*... 2·75   2·00
MSN3872 65×75 mm. 2wn. Kimilsungflower and
   Kimjongil (begonia) .... 2·75   2·00
     Nos. N3868/71 were issued both separately in large sheets and
together in *se-tenant* sheetlets of four stamps.

1274 Chimpanzee
(*Pan troglodytes*) and
Rhinoceros

(Des An Chol. Litho)

1999 (30 Apr). 40th Anniv of Central Zoo, Mt. Taesong, Pyongyang.
   T **1274** and similar vert designs. Multicoloured. P 13½.
N3873   50ch. Type **1274** 70   55
         a. Booklet pane. Nos. N3873/5,
           each ×2... 5·25
N3874   60ch. Manchurian crane (*Grus
         japonensis*) and deer 85   65
N3875   70ch. Common zebra (*Equus
         burchelli*) and kangaroo .... 1·00   75
N3873/3875   *Set of 3*... 2·30   1·80
MSN3876 95×75 mm. 2wn. Tiger (*Panthera tigris
coreensis*).. 2·75   2·00

1275 Light Industry Hall

1276 Methods of
Communication, Satellite and
Globe

(Des Choe Chol Man. Litho)

1999 (2 May). Three Revolutions Museum, Ryonmotdong, Pyongyang.
   T **1275** and similar horiz design. Multicoloured. P 11½.
N3877   60ch. Type **1275** 85   65
N3878   80ch. Heavy Industry Hall .... 1·10   85

(Des Kim Hae Yong. Litho)

1999 (8 May). 20th Anniv of Asia–Pacific Telecommunications Union.
   P 13½.
N3879   **1276**   1wn. multicoloured .... 1·40   1·10

1277 Monument

1278 Seagulls

(Des Jon Kum Hui. Litho)

1999 (19 May). 60th Anniv of Victory in Battle of Musan. P 11½.
N3880   **1277**   10ch. multicoloured 30   20

(Des Ri Yong Jin. Litho)

1999 (20 May). 190th Birth Anniv of Charles Darwin (naturalist).
   T **1278** and similar vert designs. Multicoloured. P 11½.
N3881   30ch. Type **1278** 40   30
         a. Sheetlet of 5. Nos. N3881/5 .... 6·50
N3882   50ch. Bats 70   55
N3883   1wn. Dolphins .... 1·40   1·10
N3884   1wn.20 Man on horseback .... 1·70   1·30
N3885   1wn.50 Dancer .... 2·10   1·60
N3881/3885   *Set of 5*... 5·75   4·25
MSN3886 76×67 mm. 2wn. Charles Darwin (26×39
   mm). P 13½×12 .... 3·50   2·75
     Nos. N3881/5 were issued together in *se-tenant* sheetlets of
five stamps, each stamp with a *se-tenant* label showing part of the
skeleton of the subject depicted.

1279 "Princess Margarita
in a White Dress"

1280 Rimyongsu Power
Station

(Des Ri Yong Jin. Litho)

1999 (30 May). 400th Birth Anniv of Diego Velazquez (artist). T **1279**
   and similar vert designs. Multicoloured. P 12.
N3887   50ch. Type **1279** 70   55
         a. Booklet pane. Nos. N3887/9,
           each ×2... 12·50
N3888   50ch. "Men drawing Water from a
         Well".. 70   55
N3889   3wn.50 "Self-portrait" .... 4·50   3·50
N3887/3889   *Set of 3*... 5·25   4·25
MSN3890 68×118 mm. No. N3889. P 12×11½ .... 4·75   3·75
     Nos. N3887/8 were issued both separately in large sheets and
together in *se-tenant* sheetlets of three stamps with No. N3889.
     No. N3889 was only available in *se-tenant* sheetlets with Nos.
N3887/8 or in booklet panes.

(Des Jon Kum Hui. Litho)

1999 (2 June). Hydro-electric Power Stations. T **1280** and similar
   horiz design. Multicoloured. P 11½.
N3891   50ch. Type **1280** 70   55
N3892   1wn. Jangjasan Power Station............. 1·40   1·10

1281 Players tackling

1282 The Earth, Space
Rocket and Mars

(Des Ri Song Nam and An Chol. Litho)

1999 (8 June). Third Women's World Football Championship, U.S.A. T **1281** and similar horiz designs. Multicoloured. P 13½.

N3893	1wn. Type **1281**	1·40	1·10
	a. Sheetlet of 4. Nos. N3893/6	8·50	
	b. Booklet pane. Nos. N3893/6	8·50	
N3894	1wn.50 Player No. 3 and player wearing blue and white strip tackling	2·10	1·60
N3895	1wn.50 Player and goal keeper........	2·10	1·60
N3896	2wn. Player No. 7 and player wearing blue strip........	2·75	2·10
N3893/3896 Set of 4		7·50	5·75

Nos. N3893/6 were issued together in *se-tenant* sheetlets of four stamps and in booklets containing a strip of four stamps.

(Des Yun Chol Su. Litho)

1999 (10 June). Exploration of Planet Mars. Sheet 110×75 mm. containing T **1282** and similar vert designs. Multicoloured. P 11½.

MSN3897 2wn. Type **1282**; 2wn. Satellite orbiting Mars; 2wn. Probe landing on Mars..............	8·50	6·50

1283 Man with Candlesticks

(Des Choe Chol Man. Litho)

1999 (10 June). The Nation and Destiny (Korean film). T **1283** and similar horiz designs showing scenes from the film. Multicoloured. P 11½.

N3898	1wn. Type **1283**	1·30	95
	a. Sheetlet. Nos. N3898/3901	5·50	
N3899	1wn. Woman holding gun and man in white suit....................	1·30	95
N3900	1wn. Man behind bars....................	1·30	95
N3901	1wn. Man with protective goggles on head..............	1·30	95
N3898/3901 Set of 4		4·75	3·50

Nos. 3898/901 were issued together in *se-tenant* sheetlets of four stamps.

Booklets containing a strip of two blocks were also issued.

1284 Samil Lagoon

(Des Ri Yong Jin. Litho)

1999 (15 June). Mt. Kumgang. T **1284** and similar multicoloured designs. P 12.

N3902	20ch. Type **1284**	30	20
N3903	40ch. Samson Rocks (vert).....................	55	45
N3904	60ch. Rock, Kumgang Sea..................	85	65
N3905	80ch. Kuryong Waterfall (vert).............	1·00	75
N3906	1wn. Kwimyon Rock (vert)	1·30	95
N3902/3906 Set of 5		3·50	2·75

1285 Emblem, Girl and Dove

1286 France 1870 20c. Stamp and North Korea 20ch. 1946 Stamp

(Des Ri Yong Jin. Litho)

1999 (20 June). 125th Anniv of Universal Postal Union. Sheet 87×67 mm. P 11½.

MSN3907 **1285** 2wn. Multicoloured.............................	3·00	2·40

(Des Choe Chol Man. Litho)

1999 (2 July). Philexfrance 99 International Stamp Exhibition, Paris. Sheet 102×77 mm. P 12.

MSN3908 **1286** 2wn.50 multicoloured.......................	3·50	2·50

1287 Mercedes Motor Car

1288 Chinese Characters and Mangyong Hill

(Des Kim Chol Ung. Litho)

1999 (8 July). Fifth Death Anniv of Kim Il Sung. T **1287** and similar horiz designs. Multicoloured. P 11½.

N3909	1wn. Type **1287**	1·70	1·30
	a. Horiz pair. Nos. N3909/10...........	3·15	2·75
N3910	1wn. Railway carriage......................	1·70	1·30

Nos. N3909/10 were issued together in *se-tenant* sheetlets of two stamps.

(Des Jo Jong Gu. Litho)

1999 (10 July). 105th Birth Anniv of Kim Hyong Jik (revolutionary). P 11½.

N3911 **1288** 10ch. multicoloured.................................	30	20

1289 Patterned Vessel

(Des Pak Kyong Ryong and Choe Chol Man. Litho)

1999 (15 July). Ceramics. T **1289** and similar horiz designs. Multicoloured. P 13½.

N3912	70ch. Type **1289**......................	1·00	75
N3913	80ch. Wit and Beauty jar................	1·10	85
N3914	1wn. Patterned vase...................	1·30	95

N3915	1wn.50 Celadon kettle	2·00	1·50
N3916	2wn.50 White china vase	3·25	2·50
N3912/3916 Set of 5		7·75	6·00

N3924	40ch. Hurdles	60	45
N3925	80ch. Discus	1·20	80
N3923/3925 Set of 3		2·00	1·40

1290 Silver Carp
(*Hypophthalmichthys molitrix*)

1291 Map and Crowd

(Des Kim Yong Hwa and Kim Chol Ung. Litho)

1999 (20 July). Fish Breeding. T **1290** and similar horiz designs. Multicoloured. P 13½.

N3917	50ch. Type **1290**	70	55
N3918	1wn. Common carp (*Cyprinus carpio*)	1·40	1·10
N3919	1wn.50 Spotted silver carp (*Aristichthys nobilis*)	2·10	1·60
N3917/3919 Set of 3		3·75	3·00

Booklets containing a strip of six stamps consisting of two examples of each, were also issued.

(Des Jo Jong Gu. Litho)

1999 (5 Aug). Year of National Independence and Solidarity. P 11½.
N3920 **1291** 40ch. multicoloured 55 45

1292 Samjiyon with Maps and
Japan and Korea

(Des Choe Chol Man. Litho)

1999 (16 Aug). 40th Anniv of Repatriation of Korean Nationals in Japan. P 11½.
N3921 **1292** 1wn.50 multicoloured .... 2·50 1·90

1293 Symbols of Prosperity

1294 100-metre Race

(Des Jo Jong Ku. Litho)

1999 (17 Aug). P 11½.
N3922 **1293** 40ch. multicoloured 55 45

(Des Kim Chol Ung. Litho)

1999 (18 Aug). World Athletics Championships, Seville, Spain. T **1294** and similar vert designs. Multicoloured. P 11½.
N3923   30ch. Type **1294** 45 35

1295 *Acalypha hispida*

1296 "Play a Flute to
call the Phoenix"

(Des Jon Kum Hui. Litho)

1999 (20 Aug). Plants presented to Kim Il Sung. T **1295** and similar vert designs. Multicoloured. P 11½.

N3926	40ch. Type **1295**	75	55
	a. Sheetlet. Nos. N3926/31	4·75	
N3927	40ch. *Allamanda neriifolia*	75	55
N3928	40ch. *Begonia x hiemalis*	75	55
N3929	40ch. *Fatsia japonica*	75	55
N3930	40ch. *Streptocarpus hybrida*	75	55
N3931	40ch. *Streptocarpus rexii*	75	55
N3926/3931 Set of 6		4·00	3·00

Nos. N3926/31 were issued together in *se-tenant* sheetlets of six stamps, each sheetlet forming a composite design.

(Des An Chol. Litho)

1999 (21 Aug). CHINA 1999 International Stamp Exhibition and 22nd U.P.U. Congress, Beijing. T **1296** and similar vert designs. Multicoloured. P 11½.
MSN3932 40ch. Type **1296**; 40ch. "Relics kept in a Bamboo Field"; 40ch. "Six Friends in a Pine Forest"; 40ch. "Lady's Morning Dressing" .... 3·00 2·20

1297 *Grifola frondosa*

1298 *Aporocactus
flagelliformis*

(Des Jon Kum Hui. Litho)

1999 (25 Aug). Mushrooms. T **1297** and similar horiz designs. Multicoloured. P 11½.

N3933	40ch. Type **1297**	75	55
N3934	60ch. *Lactarius volemus*	1·00	80
N3935	1wn. *Coriolus versicolor*	1·80	1·30
N3933/3935 Set of 3		3·25	2·40

(Des Choe Chol Man. Litho)

1999 (1 Sept). Cacti. T **1298** and similar vert designs. Multicoloured. P 11½.

N3936	40ch. Type **1298**	75	55
N3937	50ch. *Astrophytum ornatum*	90	65
N3938	60ch. *Gymnocalycium michano vichii*	1·00	80
N3936/3938 Set of 3		2·40	1·80

Nos. 3939/41 *are vacant.*

1299 Rat

1300 Shrimp
(*Pandalus hypsinotus*)

(Des Zhang Hui. Litho)

1999 (10 Sept). Animals of the Eastern Zodiac. Two sheets, each 110×160 mm, containing T **1299** and similar circular designs. Multicoloured. P 14.
MSN3942 Two sheets. (a) 10ch. Type **1299**; 10ch.
Ox; 10ch. Tiger; 10ch. Rabbit; 10ch. Dragon;
10ch. Snake. (b) 10ch. Horse; 10ch. Sheep;
10ch. Monkey; 10ch. Cockerel; 10ch. Dog;
10ch. Sow and piglets (each sold at 1wn.) .... 3·50   2·75
No. **MS**N3942 was perforated 10 around the circular design contained within an outer square perforated 12½.

(Des Ha Kyong Guk and An Chol. Litho)

1999 (10 Sept). T **1300** and similar vert designs. Multicoloured. P 11½.
N3943   50ch. Type **1300**   90   65
                a. Booklet pane. Nos. 3943/5,
                      each×2 ....   7·50
N3944   70ch. Shrimp (*Penaeus orientalis*) ....   1·20   90
N3945   80ch. Lobster (*Homarus vulgaris*)........   1·50   1·10
N3943/3945 Set of 3...   3·25   2·40

1301 Jong Song Ok (marathon runner)

(Des Kim Hae Yong, Cloe Chol Man. Litho)

1999 (20 Sept). Victory of Jong Song Ok at World Athletics Championship, Seville. P 13½.
N3946 **1301** 40ch. multicoloured   75   55
                a. Booklet pane. No. N3946×6.......   4·75
MSN3947 90×70 mm. 2wn. Jong Song Ok (vert) ....   3·50   2·75

1302 Mt. Kumgang, North Korea

(Des An Chol and Li Defu. Litho)

1999 (5 Oct). 50th Anniv of North Korea–China Diplomatic Relations. T **1302** and similar horiz designs. Multicoloured. P 12½×12.
N3948   40ch. Type **1302**   75   55
                a. Pair. Nos. N3948/9 ....   1·90   1·50
N3949   60ch. Mt. Lushan, China..........................   1·00   80
MSN3950 142×93 mm. No. N3948/9 ....   2·10   1·70
No. N3948/9 were issued together in horizontal or vertical pairs within the sheet.
No. **MS**N3950 was issued with two labels featuring Korean and Chinese script.

1303 Deng Xiaoping

(Des Zhu Zuwei. Litho)

1999 (10 Nov). Return of Macao to China. Two sheets containing T **1303** and similar multicoloured designs. P 13½. (**MS**N3951a/b) or 12½ (**MS**N3951c/d)
MSN3951 Four sheets. (a) 155×100 mm. 20ch. Type
1303 (green frame); 20ch. Jiang Zemin (President of People's Republic of China) and He Houhua (mayor of Macau Special Administrative Region) (green frame); 80ch. Mao Tse-tung (green frame). (b) 155×100 mm. as No. **MS**N3951a but with gold frames. (c) 90×122 mm. 1wn. Jiang Zemin (green frame) (circular design). (d) As **MS**N3951c but with gold frame...   8·25   6·75

1304 Steel Worker holding Torch

1305 Yellow Dragon

(Des An Chol. Litho)

2000 (1 Jan). New Year. 40th Anniv of April 19th Rising. P 11½.
N3952 **1304** 10ch. multicoloured   30   20

(Des An Choi. Litho)

2000 (1 Jan). Koguryo Era Tomb Murals, Jian. T **1305** and similar multicoloured designs. P 11½.
N3953   70ch. Type **1305** ....   1·20   90
                a. Booklet pane. No. N3953×8.........   9·75
MSN3954 90×60 mm. 1wn.60 Blue dragon (51×33 mm). P 11½×12 ....   3·00   2·20

1306 Weeding

1307 Views across Lake Chou

(Des Kim Hae Yong. Litho)

2000 (25 Jan). "Rural Life" (anon). T **1306** and similar vert designs showing details from the painting. Multicoloured. P 13½.

N3955	40ch. Type **1306**	75	55
N3956	40ch. Hemp cloth weaving	75	55
N3957	40ch. Threshing	75	55
N3958	40ch. Riverside market	75	55
N3955/3958	Set of 4	2·75	2·00

(Des Choe Chol Man. Litho)

2000 (30 Jan). Mt. Paektu. T **1307** and similar horiz designs. Multicoloured. P 13½.

N3959	20ch. Type **1307**	45	35
N3960	20ch. Eagle-shaped rock formation ...	45	35
N3961	20ch. Owl-shaped rock formation	45	35
N3959/3961	Set of 3	1·20	95

1308 Chuibari Mask Dance   **1309** Cat

(Des Kim Hae Yong. Litho)

2000 (3 Feb). Pongsan Mask Dance. T **1308** and similar vert designs depicting masks and characters from component dances. Multicoloured. P 11½.

N3962	50ch. Type **1308**	90	65
N3963	80ch. Ryangban Mask Dance	1·50	1·10
N3964	1wn. Malttugi Mask Dance	2·10	1·60
N3962/3964	Set of 3	4·00	3·00

(Des Ri Yong Jin. Litho)

2000 (6 Feb). Cats. T **1309** and similar vert designs. Multicoloured. P 13½.

N3965	50ch. Type **1309**	1·00	80
	a. Booklet pane. Nos. N3965×2 and Nos. N3966/7 each ×3		
N3966	50ch. Three kittens	1·00	80
N3967	50ch. Mother and kittens	1·00	80
N3965/3967	Set of 3	2·75	2·20

1310 Singapura Cat   **1311** Log Cabin (birthplace, Mt. Paekdu)

2000 (10 Feb). Fauna. T **1310** and similar vert designs. Multicoloured. P 13½.

N3968	2wn. Type **1310**	3·75	2·75
	a. Sheetlet of 4. Nos. N3968/71	16·00	
N3969	2wn. Blue Abyssinian cat	3·75	2·75
N3970	2wn. Oriental cat	3·75	2·75
N3971	2wn. Scottish fold tabby cat	3·75	2·75
N3972	2wn. Shiba inu	3·75	2·75
	a. Sheetlet of 4. Nos. N3972/5	16·00	

N3973	2wn. Yorkshire terrier	3·75	2·75
N3974	2wn. Japanese chin	3·75	2·75
N3975	2wn. Afghan hound	3·75	2·75
N3976	2wn. Przewalski's horse	3·75	2·75
	a. Sheetlet of 4. Nos. N3976/9	16·00	
N3977	2wn. Grey cob	3·75	2·75
N3978	2wn. White horse rearing	3·75	2·75
N3979	2wn. Donkeys	3·75	2·75
N3980	2wn. Panda in tree	3·75	2·75
	a. Sheetlet of 4. Nos. N3980/3	16·00	
N3981	2wn. Panda eating	3·75	2·75
N3982	2wn. Panda scratching against tree	3·75	2·75
N3983	2wn. Mother and cub	3·75	2·75
N3984	2wn. Two polar bears (*Ursus maritimus*)	3·75	2·75
	a. Sheetlet of 4. Nos. N3984/7	16·00	
N3985	2wn. Mother and cub	3·75	2·75
N3986	2wn. Standing bear	3·75	2·75
N3987	2wn. Bear lying down	3·75	2·75
N3988	2wn. Mexican lance-headed rattlesnake (*Crotalus polystictus*)	3·75	2·75
	a. Sheetlet of 4. Nos. N3988/91	16·00	
N3989	2wn. Scarlet king snake (*Lampropeltis triangulum elapsoides*)	3·75	2·75
N3990	2wn. Green tree python (*Chondropython viridis*)	3·75	2·75
N3991	2wn. Blood python (*Python curtus*)	3·75	2·75
N3992	2wn. Corythosaurus	3·75	2·75
	a. Sheetlet of 4. Nos. N3992/5	16·00	
N3993	2wn. Psittacosaurus	3·75	2·75
N3994	2wn. Megalosaurus	3·75	2·75
N3995	2wn. Muttaburrasaurus	3·75	2·75
N3996	2wn. Burmeister's porpoise (*Phocoena spinipinnis*)	3·75	2·75
	a. Sheetlet of 4. Nos. N3996/9	16·00	
N3997	2wn. Finless porpoise (*Neophocaena phocaenoides*)	3·75	2·75
N3998	2wn. Bottle-nosed dolphin (*Tursiops truncatus*)	3·75	2·75
N3999	2wn. Curvier's beaked whale (*Ziphius cavirostris*)	3·75	2·75
N4000	2wn. Port Jackson shark (*Heterodontus portusjacksoni*) ..	3·75	2·75
	a. Sheetlet of 4. Nos. N4000/3	16·00	
N4001	2wn. Great hammerhead shark (*Sphyrna mokarran*) (inscr "mokkarran")	3·75	2·75
N4002	2wn. Zebra shark (*Stegostoma fasciatum*)	3·75	2·75
N4003	2wn. Ornate wobbegong (*Orectolobus ornatus*)	3·75	2·75
N4004	2wn. Ruddy shelduck (*Tadorna ferruginea*)	3·75	2·75
	a. Sheetlet of 4. Nos. N4004/7	16·00	
N4005	2wn. European widgeon (*Anas penelope*)	3·75	2·75
N4006	2wn. Mandarin drake (*Aix galericulata*)	3·75	2·75
N4007	2wn. Hottentot teal (*Anas hottentota*)	3·75	2·75
N4008	2wn. Little owl (*Athene noctua*)	3·75	2·75
	a. Sheetlet of 4. Nos. N4008/11	16·00	
N4009	2wn. Ural owl (*Strix uralensis*)	3·75	2·75
N4010	2wn. Great horned owl (*Bubo virginianus*)	3·75	2·75
N4011	2wn. Snowy owl (*Nyctea scandiaca*)	3·75	2·75
N4012	2wn. Slaty-headed parakeet (*Psittacula himalayana*)	3·75	2·75
	a. Sheetlet of 4. Nos. N4012/15..	16·00	
N4013	2wn. Male eclectus parrot (*Eclectus roratus*)	3·75	2·75
N4014	2wn. Major Mitchell's cockatoo (*Cacatua leadbeateri*)	3·75	2·75
N4015	2wn. Female eclectus parrot (*Eclectus roratus*)	3·75	2·75
N4016	2wn. Indian leaf butterfly (*Kallima paralekta*)	3·75	2·75
	a. Sheetlet of 4. Nos. N4016/19 ..	16·00	
N4017	2wn. Spanish festoon (*Zerynthia rumina*)	3·75	2·75
N4018	2wn. Male and female emerald swallowtails (*Papilio palinurus*)	3·75	2·75
N4019	2wn. *Bhutanitis lidderdalii*	3·75	2·75

N4020	2wn. Bumble bee	3·75	2·75
	a. Sheetlet of 4. Nos. N4020/3	16·00	
N4021	2wn. Bumble bee on flower	3·75	2·75
N4022	2wn. Honey bee (*Apis mellifera*)	3·75	2·75
N4023	2wn. Honey bee attacking spider	3·75	2·75
N4024	2wn. *Micrommata virescens* (spider)	3·75	2·75
	a. Sheetlet of 4. Nos. N4024/7	16·00	
N4025	2wn. *Araneus quadratus* (spider)	3·75	2·75
N4026	2wn. *Dolomedes fimbriatus* (spider)...	3·75	2·75
N4027	2wn. *Aculepeira ceropegia* (spider)	3·75	2·75
N3968/4027	Set of 60	£200	£150

Nos. N3968/71, N3972/5, N3976/9, N3980/3, N3984/7, N3988/91, N3992/5, N3996/9, N4000/3, N4004/7, N4008/11, N4012/15, N4016/19, N4020/3 and N4024/7 respectively were issued together in *se-tenant* sheetlets of four stamps.

Nos. N3980/3 are wrongly inscr "Aculepeira ceropegia".

(Des Ha Kyong Guk and Jon Kum Hui. Litho)

2000 (16 Feb). 58th Birth Anniv of Kim Jong Il. P 11½.

N4028	**1311**	40ch. multicoloured	75	55

1312 Styracosaurus   1313 Peacock (*Inachis io*)

(Des An Chol. Litho)

2000 (5 Mar). Dinosaurs. Sheet 120×80 mm. containing T **1312** and similar multicoloured designs. P 13½.

MSN4029 1wn. Type **1312**; 1wn. Saltasaurus (29×41 mm); 1wn. Tyrannosaurus ... 6·25 5·00

(Des Kim Hae Yong. Litho)

2000 (25 Mar). Butterflies. T **1313** and similar horiz designs. Multicoloured. P 11½.

N4030	40ch. Type **1313**	90	65
	a. Sheetlet of 4. Nos. N4030/4	6·25	
	b. Booklet pane. Nos. N4030/4 ×2 plus 3 labels	12·50	
N4031	60ch. Swallowtail (*Papilio machaon*)	1·20	90
N4032	80ch. Mimic (*Hypolimnas misippus*)....	1·50	1·10
N4033	1wn.20 Papilio bianor Cramer	2·40	1·80
N4030/4033	Set of 4	5·50	4·00

Nos. N4030/3 were issued together in *se-tenant* sheetlets of four stamps.

No. 4034 is vacant.

1314 Patas Monkey (*Erythrocebus patas*)   1315 Red Flag, Top of Chollima Statue and Emblem

(Des Kim Chol Ung. Litho)

2000 (25 Mar). Primates. T **1314** and similar vert designs. Multicoloured. P 11½.

N4035	50ch. Type **1314**	1·00	80
	a. Booklet pane. Nos. N4035/6 each ×4	4·25	
N4036	50ch. Western tarsier (*Tarsius spectrm*)	1·00	80
MSN4037	Sheet 75×65 mm. 2wn. Mona monkey (*Cercopithecus mona*)	4·25	3·00

Nos. N4035/6 were issued both separately in sheets of ten (2×5) and together in sheetlets of four stamps.

(Des Ri Yong Jin. Litho)

2000 (28 Mar). 55th Anniv of Korean Worker's Party (1st issue). P 11½.

N4038	**1315**	10ch. Multicoloured	30	20

See also Nos. N4083/**MS**N4084.

1316 Demonstrators   1317 Kim Il Sun Flower

(Des O Sol Rim. Litho)

2000 (1 Apr). 40th Anniv of 19 April Uprising, South Korea. P 11½.

N4039	**1316**	10ch. multicoloured	30	20

(Des Choe Chol Man. Litho)

2000 (15 Apr). 88th Birth Anniv of Kim Il Sung. P 11½.

N4040	**1317**	40ch. multicoloured	90	65

1318 Mun Ik Hwan   1319 Symbols of Technology, Globe, Flag and Chollima Statue

(Des O Sol Rim. Litho)

2000 (25 Apr). Sixth Death Anniv of Mun Ik Hwan (National Reunification Prize winner). P 13½.

N4041	**1318**	50ch. multicoloured	1·00	80

(Des Yun Chol Su and Kim Chol Ung. Litho)

2000 (5 May). New Millennium. 55th Anniv of Korean Worker's Party. T **1319** and similar vert design. Multicoloured. P 13½.

N4042	40ch. Type **1319**	90	65
N4043	1wn.20 Dove with envelope, globe and satellites	2·40	1·80

1320 *Cattleya intermedia*   1321 Okryu Bridge (River Taedong)

(Des Choe Chol Man. Litho)

2000 (15 May). Orchids. T **1320** and similar vert designs. Multicoloured. P 13½.

N4044	20ch. Type **1320**	45	35
	a. Booklet pane. Nos. N4044/5 each ×2 and N4046 ×4	9·25	
N4045	50ch. *Dendrobium moschatum*	1·00	80
N4046	70ch. *Brassolaeliocattleya*	1·50	1·10
N4044/4046 *Set of 3*		2·75	2·00
MSN4047 85×60 mm. 2wn. *Laeliocattleya*		4·25	3·00

(Des An Chol. Litho)

2000 (21 May). Bridges. T **1321** and similar horiz designs showing bridges. Multicoloured. P 13½.

N4048	20ch. Type **1321**	60	45
	a. Booklet pane. Nos. N4048 ×2 and N4049/50 each ×3	12·50	
N4049	30ch. Ansan Bridge (River Pothong)	90	65
N4050	1wn. Rungna Bridge (River Taedong)	2·75	2·00
N4048/4050 *Set of 3*		3·75	2·75

1322 Okryugum and Jaengggang Dancers

1323 Half Moon (Yun Kuk Yong)

(Des Ri Yong Jan. Litho)

2000 (30 May). AIR. WIPA 2000 International Stamp Exhibition, Vienna. Traditional Instruments and Folk Dances. Sheet 150×84 mm. containing T **1322** and similar vert designs. Multicoloured. P 13½.

MSN4051 1wn. Type **1322**; 1wn.50 Oungum and Full Moon Viewing; 1wn.50 Janggo (drum) and Trio	8·00	6·75

The 1 won stamp does not carry an airmail inscription.

(Des Kim Hae Yong. Litho)

2000 (1 June). Children's Songs. T **1323** and similar vert designs. Multicoloured. P 12×12½.

N4052	40ch. Type **1323**	90	65
N4053	60ch. Kangnam Nostalgia (Kim Sok Song and An Ki Yong)	1·20	90
MSN4054 95×80 mm. 1wn.50 Spring in Home Village (Ri Won Su and Hong Ran Pha)		3·00	2·20

1324 Pearly Nautilus (*Nautilus pompilius*)

1325 Drake and Duck

(Des Ha Kyong Guk. Litho)

2000 (15 June). Cephalopods. T **1324** and similar vert designs. Multicoloured. P 11½.

N4055	40ch. Type **1324**	90	65
	a. Booklet pane. Nos. N4055 ×4 and N4056 /7 each ×2	12·50	
N4056	60ch. Common octopus (*Octopus vulgaris*)	1·20	90
N4057	1wn.50 Squid (*Ommastrephes sloanei pacificus*)	3·00	2·20
N4055/4057 *Set of 3*		4·50	3·50
MSN4058 60×70 mm. 1wn.50 No. N4057		3·00	2·20

No. N4057 was issued only in the *se-tenant* booklet pane and the miniature sheet.

(Des Kim Hae Yong. Litho)

2000 (16 June). Mandarin Ducks. T **1325** and similar vert designs. Multicoloured. P 12×12½.

N4059	50ch. Type **1325**	1·10	80
	a. Booklet pane. Nos. N4059×4, N4060×3	8·00	
N4060	50ch. Drake with duck and couple on bridge	1·10	80
MSN4061 92×75 mm. 1wn. Duck, drake and ducklings		2·10	1·60

1326 Table Tennis

(Des Choe Chol Man and Jon Kum Hui. Litho)

2000 (7 July). World Expo 2000 International Stamp Exhibition, Anaheim, California. Sport. T **1326** and similar horiz. Multicoloured. P 13½.

N4062	80ch. Type **1326**	1·70	1·30
	a. Sheetlet of 6. Nos. N4062/4 each ×2	12·50	
	b. Booklet pane. Nos. N4062 ×3 and N4063/4 each ×2	14·50	
N4063	1wn. Basketball	2·00	1·50
N4064	1wn.20 Baseball	2·40	1·90
N4062/4064 *Set of 3*		5·50	4·25

Nos. N4062/4 were issued together both in *se-tenant* sheetlets of six stamps and in booklets.

1327 Sungri-61 NA

(Des Kim Chol Ung. Litho)

2000 (24 July). Trucks. T **1327** and similar horiz designs. Multicoloured. P 12.

N4065	40ch. Type **1327**	90	70
	a. Strip of 3. Nos. N4065/7	5·75	
N4066	70ch. Tipper truck	1·70	1·30
N4067	1wn.50 Konsol 25 ton dump truck	3·00	2·30
N4065/4067 *Set of 3*		5·00	3·75

Nos. N4065/7 were issued together in horizontal *se-tenant* strips of three stamps within the sheet.

1328 Ri Tae Hun (artillery
company commander) and
76 mm. Field Gun

(Des An Chol. Litho)

2000 (27 July). Weaponry. T **1328** and similar horiz designs.
Multicoloured. P 11½.

N4068	60ch. Type **1328**	1·40	1·10
	a. Strip of 3. Nos. N4068/70	5·50	
N4069	80ch. Ko Hyon Bin (tank commander) and T-34 tank	1·80	1·40
N4070	1wn. Squadron leader Paek Ki Rak and Yakolev Yak-9P pursuit Plane	2·10	1·60
N4068/4070	Set of 3	4·75	3·75

Nos. N4068/70 were issued together in horizontal *se-tenant* strips
of three in sheetlets of six stamps.

1329 Fluorite   (**1330**)

(Des Jon Kum Hui. Litho)

2000 (15 Aug). Minerals. T **1329** and similar horiz designs.
Multicoloured. P 13½.

N4071	30ch. Type **1329**	60	45
	a. Booklet pane. Nos. N4071/2 each ×3, N4073 ×2	13·50	
N4072	60ch. Graphite	1·40	1·10
N4073	1wn.60 Magnesite	3·50	2·75
N4071/4073	Set of 3	5·00	3·75
MSN4074	74×74 mm. 1wn.60 No. N4073	3·75	3·00

2000 (15 Aug). Indonesia 2000 International Stamp Exhibition,
Jakarta.
Nos. N4059/**MS**N4061 optd as T **1330**, No. **MS**N4061 optd in the
margin.

N4075	50ch. Multicoloured	1·10	90
	a. Booklet pane. No. N4075 ×4, N4076 ×3	2·30	1·90
N4076	50ch. multicoloured	1·10	90
MSN4077	1wn. multicoloured	2·30	1·90

The overprint on No. **MS**N 4061 is larger, 23×11 mm.

1331 Swimming

(Des Ri Yong Jin. Litho)

2000 (15 Sept). Olympic Games, Sydney. Triathlon. Sheet 78×110
mm. containing T **1331** and similar horiz designs. Multicoloured.
P 13½.
MSN4078   80ch. Type **1331**; 1wn.20 Cycling; 2wn.
Running .... 9·00   7·75

1332 Sanju Falls

(Des Kim Chol Ung. Litho)

2000 (27 Sept). Myohyang Mountain. T **1332** and similar horiz
designs. Multicoloured. P 13½.

N4079	40ch. Type **1332**	90	70
N4080	40ch. Inho rock	90	70
N4081	1wn.20 Sangwon valley	2·75	2·10
N4079/4081	Set of 3	4·00	3·25

(**1333**)

2000 (6 Oct). Espana 2000 International Stamp Exhibition, Madrid.
No. **MS**N4029 optd in the margin with T **1333**
MSN4082 120×80 mm. 1wn. Type **1312**; 1wn.
Saltasaurus; 1wn. Tyrannosaurus .... 6·25   5·00

1334 Anniversary Emblem and
Party Museum

(Des Jon Gum Hui. Litho)

2000 (10 Oct). 55th Anniv of Korean Worker's Party (2nd issue).
T **1334** and similar multicoloured designs. P 13½.

N4083	10ch. Type **1334**	30	25
MSN4084	120×85 mm. 50ch. Kim Il Sung (35×56 mm); 50ch. Kim Jong Il (35×56 mm); 50ch. Kim Jong Suk (35×56 mm)	3·50	2·75

1335 Flag, Bulldozer and Fields

(Des Kim Chol Ung. Litho)

2000 (15 Oct). Land Re-organisation. P 13½.
N4085 **1335** 10ch. multicoloured 30   25

1336 Potatoes, Pigs, Fields and Scientist

1337 Kim Jong Il and Pres. Jiang Zemin

(Des Jon Gum Hui. Litho)

2000 (20 Oct). Taehongdan (potato production centre). T **1336** and similar horiz designs. Multicoloured. P 11½.
N4086   40ch. Type **1336** 90   70
MSN4087 110×92 mm. 2wn. Kim Il Sung with
    farmers in potato field (42×34 mm)........................ 4·50   3·50

(Des An Chol. Litho)

2000 (21 Oct). Visit of Kim Jong Il to People's Republic of China. Sheet 110×80 mm. P 12×12½.
MSN4088 **1337** 1wn.20 multicoloured........................ 2·75   2·20

1338 Kim Jong Il and Pres. Kim Dae Jung

1339 Kim Jong Il and Pres. Putin

(Des Yun Chol Su. Litho)

2000 (23 Oct). North Korea–South Korea Summit Meeting, Pyongyang. Sheet 85×110 mm. P 11½×12.
MSN4089 **1338** 2wn. multicoloured............................ 4·50   3·50

(Des Jon Kum Hui. Litho)

2000 (24 Oct). Visit of Pres. Vladimir Putin of Russian Federation. Sheet 94×108 mm. P 11½×12.
MSN4090 **1339** 1wn.50 multicoloured........................ 3·50   2·75

1340 Soldiers crossing River Amnok

1341 Chinese and Korean Soldiers

(Des an Chol. Litho)

2000 (25 Oct). 50th Anniv of Chinese People's Volunteers Participation in Korean War (1st issue). Sheet 139×164 mm. containing T **1340** and similar horiz designs. Multicoloured. P 13½.
MSN4091 10ch. Type **1340**; 10ch. Battle; 50ch.
    Chinese and Korean soldiers; 50ch. Mao Tse-tung
    and Chinese leaders; 80ch. Soldiers and gun
    emplacement.. 4·50   3·50
See also No. N4092.

(Des Ri Yong Jin. Litho)

2000 (25 Oct). 50th Anniv of Chinese People's Volunteers Participation in Korean War (2nd issue). P 13½.
N4092 **1341** 30ch. multicoloured 75   60

1342 *Aquilegia oxysepala*

1343 Women presenting Prisoners with Flowers

(Des Ha Kyong Guk. Litho)

2000 (5 Nov). Alpine Flowers. T **1342** and similar vert designs. Multicoloured. P 13½.
N4093   30ch. Type **1342** 75   60
N4094   50ch. Brilliant campion (*Lychnis
                fulgens*).. 1·20   95
N4095   70ch. Self-heal (*Prunela vulgaris*) .... 1·70   1·30
N4093/4095 Set of 3.. 3·25   2·50

(Des Choe Chol Man. Litho)

2000 (20 Dec). Repatriation of Long-term Prisoners of War. Two sheets containing horiz designs as T **1343**. Multicoloured. P 13½.
MSN4096 Two sheets. (a) 139×87 mm. 80ch. Type
    1343; (b) 165×120 mm. 1wn.20 Prisoners and
    crowd .... 4·50   3·75

1344 Flag, Factories and Trees

(Des Ri Jong Jin. Litho)

2001 (1 Jan). New Year (1st issue). P 11½.
N4097 **1344** 10ch. multicoloured................................ 30   25

1345 White Snake meeting Xu Xian

(Des Ri Yong Jin. Litho)

2001 (1 Jan). New Year (2nd issue). Tale of the White Snake. T **1345** and similar multicoloured designs. P 12 (**MS**N4102) or 12½×12 (others).

N4098	10ch. Type **1345**	30	25
	a. Booklet pane. Nos. N4098/4101, each ×2	8·25	
	b. Sheetlet of 4. Nos. N4098/4101	4·25	
N4099	40ch. Stealing the Immortal Grass	90	75
N4100	50ch. White and Green snakes and Xu Xian	1·10	90
N4101	80ch. Flooding of Jinshan Hill	1·70	1·40
N4098/4101	Set of 4	3·50	3·00
MSN4102	105×80 mm. 1wn.20 White snake and Green snake (32×52 mm)	2·75	2·30

Nos. N4098/4101 were issued in large sheets, *se-tenant* sheetlets of four stamps and, each ×2, in booklets of eight stamps.
The booklet pane has a white margin around the block.

1346 E. Lasker and J-R. Capablanca

1347 White Suit and Black Hat

(Des An Chol. Litho)

2001 (5 Jan). World Chess Champions. 165th Birth Anniv of Wilhelm Steinitz (19th-century champion) (**MS**N4109). T **1346** and similar multicoloured designs. P 11½ (**MS**N4109) or 13½. (others).

N4103	10ch. Type **1346**	35	30
	a. Sheetlet of 6. Nos. N4103/8 plus 3 labels	6·50	
	b. Booklet pane. Nos. N4103/8	6·50	
N4104	20ch. A. Alekhine and M. Euwe	65	55
N4105	30ch. M. Botvinnik and V. Smylov	80	70
N4106	40ch. T. Petrosian and M. Tal	1·00	85
N4107	50ch. B. Spassky and R. Fisher	1·20	95
N4108	1wn. A. Karpov and G. Kasparov	2·30	1·90
N4103/4108	Set of 6	5·75	4·75
MSN4109	105×80 mm. 2wn.50 Wilhelm Steinitz (32×52 mm)	6·25	5·25

Nos. N4103/8 were issued together in *se-tenant* sheetlets of six stamps plus three labels and in booklets of six stamps.

(Des Kim Hae Yong. Litho)

2001 (19 Jan). Ri-Dynasty Men's Costumes. T **1347** and similar vert designs. Multicoloured. P 12×12½.

N4110	10ch. Type **1347**	35	30
	a. Booklet pane. Nos. N4110, N4111 ×2, N4112/3	5·75	
N4111	40ch. White suit with blue waistcoat	1·00	85
N4112	50ch. White trousers, brown jacket and pagoda-shaped hat	1·20	95
N4113	70ch. Knee-length pale blue coat, black hat and stick	1·60	1·40
N4110/4113	Set of 4	3·75	3·25
MSN4114	110×80 mm. 1wn.50 Blue knee-length coat with ornamental cummerbund and black boots	3·50	3·00

1348 Small Appliance (fire)

(Des Kim Chol Ung. Litho)

2001 (20 Jan). Fire Engines. T **1348** and similar horiz designs showing engines and fire hazards. Multicoloured. P 12½×12.

N4115	20ch. Type **1348**	50	40
	a. Booklet pane. Nos. N4115/8, each×3	11·50	
	b. Sheetlet of 5. Nos. N4115/19 plus label	8·75	
N4116	30ch. Large engine with hydraulic ladder (oil can)	65	55
N4117	40ch. Small engine with two-door cab and closed back (match)	1·00	85
N4118	60ch. Small engine with ladder, spotlight and external hose reel (gas canister)	1·50	1·20
N4119	2wn. Older-style engine (cigarette)	5·00	4·25
N4115/4119	Set of 5	7·75	6·50
MSN4120	95×90 mm. 2wn. As No. N4119 (32×52 mm)	5·25	4·50

Nos. N4115/19 were issued in large sheets and *se-tenant* sheetlets of five stamps plus a label. Nos. N4115/18, each ×3, were also issued in booklets of twelve stamps.

1349 Black-naped Oriole (*Oriolus chinensis*)

1350 Jjong Il Peak and Flower

(Des Jon Kum Hui. Litho)

2001 (1 Feb). HONG KONG 2001 International Stamp Exhibition. Sheet 72×80 mm. P 11½.

MSN4121	**1349** 1wn.40 multicoloured	3·25	2·75

(Des Jon Kum Hoi. Litho)

2001 (10 Feb). 59th Birth Anniv of Kim Jong Il. P 13½.

N4122	**1350** 10ch. multicoloured	35	30

1351 Flag and Symbols of Industry and Agriculture

(Des Yun Chol Su. Litho)

2001 (5 Mar). New Millennium. Rodong Sinmun, Josoninmingun and Chongnyonjonwi Newspapers Joint Editorial. P 12½×12.

N4123	**1351** 10ch. multicoloured	35	30

1352 Log Cabin (revolutionary headquarters, Mt. Paekdu)

(Des Yun Chol Su. Litho)

2001 (7 Mar). P 11½.
N4124 **1352** 40ch. multicoloured .... 1·00   85

1353 Family Home, Mangyongdae

(Des Kim Hae Yong. Litho)

2001 (10 Apr). 89th Birth Anniv of Kim Il Sung. T **1353** and similar
  multicoloured designs. P 13½.
N4125   10ch. Type **1353**   50   30
MSNN4126 170×103 mm. 80ch. ×8, Eight different
  portraits of Kim Il Sung (vert) .... 16·00 14·00

1354 Kim Jong Il

(Des Kim Hae Yong. Litho)

2001 (25 Apr). Army as Priority. Sheet 140×75 mm. P 13½.
MSNN4127 **1354** 1wn. multicoloured .... 2·50   2·10

1355 Pyongyang—Kaesong Motorway

(Des Kim Choi Ung. Litho)

2001 (7 May). Roads. T **1355** and similar horiz designs. Multicoloured.
  P 13½.
N4128   40ch. Type **1355** ....   1·00   85
N4129   70ch. Pyongyang—Hyanngsan
              expressway ....   1·60   1·40
N4130   1wn.20 Pyongyang—Nampo
              motorway ....   3·00   2·50
N4131   1wn.50 Pyongyang—Wonsan
              expressway ....   3·50   3·00
N4128/4131 *Set of 4* ....   7·25   7·00

1356 Ryongwang Pavilion, Pyongyang

(Des Jon Kum Hui. Litho)

2001 (15 May). Cultural Heritage. Pavilions. T **1356** and similar horiz
  designs. Multicoloured. P 13½.
N4132   40ch. Type **1356** ....   1·00   85
            a. Booklet pane. Nos. N4132/5 ......   12·00
N4133   80ch. Inphung, Kanggye ....   2·00   1·70
N4134   1wn.50 Paeksang, Anju ....   3·50   3·00
N4135   2wn. Thonggun, Uiju ....   5·00   4·25
N4132/4135 *Set of 4* ....   10·50   8·75

1357 Man with raised Arm

(Des Ha Kyong. Litho)

2001 (5 June). P 13½.
N4136 **1357** 10ch. Multicoloured   35   30

1358 Blue-throat (*Luscinia svecica*)

(Des Jon Kum Hui. Litho)

2001 (9 June). Birds. T **1358** and similar horiz designs. Multicoloured.
  P 11½.
N4137   10ch. Type **1358**   35   30
            a. Sheetlet. No. N4137/42 ....   13·00
            b. Booklet pane. Nos. N4137/8,
              each ×2: N4139/42 ....   14·00
N4138   40ch. Grey lag goose (Anser anser) ....   1·00   85
N4139   80ch. Short-tailed albatross
              (*Diomedea albatrus*) ....   2·00   1·70
N4140   1wn. Little ring plover (*Charadrius
              dubius*) ....   2·50   2·10
N4141   1wn.20 Common guillemot (*Uria aalge*)   3·00   2·50
N4142   1wn.50 House martin (*Delichon urbica*)   3·50   3·00
N4137/4142 *Set of 6* ....   11·00   9·50
  Nos. N4137/42 were issued in *se-tenant* sheetlets of six stamps
with an enlarged illustrated border inscribed for Beligica 2001
International Stamp Exhibition.

1359 Mao Zedong

(Des Zhu Zu Jin. Litho)

2001 (15 June). 80th Anniv of Chinese Communist Party. Three sheets, each 152×67 mm. containing T **1359** and similar horiz designs. Multicoloured. P 11½.

MSN4143	(a) 80ch. Type **1359**; (b) 80ch. Deng		
	Xiaping; (c) 80ch. Jiang Zemin	6·00	5·00

1360 Woljong Temple, Mt. Kuwol

(Des Kim Chol Ung. Litho)

2001 (9 July). Kumol Mountain. T **1360** and similar horiz designs. Multicoloured. P 13½.

N4144	10ch. Type **1360**	35	30
	a. Sheetlet. Nos. N4144/8 plus label...	10·00	
	b. Booklet pane. Nos. N4144/8 plus label	10·00	
N4145	40ch. Revolutionary building	1·00	85
N4146	70ch. Potnamu Pavilion	1·60	1·40
N4147	1wn.30 Tak Peak	3·25	2·75
N4148	1wn.50 Ryongyon Falls	3·50	3·00
N4144/4148	Set of 5	8·75	7·50

Nos. N4144/8 were issued in *se-tenant* sheetlets of five stamps plus a label showing mountain.

1361 *Rheum coreanum*

(Des Jon Kum Hui. Litho)

2001 (20 July). Endangered Species. Plants. T **1361** and similar horiz designs. Multicoloured. P 13½.

N4149	10ch. Type **1361**	35	30
	a. Booklet pane. Nos. N4149, N4151, each ×2; N4150, N4152	10·50	
N4150	40ch. *Forsythia densiflora*.....................	1·00	85
N4151	1wn. *Rhododendron yedoense*	2·50	2·10
N4152	2wn. *Iris setosa*.....................................	5·00	4·25
N4149/4152	Set of 4	8·00	6·75

1362 *Eria pannea*

(Des Kim Hae Yong. Litho)

2001 (1 Aug). Orchids. T **1362** and similar vert designs. Multicoloured. P 13½.

N4153	10ch. Type **1362**	35	30
	a. Sheetlet. Nos. N4153/6................	7·75	

	b. Booklet pane. Nos. N4153/4; N4155 ×2; N4156/7....................	15·00	
N4154	40ch. *Cymbidium*	1·00	85
N4155	90ch. *Sophrolaeliocattleya*	2·10	1·80
N4156	1wn.60 *Cattleya trianae*........................	4·00	3·25
N4157	2wn. *Cypripedium macranthum*	5·00	4·25
N4153/4157	Set of 5	11·00	9·50
MSN4158	142×96 mm. No. N4157.........................	5·25	4·50

Nos. N4153/6 were issued in *se-tenant* sheetlets of four stamps with an enlarged illustrated margin inscribed for Philanippon '01 International Stamp Exhibition.

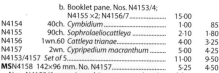

1363 Pibaldo Lighthouse

(Des Choe Chol Man. Litho)

2001 (18 Aug). Lighthouses. T **1363** and similar horiz designs. Multicoloured. P 13½.

N4159	40ch. Type **1363**	1·00	85
	a. Sheetlet. Nos. N4159/62	8·50	
	b. Booklet pane. Nos. N4159/60; Nos. 4161/2, each ×2...........	14·50	
N4160	70ch. Soho, Hamhung	1·60	1·40
N4161	90ch. Komalsan, Chongjin	2·10	1·80
N4162	1wn.50 Alsom, Rason..............................	3·50	3·00
N4159/4162	Set of 4	7·50	6·25
MSN4163	81×95 mm. No. N4162............................	3·75	3·25

Nos. N4159/61 were issued separately in sheets, Nos. N4159/62 were issued together in *se-tenant* sheetlets of four stamps.

1364 Kim Po Hyon

(Des Yun Chol Su. Litho)

2001 (19 Aug). 130th Birth Anniv of Kim Po Hyon. Sheet 80×90 mm. P 13½.

MSN4164	**1364**	1wn. black and bronze	2·50	2·10

1365 Black Stork (*Ciconia nigra*)

(Des Choe Chol Man. Litho)

2001 (2 Sept). Endangered Species. Fauna. T **1365** and similar horiz designs. Multicoloured. P 13½.

N4165	10ch. Type **1365**........................	35	30
	a. Sheetlet. Nos. N4165/68 plus label..	5·25	

b. Booklet pane. Nos. N4165/6;
Nos. N4167 ×2; N4168 .... 7·00
N4166 40ch. Cinereous vulture (*Aegypius monchus*) .... 1·00 85
N4167 70ch. Chinese water deer (*Hydropotes inermis*)............................. 1·60 1·40
N4168 90ch. Goral (*Nemorhaedus goral*)........ 2·10 1·80
N4169 1wn.30 Northern eagle owl (*Bubo bubo*) 3·25 2·75
N4165/4169 *Set of 5*.. 7·50 6·50
MSN4170 106×81 mm. No. N4169.................. 3·50 3·00

Nos. N4165/8 respectively were issued separately in sheets, Nos. N4165/9 were issued together in *se-tenant* sheetlets of five stamps plus a label inscribed with North Korean Conservation Union emblem.

1366 Deng Ya Ping receiving Gold Medal for Table Tennis from Juan Antonio Samaranch (Olympic president)

(Des Zhu Zu Wei and Ying Ming Yang. Litho)

2001 (10 Sept). Olympic Games 2008, Beijing. Sheet 152×115 mm. containing T **1366** and similar circular designs. Multicoloured. P 11½.
MSN4171 56ch. ×5, Type **1366**; Jiang Zemin (pres. People's Republic of China); Wang Jun Xia (athletics); Li Ning (gymnast); Fu Ming Xia (diver) 7·50 6·25

1367 Cycle Football   **1368** Yuri Gagarin

(Des An Chol. Litho)

2001 (20 Sept). Cycling. Sheet 90×145 mm. containing T **1367** and similar vert designs. Multicoloured. P 12.
MSN4172 10ch. Type **1367**; 40ch. Road racing; 1wn. Cyclo-cross; 2wn. Indoor racing .... 9·75 8·25

(Des An Chol. Litho)

2001 (25 Sept). Space Exploration. T **1368** and similar vert designs. Multicoloured. P 11½.
N4173 10ch. Type **1368** (cosmonaut)............. 35 30
a. Booklet pane. Nos. N4173/6...... 10·00
N4174 40ch. Apollo 11 space ship .... 1·00 85
N4175 1wn.50 Kwangmyongsong satellite....... 3·50 3·00
N4176 2wn. Edmund Halley (astronomer). Halley's comet and Giotto satellite................................. 5·00 4·25
N4173/4176 *Set of 4*.. 8·75 7·50
MSN4177 140×197 mm. Nos. N4173/6.......................... 9·75 8·25

1369 Presidents Vladimir Putin and Kim Jong Il   **1370** Presidents Kim Jong Il and Jiang Zemin

(Des Ha Kyong Guk. Litho)

2001 (12 Oct). Visit of Kim Jong Il to Russia. Sheet 92×105 mm. P 12½×11½.
MSN4178 **1369** 1wn.50 multicoloured........................ 3·50 3·00

(Des Kim Hae Yong. Litho)

2001 (25 Oct). Meeting between Pres. Kim Jong Il and Jiang Zemin (Pres. People's Republic of China). Sheet 72×104 mm. P 11½.
MSN4179 **1370** 1wn.50 multicoloured .... 3·50 3·00

1371 Kim Jong Suk protecting Kim Il Sung during Battle

(Des Jon Kum Hui. Litho)

2001 (24 Nov). 84th Birth Anniv of Kim Jong Suk (revolutionary fighter). Sheet 168×100 mm. P 12½×11½.
MSN4180 **1371** 1wn. 60 multicoloured...................... 4·00 3·25

1372 Kim Jong Il inspecting Troops

(Des Ri Yong Jin. Litho)

2001 (1 Dec). Tenth Anniv of Kim Jong Il's election as Supreme Commander of Korean People's Army. Sheet 90×110 mm. P 11½.
MSN4181 **1372** 1wn. multicoloured............................ 2·50 2·10

1373 Chollima Statue   **1374** Grey Horse

(Des Kim Hae Yong. Litho)

2002 (1 Jan). New Year. P 13.
N4182   **1373**   10ch. multicoloured   35   30

(Des Kim Hae Yong. Litho)

2002 (1 Jan). New Year. ("Year of the Horse"). "Ten Horses" (paintings by Wang Zhi Cheng) (Nos. N4183/6). T **1374** and similar multicoloured designs. P 13½.
N4183	10ch. Type **1374**	35	30
	a. Booklet pane. Nos. N4183, N4184/5, each ×2 and N4186 ...	13·50	
N4184	40ch. Bay	1·00	85
N4185	60ch. Skewbald	1·50	1·20
N4186	1wn.30 Piebald.	3·25	2·75
N4183/4186	*Set of 4*	5·50	4·50

MSN4187 (a) 106×80 mm. 1wn.60 "Jiu Fang Gao" (painting by Xu Bei Hong) (36×57 mm); (b) 168×104 mm. Nos. N4183/6 and **MS**N4187a ....   14·00   11·50

1375 Flower Basket   **1376** Zeppelin LZ1

(Des Kim Chol Ung. Litho or litho and embossed (**MS**N4189))

2002 (1 Feb). 60th Birth Anniv of Kim Jong Il. T **1375** and similar vert designs. Multicoloured. P 13½. (10ch. and 1wn.50), 12×12½ (1wn.20) or 11½×12 (2wn.)
N4188   10ch. Type **1375**   35   30
MSN4189 Three sheets. (a) 124×94 mm. 1wn.20×3, Kim Il Sung (father) (32×52 mm); Kim Jong Il as child (32×52 mm); Kim Jong Suk (mother) (32×52 mm). (b) 105×85 mm. 1wn.50 Kim Jong Il with soldiers (45×34 mm). (c) 77×117 mm. 2wn. Kim Jong Il as young man (42×64 mm) ....   18·00   16·00

(Des An Chol. Litho)

2002 (5 Feb). Centenary of First Zeppelin Airship Flight. T **1376** and similar horiz designs. Multicoloured. P 12×13½. (**MS**N4193a) or 12 (others).
N4190	40ch. Type **1376**	80	70
	a. Booklet pane. Nos. N4190/ **MS**N4193a	10·50	
N4191	80ch. LZ.	1·60	1·40
N4192	1wn.20 Zeppelin NT	2·50	2·10
N4190/4192	*Set of 3*	4·50	3·75

MSN4193 (a) 110×80 mm. 2wn.40 Zeppelin NT (different); (b) 132×110 mm. Nos. N4190/ **MS**N4193a ....   15·00   13·00

1377 Banner, Torch   **1378** *Collybia confluens*
and Soldiers

(Des Yun Chol Su. Litho)

2002 (25 Feb). Rodong Sinmun, Josoninmingun and Chongnyonjonwi Newspapers Joint Editorial. P 13½.
N4194   **1377**   10ch. Multicoloured   35   30

(Des Jon Kum Hui. Litho)

2002 (25 Feb). Fungi. T **1378** and similar horiz designs. P 13½.
N4195	10ch. Type **1378**	35	30
	a. Block of 5. Nos. N4195/9 plus label.	8·50	
	b. Booklet pane. Nos. N4195/9 plus label	8·50	
N4196	40ch. *Sparassis laminosa*	80	70
N4197	80ch. Grisette (*Amanita vaginata*) (inscr "Amanjta").	1·60	1·40
N4198	1wn.20 *Russla integra*	2·50	2·10
N4199	1wn.50 Scaly pholita (*Pholita squarrosa*)	3·00	2·60
N4195/4199	*Set of 5.*	7·50	6·25

Nos. N4195/9 were issued in *se-tenant* blocks of five stamps and a label within the sheet.

1379 Family Home,   **1380** Kang Pan Sok
Mangyongdae

(Des Jon Kum Hui (N4200) or Yun Chol Su (**MS**N4201). Litho or litho and embossed (**MS**N4201d)

2002 (15 Mar). 90th Birth Anniv of Kim Il Sung. T **1379** and similar multicoloured designs. P 11½×12 (2wn.) or 13½. (others).
N4200   10ch. Type **1379**   35   30
MSN4201 (a) 105×85 mm. 1wn.50 Kim Il Sung as young man (45×54 mm). (b) 105×85 mm. 1wn.50 With Kim Jong Suk (wife) (45×54 mm). (c) 105×85 mm.; 1wn.50 With Kim Chaeck (revolutionary) (45×54 mm); (d) 76×117 mm. 2wn. Wearing black jacket (42×64 mm) ....   13·50   12·00

(Des Kim Hae Yong. Litho)

2002 (21 Mar). 110th Birth Anniv of Kang Pan Sok (mother of Kim Il Sung). Sheet 70×100 mm. P 11½.
MSN4202 **1380** 1wn. multicoloured............................   2·00   1·70

1381 Emblem, Doves, Dancers and Music

1382 Electric Locomotive

(Des Kim Hae Yong. Litho)

2002 (25 Mar). 20th April Spring Friendship Art Festival. P 13½.
N4203 **1381** 10ch. Multicoloured 35   30

(Des Kim Chol Ung. Litho)

2002 (10 Apr). 20th-century Locomotives. T **1382** and similar horiz designs. Multicoloured. P 13½.

N4204	10ch. Type **1382**..........................	35	30
	a. Booklet pane. Nos. N4204/		
	MSN4208..........................	11·50	
N4205	40ch. Electric locomotive (different) ..	80	70
N4206	1wn.50 Steam locomotive	2·75	2·30
N4207	2wn. Steam locomotive (different)	3·50	3·00
N4204/4207 *Set of 4*....................................		6·75	5·75
MSN4208 65×55 mm. 2wn. Diesel locomotive		3·50	3·00

1383 Inscription

2002 (20 Apr). Birth Centenary of He Baozhen (first wife of Liu Shaoqi (Chinese politician)). Sheet 150×110 mm. containing T **1383** and similar multicoloured designs. Litho. P 13½.
MSN4209 10ch. Type **1383**; 20ch. Arch; 30ch. Building; 40ch. Family (33×45 mm); 1wn. He Baozhen and Liu Shaoqi (33×45 mm) .... 4·00   3·50

1384 *Cristaria plicata*

2002 (21 Apr). Shellfish. T **1384** and similar horiz designs. Multicoloured. Litho. P 13½.

N4210	10ch. Type **1384**	35	30
	a. Booklet pane. Nos. N4210/11,		
	each ×2, N4212/13..................	6·25	
N4211	40ch. *Lanceolaria cospidata*..................	65	55
N4212	1wn. *Schistodesmus lampreyanus*.......	1·60	1·40
N4213	1wn.50 *Lamprotula coreana*	2·50	2·10
N4210/4213 *Set of 4*....................................		4·50	4·00

1385 Soldiers

(Des Kim Chol Ung. Litho)

2002 (25 Apr). 70th Anniv of Korean People's Army. T **1385** and similar multicoloured design. P 12½×12.
N4214   10ch. Type **1385**...................... 35   30
MSN4215 60×85 mm. 1wn.60 Kim Il Sung and Kim Jong Il (39×51 mm). Perf and imperf........................ 3·25   2·75

1386 Actors

(Des Kim Hae Yong and Kim Chol Ung (N4216/19) or Jon Kum Hui (MSN4220). Litho)

2002 (28 Apr). Arirang Festival. T **1386** and similar horiz design. P 12.

N4216	10ch. Type **1386**	35	30
N4217	20ch. Animation and cartoon		
	characters................................	50	40
N4218	30ch. Dancer holding fan........................	65	55
N4219	40ch. Dancers	80	70
N4216/4219 *Set of 4*....................................		2·10	1·80
MSN4220 120×93 mm. 1wn. Woman holding			
tambourine (54×45 mm). P 13½		2·00	1·70

1387 Ri Rang and Song Bu

1388 Symbols of Modern Industry

(Des O Sol Rim. Litho)

2002 (28 Apr). Arirang Legend. Sheet 176×88 mm. containing T **1387** and similar vert designs. Multicoloured. P 13½.
MSN4221 10ch. Type **1387**; 40ch. As young adults; 50ch. Ri Rang killing landlord; 1wn.50 Song Bu .... 4·25   3·50

(Des Ha Kyong Guk. Litho)

2002 (2 May). Science and Technology. P 13½.
N4222 **1388** 10ch. multicoloured 35   30

1389 Squid-shaped Stalactite

(Des Choe Chol Man. Litho)

2002 (25 May). Ryongmun Cavern. Sheet 160×105 mm. containing T **1389** and similar vert designs. Multicoloured. P 11½.
MSN4223 10ch. Type **1389**; 20ch. Chandelier-
shaped stalactite; 30ch. Hill-shaped stalagmite;
40ch. Stalagmite with rough surface ....   2·00   1·70

1390 Monument

(Des O Sol Rim. Litho)

2002 (30 May). 30th Anniv of Charter of Three Principles for Re-unification. P 13½.
N4224 **1390** 10ch. multicoloured   35   30

1391 *Stauropus fagi*

(Des Kim Hae Yong. Litho)

2002 (30 June). Butterflies. T **1391** and similar vert designs. Multicoloured. P 11½×12 (N4225a) or 12×11½ (others).
N4225   10ch. Type **1391**   35   30
          a. Booklet pane. Nos. N4225,
             N4226×2 and N4227/8............... 8·00
N4226   40ch. *Agrias claudina*   65   55
N4227   1wn.50 *Catocala nupta*..........................   2·50   2·10
N4228   2wn. Blue morpho (*Morpho rhetenor*)   3·25   2·75
N4225/4228 *Set of 4*..   6·00   5·25

(1392)

2002 (30 June). 16th Chinese Communist Party Conference, Beijing. Nos. **MS**N 4143a/c optd in the margin with T **1392**.
MSN4229 Three sheets. (a) 80ch. Type **1359**;
(b) 80ch. Deng Xiaoping; (c) 80ch. Jiang Zemin.....   6·00   5·00

1393 Child and Old Man

1394 Kim Jong Suk as Child

2002 (5 July). 50th Anniv of Free Medical Care. Litho. P 12.
N4230 **1393** 10ch. Multicoloured   35   30

(Des Jon Kum Hui. Litho)

2002 (20 July). 85th Birth Anniv of Kim Jong Suk (wife of Kim Il Sung). Sheet containing T **1394** and similar vert designs. Multicoloured. P 13½.
MSN 4231 10ch. Type **1394**; 40ch. As young
woman; 1wn. Wearing uniform; 1wn.50 In
middle age ....   5·00   4·25

1395 Workers, Soldiers and Symbols of Industry

1396 Returnees

(Des Kim Myong Sik. Litho)

2002 (30 July). 30th Anniv of Constitution. P 11½.
N4232 **1395** 10ch. multicoloured   35   30

(Des Jon Kum Hui. Litho)

2002 (20 Sept). Red Cross and Red Crescent (humanitarian organizations) Day. T **1396** and similar vert designs. Multicoloured. P 13½.
N4233   3wn. Type **1396**   35   30
          a. Booklet pane. Nos. N4233/4,
             each ×2; N4235/6 .... 7·25
N4234   12wn. Red Cross workers...................   80   70
N4235   80wn. Family (AIDS awareness)............   1·60   1·40
N4236   150wn. Humanitarian aid to flood
             victims...   3·00   2·50
N4233/4236 *Set of 4*...   5·25   4·50
MSN4237 (a) 150×115 mm. Nos. N4233/4 and
N4236, each ×2; (b) 85×113 mm. No. N4235 ....   1·80   1·50

1397 Hong Chang Su

(Des Kim Chol Ung. Litho)

2002 (25 Sept). Hong Chang Su—2000 World Super-Flyweight
Champion. Sheet 110×75 mm. P 11½.
N4238 **1397** 75wn. multicoloured .... 1·60   1·40

1398 Kim Jong Il and President Vladimir Putin

2002 (15 Oct). Kim Jong Il's Visit to Russia. Two sheets containing
T **1398** and similar multicoloured design. Litho. P 13½.
MSN4239 (a) 85×70 mm. 70wn. Type **1398**; (b)
120×100 mm. 120wn. President Putin and Kim
Jong Il shaking hands (vert) .... 4·00   3·50

1399 Seal-point
Shorthair Cat

1400 Iron Pyrite

(Des Ha Kyong Guk. Litho)

2002 (20 Oct). Cats and Dogs. T **1399** and similar vert designs.
Multicoloured. P 12.
N4240   3wn. Type **1399** 25   20
   a. Booklet pane. Nos. N4240/1,
    each ×2; N4242/3 .... 7·50
N4241   12wn. Pungsan dog 35   30
N4242   100wn. White shorthair cat ...... 2·50   2·10
N4243   150wn. Black and white shorthair cat ... 3·50   3·00
N4240/4243 Set of 4 .... 6·00   5·00
MSN4244 57×70 mm. 150wn. Cavalier King Charles
spaniel .... 3·75   3·25

(Des Kim Myong Sik. Litho)

2002 (25 Oct). T **1400** and similar horiz designs.
Multicoloured. P 13½.
N4245   3wn. Type **1400** 25   20
   a. Strip of 4. Nos. N4245/8 .... 7·25
   b. Block of 4. Nos. N4245/8 ..... 7·25
   c. Booklet pane. Nos. N4245,
    N4246 ×2, N4247/8 .... 8·00
N4246   12wn. Magnetite 35   30
N4247   130wn. Calcite .... 3·00   2·50
N4248   150wn. Galena .... 3·50   3·00
N4245/4248 Set of 4 .... 6·50   5·50

1401 Prime Minister Koizumi Junichiro and Kim
Jong Il signing Declaration

2002 (25 Oct). Japan—Korea Bilateral Declaration. Two sheets
containing T **1401** and similar horiz design. Multicoloured.
Litho. P 13½.
MSN4249 (a) 90×80 mm. 120wn. Type **1401**; (b)
75×65 mm. 150wn. Prime Minister Junichiro and
Kim Jong Il shaking hands .... 5·75   5·25

1402 Family Home,
Mangyongdae

1403 Workers and
Soldiers

(Des Kim Hae Yong (1wn.), Kim Chol Ung (3wn. and 200wn.), Ha
Kyong Guk (5wn.), Jon Kum Hui (10wn.), An Chol (12wn., 20wn. and
50wn.), Kim Myong Sik (30wn.), O Sol Rim (40wn.) and Kong Kyong
Su (70wn. and 100wn.). Litho)

2002 (20 Nov). National Symbols. T **1402** and similar designs. P 13½.
(17×26 mm.) or 11½ (others).
N4250   1wn. purple-brown 15   15
N4251   3wn. myrtle green (vert) 15   15
N4252   5wn. agate 25   20
N4253   10wn. bright crimson (vert) 25   20
N4254   12wn. deep claret (17×26 mm) ... 35   30
N4255   20wn. bright scarlet and deep
    ultramarine (17×26 mm) ... 50   40
N4256   30wn. deep rose red (vert) 65   55
N4257   40wn. greenish blue (vert) ...... 1·00   85
N4258   50wn. purple brown (17×26 mm) ... 1·20   95
N4259   70wn. sepia (17×26 mm) .... 1·60   1·40
N4260   100wn. purple brown (17×26 mm) ... 2·50   2·10
N4261   200wn. bright crimson (17×26 mm) ... 5·00   4·25
N4250/4261 Set of 12 .... 12·00   10·50
Designs—1wn. purple Paeku; 3wn. Mount Paeku; 5wn. Hoeryong;
10wn. Kimilsungia; 12wn. Torch (Tower of Juche Idea); 20wn. Flag;
30wn. Kimjongilia; 40wn. Magnolia blossom; 50wn. National emblem;
70wn. Chollima statue; 100wn. Victorious Fatherland monument;
200wn. Workers Party monument.

(Des An Chol. Litho)

2003 (1 Jan). New Year. P 13½.
N4262 **1403** 3wn. multicoloured 25   20

1404 Bald Eagle steals Young
Antelope

(Des An Chol. Litho)

2003 (1 Jan). Antelope defeats Bald Eagle (fairy tale). T **1404** and
similar horiz designs. Multicoloured. P 13½.

N4263	3wn. Type **1404**	25	20
	a. Booklet pane. Nos. N4263/6, each ×2	12·00	
N4264	50wn. Antelopes unite to defeat eagle	1·30	1·10
N4265	70wn. Eagle eating fish poisoned by antelopes	1·70	1·40
N4266	100wn. Mother antelope and rescued baby	2·50	2·10
N4263/4266	Set of 4	5·25	4·25
MSN4267	110×80 mm. 150wn. Antelopes carrying fruit (54×45 mm)	3·25	2·75

1405 Greeting Full Moon
(January 15th festival)

1406 Soldier

(Des Kim Hae Yong. Litho)

2003 (20 Jan). Folk Festivals. T **1405** and similar vert designs.
Multicoloured. P 12.

N4268	3wn. Type **1405**	25	20
N4269	12wn. Dance greeting full moon (January 15th)	35	30
N4270	40wn. Swinging (Surinal festival)	1·00	85
N4271	70wn. Woman and child (Hangawi festival)	1·70	1·40
N4272	140wn. Peasant dance (Hangawi)	3·25	2·75
N4268/4272	Set of 5	6·00	5·00
MSN4273	110×90 mm. 112wn. Wrestling (Surinal)	2·75	2·40

(Des Kim Chol Ung. Litho)

2003 (14 Feb). Rodong Sinmun, Josoninmingun and Chongnyonjonwi
Newspapers Joint Editorial. P 13½.

N4274	**1406** 12wn. multicoloured	50	40

1407 Weapons

1408 Ode Monument

(Des Kim Chol Ung. Litho)

2003 (15 Feb). Withdrawal from NPT. P 13½.

N4275	**1407** 30wn. multicoloured	85	70

(Des Kim Myong Sik. Litho)

2003 (16 Feb). 61st Birth Anniv of Kim Jong Il. T **1408** and similar horiz
design. Multicoloured. P 12½×12 (3wn.) or 12×11½ (75wn.)

N4276	3wn. Type **1408**	25	20
MSN4277	90×60 mm. 75wn. Mt. Paektu (64×42 mm)	1·80	1·60

1409 Paekmagang (cargo
ship) (⅔-size illustration)

(Des Ha Kyong Guk. Litho)

2003 (18 Feb). Ships. T **1409** and similar horiz designs. Multicoloured.
P 13.

N4278	15wn. Type **1409**	40	35
	a. Booklet pane. Nos. N4278/79 and 4280/1, each ×2	11·00	
N4279	50wn. Konsol (dredger)	1·20	1·00
N4280	70wn. Undok No. 2 (passenger ship)	1·70	1·40
N4281	112wn. Piryugang (cargo ship)	2·75	2·40
N4278/4281	Set of 4	5·50	4·75
MSN4282	78×52 mm. 150wn. Pyongyang No. 1 (pleasure cruiser)	3·25	2·75

1410 Zis

1411 Book Cover

(Des O Sol Rim. Litho)

2003 (20 Feb). Kim Il Sung's Presidential Cars. T **1410** and similar horiz
designs. Multicoloured. P 12×11½.

N4283	3wn. Type **1410**	25	20
	a. Booklet pane. Nos. N4283/4 and N4285/6, each ×2	8·75	
N4284	14wn. Gaz	40	35
N4285	70wn. Pobeda	1·70	1·40
N4286	90wn. Mercedes Benz	2·20	1·80
N4283/4286	Set of 4	4·00	3·50
MSN4287	100×80 mm. 150wn. "Delaying His Urgent Journey" (painting by Kim Sam Gon) (64×42 mm)	3·25	2·75

(Des Choe Chol Man. Litho)

2003 (15 Mar). 30th Anniv of Publication of "On the Art of the Cinema" by Kim Jong Il. Sheet 95×75 mm. P 12½×12.
MSN4288 **1411** 120wn. Multicoloured .... 3·00 2·50

1412 Trumpeter and Symbols of Journey

1413 Soldier and Workers

(Des Kim Chol Ung. Litho)

2003 (16 Mar). 80th Anniv of Kim Il Sung's 250 Mile Journey for Learning. P 11½.
N4289 **1412** 15wn. multicoloured 50 40

(Des Choe Chol Man. Litho)

2003 (29 Mar). Korean People's Army. P 11½.
N4290 **1413** 3wn. multicoloured 25 20

1414 Flags and Emblem

1415 Birthplace, Mangyongdae and Kimilsungia

(Des Kim Chol Ung. Litho)

2003 (9 Apr). Tenth Anniv of Election of Kim Jong Il as Chairman of National Defence Commission. T **1414** and similar multicoloured designs. P 11½ (vert) or 11½×12 (horiz).
N4291 **1414** 3wn. Type **1414** 25 20
MSN4292 175×75 mm. 12wn. Kim Jong Il with computers (51×49 mm); 70wn. With soldiers (51×49 mm); 112wn. With raised hand (51×49 mm) .... 5·75 5·00

(Des Choe Chol Man. Litho)

2003 (15 Apr). 91st Birth Anniv of Kim Il Sung. P 11½.
N4293 **1415** 3wn. multicoloured 25 20

1416 Order of Suhbaatar (Mongolia)

1417 Pantala flavescens

(Des Choe Chol Man. Litho)

2003 (15 Apr). Kim Il Sung's Medals and Orders. T **1416** and similar multicoloured designs. P 12.
N4294 12wn. Type **1416** 35 30
N4295 35wn. Order of Grand Cross (Madagascar) .... 1·00 85
N4296 70wn. Order of Lenin (USSR) .... 2·20 1·80
N4297 140wn. Order of Playa Giron (Cuba) ...... 4·25 3·50
N4294/4297 *Set of 4*... 7·00 5·75
MSN4298 108×91 mm. 120wn. Fidel Castro (president of Cuba) and Kim Il Sung (horiz)............. 3·25 2·75

(Des Jon Kum Hui. Litho)

2003 (20 Apr). Insects. T **1417** and similar vert designs. Multicoloured. P 13½.
N4299 15wn. Type **1417** 50 40
a. Booklet pane. Nos. N4299/300, each ×2 and Nos. N4301/2......... 20·00
N4300 70wn. *Tibicen japonicus* .... 1·70 1·40
N4301 220wn. *Xylotrupes dichotomus* .... 5·75 5·00
N4302 300wn. *Lycaena dispar* .... 8·50 7·00
N4299/4302 *Set of 4*... 15·00 12·50
MSN4303 150×85 mm. Nos. N4299/302 .... 17·00 16·00

1418 Glutinous Rice Cakes

(Des Kim Hae Yong. Litho)

2003 (1 May). Traditional Food. T **1418** and similar horiz designs. Multicoloured. P 12.
N4304 3wn. Type **1418** 25 20
N4305 30wn. Tongkimchi................................. 85 70
N4306 70wn. Sinsollo .... 2·00 1·70
N4304/4306 *Set of 3*... 2·75 2·30
MSN4307 100×83 mm. 120wn. Pyongyang raengmyon.. 3·25 2·75

1419 Victory Monument, Taechongdan Hill

(Des Jon Kim Hui. Litho)

2003 (19 May). Sheet 98×71 mm. P 12.
MSN4308 **1419** 90wn. multicoloured .... 2·75 2·30

1420 Manse Pavilion

(Des An Chol and Kong Kyong Su. Litho)

2003 (30 May). Ryangchon Temple, Kowon, South Hamgyong Province. T **1420** and similar horiz designs. Multicoloured. P 13½.

N4309	3wn. Type **1420**	25	20
N4310	12wn. Three statues	35	30
N4311	40wn. Buddha and two saints (painting)	1·20	1·00
N4312	50wn. Buddha and four saints (painting)	1·50	1·30
N4309/4312	Set of 4	3·00	2·50
MSN4313	100×80 mm. 120wn. Taeung Hall	3·00	2·50

1421 Music Score

(Des Choe Chol Man. Litho)

2003 (1 June). "We are One" (song). Sheet 70×100 mm. P 13½.
MSN4314 **1421** 60wn. multicoloured .... 1·50 1·30

1422 Tigers

(Des Kim Myong Sik and Ha Kyong Guk. Litho)

2003 (10 June). Animals. Sheet 157×72 mm. containing T **1422** and similar vert designs. Multicoloured. P 13½.
MSN4315 3wn. Type **1422**; 70wn. Bears; 150wn. Wild boar; 230wn. Deer .... 12·50 11·50
  a. Booklet pane. No. **MS**N4315 ..... 12·50
The booklet pane, No. **MS**N4315a has white margins all round.

1423 Public Bonds   **1424** Distinguished Service Medal

(Des Kim Hae Yong. Litho)

2003 (25 July). Public Bond Purchase Campaign. P 13.
N4316 **1423** 140wn. multicoloured .... 3·75 3·00

(Des Kim Myong Sik. Litho)

2003 (27 July). 50th Anniv of Liberation. T **1424** and similar multicoloured designs. P 13½ (N4317) or 12 (others).
N4317 3wn. Type **1424** 25 20
MSN4318 Three sheets, all 146×106 mm. (a) 12wn. Kim Il Sung and radio microphone (38×31 mm); 35wn. Kim Il Sung with soldiers (38×31 mm); 70wn. Kim Il Sung signing document (38×31 mm); 140wn. Kim Il Sung (43×43 mm) (circular). (b) 12wn. Kim Il Sung with soldiers (38×31 mm); 35wn. Kim Il Sung inspecting soldier's weapons (38×31 mm); 70wn. Kim Il Sung and Kim Jong Il (38×31 mm); 140wn. Kim Il Sung (43×43 mm) (circular). (c) 12wn. Kim Jong Il receiving bouquet (38×31 mm); 35wn. Kim Jong Il with soldiers (38×31 mm); 70wn. Kim Jong Il with unit commander (38×31 mm); 140wn. Kim Jong Il (43×43 mm) (circular)...................................... 20·00 18·00
MSN4319 65×90 mm. 120wn. President Kim Il Sung 3·00 2·50

1425 *Minicattleya*   **1426** Japanese White-necked Crane (*Grus vipio*)

(Des Jon Kum Hui. Litho)

2003 (28 July). Orchids. T **1425** and similar horiz designs. Multicoloured. P 13½.

N4320	75wn. Type **1425**	2·00	1·70
	a. Block of 4. Nos. N4320/3	13·50	
	b. Booklet pane. Nos. N4320/3.......	13·50	
N4321	100wn. *Phalaenopsis aphrodite* (inscr "Phalanops")..................................	2·50	2·10
N4322	150wn. *Calanthe discolor*	3·75	3·25
N4323	200wn. *Dendrobium snowflake* (inscr "Den.")......................................	5·00	4·25
N4320/4323	Set of 4.................................	12·00	10·00

Nos. N4320/23 were issued in *se-tenant* blocks of four stamps within the sheet, each block forming a composite design.

The stamps of booklet pane No. N4320b form a horizontal strip of four stamps

(Des An Chol. Litho)

2003 (4 Aug). Birds. T **1426** and similar vert designs. Multicoloured. P 12 (**MS**N4329) or 13½. (others).

N4324	12wn. Type **1426**	35	30
	a. Booklet pane. Nos. N4324/5;		
	N4326 ×2 and N4327/8	17·00	
N4325	70wn. Black-crowned night heron (*Nycticorax nycticorax*)	2·10	1·80
N4326	100wn. Domestic pigeon (*Columba livia domestica*)	3·00	2·50
N4327	120wn. Cockatiel (*Nymphicus hollandicus*)	3·50	3·00
N4328	150wn. Tawny owl (*Strix aluco*)	4·25	3·75
N4324/4328	Set of 5	12·00	10·00
MSN4329	70×90 mm. 225wn. Inscr "Pseudogyps africanus" (39×51 mm)	6·75	6·00

The booklet pane, No. N4324a has white margins all round.

1427 Adelie Penguin (*Pygoscelis adeliae*)

(Des Kim Hae Yong. Litho)

2003 (20 Aug). Arctic and Antarctic Fauna. Sheet 160×114 mm. containing T **1427** and similar horiz designs. Multicoloured. P 12.

MSN4330	15wn. Type **1427**; 70wn. Walrus (*Odobenus rosmarus*); 140wn. Polar bear (*Thalarctos maritimus*); 150wn. Bowhead whale (*Balaena mysticetus*) (inscr "mysticegus"); 220wn. Spotted seal (*Phoca largha*)	16·00	14·50
	a. Booklet pane. No. **MS**N4330	16·00	14·50

The stamps and margins of **MS**N4330 form a composite design. The booklet pane, No. **MS**N4330a has narrow margins at top and bottom.

1428 *Pholiota flammans*　**1429** Exhibition Hall

(Des Jon Kum Hui and An Col. Litho)

2003 (5 Sept). Fungi. T **1428** and similar horiz designs. Multicoloured. P 13½.

N4331	3wn. Type **1428**	25	20
	a. Block of 4. Nos. N4331/4	6·25	
	b. Booklet pane. Nos. N4331/ **MS**N4335	13·50	
N4332	12wn. *Geastrum fimbriatum*	35	30
N4333	70wn. *Coprinus atramentarius*	1·90	1·60
N4334	130wn. *Pleurotus cornucopiae*	3·50	3·00
N4331/4334	Set of 4	5·50	4·50
MSN4335	80×65 mm. 250wn. *Elfvingia applanata*	6·75	6·00

Nos. 4331/4 were issued in *se-tenant* blocks of four stamps within the sheet.
The stamps of booklet pane No. N4331b form a horizontal strip of five stamps.

(Des Choe Chol Man. Litho)

2003 (5 Sept). National Stamp Exhibition. T **1429** and similar multicoloured design. P 13½.

N4336	3wn. Type **1429**	25	20
N4337	60wn. Stamps and display stands (horiz)	1·70	1·50

1430 Emblem and Flag　(**1431**)

(Des Kim Myong Sik. Litho)

2003 (9 Sept). 55th Anniv of Democratic Peoples' Republic of Korea. T **1430** and similar multicoloured designs. P 12×11½ (N4338), 12½×12 (**MS**N4339) or 14½ (**MS**N4340).

N4338	3wn. Type **1430**	25	20
MSN4339	Four sheets, each 65×120 mm. (a) 60wn. "The Birth of New Korea"; 60wn. "On the Road supporting Kim Il Sung"; 60wn. "Braving Rain of Bullets"; 60wn. "Giving command for Counter Offensive"; (c) 60wn. "We Trust and Follow You"; 60wn. "Kim Il Sung at Power Plant"; (d) 60wn. "Victory Assured"; 60wn. "Keeping up Shongun Politics"	13·50	12·50
MSN4340	75×105 mm. 120wn. Kim Il Sung (43×43 mm) (circular)	3·50	3·00

2003 (4 Oct). Bangkok 2003 International Stamp Exhibition, Thailand. No. **MS**N4244 optd in the margin with T **1431**.

MSN4341	57×70 mm. 150wn. Cavalier King Charles spaniel	3·75	3·25

1432 Mao Zedong

2003 (26 Dec). 110th Birth Anniv of Mao Zedong (Chinese leader 1945–1976). T **1432** and similar horiz designs. Imperf. (140wn.) or p 13½.

N4342	20wn. Type **1432**	70	60
	a. Strip of 2. Nos. N4342 and N4344 plus label	1·60	1·40
N4343	20wn. During the "Long March"	70	60
	a. Strip of 2. Nos. N4343 and N4345 plus label	1·60	1·40
N4344	30wn. With female companion	85	75
N4345	30wn. Seated in room of men	85	75
N4346	30wn. Addressing partisans	85	75
	a. Strip of 2. Nos. N4346/7 plus label	1·80	1·60
N4347	30wn. With partisans wearing long coat	85	75
N4348	30wn. Addressing crowd in Beijing	85	75
	a. Strip of 2. Nos. N4348/9 plus label	1·80	1·60
N4349	30wn. With people from many nations	85	75
N4342/4349	Set of 8	5·75	5·25

Nos. N4342 and N4344, Nos. N4343 and N4345, N4346/7 and N4348/9, respectively, were each issued in horizontal *se-tenant* strips of two stamps surrounding a central ½-stamp size label within the sheets.

Two sheets containing N4342/5 and N4346/9 respectively were on sale for 140wn. Each

No. N4350 is vacant.

1433 Workers and Soldiers

1434 *Cebus apella*

(Des Choe Chol Man. Litho)

2004 (1 Jan). New Year. P 13½.
N4351 **1433** 3wn. multicoloured 25 25

(Des An Chol. Litho)

2004 (1 Jan). Monkeys. T **1434** and similar vert designs. Multicoloured. P 13½.

N4352	3wn. Type **1434**	25	25
	a. Booklet pane. Nos. N4352/5	7·25	
N4353	60wn. *Papio doguera*	1·70	1·50
N4354	70wn. *Cercopithecus aethiops*	2·10	1·80
N4355	100wn. *Saguinus oedipus*	3·00	2·50
N4352/4355	*Set of 4*	6·25	5·50
MSN4356	71×85 mm. 155wn. *Macaca mulatta*	4·25	3·75

1435 Children

1436 Yong Liwei

(Des Kim Hae Yong. Litho)

2004 (22 Jan). Lunar New Year. P 13½.
N4357 **1435** 3wn. multicoloured 25 25

(Des Choe Chol Man. Litho)

2004 (30 Jan). Yong Liwei–First Chinese Astronaut. T **1436** and similar multicoloured design. P 13½.

N4358	91wn. Type **1436**	2·50	2·30
	a. Booklet pane. Nos. N4358/9, each ×2	11·00	
N4359	98wn. Returned space capsule (54×45 mm)	2·75	2·40
MSN4360	142×100 mm. Nos. N4358/9	5·50	4·75

Nos. N4358/**MS**N4360 were also available with the booklet cover and the margin of **MS**N4360 overprinted for Hong Kong 2004 Exhibition.

(**1437**)

1438 Book, Weapons and Slogan

(Des An Chol. Litho)

2004 (30 Jan). Hong Kong 2004 International Stamp Exhibition. Nos. N4352/**MS**N4356 overprinted with T **1437**. P 13½.

N4361	3wn. multicoloured	25	25
N4362	60wn. multicoloured	1·70	1·50
N4363	70wn. multicoloured	2·10	1·80
N4364	100wn. multicoloured	3·00	2·50
N4361/4364	*Set of 4*	6·25	5·50
MSN4365	71×85 mm. 155wn. multicoloured	4·25	3·75

(Des Jon Kum Hui. Litho)

2004 (15 Feb). Rodong Sinmun, Josoninmingun and Chongnyonjonwi Newspapers Joint Editorial. P 13½.
N4366 **1438** 3wn. multicoloured 25 25

Nos. N4367/71 and Type No. **1439** have been left for "Birth Anniv of Kim Jong Il", issued on 16 February 2004.

1440 Kim Jong Il

(Des Kim Hae Yong and Choe Chol Man. Litho)

2004 (19 Feb). 30th Anniv of Publication of Juche Idea Programme. Sheet 151×80 mm. P 13½.
MSN4372 **1440** 120wn. multicoloured .... 3·50 3·00

1441 Fields and Goat Herd

(Des Kim Chol Ung. Litho)

2004 (25 Feb). 40th Anniv of Publication of "Thesis on Rural Socialist Question" by Kim Il Sung. T **1441** and similar multicoloured design. P 13½.

N4373	3wn. Type **1441**	25	25
MSN4374	117×86 mm. 120wn. Kim Il Sung and farmer (49×51 mm)	3·25	2·75

1442 Sokgundo Lighthouse

(Des Kim Chol Ung. Litho)

2004 (20 Mar). Lighthouses. T **1442** and similar vert designs. Multicoloured. P 13½.

(a) Booklet Stamps.

N4375	3wn. Type **1442**	25	25
	a. Booklet pane. Nos. N4375/8	8·75	
N4376	12wn. Yubundo	50	45
N4377	100wn. Jangdokdo	2·50	2·30
N4378	195wn. Amryongdan	5·25	4·50
N4375/4378	Set of 4	7·75	6·75

(b) Miniature Sheet.

MSN4379	131×121 mm. Nos. N4375/8	8·75	7·50

1443 Korean Chess

(Des Jon Kum Hui. Litho)

2004 (20 Mar). Board Games. T **1443** and similar horiz designs. Multicoloured. P 13½.

(a) Booklet Stamps.

N4380	3wn. Type **1443**	25	25
	a. Booklet pane. Nos. N4380/1, N4382 ×2 and N4383	9·00	
N4381	12wn. Go	50	45
N4382	90wn. Yut	2·40	2·10
N4383	120wn. Koni	3·25	2·75
N4380/4383	Set of 4	5·75	5·00

(b) Miniature Sheets.

MSN4384	110×114 mm. Nos. N4380/3	6·75	6·00
MSN4385	97×81 mm. 98wn. Men and child playing chess (54×45 mm)	2·50	2·30

1444 Birthplace, Mangyongdae

(Des Kim Hae Yong. Litho)

2004 (15 Apr). 92nd Birth Anniv of Kim Il Sung. T **1444** and similar multicoloured design. P 11½.

N4386	3wn. Type **1444**	25	25
MSN4387	94×76 mm. 120wn. Kim Il Sung (39×51 mm)	3·25	2·75

1445 18th-century Map of Korea

1446 *Calcinoplax antiqua*

(Des Jon Kum Hui. Litho)

2004 (20 Apr). Tok Islet. T **1445** and similar multicoloured designs. P 13½.

(a) Booklet Stamps.

N4388	3wn. Type **1445**	25	25
	a. Booklet pane. Nos. N4388/91	7·25	
N4389	12wn. Western islet	50	45
N4390	106wn. Eastern islet	3·00	2·50
N4391	116wn. Both islets (circular) (45×45 mm)	3·25	2·75
N4388/4391	Set of 4	6·25	5·25

(b) Miniature Sheets.

MSN4392	101×121 mm. Nos. N4388/90	3·75	3·25
MSN4393	160×81 mm. 116wn. No. N4391	3·50	3·00

2004 (20 Apr). Fossils. T **1446** and similar horiz designs. Multicoloured. Litho. P 13½.

N4394	3wn. Type **1446**	25	25
	a. Booklet pane. Nos. N4394/8	10·00	
N4395	12wn. *Podozamites lanceolatus*	50	45
N4496	70wn. *Comptonia naumannii*	1·90	1·70
N4397	120wn. *Tingia carbonica*	3·25	2·75
N4398	140wn. *Clinocardium asagaiense*	3·75	3·25
N4394/4398	Set of 5	8·75	7·50
MSN4399	135×86 mm. Nos. N4394/6 and N4398	6·75	5·75
MSN4400	102×76 mm. 120wn. No. N4397	3·50	3·00

1447 *Notocactus leninghausii*

(Des Jon Kum Hui. Litho)

2004 (2 June). Cacti. T **1447** and similar horiz designs. Multicoloured.
P 13½.

(a) Booklet Stamps.

N4401	70wn. Type **1447**	1·70	1·50
	a. Booklet pane. Nos. N4401/4	10·50	
N4402	90wn. Echinocactus grusonii	2·30	2·00
N4403	100wn. Gymnocalycium baldianum	2·50	2·30
N4404	140wn. Mammillaria insularis	3·75	3·25
N4401/4404 *Set of 4*		9·25	8·25

(b) Miniature Sheet

MSN4405	148×93 mm. Nos. N4401/4	10·50	9·50

Nos. N4401/N4405 were also available (issued 28 August 2004)
with the booklet cover and the margin of **MS**N4405 overprinted for
Singapore 2004 Exhibition.

1448 Kim Jong Il and Hu Jintao

(Des Kim Hae Yong. Litho)

2004 (18 June). Kim Jong Il's visit to China. Three sheets containing
T **1448** and similar multicoloured designs. P 13½.

N4406	3wn. Type **1448**	25	25
	a. Booklet pane. Nos. N4406/14	8·75	
N4407	3wn. With Wen Jiabao	25	25
N4408	12wn. With Jiang Zemin	35	30
N4409	12wn. With Jia Qinglin	35	30
N4410	40wn. With Wu Bangguo	1·00	90
N4411	40wn. Seated with Zeng Qinghong	1·00	90
N4412	60wn. With Huang Guo and others	1·60	1·40
N4413	60wn. Inspecting Tianjin (new city)	1·60	1·40
N4414	74wn. With Hu Jintao (41×60 mm)	2·10	1·80
N4406/4414 *Set of 9*		7·75	6·75
MSN4415	Two sheets, each 160×130 mm. (a) Nos. N4406, N4408, N4410 and N4412; (b) Nos. N4407, N4409, N4411 and N4413	6·50	5·50
MSN4416	90×120 mm. N4414 (41×60 mm)	2·30	2·00

1449 Flag

(Des Choe Chol Man and Kim Hae Yong. Litho)

2004 (19 June). 40th Anniv of Kim Il Jong at WPK. T **1449** and similar
multicoloured designs. P 13½.

N4417	3wn. Type **1449**	25	25
MSN4418	Three sheets, each 150×75 mm. (a) Size 54×45 mm. 12wn. Kim Il Jong at desk; 100wn. With paintings. (b) Size 54×45 mm. 12wn. Inspecting power station; 100wn. With soldiers. (c) Size 54×45 mm. 12wn. Wearing safety hat and glasses; 100wn. Kim Il Jong	9·00	7·75
MSN4419	84×100 mm. Size 42×60 mm. 130wn. Kim Il Sung and Kim Il Jong	2·10	1·80

1450 Monument and
Kimilsungia

(Des Kim Chol Ung. Litho)

2004 (8 July). Kim Il Sung Commemoration. T **1450** and similar
multicoloured design. P 11½ (3wn.) or 12 (others).

N4420	3wn. Type **1450**	25	25
MSN4421	Four sheets, each 116×120 mm. (a) Size 51×39 mm. 12wn. Kim Il Sung with workers; 116wn. With farmers. (b) Size 51×39 mm. 12wn. With soldiers; 116wn. With children. (c) Size 51×39 mm. 12wn. With Kim Il Jong at Academy; 116wn. With Kim Il Jong on Mt. Paektu. (d) Size 51×39 mm. 12wn. With Mun Ik Hwan; 116wn. Holding telephone.	12·50	11·00
MSN4422	70×90 mm. Size 39×51 mm. 112wn. Kim Il Sung	2·75	2·40

1451 Kim Hyong Jik and Kim Il
Sung as a Child (statue)

1452 Deng Xiaoping as
Young Man

(Des An Chol. Litho)

2004 (10 July). 110th Birth Anniv of Kim Yong Jik (father of Kim Il
Sung). Sheet 150×96 mm. P 11½

MSN4423	**1451** 112wn. multicoloured	2·75	2·40

2004 (15 July). Birth Centenary of Deng Xiaoping (Chinese leader).
T **1452** and similar multicoloured designs. Litho. P 12 (**MS**N4429)
or 13½. (others).

N4424	3wn. Type **1452**	25	25
	a. Pair. Nos. N4424/5	65	60
N4425	12wn. Wearing shorts	35	30
N4426	35wn. Wearing uniform	85	75
	a. Pair. Nos. N4426/7	2·10	1·90
N4427	50wn. Giving speech	1·20	1·10
N4424/4427 *Set of 4.*		2·40	2·20
MSN4428	175×115 mm. Nos. N4424/7; 70wn. Visiting shopping centre (51×39 mm)	5·25	4·50
MSN4429	100×70 mm. 80wn. Deng Xiaoping (51×39 mm)	2·10	1·80

Nos. N4424/5 and Nos. N4426/7 were issued in *se-tenant* pairs
within the sheet, the pairs separated by a stamp sized label.

1453 Boxing

1454 *Carassius auratus*

2004 (10 Aug). Olympic Games, Athens. T **1453** and similar vert designs. Litho. P 13½.

N4430	3wn. Type **1453**	25	25
	a. Horiz strip of 4. Nos. N4430/3 ...	6·50	
N4431	12wn. Football	35	30
N4432	85wn. High jump	2·30	2·00
N4433	140wn. Gymnastics	3·50	3·00
N4430/4433 *Set of 4*		5·75	5·00

Nos. N4430/3 were issued in horizontal *se-tenant* strips of four stamps within the sheet.

2004 (10 Aug). Fish. Sheet 110×140 mm. containing T **1454** and similar horiz designs. Multicoloured. P 13½.
MSN4434 3wn. Type **1454**; 12wn. *Tilapia nilotica*; 140wn. *Ophiocephalus argus*; 165wn. *Clarias gariepinus* .... 8·50 7·50

1455 Mercedes Benz Fire Appliance

(Des Kim Myong Sik and O Sol Rim. Litho)

2004 (15 Aug). Fire Engines. T **1455** and similar horiz designs. Multicoloured. P 13½.

N4435	3wn. Type **1455**	30	25
	a. Booklet pane. Nos. N4435/8......	4·25	
N4436	12wn. Fire truck	35	30
N4437	40wn. Jelcz fire appliance	1·00	90
N4438	105wn. Mercedes Benz without ladders, facing right	2·50	2·30
N4435/4438 *Set of 4*		3·75	3·50
MSN4439 115×88 mm. Nos. N4435/8		4·25	3·50
MSN4440 85×75 mm. 97wn. Mercedes Benz with ladders, facing left		2·40	2·10

1456 Airbus A340–600

(Des Choe Chol Man. Litho)

2004 (20 Aug). Aircraft. T **1456** and similar horiz designs. Multicoloured. P 13½.

N4441	3wn. Type **1456**	30	25
	a. Horiz. pair. Nos. N4441/2	8·75	2·75
	b. Booklet pane. Nos. N4441/4......	3·00	
N4442	97wn. *Concorde*	2·50	2·30

N4443	104wn. *Graff Zeppelin* II	2·75	2·40
	a. Horiz pair. Nos. N4443/4	6·00	5·25
N4444	116wn. Junkers	3·00	2·50
N4441/4444 *Set of 4*		7·75	6·75
MSN4445 126×158 mm. Nos. N4432/5		8·75	7·50

Nos. N4441/2 and N4443/4, respectively each form a composite design. The two pairs combine with the margin in **MS**N4445 to form a composite design of an airfield.

The stamps of booklet pane No. N4441b have cream margins.

1457 Kim Il Sung and Prime Minister Koizumi

1458 An Jung Gun

(Des Choe Chol Man. Litho)

2004 (25 Aug). Kim Il Jong's Meeting with Japanese Prime Minister Junichiro Koizumi. Sheet 150×75 mm. P 12.
MSN4446 **1457** 220wn. Multicoloured...................... 5·25 4·50

(Des Jon Kum Hui)

2004 (21 Sept). 125th Birth Anniv of An Jung Gun (revolutionary). Sheet 68×90 mm. P 13½.
MSN4447 **1458** 112wn. multicoloured .... 2·50 2·30

1459 Kim Jong Suk's Pistol

(Des Jon Kum Hui. Litho)

2004 (22 Sept). Kim Jong Suk (Kim Il Sung's wife and revolutionary fighter) Commemoration. T **1459** and similar horiz design. Multicoloured. P 13½. (3wn.) or 12 (97wn.).
N4448 3wn. Type **1459** 25 25
MSN4449 103×85 mm. 97wn. Kim Jong Suk (85×42 mm) .... 2·50 2·30

1460 *Anser cygnoides*

2004 (30 Sept). Swan Goose (*Anser cygnoides*). T **1460** and similar horiz designs. Multicoloured. Litho. P 11½.
N4450 3wn. Type **1460** 30 25
a. Booklet pane. Nos. N4450/3...... 9·00

N4451	97wn. Facing left............................	2·75	2·30
N4452	104wn. Two geese	2·75	2·50
N4453	120wn. Two geese swimming..................	3·00	2·75
N4450/4453 Set of 4..............................		8·00	7·00

The stamps of booklet pane N4450a. have white margins.

1461 Temple Building

2004 (5 Oct). Simwon Temple. T **1461** and similar horiz design. Multicoloured. P 12 (3wn.) or 13½. (97wn.).

| N4454 | 3wn. Type **1461** | 30 | 25 |
| **MS**N4455 | 120×80 mm. 97wn. Buddha (56×42 mm) | 3·00 | 2·50 |

1462 Diesel Locomotive

2004 (5 Nov). Railways. T **1462** and similar horiz designs. Multicoloured. P 11½.

N4456	15wn. Type **1462**	55	45
	a. Booklet pane. Nos. N4456/60 ...	12·00	
N4457	40wn. Yellow locomotive..................	1·10	95
N4458	75wn. Electric locomotive	2·10	1·90
N4459	120wn. Older electric locomotive..........	3·50	3·00
N4460	150wn. Red locomotive....................	4·25	3·75
N4456/4460 Set of 5............................		10·50	9·50
MSN4461	165×91 mm. Nos. N4456/8 and N4460...	11·50	10·50
MSN4462	95×58 mm. 120wn. No. N4459	3·75	3·25

Nos. N4463/**MS**N4464 and Type No. 1463 have been left for "45th Anniv of Repatriation" issued 16 December 2004 not yet received.

MARIO CESAR KINDELAND MESA
(CUBA)

(**1464**)   **1465** Soldier

2004 (20 Dec). Olympic Games, Athens. Nos. N4430/3 overprinted in silver as T **1464** with medal winners' names and country. Multicoloured. Litho. P 13½.

N4465	3wn. Boxing (Mario Cesar Kindelan Mesa) (Cuba)...................	30	25
	a. Horiz. strip of 4. Nos. N4465/8	6·75	
N4466	12wn. Football (Argentina)	35	30
N4467	85wn. High jump (Yelena Slesarenko) (Russia)........................	2·30	2·00
N4468	140wn. Gymnastics (Teng Haibin) (China).........................	3·50	3·00
N4465/4468 Set of 4............................		5·75	5·00

2005 (1 Jan). New Year. Litho. P 11½.

| N4469 | **1465** | 3wn. multicoloured................... | 30 | 25 |

1466 Chick   **1467** Kim Il Sung

(Des Jon Kum Hui. Litho)

2005 (1 Jan). New Year. Year of the Rooster. T **1466** and similar vert designs showing carved wooden fowl (N4470/**MS**4476). Multicoloured. Litho. P 11½.

N4470	3wn. Type **1466**	30	25
	a. Booklet pane. Nos. N4470/5......	9·75	
N4471	12wn. Hen	35	30
N4472	30wn. Hen sitting on eggs	90	75
N4473	70wn. Hen pecking	2·00	1·70
N4474	100wn. Rooster	2·50	2·20
N4475	140wn. Basket of eggs	3·50	3·00
N4470/4475 Set of 6............................		8·50	7·50
MSN4476	84×112 mm. Nos. N4470, N4473/5........	8·50	7·50
MSN4477	80×130 mm. 97wn. Hen and chicks (painting) (50×60 mm)	2·50	2·20

The booklet pane No. N4470a. and the stamps of **MS**N4476 form a composite design.

Nos. N4470 and N4473 were also issued in individual sheets, the stamps from the booklet have yellow borders, whilst those from the sheet have white borders.

2005 (22 Jan). 80th Anniv (2003) of Kim Il Sung's 250 Mile Journey for Learning. Sheet 125×90 mm. Litho. P 12×12½.

| **MS**N4478 | **1467** 120wn. multicoloured................ | 3·00 | 2·50 |

1468 Statue

2005 (8 Feb). 45th Anniv of Chongsanri Method. Sheet 136×95 mm. Litho. P 13½.

| **MS**N4479 | **1468** 120wn. multicoloured................ | 3·00 | 2·50 |

The stamps and margins of No. **MS**N4479 form a composite design.

1469 Sunset

2005 (10 Feb). Landscapes. Sheet 136×95 mm. containing T **1469** and similar horiz designs. Multicoloured. Litho. P 12½×12.
MSN4480 3wn. Type **1469**; 12wn. Snow covered
weapons; 40wn. Flowering trees and mountain;
50wn. Waterside town; 60wn. Waterfall in
autumn; 70wn. Tractors working in fields; 80wn.
Flower fields; 100wn. Paddy fields .... 9·50   8·50

1470 Flowers and Mount   **1471** Monuments
Paektu

2005 (16 Feb). 63rd Birth Anniv of Kim Jong Il. T **1470** and similar multicoloured designs. Litho. P 13½.
N4481   3wn. Type **1470** 30   25
MSN4482 Two sheets, each 192×60 mm. (a)
50wn. ×3, Snow covered peaks, left; Snow
covered main peak at sunrise; Snow covered
peaks, right. (b) 50wn. ×3, Peaks and clouds, left;
Peaks and lake; Peaks and lake, right. 30   7·75
The stamps of Nos. MSN4482a/b, each form a composite design of a mountain range.

2005 (28 Feb). Rodong Sinmun, Josoninmingun and Chongnyonjonwi Newspapers Joint Editorial. Litho. P 13½.
N4483   **1471**   3wn. multicoloured 30   25

1472 Orchid   **1473** Kimilsungii and
Birthplace, Mangyongdae

2005 (13 Apr). 40th Anniv of Orchid Festival. T **1472** and similar multicoloured design. Litho. P 13½.
N4484   3wn. Type **1472** 30   25
MSN4485 107×80 mm. 120wn. Kim Il Sung and
President Sukarno of Indonesia (54×45 mm).......... 3·00   2·50

2005 (15 Apr). 93rd Birth Anniv of Kim Il Sung. T **1473** and similar vert design. Multicoloured. Litho. P 13½.
N4486   3wn. Type **1473** 30   25
MSN4487 105×78 mm. 112wn. Kim Il Sung (39×51
mm) .... 2·75   2·30

1474 Pack Yong Sun   **1475** Panda

(Des Choe Chol Man. Litho)

2005 (30 Apr). World Table Tennis Championship, Shanghai. T **1474** and similar horiz designs. Multicoloured. Litho. P 11½.
N4488   3wn. Type **1474** 30   25
           a. Booklet pane. Nos. N4488/93 ... 5·25
N4489   5wn. Mao Zedong.................................... 30   25
N4490   12wn. Wang Liqin.................................... 35   30
N4491   20wn. Jan-Ove Waldner 70   60
N4492   30wn. Zhang Yining................................ 90   75
N4493   102wn. Werner Schlager .... 2·50   2·20
N4488/4493 Set of 6... 4·50   4·00
MSN4494 155×187 mm. Nos. N4488/93 .... 5·25   4·75

(Des Han Song Rim and An Chol. Litho)

2005 (3 May). Giant Panda (*Ailuropoda melanoleuca*). T **1475** and similar vert designs. Multicoloured. P 13½.
N4495   15wn. Type **1475** 55   45
           a. Booklet pane. Nos. N4495/9...... 10·50
N4496   45wn. Walking .... 1·20   1·00
N4497   70wn. Two pandas .... 2·00   1·70
N4498   120wn. Mother and cub .... 3·00   2·50
N4499   140wn. Eating bamboo..................... 3·50   3·00
N4495/4499 Set of 5... 9·25   7·75
MSN4500 150×105 mm. Nos. N4495/9...................... 10·50   9·25
MSN4501 80×130 mm. 120wn. Mother and cub ...... 3·25   2·75
Nos. N4495/6 and N4499 were also issued in individual sheets.

Nos. N4502/6 and Type **1476** have been left for "Flora and Fauna", issued 5 May 2005, not yet received.

1477 Family

2005 (25 May). 50th Anniv of Korean Residents in Japan Association (Chongryon). T **1477** and similar vert design. Multicoloured. Litho. P 13½.
N4507   3wn. Type **1477** 30   25
MSN4508 85×102 mm. 130wn. Kim Il Sung and
Chongryon leader (45×54 mm).............................. 3·25   2·75

1478 *Panthera tigris altaika*

(Des An Chol and A. Puharihin. Litho)

2005 (1 June). Far Eastern Animals. T **1478** and similar horiz design. Multicoloured. P 13½.
N4509   40wn. Type **1478** .... 1·10   95
           a. Horiz. strip of 2. Nos. N4509/10
             plus label .... 2·30   2·00
           b. Booklet pane. Nos. N4509a ×2   4·75
N4510   40wn. *Martes zibellina*...................... 1·10   95
Nos. 4509/10 were issued in horizontal *se-tenant* strips of two stamps surrounding a central stamp size label.
Stamps of a similar design were issued by Russia.

1479 General's Tomb, Koguryo

(Des Choe Chol Man. Litho)

2005 (14 June). Relics and Remains of Koguryo Dynasty (277BC–668AD). T **1479** and similar multicoloured designs. P 13½.

N4511	3wn. Type **1479**	30	25
	a. Booklet pane. Nos. N4511/15 ..	11·00	
N4512	70wn. Hunting (tomb mural)	2·00	1·70
N4513	97wn. King Kwanggaetho's		
	mausoleum (37×56 mm)	2·40	2·10
N4514	100wn. Fortress, Mt. Songsan	2·50	2·20
N4515	130wn. Gilded arrow heads	3·25	2·75
N4511/4515	*Set of 5*	9·50	8·00
MSN4516	135×120 mm. Nos. N4511/12 and		
	N4514/15	8·00	7·00
MSN4517	130×90 mm. 97wn. No. N4513	2·50	2·20

1480 Kim Chol Ju

2005 (14 June). Kim Chol Ju (revolutionary) Commemoration. Sheet 75×100 mm. Litho. P 13½.

MSN4518	**1480** 170wn. multicoloured	4·50	3·75

1481 Kim Jong Il and Kim Dae-jung (President South Korea 1998–2003)

2005 (15 June). Fifth Anniv of North–South Joint Declaration. Two sheets containing T **1481** and similar multicoloured designs showing Kim Il Jong and Kim Dae-jung. P 13½. (**MS**N4520 and vert stamps of **MS**N4519) or 11½ (horiz stamps of **MS**N4519)

MSN4519 120×125 mm. 112wn. ×4, Type **1481**;		
Kim Jong Il and Kim Dae-jung (different); At		
banquet (horiz); At conference table (horiz)	13·50	12·50
MSN4520 90×110 mm. 167wn. Shaking hands		
(54×45 mm)	4·50	3·75

1482 White Tiger

(Des Jon Kum Hui. Litho)

2005 (10 July). White Tiger (*Panthera tigris altaika*). T **1482** and similar vert designs. Multicoloured. P 12×12½ (Nos. N4521/4 and **MS**N4525) or 11½×12 (**MS**N4526).

N4521	3wn. Type **1482**	30	25
	a. Booklet pane. Nos. N4515/8	9·50	
N4522	12wn. Snarling head	35	30
N4523	130wn. Head and shoulders	3·25	2·75
N4524	200wn. Snarling facing right	5·25	4·75
N4521/4524	*Set of 4*	8·25	7·25
MSN4525	160×100 mm. Nos. N4521/4	9·50	8·50
MSN4526	131×105 mm. 150wn. Mother and cubs		
	(42×64 mm)	4·00	3·50

1483 Map of Korea

2005 (25 July). Sheet 113×89 mm. Litho. P 11½×12.

MSN4527	**1483** 130wn. multicoloured	3·25	2·75

1484 Soldier

1485 Monument

2005 (27 July). Period of Struggle. Litho. P 12×12½.

N4528	**1484** 3wn. multicoloured	30	25

2005 (15 Aug). 60th Anniv of National Liberation. T **1485** and similar multicoloured designs showing Kim Il Sung. Litho. P 13½.

N4529	3wn. Type **1485**	30	25

MSN4530 Two sheets, each 111×145 mm. (a) 60wn ×4, Kim Il Sung at home (horiz); On horseback (horiz); With fighters in woodland (horiz); Planning strategy (horiz); 102wn. In uniform (44×44 mm. circular). (b) 60wn. ×4, On board ship (horiz); With workers (horiz); Giving speech (horiz); With family (horiz); 102wn. At microphone (44×44 mm. circular) .... 20·00   19·00

MSN4531 98×126 mm. 128wn. Kim Il Sung (44×44 mm. circular).............................. 3·25   2·75

(**1486**)

(Des Han Song Rim and An Chol. Litho)

2005 (19 Aug). Taipei 2005 International Stamp Exhibition. Nos. N4490/2, N4494 and **MS**N4496 overprinted as T **1486**. Multicoloured. P 13½.

N4532	15wn. As Type **1475**	55	45
N4533	45wn. Walking (As N4491)	1·20	1·00
N4534	70wn. Two pandas (As N4492)	2·10	1·90
N4535	140wn. Eating bamboo (As N4494)	3·50	3·00
N4532/4535 *Set of 4*		6·50	5·75

MSN4536 80×80 mm. 120wn. Mother and cub (As MSN4496).............................. 3·00   2·50

1487 Red Robes

1488 Marchers

(Des Kim Hae Yong. Litho)

2005 (30 Aug). National Costume. T **1487** and similar vert designs showing costumes. Multicoloured. P 11½ (Nos. N4537/40 and **MS**N4541) or 12 (**MS**N4542).

N4537	3wn. Type **1487**	30	25
	a. Booklet pane. Nos. N4537/40 ...	8·25	
N4538	80wn. Blue and yellow robe	2·20	1·90
N4539	100wn. Green and cream robe with cranes	2·50	2·20
N4540	120wn. Brocade coat	3·00	2·50
N4537/4540 *Set of 4*		7·25	6·25

MSN4541 140×80 mm. Nos. N4537/40.............................. 8·25   7·25

MSN4542 70×94 mm. 140wn. Children (39×51 mm.) .... 3·50   3·00

2005 (8 Sept). Joint Slogans. Litho. P 12×12½.

N4543	**1488** 3wn. multicoloured	30	25

1489 Monument

1490 Queen emerging

2005 (10 Oct). 60th Anniv of Korean Workers Party. T **1489** and similar multicoloured designs. Litho. P 13½. (No. N4544) or 12 (others).

N4544	3wn. Type **1489**	30	25

MSN4545 Two sheets, each 153×125 mm. Horiz, size 51×39 mm. (a) 12wn. Kim Il Sung; 30wn. Kim Il Sung and Kim Jong Il; 60wn. Kim Il Sung with military leaders; 90wn. Kim Jong Il. (b) 12wn. Early discussions; 30wn. Joining together; 60wn. Planning; 90wn. Giving speech; .... 10·50   9·75

MSN4546 Two sheets, each 81×100 mm. Circular, size 46×46 mm. (a) 120wn. Kim Jong Il. (b) 120wn. Kim Il Sung.............................. 6·00   5·50

(Des Jo Son Il. Litho)

2005 (20 Oct). Bees (*Apis mellifera*). T **1490** and similar horiz designs showing bees. Multicoloured. P 11½.

N4547	3wn. Type **1490**	30	25
	a. Booklet pane. Nos. N4547/50 ...	9·50	
N4548	12wn. Two bees and grubs	35	30
N4549	128wn. Bee and honey	3·25	2·75
N4550	200wn. Bee in flight	5·25	4·75
N4547/4550 *Set of 4*		8·25	7·25

MSN4551 140×80 mm. Nos. N4547/50.............................. 9·75   9·00

The stamps of booklet pane No. N4547a and **MS**N4551 each form a composite design of bees in the hive.

1491 "60" and Emblem   **1492** Pagoda

2005 (24 Oct). 60th Anniv of United Nations. Litho. P 13½.

N4552	**1491** 15wn. multicoloured	30	25

2005 (31 Oct). Relics of Kaesong (1st issue). Two sheets, each 180×125 mm. containing T **1492** and similar multicoloured designs. Litho. P 12×11½ (horiz) or 13 (circular).

MSN4553 Two sheets. (a) 35wn. ×3, Type **1492**; Monument; Pagoda (different); 75wn. Buildings (64×42 mm). (b) 35wn. ×3, Small building; Steps; Tablet (32×32 mm. circular); 75wn. Gateway (64×42 mm). .... 5·75   5·00

Nos. **MS**N4553a/b each contain three stamp size labels showing relics from the site. The larger stamps in each sheet merge with the margins to form a composite background design.

See also No. **MS**N4556.

1493 Kim Hyong Gwon

2005 (4 Nov). Birth Centenary of Kim Hyong Gwon (revolutionary).
Sheet 75×110 mm. Litho. P 11½×12.
MSN4554 **1493** 120wn. multicoloured.......................... 3·00   2·50

1494 Manuscript and "X"

2005 (17 Nov). Centenary of False Five Point Treaty. Litho. P 12.
N4555 **1494** 12wn. multicoloured 35   30

2005 (18 Nov). Relics of Kaesong (2nd issue). Three sheets, each
180×125 mm. containing multicoloured designs as T **1492**.
Litho. P 12×11½ (horiz) or 13 (circular).
MSN4556 (a) 35wn. ×2, Bridge; Statue; 75wn.
Waterfall (42×64 mm). (b) 35wn. ×2, Yeongjo of
Joseon (32×32 mm. circular); Gateway (45×33
mm); 75wn. Burial mound (64×42 mm). (c)
35wn. ×6, Raised building and tunnel; Two burial
mounds; Stone bridge; Steps and gateway;
Buddha; Pillars and mound................................. 14·00 13·00
No. **MS**N4556a contains four stamp size labels, No. **MS**N4550b
contains two vertical labels and **MS**N4556c contains six labels laid
checkerboard fashion with the stamps, in each case the labels show
relics from the site. The larger stamps in **MS**N4550a/b merge with the
margins to form composite background designs.

1495 President Hu Jintao and
Kim Il Jong

1496 Flowers and Mountain

2005 (15 Dec). Visit of President Hu Jintao to Korea. Sheet 149×118
mm. containing T **1495** and similar multicoloured designs. Litho.
P 11½ (horiz) or 13½. (vert).
MSN4557 35wn. ×3, Type **1495**; With business
men; Seated at flower strewn table; 102wn.
Shaking hands (36×57 mm) .... 5·50   4·75

2006 (1 Jan). New Year. P 13½.
N4558 **1496** 3wn. multicoloured 30   25

1497 Dog   **1498** Kim Il Sung

2006 (1 Jan). New Year. Year of the Dog (1st issue). T **1497** and similar
vert designs. Multicoloured. Litho. P 13½.
N4559   3wn. Type **1497**   30   25
              a. Booklet pane. Nos. N4559/63 ...   8·75
N4560   15wn. Hound   55   45
N4561   70wn. White and brown Spitz type ..... 2·00   1·70
N4562   100wn. Black and white Spitz type .... 2·50   2·20
N4563   130wn. Spaniel..................................... 3·25   2·75
N4559/4563 *Set of 5*.. 7·75   6·50
MSN4564 150×104 mm. Nos. N4559/63 plus stamp
size label. .... 9·00   8·00
MSN4565 80×80 mm. 130wn. No. N4563 .... 3·50   3·00
Nos. N4559 and N4561 were also issued in individual sheets, the
stamps from the booklet have coloured borders, whilst those from
the sheet have white borders.
See also Nos. N4568/9.

2006 (17 Jan). 60th Anniv of Kim Il Sung's Socialist Youth League. Two
sheets containing T **1498** and similar vert designs. Multicoloured.
P 13½. (**MS**N4566) or 11½ (**MS**N4567)
MSN4566 115×80 mm. 3wn. Type **1498**; 111wn.
Kim Il Sung and young people; 150wn. Passing
torch .... 7·00   6·50
MSN4567 130×115 mm. 128wn. With young
socialists (42×64 mm).................................... 3·25   2·75
The stamp and margins of No. **MS**N4567 form a composite
design.

1499 Dog   **1500** Revolutionary Tools

2006 (29 Jan). New Year. Year of the Dog (2nd issue). T **1499** and
similar multicoloured design. Litho. P 11×11½ (12wn.) or 11½
(70wn.).
N4568   12wn. Type **1499** 35   30
MSN4569 80×130 mm. 70wn. Mastiff (painting)
(50×60 mm) .... 2·00   1·80

2006 (9 Feb). Rodong Sinmun, Josoninmingun and Chongnyonjonwi
Newspapers Joint Editorial. Litho. P 13½.
N4570 **1500** 3wn. multicoloured 30   25

1501 Ice Dance   **1502** Mount Paektu and
                                   Flowers

2006 (10 Feb). Winter Olympic Games, Turin. T **1501** and similar vert
designs. Multicoloured. Litho. P 13½.
N4571   15wn. Type **1501** 55   45
              a. Booklet pane. Nos. N4571/4...... 9·25
N4572   85wn. Ice hockey .... 2·30   2·00
N4573   110wn. Ski jump .... 2·75   2·30
N4574   135wn. Speed skating .... 3·50   3·00
N4571/4574 *Set of 4*.. 8·25   7·00
MSN4575 140×112 mm. Nos. N4571/4 .... 9·25   8·50

2006 (16 Feb). 64th Birth Anniv of Kim Jong Il. T **1502** and similar vert designs. Multicoloured. Litho. P 13½.

N4576	3wn. Type **1502**	30	25

MSN4577 140×76 mm.12wn. *Polemorium racemosum*; 45wn. *Lilium concolor*; 100wn. *Taraxacum platycarpum*; 140wn. *Parnassia palustris* .... 9·00　8·00

1503 Crop Research Institute

2006 (4 Mar). Kim Jong Il's Visit to China. Two sheets containing T **1503** and similar multicoloured designs showing Kim Jong Il. P 12.

MSN4578 170×120 mm. 3wn. Type **1503**; 12wn. Fibre optic production; 35wn. Outside at Three Gorges Dam; 70wn. Inside at Guangzhou International Conference and Exhibition Centre; 100wn. Inside at Gree Air-Conditioner Production Company; 120wn. Outside at Yandian Port .... 10·00　9·00
MSN4579 160×120 mm. 102wn. With President Hu Jintao (42×64 mm) .... 2·50　2·20

1504 Irrigation

2006 (5 Mar). 60th Anniv of Agrarian Reform Law . T **1504** and similar horiz design. Multicoloured. Litho. P 11½ (12wn.) or 12 (150wn.).

N4580	12wn. Type **1504**	35	30

MSN4581 96×72 mm. 150wn. Kim Il Sung and farmer (51×39 mm) .... 4·00　3·50
No. N4580 has a *se-tenant* label.

1505 As Type 3

1506 Pibong Falls

2006 (12 Mar). 60th Anniv of First Postage Stamps. Sheet 100×80 mm. Litho. P 12

MSN4582 **1505** 158wn. multicoloured .... 4·25　3·75

2006 (15 Mar). Mount Kumgang. T **1506** and similar multicoloured designs. Litho. P 12×12½ (vert) or 12½×12 (horiz).

N4583	3wn. Type **1506**	30	25
N4584	12wn. Podok Hermitage	35	30
N4585	35wn. Sokka Peak	1·00	85
N4586	50wn. Jipson Peak	1·30	1·20
N4587	70wn. Chongsok rocks (horiz)	2·00	1·70
N4588	100wn. Sejon Peak (horiz)	2·50	2·20
N4589	120wn. Chonhwa rock (horiz)	3·00	2·50
N4590	140wn. Piro Peak (horiz)	3·50	3·00
N4583/4590 *Set of 8*		12·50	11·00

1507 Jules Verne (writer)

2006 (13 Apr). Belgica 2006 International Stamp Exhibition. T **1507** and similar multicoloured designs. Litho. P 12.

N4591	140wn. Type **1507**	3·50	3·00
N4592	140wn. *Tursiops truncatus*	3·50	3·00
N4593	140wn. Alaskan malamute dog and Birman cat	3·50	3·00
N4594	140wn. *Australopithecus afarensis* heads	3·50	3·00
N4595	140wn. "Sunflowers" (Vincent Van Gogh)	3·50	3·00
N4596	140wn. Nymphalidae and *Disa grandiflora*	3·50	3·00
N4597	140wn. Football, chess piece, table tennis bat and ball	3·50	3·00
N4598	140wn. *Tyto alba*	3·50	3·00
N4599	140wn. Ernst Grube Type S 4000-1 fire appliance (1962) (*horiz*)	3·50	3·00
N4600	140wn. Maglev train (*horiz*)	3·50	3·00
N4591/4600 *Set of 10*		32·00	28·00

1508 Kimilsungia

1509 Site of Donggang Meeting and Inaugural Declaration

2006 (15 Apr). 94th Birth Anniv of Kim Il Sung. P 11½.
N4601 **1508** 3wn. multicoloured .... 30　25
No. N4601 has a *se-tenant* label.

2006 (5 May). 70th Anniv of Foundation for the Restoration of the Fatherland. Litho. P 13½.
N4602 **1509** 3wn. multicoloured .... 30　25

1510 Pothong River Improvement Monument

2006 (21 May). 60th Anniv of Pothong River Improvement Project. Litho. P 12.
N4603 **1510** 12wn. multicoloured 35   30

1511 Necktie and Badge   **1512** Chasing Ball

2006 (6 June). 60th Anniv of Children's Union. Litho. P 13½.
N4604 **1511** 3wn. Multicoloured 30   25

2006 (9 June). World Cup Football Championship, Germany. T **1512** and similar vert designs showing two players. Multicoloured. Litho. P 13½.
N4605   3wn. Type **1512** 30   25
       a. Booklet pane. Nos. N4605/8 ...... 14·00
N4606   130wn. Tackling .... 3·25   2·75
N4607   160wn. Kicking ball into goal .... 4·25   3·75
N4608   210wn. Heading ball .... 5·75   5·00
N4605/4608 *Set of 4* .... 12·00   10·50
     Nos. N4605/8 were issued both in sheets and in booklets of four stamps.

1513 Kim Chol Ju and Zhang Weihua

2006 (12 June). 90th Birth Anniv of Kim Chol Ju (revolutionary). Sheet 65×83 mm. Litho. P 12.
MSN4609 **1513** 170wn. multicoloured .... 4·50   3·75

1514 Ri Su Bok

2006 (27 July). Ri Su Bok (poet and soldier) Commemoration. Sheet 145×85 mm. Litho. P 12.
MSN4610 **1514** 120wn. multicoloured .... 3·00   2·50
     The stamp and margin of No. **MS**N4610 form a composite design.

1515 Trapeze Artistes

2006 (10 Aug). Circus. Sheet 125×150 mm. containing T **1515** and similar multicoloured designs. Litho. P 11½ (horiz) or 11½×12 (vert).
MSN4611   3wn. Type **1515**; 12wn. Four trapeze artistes; 130wn. Acrobat; 200wn. Blindfolded juggler (42×64 mm)..... 10·00   9·25
     The stamps and margin of No. **MS**N4611 form a composite design.

1516 Kimchi

2006 (12 Aug). Traditional Food. T **1516** and similar horiz designs. Multicoloured. Litho. P 13½.
N4612   3wn. Type **1516** 30   25
N4613   12wn. Umegi 35   30
N4614   130wn. Rice cake dumplings .... 3·25   2·75
N4615   200wn. Sweet rice .... 5·25   4·75
N4612/4615 *Set of 4* .... 8·25   7·25

1517 *Megaptera nodosa*

2006 (20 Aug). Sea Mammals. T **1517** and similar horiz designs. Multicoloured. Litho. P 13½.

N4616	3wn. Type **1517**	30	25
	a. Booklet pane. Nos. N4616/19 ...	13·00	
N4617	70wn. *Balaenoptera musculus*	2·00	1·70
N4618	160wn. *Physter catodon*	4·25	3·75
N4619	240wn. *Inia geoffrensis*	6·00	5·25
N4616/4619 *Set of 4*		11·50	9·75

Nos. N4616/19 were issued both in sheets and in booklets of four stamps.

1518 Early Motor Cycle

2006 (1 Sept). Motor Cycles. T **1518** and similar horiz designs. Multicoloured. Litho. P 11½.

N4620	3wn. Type **1518**..	30	25
	a. Booklet pane. Nos. N4620/3......	14·00	
N4621	102wn. Blue motor cycle with full		
	faring	2·50	2·20
N4622	150wn. Early motor cycle	4·00	3·50
N4623	240wn. Red motor cycle with partial		
	faring	6·50	5·50
N4620/4623 *Set of 4*...		12·00	10·50
MSN4624 175×100 mm. Nos. N4620/3, each ×2.......		27·00	25·00

1519 *General Sherman* in Flames

1520 *Tyto alba*

2006 (2 Sept). 140th Anniv of Sinking of *General Sherman*. Litho. P 13½.

N4625 **1519** 130wn. multicoloured	3·25	2·75

2006 (10 Sept). Owls. T **1520** and similar vert designs. Multicoloured. Litho. P 11½.

N4626	12wn. Type **1520**......................	35	30
	a. Booklet pane. Nos. N4626/9......	11·00	
N4627	111wn. *Strix uralensis*	2·75	2·30
N4628	130wn. *Strix aluco*	3·25	2·75
N4629	160wn. *Nyctea scandiaca*...........................	4·25	3·75
N4626/4629 *Set of 4*...		9·50	8·25

Nos. 4626/9 were issued both in sheets and in booklets. The booklet stamps have ultramarine upper borders and green lower borders whilst those from sheets have green (12wn.), lilac (111wn.), bistre (130wn.) or pink (160wn.).

1521 Kim Il Sung (statue)   **1522** Ulji Mundok

2006 (1 Oct). 60th Anniv of Kim Il Sung University. Sheet 90×115 mm. Litho. P 13½.

MSN4630 **1521** 70wn. multicoloured	2·00	1·70

2006 (2 Oct). Personalities. T **1522** and similar vert designs. Multicoloured. Litho. P 13½.

N4631	3wn. Type **1522**..	30	25
N4632	12wn. So Hui	35	30
N4633	35wn. Kim Ung So	1·00	85
N4634	70wn. Kang Kam Chan...........................	2·00	1·70
N4635	102wn. Yongae Somun	2·50	2·20
N4636	130wn. Ri Kyu Bo	3·25	2·75
N4637	160wn. Mun Ik Jom	4·25	3·75
N4631/4637 *Set of 7*...		12·50	10·50

1523 Flag   **1524** Flag and Red Cross Vehicles

2006 (17 Oct). 80th Anniv of Anti-Imperialism Union. T **1523** and similar multicoloured designs. Litho. P 13½.

N4638	3wn. Type **1523**..	30	25
MSN4639 160×100 mm. 70wn. Founder members			
in the countryside (51×40 mm); 102wn. Kim Il			
Sung as young man (46×46 mm) (circular);			
120wn. Kim Il Sung and members on rail track......		9·00	7·75

No. N4640 and Type **1524** have been left for "60th Anniv of Red Cross Society", issued on 18 October 2006, not yet received.

2006 (18 Oct). 60th Anniv of Red Cross Society. P 13½.

N4640 **1524** 30wn. multicoloured	90	75

1525 Students (*Illustration reduced. Actual size 135×33 mm*)

2006 (21 Oct). 60th Anniv of Secondary Education Fund for Koreans in Japan. Sheet 150×95 mm. Litho. P 13½.
MSN4641 **1525** 110wn. multicoloured.......................... 2·75   2·30

1526 Ruler

2006 (4 Nov). 60th Anniv of UNESCO. Tomb Murals, Anak. Sheet 165×112 mm. containing T **1526** and similar multicoloured designs. Litho. P 13½. (vert) or 12½×12 (horiz).
MSN4642 3wn. Type **1526**; 70wn. Consort; 130wn. Subak (martial art) (horiz); 135wn. Procession (horiz); 160wn. Kitchen (horiz)...................................... 13·50   12·00

1527 University Buildings (*Illustration reduced. Actual size 70×33 mm*)

2006 (4 Nov). 50th Anniv of Joson University. Sheet 150×95 mm. Litho. P 13½.
MSN4643 **1527** 110wn. multicoloured.......................... 2·75   2·30

(1528)

2006 (16 Nov). Belgica 2006 International Stamp Exhibition. Owls. Nos. N4625/8 overprinted as T **1528**. Multicoloured. Litho. P 11½.
N4644   12wn. As Type **1520** 35   30
         a. Booklet pane. Nos. N4644/7...... 11·00
N4645   111wn. As No. N4627 .... 2·75   2·30
N4646   130wn. As No. N4628 .... 3·25   2·75
N4647   160wn. As No. N4629........................... 4·25   3·75
N4644/4647 *Set of 4*... 9·50   8·25

1529 Carving

2006 (24 Dec). Army's Gift to Kim Jong Il. Sheet 90×130 mm. Litho. P 11½×12
MSN4648 **1529** 130wn. multicoloured....................... 3·25   2·75
The stamp and margin of **MS**N4648 form a composite design.

1530 Bell and Snow-covered Pagoda

2007 (1 Jan). New Year. P 13½.
N4649 **1530** 3wn. multicoloured 30   25

1531 Pig

2007 (1 Jan). New Year. Year of the Pig. T **1531** and similar horiz designs. Multicoloured. Litho. P 13½.
N4650   3wn. Type **1531** 30   25
         a. Booklet pane. Nos. N4650/3...... 7·00
N4651   45wn. Pot-bellied pig .... 1·20   1·00
N4652   70wn. Saddle back .... 2·00   1·70
N4653   130wn. Large white .... 3·25   2·75
N4650/4653 *Set of 4*... 6·00   5·25
MSN4654 115×86 mm. Nos. N4650/3 .... 7·00   6·50
MSN4655 80×57 mm. 70wn. No. N4653................. 2·00   1·80
Nos. N4650 and N4651 were also issued in individual sheets, the stamps from the booklet have white borders.

APPENDIX

The following stamps have either been issued in excess of postal needs, or have not been available to the public in reasonable quantities at face value. Such stamps may later be given full listing if there is evidence of regular postal use. Miniature sheets, imperforate stamps etc., are excluded from this list.

1976
Olympic Games, Montreal. Three-dimensional stamps showing Olympic events. 5, 10, 15, 20, 25, 40ch.

1977
Olympic Games, Montreal. Three-dimensional stamps showing medals. 5, 10, 15, 20, 25, 40ch.
Olympic Games, Montreal. 1976 Olympic Games issue optd with winners' names. 5, 10, 15, 20, 25, 40ch.

1979
XIII Winter Olympic Games, 1980. Nos. N1688/94 optd. 2, 5, 10, 15, 20, 25, 40ch.

1981
Nobel Prizes for Medicine. Nos. N1955/61 optd. 7×10ch.
World Cup Football Championship, Spain (1982). Nos. N1731/40 optd. 12×20ch.
World Cup Football Championship, Spain (1982). Three-dimensional stamps. Air 20, 30ch.

1982
21st Birthday of Princess of Wales. Nos. N2108/11 and N2120/3 optd. 10, 20, 30, 40ch.; 10, 20, 30, 70ch.
Birth of Prince William of Wales. Nos. N2185/91 optd in blue or gold. 10, 20, 30, 50, 60, 70, 80ch.
World Cup Football Championship, Spain, Results. Nos. N2201/6 optd. 10, 20, 30, 40, 50, 60ch.
Birth of Prince William of Wales. Three-dimensional stamps. 3×30ch.

1983
XXIII Olympic Games, Los Angeles. 1984. Nos. N2084/8 optd. 10, 15, 20, 25, 30ch.

1984
European Royal History. 81×10ch.

Stanley
GIBBONS

The most famous name in philately

Serving collectors for over 100 years, our showroom at 399 Strand is the world's largest stamp shop, covering everything philatelic from the highest quality Penny Blacks to the latest in watermark detection technology. Whether you are an experienced collector or just starting out, our friendly team of staff is happy to help with any query you may have.

With millions of stamps in stock at any time, we cater for the requirements of all collectors - from beginner to connoisseur.

- *Over 1200 stockbooks containing stamps from 1840 to the latest issues*

- *Catalogues, albums and accessories from Stanley Gibbons and other leading names*

- *Our bookshelf section contains hundreds of rare philatelic titles from around the world*

- *Valuations available by appointment from our dedicated team of experts*

We cannot begin to do 399 Strand any justice in print so please take the time to visit our shop to judge for yourself, you will not be disappointed.

One Country Albums

Britannia Albums - ideal for collectors of all countries

We stock a range of Britannia albums for almost every country availble, including Japan and North and South Korea. Each album consists of a D ring binders made from luxury, fully padded, leather grained effect red or blue PVC containing polypropylene pockets and 120gsm white acid free leaves.

Product Code	Title	Period	Price
BH04	Japan vol. 1	1871-1955	£40.35
BH19	Japan vol. 2	1956-1980	£40.35
BH41	Japan vol. 3	1981-1995	£40.35
BH41A	Japan vol. 4	1996-2000	£35.65
BH41B	Japan vol. 5	2001-2006	£35.65
BH40A	Japan Prefecture	1989-2006	£35.65
BH40B	Japan Prefecture Booklets	1991-2002	£45.05
BE45B	North Korea vol. 1	1946-1968	£40.35
BE45C	North Korea vol. 2	1969-1976	£40.35
BE45D	North Korea vol. 3	1977-1980	£40.35
BE45E	North Korea vol. 4	1981-1983	£40.35
BE45F	North Korea vol. 5	1984-1988	£40.35
BE45G	North Korea vol. 6	1989-1993	£35.65
BE45H	North Korea vol. 7	1994-1996	£35.65
BE45J	North Korea vol. 8	1997-1999	£40.35
BE15	North Korea vol. 9	2000	£24.10
BE16	South Korea vol. 1	1894-1975	£40.35
BE16A	South Korea vol. 2	1976-1998	£40.35
BE15A	South Korea vol. 3	1999-2006	£35.65

Please contact us on the details below to find out more or to place your order.

To place your order contact us on: 01425 472363
Stanley Gibbons Ltd, 7 Parkside, Christchurch Road, Ringwood, Hampshire, BH24 3SH
www.stanleygibbons.com

 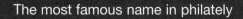

STANLEY GIBBONS

Relevant Literature

We stock a wide range of philatelic literature covering all areas of philatelic interest, including these titles we feel would be ideal for collectors of Japan and Korea:

Japanese Post Offices in China & Manchuria by John Mosher (published 1978)
£65.00

Early Japanese Postmarks And Post Offices by George A. Fisher
£15.75

The Richard W.Canman Collection Of Japan (Prices Realised)
£15.00

Philatelic Handbook For Korea 1884-1905
(published by the Korea Stamp Society)
£47.50

To order the titles, please contact us on the details below or visit or shop at 399 Strand, London, WC2R 0LX.

All prices correct as of April 2008
For more information and our entire range of philatelic literature, please visit **www.stanleygibbons.com/shop**

Foreign Stamp Catalogues: Parts 2-22

Discover the world of philately

For advanced collectors of foreign countries we have divided the world into 21 easy-to-manage volumes. Under constant revision, new editions in our series of foreign catalogues are regularly published to reflect current trends and political changes allowing you to monitor your collections. Currently available editions are listed together with their year of publication.
Publications from 2004 onwards are in full colour.

R2831-02   Part 2 Austria & Hungary, 6th edition
Covering the stamps of Austria, Lombardy and Venetia, Bosnia and Herzegovina, Austro-Hungarian Military Post, Austrian Territories acquired by Italy, Danube Steam Navigation Company, Austro-Hungarian Post Offices in Turkish Empire, United Nations Vienna Centre, Hungary, Szeged, French Occupation, Rumanian Occupation and Serbian Occupation.
£24.95

R2833-03   Part 4 Benelux, 5th edition
Covering the stamps of Belgium, the Belgian Congo, Ruanda-Urundi, Luxembourg, the Netherlands, Aruba, Netherlands Antilles, Netherlands Indies, Netherlands New Guinea and Surinam.
£24.95

R2834-02   Part 5 Czechoslovakia & Poland, 6th edition
Covering the stamps of Czechoslovakia, East Silesia, Bohemia and Moravia, the Czech Republic, Slovakia, Poland, Polish Military Post and Polish Post Offices Abroad.
£24.95

R2835-06   Part 6 France
Covering the stamps of France, Alexandretta, Algeria, Cameroon, Chad, Congo, French Equatorial Africa, French Guiana, French Guinea, French Morocco, French Polynesia, French West Africa, Gabon, Guadeloupe, Indo-China, Ivory Coast, Lebanon, Madagascar, Mali Federation, Martinique, Niger, St.Pierre et Miquelon, Senegal, Syria, Togo, Tunisia, Andorra, Monaco and the French Postal Offices in Chine, Crete, Egypt, Ethiopia, Tangier, Zanzibar and the Turkish Empire and more.
£34.95

R2836-08   Part 7 Germany 8th edition
8th edition, Germany continues to be one of the most popular stamp collecting areas and this new edition has allowed us to carefully review all the prices and take into consideration current market trends. For the first time we have included the stamps issued during the German occupation of the Channel Islands,   £29.95

R2837-04   Part 8 Italy & Switzerland, 6th edition
Covering the stamps of Italy, Liechtenstein, San Marino, Switzerland, United Nations Geneva Headquarters and Vatican City. £29.95

R2838-05   Part 9 Portugal & Spain, 5th edition
Covering the stamps of Angola, Azores, Cape Verde Islands, Macao, Madeira, Mozambique, Portuguese Guiea, Portuguese India, St Thomas and Prince Islands, Timor, Cape Juby, Cuba, Elobey, Annobon and Corisco, Fernando Poo, Ifni, Mariana Islands, Philippines, Puerto Rico, Rio Muni, Spanish Guinea, Spanish Morocco, Spanish Post Offices in Morocco and Tangier, Spanish Sahara, Spanish West Africa and Andorra.   £29.95

R2844-07   Part 15 Central America, 3rd edition
The all-new 3rd edition follows research and discoveries made by collectors and members of the trade. There has been a number of editorial additions and improvements to this issue. Covering stamps from Costa Rica, Cuba, Dominican Republic, El Salvador, Guatemala, Haiti, Honduras, Mexico and Nicaragua.
£39.95

R2845-07   Part 16 Central Asia
Covering the stamps of Afghanistan, Iran (including Bushire, the Persian Consular Post in Baku and the Russian and Indian Post Offices in Iran) and Turkey. Listings for Turkey include Foreign Post Offices in the Turkish Empire.
£27.50

R2846-07   Part 17 China, 7th edition
Covering the stamps of Municipal Posts of Treaty Ports, Chinese Empire, Chinese Republic, Chinese Provinces, Communist China, Hong Kong, Japanese Occupation of China, Foreign Post Offices in China, Chinese Post Offices in Korea, Kiaochow, Kwangchow, Macao, Manchukuo, Taiwan and Tibet.   £34.95

R2850-04   Part 21 South East Asia, 4th edition
Covering the stamps of Cambodia, Indonesia, Laos, Myanmar (Burma), Netherland Indies, the Philippines, Thailand, Timor and Vietnam. Published in colour for the first time and with new design indexes for Indonesia, the Philippines and Thailand.   £29.95

R2851-06   Part 22 United States, 6th edition
Covering US territories overseas, including the Marshall Islands, Micronesia and Palau, and the stamps of the United Nations postal administrations.
£29.95

All prices correct as of April 2008.

Stanley Gibbons Publications.
7 Parkside, Christchurch Road, Ringwood, Hampshire, BH24 3SH
E: sales@stanleygibbons.co.uk   T: +44 (0)1425 472 363
www.stanleygibbons.com

One Country Albums

If you're a Japan collector, we have the perfect way to house your collection - Lighthouse binders and pages.

Each binder holds 110 pages and has 'Nippon' embossed in gold on the spine. These popular Lighthouse binders are available in red and retail at £38.00. You can also purchase a matching slipcase for just £15.75.

The page available are as follows:

Period	No. of pages	Album pages		Album pages with mounts	
		Code	Price	Code	Price
1871-1945	65	L96-1	£67.50	L96-1SF	£140.40
1945-1957	62	L96-2	£65.50	L96-2SF	£130.00
1958-1969	50	L96-3	£51.90	L96-3SF	£103.90
1970-1979	48	L96-4	£49.90	L96-4SF	£100.80
1979-1989	59	L96-5	£62.30	L96-5SF	£123.80
1989-1994	58	L96-6	£61.30	L96-6SF	£123.80
1995-1999	64	L96-7	£67.50	L96-7SF	£134.20
2000-2002	64	L96-8	£67.50	L96-8SF	£134.20
2003-2006	82	L96-9	£82.25	L96-9SF	£165.50

Please contact us on the details below to find out more or to place your order.

All prices correct as of April 2008 and subject to change

To place your order contact us on: 01425 472363
Stanley Gibbons Ltd, 7 Parkside, Christchurch Road, Ringwood,
Hampshire, BH24 3SH
www.stanleygibbons.com

Stanley Gibbons
Roadshows

We hold regular roadshows throughout the year, covering the whole of the United Kingdom.

• Free verbal appraisals
• Put forward material for future auctions
• Excellent prices paid for selected Great Britain and Commonwealth
• Our team will be happy to examine anything remotely philatelic

So, if you were thinking of selling that single rare stamp, a part of your collection or the whole thing, then speak to our expert team first at Stanley Gibbons Ltd.

Please contact either Steve Matthews or Ryan Epps at
Stanley Gibbons Ltd. 399 Strand, London WC2R 0LX.
Telephone: +44(0)20 7836 8444   Fax: +44(0)20 7836 7342
Email: smatthews@stanleygibbons.co.uk or repps@stanleygibbons.co.uk

See more with the
Zoom Digital Microscope

R7521

The Zoom Digital Microscope is a powerful digital microscope that displays the magnified image right on to your computer screen allowing you to see intricate details of ordinary objects you never knew existed!

Features:

- Integrated Digital Camera – capture still images and VIDEO at the click of a button and view them on your PC monitor
- 26x -130x digital zoom – allows you to see details of ordinary objects you never knew existed
- 5x optical zoom
- Built in illuminator for clear and bright magnified images
- Image resolution of 640 x 489 pixels (VGA)
- Battery-free and connects right to your PC via USB
- Compatible with Windows 98SE, ME, 200, XP, Vista.

Just look at the immense detail you can capture with the microscope magnifier at up to 130x magnification

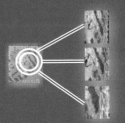

ORDER YOURS TODAY, ONLY £79.95

Price correct as of April 2008 and subject to change

Stanley Gibbons Publications, 7 Parkside, Christchurch Road, Ringwood, Hampshire, BH24 3SH
Tel: 01425 472 363 Email: info@stanleygibbons.co.uk
www.stanleygibbons.com

Stanley Gibbons Commonwealth Country Catalogues

This series of full colour catalogues lists and prices the stamps of Commonwealth countries from SG1 to date, to the level of detail familiar to users of the 'Part 1' British Commonwealth listings.

Australia
Published at the end of November 2007, this Australia volume includes the Colonial issues of New South Wales, Queensland, South Australia, Tasmania, Victoria and Western Australia.
R2871-08 £19.95

Bangladesh, Pakistan and Sri Lanka
The first edition of this new volume includes all issues of Ceylon (from 1857), as well as Bangladesh, Pakistan and Sri Lanka, with the stamps of Bahawalpur following Pakistan. Booklets and official stamps are fully listed and priced.
R2977-05 £14.95

Brunei, Malaysia & Singapore
The Brunei, Malaysia and Singapore volume includes Labuan, North Borneo and Sarawak, the stamps overprinted for the British Post Office in Bangkok, priced listings of Indian stamps used in the Straits Settlements and Thai stamps used in Northern Malaya and the various World War II occupation issues.
R2879-04 £19.95

Canada
The Canada catalogue includes the stamps of British Columbia and Vancouver Island, New Brunswick, Newfoundland, Nova Scotia and Prince Edward Island, as well as Canada itself, with priced listings of booklets, registration, special delivery and official stamps and postage dues.
R2874-05 £14.95

Cyprus, Gibraltar and Malta
As well as Cyprus, the Turkish Cypriot Posts, Gibraltar and Malta, this catalogue includes the former British Colonies in Europe of Heligoland and the Ionian Islands and the British Post Offices in Crete.
R2976-05 £14.95

East Africa
The 1st edition of the East Africa catalogue includes the stamps of Egypt, Kenya, K.U.T., the Somaliland Protectorate, Sudan, Tanzania, Uganda and the British Occupation of Italian Colonies.
R2984-06 £16.95

Eastern Pacific
This volume includes stamps from The Cook Islands, Niue And Samoa. For the first time the stamps of the German post office in Samoa are included.
R2988-07 £14.95

Falkland Islands
The Falkland Islands volume includes priced listings of Falkland stamps used in the Dependencies, as well as the issues of the Falkland Islands Dependencies, British Antarctic Territory and South Georgia and South Sandwich Islands.
R2872-04 £9.95

Hong Kong
This catalogue includes lists and prices the stamps of the commonwealth countries from SG1 to date. Hong Kong also includes the stamps of the special administrative region of the people's republic of China.
R2877-08 £9.95

India (Inc FDS)
The India volume includes stamps of the Indian Convention States and Feudatory States. The catalogue also lists and prices booklets and officials for India and the Indian States and lists the stamps overprinted for the Indian Expeditionary forces.
R2873-04 £19.95

Indian Ocean
This 1st edition of this catalogue contains the stamps of the British Indian Ocean Territory, Madagascar, the Maldive Islands, Mauritius and Seychelles.
R2986-07 £16.95

Ireland
The 2nd edition of this popular catalogue lists the stamps of Ireland from the 1922 overprints on Great Britain up to the Commemoratives of February 2006, including watermark varieties, major errors and booklets.
R2975-06 £9.95
Also available with Euro pricings
R2975-06E £9.95

Leeward Islands
This first series of colour catalogues lists and prices the stamps of Commonwealth countries This volume includes the stamps of Antigua, Barbuda, the British Virgin Islands, Leeward islands, Montserrat and St Kitts Nevis.
R2989-07 £19.95

New Zealand
The New Zealand catalogue covers the stamps of New Zealand, the Tokelau Islands, Aitutaki, the Cook Islands, Niue, Penrhyn Island and Western Samoa.
R2876-06 £14.95

Northern Caribbean
This catalogue covers issues from the Bahamas, Bermuda, Cayman Islands, Jamaica and the Turks and Caicos Islands.
R2980-06 £16.95

Southern Africa
The Southern Africa catalogue covers South Africa, with the pre-union issues of the Cape of Good Hope, Natal, New Republic, Orange Free State, Transvaal and Zululand and the Homelands issue of Bophuthatswana, Ciskeitranskei and Venda.
R2978-08 £19.95

St Helena and Dependencies
This catalogue covers the stamps of Ascension and Tristan da Cunha. It includes listings of Great Britain stamps used in Ascension
R2875-08 £9.95

Western Pacific
Covering the stamps of Fiji, the Gilbert and Ellice Islands, Kiribati, Nauru, Papua New Guinea, the Pitcairn Islands, the Solomon Islands, Tonga, Tuvalu and Vanuatu.
R2987-07 £19.95

Windward Islands
Windward Islands volume includes the stamps of Barbados, Dominica, and Grenada. Watermark varieties and booklets are all listed and the catalogue is complete to the end 2006. This is the first complete revision undertaken for six years
R2990-07 £19.95

All prices correct as of April 2008.

Stanley Gibbons Publications.
7 Parkside, Christchurch Road, Ringwood, Hampshire, BH24 3SH
E: sales@stanleygibbons.co.uk   T: +44 (0)1425 472 363
www.stanleygibbons.com

STANLEY GIBBONS
The Home of Philately since 1856

AN IMPORTANT MESSAGE TO YOU

Dear Catalogue User,

As a collector and Stanley Gibbons catalogue user for many years myself, I am only too aware of the need to provide you with the information you seek in an accurate, timely and easily accessible manner.

Naturally, I have my own views on where changes could be made, but one thing I learned long ago is that we all have different opinions and requirements.

I would therefore be most grateful if you would complete the form overleaf and return it to me (or send your answers on a separate sheet if you prefer not to cut the page out of your catalogue).

If you would like the form to be sent to you by email, let me know at hjefferies@stanleygibbons.co.uk

Very many thanks for your help.

Yours sincerely,

Hugh Jefferies,
Editor.

Hugh Jefferies (Catalogue Editor),
Stanley Gibbons Limited,
7 Parkside, Ringwood
Hampshire BH24 2LE
United Kingdom

Questionnaire

Please complete and return it to:

Hugh Jefferies *(Catalogue Editor)*
Stanley Gibbons Limited
7 Parkside, Ringwood   or   email: *hjefferies@stanleygibbons.co.uk*
Hampshire BH24 2LE
United Kingdom

Japan and Korea Catalogue 5th edition

1.   Level of detail
Do you feel that the level of detail in this catalogue is:
a)   too specialised ☐
b)   about right ☐
c)   inadequate ☐

2.   Frequency of issue
How often would you purchase a new edition of this catalogue?
a)   Annually ☐
b)   Every two years ☐
c)   Every three to five years ☐
d)   Less frequently ☐

3.   Design and Quality
How would you describe the layout and appearance of this catalogue?
a)   Excellent ☐
b)   Good ☐
c)   Adequate ☐
d)   Poor ☐

4.   *How important to you are the prices given in the catalogue:*
a)   Important ☐
b)   Quite important ☐
c)   Of little interest ☐
d)   Of no interest ☐

5.   *Would you be interested in an electronic version of this catalogue?*

a)   Yes ☐
b)   Maybe ☐
c)   No ☐

6.   *Is there anything you would like to see in this catalogue that is not currently included?* ....

....

....

....

....

....

....

....

**7.   *Would you like us to let you know when the next edition of this catalogue is due to be published?*
*If so please give your contact details below.***

Name: ....

Address:...

....

....

....

Email: ....

Telephone: ....

8.   *Would you like to be informed of the publication dates of any other Stanley Gibbons Catalogues?*
1.
2.
3.

Many thanks for your comments.

COLLECT
JAPAN & KOREA
STAMPS

From Stanley Gibbons, THE WORLD'S LARGEST STAMP STOCK

Priority order form – Four easy ways to order

Phone:
020 7836 8444
Overseas: +44 (0)20 7836 8444

Fax:
020 7557 4499
Overseas: +44 (0)20 7557 4499

Email:
lmourne@stanleygibbons.co.uk

Post: Lesley Mourne,
Stamp Mail Order Department
Stanley Gibbons Ltd, 399 Strand
London, WC2R 0LX, England

Customer Details _____

Account Number _____

Name _____

Address _____

_____ Postcode _____

Country _____ Email _____

Tel No _____ Fax No _____

Payment details

Registered Postage & Packing   £3.60

I enclose my cheque/postal order for £ _____ in full payment.
Please make cheques/postal orders payable to Stanley Gibbons Ltd.
Cheques must be in £ sterling and drawn on a UK bank

Please debit my credit card for £_____ in full payment.
I have completed the Credit Card section below.

Card Number

CVC Number

Start Date (Switch & Amex)   Expiry Date

Issue No (Switch)

Signature _____ Date_____

COLLECT
JAPAN & KOREA
STAMPS

From Stanley Gibbons, THE WORLD'S LARGEST STAMP STOCK

Condition (mint/UM/used)	Country	SG No.	Description	Price	Office use only
			POSTAGE & PACKAGING	£3.60	
			GRAND TOTAL		

Minimum price. The minimum catalogue price quoted is 10p. For individual stamps, prices between 10p and 95p are provided as a guide for catalogue users. The lowest price charged for individual stamps or sets purchased from Stanley Gibbons Ltd is £1

Please complete payment, name and address details overleaf